P9-DGB-677

PHYSICS

A BLAISDELL BOOK IN THE PURE AND APPLIED SCIENCES

CONSULTING EDITOR | *Brenton F. Stearns* | *Hobart and William Smith Colleges*

BLAISDELL PUBLISHING COMPANY

A Division of Ginn and Company | *Waltham, Massachusetts · Toronto · London*

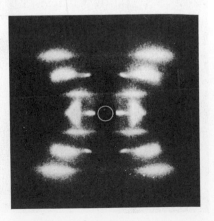

Physics:
Its Structure and
Evolution

 William A. Blanpied, Case Western Reserve University

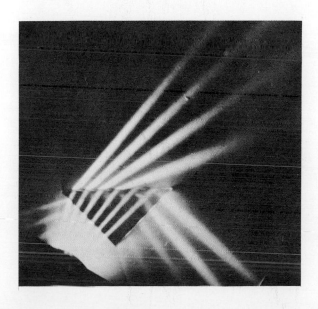

COPYRIGHT © 1969 BY BLAISDELL PUBLISHING COMPANY,
A DIVISION OF GINN AND COMPANY.
ALL RIGHTS RESERVED. NO PART OF THE MATERIAL COVERED BY
THIS COPYRIGHT MAY BE PRODUCED IN ANY FORM
OR BY ANY MEANS OF REPRODUCTION.
LIBRARY OF CONGRESS CATALOG CARD NUMBER: 69:11029
PRINTED IN THE UNITED STATES OF AMERICA.

To Sara,
the most important of
the many intelligent nonscientists
to inspire this book,

and Eric,
in the hope that he will
always regard nature with something of the
wonder and excitement he sees it with as a child.

Preface

   This book is an attempt to convey a few meaningful ideas about physics to intelligent, reasonably mature college students who do not anticipate being directly concerned with the subject during their professional careers. Although such students usually have neither the mathematical proficiency nor the training of students preparing for careers in physical science or engineering, they are certainly as intelligent, and, judging from my own experience, often equally able to comprehend the significance of important, fundamental concepts in physics. All too often in the past, nonprofessional students of physics have been offered eviscerated versions of preprofessional courses which contained little more than definitions and watered-down technique. As a result a discipline which most professional physicists regard as challenging and beautiful in its coherence frequently appeared uninspiring and totally disconnected.

   There is general agreement (at least among physicists) about the importance of physics in the liberal arts curriculum. I submit that no physics course can have much value to liberal arts students unless it tries to present physics from a physicist's point of view, showing that it *is* an exciting, living discipline which taken *in toto* represents one of the most profound achievements of the human intelligence. If the validity of this proposition is granted then I believe the outlines of a course for liberal arts students emerges almost at once. Contemporary developments based upon the fundamental concepts of special relativity and quantum mechanics should receive as serious a treatment as is possible on this level. These developments provide the justification for referring to physics as a living discipline. They link physics to the other sciences. Most important perhaps, the study of contemporary physics provides an opportunity for the liberal arts student to witness the ingenuity of the human imagination in correlating a set of experimental facts that refuse to be correlated according to a theretofore well-accepted set of hypotheses.

   It is obvious, however, that neither special relativity nor quantum mechanics can be appreciated without some understanding of the viewpoint and the achievements of classical physics as well as the reasons why the classical assumptions were ultimately judged inadequate. Beyond that, classical physics is worth studying for its own sake. Kepler, Galileo, and Newton, among many others, *also* thought of natural philosophy as a living, exciting discipline, and also faced the problem of correlating sets of experimental facts that refused to be correlated according to the then accepted postulates.

I have attempted to illustrate both the intellectual coherence and the continuing evolution of physics by focusing upon Newtonian mechanics, special relativity, and quantum mechanics, emphasizing their growth out of earlier theories, as well as the way they were modified and continue to be modified by application.

Most of the applications from classical physics have been chosen in order to illustrate the power of the Newtonian assumptions in correlating so many seemingly diverse phenomena, but I hope that most students will also find them interesting in their own right. Insofar as possible I have also tried to present classical electricity and magnetism as an extension of the basic Newtonian synthesis, while showing why the introduction of the fields requires a modification of the strict Newtonian viewpoint. A number of classical topics that have traditionally been included in basic physics courses are omitted or touched on only briefly, on the grounds that they are not essential to liberal arts students. The rotation of rigid bodies is not treated at all, geometric optics is touched in passing, and the coverage of electrical machines and circuit theory is brief. Since all three topics are rather standard and treated well in a number of basic texts, I feel that the interested student will encounter little difficulty in pursuing them on his own initiative.

Much of the selection of material from atomic, nuclear, and elementary particle physics which has been chosen both to illustrate some of the basic features of quantum mechanics and for its own intrinsic interest, admittedly reflects my own particular interests. Many of my colleagues in college teaching might contend that topics from solid state physics, for example, are just as interesting and illustrate quantum mechanical principles as well or better than the topics from elementary particle physics that I have included. Although there is considerable justice in that argument I maintain that since one of the major reasons for including contemporary material is to show that physics is still in the process of evolution, the specific choice of subject matter is less important than the way in which it is treated and the fact that it is included in the first place. I hope that the text's development of quantum mechanical principles and its treatment of atomic physics will make it possible for an instructor to introduce additional contemporary topics either by using his own notes or one or more of the many paperbacks and/or reprint articles that are now available.

A few words are in order concerning the mathematical level of the text. There is little point in denying the mathematical basis of physics, particularly of modern physics. However, I also believe an important distinction should be made between mathematical *ideas* and the mathematical *techniques* encountered in physics. Mastery of these techniques is one of the hallmarks of the professional scientist and requires considerable training and experience. Liberal arts students by definition are not going to become professional scientists, and therefore, have little reason to learn techniques, even granting that they have the mathematical background to do so.

On the other hand, many of the mathematical ideas in physics, while as unfamiliar as the physics itself, *can* be grasped by the liberal arts student who has a background in high school algebra and geometry, provided he is willing to expend some effort to that end. Once the student understands the idea of a general functional relationship between variables and of the limit of a ratio he will know enough about the differential calculus to permit him to grasp physical concepts and relations of considerable sophistication, including the meaning of a differential equation. In that sense, I use calculus in this text. A brief treatment of the technique of differentation is included for the interested student, but is virtually disconnected from the main development. In many instances sections in which I have used the idea of a derivative extensively may also be omitted at the discretion of the instructor without serious loss of continuity. Such sections are starred both in the Table of Contents and in the body of the text itself. Additional material on the calculus is relegated to a number of chapter appendices.

Despite the above disclaimer I expect that a number of my colleagues will still question whether the calculus as I have used it will be comprehensible to the liberal arts student. In anticipation of that question I would emphasize that I have written this book not for the student who is content to sit in the classroom and let physics wash over him, but rather for the student who would like to know some physics and is willing to devote some effort to that end. I have been privileged to teach physics to many such students, and have been greatly rewarded by doing so. I hope that this book will be of some aid to the many college instructors who believe, as I do, that physics does have a place both in the liberal arts curriculum and in contemporary culture, and that it will offer a glimpse of the beauty and the challenge inherent in the subject to the sort of liberal arts student I had in mind as I wrote it.

Many people have contributed, both wittingly and unwittingly, to the writing of this book. Professor Richard Feynman is no doubt the major contributor in the latter group. His beautiful and exciting *Lectures On Physics*, for beginning, preprofessional students, provided part of my motivation for wanting to offer nonprofessional students a glimpse of physics as a physicist sees it.

The structure of the text, as well as a good many of its specific treatments of topics developed from liberal arts physics courses I have taught first at Yale University and later at Case Western Reserve University. I acknowledge with gratitude the direct and indirect aid of the students who took these courses, as well as the many helpful discussions I have had with interested colleagues at both institutions. In particular, I would single out Professors Harold Cassidy and Robert Adair, of Yale, Professor MacAlister Hull, now at Oregon State University, and Professors Thomas Jenkins, Joseph Weinberg, Jonathan Reichert, and Philip Pearle of Case Western Reserve University. I am also grateful to Professor Harvey Willard, chairman of the physics department at Case Western Reserve, and Professor Richard Hoffman, director of undergraduate studies, for encouraging me in my efforts to teach liberal arts physics at the university.

I presented several of the ideas in modern physics found in the text to the participants in a Summer Institutute for College Physics Teachers held at Sagar University in India during the summer of 1967. I am grateful to Professor D. R. Bhawalkar, chairman of the physics department at Sagar, to his colleagues, and to the institute participants, in internationalizing the criticism of my preliminary draft.

A very special acknowledgement is due my consulting editor, Professor Drenton Stearns of Hobart and William Smith Colleges, whose criticisms of more than one of my drafts never failed to be complete, incisive, and constructive. I owe a debt of gratitude as well to the staff of Blaisdell Publishing Company. Thanks are also due to Mrs. Margery Young who typed the final manuscript as well as major portions of the preliminary drafts, and who responded cheerfully and efficiently when informed, on several occasions, that what she had regarded as part of a final manuscript had become penultimate at best.

Finally, I acknowledge publicly the aid and encouragement, both tangible and intangible, given to me by my wife Sara from the moment I started to write the first draft, and indeed even before then. As she knows very well, this book could not have been completed without her.

W.A.B.

Cleveland, Ohio
 April 1968

Contents

*Starred sections, in which the mathematical level is somewhat higher than in the remainder of the text, may be omitted without serious loss of continuity.

6 Symmetry principles and conservation laws   174

7 The conservation of energy   210

12   The electromagnetic field   436

13   Classical wave motion   463

There are . . . some minds which can go on contemplating with satisfaction pure quantities presented to the eye by symbols, and to the mind in a form which none but mathematicians can conceive.

There are others who feel more enjoyment in following geometrical forms which they draw on paper, or build up in the empty space before them.

Others, again, are not content unless they can project their whole physical energies into the scene which they conjure up. They learn at what rate the planets rush through space, and they experience a delightful feeling of exhilaration. They calculate the forces with which the heavenly bodies pull on one another, and they feel their own muscles straining with the effort.

To such men momentum, energy, mass are not mere abstract expressions of the results of scientific enquiry. They are words of power, which stir their souls like the memories of childhood.

For the sake of persons of these different types, scientific truth should be presented in different forms, and should be regarded as equally scientific, whether it appears in the robust form and the vivid colouring of a physical illustration, or in the tenuity and paleness of a symbolical expression.

JAMES CLERK MAXWELL
(1831-1879)

The rules of the game

1

▲▲ 1.1 The nature of scientific activity

A primary objective of physics, indeed of all the sciences, is to order the seeming infinity of observed natural processes by means of a consistent set of fundamental concepts and principles. The objective is a venerable one dating from at least the sixth century B.C. when the philosophers of the Greek cities on the Ionian coast of Asia Minor sought order in terms of natural rather than mythical causes. One of these philosophers, Anaximander of Miletus, wrote a now extant treatise called *On the Physis* in about 590 B.C. In English the word *physis* is usually rendered as "the nature of things," or "that from which things grow."* Thus both the Greek root of the English word *physics* as well as the spirit in which it was used by Anaximander are related to the central goal of contemporary physics: a search for the nature of things, for an understanding of that from which things grow.

Having noted a relationship between some of the general goals of Ionian philosophy and contemporary physics, we should also note that the procedures used in striving toward those goals, as well as our expectations of ultimate success, are very different. As anyone who has read a science column of a newspaper knows, science is concerned with understanding and interpreting naturally occurring processes. But not everyone who attempts to describe a particular facet of nature is making a scientific study. Thus it is probably easier to differentiate the sciences from other intellectual and creative activities in terms of procedures rather than specific subject matter. Both a geologist and a painter might describe the same mountain range in terms appropriate to his own profession. But only the geologist's description would be called scientific. If two geologists submit reports on the same mountain range they are likely to agree in their essential conclusions. Should they disagree there are well-defined criteria for determining (at least in principle) which report is in error. On the contrary, two artists may execute very dissimilar but nonetheless valid interpretations of the same subject. This is because an artist has the freedom to be subjective, to individualize what he sees. A scientist, on the other hand, has the responsibility to be objective, to report faithfully what is there.

---

* The etymology of the word *physis* is discussed by Giorgio de Santillana in *The Origins of Scientific Thought*, New American Library Paperback Edition, New York, 1961, p. 27.

1

The distinction between the geological and the artistic methods of describing a mountain range suggests that in a very broad sense a discipline is a science if a description of a natural system or process obtained by applying its procedures is *reproducible*. That is, it must, in principle, be independent of when it is obtained and who obtains it. Any description of a particular facet of nature is of necessity a partial description, an abstraction based upon a small number of its attributes. This is true whether the description is made by an artist, a journalist, a physician, a sociologist, or a physicist. Each constructs a different *model* of the reality he observes, emphasizing a few features of particular interest to him and ignoring the others. A simplistic interpretation of the reproducibility requirement would imply that two physicists working independently on a particular set of observations should construct identical models or *theories*. This interpretation suggests that there is a unique, well-defined method for abstracting the essential features of a physical system. On the contrary, since our knowledge of the physical universe is incomplete it is often exceedingly difficult if not impossible to know which features of a complex set of phenomena are the essential ones. Some educated guesses based upon experience with other, similar phenomena are usually in order. In these circumstances two equally competent scientists who take different approaches to the investigation of the same complex physical situation may well arrive at different interpretations. Then the reproducibility criterion requires that their theories be formulated in such a way that they can easily compare them, discuss their relative merits, reject one or the other, or, more probably, synthesize elements of both into still another theory. Since an acceptable scientific theory should be applicable to systems that differ from the one that originally inspired its creation, the elements of uncertainty that are almost always present in any new theory can be clarified, modified, or rejected by subjecting the theory to a series of experimental tests. In this way an inadequate interpretation will ultimately be rejected, while a strong theory may be generalized far beyond its original limits.

We are led, then, to a view of scientific knowledge as a growing interdependent network of these interpretations or theories which, taken as a whole, offers considerable insight into the nature of the physical universe. That network encompasses all the traditional branches of science which, though they may be distinguished from one another in terms of their subject matter, merge at their boundaries as befits their membership in the network.

Thus since the province of biology includes all processes related to living organisms it clearly merges with physiology and psychology at one of its boundaries. But changes in cell structure constitute the basis of all biological processes, and these in turn are based upon molecular rearrangements within the cells. Since chemistry deals with the types of bonds formed between atoms and molecules and the macroscopic consequences of these various combinations, it clearly overlaps the province of biology. Any description of a chemical reaction inevitably includes the net energy liberated or absorbed, and energy is in the traditional province of physics. Furthermore, the bonds between atoms and molecules are electromagnetic in character, so that again a point of contact with physics is evident.

Geology is concerned specifically with the nature of nonliving things on the earth, astronomy with the nature of extraterrestrial objects. But of course all processes on the earth are basically chemical or physical; all descriptions of planetary motion follow from the basic principles of Newtonian physics; all theories regarding processes in the interior of stars rest heavily upon nuclear physics.

Ultimately, then, the processes studied by all branches of science are related directly to the subject matter of physics. Can we go further and conclude that a thorough knowledge of physics provides an understanding of all natural process and that the other branches of science are in a sense only subdivisions of physics? Such a conclusion would ignore the model building aspect alluded to earlier, the fact that a scientist tries to comprehend a system by emphasizing a few of its attributes to the exclusion of all others.

For example, suppose a physiologist is studying the human respiratory system. It is all very well for him to know that the cells of the lungs are composed of molecules whose primary constituents are carbon and hydrogen atoms, that these atoms as well as the oxygen and nitrogen atoms inhaled into the lungs are composed of electrons, protons, and neutrons. But if he focused his attention at the subatomic or even the atomic level he would soon be lost in complexity. The total system of interest in his case involves far too many atoms, far too many subtle interactions between those atoms to permit a coherent, meaningful description to be formulated in such terms. Thus although the results of his study cannot be in conflict with biology or chemistry or physics, the physiologist must concentrate upon other attributes of his system than the biologist, the chemist, or the physicist. His model takes its place in the network that relates such dissimilar, detailed processes as the human respiratory cycle, the evolution of stars, and the production of light to each other through our contemporary knowledge of atomic and subatomic processes. To a physicist it is satisfying to know that all matter and all natural processes are probably comprehensible in terms of a few basic entities. On the other hand, the fact that these basic entities can interact and combine to yield the virtual infinity of forms observed in nature is, to him, a matter of never-ending wonder and delight.

◤◤ 1.2   The physicist's approach to nature

What, then, is physics? Textbooks written two or three decades ago before the general ideas of atomic physics had become a part of the common culture often spoke of physics as the study of matter and energy, and consequently made a subject that has challenged some of the best minds during the past several centuries seem as dry as dust. R. P. Feynman captures something of the spirit of physics when he defines it as a search for the rules of the game. He likens a physicist studying nature to a man observing a giant game of chess. By studying the sequences of moves and responses on the board the observer tries to comprehend the rules. He frames hypotheses, tries to check them by observation, modifies and extends them if appropriate. Just as he thinks he understands everything, one of the players makes a move he hasn't seen before, and as a consequence the observer may have to throw away a portion of his rule book and begin again. Ultimately he may compile a complete set of rules, and these rules will serve as his model of the game. But he cannot call himself a chess master, for understanding the rules of a game is not equivalent to playing it as an expert. For the same reason a competent physicist is not automatically equipped to do the work of a chemist, a geologist, or a biologist. However, none of these other scientists can have a really fundamental competence in his own field unless he has some acquaintance with the physicist's rule book.

What set of procedures should be used in compiling the rule book? There is no unique answer to the question. Indeed, several different approaches to the problem have been tried. As even a superficial study of the ancient Babylonian, Egyptian, Chinese, and Hindu civilizations will indicate, an interest in nature was certainly not confined to one people. Yet for a variety of reasons, only the ancient Greeks sought the simple, coherent type of natural philosophy that we have likened to a book of rules. As already noted, the Ionian philosophers of the sixth century B.C. introduced the idea that the compilation of a relatively simple rule book was possible, and tried to formulate their natural philosophy by speculating about the way they thought things should be. This approach was refined during the next centuries and culminated with the philosophy of Plato (427–347 B.C.) who taught that all forms in the visible world are but reflections of their ideal counterparts existing in what he termed the real world. Thus the idea that complex reality is best comprehended in terms of an abstract model already was present in the third century B.C. Unfortunately Plato also asserted that study of visible forms could yield little or no information about the ideal forms. The properties of the latter were to be found by pure speculation. Clearly the reproducibility requirement of modern science wouldn't be applicable to such a procedure for there would be no objective way to decide which of two alternative models of the ideal world was superior.

Aristotle (384–322 B.C.), a pupil of Plato, was much more literal minded, and sought a universal system that would be consistent with at least the broad outlines of the visible world. He conceived of natural processes in terms of the progression of things toward their ultimate, predestined forms. Application of the idea in effect precluded the possibility of learning anything from an abstract model of a particular system, since presumably the predestined form of a system is determined by the complex whole rather than upon a few of its attributes. Therefore, Aristotelian natural philosophy leads to an extensive catalogue of many observed processes rather than to a book of rules relating the processes to each other.

Throughout the Middle Ages and the Renaissance the interpretation of natural processes by Western European scholars was dominated by the teachings of the Greek philosophers, particularly Plato and Aristotle. It remained for the sixteenth- and seventeenth-century scholars to devise the procedures we now call scientific. Galileo Galilei (1564–1642) probably did more to define and codify these procedures than any other single individual (Figure 1.1). From Plato he took the idea of abstraction, or model making, reasoning that many apparently dissimilar systems would behave in the same way if their dissimilarities could somehow be neglected. (That idea is inconsistent with Aristotelian philosophy, since in that philosophy the negation of some attribute of a system alters the entire system.) Unlike Plato, Galileo insisted that the ideal, common behavior of several systems could not be discovered by pure speculation. Instead, the behavior of many systems must be studied before abstraction to the ideal is possible.

Galileo used his combined experimental-speculative approach in several investigations, the most famous being his inclined plane experiments. The length of time a real object requires to travel down a real inclined plane varies with the length of the plane, with its inclination to the horizontal, and with the roughness of the plane and the object. Given two planes of equal length inclined at the same angle to the horizontal, the measured transit time down the plane for a real object depends upon the nature of its surface and the surface of the plane. Galileo assumed that the tendency for all bodies to slide down inclined planes is more fundamental than the dissimilarities in the motion of two different bodies on the same plane. By experimenting with many different objects on many different planes he obtained enough information to conclude that the transit time for *all* objects down a completely smooth plane of a given length and inclination would be exactly the same. Finally, by comparing the speeds of objects down a plane as its inclination to the horizontal increased he was able to extrapolate to the limiting case of a vertical plane, and to conclude that all freely falling objects accelerate at the same, constant rate regardless of their dissimilarities.* Galileo's critics suggested that his conclusion was

---

* Free fall is discussed in detail in Chapters 2 and 4.

FIGURE 1.1   Title page to the first edition of Galileo's *Discourses Concerning Two New Sciences* (1638).

erroneous, for if, say, a small stone and a feather are dropped from a moderate height the stone reaches the ground well before the feather. He retorted that he was concerned with the nature of the ideal case in which they *would* strike the ground simultaneously. Given an understanding of the ideal the reasons for any observed departures from it can be studied by focusing further observations upon deviations from the ideal. In the present instance the dissimilarities between the motion of the stone and feather arise from the fact that they fall through air, which offers a different resistance for the two objects.

There are two important aspects of Galileo's approach that must be balanced in any scientific investigation: first, the need for careful and extensive observation, second, the existence of a goal or purpose that lends coherence to the observations and aids in their interpretation. Lacking the latter, the results of experiment become unrelated entries in a catalogue rather than evidence to be used in constructing an ideal model. Galileo was not interested in observing the motion of all possible bodies on all possible inclined planes. Rather, he wanted to learn what the motion of all these bodies had in common. That was his goal, and it dictated both the extent and variety of his experiments and the steps in their interpretation.

If a body of observational data is to be subject to the reproducibility requirement cited in Section 1.1, it should be formulated in a language that emphasizes the type of abstraction represented by the data which can be easily and unambiguously comprehended by other would-be investigators. Mathematics is just such a language,* as Galileo emphasized in an open letter to a critic:

> Philosophy is written in this grand book, the universe, which stands ever open to our gaze. But the book cannot be understood unless one first learns to comprehend the language and read the letters in which it is composed. It is written in the language of mathematics, and its characters are triangles, circles, and other geometric figures without which it is humanly impossible to understand a single word of it; without these, one wanders about in a dark labyrinth.†

In other words, the models of systems and processes that physicists abstract from observational data are *mathematical* models. Once a theory is verified from a particular set of processes it is desirable to test its applicability to other related processes, thereby generalizing and extending it until it takes its place in the growing network of theories which, as we noted in Section 1.1, constitutes contemporary scientific knowledge. If the results of a scientific investigation are formulated mathematically then the method of generalizing is usually unambiguous.

▲▲ 1.3 The phenomena of motion and the forces of nature

Galileo's detailed study of motion was consistent with his assumption that natural processes can best be comprehended by concentrating upon their similarities, for the word *process* implies change, and certainly motion is one of the most universally observed types of change. Galileo founded the study of *kinematics*, the mathematical *description* of motion irrespective of its cause, which constitutes the subject matter of the next two chapters. His work served as one of the principal foundations upon which Sir Isaac Newton (1642–1727) erected his monumental system of natural philosophy, enunciated in his *Philosophiae Naturalis Principia Mathematica* (*Mathematical Principles of Natural Philosophy*), first published in 1687 and usually referred to simply as the *Principia* (Figure 1.2). Newton moved beyond Galileo by incorporating the basic *causes* of motion into the book of rules. He asserted that the motion of two or more bodies is related to their *interactions*, and that these interactions are related in turn to the fundamental properties of the bodies. Thus the *Principia* provides a complete outline of one possible way to investigate the rules of the game:

> . . .the whole burden of philosophy seems to consist in this—from the phenomena of motions to investigate the forces of nature, and from these forces to demonstrate the other phenomena; . . . .‡

---

* Any system of mathematics is based upon a set of axioms and postulates assumed from the start which define the system and are not considered to be either true or false in themselves. Conclusions are then drawn from these axioms and postulates according to a defined set of procedures. Therefore, mathematics has nothing to do with natural phenomena. It is a system of logic rather than a science. The test of a proposition or conclusion in mathematics rests with its consistency with the basic axioms and postulates of the system. In contrast, the test of a scientific theory is the success with which it describes observed natural processes.

† Galileo Galilei, "The Assayer," from *Discoveries and Opinions of Galileo*, trans. by Stillman Drake, pp. 237–38. Copyright © 1957 by Stillman Drake. Reprinted by permission of Doubleday and Co.

‡ *Sir Isaac Newton's Mathematical Principles of Natural Philosophy and His System of the World*, translation revised by Florian Cajori, University of California Press, Berkeley, 1934. From Newton's Preface to the First Edition, pp. xvii and xviii.

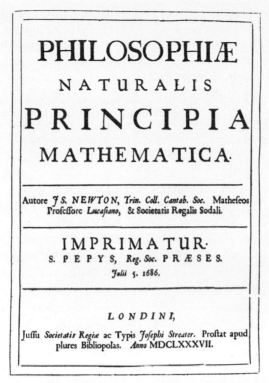

FIGURE 1.2 Title page to the first edition of Newton's *Mathematical Principles of Natural Philosophy*. (Courtesy of The Royal Society, London.)

Without a doubt, Newton's general prescription for investigating natural processes qualifies him as the founder of modern science. As we shall learn later in the text some of the detailed assumptions he made in applying his general ideas to specific problems have since been modified in the light of later experimental results. Nevertheless his basic approach, which links the motion of bodies to their properties by means of their inter-actions, is still the central working assumption in physics. Thus we might define physics as a study of matter and motion, though we would run the undoubted risk of making the subject seem terribly dull. On the other hand, as Galileo correctly noted, all natural processes involve motion. Hence if physics is defined as the study of matter and motion its subject matter includes automobiles on highways, stones in free fall, vibrating guitar strings, gas molecules colliding with each other and with the walls of their container, satellites orbiting the earth, electrons moving along a copper conductor, high velocity protons moving through a bubble chamber, rotating galaxies, and the expanding universe itself (Figure 1.3).

All of these systems and many more fall within the province of physics. Its purpose, as Feynman suggests, is to investigate the rules underlying their behavior. But physics is more than its subject matter, more than its purpose. It includes a corpus of concepts and methods which, applied to experimental data, have led to the interconnecting network of theories that Feynman calls the rules of the game. Physics, in short, is also one of the most impressive achievements of the human imagination and intellect which not only serves as the basis for all other branches of science, but is in itself an important part of the Western cultural tradition.

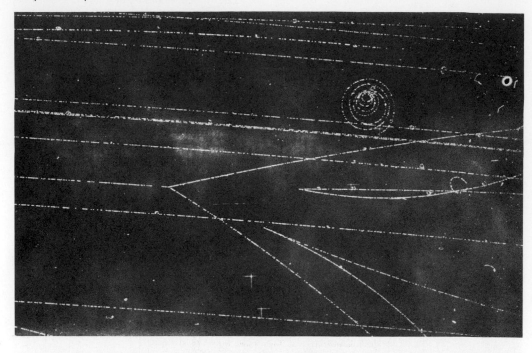

(a)

FIGURE 1.3   Two examples of matter in motion. (a) Very high velocity protons (entering from the left) interact to produce secondary particles in a liquid hydrogen bubble chamber. The motion of the particles is studied by measuring the curvatures of their tracks in a strong magnetic field. (See Chapter 9.) (Photograph courtesy of the Brookhaven National Laboratory.) (b) One of the most distant objects ever photographed: 3C295 in the constellation Bootes as seen by the 200-inch Hale telescope. The inset at the bottom shows the measured spectrum of the light from the object, and can be used to determine its velocity relative to the earth. From these data it has been concluded that 3C295 is more than two billion light years away. (Photograph from the Mount Wilson and Palomar Observatories.)

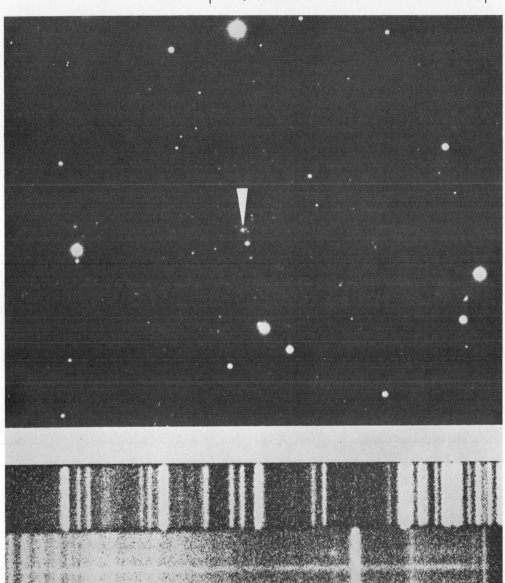

(b)

SUGGESTIONS FOR FURTHER READING ▲▲▲

The number of books and magazine articles on the history, philosophy, and methodology of physics, as well as on the influence of physics in the humanities and social sciences is far too vast to list here. Fortunately, two extended bibliographies of references in these areas already exist:

ALFRED M. BORK AND ARNOLD B. ARONS, "Resource Letter Col R-1 on Collateral Reading in Physics," *American Journal of Physics*, Vol. 35, p. 1 (1967).

MARJORIE NICHOLSON, "Science and Literature," *American Journal of Physics*, Vol. 33, p. 175 (1965).

Without a doubt one of the best general discussions about what physics is all about appears in: R. P. Feynman, R. B. Leighton, and M. Sands, *The Feynman Lectures on Physics*, Vol. 1, Addison-Wesley Publishing Co., Inc., Reading, Mass., 1963, Chapters 1–3.

Three anthologies deserve special mention:

ARNOLD B. ARONS AND ALFRED M. BORK, *Science and Ideas*, Prentice-Hall, Inc., Englewood Cliffs, N.J., 1964.

American Foundation for Continuing Education, *The Mystery of Matter*, Oxford University Press, New York, 1965.

National Science Foundation, *Exploring the Universe*, McGraw-Hill Book Co., New York, 1963.

Finally, a special volume issued on the occasion of the centennial celebration of the National Academy of Sciences contains a number of very readable articles on the state of knowledge in the various branches of science and on the place of science in contemporary society, including an address to the Academy by President John F. Kennedy: *The Scientific Endeavor*, published by The Rockefeller Institute Press, 1963.

Kinematics: the description of motion

2

There is, in nature, perhaps nothing older than motion, concerning which the books written by philosophers are neither few nor small; nevertheless I have discovered by experiment some properties of it which are worth knowing and which have not hitherto been either observed or demonstrated.*   GALILEO GALILEI

▲▲ 2.1 Motion of an automobile in one dimension. Average speed

Before attempting to understand the evolution of Newtonian dynamics it would be wise to obey Galileo's dictum quoted in Chapter 1 and turn to the development of a systematic, quantitative description of motion, leaving questions relating to particular causes for later chapters. Kinematics—the mathematical study of motion—seeks a consistent description of the observed changes in the spatial positions of physical objects. Hence we begin by finding a consistent way to locate such physical objects in time and space, then extend the description to encompass *changes* in spatial positions with time. But the nature of the various objects we might hope to describe are vastly different, as are the means used to observe them. Electrons traveling in a copper wire manifest their motion as an electric current, whereas an electron in a bubble chamber is observed only after it has passed through the chamber and left a track. The successive spatial positions of a vibrating string can be studied by means of high-speed photography, while the orbit of a planet can be established only after several months of telescopic observation. Hence it does not necessarily follow that the methods developed to describe the motion of automobiles and falling bodies will be terribly useful in describing vibrating strings or electrons. The best that can be done is to work out a consistent mathematical method to describe the motion of the more familiar types of objects and then see if the method can be generalized successfully to less familiar cases. If it can, well and good; if not, a basic reexamination will be in order.

It will be profitable to begin our mathematical study of motion by refining and generalizing some ideas familiar from common usage. One can scarcely think of a more familiar

---

* Galileo Galilei, *Dialogues Concerning Two New Sciences,* trans. by Henry Crew and Alfonso de Silvio. Copyright by The Macmillan Co., 1914; McGraw-Hill Paperback Edition, 1963, p. 147.

type of motion than that of an automobile. We want to ask what we mean by the statement: an automobile travels sixty miles per hour. Of course it is possible to think of sixty miles per hour in terms of a speedometer reading and go no further, but since we shall also want to talk about the motion of objects that do not come equipped with speedometers it would be best to inquire about the more basic meaning of the term.

When we say that an object moves we mean that it is found at different places at different times. Thus its motion may be described by listing its changing position at a number of different times. Parenthetically, it would be well to note that the automobile's motion is by no means simple. For instance, its wheels rotate on their axles and the pistons in its cylinders reciprocate many times per minute. On the microscopic level it is possible to talk about the random motion of molecules of the gas mixture that explodes in its cylinders. Nevertheless, when we speak of the motion of an automobile we usually refer implicitly to the coherent, forward motion of the entire system. Lacking an odometer, its successive positions could be measured with reference to a series of markers placed at regular intervals of, say, one-tenth of a mile along the highway. Since the automobile is an extended object different parts of it will be at different places at the same time. To make the position measurements unambiguous we can measure the position of a single point on the body—say the tip of the hood ornament. The choice is arbitrary since all points on the body of the auto maintain the same spatial relation to each other as the whole system moves forward. In fact, this is the meaning of the term "forward motion of the complete system." Odometer readings are equivalent to comparing a single moving point with mileposts on the highway.

Table 2.1 is a typical record a passenger might keep, listing correlated time and position

TABLE 2.1   *Record of Motion on Toll Road for Eight Minutes*

1	2	3	4	5	6	7	8
Clock reading	Odometer reading	t (min)	x (miles)	Δt (min)	Δx (miles)	$\bar{v} = \dfrac{\Delta x}{\Delta t}$ (miles/min)	$\bar{v}$ (miles/hr)
10:15	13,974.6	0	0.0				
				1.0	0.2	0.2	12.0
10:16	13,974.8	1	0.2				
				1.0	0.4	0.4	24.0
10:17	13,975.2	2	0.6				
				1.0	0.6	0.6	36.0
10:18	13,975.8	3	1.2				
				1.0	0.8	0.8	48.0
10:19	13,976.6	4	2.0				
				1.0	0.8	0.8	48.0
10:20	13,977.4	5	2.8				
				1.0	0.9	0.9	54.0
10:21	13,978.3	6	3.7				
				1.0	0.9	0.9	54.0
10:22	13,979.2	7	4.6				
				1.0	0.9	0.9	54.0
10:23	13,980.1	8	5.5				

measurements of an automobile on a straight, level toll road during the first eight minutes after it leaves the entrance station. He notes the initial odometer reading (say 13,974.6) and uses the symbol x_0 to designate that mileage. He also notes the initial time (10:15 A.M.), which he calls t_0. Thereafter he records the odometer reading at the end of each minute and records these correlated time and distance measurements as the raw data of columns 1 and 2.

Columns 3 and 4 are derived from the raw data of columns 1 and 2 by subtracting x_0 from each mileage entry and t_0 from each time entry. These latter columns contain information about the motion of the car during the first eight minutes and, as they involve neither the specific odometer reading nor the time of day, concentrate upon this specific trip and not upon presumably superfluous details.*

Table 2.1 does not give precise information about where the automobile was *during* each minute-long interval between measurements. But Figure 2.1, a graph of the information

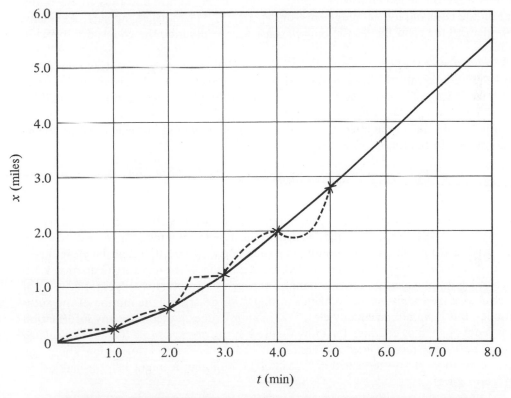

FIGURE 2.1 A graph of the data in columns 3 and 4, Table 2.1, showing the positions of an automobile on a turnpike relative to the toll booth, at one-minute intervals after leaving the booth.

---

* In fact, the derivation of columns 3 and 4 from 1 and 2 makes a rather important assumption about the description of motion: It assumes that the motion of a body during a given time interval can be described *independently* of its past history and of where or when it is described. This does not imply that past history does not in any way determine the present state of an object but only that the observed motion during a given time interval can be *described* without knowing that past history. In other words, the description of motion is to be in terms of *elapsed* distances and *elapsed* times and not in terms of *absolute* locations in time and space. This point is developed further in Chapter 6.

in column 3 plotted against column 4, permits us to make a reasonable guess about its probable position at *any* time. The vertical axis specifies distance from the starting point, the horizontal axis elapsed time. Correlated entries in the two columns appear as cross marks on the plot and show at a glance where the automobile was at the end of each of the minute-long intervals.

It is tempting to connect each of the points with straight line segments and conclude that the resulting solid line specifies the position of the car at all times. But this interpretation is not warranted by the data. It is possible to say only that the continuous line is a *reasonable* indication about where the car was at intermediate times, and for that reason is certainly very useful. But the dotted curve might just as well have been drawn through the data points, though it specifies a much less probable motion. In fact, it implies that the car stopped for a few seconds between the second and third time measurements and actually backed up for a few seconds between the fourth and fifth. Anyone who knows the length of time required to stop, reverse, and start a car would conclude that the dotted curve is a most improbable representation of the motion and thus would rule it out on the basis of physical judgment—or experience. Nevertheless, no such arguments can identify the solid line as the only *possible* way to describe the connection between points.

The motion of the vehicle may also be described by giving its speed during each of the one-minute intervals. Column 6, derived from column 4, gives the *change* in position, Δx (read "delta x"), during each of the measured intervals; column 5 is the length of each time interval, Δt (read "delta t").* Then *by definition* the average speed of the automobile during a time interval Δt is the ratio of the elapsed distance traveled during that interval to the length of the interval itself:

$$v = \frac{\Delta x}{\Delta t},\tag{2.1a}$$

Column 7, the calculated value of the average speed during each of the seven measured intervals, follows by applying Equation 2.1a to the data in columns 5 and 6, while column 8 is derived from column 7 by multiplying each entry by 60. It should be clear that a table of such average speeds, together with the definition of the quantity (Equation 2.1a) is completely equivalent to all of columns 3 through 6. In other words, specification of a set of average speeds is a convenient shorthand for describing the motion of the automobile. But it should be equally clear that column 7 does not contain any information that is not implied by columns 1–6 or by Figure 2.1. *An average speed is always calculated over a particular time interval.* Therefore, it cannot give any information about the precise position of an object within that interval, although it might help in making an informed guess.

In this section we use the term *elapsed distance* to specify distance traveled between two given points, and *average speed* as the ratio of an elapsed distance to a time interval. Later the terms *displacement* and *average velocity* will be introduced, the former specifying both the magnitude of an elapsed distance and the *direction* of motion, the latter the magnitude of an average speed and the direction of motion. These are a special type of quantity which define a direction and are known as *vectors*; elapsed distance and average speed specify only magnitudes and are called *scalar* quantities. Because we restrict the present

---

* A variable preceded by the Greek letter Δ means "change in" that variable.

discussion to motion along a straight line there is no possibility of confusing the vector quantities and the scalar quantities. Nevertheless, it would be well not to use the terms *displacement* and *average velocity* before we discuss vector quantities in more detail.

Two other remarks concerning average speed ought to be made. First that its magnitude depends both upon the *length* of the time interval over which it is measured, and second that its value may differ from one time interval to the next. The elapsed distance an automobile travels during a given *two*-minute interval is not simply twice the distance it travels during a given one-minute interval, as inspection of the table will demonstrate. Rather it is the sum of the elapsed distances during the two one-minute intervals. Hence the average speed over a particular, long time interval usually differs from the average speed over the shorter intervals that compose it. The average speed over a two-minute interval will be equal to the average speed over the two one-minute intervals if and only if the automobile travels equal distances during *any* two equal intervals and therefore travels twice as far in twice the time. This conforms with the definition of steady or uniform motion proposed by Galileo:

> By steady or uniform motion, I mean one in which the distances traversed by the moving particle during any equal intervals of time are themselves equal....
>
> We must add to the old definition...the word "any," meaning by this, all equal intervals of time; for it may happen that the moving body will traverse equal distances during some equal intervals of time and yet the distances traversed during some small portion of these time-intervals may not be equal, even though the time intervals be equal.[*]

According to this criterion the average speed of our automobile is constant after the fifth minute.

The second remark concerns the equivalence of the average speed and the successive position representations of the motion. Given the average speed of the automobile during a specific time interval it is possible to calculate its displacement during that interval by inverting Equation 2.1a:

$$\Delta x = \bar{v} \, \Delta t. \tag{2.1b}$$

But it is *not* possible to calculate its absolute position at the end of the interval (i.e., find out where it is at the end of the interval relative to the toll booth or some other reference point) unless its absolute position at the beginning of the interval is given. Nor is it possible to learn the time of day from the average speed table. In other words, columns 4 and 6 may be reproduced from column 7, but not columns 1 or 2. The concept of average speed involves *intervals* of distance and *intervals* of time and *not* locations in space and time (see footnote, p. 13). In order to reproduce the odometer reading from the speed data it is necessary to know its value at one time (for instance, that it was 13,975.8 three minutes after measurement began), just as knowledge of the clock reading at one time is sufficient to reproduce the time of day.

▶▶ 2.2 Functional relations between variables. Further examples of one-dimensional motion

Table 2.1 and Figure 2.1 record a sequence of correlated position and time measurements for an automobile, and constitute equivalent descriptions of its motion. In making

---

[*] Galileo Galilei, *Dialogues Concerning Two New Sciences*, p. 148.

such measurements we implicitly assume that equal lengths may be marked off along a road, that equal time intervals may be marked off with a clock, and that an unambiguous meaning may be assigned to these length and time intervals. Let us use the term *local event* to specify an occurrence that takes place at a given point in space, at a given instant in time, and is recorded by an observer who is stationed at that point at that time. Used in this sense the correlated entries in Table 2.1 are a series of local events. A record of the successive positions of another automobile's hood ornament by a second local observer would constitute another sequence of local events. It may be interesting to compare the positions of the two at several different times, but to do so we must be certain that the two local observers assign the same values to a given point in space and a given instant in time, and it is by no means evident that this can be done in an unambiguous way. We shall consider this question again in Chapter 11, and discover that in situations involving speeds approaching the speed of light (186,000 miles/sec or 300 million m/sec) there can be considerable disagreement between two different observers on the specification of distance and time intervals. But for the present we are dealing with much smaller speeds, and there is no difficulty in assuming that two different observers can always assign the same values to given points in space and instants in time.

Mathematically the position of the automobile and time in our example are called the *variables* describing its motion. As we have assumed that a particular instant in time may be defined unambiguously at all points in space and not merely at the position of the automobile, we adopt the viewpoint that the automobile's position depends upon time. In general, if two variables describing a particular process are related so that the numerical value assumed by one of them depends upon the numerical value of the other then the variables are said to be *functions* of each other. Thus, in our example, the variable x, specifying the position of the automobile relative to the toll booth, is a function of the variable t, specifying the elapsed time since leaving the booth. This statement is usually summarized by the expression $x = f(t)$ or $x = x(t)$, a notation that gives no explicit information on *how* x depends on t, but simply states the fact that there is a correlation between the variables. The explicit correlation might be spelled out in a number of ways: by means of a table or graph, for example, or by means of an algebraic expression. In fact, we have used the first two methods in Table 2.1 and Figure 2.1.

Extending the functional notation, the expression $x(t_1)$ means "the numerical value of the variable x at the *specific* time t_1," while $x = x(t_2) - x(t_1)$ means "the difference between the numerical values of the variable x or its elapsed distance during the interval $\Delta t = t_2 - t_1$ at specific times t_2 and t_1." In functional notation the numerical value of average speed over the time interval $\Delta t = t_2 - t_1$, must be Equation 2.1a:

$$\bar{v} = \frac{x(t_2) - x(t_1)}{t_2 - t_1}. \tag{2.1c}$$

Let us apply these ideas to the description of some other moving bodies. Figure 2.2a is a multiple time-lapse photograph of a falling body with exposures taken at intervals of $\frac{1}{30}$ of a second. Its apparent displacement during each interval can be measured directly from the photograph. If we know how much its image is reduced by the camera and enlarger, and assume no lens distortions, these apparent distance intervals may be converted into actual intervals measured in meters (or feet) and translated into graphical or tabular form (Table 2.2, Figure 2.2b). The motion of the falling body is described by a series of local events, and its position as a function of time given in Table 2.2. and Figure 2.2b.

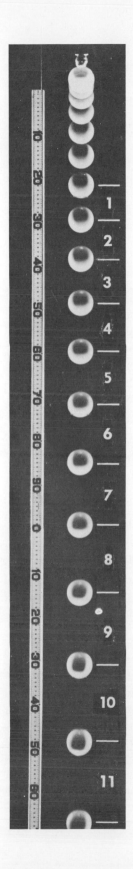

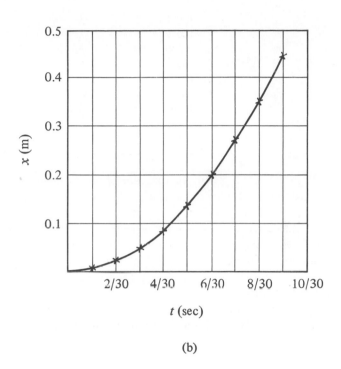

(b)

(a)

FIGURE 2.2 (a) Flash photograph of a falling billiard ball taken at intervals of $\frac{1}{30}$ of a second. The vertical scale is in centimeters (100 cm = 1 m). (From *PSSC Physics*, D. C. Heath and Co., Boston, © 1965, p. 337.) (b) A graph of the data in columns 1 and 2, Table 2.2, showing the position of a falling body relative to its starting point measured at $\frac{1}{30}$-second intervals after it begins to fall.

TABLE 2.2   *Motion of a Falling Body for Nine $\frac{1}{30}$-Sec Intervals Starting from Rest*

1	2	3	4	5
t(sec)	x(m)	Δt(sec)	Δx(m)	$\bar{v} = \dfrac{\Delta x}{\Delta t}$ (m/sec)
0	0			
$\frac{1}{30}$	0.0054	$\frac{1}{30}$	0.0054	0.16
$\frac{2}{30}$	0.022	$\frac{1}{30}$	0.017	0.51
$\frac{3}{30}$	0.049	$\frac{1}{30}$	0.027	0.81
$\frac{4}{30}$	0.087	$\frac{1}{30}$	0.038	1.14
$\frac{5}{30}$	0.136	$\frac{1}{30}$	0.049	1.47
$\frac{6}{30}$	0.196	$\frac{1}{30}$	0.060	1.80
$\frac{7}{30}$	0.267	$\frac{1}{30}$	0.071	2.13
$\frac{8}{30}$	0.348	$\frac{1}{30}$	0.081	2.43
$\frac{9}{30}$	0.441	$\frac{1}{30}$	0.093	2.79

Figure 2.3 is a schematic diagram of an arrangement for measuring the speed of an electron which traverses the straight line path shown by the dashed line. S_1, S_2, S_3, and S_4 represent the positions of counters—devices which produce short electrical impulses upon being traversed by fast, charged particles. These pulses are conveyed to a central location where a record of their arrival times is compiled. In a sense the counters are analogous to the mileposts on a highway, the arrival times of the pulses analogous to the readings on a clock. Table 2.3, giving the position of the electron as a function of time, follows at once.

However, we must not be deceived by the formal analogy between the electron and the automobile. Table 2.1 is a record of measurements by a single observer traveling with the auto, Table 2.3 a record compiled by an observer who receives his information from four different sources at four different locations in space. We may imagine that a local observer at each counter conveys his information to the central location, and must then assume that each observer agrees with the time standards of the other three. In comparing Tables 2.1 and 2.3 we also assume that an observer moving along with the electron would agree with the time and distance measurements of the stationary observers. None of these assumptions need necessarily be correct, especially since the electron's transit

TABLE 2.3   *Record of Pulses Marking the Passage of an Electron Through Counters S_1 to S_4*

1	2	3	4	5	6
t (billionths sec $= 10^{-9}$ sec)	x (m)	t (10^{-9} sec)	x (m)	$\bar{v} = \dfrac{x}{t}$ (m/billionth sec)	$\bar{v}$ (m/sec)
0	$S_1 = 0$				
		21	4.83	2.23	2.3×10^8
21	$S_2 = 4.83$				
		21	4.83	0.23	2.3×10^8
42	$S_3 = 9.66$				
		21	4.83	0.23	2.3×10^8
63	$S_4 = 14.49$				

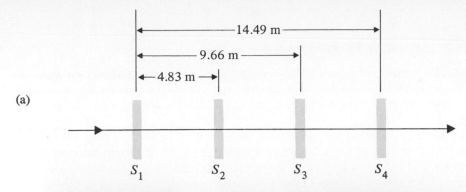

(a)

S_1 S_2 S_3 S_4

(b)

FIGURE 2.3   (a) Schematic diagram of an array of counters for measuring the speed of a high-energy electron. The arrow indicates the electron's path. (b) Apparatus used to detect high-energy particles. Protons from the Brookhaven Laboratory Alternating Gradient Synchrotron (Chapter 21) travel in the direction shown by the long arrow, and are detected by various types of counters (short arrows) along their paths. Cables carrying electrical impulses from these counters to a central control station are in an overhead rack running toward the back of the photograph. Several large electromagnets which focus and bend the charged particles, much as lenses and prisms focus and bend light (Chapter 9), separate the counters. An arrangement similar to this one could be used to detect high-speed electrons. (Photograph courtesy of the Brookhaven National Laboratory.)

time between counters is so short. However, we shall pursue the analogy between the motion of the electron and automobile unless—and until—the assumption causes difficulties. Then we shall have to make a critical reexamination of these assumptions (Chapter 11).

Figure 2.4 shows a method for measuring the apparent position of a planet relative to some fixed star. A pair of cross hairs in the eyepiece of a telescope is fixed upon the reference star, and the telescope pivoted until the planet lines up with the cross hairs. The angle through which the telescope must be moved from star to planet is the angular separation of the star and planet in degrees. If such measurements are repeated at precise, twenty-hour intervals, the angular position of the planet (say, Venus) is observed to change relative to the star. A table containing these nightly position measurements, and the apparent or angular speed of the planet derived from them could then be made. It would be useful information, yet not of the same type found in Tables 2.1, 2.2, and 2.3, for it would say nothing about the *actual* distance the planet moved in miles or meters. We must know, in addition, the distance from the earth to the planet at each point in order to convert angular intervals into actual (or *linear*) distance intervals. Furthermore, these measurements are not made by local observers stationed on the planet. Therefore, we must also assume that the time intervals between successive measurements on earth correspond to equal time intervals at the successive positions of the planet. Since the speed of light is finite this assumption will be valid only if the rate at which the distance between the planet and earth changes is small in comparison.

Finally, let us consider how we might describe the motion of a vibrating guitar string. Three successive configurations of such a string are shown in Figure 2.5. If successive points along the string are labeled $x_1, x_2, x_3, \ldots$, we could certainly compile a table recording the vertical distance of each of these points from its equilibrium position as a

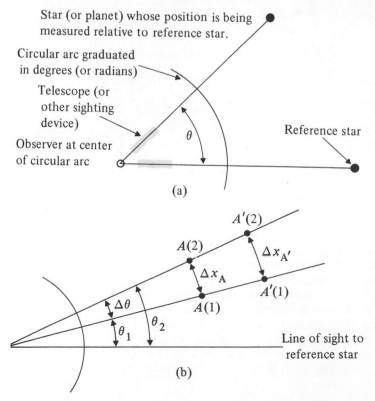

Star (or planet) whose position is being measured relative to reference star.

Circular arc graduated in degrees (or radians)

Telescope (or other sighting device)

Observer at center of circular arc

Reference star

θ

(a)

$A'(2)$

$A(2)$

$\Delta x_{A'}$

Δx_A

$A'(1)$

$\Delta \theta$

$A(1)$

θ_1 θ_2

Line of sight to reference star

(b)

FIGURE 2.4 (a) A method for measuring the angular separation, θ, between two stars, or between a reference star and a planet. (b) The angular position of planet A relative to a reference star on two successive nights (measurements 1 and 2). If the planet were at A' rather than A, the same angular displacements, $\Delta\theta$, would imply a greater actual (or linear) displacement ($\Delta x_{A'}$ greater than Δx_A). Therefore, a measured angular displacement can be translated into a linear displacement only if the distance between the observer and the planet is known.

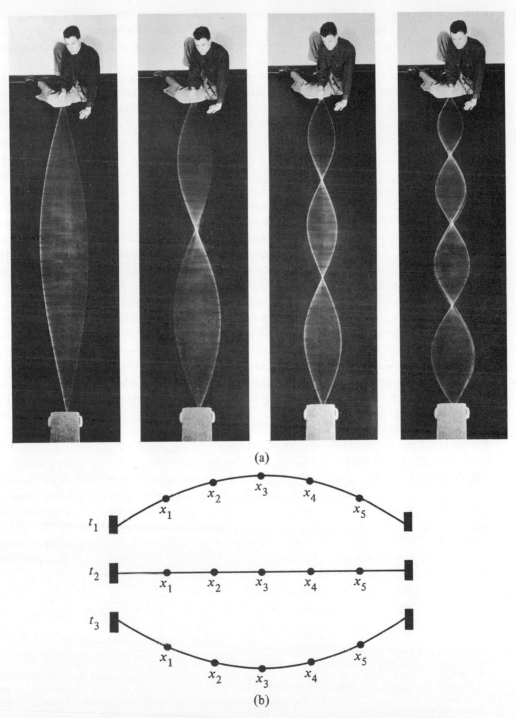

(a)

(b)

FIGURE 2.5 (a) A vibrating string. (From *PSSC Physics*, D. C. Heath and Co., Boston, © 1965, p. 651.) (b) Schematic drawing of the string in the left-most of the four cases in part a at three successive times. The time intervals between t_1 and t_2 and between t_2 and t_0 are equal.

function of time. But since the string is not rigid the spatial positions of the points relative to each other do not remain constant. Consequently, the motion of the string cannot be described in terms of the motion of one selected point. Using mathematical language, the vertical displacement of each point is a function both of time and of its distance from the end of the string. In a later chapter (Chapter 13) we shall see that it is often possible to describe the time variation of all points on a vibrating string in terms of the time variation of one selected point. Thus the description of such vibrations may be made by extending the language used to describe the motion of rigid bodies in terms of the motion of single points.

▶▶ 2.3 Classification of motion. Motion with constant speed

Whereas the description of motion we are evolving is based upon measurements of the *instantaneous* positions of an object at a number of separated points along its path, our intuitive ideas about motion imply that any object must pass along *all* points on its path. In his paradox of the arrow in flight the Greek skeptic Zeno dramatically underscored the difficulty of thinking of motion in terms of a sequence of instantaneous positions. He argued that since the path of an arrow is composed of an infinite number of points with no extension in space, then an arrow that remained for even an instant at each point on its path could never move at all! This argument makes the inconsistent assumption that a time interval may be decomposed into a *finite* number of adjacent instants. But in order to maintain a degree of symmetry between the concepts of time and space intervals on the one hand, and of instants in time and points in space on the other, it is necessary to conceive of an interval in time as divided into an *infinite* number of adjacent instants. From this point of view a moving body has an infinite number of instants available to it, and the paradox is resolved.

Despite the flaw in Zeno's argument the paradox points to a fundamental distinction between our basic intuitive feeling about motion and the sequence of instantaneous time and position measurements used as a basis for its description. When we say an object was here a few minutes ago and is there now we imply that it moved from here to there. We want a description that gives as much information as possible about *how* it traveled between the points. But as has been noted, knowledge of the position of our automobile taken at one-minute intervals gives no positive information about its position at any time within the intervals. At best it permits us to make informed guesses. More detailed information can be obtained by recording its positions more often, say every second rather than every minute. Then the corresponding points on the graph (Figure 2.1) would lie closer together leaving less uncertainty about the positions at intermediate times. Similar remarks apply to the motion of the other objects discussed in Section 2.2.*

---

*It may not always be possible to measure distance intervals over arbitrarily short time intervals without affecting the measured motion. For instance, if the distance an automobile traveled were to be measured over $\frac{1}{10}$-sec intervals, then clearly apparatus more sophisticated than a watch and odometer would be required, and this might distract the driver sufficiently to alter seriously the character of his driving. Similarly, if 200 counters were lined up at six-inch intervals to measure the speed of an electron, the character of an electron's motion would be quite seriously altered, for the electron produces a pulse in each counter as a result of its interaction with the material of that counter. But, as we shall see, with each interaction the character of the electron's motion is modified slightly so that 200 interactions completely alter the motion being measured. This important question —the effect of measurement upon the process being measured—is not taken seriously for the physics of automobiles, falling bodies, vibrating strings, and planets. But it is a very serious matter for the physics of electrons, protons, and atoms (Chapters 17 and 18).

One may wonder where the process ends, for to obtain complete information about the motion of any object would seem to require an indefinite subdivision of time intervals. But classical physics is based in part upon the assumption of regularity and predictability in the physical universe. When applied to motion this assumption suggests that if a sufficient number of correlated time and position measurements are made, an algebraic and/or geometric correlation between these sets of numbers can be found which will serve to predict the position of the body in question at all other times.

The implicit idea that a phenomenon cannot be understood until some mathematical regularity can be ascribed to it originated in ancient Greece and was forcefully restated by Galileo:

> Lines are called regular when, having a fixed and definite description, they are susceptible of definition and of having their properties demonstrated. Thus the spiral is regular, and its definition originates in two uniform motions, one straight and the other circular....Irregular lines are those which have no determinacy whatever, but are indefinite and casual and hence undefinable.... Hence to say, "Such events take place thanks to an irregular path" is the same as to say, "I do not know why they occur"....*

In other words, when we find some regularity in a series of correlated time and position measurements, or, mathematically, find an explicit functional connection between x and t, we have made the important transition from a description of points in time and space to a description of motion.

These regularities are often difficult or even impossible to find. For instance, the motion of an automobile is not the result of a few simple, predictable causes but depends on such factors as the condition of the vehicle, the condition of the highway, the skill of the driver, his whims, and his responses to the behavior of other traffic. Thus one would expect its motion to be irregular. However, after the fifth minute the motion of the automobile described in Table 2.1 is characterized by constant average speed during each succeeding one-minute interval. We might suspect that after the fifth minute the average speed over shorter time intervals is also constant, and that therefore the straight line connecting the last points on Figure 2.1 is a valid geometric description of its motion.

The corresponding algebraic description in this very special case may be obtained from Equation 2.16. By definition a body moving with constant speed travels equal distances in equal time intervals. In other words, the displacement of such a body in a given time interval is directly proportional to the length of the interval, or

$$\Delta x = \bar{v}\, \Delta t.$$

Although this equation is identical in form to Equation 2.1b there is an important distinction between them. In general the average speed of a body depends both upon the time at which it is measured and the length of the interval over which it is defined. Therefore, the numerical value used in Equation 2.1b may vary both with the lengths of the intervals Δt and with the times at which the intervals begin. But in the constant speed case, $\bar{v}$ is the same for all time intervals regardless of their length, regardless of where they begin.

If x is the position of a constant-speed object at some time t, and x_0 its position at some time t_0, then $\Delta x = x - x_0$, $\Delta t = t - t_0$, and

$$(x - x_0) = \bar{v}(t - t_0),$$

or

$$x = x_0 + \bar{v}(t - t_0). \tag{2.2}$$

---

* From *Discoveries and Opinions of Galileo*, trans. by Stillman Drake, p. 241. Copyright © 1957 by Stillman Drake. Reprinted by permission of Doubleday and Co.

Since our automobile moves with constant speed after $t = 5$ min we may choose $t_0 = 5$, $x_0 = 2.9$. Then, since $\bar{v} = 0.9$ miles/min:

$$x = 2.9 + 0.9(t - 5),$$

where x is the distance from the toll booth, t the time since leaving the toll booth. We could also have chosen $t_0 = 10\!:\!15$, $x_0 = 13{,}974.6$ so that x would be the odometer reading and t the time of day, or $x_0 = 0$, $t_0 = 0$ in which case x would be a distance from the point where the speed became constant and t the corresponding time. It is important to note again that Equation 2.2 is valid *only* for the constant speed part of the motion. During the first five minutes the average speed changes from one interval to the next and so depends on the lengths of the intervals themselves. Table 2.1 contains insufficient information on which to base an algebraic description of the motion during these minutes, especially since such descriptions imply a certain degree of confidence about their predictive abilities.

Equation 2.2 is applicable to any object moving with constant speed, and suggests the existence of at least a formal similarity between such objects. More generally, it suggests that various types of motion might be classified according to the nature of the regularity displayed by their algebraic descriptions.

For example, Table 2.3 indicates that the speed of the electron is constant over its entire path. Therefore, if $x_0 = 0$, $t_0 = 0$ in Equation 2.2 the position of the electron relative to the first counter is given as a function of time by

$$x = \bar{v}t,$$

where $\bar{v} = 2.3 \times 10^8$ m/sec.

Table 2.4, which reproduces the data on the falling body from Table 2.2, shows that the distance traveled from one time interval to the next increases with time. Therefore, the average speed of the body (column 5) is not constant, and Equation 2.2 cannot be a valid description of its motion. Column 7 of Table 2.4 lists the ratios of the elapsed distance traveled from the starting point to the *square* of the corresponding elapsed time (x/t^2). Note that this ratio is constant for all times and equal to 4.9 m/sec². Therefore, the motion is described by the equation

$$\frac{x}{t^2} = 4.9 \text{ m/sec}^2,$$

TABLE 2.4   *Motion of a Falling Body for Nine $\frac{1}{30}$-Sec Intervals Starting from Rest**

1 t(sec)	2 x(m)	3 t	4 x	5 $\bar{v}$(m/sec)	6 t^2(sec²)	7 x/t^2(m/sec²)
0	0					
$\frac{1}{30}$	0.0054	$\frac{1}{30}$	0.0054	0.16	$\frac{1}{900}$	4.9
$\frac{2}{30}$	0.022	$\frac{1}{30}$	0.017	0.51	$\frac{4}{900}$	4.9
$\frac{3}{30}$	0.049	$\frac{1}{30}$	0.027	0.81	$\frac{9}{900}$	4.9
$\frac{4}{30}$	0.087	$\frac{1}{30}$	0.038	1.14	$\frac{16}{900}$	4.9
$\frac{5}{30}$	0.136	$\frac{1}{30}$	0.049	1.47	$\frac{25}{900}$	4.9
$\frac{6}{30}$	0.196	$\frac{1}{30}$	0.060	1.80	$\frac{36}{900}$	4.9
$\frac{7}{30}$	0.267	$\frac{1}{30}$	0.071	2.13	$\frac{49}{900}$	4.9
$\frac{8}{30}$	0.348	$\frac{1}{30}$	0.081	2.43	$\frac{64}{900}$	4.9
$\frac{9}{30}$	0.441	$\frac{1}{30}$	0.093	2.79	$\frac{81}{900}$	4.9

* Cf. Table 2.2.

and the desired functional relation between x and t must be

$$x = 4.9t^2. \tag{2.3}$$

◣◣ 2.4 Instantaneous speed

Let us now return to a question first raised in Section 2.1: namely, what is the meaning of the statement "sixty miles an hour"? We have an unambiguous answer for the very special constant speed situation: a speed of sixty miles per hour implies that in any given fraction of an hour an automobile travels a distance equal to that same fraction of sixty miles. For example, it travels 1 mile in 1 min, $\frac{1}{10}$ mile in $\frac{1}{10}$ min. In principle, no matter how small the duration of the time interval the *ratio* of elapsed distance during that interval to the duration of the interval remains constant. Of course this is precisely the statement summarized by Equation 2.2.

Now as the automobile discussed in Section 2.1 moves away from the toll station our intuition about the meaning of motion suggests that its speed increases continuously from zero to the constant value 0.9 miles/h attained at the end of the first five minutes. This suggests that the concept of speed *at an instant* should be meaningful, although it is not obvious how the idea of speed defined as the ratio of a distance to a time interval of finite duration can be made consistent with the idea of speed at an *instant* of time. For obviously an object cannot move at all during a time interval of zero duration.

In order to approach the definition of instantaneous speed let us first note that *constant* speed may be defined over arbitrarily small time intervals. If a body moves with a constant speed equal to 10 m/sec, then by definition it travels 10 m in 1 sec, 1 m in $\frac{1}{10}$ sec, $\frac{1}{10}$ m in $\frac{1}{100}$ sec, $\frac{1}{100}$ m in $\frac{1}{1000}$ sec. We define the *instantaneous speed* of a body as its *average* speed over a vanishingly small time interval. From the above example it is clear that if the speed of a body is constant its instantaneous speed is always equal to its average speed. How shall we apply the definition to a body whose speed is *not* constant?

The data of Table 2.5, which records the sequential positions of a body over five one-second intervals, suggest an answer. Column 3 shows that its average speed calculated

TABLE 2.5 *Successive Position of a Moving Body over Five 1-Sec Intervals and Its Average Speed over These Intervals*

1 t(sec)	2 x(m)	3 $\bar{v} = \dfrac{\Delta x}{\Delta t}$ (m/sec)
0	0	
1	1.1	1.1
2	2.8	1.7
3	5.7	2.9
4	10.4	4.7
5	17.5	7.1

over each succeeding interval is increasing. As we have already noted, however, average speed usually depends upon the length of the interval over which it is calculated, and this is certainly true of the motion described in Table 2.5. For example, the average speed of the body between the second and third second is 2.9 m/sec. But between the second and fourth seconds we have

$$\bar{v} = \frac{10.4 - 2.8}{4 - 2} = \frac{7.6}{2} = 3.8 \text{ m/sec,}$$

while between the second and fifth seconds,

$$\bar{v} = \frac{17.5 - 2.8}{5 - 2} = \frac{14.7}{3} = 4.9 \text{ m/sec.}$$

Thus the average speed increases with the length of the time interval over which it is defined. Further, its *rate* of increase increases (from 2.9 to 3.8 vs 3.8 to 4.9). We would expect the opposite trend if the average speed were calculated over time intervals of ever *decreasing* length starting at $t = 2$ sec, i.e., 2 to 2.1 sec, then 2 to 2.01 sec, etc. That is, we anticipate an average speed that *decreases* with the length of Δt, together with a decreasing discrepancy between these average values. As the time interval over which average speed is defined becomes smaller and smaller the calculated speeds converge toward some particular value. By definition, this limiting value is the instantaneous speed at the beginning of the interval in question.

Thus instantaneous speed is really not speed *at* an instant. Rather, it is average speed defined over a time interval as the time interval becomes vanishingly small, or, in other words, as it *approaches* zero. Mathematically, the ratio $\Delta x/\Delta t$ in these circumstances is known as the *limit* of the ratio. In symbols, instantaneous speed is defined as

$$v_{\text{in}} = \lim_{\Delta t \to 0} \frac{\Delta x}{\Delta t}. \tag{2.4}$$

Henceforth the subscript will be omitted on v_{in}. The symbol v will always mean instantaneous speed and $\bar{v}$ will be reserved for average speed. Note that Equation 2.4 does *not* state that $\Delta t = 0$. In that circumstance Δx would have to equal zero, leading to the indeterminate ratio 0:0 as the value of instantaneous velocity. Rather, Equation 2.4 states that Δt *approaches* zero. The ratio $\Delta x/\Delta t$ may remain appreciable as Δt approaches zero since x is a function of t and therefore Δx and Δt become small together.

Let us use the prescription summarized by Equation 2.4 to find an expression for the instantaneous speed of a falling body as a function of time. We must first write an algebraic expression for the distance it falls during the interval starting at time t and ending at time $t + \Delta t$. Using functional notation and referring to Equation 2.3:

$$x(t) = 4.9t^2,$$

$$x(t + \Delta t) = 4.9(t + \Delta t)^2 = 4.9(t^2 + 2t\,\Delta t + \Delta t^2).$$

Therefore:

and

$$\Delta x = x(t + \Delta t) - x(t) = 9.8t\,\Delta t + 4.9\,\Delta t^2,$$

$$\frac{\Delta x}{\Delta t} = 9.8t + 4.9\,\Delta t.$$

The instantaneous speed of a falling body is defined as the limit of this expression as Δt approaches zero. Now the first term is independent of the duration of the interval Δt, while the second is directly proportional to it. Therefore, as Δt becomes arbitrarily small the dependence of the ratio on the length of the interval becomes negligible. Depending upon the precision desired, it is always possible to choose a Δt so small that it does not contribute to the value of the ratio until the third, the tenth, or the one-hundredth decimal place, for instance. Clearly Δt can never be less than zero, for that would imply a time interval that ends before it begins. Therefore, it Δt is set *equal* to zero the ratio $\Delta x/\Delta t$ attains its value for the smallest conceivable time interval starting with time t. By definition, this is the instantaneous speed of the falling body:

$$v = 9.8t. \tag{2.5}$$

Reasoning in a completely analogous manner, for any object that covers an elapsed distance that varies in direct proportion to the *square* of the elapsed time t,

$$x = kt^2, \tag{2.6a}$$

where k is a constant, the instantaneous speed must be given as a function of time by the equation

$$v = 2kt. \tag{2.6b}$$

We can also interpret instantaneous speed graphically. Figure 2.6 reproduces Figure 2.2b, the graph of elapsed distance against time for the falling body. By definition (Equation 2.1a) the average speed over the interval Δt is the ratio $\Delta x/\Delta t$. The value of Δx is represented geometrically as the vertical distance between the positions of the body at the beginning and end of the interval, while Δt is the corresponding horizontal distance. Then the average speed over the interval must be equal to the ratio of the vertical to the horizontal legs of a right triangle, or simply tan θ. As the legs decrease in length the value of θ (and therefore tan θ) also decreases, but not as the legs themselves. In the limit where the lengths of the legs approach zero the hypotenuse line touches the curve at only one point (i.e., it is *tangent* to the curve), and by definition the tangent of the angle θ in this limit is equal to the instantaneous speed at time t.

▲▲ 2.5 Acceleration. Constant acceleration. Free fall

The instantaneous speed of a body determines the rate of change of its position with time; the magnitude of its acceleration determines the rate of change of its *speed* with time.* It is a quantity that measures the rate at which a body speeds up or slows down, and is related mathematically to speed in exactly the same way as speed is related to position.

Let $v(t_1)$ be the instantaneous speed of a body at time t_1, $v(t_2)$ its instantaneous speed at a later time t_2. Then its change in speed during the interval $\Delta t = t_2 - t_1$ is $\Delta v = v(t_2) - v(t_1)$. By definition, the magnitude of the *average* acceleration during that interval is

$$\bar{a} = \frac{\Delta v}{\Delta t}. \tag{2.7}$$

Like average speed the magnitude of the average acceleration of a body depends, in general, both upon the time it is measured and the length of the time interval over which

---

* Acceleration, like displacement and velocity, is a *vector* quantity, meaning that a direction as well as a magnitude must be specified for it (see Sections 2.1 and 2.9).

The speed of an object specifies the magnitude of its velocity. In this section we deal with the magnitude of acceleration and do not consider its direction. But as there is no generally accepted term like *speed* corresponding to that magnitude we must use the full rather unwieldy phrase "magnitude of acceleration."

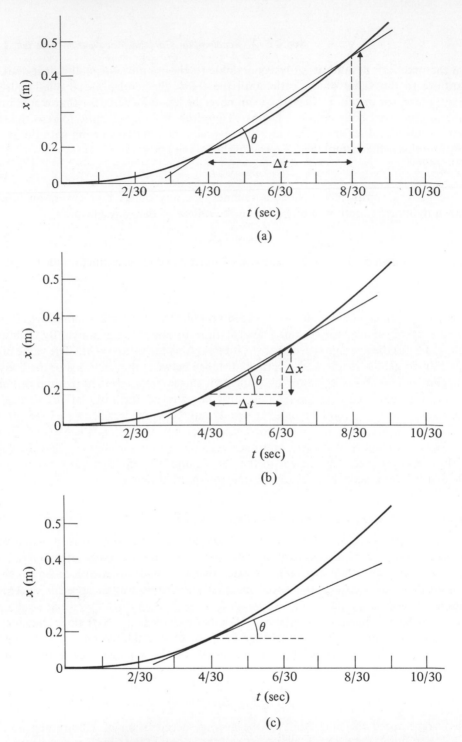

FIGURE 2.6 Geometric interpretation of the approach to a limit. The curves show the position of a falling body as a function of time (Figure 2.2b). The average speed $\bar{v} = \Delta x/\Delta t$, and is therefore proportional to $\tan \theta$, the slope of the straight line passing through the points giving the measured position of the body at the beginning and end of the interval. In part a the interval starts at $t = \frac{4}{30}$ sec and is $\frac{4}{30}$ sec long, In part b it starts at $t = \frac{4}{30}$ sec and is $\frac{2}{30}$ sec long. Finally in part c the straight line is tangent to the curve at $\frac{4}{30}$ sec so that its slope is proportional to the instantaneous speed of the body at that time.

it is measured. The magnitude of the *instantaneous* acceleration is defined analogously to instantaneous speed (Equation 2.4) as the limit of the ratio $\Delta v/\Delta t$ as t approaches zero:

$$a = \lim_{\Delta t \to 0} \frac{\Delta v}{\Delta t}. \tag{2.8}$$

Let us find an expression for the magnitude of instantaneous acceleration for a body whose elapsed distance increases in proportion to the square time, i.e., as given by Equation 2.6a:

$$x = kt^2,$$

with k a constant. According to Equation 2.6b its instantaneous speed is

$$v = 2kt.$$

Let $v(t)$ be its velocity at time t, $v(t + \Delta t)$ its velocity at a later time $t + \Delta t$. Then:

$$v = v(t + \Delta t) - v(t) = 2kt + 2k\,\Delta t - 2kt = 2k\,\Delta t,$$

and

$$\frac{\Delta v}{\Delta t} = 2k.$$

Since the ratio is a constant it is independent of Δt, and in particular retains its value when Δt becomes indefinitely small. Therefore:

$$a = 2k. \tag{2.9a}$$

Taken together, Equations 2.6a, 2.6b, and 2.9a prove that if the distance a body moves increases in direct proportion to the *square* of the elapsed time, its instantaneous speed is directly proportional to time, and the magnitude of its acceleration is constant. The explicit time dependence of the distance it travels and its instantaneous speed follow by substituting $k = \frac{1}{2}a$ into Equations 2.6a and 2.6b:

$$x = \tfrac{1}{2}at^2, \tag{2.9b}$$

$$v = at. \tag{2.9c}$$

In the early seventeenth century Galileo made the first detailed study of falling bodies. From the results of a series of inclined plane experiments, he reasoned that although the speed and magnitude of the acceleration of real falling bodies depend upon such factors as their weights, sizes, and shapes, the observed differences are not fundamental but arise from differences in retardation due to air resistance as they fall. He also concluded that all bodies would fall with the same, constant acceleration in the absence of air resistance. This constant *acceleration due to gravity* is conventionally expressed by the symbol g and a body which falls with this constant acceleration is said to be in free fall. For reasons that will be discussed in Chapter 5, the numerical value of g varies slightly over the surface of the earth. However, it is approximately 32 ft/sec/sec (summarized as 32 ft/sec²). In the metric units used in this text henceforth, $g = 9.8$ m/sec/sec (or 9.8 m/sec²). Substituting $a = g$ in Equations 2.9b and 2.9c, we arrive at equations of motion for the special case of free fall starting from rest at $t = 0$:

$$x = \tfrac{1}{2}gt^2, \tag{2.10a}$$

$$v = gt. \tag{2.10b}$$

If $g = 9.8$ m/sec², Equations 2.10 are identical with Equations 2.3 and 2.5, which were derived from the experimental data of Table 2.2.

In general the instantaneous speed of a body is not constant but rather is a function of time. If the distance it travels in a given time interval is known as a function of time, both its speed and the magnitude of its acceleration follow from an application of the appropriate definitions.

Suppose a body moves such that its distance changes in direct proportion to the cube of time:

$$x = kt^3,$$

with k a constant. Then:

$$\Delta x = x(t + \Delta t) - x(t) = k\{(t + \Delta t)^3 - t^3\},$$

$$= k\{t^3 + 3t^2\,\Delta t + 3t\,\Delta t^2 + \Delta t^3 - t^3\},$$

so

$$\frac{\Delta x}{\Delta t} = 3k\{t^2 + t\,\Delta t + \Delta t^2\},$$

and

$$v = \lim_{\Delta t \to 0} \frac{\Delta x}{\Delta t} = 3kt^2.$$

To find the magnitude of its instantaneous acceleration,

$$v = v(t + \Delta t) - v(t) = 3k\{(t + \Delta t)^2 - t^2\},$$

$$= 3k\{t^2 + 2t\,\Delta t + \Delta t^2 - t^2\}.$$

Then:

$$\frac{\Delta v}{\Delta t} = 6kt + 3k\,\Delta t,$$

and

$$a = \lim_{\Delta t \to 0} \frac{\Delta v}{\Delta t} = 6kt.$$

▲▲ 2.6 Calculation of speed and displacement from acceleration*

At this point it might be legitimate to ask why another function equal to the limit of the ratio $\Delta a/\Delta t$ is not defined, and if it is not, exactly why so much emphasis has been placed on acceleration? Hopefully, the answers will become clear with the discussion of Newton's laws of motion in Chapters 3 and 4. However, a brief preview here would be appropriate.

Newton's second law is a cause and effect relation linking force and acceleration, and implies that if the same force acts upon each of several bodies whose masses† are equal, the accelerations of the bodies will be identical. But this statement does *not* imply that the instantaneous speeds will also be identical, nor that the bodies travel equal distances in equal times. For example, a stone dropped from a 100-meter tower has the same acceleration as a toy dropped by a child playing on the floor, but the positions of the two bodies after one second will obviously be very different. Similarly the speed of a body that has

---

* This section may be omitted without serious loss of continuity.
† *Mass* is defined in Section 4.1.

been falling for five seconds is 49 m/sec, while the speed of one that has been falling for one second is only 9.8 m/sec (Equations 2.10) even though their accelerations are equal.

If the velocities and positions of all objects in a given system are known at the beginning of a particular time interval, *and* if the instantaneous force on each object is also known, then the instantaneous accelerations follow from Newton's second law. Given these accelerations, these *changes* in velocity, the *velocities* the objects will have at the end of that time interval can be calculated. These new velocities may in turn be used to find the new positions of the objects. If the forces on the objects in this *new* configuration are known, the calculations may be repeated to determine a third configuration existing at the end of a second time interval. Indeed, they may be repeated as many times as is required to determine the character of the system's motion.

In summary, calculation of the motion of a system over some definite interval of time requires that two distinct types of data be given:

1. The position and velocity of all bodies in the system at the *beginning* of the interval.
2. The acceleration of each body as a function of time *within* the interval.

Data of type 1 are called the *initial conditions* of the problem; data of type 2 are related to its *dynamics*, to the forces acting on the composite bodies of the system during the time interval of interest.

The validity of this procedure is not restricted to motion along straight line paths. Indeed it is valid for arbitrary trajectories provided the *vector* properties of velocity, acceleration, and force are used in making the calculations (Section 2.8, *et seq.*). We have used these vector terms for that reason. However, for present purposes we shall once again limit our discussion to linear motion, and write down a set of equations summarizing our procedure for the motion of a single body.

Let the time interval during which the motion is to be described start at time t_0, and let the position and instantaneous speed of the body at $t = t_0$ be $x(t_0)$ and $v(t_0)$, respectively. During the small subinterval beginning at t_0 and ending at $t_0 + \Delta t$ the instantaneous magnitude of acceleration is given by Equation 2.8:

$$a(t_0) = \frac{\Delta v}{\Delta t} = \frac{v(t_0 + \Delta t) - v(t_0)}{\Delta t}.$$

Hence the speed at the end of the subinterval is related to the speed at the beginning of the subinterval and the acceleration *during* the subinterval by:

$$v(t_0 + \Delta t) = v(t_0) + a(t_0)\,\Delta t. \tag{2.11a}$$

An equation relating the position at the end of the subinterval to the initial position and the speed *during* the subinterval follows analogously. Since

$$v(t_0) = \frac{\Delta x}{\Delta t} = \frac{x(t_0 + \Delta t) - x(t_0)}{\Delta t},$$

then

$$x(t_0 + \Delta t) - x(t_0) + v(t_0)\,\Delta t. \tag{2.11b}$$

Equations 2.11 only become exact as the duration of Δt approaches zero. If the length of the interval is finite, as it must be for any numerical calculation, the precision obtained depends on how much the acceleration and speed change during the interval, and may be improved by decreasing the length of Δt. By choosing a sufficiently small subinterval it is possible to obtain results to any desired precision.

Since $v(t_0 + \Delta t)$ and $x(t_0 + \Delta t)$ are now known they may be used as the initial conditions required to determine the speed and position at the end of another subinterval of duration Δt (i.e., a subinterval ending at time $t_0 + 2\Delta t$), provided the acceleration during that interval is given. By the same reasoning that led to Equation 2.11:

$$v(t_0 + 2\Delta t) = v(t_0 + \Delta t) + a(t_0 + \Delta t)\Delta t,$$

$$x(t_0 + 2\Delta t) = x(t_0 + \Delta t) + v(t_0 + \Delta t)\Delta t.$$

Similarly, we can immediately write the appropriate equations for the next interval:

$$v(t_0 + 3\Delta t) = v(t_0 + 2\Delta t) + a(t_0 + 2\Delta t)\Delta t,$$

$$x(t_0 + 3\Delta t) = x(t_0 + 2\Delta t) + v(t_0 + 2\Delta t)\Delta t,$$

and so on. Thus given the speed and position of a body at time $t = t_0$, only a knowledge of its acceleration is required to calculate its position and speed at all subsequent times.

▲▲ 2.7 Graphical relations between displacement, speed, and acceleration. Applications to free fall

It will be useful to introduce a geometric interpretation of Equation 2.11. Figure 2.7a is a graph of the instantaneous acceleration of an arbitrary body as a function of time starting at time t_0. According to Equation 2.11a, the change in its speed over the interval from t_0 to $t_0 + \Delta t$ is approximately equal to the product $a(t_0)\Delta t$, represented on the graph as the area of the rectangle with base Δt and height $a(t_0)$. Similarly, the change in speed during the subinterval from $t_0 + \Delta t$ to $t_0 + 2\Delta t$ is approximated as the area of the rectangle with base Δt and height $a(t_0 + \Delta t)$. Therefore, the change in speed from t_0 to $t_0 + 2\Delta t$ is approximately equal to the sum of these two rectangular areas, and the change in speed between time t_0 and any later time t is approximately equal to the sum of all such rectangular areas from t_0 to t. In the limit as the intervals Δt approach zero, the sum of all rectangular areas equals the area under the acceleration curve between t_0 and t, and by definition, this area is exactly equal to the change in speed between these time limits. It follows that the speed at time t is the sum of the speed at time t_0 and the area under the acceleration curve from t_0 to t.

There is a completely analogous connection between the area under a curve representing speed as a function of time and elapsed distance (Figure 2.7b). Therefore, given the position of a body at time t_0, its position at t may be found by adding to it the area under the speed curve from t_0 to t. In general, techniques of the integral calculus are required for the evaluation of areas under curves. However, simple geometric relations suffice if the acceleration is constant.

Figure 2.8a plots constant acceleration against time. The curve is a horizontal line, and thus the area upon the base t_0 to t is rectangular and the change in speed simply the product of the base, by the constant height a. It follows that instantaneous speed is given as a function of time by the equation:

$$v(t) = v(t_0) + a(t - t_0), \tag{2.12a}$$

which reduces to Equation 2.9c in the special case $t_0 = 0$, $v(0) = 0$.

The geometric figure under the instantaneous speed (Figure 2.8b) is composed of a triangle with altitude $a(t - t_0)$ resting upon a rectangular pedestal with altitude $v(t_0)$.

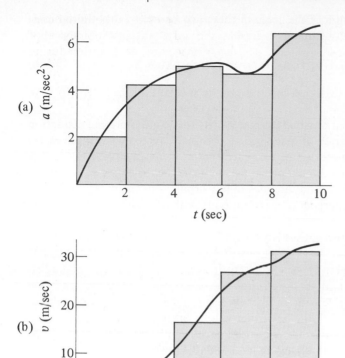

(a)

(b)

FIGURE 2.7 (a) Graphical interpretation of Equation 2.11a. The curve shows the acceleration of a body as a function of time from $t = 0$ to $t = 10$ sec. The increase in its velocity, $\Delta v = a\,\Delta t$, during each 1-sec interval is approximated by the area of the appropriate shaded rectangle. As the lengths of these time intervals approach zero, each rectangle becomes an increasingly better approximation to Δv over the interval. Therefore, the increase in the body's velocity from 0 to 10 sec is equal to the area under the a vs t curve. (b) Similarly, the elapsed distance traveled from 0 to 10 sec is equal to the area under the curve giving its velocity as a function of time. N.B.: The motion described by Figure 2.7a is not related to that described by Figure 2.7b.

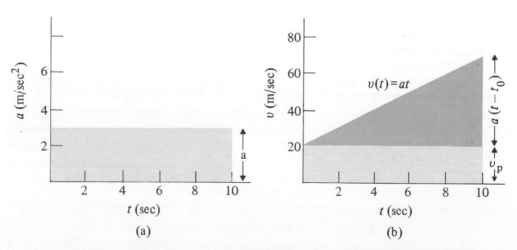

(a)

(b)

FIGURE 2.8 Geometric derivation of Equation 2.12. (a) Since the acceleration is constant, the change in velocity from $t_0 = 0$ to $t = 10$ sec is equal to area of the rectangle with base $t - t_0$ and altitude a, or $\Delta v = a\,\Delta t$ (Equation 2.12a). (b) The area under the curve for constantly increasing velocity $v = v_0 + a\,\Delta t$ ($\Delta t = t - t_0$; $t = 10$ sec, $t_0 = 0$) is composed of a triangular area with base Δt and altitude $a\,\Delta t$ on top of a rectangular pedestal with altitude v_0. Therefore, $\Delta x = v_0\,\Delta t + \frac{1}{2}a\,\Delta t^2$ Equation 2.12b.

The area under the curve is the sum of the areas of these two figures so that the position of the body is given as a function of time by:

$$x(t) = x(t_0) + v(t_0)(t - t_0) + \tfrac{1}{2}a(t - t_0)^2. \qquad (2.12b)$$

Again, Equation 2.12b reduces to Equation 2.9b in the special case $t_0 = 0$, $v(0) = 0$, $x(0) = 0$.

We have noted (Section 2.5) that any body subject solely to the gravitational attraction of the earth has constant acceleration of magnitude 9.8 m/sec² directed toward the earth. It follows that differences in the motion of two such bodies is attributable only to differences in their initial conditions. In Chapter 4 we shall use this principle to relate the motion of falling bodies, projectiles, and satellites in low orbits. For the present we must be content with the simpler comparison of a falling body with a body thrown vertically upward from the ground.

We first select a *frame of reference*, that is we decide what time we shall call t_0, what point we shall call x_0, and whether we shall let positive values of x specify the upward or downward direction. Each of these choices is arbitrary since two people can make two entirely different sets of choices and yet agree upon the description of the motion. One choice of t_0 can be made to coincide with another by setting one clock ahead or behind, a process that does not interfere with the basic interval-measuring function of the clock. Likewise, the end of a tape measure may be raised or lowered and/or the entire tape measure turned upside down without changing its length.* However, the upward direction is conventionally called positive, meaning that increasing positive values of x specify increasing distances from the ground. Likewise it is convenient to take the point $x = 0$ on the ground, and let $t = 0$ mark the beginning of the time interval during which the motion is to be followed.

Now we note that the particular acceleration we are considering always results in a downward or *negative* change in speed so that the speed of a *falling* body *increases* with time, while the speed of an *ascending* body *decreases*. Therefore, in our frame of reference rising bodies have positive speeds (their positions become more positive with time), falling bodies negative speeds, and *all* bodies the constant, negative acceleration $-g = -9.8$ m/sec².

Let an object be dropped from some height x_0 at time $t = 0$. How long does it take to reach the ground? What is the speed at the instant before it arrives? Since we know its acceleration is -9.8 m/sec² it is only necessary to define initial conditions, make the proper substitutions in Equation 2.12, and solve the equations to find the answers. According to the statement of the problem $t_0 = 0$, $x(t_0) = x_0$, and $v(t_0) = 0$ (because the body is dropped, its initial velocity is zero). Then:

$$x(t) = x_0 - \tfrac{1}{2}gt^2,$$

$$v(t) = -gt.$$

The elapsed time follows by solving the first of these equations for $x(t) = 0$, since this specifies the ground position:

$$t = \sqrt{2x_0/g}$$

---

* The fact that these operations are possible implies the existence of a set of symmetries in the physical universe (see Chapter 6).

Given this elapsed time the speed of the body immediately prior to striking the ground follows by substituting into the second equation:

$$v = -g\sqrt{2x_0/g} = -\sqrt{2x_0 g}.$$

Now consider an object thrown vertically upward with speed v_0. How high does it rise? How long does it take to rise? When does it again strike the ground? This problem differs from the previous one only in its initial conditions. Here $t_0 = 0$, $x(t_0) = 0$, $v(t_0)v_0$. Substituting into Equations 2.12:

$$x(t) = v_0 t - \tfrac{1}{2}gt^2,$$

$$v(t) = v_0 - gt.$$

On reaching its maximum height the body has zero instantaneous velocity. Therefore, solution of the second equation for $v(t) = 0$ gives the time the body requires to reach its maximum height, while substitution of this time into the first equation gives the maximum height itself.

Since the body momentarily stops when it reaches the maximum height its subsequent motion is nothing more than a case of free fall from rest, and therefore the method used in the previous problem is applicable. Alternately (and more simply) we note that since a time t is required for the rising body to decelerate to rest, and since its acceleration is -9.8 m/sec^2 regardless of whether it is rising or falling, the same time is required for the return trip over the same path. Likewise, its speed prior to striking the ground must be equal in its initial speed.

▲▲ 2.8 Motion in two and three dimensions. Cartesian coordinate systems. Vectors

The reason for restricting the algebraic and geometric apparatus we have developed to motion along a straight line may not be immediately evident, for the concept of distance along a curved path certainly has a well-defined meaning. For example, the distance an automobile travels between two points on a winding road may be measured by means of its odometer, or by referring to markers placed at equal distances along the shoulder of the highway. The speed along the path is the rate of change of elapsed distance with time, as before, and the magnitude of acceleration the rate of change of speed with time. However, the procedure requires a detailed specification of the automobile's path before the distance between two points on that path may be calculated.

A simpler procedure retains the essential features of the straight-line description already developed. Figure 2.9 shows the path of some arbitrary object between the points a and e. The horizontal and vertical axes might represent the respective east–west and north–south directions, for instance, or any other two perpendicular directions. Let us define the magnitude of the *displacement* of the object from a to e (Δs) as the length of the straight line segment between the two points, and the magnitude of the displacement between any other two points on the curve as the straight-line distance between them. Then in analogy with Equation 2.1a the average speed over the path between the points a and e is the ratio of the magnitude of the displacement, Δs, to the time interval required to move from a to e:

$$\bar{v} = \frac{\Delta s}{\Delta t}. \tag{2.13a}$$

The definitions seem both arbitrary and inadequate at first sight, since there are an infinite number of possible paths between the end points. However, we are going to be

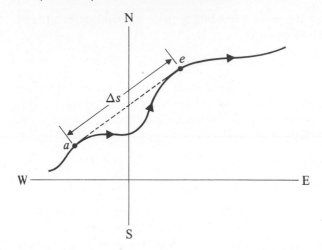

FIGURE 2.9 The magnitude of the displacement between any two points on a body's path is defined as the length of the straight line joining them.

concerned with instantaneous rather than average speeds and shall define instantaneous speed in analogy with Equation 2.4 as the limit of the ratio of the displacement magnitude to the time interval as the length of the interval approaches zero:

$$v = \lim_{\Delta t \to 0} \frac{\Delta s}{\Delta t}. \tag{2.13b}$$

As the interval Δt decreases, the distance a body travels also decreases, whether that distance is measured along the curve or along the straight line joining the positions of the body at the beginning and end of the interval. The discrepancy between the two distances also decreases. In other words, for decreasing segments of path length the actual distance between two points approaches the linear distance, and in the limit the discrepancy disappears completely. Hence there is no inconsistency in taking Equation 2.13b as the generalization of Equation 2.4.

The position of any point on a straight-line path relative to some reference point may be completely specified by one number: its distance from the reference point. In contrast, two numbers are required to specify the relative positions of two points in a plane. For example, the position of an automobile on a flat, winding road is defined by saying it is six miles north and four miles east of a toll booth, regardless of the path it took to get there. If the road is in the mountains its elevation relative to the toll booth is also required. Hence motion in a straight line may be described in terms of the variation of *one* number with time, motion restricted to a plane in terms of the variation of *two* numbers with time, and motion in space in terms of the time variation of *three* numbers.

The two numbers required to specify the position of a point in a plane may be taken as the perpendicular distances between the point and two perpendicular reference axes or *coordinate* axes. Such a system is called a rectangular or Cartesian coordinate system, in honor of René Descartes (1596–1650). The horizontal axis of such a system is usually called the *x*-axis, the vertical axis the *y*-axis, and their interaction point the *origin* (Figure 2.10a). Such a system constitutes a frame of reference in the plane, that is, a system to which all points in the plane may be referred. In describing any physical process both the position of the origin and the orientation of the perpendicular axes relative to the system described is entirely arbitrary although this is by no means obvious.* For instance, there is no fundamental reason why the direction north need be

* See footnote, p. 13.

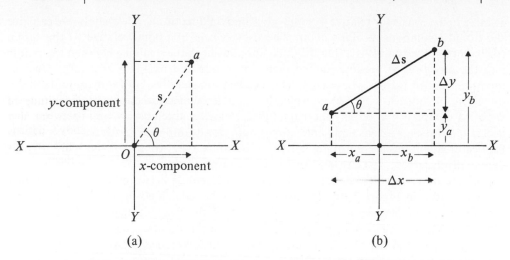

(a)   (b)

FIGURE 2.10   Specification of the position of a point in a plane in terms of the *x*- and *y*-components of its displacement relative to the origin of a Cartesian coordinate system. (b) The displacement between two points in a plane in terms of the *algebraic* differences between their *x*- and *y*-components in a Cartesian coordinate system. Since the *x*-component of point *a* is negative, the magnitude of Δx is greater than the magnitudes of either x_a or x_b.

the direction of the north geographic pole. It might just as well have been chosen as the direction of the north geographic pole or as some other direction. Once *north* is defined, however, the east–west direction is also defined by the requirement that it be perpendicular to the north–south direction.

By convention, distances along the *x*-axis to the right of the origin are positive, distances to the left negative. Similarly, distances on the *y*-axis above the origin are positive, distances below the origin negative. By definition, the distance *s* from any point in the plane to the origin is the length of the straight line connecting the point to the origin. The *x*-distance from the origin to the point (also called the *x*-component of *s*) is defined as the distance measured *along the x-axis* from the origin to the intersection of the *x*-axis and the perpendicular dropped from the point in question. The *y*-component of *s* is defined analogously with respect to the *y*-axis.

Referring to Figure 2.10a, the distances between the origin and the point *a* is related to its *x*- and *y*-components by the Pythagorean theorem:

$$s^2 = x^2 + y^2,$$

while the angle between the straight line joining the points and the *x*-axis may be found from the relation:

$$\tan \theta = \frac{y}{x}.$$

Therefore, the position of any point in a plane is specified completely by giving its *x*- and *y*-components relative to some Cartesian coordinate system.

Suppose that point *a* in Figure 2.10a represents a point on the path of a moving body. The straight-line distance *s* is its distance from the origin. However, it should be clear that specification of a particular distance does *not* uniquely define the position of a point in a plane. We must also give the direction of the line joining the point and the origin relative to the x-axis (or relative to some other known direction). Alternately, we can give the x- and y-components of the point. The *displacement* of a point relative to the origin (or to some other point) is a quantity that specifies both the distance between the points and the direction of the line joining them. It is our first example of a large class of quantities called *vectors* whose complete specification requires both a magnitude and a direction, in contrast with *scalars*, which have no associated direction and which may be specified completely in terms of a magnitude. Velocity, acceleration, and force are also vector quantities, whereas mass and temperature, for example, are scalars. The symbols for vector quantities are normally written in boldface type; thus **s**, **v**, and **a** are used to denote displacement, velocity, and acceleration, respectively.

Both the magnitude and direction of the displacement Δ**s** between *any* two points on a curve (*b* and *a* in Figure 2.10b, for instance) may be calculated in terms of the x- and y-components of the vector. The x-component of the displacement Δx is simply the difference between the respective x-components of the points referred to the origin, while the y-component of displacement, Δy, is the difference between the respective y-components. Therefore,

$$\Delta s^2 = \Delta x^2 + \Delta y^2 = (x_b - x_a)^2 + (y_b - y_a)^2, \qquad (2.14a)$$

and

$$\tan \theta = \frac{\Delta y}{\Delta x}. \qquad (2.14b)$$

Generalization of these remarks to three dimensions follows in a completely natural way. A third axis called z is established in the direction mutually perpendicular to the x- and y-axes, and all points in space specified by their x-, y-, and z-components. The magnitude of the displacement Δ**s** between any two points in space follows from application of the three-dimensional Pythagorean theorem:

$$\Delta s^2 = \Delta x^2 + \Delta y^2 + \Delta z^2, \qquad (2.15)$$

while its direction is specified by two angles, usually called ϕ and θ.

▲▲ 2.9 Velocity and acceleration vectors. Vector algebra and geometry

The specification of displacements in terms of three mutually perpendicular components permits the description of any arbitrary motion in terms of three separate but related one-dimensional motions, and therefore uses all of the algebraic and geometric apparatus we have already developed. Generalizing from the one-dimensional case (Equation 2.13) the *velocity* of a body during a time interval Δt is defined as the ratio of its displacement to the duration of that interval:

$$\mathbf{v} = \lim_{\Delta t \to 0} \frac{\Delta \mathbf{s}}{\Delta t}. \qquad (2.16a)$$

Likewise, instantaneous velocity is defined as the limit of that ratio as the time interval approaches zero. Velocity is a vector quantity, as has already been noted. Its magnitude is usually called speed, which is consistent with our usage. Acceleration, which is also a vector, is likewise defined by generalizing from the one-dimensional case (Equations 2.7 and 2.8):

$$\mathbf{a} = \lim_{\Delta t \to 0} \frac{\Delta \mathbf{v}}{\Delta t}. \qquad (2.16b)$$

By means of the same generalization leading to Equation 2.16a we define the x-, y-, and z-*components* of velocity in terms of the time rates of change of the three displacement components:

$$v_x = \lim_{\Delta t \to 0} \frac{\Delta x}{\Delta t}, \tag{2.17a}$$

$$v_y = \lim_{\Delta t \to 0} \frac{\Delta y}{\Delta t}, \tag{2.17b}$$

$$v_z = \lim_{\Delta t \to 0} \frac{\Delta z}{\Delta t}. \tag{2.17c}$$

By combining these definitions with Equation 2.15, which gives displacement in terms of its components, we arrive at an expression for the magnitude of velocity (or speed) in terms of the three velocity components:

$$v = \sqrt{v_x^2 + v_y^2 + v_z^2}. \tag{2.18a}$$

For motion confined to a plane the z-component of displacement remains constant, so $v_z = 0$ and the right-hand side of Equation 2.18a contains but two terms. Combining Equations 2.14b and 2.17, the direction of the instantaneous velocity vector is given by:

$$\tan \theta_v = \frac{v_y}{v_x}. \tag{2.18b}$$

Each of the components of velocity may be a different function of time. Therefore, either the magnitude of the total instantaneous velocity (Equation 2.18a) or its direction or both may change with time.

It is convenient and reasonable to generalize the geometric description of the displacement vector $\Delta \mathbf{s}$ to the description of *all* vectors. Figure 2.11 shows such a representation of the vector $\mathbf{A}$ in a rectangular coordinate system. The length of the line segment is proportional to the magnitude of the vector; its angle of inclination to the x-axis specifies its direction in the plane. This vector might be the velocity of a body at some instant of time, in which case the length of the arrow would indicate its speed at that instant, and the angle θ its instantaneous direction. Or it might represent the acceleration of the body or its momentum or the force upon it or any one of a number of the other vectors to be encountered in later chapters.

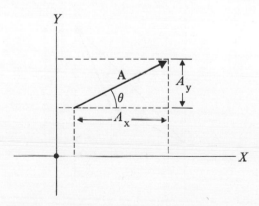

FIGURE 2.11 Geometric representation of the vector **A**.

By analogy, with displacement and velocity, any vector may be completely defined by giving its *x*-, *y*-, and *z*-components relative to some coordinate system. If its magnitude and/or its direction changes in time, then one or all of its components will also depend on time. Thus the motion of an automobile in three dimensions (traveling on a winding mountain road, for instance) could be specified by expanding Table 2.1, that is, by giving a column for each of the three components of displacement from some arbitrary origin rather than simply one column specifying the one-dimensional displacement from the toll booth.

Algebraic rules for finding the components of vectors in a plane follow immediately from their geometric representation. Referring to Figure 2.11, if A is the magnitude of the vector **A** and θ its angle of inclination to the *x*-axis, then the components A_x and A_y are:

$$A_x = A \cos \theta, \tag{2.19a}$$

$$A_y = A \sin \theta. \tag{2.19b}$$

Conversely, given the components of a vector, A_x and A_y, its magnitude and direction also follow from Figure 2.11:

$$A = \sqrt{A_x^2 + A_y^2}, \tag{2.20a}$$

$$\tan \theta = \frac{A_y}{A_x}, \tag{2.20b}$$

in analogy with Equations 2.15 and 2.17.

Since vectors are a special type of quantity having both magnitude and direction, they cannot be combined according to the rules of ordinary algebra. A special algebra— vector algebra—must be employed. The basis of this new algebra is really not difficult to understand. Equations 2.19 and 2.20, together with Figure 2.12, give prescriptions for analyzing a vector into its components and for combining components into a vector. Since the components are simply numbers *they* may be treated according to the rules of ordinary algebra.

Figure 2.12 illustrates the geometric addition of two vectors **A** and **B**. **A** might represent a given straight-line displacement from the origin; **B** another such displacement following the first. Then the vector sum (or *resultant*) of **A** and **B**,

$$\mathbf{C} = \mathbf{A} + \mathbf{B},$$

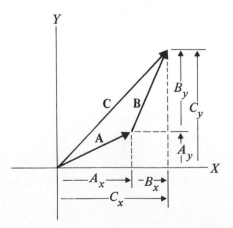

FIGURE 2.12 Geometric interpretation of vector addition, $\mathbf{C} = \mathbf{A} + \mathbf{B}$.

is the vector which connects the tail of **A** to the head of **B**, the vector which represents displacement from the origin to the point *b* in a single step. The geometric prescription for finding the sum of several vectors follows by a simple extension of this reasoning: lay the tail of the second on the head of the first, the tail of the third on the head of the second, etc. By definition, the sum of the vectors is represented by the line connecting the *tail* of the first vector with the *head* of the last.

The algebraic method for adding (and subtracting) vectors is also straightforward. According to Figure 2.12, the *x*- and *y*-components of the vector **C** are the sums of the respective *x*- and *y*-components of the vectors **A** and **B**:

$$C_x = A_x + B_x, \tag{2.21a}$$

$$C_y = A_y + B_y. \tag{2.21b}$$

But according to Equation 2.19,

$$A_x = A \cos \theta_A, \qquad B_x = B \cos \theta_B,$$
$$A_y = A \sin \theta_A, \qquad B_y = B \sin \theta_B,$$

while Equations 2.20 give

$$C = \sqrt{C_x^2 + C_y^2},$$

$$\tan \theta_C = \frac{C_y}{C_x}.$$

Therefore, to add vectors:

1. Find their *x*- and *y*-components by using Equations 2.19;
2. Find the *x*- and *y*-components of the resultant vector **C** by adding the respective *x*- and *y*-components of **A** and **B**;
3. Given its components, the magnitude and direction of **C** follow by applying Equations 2.20.

The rule for finding the difference of two vectors:

$$\mathbf{C} = \mathbf{A} - \mathbf{B}$$

follows from a simple modification of this procedure, the components being given by the differences of the components of **A** and **B** rather than by their sums:

$$C_x = A_x - B_x, \tag{2.21c}$$

$$C_y = A_y - B_y. \tag{2.21d}$$

Multiplication of a vector **A** by a scalar *a*,

$$\mathbf{C} = a\mathbf{A}, \tag{2.22a}$$

implies that both components of **A** are to be multiplied by the scalar:

$$C_x = aA_x,$$

$$C_y = aA_y.$$

Following Equations 2.20,

$$C = C_x^2 + C_y^2 = a^2 A_x^2 + a^2 A_y^2$$

$$= aA_x^2 + A_y^2 = aA, \tag{2.22b}$$

and

$$\tan \theta_c = \frac{C_y}{C_x} = \frac{aA_y}{aA_x} = \frac{A_y}{A_x} = \tan \theta_A. \qquad (2.22c)$$

In other words, multiplication of a vector by a scalar changes the magnitude of the vector while leaving its direction unaltered.

▲▲ 2.10   Centripetal acceleration

Acceleration is defined as the rate of change of velocity with time (Equation 2.8). For motion in one dimension the meaning of that definition is reasonably clear. However, in the two-dimensional case not only the magnitude but also the direction of velocity may change with time. Therefore, acceleration is itself a vector, and its meaning becomes broader.

Figure 2.13a shows the trajectory of a body moving in a plane. The vectors $\mathbf{v}(t)$ and $\mathbf{v}(t + \Delta t)$ represent its instantaneous velocity at two points along the trajectory (at times

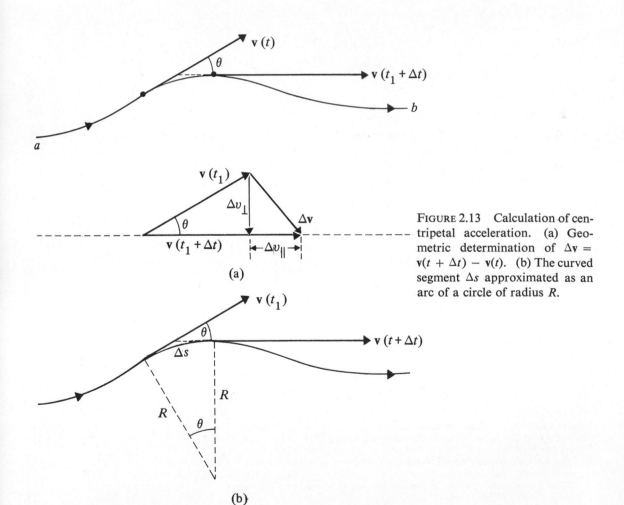

FIGURE 2.13   Calculation of centripetal acceleration. (a) Geometric determination of $\Delta \mathbf{v} = \mathbf{v}(t + \Delta t) - \mathbf{v}(t)$. (b) The curved segment Δs approximated as an arc of a circle of radius R.

t and $t + \Delta t$, respectively). Clearly *both* the magnitude and direction of its velocity vector depend on time. According to Equation 2.16b the average acceleration of the body over the time interval is the ratio of the change in the velocity *vector* during that interval to the length of the interval:

$$\mathbf{a} = \frac{\Delta v}{\Delta t} = \frac{\mathbf{v}(t + \Delta t) - \mathbf{v}(t)}{\Delta t}.$$

The instantaneous acceleration is the value of this ratio as $\Delta t \to 0$.

It is often convenient to express the components of the vector difference $\Delta \mathbf{v} = \mathbf{v}(t + \Delta t) - \mathbf{v}(t)$ in a coordinate system with one axis in the direction of the velocity vector at time $t + \Delta t$ and one perpendicular to the velocity vector. Let us call these directions the parallel and perpendicular directions, respectively. The resolution of $\Delta \mathbf{v}$ into these components is illustrated in Figure 2.13a:

$$v_{\parallel} = v(t + \Delta t) - v(t) \cos \theta,$$

$$v_{\perp} = v(t) \sin \theta,$$

where θ is the angle between the direction of the velocity at time $t + \Delta t$ and its direction at time t. Therefore, the components of the average acceleration are:

$$a_{\parallel} = \frac{v(t + \Delta t) - v(t) \cos \theta}{t},$$

$$a_{\perp} = \frac{v(t) \sin \theta}{t}.$$

As the time interval Δt approaches zero the difference between $\mathbf{v}(t + \Delta t)$ and $\mathbf{v}(t)$ becomes small as does the angle between their directions. But for very small angles $\cos \theta$ approaches unity. Therefore, the instantaneous magnitude of the parallel acceleration component is:

$$a_{\parallel} = \lim_{\Delta t \to 0} \frac{\Delta v}{\Delta t}, \tag{2.23a}$$

where Δv is the change in the *magnitude* of the velocity, or in the speed.

Similarly, as Δt and therefore $\Delta \theta$ become very small, the value of $\sin \theta$ approaches the value of θ itself (measured in radians*) so that the instantaneous value of the perpendicular component is related to the change in the *direction* of the velocity:

$$a_{\perp} = v(t) \times \lim_{\Delta t \to 0} \frac{\Delta \theta}{\Delta t}.$$

Now since s, the segment of arc between which the moving body has the respective velocities $\mathbf{v}(t + \Delta t)$ and $\mathbf{v}(t)$, also becomes small when Δt approaches zero, the shape of the segment may be approximated as the arc of a circle of radius R (Figure 2.13b). The

---

* The magnitude of an angle, measured in *radians*, is defined as the ratio of the length of the arc of a circle subtended by that angle to the radius of that circle. If the angle is very small then the length of the subtended arc is only slightly larger than the length of the perpendicular straight line dropped from the intersection of the arc and one of the two radial lines enclosing the angle and the other. Hence the ratio of this perpendicular line to the radius, which defines the sine of the angle, is approximately equal to the ratio of the arc to the radius, which measures the angle in radians.

If the two radial lines are perpendicular, the subtended arc is one-quarter the circumference of a circle, or $\pi R/2$. Therefore, by definition $\pi/2$ radians = 90 degrees, or 1 radian = (about) 57.3°. (See also Appendix B.)

angle θ measured in radians is related to Δs and R by $\theta = \Delta s/R$. Hence the change in θ with time may be expressed in terms of a change in the arc lengths:

$$\lim_{\Delta t \to 0} \frac{\Delta \theta}{\Delta t} = \frac{1}{R}\left(\lim_{\Delta t \to 0} \frac{\Delta s}{\Delta t}\right).$$

But by definition (Equation 2.13b) the limit of the ratio $\Delta s/\Delta t$ is simply $v(t)$, the magnitude of the instantaneous velocity along the curve at time t. Therefore:

$$\lim_{\Delta t \to 0} \frac{\Delta \theta}{\Delta t} = \frac{1}{R}\left(\lim_{\Delta t \to 0} \frac{\Delta s}{\Delta t}\right) = \frac{v(t)}{R},$$

and finally,

$$a_\perp = v(t) \times \left(\lim_{\Delta t \to 0} \frac{\Delta \theta}{\Delta t}\right) = \frac{v^2(t)}{R}. \tag{2.23b}$$

In summary, the instantaneous acceleration vector of a body in a curved path may be expressed in terms of a component parallel to its instantaneous velocity (Equation 2.23a) and a component perpendicular to the instantaneous velocity with magnitude $v^2(t)/R$ (Equation 3.23b).

Two important special cases deserve particular attention. If the trajectory of a body is a straight line, then the direction of its velocity does not change, and the perpendicular component of acceleration (Equation 2.23b) is zero. Therefore, the acceleration vector is in the direction of the motion and given by Equation 2.23a, identical in this case with Equation 2.8, which it must be, of course.

On the other hand, if a body moves in a circular path with constant *speed* (i.e., with the magnitude of **v** constant), the parallel component (Equation 2.23a) is zero, and the acceleration remains perpendicular to the trajectory and has the constant magnitude $a = v^2/R$ (Equation 2.23b). That is, a change in the *direction* of velocity, even without a change in speed, implies an acceleration. Because the acceleration vector of a body in uniform circular motion always points toward the center of the circle, it is called *centripetal* (or center-seeking) acceleration.

▶▶ 2.11 Standards and units

All of the mathematical apparatus developed in the foregoing sections has but one objective: to provide a set of convenient, consistent methods for describing *quantitatively* the observed motion of physical objects. In succeeding chapters other quantities used to represent the behavior of systems, quantities such as mass, momentum, force, charge, and energy, will be introduced. Like velocity and acceleration, these constitute the vocabulary of physics; the experimentally determined relations between them constitute its grammar. If the behavior of a particular system is to be represented in terms of numerical relationships between such quantities, it follows that consistent and universally comprehensible methods of measuring them and of expressing the results of such measurements must be established. Standards of measurement and systems of units based upon these standards fulfill these objectives.

Any measurement of a velocity reduces, fundamentally, to measurement of a length and measurement of a time interval. Similarly, measurement of an acceleration reduces to measurements of velocity and time and therefore once again to a measurement of length and time. If standards and units are established for measuring length and time, then prescriptions for measuring velocity and acceleration, as well as the units used for expressing the results of such measurements, follow at once.

The concept of length is based upon the intuitive idea of extension in space, the concept of time upon the equally intuitive idea of duration. Measurement of length involves comparison with an object of known extension in space; measurement of a time interval involves comparison with a system whose behavior repeats itself after a known constant duration. In other words, for the purpose of defining basic physical concepts, length is nothing more than a quantity measured with a "meter stick"; time is simply a quantity measured with a "clock." The question of how a length measured by laying a real meter stick beside an object is to be compared with a length determined by reflecting a radar signal from Mars is nontrivial, as is the question of comparing a time interval measured with a stopwatch with electronically determined times on the order of billionths of seconds.

If for the moment we assume that some consistency can be established, then a satisfactory universal standard of length may be defined as the length of a particular bar of metal that is kept at a constant temperature in a corrosion-free environment. The basic requirement is that the standard length never vary. Secondary standards of length may be defined by comparison with this primary standard.

Similarly, a primary standard of time may be defined in terms of some process whose repetition rate is constant, and secondary standards defined in terms of that process. Only one other primary standard besides length and time is required to define all the quantities used in physics: mass, which is a concept based upon the intuitive idea of inertia or the resistance of a body to change in velocity. Since mass and weight are closely related (Chapter 4), the primary standard of mass may be defined in terms of the weight of some arbitrary piece of metal which, like the standard of length, is kept at a constant temperature in a corrosion-free environment. Questions relating to how one determines that a standard does not vary (especially the standard of time) are again nontrivial. If the period of the earth about the sun defines one year, how is it possible to determine whether or not the length of a year is constant? In fact, it would not be possible if the revolution of the earth about the sun were the only periodic motion in nature. But there are others, the rotation of the earth on its axis, the oscillation of a pendulum of a specific length, and many atomic processes, for example. If none of these periods changes relative to each other then we may assume all are constant. If some variation is observed it should be possible to determine which is the most nearly constant and choose it as the primary standard.

The metric system is universally accepted for scientific purposes. Its units of length, mass, and time are the meter, the kilogram, and the second; the system of units based upon this primary triad is called the mks system. The centimeter ($\frac{1}{100}$ meter) and the gram ($\frac{1}{1000}$ kilogram) are also commonly employed and are the basis of the cgs system. The former system is used in this text.

Formerly, the international meter was defined as the length of a particular bar of platinum-irridium alloy kept at the International Bureau of Weights and Measures in Paris; the international kilogram, the mass of a cylinder of the same alloy kept in the same location; while the second was defined as a particular fraction of an astronomically determined year—i.e., the period of revolution of the earth about the sun.* Today,

---

* Specifically, the second is defined as 1/31,556,925.9747 of the tropical year 1900, where a tropical year is defined as the time interval between two successive passages of the sun through the vernal equinox.

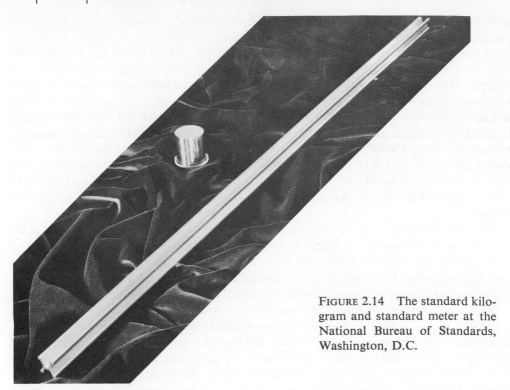

FIGURE 2.14 The standard kilogram and standard meter at the National Bureau of Standards, Washington, D.C.

however, atomic definitions have replaced the classical standard of length. The meter is defined in terms of the wavelength of light emitted in a particular atomic process, and redefinition of the second in terms of the duration of another atomic process is imminent.

Given standards and units of length and time, the dimensions of all derived quantities follow immediately from the equations defining those quantities. Let L and T symbolize the units of length and time, respectively. Then since speed is defined as the ratio of a distance to a time (Equations 2.1 and 2.4) it must have the dimensions L/T, or m/sec in the mks system. Likewise, acceleration (Equations 2.7 and 2.8) is defined as the ratio of a velocity to a time interval and so has dimensions $L/T/T$, or L/T^2, or specifically m/sec^2 in the mks system.

The symbolic L-T notation is useful in checking to make certain that the dimensions of all terms on the left and right sides of any equation are the same. Consider for instance Equation 2.12b, which gives the one-dimensional displacement of a body with constant acceleration as a function of time:

$$x(t) = x(t_0) + v(t_0)(t - t_0) + \tfrac{1}{2}a(t - t_0)^2.$$

Since $x(t)$ and $x(t_0)$ are both lengths then the other two terms must also have the same dimension. Then the dimensions of the term $v(t_0)(t - t_0)$ are

$$\frac{L}{T} \times T = L,$$

and the dimensions of the term $\frac{1}{2}a(t - t_0)^2$,

$$\frac{L}{T} \times T^2 = L.$$

All terms have the dimensions of length; hence the equation itself is dimensionally consistent.

Consistency of units is also required in any numerical problem. It would be meaningless, for example, to express a velocity in m/sec, a displacement in centimeters and a time in hours and then use these inconsistent units in Equation 2.12b. All units must be converted into either mks or cgs units before making numerical calculations.

APPENDIX TO CHAPTER 2 | *The derivative of a function*

The mathematical description of motion developed in this chapter is based upon finding a correlation between the successive spatial positions of a moving object and time. Once such a functional relationship is found, the instantaneous velocity of the object at any given time may be calculated by finding the limit of the ratio $\Delta x/\Delta t$ as Δt approaches zero (Equation 2.4, Section 2.4).

All of the functions that have been discussed concern relations between displacement and time. But since the word *function* implies nothing more than the existence of some correlation between a pair of variables, the concept has a much broader application. For example, the pressure of a given volume of gas depends upon its temperature, so the pressure is a *function* of temperature, a fact which may be summarized by the statement $p = p(T)$. By making an appropriate series of measurements with various gases it is possible to find a number of different algebraic, graphical, or tabular relationships that spell out the functional dependence explicitly. These relations differ from one another depending upon the gas used, the temperature range considered, and a number of other factors. However, given *some* explicit functional relation it becomes possible to study further properties of the gas by studying the mathematical behavior of the function.

Since the pressure of a gas depends upon its temperature it follows that a change in temperature leads to a change in pressure, and that therefore the rate of change of pressure with temperature is an important characteristic of the gas. If $p(T_2)$ is the pressure of the gas at a temperature T_2, and $p(T_1)$ the pressure at T_1 then the *average* rate of change of pressure with respect to temperature over the range T_2 to T_1 is

$$\frac{p(T_2) - p(T_1)}{T_2 - T_1}, \tag{A2.1}$$

or more concisely,

$$\frac{\Delta p}{\Delta T}. \tag{A2.2}$$

The rate of change of pressure with temperature at a specific temperature T follows from the average rate of change in exactly the same way that instantaneous velocity follows from average velocity: it is the limit of the ratio as the denominator approaches zero (Section 2.4).

The rate of change of one member of a pair of correlated variables with respect to the other is defined as the limiting value of the ratio of the changes in the variables as the denominator approaches zero. This limiting value of the ratio is called the *first derivative* of the first variable with respect to the second. Thus, for instance, the instantaneous speed of an object moving in a straight line is the first derivative of its elapsed distance with respect to time, written as dx/dt. That is:

$$\frac{dx}{dt} = \lim_{\Delta t \to 0} \frac{\Delta x}{\Delta t},$$

so that the defining equation for instantaneous speed (Equation 2.4) becomes

$$v = \frac{dx}{dt}. \tag{A2.3}$$

Similarly, the magnitude of instantaneous acceleration is defined as the first derivative of speed with respect to time so that (Equation 2.8):

$$a = \frac{dv}{dt}, \tag{A2.4}$$

and from Equation A2.2 the rate of change of the pressure of a gas with temperature is written as dp/dT. In general, if some variable y is a function of some other variable x then the rate of change of y with respect to x is the first derivative dy/dx defined as:

$$\frac{dy}{dx} = \lim_{\Delta x \to 0} \frac{\Delta y}{\Delta x}. \tag{A2.5}$$

Since rates of change are characteristic of the mathematical relationship between two cor-related variables, the calculation of first derivatives is an important mathematical technique. To find the first derivative of any explicitly stated function it is only necessary to carry out the procedure implied by Equation A2.5. Once the derivative for a specific algebraic form is known it may be catalogued for future use.

First derivatives for the functional forms $y = kx^2$ and $y = kx^3$ were calculated in Sections 2.4 and 2.5, although the results were not explicitly called first derivatives. As a further example let us calculate the first derivative of y with respect to x for the relation $y = x^n$, where n is any constant. By definition:

$$\Delta y = (x + \Delta x)^n - x^n.$$

Applying the binomial expansion (Appendix D):

$$(x + \Delta x)^n = x^n + nx^{n-1} \Delta x + \frac{n(n-1)x^{n-2}(\Delta x)^2}{2} + \cdots,$$

so, approximately,

$$\frac{\Delta y}{\Delta x} = nx^{n-1} + \frac{n(n-1)x^{n-2} \Delta x}{2} + \cdots.$$

This approximation is sufficient for calculating the first derivative, since all terms but the first must vanish for $\Delta x \to 0$. Therefore:

$$\frac{dy}{dx} = nx^{n-1}.$$

Table A2.1 contains a short list of derivatives for some simple functional relations derived by applying the definition, as in the preceding example. In this table a and n are constants; x, y, u, and v variables; $y(x)$, $u(x)$, and $v(x)$ functions of x; dy/dx, du/dx, and dv/dx their first derivatives with respect to x. Since the derivative of a sum of functions is the sum of the separate derivatives (next to last entry in Table A2.1), the derivatives of rather complex functions may be calculated by repeated reference to this short catalogue.

TABLE A2.1

If $y(x) =$	then $dy/dx =$
x	1
ax	a
ax^2	$2ax$
ax^n	nax^{n-1}
a	0
$au(x)$	$a\,du/dx$
$u(x) + v(x)$	$du/dx + dv/dx$
$u(x)v(x)$	$u(x)\,dv/dx + v(x)\,du/dx$

SUGGESTIONS FOR FURTHER READING ▲▲▲

All introductory physics texts treat the subject of kinematics and vector algebra. Three that treat the subjects on somewhat the same level as this text are:

K. R. ATKINS, *Physics*, John Wiley and Sons, Inc., New York, 1965, Chapters 3, 4, and 5.

ARTHUR BEISER, *The Mainstream of Physics*, Addison-Wesley Publishing Co., Inc., Reading, Mass., 1962, Chapters 1 and 3.

JAY OREAR, *Fundamental Physics*, John Wiley and Sons, Inc., New York, 1961, Chapter 2.

Two that treat the subjects on a slightly more advanced level are:

ARNOLD B. ARONS, *Development of Concepts of Physics*, Addison-Wesley Publishing Co., Inc., Reading, Mass., 1965, Chapters 1 and 3.

R. P. FEYNMAN, R. B. LEIGHTON, AND M. SANDS, *The Feynman Lectures on Physics*, Vol. 1, Addison-Wesley Publishing Co., Inc., Reading, Mass., 1963, Chapter 8.

Arons' Chapter 3 also provides an excellent introduction to the use of the calculus in physics.

PROBLEMS AND EXERCISES ▲▲▲

2.1. The average speed of a body during any time interval generally depends upon the length of that interval. Calculate the average speed of the automobile in Table 2.1 over the intervals between the first and fourth minutes and between the first and third minutes. Are your answers equal? Should they be?

2.2. (a) Suppose that columns 1 and 2 (Table 2.1) are extended as follows:

10:24	13,981.3
10:25	13,982.4
10:26	13,983.3
10:27	13,984.3

Complete the remaining columns of the table and extend Figure 2.1 accordingly.

(b) Suppose the average speed (in miles/hr) during the next four time intervals in Table 2.1 are:

$$0.9 \quad 1.0 \quad 1.1 \quad 1.1$$

Complete the remaining columns and extend Figure 2.1 accordingly.

2.3. The dotted line in Figure 2.1 indicates that the automobile stopped for a few seconds between the second and third minutes and reversed direction between the fourth and fifth. Make up a table (similar to Table 2.1) that might lead to a graph of this type.

2.4. (a) Based upon Figure 2.1, what is the best estimate you can make about the position of the automobile 1.5 sec after leaving the toll station? 4.75 min after leaving the station?

(b) Based on Figure 2.2b what is your best estimate of the falling body's position $\frac{13}{90}$ sec after it is dropped?

(c) What is your best estimate of the position of the electron in Table 2.3 50 billionths sec after it leaves counter S_1?

2.5. Referring to Table 2.1 distinguish between the idea of speed *at* $t = 1$ min and speed *over the interval* from $t = 1$ to $t = 2$ min.

2.6. Is the information in Table 2.1 sufficient to calculate the instantaneous speed of the automobile at $t = 3$ min? If not, make an informed guess.

2.7. (a) Using Table 2.2 (or Figure 2.2b or both) calculate the average speed of the falling body over the intervals:

   i. $t = \frac{2}{30}$ to $\frac{7}{30}$ sec.
   ii. $\frac{3}{30}$ to $\frac{6}{30}$ sec.
   iii. $\frac{4}{30}$ to $\frac{5}{30}$ sec.

(b) Based on your answers to part a what is your best estimate of the instantaneous speed at $t = \frac{9}{60}$ sec?

(c) Repeat part a for the three intervals:

   i. $\frac{3}{30}$ to $\frac{8}{30}$ sec.
   ii. $\frac{4}{30}$ to $\frac{7}{30}$ sec.
   iii. $\frac{5}{30}$ to $\frac{6}{30}$ sec.

(d) Based on your answers to part c estimate the instantaneous speed at $t = \frac{11}{60}$ sec.

(e) Are your answers equal? Should they be? Why?

N.B.: In following the procedure of parts a and b and of parts c and d you have taken a limit of average speed as the time interval over which it is defined approaches zero.

2.8. Express the following statements in mathematical form:

(a) x is directly proportional to y.

(b) x is directly proportional to y with proportionality constant 3.7. With proportionality constant C.

(c) x is equal to 3.7 times y.

(d) x is directly proportional to the cube of y.

(e) The value of x (some indefinite function of y) evaluated for $y = y_1$.

(f) The difference between the value of x (some indefinite function of y) evaluated at y_2 and y_1.

2.9. (a) Find explicit numerical answers for Problem 2.8 e and f for $y_2 = 60$, $y_1 = 30$ if the functional relationship between x and y is $x = 3y^2 + 6y$.

(b) Repeat part a for the functional relationship $x = \sin(y)$.

2.10. Plot graphs of the relations (a) $x = 4t^3$ and (b) $x = 100/t$ for 1-sec intervals from $t = 0$ to $t = 5$ sec.

2.11. Plot graphs of the relations (a) $v = 12t^2$ and (b) $v = -100/t^2$ for 1-sec intervals from $t = 0$ to $t = 5$ sec. Do you see any relation between this and the previous problem?

2.12. (a) Calculate and plot the values of the average acceleration for the motion described by $v = 12t^2$ over the first 1-sec interval.

(b) Repeat for $v = -100/t^2$.

2.13. Estimate the instantaneous acceleration at $t = 1$ sec for the motion described by $v = 12t^2$ by calculating the average acceleration over decreasing time intervals starting at $t = 1$ sec. Repeat for $t = 3$ sec.

2.14. Repeat Problem 2.13 for $v = -100/t^2$.

2.15. Suppose the magnitude of the acceleration of some body were given as a function of time by the equation:

$$a = kt.$$

Write an expression for its speed as a function of time.

2.16. A ball is thrown straight upward from a platform 172 m above the ground with an initial speed of 29.4 m/sec.

(a) How long does it continue to rise?
(b) How far does it rise above the platform?

2.17. Suppose the platform in the previous problem is removed immediately after the ball is thrown.

(a) What time elapses between the instant the ball is thrown upward and the time it strikes the ground?
(b) What is its speed on striking the ground?

2.18. A ball is thrown straight *downward* from the 172-m platform with initial speed 29.4 m/sec.

(a) How long does it continue to fall?
(b) With what speed does it strike the ground?
(c) How long would the ball continue to fall if it were dropped from rest?

2.19. One meter is about 0.33 ft (1 ft = 0.305 m). Express the following in mks units:

(a) Your height.
(b) 1 in.
(c) 1 mile.
(d) 60 miles/hr (in m/sec).
(e) The distance to the sun (93 million miles).
(f) 5 sq ft.

2.20. Express the following in kilograms. A 1-kg mass is equivalent to a weight of about 2.2 lb.

(a) Your weight.
(b) 1 oz.
(c) 1 ton.

2.21. The *radian* is defined in a footnote in Section 2.10 and also in Appendix B as the arc of a circle subtended by an angle θ to the radius of the circle:

$$\theta \text{ (in radians)} = \frac{s}{R}.$$

Estimate the angles in radians subtended by:

(a) A 25-cent piece held at arm's length.
(b) A 6-ft man 100 ft away.
(c) The full moon (radius, 1000 miles; distance from earth, 240,000 miles).

2.22. How far away must a 25-cent piece be held if it is to subtend the same angle as the moon?

2.23. (a) What is the approximate angular displacement of the sun (in radians) between 12 noon and 1:00 P.M. on a day in late April?
(b) The radius of the earth is about 4000 miles. From your answer to part a, about how far does a point on the equator move in one hour due to the earth's rotation on its axes?

2.24. Since $\pi/2$ radians $= 90°$, 1 radian is about $57.3°$. (See footnote in Section 2.10 and Appendix B.) Express the following radian measurements in degrees: 0.02, 0.1, 0.3, 1.0, $\pi/2$, 2.0, π.

2.25. (a) The x- and y-components of the end points of a line in a plane are $x_2 = 4$, $y_2 = 3$, $x_1 = 0$, $y_1 = 0$, respectively. How long is the line? What is the tangent of its angle to the x-axis? Sketch the line and its components.

(b) A line in a plane is fourteen units long and makes a $30°$ angle to the x-axis. What are its x- and y-components?

2.26. (a) A vector **A**, six units long, lies on the x-axis. Another vector **B**, ten units long, makes a $45°$ angle with the x-axis. Find their sum both graphically and algebraically.

(b) A vector ten units long makes a $30°$ angle with the x-axis. What vector when added to the first yields a vector fourteen units long and in the y-direction? Solve both graphically and algebraically.

2.27. (a) A cannon, inclined at $60°$ to the horizontal, fires a shell with velocity 1000 m/sec. What are the horizontal and vertical components of the shell's velocity at the moment it leaves the cannon?

(b) A boat starts across a stream with velocity 15 miles/hr perpendicular to the direction of the stream which flows with velocity 5 miles/hr. What is the total velocity (magnitude and direction) of the boat relative to the stream?

2.28. A pair of country roads run in the north–south and east–west directions, respectively. An automobile leaves their junction and travels due west. After one minute it has traveled 0.7 miles, after two minutes 1.5 miles. It then turns onto a side road. Thereafter its distances (in miles) from the north–south and the east–west roads at the end of one-minute intervals are:

Measurement	Distance from N–S	Distance from E–W
1	2.0	0.4
2	2.4	1.1
3	2.9	1.6
4	2.9	2.4

(a) Plot the successive positions of the automobile starting from the junction. Make your choice of axes and origin clear and explicit.

(b) What is the displacement of the auto from the junction after two minutes? After three minutes? *During* the third minute?

(c) Calculate the displacement after three minutes from the displacement *after* two minutes and the displacement *during* the third minute by using vector algebra.

(d) What are the average velocity components during the fourth and fifth minutes after the automobile leaves the junction? What is the total average velocity (magnitude and direction) during these same time intervals?

(e) Calculate the magnitude and direction of the average velocity over the two-minute interval from the fourth to the sixth minute by using vector algebra and your answers to part d.

(f) Using vector subtraction find the change in average velocity from the fourth- to the fifth-minute intervals, and from your answer calculate the average acceleration over the two-minute interval from the fourth to the sixth minute.

2.29. (a) An automobile travels at 30 m/sec around a 20-m radius curve. What is the magnitude and direction of its centripetal acceleration?

(b) What would the radius of the curve have to be such that the centripetal acceleration of an automobile rounding it at 15 m/sec would be the same as in part a?

(c) What would the speed of an automobile on a 10-m radius curve have to be so that the centripetal acceleration of an automobile rounding it would be the same as in part a?

2.30. A stone is tied to the end of a 3-m long string and whirled about in a vertical circle. What is the speed of the stone such that its centripetal acceleration is equal in magnitude to its acceleration due to gravity?

2.31. (a) The moon is 240,000 miles from the earth and makes one revolution about it in approximately 28 days. What is the magnitude of its centripetal acceleration? Where is it directed? (Assume a circular orbit.)

   (b) A satellite in a low circular orbit about the earth (radius, 4000 miles) makes one complete revolution in about 84 min. What is its centripetal acceleration? Where have you seen your answer before?

2.32. Referring to the Chapter appendix show that if:

$$y = ax^n \qquad (a \text{ and } n \text{ constants}),$$

then

$$\frac{dy}{dx} = nax^{n-1}.$$

[HINT: Use the first terms in the binomial expansion $(a + b^n = a^n + na^{n-1}b + \cdots.)$]

2.33. Show that if:

(a) $y = \sin(x)$,   then $dy/dx = \cos(x)$.
(b) $y = \cos(x)$,   then $dy/dx = -\sin(x)$.

[HINT: Use the relations:

  i. $\sin(x + \Delta x) = \sin x \cos \Delta x + \cos x \sin \Delta x$,
  ii. $\cos(x + \Delta x) = \cos x \cos \Delta x - \sin x \sin \Delta x$,

and the fact that for very small Δx the following approximations are valid:

$$\sin \Delta x \cong \Delta x, \qquad \cos \Delta x \cong 1.]$$

The problem of motion: an historical survey

3

▲▲ 3.1 The Aristotelian world view

Concerning the ancient problem of understanding the causes of motion, the historian Herbert Butterfield has written:

> Of all the intellectual hurdles which the human mind has confronted and has overcome in the last fifteen hundred years, the one which seems to me to have been the most amazing in character and the most stupendous in the scope of its consequences is the one relating to the problem of motion—the one which perhaps was hardly disposed of by Galileo, though it received a definitive form of settlement shortly after his time in the full revised statement of what every schoolboy learns to call the law of inertia. On this question of motion the Aristotelian teaching, precisely because it carried such an intricate dovetailing of observations and explanations—that is to say, precisely because it was part of a system which was such a colossal intellectual feat in itself—was hard for the human mind to escape from, and gained a strong hold on medieval scholastic thought.*

It is often assumed the Greek and medieval philosophies failed to come to grips with the problem because they did not *observe* motion. The implication is that had Aristotle made more and better observations he might have preempted Newton by stating the latter's three laws of motion some twenty centuries earlier. Butterfield presents convincing arguments to the contrary: it was not that Aristotle and his successors observed *less* than, say, Galileo; it was simply that they did not observe from the same quantitative point of view that Galileo introduced (Section 1.2). They observed from a different point of view *not* because they were any less intelligent but simply because the quantitative approach of Galileo was irrelevant to their fundamental metaphysical system.

Science is much more than a collection of facts fitted into a predetermined pattern. Rather it is an attempt to work out a system relating and ordering these facts, these observed physical processes. Every high school physics student is taught Newton's first law, the law of inertia: that every body remains at rest or moves with constant velocity along a straight line unless acted upon by an outside force. But has that student ever *observed* such a case of force-free motion? If after a moment's thought he replies that he has seen films of astronauts floating near their capsules, he might forgive Aristotle for

---

* Herbert Butterfield, *The Origins of Modern Science: 1300–1800*, G. Bell and Sons, Ltd., London, 1950, p. 3.

54

not making similar observations and indeed wonder how Galileo and Newton ever did formulate the law of inertia in the first place!* Similarly, every high school student "knows" that the force of gravity causes a stone to fall. But lacking some definition of force other than the semi-intuitive, inadequate pushing-pulling motion, how can he understand that statement?

From the Newtonian point of view the force of gravity is to be understood in terms of the interaction of the earth with the falling stone. In a similar context the motion of an automobile coasting on a superhighway at 60 mph is impeded only by the friction of its bearings and the resistance offered by the air. Therefore, it comes close to obeying the law of inertia.

But it is not obvious that *anyone* who compares the motion of an automobile with the motion of a falling stone will immediately adopt the Newtonian viewpoint as the basis of his ordering system. Is it entirely obvious that the motion of the coasting automobile is an approximate example of force-free motion, while the motion of a falling stone is a prime example of the interaction of two bodies? Aristotle (384–322 B.C.) considered motion in the broad context of change in general and made the basic assumption that no change can be considered separately from the purpose of that change. Just as a boy grows because he is to become a man and contains as a boy something of the man he is to become, so in the Aristotelian system a stone falls because its purpose is fulfilled in returning to earth. No interaction is implied; the stone falls because it is *natural* for it to fall. Its very quality of being a stone implies the fact that it *must* fall, and since its motion is natural, there is no further need of discussing it.

Aristotle incorporated this basic idea into a model of the entire universe. Fixing the earth as a sphere at the center he divided his universe into a sublunar, or terrestrial region, and a celestial region. Assuming that all terrestrial matter was composed of one or more of the four elements, earth, water, air, and fire that were first proposed by the Ionian philosophers in the sixth century B.C., he next assigned to each its natural abode: the sphere of earth at the center surrounded by concentric spheres of water, air, and fire, respectively. The sphere of fire extended throughout the sublunar regions. Beyond in the celestial regions moved the sun, moon, planets, and fixed stars, all composed of a fifth ethereal element.

The celestial regions were regarded as perfect, unchanging. Here the sun, moon, stars, and planets orbited forever about a fixed earth in paths based upon a combination of several uniform, circular motions because that uniform, circular motion was regarded as natural in these regions. Beyond them lay the sphere of the fixed stars and enclosing the entire system the sphere of the Prime Mover, supplying motivation for the celestial realms. Only the terrestrial regions were changeable and imperfect, as witnessed, for example, by the fact that earthlike continents protruded above the sphere of the oceans.

By implication, rest is the preferred state in the terrestrial or sublunar regions, for when left to their own devices all bodies return to their natural abodes. A stone falls not only through air but also through water. Rain falls through air, whereas fire rises to its natural sphere. Hence it becomes necessary to account for all unnatural—or violent—motion, and to do so Aristotle asserted, *on the basis of observations*, that all such violent motion required application of a mover or of a force. Thus force was immediately related to the idea of muscular effort. In the Aristotelian system all forces are contact forces. The Newtonian generalization of the concept to include action at a distance (and therefore

---

* In fact, as we shall see in Chapter 5, even such an astronaut is really not in a force-free state.

FIGURE 3.1 Plato and Aristotle surrounded by other notables in Greek philosophy and mathematics, in a detail from Raphael's *School of Athens*. Plato points upward to emphasize his concern with the ideal world, Aristotle's downward gesture indicates his primary concern with more tangible, observable things. (Photograph courtesy of Dr. Franz Stoedtner, Dusseldorf, West Germany.)

gravitation) is not necessary, since free fall—the principle case of motion observed to take place *without* an obvious mover—is natural in the Aristotelian system and thus by definition force-free.

The Aristotelian system sought to order the universe with the teleological idea that all change implied a preordained purpose for that change. It was more than a system of physics as we now understand the word, for it embraced not only physics, astronomy, and biology but also such nonscientific areas as ethics and political philosophy. When Western Europe rediscovered the system during the twelfth century, it was easily adapted to the philosophical needs of medieval Christendom, the primary purpose for change being interpreted as the purpose of God. Man created in the image of God had obviously been placed on earth—the center of Aristotle's universe—to fulfill God's purpose. And all events, natural and unnatural, could be interpreted as being manifestations of God's purpose and meant for the benefit, instruction, or punishment of man.

◣◣ 3.2 The idea of uniform circular motion in astronomy

The preceding brief summary does justice neither to the system of Aristotle nor the scholastic philosophy based upon it. Clearly the Aristotelian-scholastic universe had a tremendous appeal not only because it fused together so many diverse elements but also because it easily adapted itself to the Christian concept of a God Who ruled through just, changeless laws and Who maintained a special, personal interest in man created in His image.

As early as Greek times it was known that there were specific *quantitative* difficulties inherent in the system of terrestrial dynamics and these became increasingly evident after its revival in the twelfth century. Concurrently, the ancient problem of planetary motion was revived, and assumptions accepted since the time of Plato began to be questioned.

Even a superficial observer is likely to be struck by the uniqueness and the order displayed in the night sky. The stars are not uniformly distributed to his view. Some are sprinkled at random about the heavens, while others seem to be grouped into recognizable patterns or constellations. Nor is the appearance of the individual stars identical. Rather they differ in color, apparent size, and apparent brightness. Yet despite the seemingly infinite variety displayed by the stars, each night the complete pattern describes its stately progression from east to west just as the sun runs its course by day (Figure 3.2).

The motion of seven objects visible to the naked eye—the sun, the moon, and the five planets—deviates from the simple regularity of the stars. These deviations were already known to the Babylonians, and led generations of scholars in later centuries to devote themselves to the problem of planetary motion. If the mind can grasp, be pleased and at ease with an orderly system, it is troubled by discrepancies in that order and is disturbed by the gap between what is and what it believes should be.

Well before the time of Plato (427–347 B.C.), the Greeks had conceived of the stars as bits of ethereal substances fixed to a great sphere that revolved about the earth once each day. The five visible planets, Mercury, Venus, Mars, Jupiter, and Saturn, also appear to move around the earth from east to west, but their motion is less simple than that of the fixed stars. Hence they were called *wandering stars* or *planets*. Chapter 2 (Figure 2.4) describes briefly a method for measuring the position of a planet relative to a given reference star. Since the apparent position of the stars remains fixed relative to one another, they are called *fixed*.

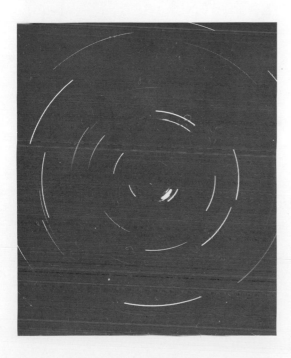

FIGURE 3.2 One-hour time exposure with the camera directed toward the North Star. From such an observation it might seem plausible that the stars rotate with uniform, circular motion about the earth. (Yerkes Observatory photograph.)

But the positions of the planets change relative to the fixed stars, and the motion of each differs in its particulars from the motion of the others. Figure 3.3 shows schematically the successive positions of a planet observed at equal intervals of time, say, nightly or weekly. Relative to the earth, both the stars and the planet advance toward the west, apparently revolving about the earth. For a time the planet apparently moves faster than the stars. However, its velocity relative to them (its apparent displacement between two successive measurements divided by the time between measurements) is not constant. It appears to accelerate, then decelerate, and stop briefly. When it appears to move once again, its motion is reversed (or retrograde), i.e., it moves with velocity slower than the velocity of the stars. This retrogression continues until the planet stops once again and then starts to advance.

It is not at all difficult to understand the general reason for this involved apparent motion in terms of an heliocentric model of the solar system. The earth, like the other five visible planets, is a satellite of the sun. Therefore, the apparent position of any one planet relative to the stars depends upon the position of *both* the earth and the planet in question, as Figure 3.3. shows very clearly. The earth moves more rapidly than Mars.

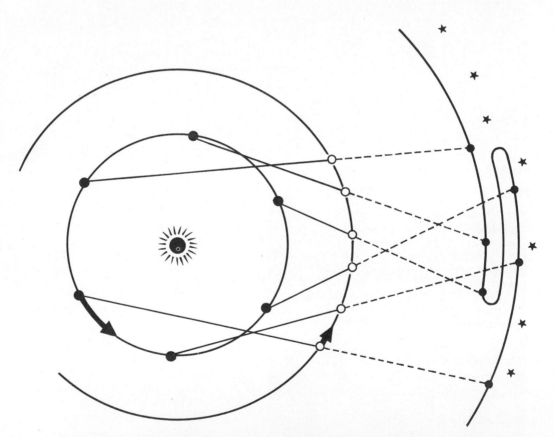

FIGURE 3.3   Apparent motion of one of the outer planets (Mars, for instance— open circles) seen from the earth (closed circles). Since the earth moves more rapidly than Mars, the latter planet, viewed against the background of "fixed" stars, apparently accelerates, decelerates, and changes direction. (From Thorton Page, *Stars and Galaxies*, Fig. I–6. © 1962.) By permission of Prentice-Hall, Inc., Englewood Cliffs, N.J.

When both planets are on the same side of the sun and the earth is catching up with or passing Mars, the planet appears to move backwards or retrogress. At other times (when the planets are on opposite sides of the sun, for instance) its motion appears to be more rapid than that of the stars.* However, almost all of the Greek philosophers† believed that the earth was fixed and immovable. Therefore, the apparent motion of the planets had to be explained in terms of the geocentric viewpoint, and this was no simple task.

The doctrine of uniform, circular motion was the dominant astronomical idea inherited from the Greeks by medieval European scholars. The fundamental concept derived from Plato who sought to express the order of the universe in terms of geometry. From considerations of symmetry he argued that the sphere is the most perfect geometric figure and that it follows from this that all celestial bodies, being perfect, must move in circular orbits centered upon the earth:

> Wherefore he made the world in the form of a globe, round as from a lathe having its extremes in every direction equidistant from the centre, the most perfect and the most like itself of all figures; for he considered that the like is infinitely fairer than the unlike. . . .
> . . .he made the universe a circle moving in a circle, one and solitary. . . .‡ *Timaeus*

It is not particularly difficult to construct a model of the universe in terms of a number of concentric spheres, each centered upon the earth, each bearing a planet or the sun or the moon or the fixed stars, each revolving about the earth with its own characteristic motion. In order to agree with the observed motion of the planets well known in Plato's time, the spheres bearing the planets would have to move in a series of fits and starts, now more rapidly, now less rapidly, than the sphere of the fixed stars. And yet Plato insisted that all motion of celestial bodies must be based upon *uniform*, circular motion, and Figure 3a shows that the planets simply do not move in that manner. But Plato was not a physicist in the modern sense nor even in the Aristotelian sense. In fact, the explanation of natural phenomena was not a terribly important part of his philosophy. On the contrary, his major interest was in the ideal world of which the visible world was but an imperfect copy. He expressed a low opinion of those who believed that the nature of the ideal world could be inferred from observation of the visible:

> I should rather say that those who elevate astronomy into philosophy treat it in such a way as to make us look downwards and not upwards. . . .
> . . .whether a man gapes at the heavens or blinks on the ground, when seeking to learn some particular of sense, I would deny that he can learn, for nothing of that sort is matter of science; . . . .
> . . .the starry heaven which we behold is wrought upon a visible ground, and therefore . . .must necessarily be deemed inferior far to the true motions with which the real swiftness and the real slowness move in their relation to each other. . . .§
> *The Republic, Book VII*

In Plato's real world the basis of all celestial motion must be constant, circular motion. The astronomer's task became reconciliation of the nonuniform "appearance" with Platonic "reality," a task to which a pupil of Plato's, the brilliant mathematician

---

* The distance to the stars is so enormous relative to the dimensions of the earth's orbit that they do not change their apparent positions appreciably during the course of a year (see Figure 3.9).

† Aristarchus (third century B.C.) advocated a heliocentric model of the universe. But since none of the observational evidence available at his time favored his viewpoint, this theory was overshadowed by the dominant geocentric theory of Plato, Aristotle, and their followers.

‡ *The Dialogues of Plato*, 4th edition, Vol. III, trans. by B. Jowett, The Clarendon Press, Oxford, 1953, pp. 719–20.

§ *The Dialogues of Plato*, Vol. II, pp. 393–94.

Eudoxus, was one of the first to apply himself. In his system not one but rather a nest of several concentric spheres was assigned to the sun, to the moon, and to each planet. Each sphere centered upon the earth and rotated with constant speed about its own axis (Figure 3.4). The axis of each sphere in a nest was attached to the next larger sphere and therefore carried along by the motion of its parent. Since the axes of the spheres were not parallel, the observed orbit of the celestial body itself, attached to the inner sphere in each nest and therefore partaking of the motion of all members of the nest, could be quite complex. By adjusting the speed of each sphere and the direction of its axis with respect to the axis of its parent, it was possible to reproduce, at least in outline, the observed motion of the sun, the moon, and each planet.

The system of Eudoxus required a total of twenty-seven spheres. Calippus, a pupil of Eudoxus, refined the model by adding seven more spheres, bringing the total number to thirty-four, including the sphere of the fixed stars which surrounded the entire system. Plato enunciated his uniform, circular doctrine as allegory and was quite disdainful of

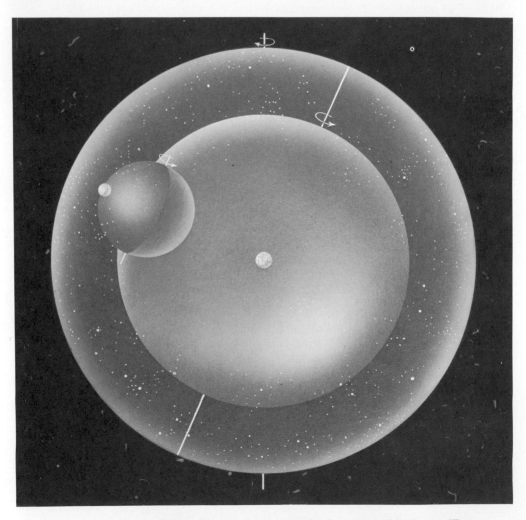

FIGURE 3.4   The motion of Mars about the earth in the system of Eudoxus. (From Thorton Page, *Stars and Galaxies*, Fig. I–5. © 1962.) By permission of Prentice-Hall, Inc., Englewood Cliffs, N.J.

observation. Eudoxus and Calippus sought a mathematical implementation of the allegory without worrying about the material nature of the spheres. But Aristotle was both literal and at pains to reconcile his philosophy with observation. In his hands the ideal, mathematical spheres of Plato and Eudoxus became real, physical, material spheres:

> The shape of the heavens must be spherical. That is the most suitable to its substance and is the primary shape in nature.*
>
> Again, it is an observed fact, and assumed in these arguments, that the whole revolves on a circle, and has been shown that beyond the outermost circumference there is neither void nor place, this provides another reason why the heavens must be spherical.†

The number of celestial spheres in the Aristotelian universe was increased to fifty-five. These were interlocked, as in the system of Eudoxus, and were assumed to be composed of a specific celestial element. The four terrestrial spheres of earth, water, air, and fire were enclosed within this celestial system as outlined in Section 3.1. Aristotle modified the Platonic allegory to his own literal ends and incorporated it into a total model of the universe.

Although the fifty-five spheres of Aristotle provided sufficient freedom to construct very complicated motions from combinations of uniform, circular rotations, the model still could not be reconciled with all observations. Among the more serious deficiencies was its failure to account for observed variations in the brightness of the planets during their cycles about the earth. These fluctuations could be easily understood by assuming that the distance between the earth and a planet changed during the course of its revolution about the earth, but no such variation could be incorporated into the spherical system. Therefore, although the general Aristotelian idea of a universe composed of concentric spheres recurs until the seventeenth century, astronomers abandoned the literal system as a working tool even during his lifetime. Instead they developed a purely mathematical system capable of reproducing the observed motion of the celestial bodies, while preserving the basic geocentric, uniform, circular requirements.

The new system was known to later ages as the Ptolemaic system in honor of Claudius Ptolemy of Alexandria who perfected it about A.D. 150. But its outlines were first conceived in the third century B.C. by Apollonius of Perga and developed more fully by Hipparchus of Rhodes in the following century. As in the system of Eudoxus, the motion of each planet is the result of several uniform, circular motions. But whereas the planets of Eudoxus are attached to real, material spheres, the planets of Ptolemy move in combined circles that have only a mathematical reality. Each moves with constant velocity in a circular orbit called its *epicycle* (Figures 3.5 and 3.6). The center of its epicycle is not the earth, however, but a geometric point which moves upon another circle, the *deferent*, with constant velocity. Viewed from the moving center of the epicycle, the planet executes uniform circular motion; viewed from the center of the deferent, the *center* of the epicycle executes uniform, circular motion, but the motion of the planet appears as a series of loops about the deferent.

Rather complicated-appearing motions can be reproduced in this way by the proper selection of the radii of the circles and of the planet about its epicycle, and of the epicycle center about its deferent. As first conceived by Hipparchus, the deferent of each planet centered upon the earth. To improve the agreement with observation, Ptolemy added

---

* Aristotle, *On the Heavens*, Book II, trans. by W. K. C. Guthrie, Loeb Classical Library, Harvard University Press, 1939, 286b, lines 10–12.
† *Ibid.*, 287b, lines 11–16.

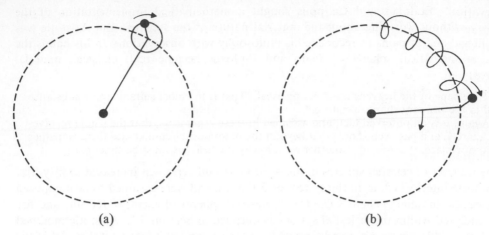

(a)   (b)

FIGURE 3.5   (a) In the Ptolemaic system the motion of a planet viewed from the center of its epicycle (small circle) is uniform and circular. (b) Since the center of the epicycle moves with uniform motion along the deferent (large circle centered on the earth), the motion of the planet seen from the earth may appear quite complicated.

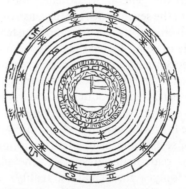

Pera eſt corpus ſolidum vna tantum ſuperficie contentum.
CSpere celeſtes decem ſunt.C Prima eſt firmamentum ſeu circumferentia.C Secunda orbis ſignorum.C Tertia orbis ſtellatus.C Quarta ſaturni.C Quinta iouis.C Sexta mar// tis.C Septima ſolis.C Octaua veneris.C Nona mercurij. CDecima lune.C Orbis ſupremus ſeu ſpera a virtute prime cauſe quem imobilis eſt mouetur que mota mouet omnes alias: τ planete mouentur contra ipſum. Iſte orbis dicitur magnus τ eſt rectus capatior τ ve locior omnibus aliis: τ eos inter ſe comprehendit τ reuoluitur in die τ no// cte reuolutione. 360.partium cum orbe ſignorum: τ reuoluit ſecum orbem ſtellarum fixarum ab oriente in occidentem. Et orbis illarum reuoluit de ipſo ad orientem in. 100. annis vnum gradum ſecundum. Ptbolomeum. Deinde alii orbes ſecudu3 quantitatem conſtrictionis'ſue τ amplitudinis: τ propter ipſum ſunt dies τ nox: τ tempora diuerſa veris τ eſtatis autuni τ bie/ mis τ ipſe permutat ſeptem planetas: τ terra eſt fixa in medio ipſius: quod ſi non eſſet nunq̅ equarentur dies τ nox: τ eſt non ſtellatus τ dicunt aliqui q̅ ipſe eſt ſpiritualis.

FIGURE 3.6   The Ptolemaic system as shown in *A Compilation of Leopold of Austria*, 1520. (Yerkes Observatory photograph.)

still more circles so that in most cases the deferent centered upon a geometric point which moves in a circle about the earth or even upon still another point which moves in a circle about the earth. The final system of Ptolemy required forty circles including the circle of the fixed stars.

To the modern mind schooled in the heliocentric theory, the system of Ptolemy seems unnecessarily complex. So also it seemed to many scholars of the late Middle Ages who sought in vain for some simplification consistent with the demands of a uniform, circular, geocentric astronomy. Nevertheless, it was able to reproduce all of the planetary data known to the Alexandrians and reproduce them to a better precision than any other system that had been proposed. Ptolemy's text was preserved and translated by Arabic astronomers who held it in such regard that they called it *The Greatest Work*. The Latinization of this Arabic designation became *Almagest*.

Claudius Ptolemy was the last of the great Alexandrian mathematical astronomers. Politically the age in which he lived was dominated by Rome, and the Romans showed little interest in philosophical innovations, borrowing their philosophy in the main from their Hellenic teachers. With the decay and collapse of Rome all interest in classical philosophy rapidly vanished from Western Europe; indeed knowledge of the intellectual accomplishments of the Greco-Roman world was all but forgotten within a few centuries. Western Europe awoke to the fact that a world existed outside its own narrow confines only in the twelfth century following the Crusades. Arabic technology was admired; Arabic translations of fragments from classical authors were discovered; and contact with the latter-day Greek culture of Byzantium was established as Western Europe made its transition from the so-called Dark Ages to the High Middle Ages. The revival of learning had begun, a gradual process which was to gain momentum slowly and eventually culminate in the Renaissance of the fourteenth and fifteenth centuries.

The rediscovery and revival of interest in classical learning took many forms. One was the evolution in the thirteenth century of the scholastic philosophy, that blend of Aristotelian and Christian philosophy which incorporated within itself the system of physics that was accepted until the seventeenth century. Another was a passion to find complete original texts of the Greek astronomers, to master the mathematics known to the Alexandrians so that these texts could be comprehended, and to revive the methods of Alexandrian observational astronomy. During the thirteenth century the Jewish and Arabic astronomers of King Alphonse X of Castile compiled tables of planetary positions based upon the rediscovered *Almagest* of Ptolemy. These were the best contemporary astronomical calculations, although they were not generally available until the invention of printing two centuries later. The tables were in great demand when published in Venice in 1483, and almost immediately were found to disagree with observation.

The latter part of the fifteenth century was an exciting epoch in European history. The Renaissance was at its peak, the Reformation about to break upon the scene; the Portuguese had started their voyages of exploration, and during the last decade of the century Columbus was to discover the New World. Trigonometry had been developed, mathematical sophistication had advanced to a level sufficient for a critical understanding of the Greek astronomers, and the invention of printing permitted the rapid and general dissemination of ideas. Although the recently published Alphonsian tables were in sufficient accord with observation for Columbus to navigate with them, they were clearly not in complete accord with observation. By the beginning of the sixteenth century, European scholars had both the interest and the sophistication to search for flaws in the system or at least to attempt a consistent simplification or modification. One such attempt which met with little favor at the time but was destined to outshine all the rest in its subsequent influence was the heliocentric model of Nicholas Copernicus.

▲▲ 3.3 The Copernican system

According to the popular view science evolves by a series of logical, well-defined steps. Observational data pertaining to some system of interest is obtained; a theory is proposed in an attempt to rationalize those data; the theory then suggests other observations by which it can be tested; the results of these tests are used to reject, accept, or modify the theory; further measurements are suggested, and a consistent understanding evolved via this well-defined interchange between theory and experiment.

Whereas these steps do give an outline of the manner in which most important ideas in science have evolved, they are too idealized and convey nothing of the difficulties which the scientists of any particular age have faced in grappling with problems on the frontiers of knowledge. Sketchy histories of science based upon this idealized "scientific method" (as it is often called) neglect and condemn to obscurity many scholars whose false, partially correct, or small but pivotal ideas contributed in some direct or indirect way to the advancement of knowledge. Conversely, they tend to neglect, to omit the incorrect ideas of the giants in the same field, leaving the consequent impression that the evolution of science depends upon the inspiration of infrequent geniuses, incapable of error, who are able to comprehend the complete solution to a problem without any assistance from their misguided contemporaries.

Posterity has been kind to Nicholas Copernicus, paying him just honor as the first man since classical times* to propose a detailed system with the sun fixed at the center of the planetary system and the earth a sixth planet orbiting about it (Figure 3.7). But that same posterity frequently ignores the fact that although the heliocentric hypothesis proved to be the key to an understanding of planetary motion in the hands of Kepler and Newton, the details of the system proposed by Copernicus are almost as complex as the details of the Ptolemaic system he sought to amend. Few men are able to make a complete break with the past, and Copernicus was no exception. He made a giant step in placing the earth in orbit, but he did not take the further step of dispensing with the uniform, circular requirement imposed by Plato so many centuries earlier.

Born in East Prussia (in a region that is now a part of Poland) in 1473, Copernicus studied in Italy from 1496 to 1506, a period of intense intellectual excitement. Manuscripts of the classical authors were widely read, discussed, and criticized. Astronomy was a primary topic of interest, new measurements were being made, and the need to modify the Ptolemaic system generally conceded. It is very probable that the heliocentric idea proposed by Aristarchus* in the third century B.C. was among the possibilities discussed. At any rate, toward the end of his Italian decade, Copernicus seems to have conceived his idea of a modification based upon a heliocentric assumption. Upon his return to Poland in 1512, he was appointed a Canon of the Cathedral of Frauenber, a post he occupied until his death in 1543. During these years he maintained his interest in astronomy, making occasional observations with instruments he constructed according to the specifications of Ptolemy and working out the details of his heliocentric theory. Copernicus probably completed the manuscript of *De Revolutionibus* about 1530, although for reasons that are not entirely clear he was reluctant to have it published,

---

* See footnote, p. 59.

NICOLAI COPERNICI

net, in quo terram cum orbe lunari tanquam epicyclo continerî
diximus. Quinto loco Venus nono mense reducitur.   Sextum
deniçp locum Mercurius tenet, octuaginta dierum fpacio circũ
currens. In medio uero omnium refidet Sol.   Quis enim in hoc

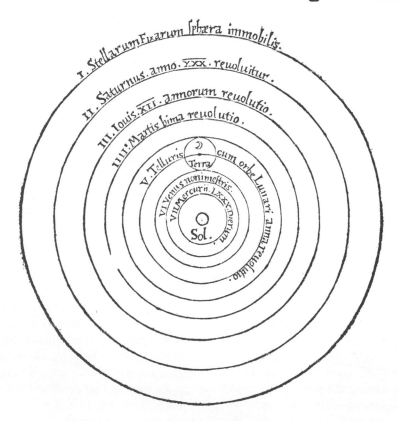

pulcherrimo templo lampadem hanc in alio uel meliori loco põ
neret, quàm unde totum fimul pofsit illuminare? Siquidem non
inepte quidam lucernam mundi, aln̄ mentem, aln̄ rectorem uo⸗
cant. Trimegiftus uifibilem Deum, Sophoclis Electra intuentẽ
omnia. Ita profecto tanquam in folio regali Sol refidens circum
agentem gubernat Aftrorum familiam. Tellus quoque minime
fraudatur lunari minifterio, fed ut Ariftoteles de animalibus ait,
maximam Luna cum terra cognationẽ habet. Cõcipit interea à
Sole terra, & impregnatur aūnno partu.   Inuenimus igitur fub
                                                                                    hae

FIGURE 3.7   The Copernican system from *De revolutionibus Orbium Coelestium*,
1566. (Yerkes Observatory photograph.)

giving his consent only after considerable urging, and more than a decade later. The book arrived from the printer's as he lay on his deathbed. According to tradition Copernicus grasped the first copy as he died.

In the "Dedication to Pope Paul III" preceding the text to *De Revolutionibus*, Copernicus explicitly announces the giant step he proposes to make:

> . . . we do not hesitate to state that the moon and earth describe annually a *circular* orbit (italics added) placed between the outer and inner planets round the sun, which rests immobile in the center of the world; and that everything which appears as a motion of the sun is in truth a motion of the earth.*

He also states the order which the planets occupy in his system in terms of their increasing distances from the sun. It is the order recognized today: Mercury, Venus, Earth, Mars, Jupiter, Saturn.

But the system also assumes that the motion basic to the planets is uniform and circular. In fact, Copernicus was motivated in part by a desire to simplify the Ptolemaic system in the *Ptolemaic spirit*. As he had written earlier:

> . . . I often considered whether there could perhaps be found a more reasonable arrangement of circles . . . in which everything would move uniformly about its proper center, *as the rule of absolute motion requires* [italics added].†

Thus bound to the uniform, circular doctrine, Copernicus was forced to assign several circles to each planet in order to reproduce the motion observed from a moving earth. The major difference between the Copernican and Ptolemaic systems was that the sun and not the earth became the pivot. Conceptionally the difference was enormous. But the detailed system set forth in *De Revolutionibus* required forty-eight circles whereas Ptolemy's *Almagest* had used only forty. In this sense the original Copernican system is more complex than the Ptolemaic!

The major virtue of the new system was its ability to explain the retrogressions of the planets as a result of their being observed from a moving earth. But to most contemporary scholars this was a dubious advantage when weighed against the incredible notion that the seemingly solid earth was not the center of the universe but actually moved, and moved at a terrifying speed at that. Philosophical, theological, and scientific objections were raised against the notion. The earth occupied a very special place as the center of the Aristotelian-scholastic universe; it was the home of man created in the image of God. To set the earth adrift and reduce it to the status of a mere solar satellite seemed to undermine the foundations of the entire philosophical system.

The concept of a moving earth was also difficult to reconcile with observation (Figure 3.8). It was argued that if the earth moved through space at the incredible rate of ten miles per second everything on its surface—people, trees, buildings—would be swept away. A century after Copernicus, Galileo argued that all bodies on a moving object partake of the motion of that object, pointing out that just as sailors are not swept into the sea by the motion of a ship, so objects on the earth are not swept into space. This is a consequence of the law of inertia which Galileo came close to stating: that a body in motion with constant velocity maintains that motion unless acted upon by some outside force. Thus a body in motion along with the earth will continue to move with the earth.

---

* Quoted in Arthur Koestler, *The Sleepwalkers*, © The Macmillan Co., New York, 1959, p. 205; reprinted by Hutchinson Publishing Group Ltd., London, © Arthur Koestler, 1959; and by A. D. Peters & Co., London. By permission of the publishers.

† From Edward Rosen, *The Commentariolus of Copernicus from Three Copernican Treatises*, Dover Publications, Inc., New York, 1954. Reprinted by permission of the publisher.

FIGURE 3.8   This composite photograph, taken and transmitted by the satellite Lunar Orbiter 1 in 1966, shows the crescent earth rising above the lunar surface. If there had been inhabitants on the moon they might well have devised a "luno-centric" model of the universe. (Courtesy of the Jet Propulsion Laboratory, California Institute of Technology.)

However, that conclusion was contrary to the Aristotelian physics current in the sixteenth century, a physics to which Copernicus himself subscribed.

Another objection to the Copernican system related to the question of stellar parallax. If the earth really moves in an orbit some 186 million miles in diameter, then the angular position of a star when viewed in summer should be quite different from the position of the same star viewed six months earlier, in winter, when the earth is 186 million miles from its position relative to the sun (Figure 3.9). But, in fact, no such parallax was observed. The only possible answer to the objection was that the stars are so far away that the diameter of the earth's orbit is negligible in comparison; therefore the parallax could not be observed with the techniques available. But the distances required are enormous, indicating a universe far larger, far more awesome than the sixteenth-century mind could conceive.*

Given these serious objections to the idea of a moving earth, together with the fact that the detailed system of *De Revolutionibus* offered no gain in simplicity vis-à-vis that of the *Almagest*, the Copernican theory gained few adherents and was largely ignored for a time. However, as the sixteenth century neared its close, a small but increasing number of scholars was able to look behind the maze of circles with which Copernicus had all but obscured his basic heliocentric idea and to recognize the fact that some theory based upon that idea might well prove simpler than any geocentric theory, even though Copernicus himself had failed in his attempt to find it.

Both the Ptolemaic and the Copernican systems permitted the calculation of tables predicting planetary positions relative to the fixed stars. Hence both provided purely

---

* In fact, stellar parallax is such a small effect that it was not observed until the nineteenth century.

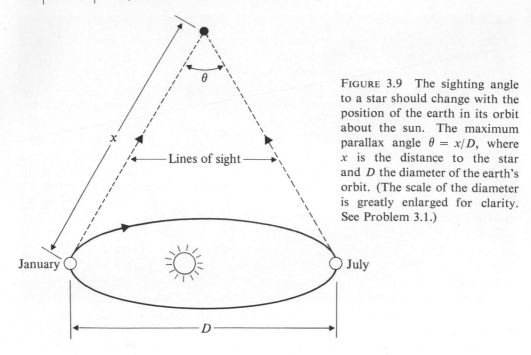

FIGURE 3.9 The sighting angle to a star should change with the position of the earth in its orbit about the sun. The maximum parallax angle $\theta = x/D$, where x is the distance to the star and D the diameter of the earth's orbit. (The scale of the diameter is greatly enlarged for clarity. See Problem 3.1.)

mathematical descriptions of the planetary system. In terms of Chapter 2 they were completely kinematic in nature; neither had anything to say about the cause, the dynamics, of the observed motion. Judged strictly from the accuracy of the prediction each was able to make, there was no reason to consider one superior to the other. But there are additional criteria for judging theories in physics. The Copernican system was criticized because objects would be swept off a moving earth. But that criticism was made from the viewpoint of Aristotelian dynamics and did not concern itself with whether or not the Copernican kinematics was valid. From a modern viewpoint the system may be criticized because the forty-eight separate circular motions cannot be rationalized in terms of interactions between the planets and the sun. Again that criticism does not deny the possibility that the kinematics may be valid.

The Ptolemaic and Copernican systems may also be criticized on more esthetic grounds. The belief that nature should be simple has been a strong article of faith among natural philosophers at least since the time of Pythagoras (fifth century B.C.). The school he founded discovered that if the string of a musical instrument is divided so that the ratio of its two lengths are equal to the ratio of certain sets of whole numbers then harmonious tones result. When the ratios are equal to the ratios of other sets of whole numbers, the result will be dissonance. They reasoned, by analogy, that since the universe must be harmonious then the distances to the planets must also be in the ratio of harmonious whole numbers. Plato also believed in simplicity but took the idea of geometric perfection as his starting point. The spirit of the Platonic idea was simplicity, and while the jumble of circles in the Ptolemaic system adhered to the letter of the Platonic circular doctrine, they most certainly violated the spirit. Indeed, Copernicus was motivated, as he himself states, by a desire to find a more harmonious arrangement of the circles. The fact that his system also turned out to be complex was the price he paid for insisting on both the uniform, circular doctrine and the requirement of observational consistency.

▲▲ 3.4 Kepler and Brahe

The lifework of the German mathematical astronomer, Johannes Kepler (1571–1630), was based upon an almost fanatical conviction that planetary motion could be described by a system that was both simple *and* quantitatively consistent with observation. In common with both the followers of Pythagoras and Plato, he sought to express what was to him a mystical harmony inherent in the universe in terms of the abstract symmetries of mathematics. Very early in his career he became convinced that Copernicus had been right in choosing the sun as the center of the planetary system, though the complexity of circles in *De Revolutionibus* was abhorrent to him. His first model was an attempt at a geometric rationalization of the planetary orbits.

Any three-dimensional figure whose faces are identical two-dimensional polygons is known as a *perfect solid*. As had been known to early Greek thinkers and was later proved by Euclid, only five such solids exist in three-dimensional space: the tetrahedron, with four equilateral triangles as its faces; the cube; the octahedron, composed of eight equilateral triangles; the dodecahedron, with twelve pentagonal faces; and the isosahedron, bounded by twenty equilateral triangles. Because of the regularity of these solids, each may be inscribed within a sphere so that all of its vertices are in contact with the sphere, or circumscribed about a sphere so that all its faces touch the figure. If one sphere is inscribed within a perfect solid and another circumscribed about the same solid, the ratios of the diameters of the two spheres will be uniquely determined, though the magnitude of the ratio itself depends upon which one of the five solids is chosen to mediate between the two spheres.

Kepler's geometric model described in his *Mysterium Cosmographicum* (published in 1596) was based upon this sort of construction (Figure 3.10). Since there are five perfect solids, it is possible to build a nest of six concentric spheres, the first inscribed within one of the solids, the second circumscribing that solid and inscribed within another, the third in turn circumscribing this second solid and inscribed within a third, etc. Several (in fact, 120) different arrangements are possible depending upon the ordering of the five solids, and in each arrangement the diameters of the six spheres have a unique ratio to

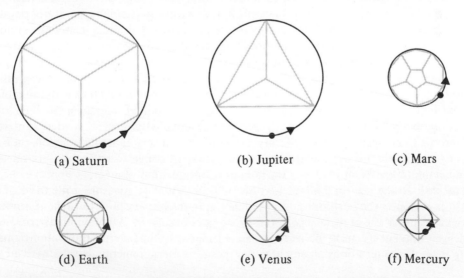

(a) Saturn   (b) Jupiter   (c) Mars

(d) Earth   (e) Venus   (f) Mercury

FIGURE 3.10   Kepler's perfect solids. (After a drawing from *PSSC Physics*, D.C. Heath and Co., Boston, © 1965, p. 363.)

one another. In the *Mysterium Cosmographicum* Kepler states that he had often wondered why there were only six planets and "not twenty or one hundred." He thought he had found the answer in the fact that only six spheres could be nested together with the five solids and reasoned further that the ratios of the spherical diameters must be equal to the ratios of the diameters of the planetary orbits to one another.

It was a charming and elegant, though somewhat naïve, idea. Unfortunately, its agreement with observational data on the planetary orbits was marginal at best. By thickening walls of his spherical shells and by fudging the data a bit, Kepler was able to argue that perhaps the system was not too much in error. In fact, there were ambiguities in the data available to him when he wrote the *Mysterium Cosmographicum*, and it soon became clear that he could construct no satisfactory system at all unless he had access to better measurements. Kepler (and every other interested scholar) knew that this better data existed but had not been published. It remained in the hands of the Danish nobleman Tycho Brahe (1546–1601), the foremost astronomer of the age.

According to his biographer Tycho Brahe's interest in astronomy was first aroused in 1560 when he observed an eclipse of the sun and marveled that so awesome an event could be predicted with such precision. Upon one particular night three years later, the planets Jupiter and Saturn were so close together that they were almost indistinguishable. He also observed that event but noted its prediction based upon the Alphonsian Tables (calculated from the *Almagest*) was a month in error, while the similar prediction based upon the Prunetic Tables (calculated from *De Revolutionibus*) was several days in error. Scandalized at these discrepancies in what to him was a system capable of limitless precision, Brahe decided that more and better observations were necessary and that no one was better qualified to make them than he. His conviction that the best possible quantitative data was prerequisite to any theoretical system was an implicit recognition of the dictum made explicitly by Galileo half a century later (Chapter 1).

Most of Brahe's observations were made during his twenty years at Uranianborg, the great observatory he constructed upon the island of Hveen to which he was granted title in 1576 by King Frederick II of Denmark. Brahe himself designed most of the great instruments with which he outfitted his observatory.* Although these varied in size and in their detailed features, making one more suitable for a particular type of observation than for another, they were all basically large, precisely-ruled circular arcs (or systems of such arcs) with provision for accurate sighting from the center along the ruled arc to the star or planet whose position relative to some reference star was being measured (Figure 2.4). The principles of most of the instruments had been known to the Alexandrian astronomers. However, the care Brahe devoted to their design, together with the money he lavished to obtain the finest materials and the most skilled craftsmen for their construction, insured him of the means to carry out his detailed program. As the years went by and his fame spread, many scholars and curiosity seekers came to Hveen for a time either to assist the master in carrying out his work, to converse with him about astronomical matters, or simply to tour the famous scientific establishment.

The task Brahe set for himself and his assistants was to measure with the highest possible precision the position of every visible star in the heavens and to make *continuous* measurements of the planetary positions to the same accuracy. All previous astronomers had been content to make occasional observations of planetary positions and to base their orbital computations upon these few position measurements. Brahe insisted on

---

* All of his work predated the telescope. Galileo first used that instrument for astronomical observation in 1609, eight years after Brahe's death.

having measurements made almost nightly and over a long period of time before he would consider fitting orbits. This was an important innovation in the practice of quantitative observation. Equally important was the care he took in estimating the precision of his measurements. Given the limitations inherent in even the best instruments, it follows that no measurement can ever be completely without error. Therefore, in attempting to find a mathematical description of a set of observational data, it is important to know just how precise the measurements really are in order to ascertain how much discrepancy between the predictions of the mathematical theory and the numerical data is tolerable. Assigning quantitative limits of accuracy to measured numerical data, now a common practice, was introduced into experimental science by Tycho Brahe. According to his own estimates his planetary measurements were precise to four minutes of arc—that is, to $\frac{1}{15}°$.* Two centuries later Robert Hooke showed that the best theoretical precision obtainable without a telescope is about two minutes of arc. Brahe pushed his observations far closer to that limit than anyone who had preceded him.

In 1597, following a series of quarrels with the successor to his original royal patron, Tycho Brahe left Denmark to become official astronomer to the Holy Roman Emperor Rudolph II, then residing in Prague. Although he transported those instruments which were portable with the intention of continuing his observations, the work he had finished at Hveen was to be his great monument. During his twenty-one years on the island Brahe and his assistants had mapped the positions of one thousand stars and, more important to the subsequent development of astronomy and physics, had compiled almost continuous tables of planetary positions. Now he felt prepared to devise his own system. Having little sympathy with the heliocentric doctrine of Copernicus and his followers, he proposed instead a compromise that simplified the planetary orbits while leaving the earth fixed at the center of the universe: let the five established planets revolve in circular orbits about the sun, while the sun and moon revolve in circles about the earth. It was an appealing idea that was to find considerable favor with many scholars who could not accept the notion of an earth that moved. But Tycho Brahe was no mathematician; his forte was observation, and he required an assistant proficient in mathematics to reconcile the details of his proposal with his own superb data. The young Johannes Kepler was just such a man. He had had a brief correspondence with Brahe concerning his *Mysterium Cosmographicum*. A subsequent invitation to come to Prague as an assistant was readily accepted by Kepler, who saw it as an opportunity to gain access to the data he required to improve his own system.

▶▶ 3.5 Kepler's three laws

Tycho Brahe and Johannes Kepler met in Prague in February, 1600. Had not each had a sufficient respect for the ability of the other to overlook personal grievances the differences in temperament between them might have ruptured the relation within a few weeks. Tycho Brahe, with a reputation based upon more than twenty years of solid achievement, treated Kepler as a servant, had no sympathy with the heliocentric hypothesis, and even less with the mystical ideas concerning perfect solids which Kepler had so passionately advocated in his *Mysterium Cosmographicum*. Nor did he give Kepler ready access to his data. Instead he assigned him the problem of Mars: to calculate an

---

*The angle subtended by the edges of a 25-cent piece held eighty feet from an observer is about 4'. The moon subtends an angle of about 30' of arc to an observer on the earth.

orbit that would describe the observed position of that planet at any time to within the accuracy of observation—four minutes of arc. Both master and assistant expected a kinematic description in terms of uniform, circular motion; both believed the problem was only to find the correct circle and the correct velocity.

Kepler boasted that he would have a solution in eight days but soon realized he had quite underestimated the difficulties involved. In fact, the problem was destined to absorb him for more than six years. Upon Brahe's death in 1601, Kepler was appointed Imperial Mathematician to the Emperor Rudolph and also inherited Brahe's data—though only after a considerable struggle with the latter's heirs.

During their short, rather unpleasant association, Kepler had absorbed Brahe's passion for accuracy and wedded that passion to his faith in the ultimate simplicity of the planetary system, a simplicity based upon a heliocentric viewpoint reflecting the grandeur of the sun.

The end result sought by both Copernicus and Kepler was a heliocentric orbit for each of the planets that would describe correctly its apparent position with respect to a moving earth. Kepler sought, in addition, to eliminate the deferents and epicycles. The difficulty of the task becomes more apparent when it is realized that abandoning the geocentric view means that a correct heliocentric orbit for the *earth* must be found before the positions of the other planets, with respect to the sun, can be translated into positions with respect to an earth-bound astronomer.

After four years of trying various circular orbits for the earth and Mars, Kepler found a solution that fit a number of Brahe's observations. As a check he picked two more observations from the notebooks and found to his dismay that they were at variance with his solution. Adjustment of the orbits made matters worse; one measurement in fact differed from his prediction by no less than eight minutes of arc!

An earlier astronomer or even a younger Kepler would have ignored such a small discrepancy or removed it by adding an epicycle. But the mature Kepler knew that Tycho's accuracy was pertinent to his problem and was convinced that the solution must be a simple one. Had Kepler's purpose been to find a mathematical system that would do no more than predict the position of a planet, as the system of Copernicus had done, then the eight minutes would have been a small discrepancy. But since Kepler sought something further—namely, the rationale underlying the mathematically correct description—he could not be satisfied. In the *Astronomia Nova* of 1609 he recounted his four years of frustration, adding:

> But for us, who by divine kindness were given an accurate observer such as Tycho Brahe, for us it is fitting that we should acknowledge this divine gift and put it to work. . . . Henceforth I shall lead the way toward that goal according to my own ideas. For if I had believed that we could ignore these eight minutes of arc I would have patched up my hypothesis accordingly. But since it was not permissible to ignore them, those eight minutes point the road to a complete reformation in astronomy.*

In other words, Kepler announces that since he cannot patch up his model in any way that will bring it into consistency with the ideas of Plato or Aristotle or Tycho Brahe or anyone else, he will be bound only by the data and otherwise follow his own ideas. It is exceedingly difficult to understand the radical nature of that step, for in the seventeenth century the idea of physical causation as we now understand it, the conviction that the

---

*Quoted by Arthur Koestler in *The Sleepwalkers*, © The Macmillan Co., New York, 1959, p. 322; reprinted by Hutchinson Publishing Group Ltd., London, © Arthur Koestler, 1959; and by A. D. Peters & Co., London. By permission of the publishers.

laws of nature manifest themselves in exact mathematical results, was virtually non-existent. Kepler's conviction that Brahe's data was not only accurate but *relevant* to the basic order he sought forced him to throw aside the uniform, circular dogma that had persisted for almost two millenia and begin anew. The whole of the subsequent development of physics, a whole new philosophy of science turned upon Kepler's dogged belief that those eight minutes of arc were relevant.

To appreciate the relationship between Kepler and Tycho it must be realized that the balance of choice between Keplerian and Copernican astronomy is very narrow. Until measurements were available whose accuracy could be relied upon within a range of four minutes, or even less, there was no need to suppose that the planetary orbits were anything other than circles eccentric to the sun. Kepler, in plotting the orbit of Mars from which he discovered the ellipticity of planetary orbits, was able to calculate the elements of a circular orbit which differed by less than ten minutes from observation. It was only because he knew that Tycho's work was accurate within about half this range that he was dissatisfied and impelled to go further. Kepler's famous first law was thus the first instance in the history of science of a discovery being made as a result of a search for a theory, not merely to cover a given set of measurements but to interpret a group of refined measurements whose probable accuracy was a significant factor.*

In addition to recounting his four years of frustration in attempting to fit a circular orbit to Brahe's Martian data and his ultimate conviction that the doctrine of uniform, circular motion had to be discarded, Kepler's *Astronomia Nova* recounts in agonizing detail two years of additional struggle in which he engaged before he had mastered the problem. In that same book he finally announced his solution in terms of two kinematic laws applicable not only to Mars but to all the planets, including the planet Earth. Taken together the two laws replace the Platonic doctrine of uniform, circular motion.

LAW 1. The orbit of a planet is an ellipse with the sun at one focus.

LAW 2. The radius vector of a planet (the line connecting the sun and the planet) sweeps out equal areas in equal times.

These laws apply to each planet individually but do not relate the orbits of the planets to each other. Finding some relationship between the orbits had been Kepler's driving ambition from the beginning. His perfect solids were an attempt to find such a relationship, and he had been motivated to join Brahe to further his aim. Finally in 1619 he published his *Harmonici Mundi*, a book containing many mystical ideas on the harmony of the universe. It included the almost casual demonstration of a proposition derived from Brahe's data which is now called Kepler's third law and was in fact the long-sought relationship between the planetary orbits:

LAW 3. The square of the period of revolution of a planet about the sun is directly proportional to the cube of its semimajor axis radius vector. (The period of a planet is its "year"—the length of time it requires to complete one revolution about the sun. Its semimajor axis is one half the greatest dimension of its elliptical orbit. See Section 3.6.)

These three kinematic laws summarize Kepler's "complete reformation in astronomy," replacing at a stroke the complex system of deferents, epicycles, and equants that had been used in every description of planetary motion since the first century B.C. The heliocentric hypothesis is explicit in all of them, as is the implication that the heliocentric hypothesis by itself is insufficient.

---

* A. R. Hall, *The Scientific Revolution: 1500–1800*, Longmans, Green and Co., London, 1954, pp. 120–21.

▲▲ 3.6   Kepler's first law: elliptical planetary orbits

Let us examine Kepler's laws in greater detail. The first deals with the shapes of the planetary orbits. The quotation of Galileo's in Section 2.3 implies that the description of the trajectory of a moving body in terms of a regular geometric figure is prerequisite to understanding the character of its motion. Pre-Keplerian astronomers had based their description of planetary motion upon the circle; Kepler used the ellipse.

Mathematically both figures are called curves of second order, or *conic sections*. In a two-dimensional plane a particular circle is defined completely in terms of the position of a point, its center, and a characteristic length, its radius. Let the origin of a two-dimensional Cartesian coordinate system be the center of a circle of radius R (Figure 3.11). Then according to the Pythagorean theorem the x- and y-components of point a on the circle are related by the equation:

$$x_a^2 + y_a^2 = R^2.$$

But the same relationship holds for the components of point b—or any other point upon the circle. Therefore, the circle itself is described by the equation:

$$x^2 + y^2 = R^2. \tag{3.1}$$

Since the variables x and y describing the circle are squared in this equation, the circle is called a curve of second order.

Roughly speaking, an ellipse is a flattened circle, defined in two dimensions by the positions of two points, its *foci* (singular: *focus*) and a characteristic distance, the sum of the distances from the two foci to any point upon the curve. It is the curve determined by the requirement that for all points upon it this sum is constant. In Figure 3.11 for instance, the sum $m_1 + m_2$ must equal the sum $n_1 + n_2$.

The center of an ellipse lies midway between its foci. An alternate method of specifying a particular ellipse is to state the length of its major axis, the line passing through foci, and the length of the minor axis, the perpendicular to the major axis at the center of the ellipse (Figure 3.12). If the length of the major and minor axes of an ellipse are $2a$ and $2b$, respectively, the center of the ellipse is the origin of a Cartesian coordinate system,

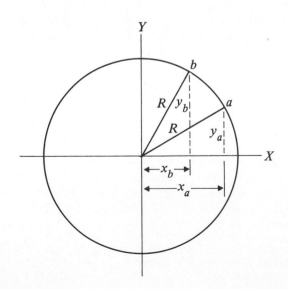

FIGURE 3.11   A circle of radius R centered at the origin of a Cartesian coordinate system.

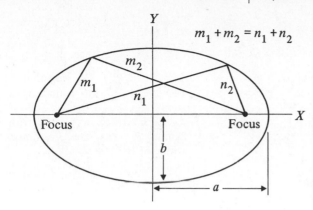

$$m_1 + m_2 = n_1 + n_2$$

FIGURE 3.12 An ellipse with semimajor axis a and semiminor axis b centered at the origin of a Cartesian coordinate system.

and the major axis coincides with the x-axis of the system, then it may be shown that the x- and y-components of any point on the ellipse are related by the equation:

$$\frac{x^2}{a^2} + \frac{y^2}{b^2} = 1. \tag{3.2}$$

In these terms Kepler's first law states that for any planet a coordinate system exists in which the x- and y-components of the planet are always related by Equation 3.2 and that in that coordinate system the sun is at one of the foci of the ellipse so described. Strictly speaking, then, Kepler's system is not helio*centric* at all; the sun does not lie at the center of a planetary orbit but at one of the two foci.

It is important to note that Kepler's first law does not deny the *possibility* of a circular orbit; it merely states that no such orbits are observed in the solar system. For a given major axis an infinite number of ellipses may be constructed differing in the length of their minor axes and therefore in their elongations. If the major and minor axes are equal, the position of two foci coincide at the center, and the ellipse degenerates into a circle. In other words, a circle is an ellipse whose foci coincide and whose major and minor axes are equal. Let $a = b = R$ in Equation 3.2. Then multiplying through by R^2,

$$x^2 + y^2 = R^2,$$

which is simply Equation 3.1 and demonstrates the degeneracy of the ellipse into a circle when its axes are equal.

To appreciate better Kepler's monumental achievement in arriving at his first law, it should be realized that the planetary ellipses are very close to being circular. Of the outer planets known in 1609, Mars has the most elongated orbit and defied his attempts to fit it with a circle for that reason. The ratio of the difference between the major and minor axes to the length of the major axis is but 0.00429, whereas it would be strictly zero for a circle. In other words, if the Martian ellipse were inscribed in a circle (Figure 3.13) the ratio of the crescent characterizing its deviation from that circle to the radius of the circle is 0.00429—or less than $\frac{1}{2}$ of 1%.*

---

* Another measure of an ellipse's elongation is its *eccentricity*,

$$\epsilon = \frac{a^2 - b^2}{a^2}.$$

The eccentricities of the orbits of Earth and Mars are 0.093 and 0.017, respectively. Mercury, with eccentricity 0.206, is difficult to observe due to its proximity to the sun, while Pluto, with eccentricity 0.246, was not discovered until 1930. An ellipse with eccentricity zero is a circle, while an ellipse with eccentricity 1 is completely flat—in other words a straight line with "foci" at its extremities.

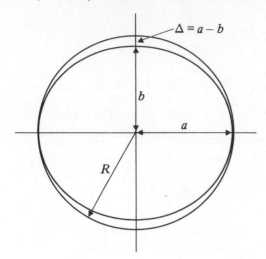

FIGURE 3.13 An ellipse with semimajor axis a and semiminor axis b inscribed in a circle with radius $R = a$. The maximum width of the crescent $\Delta = a - b$ is shown. For the orbit of Mars, the ratio $\Delta/a = 0.00429$.

▲▲ 3.7 Kepler's second law: equal areas in equal times

Kepler's second law states that as a planet moves in its elliptical orbit about the sun its radius vector (the line connecting it with the sun) sweeps out equal areas in equal intervals of time. In Figure 3.14a, $\overset{\frown}{BC}$ and $\overset{\frown}{DE}$ are two segments of such an orbit. If the time intervals the planet requires to traverse these two segments are equal, the areas $R_b\overset{\frown}{BC}$ and $R_d\overset{\frown}{DE}$ must also be equal (Figure 3.14).

Let the arcs $\overset{\frown}{BC}$ and $\overset{\frown}{DE}$ be small compared with the total circumference of the orbit, let BC' be the length of the perpendicular lines from point B to the line SC, and similarly, let DE' be the length of the perpendicular from D to the line SE. Since $\overset{\frown}{BC}$ and $\overset{\frown}{DE}$ are small the areas of the segments $R_b\overset{\frown}{BC}$ and $R_d\overset{\frown}{DE}$ are approximately equal to

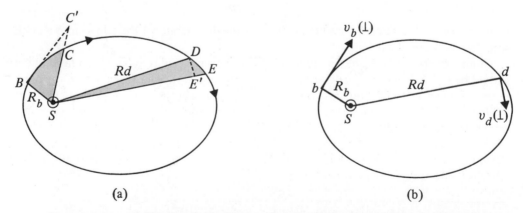

(a) (b)

FIGURE 3.14 (a) Kepler's second law states that if the time a planet requires to traverse the arc $\overset{\frown}{BC}$ is equal to the time required to traverse $\overset{\frown}{DE}$ then the areas BCS and DES are equal. (b) The components of the instantaneous velocity perpendicular to the radius vector at any point is obtained when Δt, the time required to traverse a segment of arc, approaches zero. Kepler's second law implies that $Rv_\perp = $ constant.

the areas of the triangles $R_b\widehat{BC'}$ and $R_d\widehat{DE'}$. Then according to Kepler's second law we have the *approximate* relation:

$$\frac{\frac{1}{2}BC' \times R_b}{\Delta t} = \frac{\frac{1}{2}DE' \times R_d}{\Delta t}. \tag{3.3a}$$

By definition (Equation 2.1) the ratio $BC'/\Delta t = \bar{v}_\perp(BC)$, the component of the average velocity over the arc $\widehat{BC}$ perpendicular to the radius vector $\mathbf{R}_b$, while $DE'/\Delta t = v_\perp(DE)$. As the duration of the interval Δt approaches zero the perpendicular components of the two average velocities approach the perpendicular components of the instantaneous velocities at points B and D, respectively (Equation 2.4), i.e., $v_{\perp b}$ and $v_{\perp d}$. In addition as Δt approaches zero the area of the segments $R_b\widehat{BC}$ and $R_d\widehat{DE}$ are equal to the areas of the two superimposed triangles so that Equation 3.3a becomes an exact relation. Substituting the values of the instantaneous velocity components into this equation,

$$R_b v_{b\perp} = R_d v_{d\perp}.$$

But this equation will also be valid for any other point on the orbit. Therefore, we can write Kepler's second law as:

$$Rv_\perp = \text{const.} \tag{3.3b}$$

That is, the product of the radius vector of a planet by the component of its velocity perpendicular to the radius vector remains constant over its entire orbit. Consequently, a planet moves more rapidly when near the sun than when farther away.

If there *were* a planet with a circular orbit its radius vector would be constant, and its velocity vector always perpendicular to that radius vector. According to Equation 3.3b the planet's speed would remain constant over the entire orbit. Therefore, taken together the first two laws of Kepler amend the doctrine of the uniform, circular motion: the orbital speed of a planet is constant *if and only if* its orbit is circular. Since no planet in the solar system has a circular orbit, no planet travels with uniform speed. However, Kepler's laws are also valid for all satellites, natural and artificial, that orbit the earth if the word "sun" is replaced by "Earth," and the word "planet" by "satellite." The nearly circular orbits that have been achieved by artificial satellites are characterized by nearly constant speeds, as Kepler would have expected.

▲▲ 3.8 Kepler's third law: periods of the planets

Kepler's second law (Equation 3.3b) states that the product $Rv_\perp$ is constant for every planet, but does not specify the numerical value of that constant. It will differ for each planet, as shown by the third law.

Let R be the length of the semimajor axis of a planet's orbit (Section 3.6) and T its period of revolution or "year," the time required to complete one orbit about the sun. According to the third law the square of the period is proportional to the cube of the semimajor axis, or:

$$T^2 = kR^3, \tag{3.4}$$

where k is a constant which has the same numerical value for all planets in the solar system. A convenient system of units for planetary measurements expresses distances in fractions or multiples of the earth's semimajor axis, and periods in fractions or multiples of earth years. In that system $k = 1$ year^2/earth-radius^3. Now Venus has a 225-day or

0.615-year period. Applying Equation 3.4, its semimajor axis must be 0.72 times that of the earth, in agreement with measurement.

Table 3.1 lists the mean orbital radii, the periods, and the ratio $k = R^3/T^2$ for the planets of the solar system. According to Equation 3.4 this latter quantity should be

TABLE 3.1 *Mean Distances from the Sun and Periods of the Planets Visible Without a Telescope*

Planet	$\bar{R}$*	T†	$k = \bar{R}^3/T^2$ ‡
Mercury	0.39	0.241	1.02
Venus	0.72	0.616	0.98
Earth	1.00	1.00	1.00
Mars	1.5	1.88	0.96
Jupiter	5.2	11.86	1.00
Saturn	9.5	29.46	0.99

* $\bar{R}$ in units of the mean difference from Earth to Sun.
† T in earth years.
‡ The slight variation in the ratio arises in part from the fact that the cubes of the mean distances from the sun rather than the cubes of the semimajor axes of the orbits are used.

equal for all planets. Table 3.2 lists these quantities for the moon and for a recent artificial earth satellite. Although the ratios $k = R^3/T^2$ for these earth satellites are equal, they differ from the same ratios for the planets. Evidently Kepler's third law is valid for objects in orbit about the earth as well as for objects in orbit about the sun. However, the numerical constant of proportionality in Equation 3.4 differs for the two systems, suggesting that its value depends upon the properties of the body which is central to the system.

TABLE 3.2 *Two Satellites of the Earth*

*Moon**

$\bar{R} = 2.4 \times 10^5$ miles $= 2.58 \times 10^{-3} R_e$ $k = \bar{R}^3/T^2 = 3.05 \times 10^{-6}$
$T = 27.4$ days $= 7.5 \times 10^{-2}$ years

*Low-Orbit Satellite**

$\bar{R} = 4 \times 10^3$ miles $= 4.3 \times 10^{-5} R_e$ $k = \bar{R}^3/T^2 = 3.14 \times 10^{-6}$
$T = 84$ minutes $= 1.6 \times 10^{-4}$ years

* $\bar{R}$ = mean distance from the earth. R_e = mean radius of Earth's orbit about the sun.

It is worth noting explicitly that Equation 3.4 involves the semimajor axes of the elliptical planetary orbits but *not* the semiminor axis. Therefore, two planets or two satellites with the same semimajor axes would have identical periods regardless of the degree of flattening of their orbits. Since the orbits of all planets in the solar system have different semimajor axes there is no simple way to apply this conclusion to that system, although it might conceivably be used in connection with a group of artificial satellites. But we shall find an analogous statement of the relation of considerable interest in Chapter 19 when we discuss electron orbits in atoms.

In Chapter 5 we shall use Kepler's third law as one of the observational data leading to Newton's law of gravitation. In order to prepare for that discussion let us recast Equation 3.4 into a form valid for the special case of a circular orbit, a form involving the radius of the orbit and the speed of the planet rather than its period. Because the planetary orbits are so nearly circular (Section 3.6) this alternate form is almost correct for the observed elliptical orbits as well.

The (constant) magnitude of the velocity of a planet in a circular orbit is equal to the ratio of the circumference of the orbit by the period of revolution:

$$v = \frac{C}{T}, \quad \text{or} \quad T = \frac{C}{v}.$$

But $C = 2\pi R$, where R is the radius of the orbit so that:

$$T^2 = \left(\frac{2\pi R}{v}\right)^2.$$

Substituting into Equation 3.4:

$$\left(\frac{2\pi R}{v}\right)^2 = kR^3,$$

or, rearranging factors:

$$Rv^2 = \frac{(2\pi)^2}{k}. \tag{3.5}$$

That is, the product of the radius by the square of the speed of all satellites in circular orbits about the same central body is constant.

▲▲ 3.9 Galileo's contributions to astronomy

Galileo Galilei (1564–1642) made two distinct contributions to the synthesis of celestial and terrestrial mechanics achieved by Isaac Newton in the late seventeenth century. During the early years of his career while professor at Pisa and later at Padova, he performed several series of experiments on the motion of terrestrial objects. Reasoning from the results of these experiments, he reached numerous conclusions about the character of motion. By pointing out errors and misconceptions in Aristotelian physics, in free fall, projectile motion, and in the concepts of "natural" and "violent" motion themselves, he laid the basis for modern kinematics.

Most of these results were published in his *Discourses Concerning Two New Sciences* in 1638, many years after he had completed his investigations. In 1608 his attention was diverted from the earth to the heavens by the news that a Dutchman, one Hans Lipperkey, had discovered that if two lenses were arranged in a particular fashion in a long tube, objects sighted through the tube appeared to be magnified considerably. By his own account Galileo experimented with a number of such lens arrangements until he thought he understood the operation of the device. Turning this primitive telescope (Figure 3.15) to the heavens, he was astounded by what he saw. Abandoning all other interests, he labored to improve his new instrument. After six months of feverish observation he published his *Siderius Nuncius*—or *Message from the Stars*—which must rank as one of the most extraordinary scientific reports ever written.

> Great indeed are the things which in this brief treatise I propose for observation and consideration by all students of nature. I say great, because of the excellence of the subject itself, the entirely unexpected character of these things, and finally because of the instrument by means of which they have been revealed to our senses.
>
> Surely it is a great thing to increase the numerous host of fixed stars previously visible to the unaided vision, adding countless more which have never been seen, exposing these plainly to the eye in numbers ten times exceeding the old and familiar stars.

FIGURE 3.15   The first two telescopes of Galileo, now at the Museo di Storia della Scienza, Florence, Italy. (Photograph courtesy of the Museum.)

It is a very beautiful thing, and most gratifying to the sight, to behold the body of the moon, distant from us about sixty earthly radii, as if it were no farther away than two such measures. . . . In this way one may learn with all the certainty of sense evidence that the moon is not robed in a smooth and polished surface but is in fact rough and uneven, covered everywhere, just like the earth's surface, with huge prominences, deep valleys, and chasms.*

Thus in his first paragraphs Galileo presents observational evidence contrary to the Aristotelian conception of the universe: there are at least ten times as many stars as had been previously supposed; the moon is not a perfect celestial body, but in fact its surface appears to be very much like the earth's. As he reports in a later section:

There is another thing that I must not omit, for I beheld it not without a certain wonder; this is that almost in the center of the moon there is a cavity larger than all the rest. . . .

---

* From *Discoveries and Opinions of Galileo*, trans. by Stillman Drake, p. 27. Copyright © 1957 by Stillman Drake. Reprinted by permission of Doubleday and Co.

As to light and shade, it offers the same appearance as would a region like Bohemia if that were enclosed on all sides by very lofty mountains. . . .*

Impressive as these observations were, the most startling discovery remained to be reported:

> There remains the matter which in my opinion deserves to be considered the most important of all—the disclosure of four PLANETS never seen from the creation of the world up to our own time, together with the occasion of my having discovered and studied them, their arrangements, and the observations made of their movements and alterations during the past two months.†

These "planets" (which Galileo named the Medicean planets in honor of the ruling house of Florence) were the four largest satellites of Jupiter (Figure 3.16). Galileo had discovered a system quite analogous to the earth and its satellite. Since Jupiter, a planet, had moons, one could argue that the earth too could be considered a planet.

Galileo ends the *Siderius Nuncius* by stating his conviction that he had not yet exhausted the possibilities of his new instrument:

> Time prevents my proceeding further, but the gentle reader may expect more soon.‡

This expectation proved correct. In later observations he discovered sunspots, the rotation of the sun about its axis, the phases of Venus, and the strange shape of Saturn, though his telescope was insufficient to reveal that this strange shape was due to the rings about that planet. All cast grave doubts upon Aristotelian cosmology though the heliocentric theory was *proved* by none of these discoveries: the surface of the moon is like the surface of the earth, the surface of the sun is blemished, the planet Jupiter has moons, and Venus has phases, which can only be true if it revolves about the sun and not the earth.§ Galileo had written that "Philosophy is written in that grand book, the universe, which stands ever open to our gaze" (Chapter 1). The powerful gaze of the telescope compelled one to read the book in a different sense than ever before.

Of course, Galileo's strong advocacy of the heliocentric view, enunciated most emphatically in his *Dialogues Concerning Two World Systems* (1635), brought him into conflict with those academicians who were not yet ready to abandon the Aristotelian system. At first the official position of the Catholic Church was not one of solid alliance with these academicians. Contrary to what is commonly believed, Galileo received considerable support for his work (though not for his heliocentric viewpoint) from the official Jesuit astronomers in Rome after making his first discoveries. In 1623 Maffeo Barbarini, who regarded himself a scientist and who had expressed admiration for Galileo, ascended the papal throne as Urban VIII. Galileo sought his permission to expound the arguments for the heliocentric viewpoint in contrast with the geocentric theory. He was granted permission to do so provided he present it only as a *hypothesis,* not as a fact. When the *Dialogues Concerning Two World Systems* appeared in print, Urban was furious, believing that Galileo had broken the terms of his agreement by presenting the heliocentric "hypothesis" in too favorable a light and had, in addition, publicly held him, the Pope, up to ridicule. Even though many elements in the Church supported Galileo's ideas and

---

* *Ibid.,* p. 36.
† *Ibid.,* pp. 50–51.
‡ *Ibid.,* p. 58.
§ One criticism of Copernicus had been that if the earth were a satellite of the sun and Venus revolved about the sun in an orbit interior to the orbit of the earth, then phases of Venus would be observed. Hence Galileo's discovery was a striking confirmation of one aspect of the heliocentric theory.

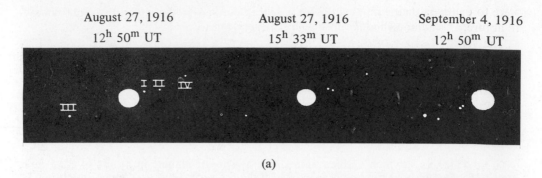

August 27, 1916
12ʰ 50ᵐ UT

August 27, 1916
15ʰ 33ᵐ UT

September 4, 1916
12ʰ 50ᵐ UT

(a)

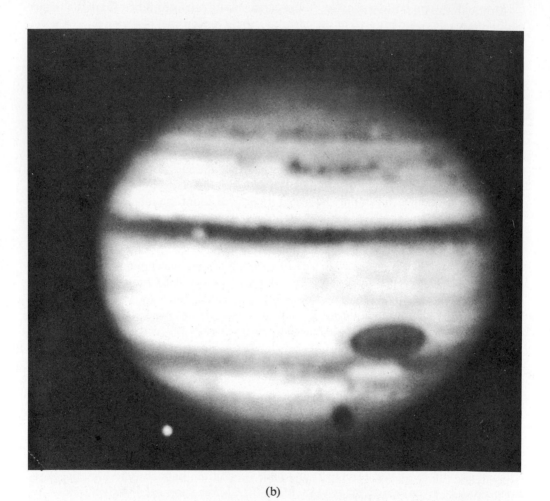

(b)

FIGURE 3.16 (a) Jupiter and the four "Medicean" satellites discovered by Galileo photographed with a ten-inch telescope at three different times. (Yerkes Observatory photograph.) (b) Jupiter and its smallest satellite, Ganymede, photographed with the Hale 200-inch telescope. The shadow cast by the satellite is clearly visible on the surface of the planet. (Photograph from the Mt. Wilson and Palomar Observatories.)

were to continue their support in private, Galileo was summoned to Rome, tried, forced to abjure, and admonished never to teach the heliocentric theory again.*

The verdict was a tragedy for Galileo. Forced to denounce the work of almost thirty years, he was kept in virtual house arrest in his villa at Arceti until his death. His books were banned in the Catholic world so that his last work—*Discourses Concerning Two New Sciences*—had to be published in Holland. But although he could renounce his work, he could not force the world to renounce it. Few could now believe in the veracity of either Aristotelian cosmology or Aristotelian physics. The stage was set for Newton, born in 1642, the year of Galileo's death.

▲▲ 3.10 Evolution of the law of inertia. Force and motion

Although the three laws of Kepler completely replace the complex tables of deferents and epicycles required in the Ptolemaic and Copernican descriptions, revealing a simplicity and harmony that the earlier systems had succeeded in almost completely concealing, the laws are still purely kinematical. They go no further in themselves toward suggesting *why* the planets move as they do and in that sense are still bound to the old spirit of astronomy as a purely mathematical exercise. But Kepler was not content with pure kinematics; all of his career had been motivated by a desire to understand the reasons for planetary motion. The simplicity manifested in his mathematical results strongly suggests the possibility of finding a basic physical mechanism underlying the whole system, thus providing a connection between physics and astronomy. He experimented with various ideas but died in 1630 without succeeding. Although he had replaced the celestial portion of the Aristotelian-based system with a far simpler scheme, he did not abandon Aristotelian dynamics. Assuming that terrestrial force concepts are applicable to the solar system, the task of finding a quantitative physical mechanism on the Aristotelian basis is formidable. According to Aristotelian dynamics a force is needed to push each planet around its orbit, a force proportional to the instantaneous orbital velocity of the planet. Aristotle had vested that motive force in a vaguely defined Prime Mover. Since the sun was granted primacy in Kepler's system, he tried at the time to locate the origin of the pushing force in some sort of invisible spokes pivoting about the sun. The first law insists upon elliptical orbits, however, suggesting that each planet must roll slowly back and forth on its spoke as it is pushed about, while the second law requires that as the planet rolls along the spoke the force with which the spoke pushes must vary. Finally, the third law implies a different, though related set of spokes for each planet. The system begins to sound as unwieldly as the interlocking spheres of Eudoxus.

Further, Aristotelian dynamics insists that the motive force be proportional to the weight of the body being moved. It is difficult to understand how the intuitive idea of weight in terms of the force required to lift a body from the surface of the earth can be extended to the planets, especially since the sun, not the earth, is the pivot of the system. The flaw in this line of reasoning appears to be centered about the concepts of force and weight, and this defect blocked the path from Kepler's kinematic laws to an understanding of the physical causation behind them, i.e., to a system of planetary dynamics.

Prior to the publication of Galileo's *Discourse Concerning Two New Sciences* in 1637, the Aristotelian assumption that rest was a preferred state had been a major mental block in all attempts to understand the causes of motion. Indeed as suggested in Section 3.1,

---

* A complete account of the trial, events leading to it, and the issues involved are given in a number of references—for instance G. de Santillana, *The Crime of Galileo*, University of Chicago Press, 1955.

this assumption seems well grounded in observation, for all terrestrial objects, when left to their own devices, come eventually to rest. The next step is the assumption that all departures from rest, that is, that all motion, require a force, though certain categories of natural motion, notably falling bodies, are excepted from the rule in the Aristotelian system. Again this assumption seems to be a good one until it is critically examined. A *moving* automobile does not come immediately to rest if its engine is turned off. Similarly, an arrow requires the force of a bow string to *set* it in motion, but the origin of the force that subsequently keeps it in motion is not at all obvious—if indeed such a force is required.

On the basis of a long series of observations Galileo reached the conclusion that a force is *not* always required to keep a body in motion. In Aristotelian terms a force must be found to keep an automobile in motion after its engine is turned off. However, Galileo's conclusions suggest that to search for that force is to ask the wrong question. *If* no force is required to *keep* the auto in motion, the correct question is why does it slow down at all? Experiments conducted *with that question in mind* lead to the conclusion that the condition of the roadbed determines the rate of the auto's deceleration. In modern terms, the deceleration results from a frictional force between auto and road. Given these data, it is possible to extrapolate to an ideal, frictionless case and assume the velocity of the automobile remains constant *unless* an external force intervenes.

Reasoning from his experiments in this manner (though obviously not from experiments with automobiles) Galileo groped toward a redefinition of the force-free state of an object. René Descartes (1596–1650) generalized the idea to the motion of all bodies in a statement of the law of inertia, and Newton rephrased the Cartesian law as his first law of motion:

Law 1. A body continues in a state of rest or in a state of uniform, linear velocity unless acted upon by an external force.

In Aristotelian physics, force-free motion is called natural motion. In essence the law of inertia redefines natural motion to include *all* constant velocity motion. It includes rest as a special case of zero (constant) velocity but no longer as a privileged case. Rest and constant velocity are dynamically equivalent in that neither requires the intervention of an external force.

Additional illumination is offered by stating Newton's first law in a more compact form. Velocity is a vector. Therefore, it only remains constant if neither its magnitude nor its direction changes. Hence:

Law 1. The velocity vector of a body in a force-free state remains constant.

Now if the constancy of a body's velocity vector is the necessary and sufficient condition for determining that it is in a force-free state, a cause must be found for any motion characterized by a *changing* velocity vector. Falling bodies accelerate, for instance. Therefore, free fall cannot qualify as force-free motion. Similarly, it would not be necessary to explain the motion of the planets if they moved in straight lines with constant velocity. But according to Kepler's second law their velocity vectors change continuously. Hence it becomes necessary to find a force that keeps them *in their orbits*, not a force that keeps them *in motion*. Neither Aristotle's Prime Mover nor Kepler's sun spokes is required.

The intuitive idea of force is related to effort, and it is convenient to retain the connection in seeking a mathematical definition of the concept of force itself. Analysis of the motion of an automobile suggests a connection between the "effort" made by the engine and the acceleration it produces. Therefore, as a first step the total, external force upon a body can be defined as a quantity proportional to the acceleration of that body:

$$\mathbf{F} \propto \mathbf{a}. \tag{3.6}$$

That force is a vector follows both from Equation 3.6 and also from its intuitive connection with effort.

Newton based his second law of motion on this intuitive proportion between force and acceleration, and that law is the connecting link between kinematics and the cause of motion. If the solar system is to be analyzed in terms of Newtonian dynamics, then the observed acceleration of the planets, implicit in Kepler's laws, must be connected with a force that is consistent with Kepler's kinematic description. Similarly the observed fact that free-fall acceleration is constant implies that a force of constant magnitude acts upon all terrestrial bodies.

A popular tradition attributes Newton's discovery of the law of universal gravitation to a minor mishap in an apple orchard. Almost certainly the tradition has no basis in fact and is too well known to bear repetition. However, it is pertinent to the assumption of universality that led to his successful synthesis. If all bodies in the universe are subject to the same consistent set of physical laws and if an apple falls from a tree not because it seeks its natural place but because the earth exerts an attractive force upon it by virtue of the second law, then the earth should exert the same force upon all bodies in its proximity. Therefore, the moon, like the apple, should fall toward the earth. But instead of falling the moon moves in accord with Kepler's laws. Newton's basic problem was to reconcile the assumption of universality with the observed differences in behavior of the apple and the moon.

SUGGESTIONS FOR FURTHER READING ▲▲▲

Possibly the best review of the history of astronomy through Kepler and Galileo in any physics text is:

GERALD HOLTON AND DUANE H. D. ROLLER, *Foundations of Modern Physical Science*, Addison-Wesley Publishing Co., Inc., Reading, Mass., 1958, Chapters 6–11.

Among the many books by historians on the same subject are:

HERBERT BUTTERFIELD, *The Origins of Modern Science*, The Macmillan Co., 1960, Chapters 1, 2, and 4.

I. BERNARD COHEN, *The Birth of a New Physics*, Science Study Series, Doubleday and Co., Garden City, New York.

There are also many books about the life and work of the major figures mentioned in this chapter, among them:

STILLMAN DRAKE, *Discoveries and Opinions of Galileo*, Doubleday and Co., Garden City, New York, 1957.

J. L. E. DREYER, *Tycho Brahe: A Picture of Scientific Life and Work in the Sixteenth Century*, Dover Publications, Inc., New York, 1963.

ARTHUR KOESTLER, *The Watershed; A Biography of Johannes Kepler*, Science Study Series, Doubleday and Co., Garden City, New York.

GIORGIO DE SANTILLANA, *The Crime of Galileo*, University of Chicago Press, 1955.

PROBLEMS AND EXERCISES ▲▲▲

3.1. What is the parallax angle of the nearest star (Alpha Centuri) between January 1 and July 1? (Alpha Centuri is four light years from the earth; assume the earth's orbit is circular with radius 1.5 $(10)^{11}$ m. The velocity of light is 3×10^8 m/sec.)

3.2. The so-called "fixed stars" are really not fixed. However, their distances from the earth are so great that changes in their positions are difficult to observe over short time intervals.

(a) If Alpha Centuri were in motion in a direction parallel to the earth's orbit how far would it have to move to give an apparent displacement of 1 sec of arc? (There are 60 sec per min of arc; 60 min per deg. See Figure 2.4.)

(b) If the velocity of the star relative to the earth were 1000 km/sec (10^6 m/sec), over what time interval would this displacement become apparent assuming the star's velocity is perpendicular to the line of sight? (Assume the net displacement of the earth during this time is negligible relative to the motion of the star.)

3.3. Plot ellipses with centers on the origin of a Cartesian coordinate system with the following semimajor and semiminor axes:

$$
\begin{aligned}
a &= 5, &b &= 4; \\
a &= 5, &b &= 3, \\
a &= 3, &b &= 3, \\
a &= 3, &b &= 2.
\end{aligned}
$$

3.4. The equation for an ellipse with major axis coincident with the x-axis of a Cartesian coordinate system but with the origin of the system at one focus rather than at the center is:

$$
\frac{(x \pm d)^2}{a^2} + \frac{y^2}{b^2} = 1,
$$

where a = the semimajor axis, b = the semiminor axis, and $d^2 = a^2 - b^2$. Plot two ellipses with $a = 5$, $b = 4$, $d = 2$: one with $x + d$, the other with $x - d$ in the equation.

3.5. One form of the equation for an *hyperbola* in Cartesian coordinates is:

$$
\frac{x^2}{a^2} - \frac{y^2}{b^2} = 1.
$$

Plot hyperbolae with:

$$
\begin{aligned}
a &= 5, &b &= 4, \\
a &= 5, &b &= 3, \\
a &= 3, &b &= 3.
\end{aligned}
$$

Compare your plots with the ellipses obtained with the same values of a and b in Problem 3.3.

3.6. The period of a satellite in low orbit about the earth (orbital radius about 6.4×10^6 m) is about 84 min. Is this consistent with Kepler's third law and the known period of the moon?

3.7. What would the radius of a satellite orbit be if its period were one-half that of the moon?

3.8. Several communications satellites have periods equal to the 24-hr rotational period of the earth so that they remain in one spot above its surface. What are the radii of their orbits relative to the center of the earth?

3.9. What would the period of an artificial earth satellite be if the semimajor axis of its orbit were 240,000 miles? [HINT: What is the radius of the moon's orbit?]

3.10. Make a tracing of Figure 3.16a showing Jupiter and several of its moons on three different nights. Are Kepler's second and third laws consistent with the figure?

3.11. The radii of three of the moons of Jupiter (in units of the radius of that planet) and the period of one of them are given below. Complete the table.

Moon	R	T
1	5.5	1.76 days
2	8.75	
3	13.9	

3.12. Suppose two earth satellites had the same perigee (distance of closest approach to earth) but one was in a circular orbit while the other was in an elliptical orbit with its major axis three times the orbital radius of the first. Using Kepler's laws compare:

(a) The periods of the satellites.
(b) Their velocities at perigee.
(c) Their velocities at apogee (farthest distance from the earth).

3.13. (a) An earth satellite is in a circular orbit of radius R, another is in an elliptical orbit whose semimajor axis is equal to the radius of the circular orbit. Which has the greater average velocity over its orbit?

(b) A third satellite has the same semimajor axis but a smaller semiminor axis than the second. Which has the greater average velocity?

3.14. Halley's comet has a 76-yr period about the sun. What is the length of its semimajor axis?

3.15. The earth is 1.47×10^{11} m from the sun in winter, 1.48×10^{11} m in summer. What is the extreme percentage variation in its orbital velocity?

3.16. In the very unlikely event that the moon were suddenly to lose its orbital velocity and crash into the earth, how long would it take to arrive?

[HINT: A straight line is a special case of an ellipse with major axis one-half its length. Although the moon's orbit would be altered by the catastrophe it would continue to obey Kepler's third law in its new "orbit."]

3.17. (a) Using Kepler's third law, plot the monthly positions of the earth and Venus for one earth year in a Cartesian coordinate system with the sun at the origin. Assume circular orbits for simplicity; let the radii of the orbits be 1.5×10^{11} and 1.0×10^{11}m, respectively.

(b) Translate the graph of part a into a plot of the positions of Venus as viewed from the earth as follows:

  i. Measure the monthly x- and y-components of the displacement of Venus from Earth from your graph.

  ii. Plot the positions of Venus given by these x- and y-components in a Cartesian system with the earth at the origin.

This is the sort of geocentric orbit the Ptolemaic theory sought to describe. Kepler's task was to proceed from (ii)—given by Brahe's data—back to (i) using elliptical rather than circular orbits.

3.18. Assume that the force causing the centripetal acceleration of the moon toward the earth originates in the earth's gravitational attraction. How must the magnitude of that attraction vary with distance to be consistent with both Newton's second law and Kepler's third law?

[HINT: Compare the expression for the centripetal acceleration of the moon with Kepler's third law in the form of Equation 3.5.]

Fundamental principles of dynamics

4

Since the Ancients . . . esteemed the science of mechanics of greatest importance in the investigation of natural things, and the moderns, rejecting substantial forms and occult qualities, have endeavored to subject the phenomena of nature to the laws of mathematics, I have in this treatise cultivated mathematics as far as it relates to philosophy. . . .

. . . the whole burden of philosophy seems to consist in this—from the phenomena of motions to investigate the forces of nature, and then from these forces to demonstrate the other phenomena. . . .

. . . I hope the principles here laid down will afford some light either to this or some truer philosophy.* ISAAC NEWTON

▲▲ 4.1 Two-body interactions and inertial mass

Newton's synthesis of terrestrial and celestial dynamics is the basis of classical physics. His *Principia Mathematica*, first published in 1687, is the definitive statement of that synthesis and includes the reasoning that led him to four laws: the three laws of motion and the law of universal gravitation.

It is both interesting and instructive to read the *Principia* and to follow directly Newton's methods. But the conceptual structure of physics has evolved considerably since 1687 so that by departing from an historical method of exposition we can take advantage of hindsight in our development of particle dynamics. While the arguments and the ordering of the topics in this chapter are not Newton's, we shall nevertheless arrive at the same general system of dynamics.

Let us restate Newton's first law, the law of inertia:

The velocity vector of a body in a force-free state remains constant.

As we noted in Chapter 3, this law may be taken as a basic postulate, a means for determining experimentally whether or not a given body is in a force-free state. If we discover that the velocity vector of a particular body is *not* constant we must conclude that it is subject to a net, external force.

---

* *Sir Isaac Newton's Mathematical Principles of Natural Philosophy and His System of the World*, translation revised by Florian Cajori, University of California Press, Berkeley, Calif. (1934). From Newton's Preface to the First Edition, pp. xvii–xviii.

FIGURE 4.1   Sir Isaac Newton, 1642–1727. (Courtesy of the Royal Society, London.)

Ultimately we shall attribute all forces to the interaction of two or more bodies. There-fore, we shall begin our development of Newtonian dynamics by formulating a completely general, experimentally-based principle that describes the results of any interaction between two bodies, provided only that the bodies interact only with each other and not with any external force. Such two-body systems are called *isolated* systems.

There are many very good approximations to such systems: two colliding billiard balls; a rifle and the bullet it fires; a rocket and the gas it ejects;* a falling body and the earth; the sun and a planet that revolves about it; the proton and orbital electron of a hydrogen atom; the α-particle and the uranium nucleus from which it is ejected in radioactive decay. In each case the detailed nature of the interactions between the pairs is quite different: the billiard balls interact by contact for a short period of time, whereas the earth and the sun interact continuously over large distances. For the present the exact nature of the inter-action between any two bodies is of no concern since we are investigating the results of any general interaction. It is worth mentioning that whereas Newton's second law is *not* valid for the atomic and nuclear systems listed above, the law of momentum conservation we are now formulating has universal applicability.

It is simple to demonstrate experimentally that two particles are interacting: *neither* obeys the law of inertia. A billiard ball imparts some of its own velocity in colliding with another. The earth moves in a *curved* path about the sun, not in a straight line. Again, it is simple (in principle) to determine that neither particle in an isolated system interacts with anything external to the system: if one member of the pair is removed, then the velocity vector of the second *will* remain constant. The velocity of billiard ball 1 is constant before and after its collision with 2; a rifle does not recoil until it is fired.

Let us first consider a series of isolated systems, each consisting of a pair of bodies whose mutual interaction is repulsive, restricting our discussion to motion along a straight line. Such a system might consist of two blocks resting on a level, frictionless surface initially separated by a compressed spring (Figure 4.2), or two bar magnets oriented with their south poles facing each other, or a rifle and its bullet.

To be specific, let us discuss in detail a series of experiments with a block and spring system, and let the spring be attached to one block so that two bodies are involved instead of three. The spring is compressed by pushing the blocks toward each other, and the system remains at rest as long as an external force keeps the spring compressed. When this restraint is removed the spring expands and the blocks move from the scene of the interaction in opposite directions (Figure 4.3). If the surface on which they move is completely frictionless we observe that the speeds of the blocks are constant, and con-clude that each is in a force-free state. But before the expansion of the spring the blocks were at rest. Therefore, as a result of the interaction the velocity vector of each has changed, in agreement with our general criterion for determining that an interaction has occurred.

For a given pair of blocks the magnitudes of the two final, constant velocities depend upon the compression of the spring: the greater the compression, the greater the velo-cities. However, it is observed experimentally that regardless of the compression of the spring the *ratio* of the magnitudes of the final velocities is constant. That is: if $v_1(A)$ and

---

*Of course the force of gravity acts upon both billiard balls, upon the rifle and bullet, and upon the rocket. But in the first examples the upward force of the billiard table exactly cancels its effect upon the billiard balls, whereas in the second and third examples the objects move so rapidly that the acceleration due to gravity has little effect upon their motion over short periods of time. Therefore we may regard all these systems as approximately isolated.

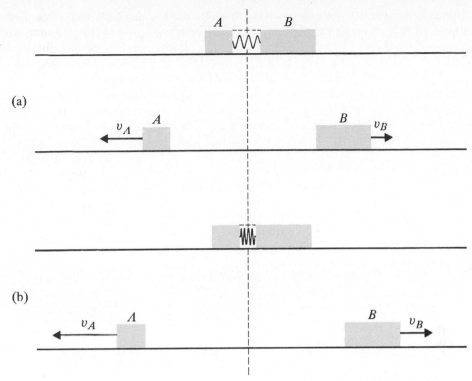

(a)

(b)

FIGURE 4.2 Operational definition of the inertial mass ratio of two interacting bodies. In part b the spring initially connecting the bodies is compressed more than in part a so that the magnitudes of the two final velocities are also greater. However, the *ratio* of the final speeds is independent of the details of the interaction and it therefore apparently measures an intrinsic property of the bodies themselves.

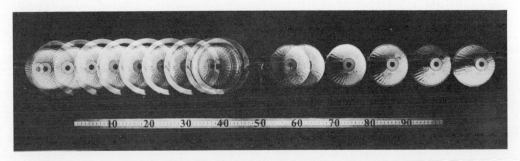

FIGURE 4.3 Multiple-flash photograph of two dry-ice pucks made at four-second intervals after they were pushed apart by a spring. The horizontal scale is in centimeters (100 c = 1 m.) (From *PSCC Physics*, D. C. Heath and Co., Boston, © 1965, p. 382.)

$v_2(A)$ are the respective final speeds of body 1 and 2 for one particular state of compression, and $v_1(B)$, $v_2(B)$ the final speeds for another state then:

$$\frac{v_2(A)}{v_1(A)} = \frac{v_2(B)}{v_1(B)},$$

or, in general,

$$\frac{v_2}{v_1} = \text{const.}, \tag{4.1}$$

regardless of the individual magnitudes of v_1 and v_2.

Equation 4.1 makes a basic statement about the nature of two-body interactions. If we let another block, say 3, interact with block 1 in the same way then it is again observed that the ratio v_3/v_1 is constant, though in general a different constant than the ratio v_2/v_1. Furthermore, the constant-speed ratio is observed for *all* possible interactions between two bodies. We might replace the springs with bar magnets oriented with adjacent south poles, push the poles together, release the blocks, and measure the speeds when the two are so far apart that their interaction is negligible. The ratio v_2/v_1 will be the same ratio that was obtained when the interaction was mediated by the spring.

From these observations we conclude that all bodies have some constant, intrinsic property that characterizes the way their velocity vectors change when they interact with other bodies. This property is called *inertia*, and the quantity that measures inertia, *inertial mass*. Let us define the ratio of the inertial masses of two bodies as the *inverse* ratio of their speeds after interaction. That is:

$$\frac{M_2}{M_1} = \frac{v_1}{v_2}. \tag{4.2}$$

According to this definition the velocity of the body with the larger inertial mass is the slower of the two. Hence we may also regard inertia as a measure of a body's intrinsic "reluctance" to having its velocity vector changed. Since the ratio v_2/v_1 is constant *regardless* of the nature of the interaction between the two bodies it follows that the ratio of their inertial masses is also constant. If this were not so the concept of inertia would have little utility.*

We may perform a set of analogous experiments to determine the ratio of the inertial mass of another body, 3, to body 1:

$$\frac{M_3}{M_1} = \frac{v_1}{v_3},$$

and determine the ratio for body 4 in the same way:

$$\frac{M_4}{M_1} = \frac{v_1}{v_4}.$$

Since it is immaterial which of the bodies we label as 1 we must also observe that:

$$\frac{M_3}{M_2} = \frac{v_2}{v_3}, \ldots$$

---

* At speeds close to the speed of light (3×10^8 m/sec) the ratio v_2/v_1 is no longer a constant independent of the speeds themselves so that internal mass becomes a function of speed (Chapter 11).

If we now arbitrarily select some body, 1, as the standard of inertial mass (in the sense of Section 2.11) and let its magnitude be one unit, then the masses of all other bodies follow from Equation 4.2. For since $M_1 = 1$ then:

$$M_2 = \frac{v_1}{v_2}, \qquad M_3 = \frac{v_1}{v_3}, \ldots$$

In the mks system a cylinder of platinum-irridium alloy kept at the International Bureau of Weights and Measures in Paris serves as the standard mass and is arbitrarily assigned a magnitude of one kilogram. Because no direction is implied in the concept of inertia, inertial mass is a scalar quantity.

▲▲ 4.2 The conservation of momentum

We have reached the important experimental conclusion that the ratio of the final speeds of two bodies that repel each other starting from rest is a constant independent of the detailed nature of the repulsive interaction between the bodies. That is,

$$\frac{M_a}{M_b} = \frac{v_b}{v_a},$$

or, rearranging factors:

$$M_a v_a = M_b v_b.$$

By writing this equation in vector form we can also indicate explicitly that the two bodies move in opposite directions following the interaction:

$$M_a \mathbf{v}_a = -M_b \mathbf{v}_a.$$

The product $M\mathbf{v}$ is called *momentum*. Since inertial mass is a scalar and velocity a vector, then momentum must be a vector in the same direction as velocity:

$$\mathbf{p} = M\mathbf{v}. \tag{4.3}$$

It is convenient to express the results of the interaction experiments in terms of the final momentum vectors of the two bodies:

$$\mathbf{p}_A = -\mathbf{p}_B,$$

or

$$\mathbf{p}_A + \mathbf{p}_B = 0.$$

That is, the total momentum vector of the two-body system, defined as the vector sum of the individual momenta, is equal to zero. Before the interaction both bodies were at rest so that the total momentum at that time was also zero. *Therefore, the total momentum of the system was not changed by the interaction between the two bodies.*

The statement $\mathbf{p}_A + \mathbf{p}_B = 0$ is a special case of the general, experimentally-based law of momentum conservation which states that the vector sum of the momenta of any number of bodies constituting an isolated system remains constant. In other words, the momentum of a system cannot be altered by interactions within the system itself. Let the respective momenta of n interacting bodies at time t_1 be $\mathbf{p}_A(t_1), \mathbf{p}_B(t_1), \mathbf{p}_C(t_1), \ldots, \mathbf{p}_n(t_1)$, and let the momenta of the same bodies at a later time t_2 be $\mathbf{p}_A(t_2), \mathbf{p}_B(t_2), \mathbf{p}_C(t_2), \ldots, \mathbf{p}_n(t_2)$. The law of momentum conservation states that

$$\mathbf{p}_A(t_1) + \mathbf{p}_B(t_1) + \mathbf{p}_C(t_1) + \cdots + \mathbf{p}_n(t_1) = \mathbf{p}_A(t_2) + \mathbf{p}_B(t_2) + \mathbf{p}_C(t_2) + \cdots + \mathbf{p}_n(t_2), \tag{4.4}$$

regardless of the nature of the interactions among the n bodies. For two interacting bodies initially at rest, $\mathbf{p}_A(t_1) = 0$, $\mathbf{p}_B(t_1) = 0$, and Equation 4.4 requires that $\mathbf{p}_A(t_2) + \mathbf{p}_B(t_2) = 0$, in agreement with our previous observations.

As a slight variant of the block and spring system let us consider the radioactive decay of uranium. In such a decay the parent nucleus—uranium—disintegrates into an α-particle (the nucleus of a helium atom) and another nucleus, thorium, whose mass is very close to being the difference between the masses of the uranium nucleus and the α-particle.* How are the velocity vectors of the ejected α-particle and the thorium nucleus related? Let the mass of the uranium nucleus be M_u, the mass of the ejected α be M_α. Then the thorium nucleus has mass $M_{th} = M_u - M_\alpha$. If the uranium nucleus is at rest before decay, the momentum of the system is zero and must remain zero throughout and subsequent to the decay. Therefore, the momenta of the decay products must be equal and opposite. If v_1 and v_2 are the magnitudes of the velocities of the α-particle and the thorium nucleus, respectively, then:

$$M_{th}v_2 = M_\alpha v_1,$$

or

$$v_2 = \frac{M_\alpha}{M_{th}}\, v_1.$$

Referring to the Periodic Table of the Elements (see Chapter 19), thorium has mass approximately 234 times the mass of a hydrogen atom, helium mass four on the same scale. Therefore:

$$v_2 = \left(\frac{4}{234}\right)v_1.$$

The thorium nucleus recoils with about 2% the velocity of the ejected alpha.

In many interactions the initial momentum of the system is not zero, and in such cases the final velocities need not be confined to one direction. Suppose a billiard ball of mass M_A and velocity v_0 collides with a second billiard ball M_B which is initially at rest. Prior to the collision the momentum of M_A is the total momentum of the system:

$$\mathbf{p}_0 = M_A\mathbf{v}_0.$$

Following the collision the velocities $\mathbf{v}_A$ and $\mathbf{v}_B$ are related to $\mathbf{v}_0$ by:

$$M_A\mathbf{v}_0 = M_A\mathbf{v}_A + M_B\mathbf{v}_B.$$

Let the x-axis of the coordinate system in which the collision is described be the direction of the incident billiard ball, and choose the origin at the interaction point (Figure 4.4a). In this system the initial momentum is entirely along the x-axis, but the final momenta need not be. We can regard the above vector equation as shorthand for two separate equations between initial and final x- and y-components of momentum. Referring to Figure 4.4a, these equations may be written in terms of the magnitudes and directions of the two final velocities:

$$M_A v_0 = M_A v_A \cos \theta_A + M_B v_B \cos \theta_B,$$
$$0 = M_A v_A \sin \theta_A + M_B v_B \sin \theta_B.$$

These are two equations in four unknowns, two magnitudes and two directions. Given any two of these four quantities the other two follow at once. The second equation implies

---

* The reason why the difference is not exact is discussed in Chapter 20.

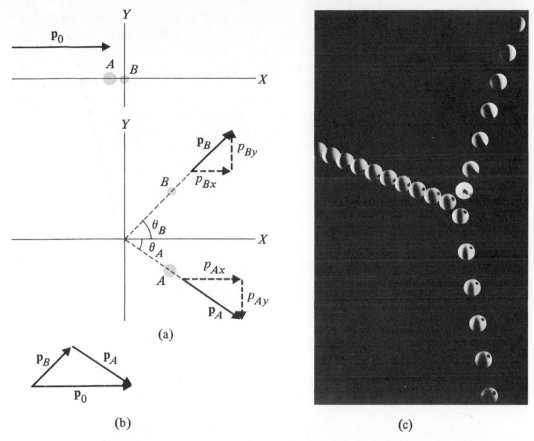

FIGURE 4.4 Momentum conservation in a two-dimensional two-body inter-action. (a) The sum of the x-components of the final momenta is equal to the magnitude of the initial momentum, and the final y-components are equal and opposite. (b) Geometric interpretation of momentum conservation. The vector sum of the final momenta is equal to the initial momentum. (c) Multiple flash photograph (rate: 30 sec) of a two-dimensional collision between equal masses. The dotted ball entered from the bottom of the picture and struck the striped ball which was originally at rest. (Photograph from *PSSC Physics*, D. C. Heath and Co., Boston, © 1965, p. 384.)

that the y-components of the final momenta must be equal and opposite to each other, a requirement that follows from the fact that the initial y-component of momentum is zero.

Several special cases should be noted. If the two balls do not scatter but instead proceed in the incident direction then $\theta_A = \theta_B = 0$, and $M_A v_0 = M_A v_A + M_B v_B$. If in addition the masses are equal, the sum of the final velocities is equal to the initial velocity. Finally, if $v_B = v_0$ then $v_A = 0$. Billiard ball A stops and transfers all of its velocity to B.

This type of collision problem has a rather natural geometric interpretation, as shown in Figure 4.4b. Since the sum of two vectors may be represented by laying the tail of the second upon the head of the first (Section 2.9), and since the vector sum of the final momenta is equal to the initial momentum it follows that the initial momentum vector, $\mathbf{p}_0$, must be the third side of the triangle formed by the final vectors $\mathbf{p}_A$ and $\mathbf{p}_B$.

Two more examples demonstrate the wide applicability of the momentum conservation law.

1. A rocket of mass M, cruising with constant velocity V, ejects a jet of gas of mass m with velocity v in a direction perpendicular to its own motion. Describe the motion of the rocket after ejection of the gas. Assume the gas is ejected in a short burst (Figure 4.5).

Let the original direction of motion be the x-axis of some coordinate system. Then the initial momentum is MV_0 in the x-direction. Since the gas is ejected with momentum mv in the y-direction, the rocket receives an equal and opposite momentum in that direction. If V_{fx} and V_{fy} are the x- and y-components of the rocket's velocity after ejection of the gas, then:

$$(M - m)V_{fx} = MV_0,$$
$$(M - m)V_{fy} = mv.$$

If m is much smaller than M, then approximately:

$$V_{fx} = V_0,$$
$$V_{fy} = -\frac{mv}{M}.$$

The magnitude and direction of the total velocity vector follow from Equation 2.18:

$$V = \sqrt{V_{fx}^2 + V_{fy}^2},$$
$$\tan \phi = \frac{V_{fy}}{V_{fx}}.$$

2. In Figure 4.6a the tracks of several antiprotons are shown in a liquid hydrogen bubble chamber (Chapter 21). A number undergo interactions with the protons that constitute the nuclei of the hydrogen atoms. Two such interactions from Figure 4.6a are sketched in Figure 4.6b. In each of these the incident antiproton and target proton annihilate each other to yield several secondary particles whose momenta may be determined from the curvature of their tracks in the chamber (Section 9.4).

Since the antiprotons travel with virtually the speed of light before their interaction, and, further, since the identities of the particles in the initial and final states are completely different, many assumptions of Newtonian physics are not applicable to the interactions. Nevertheless, the momentum of the incident antiproton is conserved in the interaction.

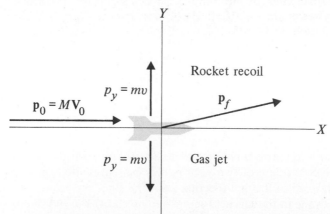

FIGURE 4.5 A rocket traveling initially in the x-direction ejects a burst of gas of mass m with velocity v in the negative y-direction. Thus the rocket receives an equal and opposite y-component of momentum and thereby alters its course.

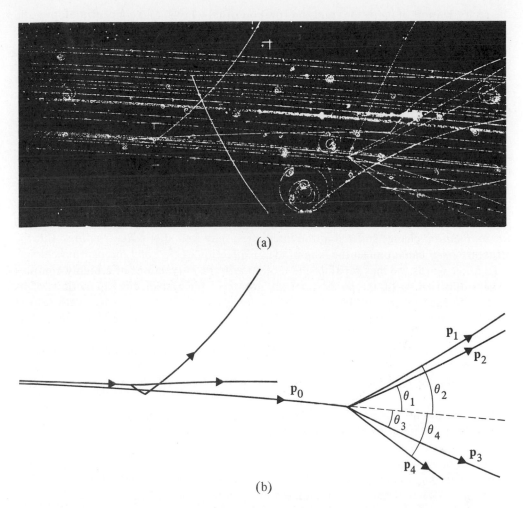

FIGURE 4.6 (a) Antiproton interactions in a liquid hydrogen bubble chamber. (b) Identification of the momentum vector of the incident antiproton ($\bar{p}_0$) and the momentum vectors of the four charged secondary particles resulting from the annihilation of the antiproton with a proton in the liquid hydrogen. (Photograph courtesy of Brookhaven National Laboratory.)

Concentrating on the four-pronged event in Figure 4.6b, we can write, as with the billiard ball in Figure 4.4:

$$p_0 = p_1 \cos \theta_1 + p_2 \cos \theta_2 + p_3 \cos \theta_3 + p_4 \cos \theta_4,$$
$$0 = p_1 \sin \theta_1 + p_2 \sin \theta_2 + p_3 \sin \theta_3 + p_4 \sin \theta_4.$$

The relation between mass, velocity, and momentum at these very high velocities is discussed in Chapter 11.

▲▲ 4.3 Centers of mass of systems of particles and extended bodies

In Chapter 2 (Section 2.1) we noted that the term "motion of an automobile" is ambiguous since, in fact, each individual part of an automobile has its own characteristic motion. However, if we are interested in the motion of the system as a whole we ignore the reciprocation of its pistons and the rotation of its wheels, and concentrate upon the changing position of an arbitrary point on the body as a function of time. This procedure permits us to talk about time variation of the positions of every other point on the body as well, since the rigid structure of the automobile implies that all points on the auto maintain an invariant spatial relationship relative to one another. In effect, we reduce the description of the automobile's motion to a description of the motion of the arbitrary point.

We have formulated the law of momentum conservation in terms of the interactions of "bodies" or "objects" without asking whether or not these entities have internal structures. It is the momentum conservation law itself which permits us to do so, for according to that law the purely internal workings of a system cannot alter its total momentum. Two bodies of the same mass and same total momentum differing only in their internal structures must undergo identical changes in their momenta when they interact in the same way with a third body. If one of the two bodies has a complex internal structure the momentum change suffered in the interaction may well alter that structure. But the structure *itself* cannot affect the magnitude or direction of the total momentum change.

In other words, we may separate the motion and the interactions of a highly complex system into two parts: the purely internal motion of the system, the interactions of its parts with each other, and the motion and interaction of the whole system with respect to other systems. The exact meaning of the word "system" is often arbitrary, depending upon the way an observer chooses to attack the problem at hand. The earth and everything upon it may be considered a "system" vis-à-vis the motion of that planet relative to the sun, while the sun with all of its comets, asteroids, planets and their attendant satellites may be regarded as a "system," the solar system, vis-à-vis the structure of the local galaxy.

When we discuss the motion and interaction of systems without regard to their internal structures it is useful to concentrate upon a point in each (as with the automobile in Chapter 2) and in effect reduce the external motion and interactions of the system to that point. In other words, we replace the system with a *particle* having the mass of the entire system, defining a particle as any entity whose motion may be represented by a single, three-dimensional, time-varying momentum vector. The abstraction permits us to develop the basic laws of dynamics without regard to the internal structure of systems, and in addition offers the possibility of discussing the internal motion of systems in terms of the particles which compose them. Hence the abstraction has a wide if by no means a universal applicability.

The external motion of a system is most simply described if the position of the particle chosen to represent that external motion is located at its *center of mass*. Let the system be composed of n particles with inertial masses $M_1, M_2, \ldots, M_n$, and let the Cartesian components of these particles be $(x_1, y_1, z_1), (x_2, y_2, z_2), \ldots, (x_n, y_n, z_n)$, respectively. Then *by definition* the coordinates of the system's center of mass are:

$$X = \frac{M_1 x_1 + M_2 x_2 + \cdots + M_n x_n}{M_1 + M_2 + \cdots + M_n}, \tag{4.5a}$$

$$Y = \frac{M_1 y_1 + M_2 y_2 + \cdots + M_n y_n}{M_1 + M_2 + \cdots + M_n}, \tag{4.5b}$$

$$Z = \frac{M_1 z_1 + M_2 z_2 + \cdots + M_n z_n}{M_1 + M_2 + \cdots + M_n}. \tag{4.5c}$$

For example, if two particles at rest compose the system it is always possible to choose a coordinate system in which both of the particles lie on the x-axis (Figure 4.7a). Then their center of mass also lies on the x-axis and has the x-coordinate:

$$X = \frac{M_1 x_1 + M_2 x_2}{M_1 + M_2}.$$

If in addition the position of M_1 is chosen as the origin of the system then $x_1 = 0$ and

$$X = \left(\frac{M_2}{M_1 + M_2}\right) x_2.$$

In the special case $M_1 = M_2$, $X = x_2/2$ so that the center of mass lies midway between the particles. If the masses of the particles are not equal their center of mass will lie closer to the more massive member of the pair. For example in the case $M_2 = 3M_1$, $X = \frac{3}{4}x_2$. The center of mass is located three-fourths of the distance between M_1 and M_2 (Figure 4.7b).

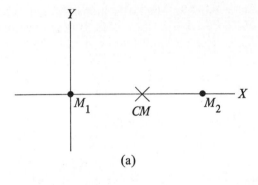

(a)

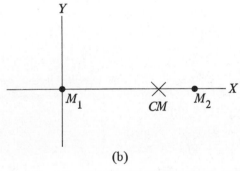

(b)

FIGURE 4.7 (a) The center of mass of two equal mass particles is midway between them. (b) If the masses of the two particles are not equal (here $M_2 = 3M_1$), their center of mass is nearer the more massive particle. (c) The center of mass of three particles. ($M_2 = 3M_1$, $M_3 = 2M_1$).

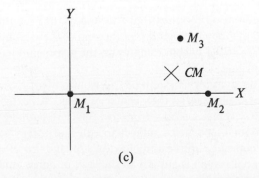

(c)

Finding the center of mass of three particles that do not lie in a straight line requires the use of a two-dimensional coordinate system and both Equations 4.5a and 4.5b (Figure 4.7c), while generally all three of these equations must be used to find the center of mass of a system with four or more particles. The center of mass of a continuous, extended object may be located by imagining that the body is composed of a great many particles, and applying Equations 4.5. Often this procedure requires that techniques of the integral calculus be introduced in order to evaluate the sums. However, if the body has a regular shape, geometric considerations often suffice in fixing its center of mass. For example, the symmetry of a sphere implies that its center of mass coincides with its geometric center.

It is interesting to note that momentum conservation is equivalent to the assertion that the center of mass of an isolated two-particle system is not altered by interactions between the particles, but moves as if it were subject to the law of inertia. If two particles move relative to each other in the xy-plane then the position of their center of mass also changes with time. According to Equations 4.5 it has velocity components:

$$V_x = \frac{\Delta X}{\Delta t} = \frac{M_1(\Delta x_1/\Delta t) + M_2(\Delta x_2/\Delta t)}{M_1 + M_2} = \frac{M_1 v_{x1} + M_2 v_{x2}}{M_1 + M_2}, \tag{4.6a}$$

$$V_y = \frac{\Delta Y}{\Delta t} = \frac{M_1(\Delta y_1/\Delta t) + M_2(\Delta y_2/\Delta t)}{M_1 + M_2} = \frac{M_1 v_{y1} + M_2 v_{y2}}{M_1 + M_2}, \tag{4.6b}$$

which, upon rearranging terms becomes:

$$(M_1 + M_2)V_x = M_1 v_{x1} + M_2 v_{x2} = p_{x1} + p_{x2}, \tag{4.7a}$$

$$(M_1 + M_2)V_y = M_1 v_{y1} + M_2 v_{y2} = p_{y1} + p_{y2}. \tag{4.7b}$$

However, $p_{x1} + p_{x2}$ and $p_{y1} + p_{y2}$ are the total x- and y-components of the system's momentum, and these remain constant regardless of the interaction between the particles. Likewise, $(M_1 + M_2)V_x$ and $(M_1 + M_2)V_y$ are equal to the momentum components of a particle having the total mass of the system and located at its center of mass. In other words, these equations imply that the external motion of the system is equivalent to the motion of such a particle, which is just the point discussed earlier in this section.

Consider in particular a collision between two billiard balls of equal mass with billiard ball 1 incident upon 2 with velocity v_0 and along the x-axis (Figure 4.8). Before the collision $p_x = M_1 v_0$, $p_y = 0$, and Equations 4.6 imply:

$$V_x = \frac{M_1}{M_1 + M_2} v_0 = \frac{v_0}{2},$$

$$V_y = 0.$$

After the collision, momentum conservation requires that the sum of the x-components of the momenta be equal to the original momentum and that the sum of the y-components be zero. Therefore, the center of mass of the system remains on the x-axis and has speed $v_0/2$ as before the collision.

We have shown that the external behavior of a system of two isolated particles may be reduced to the motion of a single particle located at their center of mass. An extension of the proof to multiparticle isolated systems is straightforward. The remainder of this chapter is concerned with the behavior of particles subject to external forces, in other words, with situations involving the concept of force and Newton's second law of motion. Just as the center of mass of an isolated system is subject to the law of inertia, the center

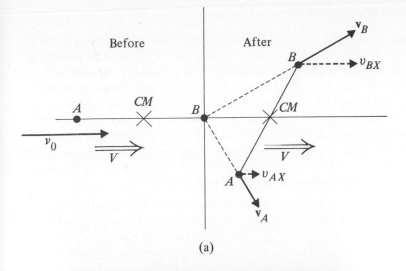

(a)

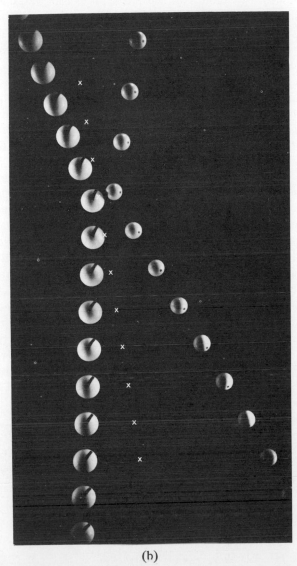

(b)

FIGURE 4.8 (a) Collision of two
equal mass particles. The motion
of the center of mass is unaffected
by the interaction. (b) Multiple
flash photograph showing the
collision of two bodies with a
mass ratio of 7/3, both of which
were in motion before the collision. The crosses show the
position of the system's center
of mass which moves with constant velocity. (From *PSSC
Physics*, D. C. Heath and Co.,
Boston, © 1965, p. 389.)

of mass of a system subject to external forces behaves as if the system's entire mass were concentrated at that point. This statement retains its validity even if the constituents of the system do not retain their proximity to each other. The motion of projectiles is considered in a later section. If such a projectile (a shell, for instance) explodes at some point along its trajectory then no matter how many fragments result from the explosion, their center of mass continues to move as if nothing had happened, and their total momentum remains equal to the changing momentum of that center of mass.

▲▲ 4.4 The force vector. Newton's second and third laws of motion

The broad applicability of the momentum conservation law is suggested by the examples in Section 4.2. However, these examples also show that the law by itself is insufficient to specify completely the results of an interaction between two bodies. The final velocity vectors of two billiard balls are not uniquely specified by the initial velocity of the incident sphere. Specification of two vectors in a plane requires four variables, two magnitudes and two directions, while momentum conservation yields only two equations. If the incident *and* one of the final velocity vectors is specified, the other final vector follows from momentum conservation. But there is no way to calculate *both* velocity vectors by using the momentum conservation law alone.

This state of affairs should not be surprising. Since the momentum conservation law imposes no restriction upon a system save its isolation, the law cannot yield specific conclusions related to details of specific types of interactions. But since physics is concerned with such details it is desirable to define a new quantity capable of acting as a link between the momentum change which is the *effect* of an interaction, and the properties of the particles which *cause* them to interact. This quantity is called *force*; it is defined by Newton's second law of motion. It is important to note at the outset that the utility of the force concept as we are about to define it depends very much upon the extent to which a system can be regarded as a collection of interacting particles, i.e., as a group of entities each specified by a single, well-defined time-varying momentum vector. In dealing with atomic and subatomic processes it is necessary to modify the meaning of the word particle, and the Newtonian idea of force ceases to be such a useful one. But in all cases encountered in the next few chapters, the use of the force concept and of Newton's second law is completely justified.

Consider two particles which interact continuously and over a distance rather than instantaneously and by contact. Such "particles" might be the poles of two long bar magnets that attract or repel each other according to the orientation of the magnets, the earth and a falling stone, or two blocks at the ends of an expanding spring. If the two particles comprise an isolated system, then regardless of the specific nature of the inter-action between them, the *change* in momentum of the first during any time interval Δt must be equal in magnitude and opposite in direction to the change in momentum of the second over the same time interval.

Figure 4.9 shows two successive positions of two particles attracting each other along the line drawn between them. If their respective momenta at time t_1 are $\mathbf{p}_1(t_1)$ and $\mathbf{p}_2(t_2)$, and their momenta at a later time t_2 are $\mathbf{p}_1(t_2)$ and $\mathbf{p}_2(t_2)$, the respective changes in their momenta during the time interval $\Delta t = t_2 - t_1$ are

$$\Delta\mathbf{p}_1 = \mathbf{p}_1(t_2) - \mathbf{p}_1(t_1),$$

$$\Delta\mathbf{p}_2 = \mathbf{p}_2(t_2) - \mathbf{p}_2(t_2),$$

(a)

(b)

FIGURE 4.9 (a) The positions of two particles attracting each other and their momentum vectors at time t_1 and time t_2, a short interval Δt later. (b) The equal and opposite changes in the two momentum vectors during the time interval, Δt, are obtained by taking the vector differences at the two times.

and according to the law of momentum conservation:

$$\Delta \mathbf{p}_2 = -\Delta \mathbf{p}_1.$$

The *average* force upon the mass M_2 during the time interval Δt due to its interaction with M_1 is defined as the ratio of the change in its momentum vector during the time interval Δt to the length of the interval itself:

$$\mathbf{F}_{av} = \frac{\Delta \mathbf{p}_2}{\Delta t}. \tag{4.8a}$$

Force is therefore a quantity that measures the strength of an interaction, since its magnitude depends upon how rapidly momentum changes. A small change in momentum during a time interval of a particular length implies a smaller force than a larger change during the same time interval. Since momentum is measured in kilogram-meters per second, force must be measured in kilogram-meters per square second. A shorthand unit of force in the mks system is the *newton* (N), equal to 1 kg-m/sec².

The specific force characterizing the interaction between two bodies may depend upon a number of properties of the bodies: their masses, for example, or their electric charges. It almost always depends upon their separation and sometimes upon their velocities relative to each other. Since the bodies move as a result of their mutual interaction, it follows that the force between them usually changes as their positions change, and hence becomes a function of time. Thus the average force upon a particle over a particular interval will depend upon the length of the interval itself, just as with the average velocity of an accelerating body depends upon the length of the time interval over which it is calculated.

The *instantaneous* force upon a particle is derived from average force in the same way that instantaneous velocity is derived from average velocity (Chapter 2). The time interval in which the momentum change is measured is permitted to approach zero. Although the change in momentum *itself* will become vanishingly small as the time interval becomes small, the *ratio* $\Delta \mathbf{p}_2 / \Delta t$ need not go to zero because $\Delta \mathbf{p}_2$ and Δt become small *together*. That is,

$$\mathbf{F} = \lim_{\Delta t \to 0} \frac{\Delta \mathbf{p}_2}{\Delta t}. \tag{4.8b}$$

A good deal of the material in this and the next few chapters is concerned with various types of forces between particles. We shall discover that the behavior of many important forces can be expressed as simple functions of the properties of the interacting particles. The gravitational force upon an object close to the earth's surface is directly proportional to its mass. The force exerted by a compressed spring is directly proportional to its degree of compression. The gravitational force between two particles is directly proportional to the product of their masses and inversely proportional to the square of their separation, while the electrostatic force between two charged particles is directly proportional to the product of their charges and, again, inversely proportional to the square of their separation. If it were not possible to relate the time rate of change of momentum to the properties of particles in such a simple way in so many cases, then introduction of the force concept would serve little or no purpose. Indeed as we have already noted we shall dispense with the concept when dealing with the interactions of elementary particles and also with interactions at very large velocities, for in these cases the use of force becomes quite cumbersome.

Many texts regard Equation 4.8b as a law relating two independently defined quantities rather than as a definition of force. Doubtless Newton had the former interpretation in mind. However, that interpretation requires an independent definition of force, and it is difficult or impossible to find such a definition that does not eventually reduce itself to standardization in terms of some particular force, or, in other words, that does not tie itself to some specific property of matter. Since we shall be concerned chiefly with the applications of the force concept, the question of whether Equation 4.8b is a law or a definition should not trouble us further. It is sufficient to note that there is by no means any general agreement on the answer to that question.

Thus far we have restricted the idea of force to two-body interactions. But a particle may interact simultaneously with more than one other particle. For example, a falling body experiences a gravitational force as well as a retarding force due to its interaction with the air molecules, the moon is attracted by both the earth and the sun, an atom in a crystal interacts with all adjacent atoms.

Figure 4.10a shows a particle M_1 interacting with two others which exert the respective forces F_1 and F_2 upon it. If either of the forces acted separately, then, according to Equation 4.8a, it would cause a change in the momentum of M_1 proportional to $\mathbf{F} \, \Delta t$ during the time Δt. But since the forces act simultaneously the resultant momentum change must be the vector sum of the two separate momentum changes. Referring to Equation 4.8a once again we arrive at the principle of superposition of forces: the *net* force acting upon a particle is the vector sum of all the separate forces upon it.

If F_{1x} and F_{1y} are the x- and y-components of the force $\mathbf{F}_1$ in some coordinate system and F_{2x} and F_{2y} the corresponding components of force $\mathbf{F}_2$ (see Figure 4.10a and Equation 2.9) then according to Equations 2.21 the components of the net force on M_1 are:

$$F_{nx} = F_{1x} + F_{2x},$$
$$F_{ny} = F_{1y} + F_{2y},$$

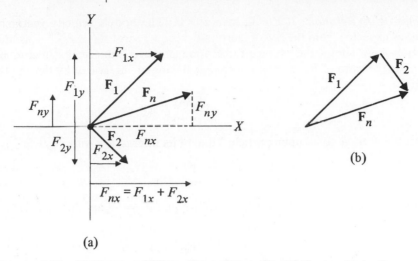

(a)

(b)

FIGURE 4.10   (a) Vector addition of two forces, $\mathbf{F}_1$ and $\mathbf{F}_2$, to obtain the resultant $\mathbf{F}_n$.   (b) Geometric method of vector addition.

and (Equations 2.20) the magnitude and direction of the vector $\mathbf{F}_n$ are given by

$$F_n = \sqrt{F_{nx}^2 + F_{ny}^2},$$

$$\tan \theta = \frac{F_{ny}}{F_{nx}}.$$

The net force may also be determined geometrically by placing the tail of $\mathbf{F}_2$ upon the head of $\mathbf{F}_1$ and closing the triangle (Figure 4.10b). Generalization of these considerations to three or more forces is straightforward.

We are now in a position to give a general definition of force in terms of the rate of change of the momentum of a particle with time. By definition a force acts upon any particle whose momentum is changing for any reason whatsoever and continues to act so long as the momentum changes. This is true even if the detailed nature of the force is unknown. *The net instantaneous force upon a particle is equal to the rate of change of its momentum with time.*

$$\mathbf{F} = \lim_{\Delta t \to 0} \frac{\Delta \mathbf{p}}{\Delta t}. \tag{4.9}$$

This is Newton's second law of motion. It is also a statement of the basic procedure to be followed in Newtonian dynamics: *look for the forces acting upon a body whose momentum is changing.**

If the mass of a body remains constant while an external force acts upon it, then:

$$\lim \frac{\Delta \mathbf{p}}{\Delta t} = M \lim_{\Delta t \to 0} \frac{\Delta \mathbf{v}}{\Delta t} = M\mathbf{a} \qquad \text{(if } M = \text{const)}$$

Substituting into Equation 4.9:

$$\mathbf{F} = M\mathbf{a}. \tag{4.10}$$

This is the familiar statement of Newton's second law and agrees with the qualitative discussion in Section 3.11: *the total instantaneous force applied to a body is equal to its*

---

* See the quotation from Newton at the beginning of this chapter.

mass times its acceleration. If $\mathbf{F} = 0$, then $\mathbf{a} = 0$. The body's velocity vector remains constant, as expected from the law of inertia.

Equation 4.8a defines the average force upon particle 1 due to its interaction with particle 2 as the ratio of its momentum change during an interval Δt by the length of the interval:

$$\mathbf{F}_{21} = \frac{\Delta \mathbf{p}_1}{\Delta t}.$$

Likewise, the average force upon particle 2 due to its interaction with particle 1 is

$$\mathbf{F}_{12} = \frac{\Delta \mathbf{p}_2}{\Delta t}.$$

But according to the law of momentum conservation, $\Delta \mathbf{p}_1 = -\Delta \mathbf{p}_2$ during the time interval Δt, and thus:

$$\mathbf{F}_{12} = -\mathbf{F}_{21}. \tag{4.11}$$

The two interacting bodies exert equal and opposite forces upon each other. This is Newton's third law of motion. In words:

- If a body A exerts a force $\mathbf{F}_A$ upon a body B, then the body B exerts an equal and opposite force $\mathbf{F}_B$ upon A:
$$\mathbf{F}_A = -\mathbf{F}_B.$$

Newton's first two laws deal with the results of applying (or *not* applying) forces to single bodies. In contrast, the third law states quite specifically that there is a certain symmetry inherent in the concept of force; that forces never act alone, but in pairs; in short, that Newtonian dynamics deals with the *interactions* between bodies and not with isolated forces. The importance of Newton's third law (or equivalently, the momentum conservation law) is often overlooked, since so many problems deal with the effect of particular forces on single particles. But Ernst Mach called the third law Newton's most important contribution to dynamics. Since historically it is the first succinct statement of the interaction point of view, developments in contemporary physics have more than sustained Mach's judgment.

▲▲ 4.5 Free fall, weight, and the principle of equivalence

In effect, all of classical physics may be regarded as a series of applications of the Newtonian laws and concepts to a wide range of detailed problems. There were a host of physical situations that Newton did not consider or encounter; many of the ideas of his *Principia* were to be modified, extended, or generalized as they were applied to new problems by later scientists. Nonetheless, the three laws and their implications are the foundation upon which the edifice of physics rises, the fundamental revisions of the present century notwithstanding.

Application of the second law to the free-fall problem is both straightforward and informative. Since the acceleration of a freely falling body is $g = 9.8$ m/sec^2 directed toward the center of the earth, a constant force acts upon such a body as it falls. The magnitude and direction of that force, the force of terrestrial gravitation, follow from Newton's second law (Equation 4.10) with $\mathbf{a} = \mathbf{g}$:

$$\mathbf{F} = M_i \mathbf{g}, \tag{4.12a}$$

where M_i is the inertial mass of the falling body.

Now Newtonian mechanics assumes that this particular force results from the body's interaction with the earth. If so, the body should be subject to the same force whenever it is in the proximity of the earth. For instance, a downward force of magnitude $M_i g$ must act upon the body when it lies at rest on a table. But in that case it can only remain at rest if the table, or the floor or the muscles of a man or anything else that keeps it at rest exerts an equal, *upward* force.

From common experience we know that the heavier a body the greater the upward force required to keep it from falling. Therefore, we define the *weight* of a body **W** as the force of gravity upon it, so that according to Equation 4.12a:

$$\mathbf{W} = M_i \mathbf{g}. \tag{4.12b}$$

The inertial mass of a body measures its intrinsic ability to resist changes in velocity resulting from the application of *any* force. Let us define another property of a body proportional to its weight which measures its intrinsic ability to interact with the earth and call that property *gravitational mass, M_g*:

$$\mathbf{W} = \mathbf{C} M_g, \tag{4.12c}$$

where **C** is a vector constant whose direction is toward the center of the earth but whose magnitude is as yet unspecified. Combining Equations 4.12b and 4.12c,

$$\mathbf{C} M_g = M_i \mathbf{g},$$

or, rearranging factors,

$$\mathbf{g} = \mathbf{C}\left(\frac{M_g}{M_i}\right). \tag{4.12d}$$

A body's acceleration due to gravity is proportional to the ratio of its gravitational to its inertial mass. But Galileo reached the experimental conclusion that *all* bodies in free fall have their magnitudes of acceleration $g = 9.8$ m/sec² regardless of their size, shape, or composition. This conclusion is consistent with Equation 4.12d if and only if the ratio of gravitational to inertial mass is the same for all bodies. The numerical value of this ratio depends upon the units chosen for gravitational mass. If the kilogram is selected, the ratio M_g/M_i will be unity, and the constant **C**, the acceleration due to gravity. Since gravitational and inertial mass appear to be equal experimentally the subscripts g and i will henceforth be omitted and the common quantity—mass—labeled simply M. Substituting $\mathbf{C} = \mathbf{g}$ in Equation 4.12b,

$$\mathbf{W} = M\mathbf{g}. \tag{4.13}$$

The weight of a body, the gravitational force exerted upon it by the earth, is a vector equal to the product of its mass by the acceleration due to gravity.

Equation 4.13 has far-reaching implications in illuminating the nature of the gravitational interaction. Conceptually, inertial and gravitational mass are quite distinct quantities. One of them measures the resistance to all changes in velocity; the other measures the strength of one particular force. The observation that free-fall acceleration is the same for all bodies implies *that the gravitational force acts upon a body in proportion to the body's ability to resist accelerations caused by any force whatsoever.* This conclusion is the basic postulate of Einstein's general theory of relativity which will be touched upon in Chapter 11. Some of the more immediate implications of the equality $M_i = M_g$ will be explored in Chapter 5.

▲▲ 4.6 Effect of a force that is not in the direction of motion

Newton's second law of motion (Equation 4.10) defines the instantaneous force upon a body as a vector in the direction of its acceleration at that instant. If a constant force acts upon a body in the direction of its velocity vector (as in free fall from rest), the resultant acceleration is also in the direction of the velocity vector.

However, there is no reason why a force need be applied to a body in the direction of its motion. Figure 4.11a shows the velocity vector of a particle located at the point with coordinates x_0, y_0, at time t. If the velocity at this time has magnitude v_0 and angle θ_0, its components are (Equations 2.19):

$$v_x(t_0) = v_0 \cos \theta_0,$$
$$v_y(t_0) = v_0 \sin \theta_0.$$

As long as no force is applied the velocity vector remains constant and the particle moves along the path indicated by the dotted line in the figure. In that event its coordinates at

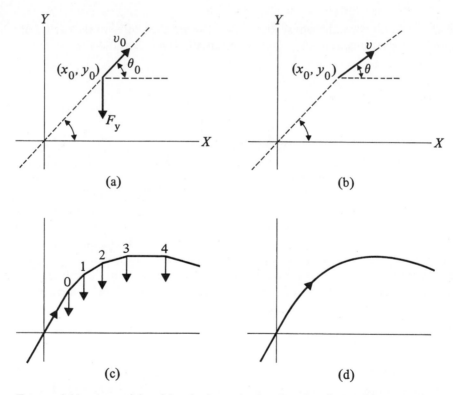

(a)

(b)

(c)

(d)

FIGURE 4.11   A particle with velocity $\mathbf{v}_0$ in the direction θ_0 is subject to a force F_y for a very short time interval at the point (x_0, y_0). If the force had *not* been applied the particle would have continued on the dashed path shown in part a. However, the force changes the y-component of the momentum so that the particle follows the path shown in part b. When no force acts the particle obeys the law of inertia. Part c shows the trajectory of a particle subject to short duration forces of equal magnitude and direction at points 0, 1, 2, 3, and 4. If the force acts continuously the effect is a continuous series of "hammer blows" so that the trajectory becomes a smooth curve (part d).

a later time t would be specified by the equations for motion with constant velocity (Equation 2.2):

$$x = x_0 + v_0(\cos \theta_0)(t - t_0),$$
$$y = y_0 + v_0(\sin \theta_0)(t - t_0).$$

But suppose the particle is subject to a force of very short duration Δt in the negative y-direction while at the point (x_0, y_0), i.e., subject to a downward "hammer blow." It receives an instantaneous acceleration *in the direction of the force* as long as that force is applied (Equation 4.10):

$$a_y = \frac{F}{M},$$

so that the y-component of its velocity changes by an amount

$$\Delta v_y = \frac{F}{m} \Delta t.$$

When the (virtually) instantaneous force is removed the velocity component of the particle in the y-direction is, therefore,

$$v_y(t_0 + \Delta t) = v_y(t_0) + \frac{F}{m} \Delta t,$$

whereas the x-component of the velocity remains unaltered since no force acted in that direction. The magnitude and direction of the velocity after the blow is given in terms of its components by Equations 2.18:

$$v = \sqrt{v_x^2 + v_y^2},$$

$$\tan \theta = \frac{v_y}{v_x},$$

showing that both the magnitude and the direction of the velocity vector are altered by the force.

It is important to recall that the particle accelerates *only* during the time the force is applied. Subsequently (as previously) it obeys the law of inertia and proceeds along the dotted path shown in Figure 4.11b unless and until another force acts upon it. If forces of the same magnitude and direction were applied for time intervals of equal duration at points 1, 2, 3, and 4, the trajectory of the particle would be something like that shown in Figure 4.11c. While a force is applied the particle accelerates *in the direction of the force*; when not subject to a force the particle obeys the law of inertia. Neither the magnitudes nor the directions of the forces acting at points 0, 1, 2, 3, and 4 need be equal. If they are not, the accelerations (and therefore the changes in direction) at these points would also differ.

The effect of a force that continuously acts upon a particle can be understood by regarding it as a continuous series of hammer blows, each of duration approaching zero, and each resulting in an instantaneous acceleration proportional to its magnitude and in its own direction. The resulting trajectory of the particle will be a continuous curve (Figure 4.11d). If $\mathbf{F}(t)$ is the instantaneous force vector at time t, then the instantaneous acceleration vector at that time follows from Newton's second law. Give the acceleration at all times within a given interval *and* the position and the velocity vectors at the beginning of the interval, the motion of the particle may be calculated throughout the interval, usually by the step by step "hammer blow" approximation. In principle nothing more is required to apply Newtonian dynamics to any particular problem.

▲▲ 4.7 Free fall, projectile motion, and satellite motion

All bodies subject to no force other than the gravitational attraction of the earth accelerate toward the earth with the constant magnitude $g = 9.8$ m/sec^2 *regardless* of the magnitude or direction of their velocities. Hence in a time t all such bodies "fall" a distance $y = \frac{1}{2}gt^2$ (Equations 2.10) from the paths they would follow in the absence of the gravitational attraction.

Let us use this principle to compare free fall from rest with the motion of a body thrown vertically upward with velocity v_0 (Section 2.7). In the absence of gravity an object dropped from a height y_0 would simply remain at the point where it was "dropped," while the body thrown upward would rise with constant velocity to a height $v_0 t$ in t sec. Instead, the object dropped from rest falls from its original position a distance $\frac{1}{2}gt^2$ in t sec. The second body "falls" a like distance from its inertial position (the position it would occupy if no force acted upon it) so that in t sec its position is given by:

$$y = v_0 t - \tfrac{1}{2}gt^2.$$

Suppose a shell is fired from a horizontally inclined cannon located on a cliff of height y_0. In the absence of gravity the shell would describe a path in the horizontal, x-direction parallel to the ground (Figure 4.12a) traveling with its initial muzzle velocity v_0. After t sec its y-coordinate would still be y_0, its x-coordinate $v_0 t$. But the gravitational force, acting like a continuous series of hammer blows, causes a departure from this horizontal path. The shell "falls" a distance $\frac{1}{2}gt^2$ in t sec so that its y-coordinate at time t is

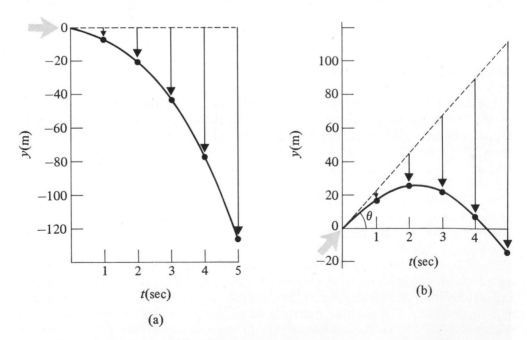

FIGURE 4.12 A projectile "falls" exactly the same distance each second from its initial trajectory as a body in free fall. (a) A horizontally-fired projectile. (b) A projectile fired at an angle θ to the horizontal.

$y_0 - \frac{1}{2}gt^2$, and strikes the ground at the same time as another shell that was dropped from the cliff in coincidence with the firing of the cannon. Since no force acts in the *x*-direction the motion in that direction can have no effect upon the rate at which the shell "falls," and vice versa. All bodies projected horizontally from the cliff strike the level ground at the same time regardless of their horizontal velocities, although the greater the horizontal velocity the greater the horizontal distance traversed by a shell in the time allotted.

Now consider the motion of a projectile fired with velocity v_0 from a cannon resting on level ground and inclined at an angle θ_0 to the horizontal (Figure 4.12b). At time $t = 0$ its velocity components are

$$v_x = v_0 \cos \theta,$$
$$v_y = v_0 \sin \theta.$$

In the absence of gravity the motion of the shell would be described by the equations:

$$x = v_x t,$$
$$y = v_y t.$$

However, in time t the shell "falls" a distance $\frac{1}{2}gt^2$. Therefore, its equations of motion are

$$x = v_x t, \tag{4.14a}$$
$$y = v_y t - \tfrac{1}{2}gt^2, \tag{4.14b}$$

where once again the motion in the two perpendicular directions is considered separately.

Thus by clearly separating the effects of acceleration and the effects of its initial velocity and position upon the subsequent motion of a body, we can very easily relate projectile motion to free fall. As Newton was the first to suggest we may also relate free fall to the motion of satellites. Let a horizontally inclined cannon be fired from the top

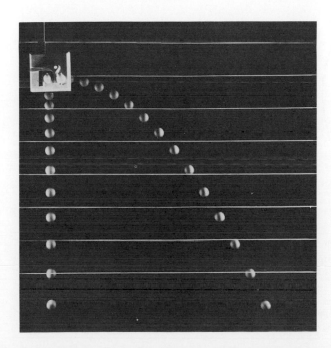

FIGURE 4.13 Multiple flash photograph of two golf balls released simultaneously from the mechanism shown. The pulse rate was 30/sec. (From *PSSC Physics*, D. C. Heath and Co., Boston, © 1965, p. 92.)

of a tall tower or a high mountain. The length of time its shell remains aloft depends only upon the height of the tower and not upon its muzzle velocity *provided* the distance it travels from the tower is small relative to the distance over which the curvature of the earth is appreciable. Otherwise the ground cannot be assumed level, and the shell must fall farther to reach the earth. In fact, if the shell's initial velocity is sufficiently high it will "fall" at precisely the same rate that the earth's surface curves away from the horizontal. Therefore it will remain at the same distance above the earth's surface and eventually return to its starting point, the tower. As there is no reason for the shell to stop there it will continue to orbit the earth, "falling" like any other projectile but never reaching the surface because the surface itself is "falling" along with it.

What is the critical velocity above which a projectile becomes a satellite? Figure 4.14b (due to R. P. Feynman*) shows the essential features of the problem. A projectile fired from the North Pole would move horizontally along a straight line path tangent to the earth if it obeyed the law of inertia. Instead, it falls. To maintain an orbit, the distance it falls in traveling a horizontal distance x must be equal to the distance the earth's surface "falls" over the same distance. The triangle with legs x, y is similar to the triangle with legs $2R - y$, and x (R the radius of the earth). Therefore:

$$\frac{y}{x} = \frac{x}{2R - y},$$

or, since y is small compared with R:

$$x = \sqrt{2Ry}.$$

But we know that $x = v_x t$, $y = \frac{1}{2}gt^2$. Therefore:

$$v_x = \sqrt{gR_e} \tag{4.15a}$$

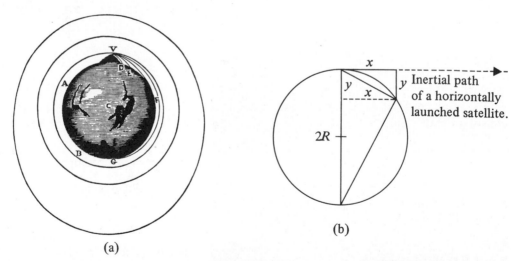

(a)

(b)

FIGURE 4.14 (a) A drawing from Newton's *Principia* detailing his arguments on satellite launching. (From *PSSC Physics*, D. C. Heath and Co., Boston, © 1965.) (b) Essential geometry of Newton's satellite problem.

---

* Feynman, Leighton, and Sands, *The Feynman Lectures in Physics*, Vol. I, Chapter 7, Addison-Wesley Publishing Co., Reading, Mass., 1963.

is the critical, initial velocity the horizontally fired projectile must have to remain in orbit. Substituting $R_e = 4000$ miles $= 6.4 \times 10^6$ m, and $g = 9.8$ m/sec^2, we find $v_x = 4.97$ m/sec.

We can also express this result in terms of the period of the satellite T, the time it requires to complete one orbit (Section 3.9). Since the circumference of the earth is equal to $2\pi R_e$ then the period is equal to $2\pi R_e/v_x$, or, rearranging factors:

$$v_x = \frac{2\pi R_e}{T}.$$

Substituting in Equation 4.15a:

$$\frac{2\pi R_e}{T} = gR_e,$$

or:

$$T^2 = \frac{(2\pi)^2 R}{g}, \tag{4.15b}$$

which yields a period of about eighty-four minutes, very nearly equal to the measured period of a satellite in low orbit* (Figure 4.15). Hence we have established the dynamic equivalence of free fall and satellite motion. The two cases differ *only* in their initial conditions.

Can we also regard the moon as a very large stone falling toward the earth? It certainly has mass and so must fall like any other projectile provided the gravitational force exerted by the earth extends to its orbit. However, it is easy to show that the strength of that force on the moon cannot be $M_m g$ with $g = 9.8$ m/sec. If it were, then, approximating the moon's orbit as a circle, Equation 4.15b would be directly applicable with R equal to the radius of that orbit. But that equation requires that the square of its period of revolution be directly proportional to the radius, whereas Kepler's third law (Equation 3.4) requires that the square of the period be proportional to the *cube* of the radius. Therefore, the value of g cannot be constant but must decrease with distance. If we assume it is inversely proportional to the square of R:

$$g = \frac{k}{R^2},$$

with k some constant, then substituting into Equation 4.15b we arrive at an equation consistent with Kepler's third law:

$$T^2 = \frac{2\pi^2}{k} R^3.$$

So we seem to have evidence for the assertion that the gravitational force between two bodies varies inversely as the square of their separation.

We shall return to this problem in Chapter 5.

▲▲ 4.8 Centripetal force

A particle of mass M moving in a circle of radius r with the *magnitude* of its velocity constant is nevertheless not moving with constant velocity simply because the *direction*

---

* Since the earth rotates as the satellite revolves about it the time required for the projectile to return to its tower will be about six minutes greater or slightly less than eighty-four minutes, depending on whether the satellite moves in the direction of the earth's rotation or in the opposite direction.

FIGURE 4.15 View of the earth and docked Agena target vehicle as seen from Gemini VIII (1966.) (Courtesy of the National Aeronautics and Space Administration.)

of its velocity is changing. It follows that the particle is subject to an external force, a force that keeps it in a circular path rather than permitting it to follow its preferred inertial trajectory and fly off on a tangent to the circle.

Expressions for the acceleration of a particle moving along a curved trajectory were derived in Section 2.10. Equation 2.23b is applicable to the special case of circular motion with the magnitude of velocity constant. The instantaneous acceleration of the particle is directed toward the center of the circle and has magnitude $a = v^2/r$. Thus according to Newton's second law the force is also directed toward the center of the circle and has magnitude:

$$F_c = \frac{Mv^2}{r}.$$ (4.16)

This force that must act upon the particle to keep it in its circular path is called the *centripetal* (or "center-seeking") force.

The motion of a particle in a circular path is the *effect* of an applied force, just like the accelerated motion of any other body. It is *not* the *cause* of a force. Equation 4.16 implies that a body of mass M can move with speed v in a circular orbit of radius r *only* if a force of magnitude Mv^2/R is applied. A force of a different magnitude cannot maintain the body with that velocity in an orbit of that radius. The *source* of the force that results in the acceleration is not identified by the equation and must be sought from other data. For instance, when an automobile rounds a curve, it accelerates toward the center of the curve. The force producing the acceleration is obtained from the friction between the tires and the roadbed. If friction is insufficient, the auto (which prefers to obey the law of inertia) goes off the curve, an effect which is often mistakenly attributed to a so-called "centrifugal" force. In reality it is simply a result of the law of inertia which must apply when the centripetal force is insufficient to maintain the required centripetal acceleration.

The centripetal force on a low-orbit satellite is supplied by the gravitational force of the earth and must be equal, therefore, to Mg, the weight of the satellite:

$$Mg = \frac{Mv^2}{R},$$

where v is its orbital velocity and R its orbital radius, approximately the radius of the earth. Rearranging factors,

$$v = \sqrt{gR},$$

the same result obtained in Section 4.7 (Equation 4.15a) by considering the motion of the satellite as a special case of projectile motion.

▲▲ 4.9 Simple harmonic motion: qualitative features

In this and the foregoing chapters we have treated all bodies as completely rigid, assuming that the distance between all points on any body remain fixed regardless of the applied force. In fact, we have shown that we can reduce the motion of any system to the motion of a single point if by "motion" we mean motion of the system as a whole and not of its internal parts relative to one another (Section 4.3).

It is well known from common experience that no body is completely rigid. Even the hardest steel can be stretched, compressed, twisted, or generally deformed if a sufficient external force is applied to it. Usually the degree of deformation increases with the magnitude of the applied force. Robert Hooke (1635–1703) found that the amount a spring is stretched or compressed by an external force is directly proportional to the magnitude of the force *provided* the amount of stretching (or compression) is small. That is,

$$F = ky, \tag{4.17a}$$

where F is the magnitude of the applied force, y the amount of stretching (or compression), and k a constant (see Figure 4.16a). The stiffness of a particular spring is characterized by the value of that constant, with a large value implying a more rigid spring than a small one.

The Hooke's law force (Equation 4.17a) is perhaps the simplest example of a non-constant force. Its use is not restricted to springs for it turns out that the deformation of most bodies is directly proportional to the magnitude of the applied force if the deformation remains small. However, the dependence of deformation upon force may become quite complicated if this condition is not satisfied.

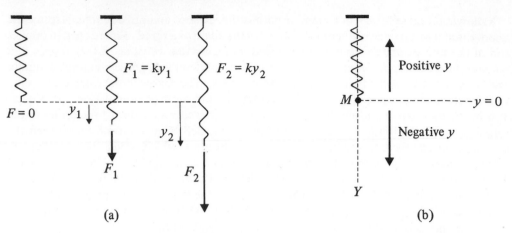

FIGURE 4.16   (a) According to Hooke's law the elongation of a spring is directly proportional to the external force applied to stretch it. (b) Definition of coordinates for analyzing the motion of an harmonic oscillator. The system is shown in its equilibrium configuration.

If a mass at rest at the end of a spring exerts a downward force proportional to its weight, then by Newton's third law the spring must exert an equal *upward* force on the mass. If the spring is stretched still farther by pulling down on the mass, Hooke's law requires that the total force on the spring be proportional to the total stretching, while Newton's third law *continues* to require that the spring exert an upward force on the mass which is equal in magnitude to the total downward force.

The opposite situation is encountered when the spring is compressed. It exerts a force whose tendency is to restore itself to its nonstretched equilibrium state. Since Hooke's law requires that this force be directly proportional to the amount of stretching or compression, it is called a *linear restoring force.*

We want to determine the motion of a spring with an attached mass which is stretched a certain distance and then released. As we have shown earlier in this chapter the motion of any system is completely determined if its initial position and velocity and the force acting upon it are given. Therefore, we shall be able to generalize our results to describe the motion of any system subject to a linear restoring force.

Let the spring hang in the y-direction, and let $y = 0$ be the position of the mass when the system is at equilibrium (i.e., the point at which the mass comes to rest after being attached to the spring and stretching it in accord with Hooke's law). For convenience, call the upward y-direction positive (Figure 4.16b). If the mass is displaced a distance y from its equilibrium position, the spring exerts a restoring force proportional to y:

$$F = -ky. \tag{4.17b}$$

Equation 4.17b gives the force exerted by the spring for both compression and elongation since in both instances the direction of the force is opposite the direction of the displacement. If the mass is pulled down a distance y below its equilibrium point and then released, the force at that instant will be $-ky$ which, by Newton's second law, results in an instantaneous acceleration toward the equilibrium position, of magnitude:

$$a = -\frac{k}{M} y. \tag{4.17c}$$

Following the general procedure of Section 4.6 the instantaneous force may be approximated as an upward hammer blow lasting for a very short time interval. At the end of the interval the upward acceleration has resulted in an increase in the velocity of the mass from the nonzero value it had at the instant of release, which in turn means that the mass is slightly nearer its equilibrium position. Since y decreases during this first time interval then, according to Equation 4.17b, the force on the mass also decreases. Therefore, the magnitude of the "hammer blow" exerted by the spring during the *next* time interval, will be slightly smaller than the previous blow, and the acceleration will also decrease. In other words the upward velocity continues to increase, although its *rate* of increase becomes smaller as the mass moves closer to equilibrium. When the mass actually reaches the equilibrium point the force exerted upon it by the spring is zero (Equation 4.17b). But its velocity is *not* zero, since it has been continually accelerated upward from the moment of its release. Therefore (Newton's first law) it continues to move through the equilibrium point, and its displacement becomes negative.

However, a negative displacement implies compression, and so Equation 4.17b specifies a downward force. Immediately after it passes through the equilibrium position the mass is subject to a small downward "tap" from the hammer (small, since y is still close to zero), and this downward tap results in a very small deceleration. As the upward motion of the mass continues to compress the spring, the magnitude of the downward force continues to increase, and the mass eventually comes to rest.

Because the magnitude of the upward restoring force for a downward displacement is equal to the magnitude of the downward restoring force for an equivalent upward displacement there is a symmetry about the problem, and we conclude that the mass comes to rest at a distance *above* equilibrium that is exactly equal to its initial displacement *below* equilibrium. This maximum departure distance from equilibrium is called the *amplitude* of the motion.

Because of the symmetry involved the subsequent motion from $y = y_0$ to $-y_0$ mirrors the previous motion (Figure 4.17). The mass accelerates downward to the equilibrium point, then decelerates until it comes to rest at its original starting position y_0. The initial conditions are exactly reproduced, for the mass is momentarily at rest and its displacement and the upward force upon it are what they were at the instant of its release. The system has no "memory" of how it reached that point, whether it was pulled down manually from equilibrium, or arrived by some other means. Since the initial conditions are reproduced it will retrace its motion exactly, reproduce the initial conditions once again, and once again proceed to retrace its steps.

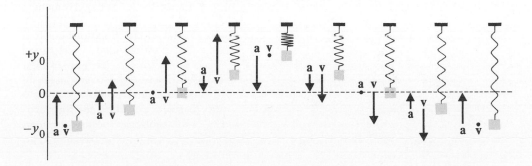

FIGURE 4.17 The position, and the acceleration and velocity vectors of an oscillating spring during one cycle of its motion.

Any system whose motion is characterized by an indefinite succession of cycles that are in every way identical is called *periodic*. The time T required for one complete cycle is called the *period* of the system.* The motion of a particle subject to a force directly proportional to the negative of its displacement from equilibrium (a linear restoring force) is called *simple harmonic motion*, of which the mass-spring system detailed in this section and the next is the most common example.

▲▲ 4.10 Simple harmonic motion: algebraic treatment

We shall now derive a very useful connection between circular motion with constant speed (Section 4.8) and simple harmonic motion. Figure 4.18 shows a particle of mass M in a circular orbit of radius r. For convenience the center of the circle is placed at the origin of a Cartesian coordinate system. If θ is the angle between the y-axis and the radius vector of the particle at time t the y-coordinate of the particle is

$$y = r \cos \theta, \tag{4.18a}$$

and its velocity component in the y-direction must be

$$v_y = -r \sin \theta, \tag{4.18b}$$

since the total velocity remains perpendicular to the radius vector at all times. The acceleration of the particle is centripetal, or magnitude v^2/r, and directed along the radius vector toward the origin. Therefore, the y-component of acceleration at time t is:

$$a_y = -\frac{v^2}{r} \cos \theta. \tag{4.18c}$$

The uniform circular motion of the particle may be represented either in terms of the constant speed v which measures the rate of change of its actual spatial position with

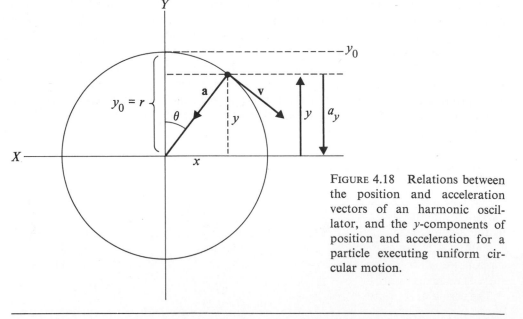

FIGURE 4.18 Relations between the position and acceleration vectors of an harmonic oscillator, and the y-components of position and acceleration for a particle executing uniform circular motion.

*This definition of periodic motion is applicable to the motion of a planet about the sun, since each orbit is a repetition of the previous orbit. In this case the period of the planet is simply its "year."

respect to time, or in terms of the time rate of change of θ, the angle between its radius vector and the y-axis. If $t = 0$ when $\theta = 0$ (i.e., when the radius vector coincides with the y-axis) then since the increase in θ is proportional to time we may write:

$$\theta = \omega t, \tag{4.19}$$

the constant ω (Greek "omega") being the *angular velocity* of the particle. The circular arc s of radius r is related to the angle θ that subtends the arc by

$$s = r\theta, \tag{4.20a}$$

with θ measured in radians. (See Appendix B to the text.) By definition the speed along the orbit is the rate of change of s with time. Since ω is defined as the rate of change of the angle θ with respect to time, then if r is constant:

$$\frac{\Delta s}{\Delta t} = r \frac{\Delta \theta}{\Delta t},$$

or:

$$v = r\omega. \tag{4.20b}$$

Substituting Equations 4.19 and 4.20b in Equations 4.18,

$$y = r \cos \omega t,$$
$$v_y = -\omega r \sin \omega t,$$
$$a_y = -\omega^2 r \cos \omega t.$$

However, the radius r is equal to y_0, the maximum value of the particle's y-component, so:

$$y = y_0 \cos \omega t, \tag{4.21a}$$
$$v_y = -\omega y_0 \sin \omega t, \tag{4.21b}$$
$$a_y = -\omega^2 y_0 \cos \omega t. \tag{4.21c}$$

Comparing Equations 4.21a and 4.21c:

$$a_y = -\omega^2 y, \tag{4.22a}$$
$$F_y = -M\omega^2 y. \tag{4.22b}$$

Simple harmonic motion is defined in Section 4.9 as the motion of a particle subject to a force that is directly proportional to its displacement from equilibrium, or, equivalently, motion characterized by an acceleration proportional to the negative of displacement. Since Equations 4.22 express these proportions it follows that the y-component of the displacement of a particle executing uniform, circular motion is equivalent to simple harmonic motion along the y-axis. Conversely, simple harmonic motion may be regarded as the y-component of a uniform, circular motion. Evidently equations analogous to Equations 4.22 can also be derived for the x-component of a particle in uniform, circular motion, provided the angle θ were defined relative to the x- rather than the y-axis. Thus these statements apply to motion along that axis as well.

The period of the particle in the circular orbit is related to its speed by:

$$T = \frac{2\pi r}{v},$$

or, using Equation 4.20b,

$$T = \frac{2\pi}{\omega}. \tag{4.23}$$

Similarly, the period of an harmonic oscillator is the time the system requires to complete one cycle of its motion. Since the y-component of the circular motion completes one cycle during the time the particle completes one circular orbit it follows that Equation 4.23 gives the period of the y-component of the motion as well.

It is now simple to apply these relations to obtain equations of motion for the oscillating spring. The constant may be expressed in terms of the constants of the spring system by comparing Equations 4.17c and 4.22a:

$$\omega^2 = \frac{k}{m}, \tag{4.24a}$$

or from Equation 4.23,

$$T = 2\pi \sqrt{\frac{M}{k}}. \tag{4.24b}$$

The period of an oscillating spring is directly proportional to the square root of the attached mass and inversely proportional to the square root of the spring constant. This is certainly in accord with qualitative observation. The greater the mass attached to a spring the more sluggish its motion, while the stiffer a spring, the more rapid its oscillation. It is useful to express the equations for simple harmonic motion (Equations 4.21) in terms of the period by substituting Equation 4.23:

$$y = y_0 \cos \left(\frac{2\pi t}{T}\right), \tag{4.25a}$$

$$v = \frac{-2\pi y_0}{T} \sin \left(\frac{2\pi t}{T}\right). \tag{4.25b}$$

These equations show that the position and velocity of the mass at any time t is determined by the ratio t/T. The trigonometric functions $\sin \theta$ and $\cos \theta$ have well-known periodicity properties as functions of their argument θ (Figure 4.19). As θ increases from 0 to $\pi/2$ radians (0 to 90°), $\cos \theta$ decreases from 1 to 0 while $\sin \theta$ increases from 0 to 1. Likewise (Figure 4.20), since as t increases from 0 to $T/4$ the argument $2\pi t/T$ increases from 0 to $\pi/2$, it follows that y decreases from y_0 to 0 during the first quarter cycle of the motion whereas v increases from 0 to $-2\pi(y_0/T)$. The magnitude of the instantaneous velocity is a maximum when the mass passes through equilibrium, in accord with the qualitative discussion of Section 4.9.

As t continues to increase and the argument successively becomes π, $3\pi/2$, and 2π, $\cos (2\pi t/T)$ decreases to -1, increases again to 0, and finally to $+1$ again, while $\sin (2\pi t/T)$ goes to 0, to $+1$, and once more to zero. When $t = T$, one cycle of the motion is completed, and the initial conditions are reproduced. For θ between 2π and 4π radians both $\sin \theta$ and $\cos \theta$ are equal to their values at $\theta - 2\pi$. In general for θ between $2n\pi$ and $2(n + 1)\pi$:

$$\sin \theta = \sin (\theta - 2n\pi),$$
$$\cos \theta = \cos (\theta - 2n\pi),$$

with $n = 1, 2, 3, \ldots.$ Comparing with Equations 4.25 it follows that the motion during any cycle from $t = nT$ to $t = (n + 1)T$ is a faithful reproduction of the first cycle from $t = 0$ to $t = T$.

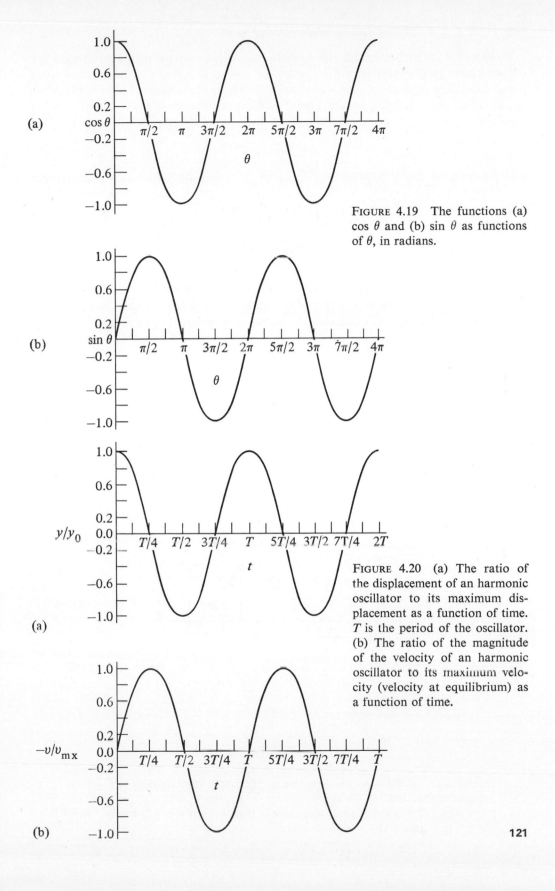

(a)

FIGURE 4.19 The functions (a) cos θ and (b) sin θ as functions of θ, in radians.

(b)

(a)

FIGURE 4.20 (a) The ratio of the displacement of an harmonic oscillator to its maximum displacement as a function of time. T is the period of the oscillator. (b) The ratio of the magnitude of the velocity of an harmonic oscillator to its maximum velocity (velocity at equilibrium) as a function of time.

(b)

Equations 4.25 are not unique representations of the harmonic oscillator motion but depend rather on choosing the initial conditions $y = y_0$, $v = 0$ at $t = 0$. Another set of initial conditions might be chosen with equal validity. In that case the initial angle of the radius vector of the reference circle (Figure 4.21) corresponding to the harmonic motion would be some nonzero angle θ_0 so that Equation 4.19 would be generalized to

$$\theta = \theta_0 + \omega t,$$

with the constant θ_0 called the *phase angle* of the system. Equations 4.25 would become:

$$y = y_0 \cos \left(\frac{2\pi t}{T} + \theta_0 \right),$$

$$v = \frac{-2\pi y_0}{T} \sin \left(\frac{2\pi t}{T} + \theta_0 \right).$$

In particular, if the description of the motion starts one-quarter cycle after the spring is released from rest then at $t = 0$, $y = 0$, and $v = -2\pi y_0/T$. As may be verified by substituting $\theta_0 = -\pi/2$ into either of the above sets of equations the motion is then described by the equations:

$$y = +y_0 \sin \left(\frac{2\pi t}{T} \right), \tag{4.25c}$$

$$v = \frac{+2\pi y_0}{T} \cos \left(\frac{2\pi t}{T} \right). \tag{4.25d}$$

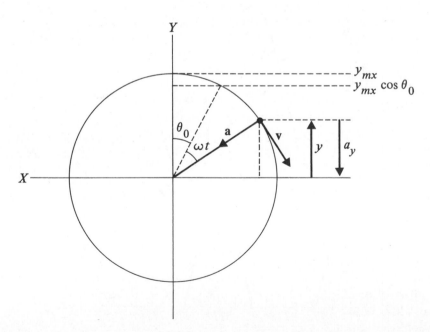

FIGURE 4.21   If the oscillator is not at its maximum displacement at $t = 0$ its position at that time may be expressed as $y_0 = y_{mx} \cos \theta_0$, where θ_0 is a constant *phase angle*. The subsequent displacement is then written $y = y_{mx} \cos(\omega t + \theta_0)$. ($\theta_0 = 0$ in Figure 4.18.)

▲▲ 4.11 Simple harmonic motion: numerical treatment*

Most interactions in nature do not involve constant forces but instead forces that vary both with time and with the positions of the particles involved. The harmonic oscillator that we have been considering is an example of the motion of a body subject to one particular type of nonconstant force. In general the manner in which the fundamental forces vary is even more complex. For example, the gravitational force between two particles varies as the inverse square of their separation (Equation 4.15b and Chapter 5), as does the electrostatic force between two charged particles at rest. The magnetic force between two moving charges depends not only upon their separation but also upon their relative velocities. Since the acceleration of two interacting particles may change both their separation and in their velocities, the force between them will also vary with time if it depends upon their positions and velocities. But if the force varies, then so must the acceleration of the particles, and this in turn affects their velocities, etc.

The principles involved in finding the position and velocity of a particle accelerated by such nonconstant forces are no different from the constant-force calculations considered in the gravitational case, for the general "hammer blow" procedure of Section 4.6 is not limited to constant forces. If the positions and velocities of the particles are known when a force of known magnitude and direction is applied to them, then the result of the force on their motion over a short time interval may be calculated, and the new positions and velocities used as initial conditions to determine the effect of the force over the next time interval.

The equations of motion for an oscillating spring were derived in Section 4.10 by first demonstrating the special connection between circular and simple harmonic motion. Special relations of this sort usually do not exist in more complicated situations so that derivation of equations of motion requires considerable mathematical sophistication. However, it is always possible to obtain excellent though approximate numerical solutions to such problems by carrying out the "hammer blow" procedure in detail. Let us go through such a calculation for the harmonic oscillator problem in order to demonstrate the power and generality of the method in a case where we know the answers in advance.

The kinematic equations required to calculate the approximate step-by-step motion of a particle are the three-dimensional generalizations of Equations 2.11 which in turn follow from the definitions of instantaneous velocity and instantaneous acceleration. They relate $s_0(t_0 + \Delta t)$ and $v(t_0 + \Delta t)$, the displacement and velocity vectors of a particle at the end of a short time interval Δt, to its position and velocity vector at the *beginning* of the interval and its acceleration *during* the interval:

$$v(t_0 + \Delta t) = v(t_0) + a(t)\Delta t, \tag{4.26a}$$

$$s(t_0 + \Delta t) = s(t_0) + v(t)\Delta t. \tag{4.26b}$$

These are vector equations, shorthand for three equations each: one relating x-components, one y-components, and one z-components.

Given the instantaneous force on the particle, Newton's second law gives the acceleration required in Equation 4.26a and the velocity so calculated may then be used in Equation 4.26b. These two equations involve instantaneous positions, velocities, and accelerations, but a nonzero time interval, Δt. Therefore, they are strictly valid only if $a(t)$ is constant. If the instantaneous acceleration varies considerably during the chosen

---

* This section may be omitted without serious loss of continuity.

time interval Δt, then some average value must be used in the equations, and the calculated velocity, $\mathbf{v}(t_0 + \Delta t)$, will be only approximate. However, approximation may be made as good as desired by choosing the time intervals small enough so that the variation of the acceleration during any interval is also small.

There is an ambiguity in both Equations 4.26. The position at the end of the time interval depends upon the instantaneous velocity *during* the interval, but Equation 4.26a yields a velocity at the *end* of the interval. If Δt is sufficiently small the instantaneous velocity during the interval is approximated very well by the velocity at the midpoint of the interval, i.e., at time $t_0 + \Delta t/2$, which is related in turn to the acceleration at the beginning of the interval and the velocity at the midpoint of the *previous* interval by

$$\mathbf{v}\left(\frac{t_0 + \Delta t}{2}\right) = \mathbf{v}\left(\frac{t_0 - \Delta t}{2}\right) + a(t_0)\,\Delta t, \tag{4.27a}$$

so that Equation 4.26b becomes

$$\mathbf{s}(t_0 + \Delta t) = \mathbf{s}(t_0) + \mathbf{v}\left(\frac{t_0 + \Delta t}{2}\right)\Delta t. \tag{4.27b}$$

These equations, together with Newton's second law of motion, provide the machinery required to generate the trajectory of any particle subject to a known force in terms of a great many short steps, each as good an approximation as desired to the actual motion during an interval of length Δt. The continuously acting force is approximated by a rapid, discrete succession of "hammer blows." The position and velocity of the particle resulting from the first blow are the position and velocity it has when it receives the second blow, etc. Many calculations, many blows very close together may be required to follow a trajectory for a long period of time, but there is nothing more to the principles than is summarized by Newton's second law and Equations 4.27. The rest is arithmetic, and modern electronic computers specialize in doing a great deal of arithmetic very rapidly.

In the harmonic oscillator problem the motion is confined to the y-direction so that Equations 4.27 reduce to relations between y, v_y, and a_y. The required acceleration is obtained from Equation 4.17c:

$$a(t) = -\left(\frac{k}{m}\right)y(t).$$

Let us simplify the calculations by considering the special case $(k/m) = 1$ so that $a(t) = -y(t)$. A solution for the more general case merely requires a bit more arithmetic. Our initial conditions are determined by the fact that the system is set into oscillation by pulling the mass down a distance y_0 from equilibrium and releasing it at time $t = 0$ (Figure 4.17). Then $y(0) = y_0$, $v(0) = 0$. Finally, let us carry out the calculations for successive time intervals $\Delta t = 0.1$ sec.*

Equation 4.27a with $t = 0$ relates the velocity at $t + \Delta t/2 = 0.05$ sec to the velocity at $t - \Delta t/2 = -0.05$ sec, a time before the motion begins. A special starting equation is required relating the velocity at $t = \Delta t/2$ to the initial velocity, the initial acceleration,

---

* This calculation is adapted from the material in R. P. Feynman, R. B. Leighton, and M. Sands, *The Feynman Lectures in Physics*, Vol. I, Chapter 9, Addison-Wesley Publishing Co., Reading, Mass., 1963.

and the length of the first half interval of time. Since $a = \Delta v / \Delta t$ as $\Delta t \rightarrow 0$ then setting $\Delta t = \Delta t/2$ we may write:

$$v\left(\frac{\Delta t}{2}\right) = v(0) + a(0)\frac{\Delta t}{2}, \tag{4.27c}$$

or

$$v(0.05) = 0.00 - y_0 \times 0.05 = -0.05y_0,$$

since $a(0) = -y(0)$. Substituting this calculated velocity at $t = 0.05$ sec into Equation 4.27b we obtain the approximate position at the end of the first time interval:

$$y(0.1) = y_0 - 0.05y_0 \times 0.1 = 0.995y_0.$$

The first "hammer blow" results in an upward velocity of 0.05 m/sec and a displacement $0.995y_0$ m, $\frac{1}{2}\%$ smaller than the initial displacement.

The mass is now ready to receive the second blow. Its instantaneous acceleration is $-0.995y_0$ m/sec². Substituting this value for $a(0.1)$ into Equation 4.27a with $t = 0.1$ and $\Delta t = 0.1$:

$$v(0.15) = v(0.05) - y(0.1)\,\Delta t,$$
$$= -0.05y_0 - 0.995y_0 \times 0.1,$$
$$= -0.150y_0.$$

to a precision of three decimal places. To find the position of the mass after the second "hammer blow" substitute this value of the velocity into Equation 4.27b evaluated at $t = 0.2$ sec:

$$y(0.2) = y(0.1) + v(0.15)t$$
$$= 0.980y_0.$$

Table 4.1 gives the results of these calculations continued to $t = 1.6$ sec. For comparison, values of cos (t) and sin (t) are listed in columns 5 and 6. The remarkable agreement between columns 2 and 3 and 5 and 6 is no accident, of course, but merely demonstrates that our numerical calculation agrees with the analytical solution obtained in the foregoing section (Equation 4.25).

If Table 4.1 were continued beyond $t = 1.60$, y would become more negative, $a = -y$ more positive, and hence v decreasingly negative once again. At about $t = 3.14$ sec, $y = y_0$, $v = 0$, and $a = y_0$, the mirror image of the initial conditions at $t = 0$. Continuing to $t = 3.20, 3.30$, etc. the mass starts to move back toward equilibrium with v positive and increasing until $y = 0$, $v = +y_0$. Thereafter v decreases until at about $t = 6.28$ sec the initial conditions are reproduced ($y = y_0$, $v = 0$). For times greater than 6.28 sec the motion is described in Table 4.1 with $(t - 6.28)$ substituted for t. The system is periodic with period $T = 6.28, \ldots, -2\pi$ sec, in agreement with Equation 4.24b with $\sqrt{k/m} = 1$.

Equations 4.25, the analytical solutions to the harmonic oscillator problem, are more convenient to apply than the numerical solution of Table 4.1 since they permit us to calculate $y(t)$ and $v(t)$ by consulting a table of sines and cosines whereas the numerical calculations may be quite laborious. But the power of the numerical method should be recognized. There are far more complicated forces in nature than the linear restoring force, and these result in particle trajectories that cannot be expressed in terms of exact functions. There are other trajectories expressible in terms of functional solutions so

TABLE 4.1

1	2	3	4	5	6
t	$y = y_0 \times$	$v = y_0 \times$	$a = y_0 \times$	$\cos(t)$	$\sin(t)$
0.00	1.000	0.000	−1.000	1.000	0.000
0.05		−0.050			0.050
0.10	0.995		−0.995	0.995	
0.15		−0.150			0.149
0.20	0.980		−0.980	0.980	
0.25		−0.248			0.247
0.30	0.955		−0.955	0.955	
0.35		−0.343			0.343
0.40	0.921		−0.921	0.921	
0.45		−0.435			0.435
0.50	0.877		−0.877	0.878	
0.55		−0.523			0.523
0.60	0.825		−0.825	0.825	
0.65		−0.605			0.605
0.70	0.764		−0.764	0.765	
0.75		−0.682			0.682
0.80	0.696		−0.696	0.697	
0.85		−0.751			0.751
0.90	0.621		−0.621	0.622	
0.95		−0.814			0.814
1.00	0.540		−0.540	0.540	
1.05		−0.868			0.868
1.10	0.453		−0.453	0.454	
1.15		−0.913			0.913
1.20	0.362		−0.362	0.362	
1.25		−0.949			0.949
1.30	0.267		−0.267	0.268	
1.35		−0.976			0.976
1.40	0.169		−0.169	0.170	
1.45		−0.993			0.993
1.50	0.070		−0.070	0.071	
1.55		−1.000			1.000
1.60	−0.030		0.030	−0.029	

complicated that it is virtually inpossible to understand the character of the solutions *without* making tables of numerical values or plotting a series of graphs. In fact, these categories embrace 90% of the really interesting problems in physics. One of them is the derivation of Kepler's first law from Newton's law of gravitation, as presented in Chapter 5.

APPENDIX TO CHAPTER 4 | *Differential equations*

Obtaining explicit equations of motion for a particle subject to an external force usually requires the solution of a differential equation. The magnitudes of instantaneous velocity and instantaneous acceleration are defined in the appendix to Chapter 2 as first derivatives with respect to time:

$$v = \frac{dy}{dt}, \tag{4.28a}$$

$$a = \frac{dv}{dt}. \tag{4.28b}$$

Thus acceleration is the first derivative of the first derivative of displacement, or the second derivative of displacement with respect to time:

$$a = \frac{d}{dt}\left(\frac{dy}{dt}\right). \tag{4.28c}$$

These equations express the same kinematical relations as Equations 4.27 in the more compact notation of the calculus. For the harmonic oscillator $F = -ky$, and Newton's second law yields $a = -(k/M)y$. Then:

$$\frac{d}{dt}\left(\frac{dy}{dt}\right) = -\frac{k}{M}y. \tag{4.29}$$

This is the *differential equation* of the system, an equation relating the second derivative of displacement with time to the displacement itself. Other systems involving other forces are also characterized by differential equations, the force being described by an expression on the right-hand side. Equations 4.27 follow from Equation 4.29 if the derivatives are expressed in terms of their limiting definitions (Chapter 2). Therefore, the differential equation is an alternate, more compact prescription for finding y as a function of t.

To solve a differential equation it is necessary to find a function whose second derivative with respect to time is equal to the expression on the right of the equal sign [$(-k/m)y$ in Equation 4.29]. That function then describes the motion of the system. Often no such function exists. Either it must be approximated, or the motion calculated numerically as in Section 4.11. However, the differential equation for the harmonic oscillator is soluble in terms of the trigonometric functions. As we shall see, the solution is not unique but depends upon the initial conditions of the problem.

It was shown in the problems accompanying the appendix to Chapter 2 that the first derivative of $\sin x$ with respect to x is $\cos x$, while the first derivative of $\cos x$ with respect to x is $-\sin x$:

$$\frac{d(\sin x)}{dx} = \cos x,$$

$$\frac{d(\cos x)}{dx} = -\sin x.$$

Therefore,

$$\frac{d}{dx}\frac{d(\sin x)}{dx} = \frac{d}{dx}(\cos x) = -\sin x.$$

That is, the second derivative of $\sin x$ with respect to x is the negative of $\sin x$. Similarly, the second derivative of $\cos x$ is $-\cos x$. Therefore, both functions satisfy the differential equation, Equation 4.29a, as may be verified by direct substitution. In fact, these are the only two functions that *do* satisfy Equation 4.29a. Referring to the table of derivatives in the appendix to Chapter 2, it follows that the functions obtained by multiplying the sine and cosine functions by constants are also solutions to the differential equation, as is the sum of two such functions. Thus the most general solution to Equation 4.29a (for $k/m = 1$) is

$$y(t) = A \sin(t) + B \cos(t).$$

If k/M is not unity the functions depend not upon t but upon $t\sqrt{(k/M)}$, or (since $T = 2\pi M/k$) upon $2\pi(t/T)$:

$$y(t) = A \sin\left(\frac{2\pi t}{T}\right) + B \cos\left(\frac{2\pi t}{T}\right), \tag{4.30a}$$

and since $v = dy/dt$:

$$v(t) = \frac{2\pi}{T}\left\{A \cos\left(\frac{2\pi t}{T}\right) - B \sin\left(\frac{2\pi t}{T}\right)\right\}, \tag{4.30b}$$

with the expression $2\pi(t/T)$ expressed in radians. (The multiplicative factor $2\pi/T$ in Equation 4.30b arises from the fact that the derivative dy/dt is taken with respect to t and not with respect to the whole factor $2\pi(t/T)$.)

The constants A and B in Equations 4.30 are related to the choice of the initial conditions of the motion. Substituting $y(0) = y_0$ into Equation 4.30a,

$$y_0 = A \sin(0) + B \cos(0).$$

Since $\sin(0) = 0$ and $\cos(0) = 1$, then $B = y_0$. To evaluate A, let $v(0) = 0$ in Equation 4.30b:

$$0 = A \cos(0) - B \sin(0).$$

So $A = 0$. Therefore, the solution for the initial conditions $y(0) = y_0$, $v(0) = 0$ reduces to

$$y(t) = y_0 \cos\left(\frac{2\pi t}{T}\right), \tag{4.31a}$$

with the velocity of the system given by:

$$v(t) = \frac{-2\pi}{T} y_0 \sin\left(\frac{2\pi t}{T}\right), \tag{4.31b}$$

in agreement with Equations 4.25a and 4.25b.

Equations 4.31a and 4.31b were derived from the general solution (Equation 4.22) for a specific set of initial conditions. But different choices of initial conditions are possible. If the spring were already oscillating when measurements began then it would be convenient, perhaps, to choose $t = 0$ as the time when the spring passes through its equilibrium position. In that case,

$$y(0) = 0,$$

$$v(0) = v(\text{max}) = \frac{2\pi}{T} y_0,$$

which, when substituted into Equations 4.30 lead to the particular solutions

$$y(t) = y_0 \sin\left(\frac{2\pi t}{T}\right), \tag{4.31c}$$

$$v(t) = \frac{2\pi}{T} y_0 \cos\left(\frac{2\pi t}{T}\right). \tag{4.31d}$$

These equations are also a correct description of the motion of the harmonic oscillator, although the motion they describe begins one-quarter cycle earlier than the motion described by Equations 4.31a and 4.31b, in agreement with Equations 4.25c and 4.25d.

Since the trigonometric functions are most often associated with triangular measurement it may seem strange at first to encounter them in a problem that involves no obvious angle. Of course the connection between circular motion and simple harmonic motion makes their use here seem somewhat more rational. But the periodic nature of the functions is a more general property than is their association with triangulation. Any differential equation may be solved numerically by using the methods of Section 4.11 , and the solution expressed in tabular form. The same numerical method may be used to find a solution to any differential equation whether or not the equation involves motion. If a differential equation of a particular form is encountered frequently, tabulating its numerical solution once and for all may be worthwhile. In that case it is also convenient to give the tabulated function a special name. The special function is then defined as that function which satisfies the original differential equation—the differential equation whose solution is expressed numerically by the oft-used table.

The sine and cosine function may be defined in this way: as functions satisfying the differential equation of the form

$$\frac{d}{dx}\left(\frac{dy}{dx}\right) = -y(x). \tag{4.32}$$

Since Equation 4.32 may be regarded as a purely mathematical statement about the relationship between the variables y and x, a relationship spelled out more explicitly by the tabulated dependence of y on x obtained by solving Equation 4.32 numerically, the differential equation may appear in physical problems whose contexts are quite different. The motion of an harmonic oscillator is one such problem. The relationships between the sides and angles of triangles is another. Therefore, the differential equation (4.32) is a general prescription for solving both problems. Reduced to its simplest terms it says: "Look up a table of numbers used so often that it is given the heading 'sine' or 'cosine'."

SUGGESTIONS FOR FURTHER READING ▲▲▲

All introductory texts in physics discuss momentum conservation and Newton's laws at length, though usually not in the order presented in this chapter. Six, arranged in increasing order of difficulty are:

GERALD HOLTON AND DUANE H. D. ROLLER, *Foundations of Modern Physical Science*, Addison-Wesley Publishing Co., Inc., Reading, Mass., 1958, Chapters 4 and 5.

JAY OREAR, *Fundamental Physics*, John Wiley and Sons, Inc., New York, 1961, Chapter 3.

K. R. ATKINS, *Physics*, John Wiley and Sons, Inc., New York, 1965, Chapters 6, 7, and 8.

ARNOLD B. ARONS, *Development of Concepts of Physics*, Addison-Wesley Publishing Co., Inc., Reading, Mass., 1965, Chapters 5, 6, 9, and 17.

R. P. FEYNMAN, R. B. LEIGHTON, AND M. SANDS, *The Feynman Lectures on Physics*, Vol. 1, Addison-Wesley Publishing Co., Inc., 1963, Chapters 9, 10, and 12.

CHALMER SHERWIN, *Basic Concepts of Physics*, Holt, Rinehart, and Winston, Inc., New York, 1961, Chapters 2 and 3.

Feynman (Chapter 9) and Sherwin (Chapter 2) develop the subject using differential equations, including numerical methods of solution. Both treatments go considerably deeper than this chapter but are consistent with it. Feynman's chapter is especially worth reading.

PROBLEMS AND EXERCISES ▲▲▲

4.1. Find the centers of mass of the following systems:

(a) Two particles of equal mass three meters apart.

(b) Two particles, one with five times the mass of the other, three meters apart.

(c) Two particles—the more massive at the origin of a Cartesian system, the other with half the mass of the first and at the point $x = +7.0$, $y = -3.6$.

(d) Three particles—the two in part c and a third with mass equal to the mass of the particle at the origin and located at $x = 0$, $y = +5.0$.

(e) A homogeneous, solid sphere.

(f) A homogeneous, solid right circular cylinder.

4.2. (a) Suppose one of the particles in Problem 4.1a moves toward the other with speed 0.2 m/sec, while the other remains at rest. Plot the speed of the first and the speed of the system's center of mass as a function of time.

(b) Repeat for the particles in Problem 4.1b.

(c) Suppose the particle at $x = +7.0$, $y = -3.6$ in Problem 4.1c starts to move parallel to the y-axis with velocity 0.5 m/sec, while the other particle remains at rest at the origin. Plot the position of the moving particle and of the system's center of mass during the first five seconds after the particle starts to move.

4.3. (a) Two equal mass particles approach each other, collide, and reverse their directions. Prior to the collision the speed of the first is twice that of the second; after the collision its speed is one-half its value before collision. What is the final speed of the second particle?

(b) Two particles, the first with mass twice that of the second, approach each other with equal speeds. The more massive of the two rebounds with one-half its original speed. What is the final velocity (magnitude and direction) of the second?

4.4. Two particles, M_1 and M_2, slide toward each other, collide, and scatter. M_1 is twice as massive as M_2 and travels toward the collision point with half the velocity.

(a) What is the velocity of their center of mass?

(b) What can you say about their individual velocities and the sum of their scattering angles after the collision?

4.5. A particle collides with another, equal-mass particle which is initially at rest and scatters at an angle 30° to its original direction. The speeds of the two are equal following the collision. What is the scattering angle of the second particle?

[HINT: Solve the problem using the geometric method of vector addition.]

4.6. According to Kepler's second law the velocity of a planet in its elliptical orbit is not constant. Is this consistent with momentum conservation? Explain.

4.7. In the radioactive decay calculation of Section 4.2 the uranium nucleus is at rest when it decays. What is the final velocity of the thorium nucleus if the uranium nucleus moves with constant velocity v_0 before decay and emits the alpha-particle with velocity v_1 in the direction of its motion? What is the difference between the thorium recoil velocity and the initial velocity of the uranium nucleus? (Compare your answer with the velocity derived in the example and comment on the comparison.)

4.8. A toy rocket of mass M is at rest on a horizontal, frictionless table. At a certain time (call it t_0) it ejects a small pellet of mass m with velocity v from its tail. Thereafter it ejects five more such pellets at 30-sec intervals. Plot the velocity and position of the rocket as a function of time.

4.9. Suppose the rocket in Problem 4.8 ejects a continuous stream of n pellets of mass m in 30 sec. What is its velocity at the end of the 30 sec? Its acceleration during the 30 sec? Afterwards? (Assume the total ejected mass is small compared with the mass of the rocket.)

4.10. (a) According to Newton's third law a stone attracts the earth toward it as it falls. Why isn't the motion of the earth toward the stone apparent?

(b) Again according to the third law what effect should the motion of the moon have upon the earth? Is the effect observable?

[HINT: Consider Newton's second law.]

4.11. A bullet of mass m is fired into a block of mass M and embeds itself in it. The block rests upon a level, frictionless table a height d above the floor. After the collision the block slides across the table, falls off the edge, and comes to rest on the floor. Derive expressions for:

(a) The horizontal speed of the block as it leaves the table, and

(b) the initial speed of the bullet in terms of the mass of the block, the acceleration due to gravity, the height of the table, and the distance from the edge of the table to the point where the block strikes the floor.

4.12. It is shown in Chapter 8 that the magnitude of the force exerted by an electric field E on a particle of charge q is

$$F = qE.$$

(a) If the mass of such a particle is M what is its acceleration?

(b) A particle of mass M and charge q is placed in an electric field which is constant in the x-direction. Write an expression for the magnitude of its displacement, x, as a function of time. (Assume the particle is at rest at the origin at $t = 0$.)

4.13. A particle with mass 1 kg travels along the x-axis of a Cartesian system with constant speed. At the origin it is subject to an upward force of 1000 newtons for 0.01 sec. Plot the subsequent path of the particle for the following values of v_x:

(a) $10\sqrt{3}$ m/sec ($= 17.32$ m/sec).

(b) 10 m/sec.

(c) $10/\sqrt{3}$ m/sec ($= 5.77$ m/sec).

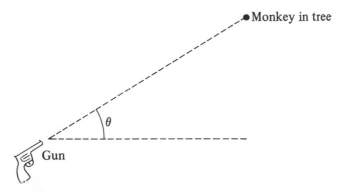

4.14. A hunter with no knowledge of physics wants to shoot a monkey hanging from the top branch of a tree. He aims his rifle at the animal as if he expected the bullet to follow his line of sight. The monkey, who is also ignorant of physics, decides to outwit the hunter and releases his hold just as the gun fires. What happens? Why?

4.15. A cannon located on a level plane and inclined at 30° to the horizontal fires a projectile with speed 500 m/sec.

(a) How long does the shell take to reach its maximum height?

(b) How high does it rise?

(c) At what horizontal distance from the cannon does the shell strike the ground?

4.16. The cannon in the previous problem is located on a cliff 124 m above a level plane.

(a) How long does its projectile stay aloft?

(b) At what distance from the cliff does it strike the ground?

4.17. Determine the range of a projectile (i.e., the distance from the cannon at which it strikes the earth) fired at a speed of 500 m/sec for a cannon inclined at 30°, 45°, and 60° to the horizontal. Plot your results and estimate the angle for which the range is a maximum. Is your estimate reasonable?

4.18. When a certain projectile is at its maximum height 490 m above the ground, traveling with horizontal velocity 250 m/sec and vertical velocity zero, it explodes into two equal mass fragments. The first is propelled straight upward with a velocity of 5 m/sec.

(a) When do the fragments strike the ground?
(b) At what horizontal distance from the explosion point does each one strike the ground?

4.19. (a) The acceleration due to gravity on the surface of the moon is approximately one-sixth the terrestrial value (Chapter 5). Two identical cannons—one on earth, the other on the moon, are inclined at 30° to the horizontal and fire shells with initial velocity 100 m/sec.
How long do the shells remain aloft? How high do they rise? What horizontal distance do they travel before striking the ground?

(b) What minimum horizontal velocity must be given a shell if it is to go into orbit about the moon? (The radius of the moon is about 1000 miles.)

(c) What is the period of such a satellite? (Figure 3.7 shows a photograph taken by one.)

4.20. (a) Find an equation for the trajectory of a projectile by eliminating t between Equations 4.14a and 4.14b. Let $x(0) = 0$, $y(0) = 0$.

(b) The range of a projectile is defined as the maximum horizontal distance it travels before striking the ground. Find an expression for range based upon your answer to part a and show that for a given muzzle velocity the maximum range is attained for an inclination angle $\theta = 45°$.

4.21. A one-kilogram mass is attached to a spring with Hooke's law constant 500 newtons/meter which is in turn attached to a string. The entire system is whirled about in a horizontal circle centered at the free end of the string. The combined length of the string and unextended spring is one meter. Plot the extension of the spring as a function of the orbital speed of the mass.

4.22. Motorists are often advised to accelerate going into a curve and decelerate coming out. Why?

[HINT: Consider the geometric addition of the pertinent force vectors.]

4.23. In one type of amusement-park ride, victims are strapped into gondolas which are then rotated in approximately 10-m radius vertical circles. For what minimum orbital speed could the victims remain in their seats regardless of whether or not they are strapped in? Why is this possible?

4.24. The moon moves in an approximately circular orbit of radius 3.8×10^8 m with a period of about twenty-eight days. Its mass is 7.5×10^{22} kg. What is the magnitude of the centripetal force upon it? What is the origin of that force?

4.25. How does the period of a simple harmonic oscillator change if:

(a) Its mass is doubled?
(b) Its spring constant is doubled?
(c) Its amplitude is doubled?
(d) Its maximum velocity is doubled?

4.26. A 0.1 kg mass is attached to the end of a spring with force constant $k = 1000$ newtons/meter.

(a) What is its period of oscillation?
(b) If the initial displacement from equilibrium is 0.1 m, what is its maximum velocity?

4.27. (a) How long a time is required for the mass in the previous problem to return to one-half the distance from its equilibrium position after its release? What is its velocity at that point (relative to its maximum velocity)?

(b) When does the mass in the previous problem attain one-half its maximum velocity? Where is it when it does?

4.28. (a) Plot the position and velocity of the oscillator in Problem 4.26 from $t = 0$ to $2T$.

(b) Repeat for an oscillator with $M = 0.4$ kg, $k = 1000$ newtons/m.

4.29. Describe the subsequent motion of the mass in Problem 4.26 if it becomes detached from the spring at:

(a) $x - 0.1$ m (from equilibrium).
(b) $x = 0.05$ m.
(c) $x = 0$.

4.30. Devise a method for determining the speed of a bullet that is fired into a mass attached to a horizontally oriented spring by observing the subsequent oscillations of the system.

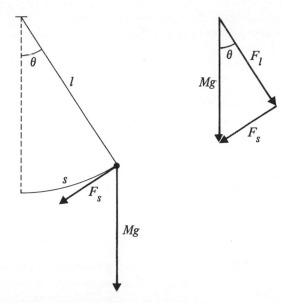

4.31. You are in a position to analyze the motion of a simple pendulum by treating it as an analogue of the harmonic oscillator. Go through the analysis by following the steps below. If you have difficulty at any point refer to the series of hints at the end of the question, but do not look at any step beyond the point where you are having trouble.

The simple pendulum consists of a mass M suspended from a string of length l. When the mass is pulled aside and released the system oscillates.

(a) When the string makes an angle θ with the vertical there is a component of the mass's weight along the direction of the arc, s. Show, by means of a diagram, that the magnitude of this component is:

$$F_s = -Mg \sin \theta.$$

(b) What is the acceleration of the mass along the arc when the string makes an angle θ with the vertical?

(c) The arc s is related to θ and l. What is the relationship? (Express θ in radians.)

(d) F_s is a restoring force since it increases with θ and is in the direction tending to restore the system to equilibrium ($\theta = 0$). However, the force is not linear but varies with the sine of the angle. Under what conditions will the force be approximately linear?

(e) Given the conditions of your answer to part d, express the restoring force and the acceleration along the arc in terms of l and s rather than in terms of θ.

(f) Compare the mathematical forms of the equations for the acceleration of the pendulum and the acceleration of the harmonic oscillator. To which harmonic oscillator variables do the pendulum variables a_s and s correspond? To which harmonic oscillator constants do the pendulum constants g and l correspond?

(g) Write an expression for the period of the pendulum as a function of g/l.

(h) Write an equation for s as a function of time and also for θ as a function of time given the initial condition that the pendulum is released from rest at $t = 0$.

(i) Assuming the initial conditions $\theta(0) = 0.05$ radians (about $3°$) and the pendulum released from rest at $t = 0$, and given $l = 1.09$ m, what is the period of the pendulum?

(j) What is the value of θ at $t = \pi/12$ sec? At $t = \pi/6$ sec?

Hints for Question 4.31

(a) The force diagram and spatial configuration of the system are similar triangles. F_s is perpendicular to F_l, the component along the string, just as the arc is perpendicular to the string at the intersection point of arc and string. Therefore:

$$F_s = - Mg \sin \theta.$$

(b) $a_s = -g \sin \theta$.

(c) $s = l\theta$.

(d) If θ is small then $\sin \theta$ is approximately equal to θ in radians. Hence for small θ the restoring force is proportional to the angular displacement of the string from the vertical:

$$F_s = - Mg \, \theta.$$

(e) Since $s = l\theta$:

$$F_s = - M\left(\frac{g}{l}\right)s,$$

$$a_s = -\left(\frac{g}{l}\right)s.$$

(f) Equation 4.17c for the acceleration of the harmonic oscillator is:

$$a = -\left(\frac{k}{m}\right)y.$$

Therefore, y corresponds to s, a to a_s, and (k/m) to (g/l).

(g) In analogy with Equation 4.24b,

$$T = 2\pi \sqrt{l/g}.$$

(h) In analogy with Equation 4.25a, the equation of motion for arbitrary initial conditions must be

$$s(t) = s_0 \cos\left(\frac{2\pi t}{T}\right).$$

Also since $s = l\theta$, and $s_0 = l\theta_0$:

$$\theta(t) = \theta_0 \cos\left(\frac{2\pi t}{T}\right).$$

(i) Since $l = 1.09$, $l/g = 1/9$, and $T = 2\pi/3$.

(j) At $t = \pi/12$ sec, $2\pi(t/T) = \pi/4$ ($45°$), $\cos(\pi/4) = 0.707$. So $\theta = 0.707 \times \theta_0 = 0.035$ radians. At $t = \pi/6$, $2\pi(t/T) = \pi/2$, $\cos(\pi/2) = 0$. Therefore, the bob is passing through equilibrium.

The universal law of gravitation

5

...by the propositions mathematically demonstrated... I derive from the celestial phenomena the forces of gravity with which bodies tend to the sun and the several planets. Then from these forces, by other propositions which are also mathematical, I deduce the motion of the planets, the comets, the moon, and the sea.*

ISAAC NEWTON

▲▲ 5.1 Newton and the development of physics

The three laws of Johannes Kepler derived from Tycho Brahe's observational data describe the motion of all planets in the solar system, and are applicable as well to all satellites of a particular planet. By combining his own laws of motion with the third law of Kepler, Isaac Newton derived a law relating the strength of the gravitational interaction between two bodies to the separation of the bodies and to their respective gravitational masses. He then showed that Kepler's first law is a necessary consequence of the gravitational law by demonstrating that the trajectory of any planet subject to the gravitational force of the sun must be elliptical.

There are many consequences of the gravitational law besides its ability to rationalize Kepler's planetary kinematics. It leads to the correct trajectories for all comets, both those that are permanent members of the solar system and those that make but one visit. It implies that there must be small corrections to Kepler's laws, since any planet must interact not only with the sun but with all other bodies in the solar system as well. Indeed, it was this latter implication that led to the dramatic discovery of the planet Neptune in the nineteenth century.

When applied to motion of objects near the earth, the law leads directly to Galileo's free-fall kinematics and is basic to the calculation of artificial satellite orbits. It is the gravitational force between the particles composing the earth that holds the earth together and is responsible for its nearly spherical shape. Likewise, the gravitational attraction between the atoms of the sun not only holds it together but compresses its total mass sufficiently to raise its internal temperature to the point where the thermonuclear

---

* *Sir Isaac Newton's Mathematical Principles of Natural Philosophy and His System of the World,* translation revised by Florian Cajori, University of California Press, Berkeley, Calif. (1934). From Newton's Preface to the First Edition, p. xviii.

FIGURE 5.1 Jupiter and its smallest satellite, Ganymede. The motion of Ganymede about Jupiter and of Jupiter about the sun are completely consistent with predictions based on Newton's law of gravitation. (Photograph from the Mt. Wilson and Palomar Observatories.)

FIGURE 5.2 Spiral nebula in the constellation Virgo as seen by the Hale 200-inch telescope. Galaxies such as this one are systems containing billions of stars bound together by their mutual gravitational attraction. (Photograph from the Mt. Wilson and Palomar Observatories.)

reactions responsible for its heat and light are initiated. A similar mechanism operates in the stars.

On a larger scale the gravitational interaction between the stars binds them together into galaxies and the galaxies into clusters. The gravitational force is one of the four basic interactions which taken together are believed to be responsible for all the phenomena in the physical universe. The others are the electromagnetic interaction between all charged particles, and the strong and weak interactions which manifest themselves only over distances characteristic of atomic nuclei. Although the gravitational interaction is the weakest of the four, it is the only means by which two uncharged bodies can interact regardless of the distance separating them. Thus it is this interaction alone, so insignificant on the subatomic level, that binds the stars, galaxies, and clusters into a universe.

The almost universal admiration accorded Newton by his contemporaries is well summarized by a famous couplet of Alexander Pope's:

> Nature and nature's laws lay hid in night;
> God said: "Let Newton be," and all was light.

Expressing his own respect, the eighteenth-century French mathematical physicist Laplace stated emphatically that Newton was not only the greatest philosopher who had ever lived but also the most fortunate: God had created but one universe, and thus but one man—Newton—could be granted the glory of revealing its laws.

Of course Newton did not solve all problems of the physical universe nor even touch upon most of them. But the sentiments expressed by Pope and Laplace—grossly oversimplified though they may be—suggest their estimation of Newton's achievement in comprehending the order of the planetary system in terms of simple, universal laws and in unifying the laws of celestial and terrestrial motion.

▲▲ 5.2 Deduction of Newton's gravitational law from Kepler's third law

While Kepler derived his laws for the motion of the planets about the sun, they are also applicable to the motion of the satellites of the planet earth:

LAW 1. The orbit of a satellite (natural or artificial) is an ellipse with the earth at one focus.

LAW 2. The radius vector of the satellite sweeps out equal areas in equal intervals of time, or (Equation 3.3):

$$Rv_\perp = \text{const.}$$

LAW 3. The square of the period of revolution of a satellite about the earth is proportional to the cube of its semimajor axis (Equation 3.4):

$$T^2 = k_e R^3,$$

where k_e is constant for all satellites in the earth's system but is different from the analogous constant applicable to the planetary orbits. (See Tables 3.1 and 3.2.) Alternately the law may be expressed in the form (Equation 3.5):

$$\bar{v}^2 R = \frac{(2\pi)^2}{k_e},$$

where $\bar{v}$ is the mean orbital velocity of the planet.

If the gravitational force on the moon were known, then, given its position and velocity vectors at any time, the detailed method discussed in Section 4.11 could be used to calculate its orbit. However, Newton did not know that force and so had to reverse the procedure in his (successful) attempt to derive the force from the observed motion.

As shown in Chapter 4 (Section 4.7), the motion of falling bodies, projectiles, and satellites in low, circular orbits are dynamically equivalent. The acceleration of each results from the application of the constant gravitational force of the earth. The three cases differ only in their initial conditions: the falling body is dropped from rest, the projectile fired at an angle to the earth's surface, the satellite launched with a velocity so large that it falls at least at the same rate that the earth's surface curves.

Presumably the moon's orbit can be understood by an extension of this reasoning: the moon "falls" toward the earth because of the gravitational force upon it, but remains in its elliptical orbit because it has a sufficiently high orbital velocity. There is no reason to assume that the magnitude of the gravitational force on the moon is equal to the force on the low-orbiting satellite, however. On the contrary, as we saw in Chapter 4 (Section 4.7, Equation 4.15b), such an assumption contradicts Kepler's third law. Nevertheless, we may use the motion of the satellite as a guide in finding the orbital force upon the moon. Since the direction of its velocity vector changes continuously, the moon must be subject to a centripetal force. Assuming for simplicity that the orbit is circular the magnitude of this force is (Equation 4.16):

$$F_c = \frac{M_m v^2}{R},$$ (5.1a)

where M_m is the mass of the moon, v its orbital velocity, and R its orbital radius. This force accelerates the moon toward the center of its orbit, and as the earth occupies this central position it is reasonable to assume that the centripetal force originates in the gravitational interaction of earth and moon.

If the centripetal force that keeps the moon in orbit *is* supplied by the gravitational attraction of the earth, and if the magnitude of this force is F_g, then:

$$F_g = \frac{M_m v^2}{R}.$$ (5.1b)

Kepler's third law provides another relationship between the velocity of the moon and the radius of its orbit (Equation 3.5):

$$v^2 R = \frac{(2\pi)^2}{k_e}.$$

Multiplying each side of this equation by the ratio M_m/R^2 gives an alternate statement of the third law:

$$\frac{M_m v^2}{R} = \frac{(2\pi)^2 M_m}{k_e R^2}.$$

But the expression on the left side of the equation is just the centripetal force upon the moon, and it has been assumed that this force is supplied by the gravitational attraction of the earth. Therefore, substituting into Equation 5.1b,

$$F_g = \frac{(2\pi)^2 M_m}{k_e R^2}.$$ (5.2)

That is, in order to be consistent with Kepler's third law, the gravitational force on the moon must be directly proportional to its mass and inversely proportional to the square of its distance from the earth, a conclusion we also reached at the end of Section 4.7.

The emphasis to this point has been on the gravitational force exerted upon the moon by the earth. But Newton's third law requires that if the earth exerts a gravitational force on the moon the moon must exert an equal and opposite force on the earth. That is, the third law emphasizes the gravitational *interaction* between the two bodies. It is plausible to assume that since the force on the moon is directly proportional to the mass of the *moon* (Equation 5.2) the force must also be directly proportional to the mass of the *earth*; or, mathematically:

$$\frac{(2\pi)^2}{k_e} = GM_e,$$

where G, the constant of proportionality, is called the *universal gravitational constant*.* Substituting in Equation 5.2,

$$F_g = G\left(\frac{M_e M_m}{R^2}\right). \tag{5.3}$$

The gravitational force between the earth and moon is directly proportional to the respective masses of the bodies and inversely proportional to the square of the distance between them. The universal gravitational constant G is assumed to be independent of either mass and characterizes the strength of the interaction itself.

If we assume that Equation 5.3 is not limited to the interaction between the earth and moon but rather that it describes the gravitational force between any two bodies whatsoever then we elevate G into a universal constant of nature. The statement

$$F_g = \frac{GM_1 M_2}{R^2} \tag{5.4a}$$

is Newton's universal law of gravitation. The burden of testing its universal applicability lies in its consistency with observational evidence.

Equation 5.4a specifies the magnitude of the gravitational force between two bodies of mass M_1 and M_2, but makes no statement about the direction of the force. However, the derivation of the equation requires that the force be attractive and directed along the line joining the two bodies. We can incorporate the direction of the force into the statement of the law by introducing the vector $\mathbf{R}/R$, which has unit magnitude and direction *outward* along the radius vector between the bodies. Then since the direction of the gravitational force is *inward* along the radius vector, the full statement of the gravitational law may be written as

$$\mathbf{F}_g = -G\frac{M_1 M_2}{R^2}\frac{\mathbf{R}}{R}. \tag{5.4b}$$

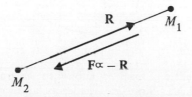

FIGURE 5.3 Radius and force vectors for Newton's gravitational law. The position of M_1 relative to M_2 is specified by the vector $\mathbf{R}$ whose direction is outward from M_2. Since the force between M_1 and M_2 is attractive, it must be in the direction $-\mathbf{R}$.

---

* This constant G must not be confused with g, the acceleration due to gravity. (See Section 5.3.)

In many applications only the magnitude of the force is pertinent so that Equation 5.4a is sufficient.

▲▲ 5.3 The gravitational force between extended bodies. Acceleration due to gravity on the earth and moon

The derivation of the gravitational law assumes both Kepler's third law and Newton's second law of motion. But the application of the second law in its simplest form is restricted to the motion of particles. If a body is so large that the force upon it varies from one part to another some average force must be calculated before the second law can be applied. Conversely, the gravitational force exerted by an extended body is the total force exerted by all its component particles.

Figure 5.4a shows a particle of mass M_1 subject simultaneously to a gravitational force $\mathbf{F}_{12}$ exerted by mass M_2 and a force $\mathbf{F}_{13}$ exerted by mass M_3. The acceleration experience by M_1 is due to the net force upon it, the vector sum of the forces $\mathbf{F}_{12}$ and $\mathbf{F}_{13}$.

We may regard the extended body of Figure 5.4b as a composite of a great many particles the sum of whose masses is equal to the mass of the body itself. Each of these

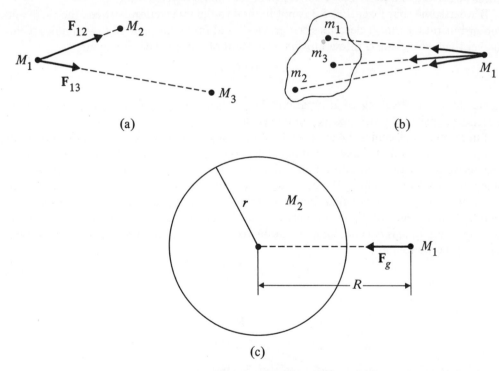

(a)

(b)

(c)

FIGURE 5.4 (a) A particle of mass M_1 subject to the gravitational force of two equal masses, M_2 and M_3. Since M_3 is twice as far away from M_1 as M_2 is, it exerts only one-quarter the force upon it. The total force on M_1 is the vector sum $\mathbf{F}_{12} + \mathbf{F}_{13}$. (b) The gravitational force exerted on a particle by an extended body may be calculated by breaking up the body into many equal mass particles and taking the vector sum of the forces between each particle and M_1. (c) The gravitational force exerted by a sphere of mass M_2 upon a particle of mass M_1 located outside the sphere is equal to the force the sphere would exert on M_1 if all its mass were concentrated at its center.

component particles exerts a gravitational force upon the particle M_1 inversely proportional to the square of its distance from M_1. The total gravitational force upon M_1 due to the extended body is the vector sum of these individual contributions, and in general, must be calculated using the methods of the integral calculus. However, it may be shown that the gravitational force exerted upon a particle by a solid, homogeneous sphere (Figure 5.4c) is just the gravitational force that would be exerted upon the particle if the entire mass of the sphere were concentrated at its center.

Neither the earth nor the moon is perfectly spherical. But since their separation is much larger than their respective radii, the spherical approximation gives very good results when used to calculate the gravitational force between them. The same spherical approximation is applicable to the gravitational force between the earth and any body near its surface.

Suppose an object of mass m is dropped from a 100-m tower. As it starts to fall it is subject to the gravitational force

$$\frac{GM_e m}{(R_e + 100)^2},$$

since the force exerted upon it by the earth is calculated by assuming that the entire mass of the earth is concentrated at its center. Upon reaching the surface the magnitude of the force is

$$\frac{GM_e m}{R_e^2}.$$

But R_e, the radius of the earth, is 4000 miles or 6.4×10^6 m. Thus the change in the gravitational force over the 100 m is so small that it would be detectable only with the most delicate measurements, and there is virtually no inaccuracy in assuming that during the entire course of its free fall, the distance between the body and the center of the earth is simply the radius of the earth. From the law of gravitation the magnitude of the force exerted on the falling body must be:

$$F_g = \frac{GM_e m}{R_e^2},$$

resulting in an acceleration of magnitude:

$$ma = \frac{GM_e m}{R_e^2},$$

or, canceling the mass m on both sides of the equation:

$$a = \frac{GM_e}{R_e^2},$$

which must be the acceleration due to gravity, g, measured as 9.8 m/sec^2:

$$g = \frac{GM_e}{R_e^2}. \tag{5.5}$$

Equation 5.5 states that the acceleration of a body by the gravitational attraction of the earth is independent of the mass of the body, precisely Galileo's experimental conclusion. Given the numerical value of the constant G and the mass and radius of the earth, the expression GM_e/R_e^2 should be equal to 9.8 m/sec^2 if Newton's law of gravitation is consistent with Galileo's free-fall kinematics. Conversely, given G, R_e, and g, the mass of the earth follows from Equation 5.5. Thus when Henry Cavendish made an experimental determination of *G* in 1798, he was said to have weighed the earth (Section 5.4).

For several reasons the acceleration due to gravity, **g**, varies slightly over the terrestrial surface.* First, the earth is not quite spherical. Rather, its radius is greater at the equator than at the poles and greater at the top of a mountain than at its base. Effects of nonuniform density are also important. Since each "particle" composing the earth attracts a stone with a force that varies inversely as square of its distance from that stone, a large irregularity near the point where the stone is dropped will have a relatively large effect. For instance, if a body is dropped near the base of a mountain it will be attracted slightly in the direction of the mountain, if dropped over a large subterranean cavern a slight reduction in *g* due to the absence of nearby "particles" will be observed. (In fact, this is the basis of one method of detecting the probable presence of underground oil deposits.)

Finally, there is a slight reduction in the gravitational acceleration due to the rotation of the earth on its axes. Since a body on the earth's surface rotates along with the earth, a very small centripetal force must be exerted to keep it upon the surface, and this force, supplied by the earth's gravitational attraction, is subtracted from the measured weight of the body, *M***g**. As both the velocity at the surface and the radius of the circle of rotation vary with the distance from the earth's axis (Figure 5.5) and therefore with latitude, the centripetal reduction of **g** is a maximum at the equator and zero at the poles.

All of these small corrections to the value of **g** given by Equation 5.5 have been calculated to considerable precision. In all cases the calculations are in agreement with measurements. Therefore, Newton's law of gravitation is successful in unifying the motion of falling apples and the motion of the moon in its orbit.

If a body were dropped from a tower on the moon, then in analogy with the reasoning that led to Equation 5.5, the acceleration due to lunar gravitation would be

$$g_{\mathrm{m}} = \frac{GM_{\mathrm{m}}}{R_{\mathrm{m}}^2}, \tag{5.6a}$$

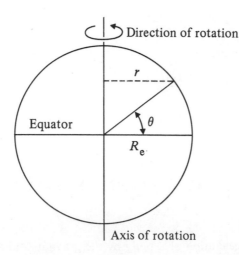

FIGURE 5.5 Effect of the earth's rotation on **g**. The distance *r* from a point on the earth's surface to the axis of rotation is $R_{\mathrm{e}} \cos \theta$, where R_{e} is the radius of the earth and θ the latitude angle of the point. The speed of the point due to rotation = $2\pi r/T$, where $T = 1$ day. Therefore, the centripetal acceleration of the point is $(2\pi/T)^2 R_{\mathrm{e}} \cos \theta$.

---

* According to the *American Institute of Physics Handbook*, the value of *g* at the equator at sea level is 9.780495 m/sec², and at sea level at the poles 9.8322131 m/sec². At Denver, Colorado, 1 mile above sea level *g* = 9.79609 m/sec², while at a point at the same latitude at sea level *g* = 9.80081 m/sec².

where the subscript m refers to the moon. The ratio of the accelerations due to lunar and terrestrial gravitation is found by dividing Equation 5.6a by Equation 5.5:

$$\frac{g_m}{g_e} = \frac{M_m/R_m^2}{M_e/R_e^2}. \tag{5.6b}$$

Rearranging terms and substituting known values for the masses and radii:

$$g_m \cong \frac{g_e}{6}.$$

Since the *definition* of weight is the product of mass by the acceleration due to gravity (Equation 4.13) it follows that the weight of a body on the moon will be approximately one-sixth its weight on earth.

▶▶ 5.4 The Cavendish experiment; measurement of the gravitational constant

One of the most dramatic demonstrations of the universality of the gravitational law was provided by Henry Cavendish in 1798, over one hundred years after the publication of Newton's *Principia*. Using a delicate instrument known as a torsion balance he showed directly that the effect of the gravitational interaction between bodies with masses on the order of a few grams or kilograms is observable, and used this demonstration to provide the first precise measurement of the universal constant G.

It is not difficult to understand why a delicate apparatus is required to observe the gravitational force between small masses. Anticipating Cavendish's result, the value of G in the mks system is 6.67×10^{-11} newtons-m^2/kg^2. Then according to the law of gravitation the force between two 1-kg spheres whose centers are separated by 5 cm (0.05 m) is only 2.67×10^{-8} newtons to be compared, for example, with the 9.8-newton force exerted upon each of the spheres by the gravitational attraction of the earth. Using Newton's second law the acceleration of the masses resulting from the small force between them is 2.67×10^{-8} m/sec^2. If each mass were to maintain this constant acceleration, then in a time t each would move a distance $x = \frac{1}{2}at^2$, requiring 860 sec (or about 14 min) to travel 1 cm. However, two 1-kg masses placed side by side upon a laboratory table do not move toward each other simply because their mutual attraction is insufficient to overcome the frictional force exerted upon them by the table, a force considerably greater than 10^{-8} newtons for even the most highly polished surfaces. The effects of the gravitational force between two masses of this size can only be observed if the other forces upon them are negligible. The Cavendish torsion balance was designed to achieve this end.

A schematic drawing of the apparatus is shown in Figure 5.6. It consists of two pairs of spheres. The two small spheres (*a* and *b*), with masses on the order of 0.01 kg, are connected by a rigid rod which is in turn suspended at its center from a fine metallic fiber. When the large spheres (*A* and *B* with masses on the order of 1 kg) are in the positions indicated by the dashed lines, each is equidistant from the small spheres and hence exerts equal forces upon them. But when moved to the positions indicated by the solid lines each large sphere exerts a much larger force upon the adjacent small sphere than it does upon the other. If the arrangement is completely symmetric so that the force upon each of the small spheres is equal in magnitude, each will then begin accelerating toward the nearest large sphere. Measurement of this initial acceleration and the masses of the small spheres suffices to determine the magnitude of the force between the pairs of spheres. Given the masses of the large spheres and the distance between the centers of

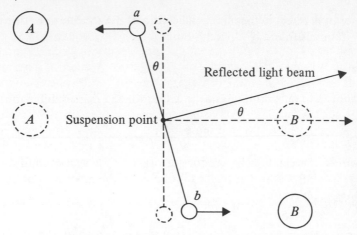

FIGURE 5.6   Essential features of the Cavendish apparatus for determining *G*. When the large spheres are in the neutral positions indicated by the dashed circles, they exert equal and opposite forces on each of the small spheres. But if *A* is closer to *a*, and *B* closer to *b*, the unbalanced forces on the small spheres rotate the connecting rod between them, which in turn twists the suspending fiber. Equilibrium is reestablished when the magnitude of the gravitational force on the system *ab* is equal to the restoring force exerted by the twisted fiber.

the large and small spheres, the universal gravitational constant *G* is the only remaining unknown factor in Equation 5.4 and is therefore determined.

As we have noted, the magnitude of the gravitational force between small objects is so small that it is entirely masked unless the other forces upon the masses are negligible in comparison. Hence the Cavendish apparatus must be delicately balanced so that extraneous forces upon one part of the system are canceled by equal forces upon the symmetric parts. As the small spheres accelerate toward the large spheres they twist the suspending wire in a clockwise direction, a distortion that may be measured by noting the rate of change of the angle θ. As this angle increases the twisted fiber exerts a restoring force upon the suspended masses in the clockwise direction which is directly proportional to the angle θ, much as a distorted spring exerts a restoring force upon the mass that elongates it (Section 4.9). Hence, as the small masses move toward their larger neighbors they are subject to an opposing force exerted upon them by the twisted suspension so that their acceleration is not constant, but changes with time. At the equilibrium position the gravitational force between the pairs of spheres will be equal and opposite to the force exerted by the twisted suspension and the net force upon the small spheres zero. Given this equilibrium angle (Figure 5.6) and the constant for the fiber (analogous to the Hooke's law constant for the spring in Equation 4.17b) the gravitational force upon the small spheres (and the value of *G*) follow at once.

Because the force exerted by the fiber is proportional to the amount it is twisted, then, pursuing the analogy with the spring system of Chapter 4, the suspended masses and their connecting rod would be expected to perform rotational oscillations about the equilibrium angle with a period proportional to the square root of the pertinent proportionality constant (Equation 4.24b). Hence a measurement of the period of these oscillations suffices to determine the requisite proportionality constant, whereas observation of the amplitude of the oscillations—the extremes of the angles θ attained by the oscillating system—is tantamount to a measurement of the midpoint between them, the equilibrium angle at which the gravitational force is equal to the restoring force exerted by the fiber.

Even with a fiber that exerts only an infinitesimal restoring force the angle of twisting is so small that it is usually measured by observing the deflection of a beam of light by a small mirror that is attached to the rod connecting the small spheres and rotates along with them. The best contemporary value of G obtained from similar measurements is 6.670×10^{-11} newtons-m^2/kg^2. Although the value of this constant implies but a tiny force on the laboratory scale, it is the same force that, on the cosmic scale is sufficient to bind the moon to the earth, the planets to the sun, and the stars into galaxies. The observation of this force in the laboratory is a striking demonstration of its universality.

▲▲ 5.5 Applications of the gravitational law; masses of the Sun and Jupiter

If the law of gravitation is truly universal it should be capable of extension to the entire planetary system. Indeed, application of the law led to many of the advances in astronomy during the eighteenth and nineteenth centuries. It is not surprising that universal gravitation should be the basis for understanding Kepler's planetary kinematics, since the third law applied to the orbit of the moon was a partial basis for the gravitational law. It is useful to derive that third law of Kepler for the planetary orbits from the assumption that Equation 5.6 is a valid description of the gravitational interaction between the sun (mass M_s) and a planet (mass M_p) separated by a distance R_{sp}:

$$F = \frac{GM_sM_p}{R_{sp}^2}.$$

For simplicity assume the planetary orbits are circular. If a planet has velocity v there must be a centripetal force $M_p v^2 / R_{sp}^2$ upon it, a force supplied by its gravitational interaction with the sun. Hence:

$$\frac{M_p v^2}{R_{sp}} = \frac{GM_sM_p}{R_{sp}^2}. \tag{5.7a}$$

The period of a planet is defined as the time required for the completion of one orbit about the sun. Therefore, it is the ratio of the circumference of the orbit to the orbital speed. For the assumed circular orbit,

$$T = \frac{C}{v} = \frac{2\pi R_{sp}}{v},$$

so that

$$v^2 = \left(\frac{2\pi R_{sp}}{T}\right)^2.$$

Substituting this expression into Equation 5.7a yields

$$\frac{4\pi^2 M_p R_{sp}}{T^2} = \frac{GM_sM_p}{R_{sp}^2}.$$

Canceling the mass of the planet on each side of this expression and rearranging terms, we find

$$T^2 = \left(\frac{4\pi^2}{GM_s}\right)R^3. \tag{5.7b}$$

For any planet in the solar system the expression in parentheses is constant. Therefore, Equation 5.7b is a statement of Kepler's third law. The constant k in Equation 3.3 ($T^2 = kR^3$) may be expressed in terms of G and M_s by referring to Equation 5.7b:

$$k = \frac{4\pi^2}{GM_s}.$$

That is, the constant appearing in Kepler's empirically-based third law for the planetary orbits is inversely proportional to the mass of the sun. Since the derivation of Equation 5.7b could be repeated for any satellite orbiting about a central planet it follows that the constant k which characterizes any such system must be proportional to the mass of its central body. We can also arrive at the same conclusion by noting that if two identical bodies were in orbits of identical radii about the sun and the earth, for example, then the period of revolution about the sun would be the smaller of the two since the more massive sun would exert a greater force than the earth, implying a greater centripetal acceleration and, therefore, a greater velocity to maintain the orbit (Equation 5.7a).

Since the constant k pertinent to the motion of the planets about the sun has been accurately determined, knowledge of the value of the universal gravitational constant G (Section 5.4) and Equation 5.7b lead immediately to a numerical value for the mass of the sun. Given M_s it is then possible to determine the mass of any planet that has satellites of its own.

For example, the planet Jupiter has nine satellites. Let T_m be the period of one of these moons about Jupiter, M_j the mass of Jupiter, and R_{jm} the distance between Jupiter and the moon in question. In analogy with Equation 5.7b:

$$T_m^2 = \left(\frac{4\pi^2}{GM_j}\right)R_{jm}^3.$$

Similarly, if M_s is the mass of the sun, T_j the period of Jupiter about the sun, and R_{sj} the distance from the sun to that planet:

$$M_j = M_s\left(\frac{T_j}{T_m}\right)^2\left(\frac{R_{jm}}{R_{sj}}\right)^3,$$

which gives the mass of the planet in terms of the mass of the sun and the measurable periods and radii.

▲▲ 5.6 Numerical determinations of planetary orbits*

The solar system is characterized by the presence of one very massive body—the sun—which interacts through its gravitational force with a number of smaller bodies. Since the sun's attraction accelerates the planets, Newton's third law requires that the planets must also accelerate the sun. But since the accelerations of the sun and a particular planet that result from their mutual interaction are inversely proportional to the respective masses, the acceleration of the sun will be small and to an excellent approximation it may be assumed stationary with respect to the stars.

Calculation of a planetary orbit is no different in principle from the calculation of any other particle trajectory. If the positions of the planet and the sun are known at some

---

* The detailed calculations of this section are based on material in R. P. Feynman, R. B. Leighton, and M. Sands, *The Feynman Lectures in Physics*, Vol. 1, Chapter 9, Addison Wesley Publishing Co., Reading, Mass., 1963. This section may be omitted without serious loss of continuity.

time (call it $t = 0$) the magnitude of the gravitational interaction follows from Equation 5.4. In terms of Section 4.6, this equation specifies the strength of the "hammer blow" the planet receives in the direction of the sun during the next short time interval Δt. Given in addition the velocity vector of the planet at $t = 0$, both its position and its velocity at the end of the interval Δt may be calculated, and this information is sufficient to permit the calculation of both the strength of the next hammer blow and the change in position and velocity resulting from it.

Figure 5.7 shows the position of the planet and the sun at some time t in a Cartesian coordinate system with the sun at the origin. The gravitational force between the two bodies acts along the radius vector of the planet and has components in both the x- and y-directions. As the planet moves, the angle between its radius vector and the x-axis changes so that the components F_x and F_y change both because the magnitude of the total force varies inversely as R^2, and because the angle θ is itself a function of time. In terms of F_R and θ, the components of the force are

$$F_x = F_R \cos \theta,$$
$$F_y = F_R \sin \theta.$$

However, the position components, x and y, together with the radius vector R, form a right triangle. Therefore:

$$\cos \theta = \frac{x}{R},$$

$$\sin \theta = \frac{y}{R},$$

so that

$$F_x = F_R\left(\frac{x}{R}\right),$$

$$F_y = F_R\left(\frac{y}{R}\right).$$

These equations express the force components in terms of magnitude of the total force, the radius vector, and the components of the radius vector. Replacing F_R by the explicit expression for the gravitational force (Equation 5.4a) yields:

$$F_x = -GM_sM_p\left(\frac{x}{R^3}\right), \tag{5.8a}$$

$$F_y = -GM_sM_p\left(\frac{y}{R^3}\right), \tag{5.8b}$$

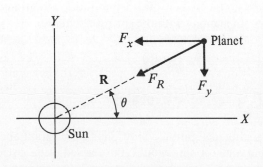

FIGURE 5.7 Cartesian coordinate system for calculating the orbit of a planet. The gravitational force exerted by the sun acts along the radius vector **R** (see Figure 5.3) and has components in both the x- and y-directions. As the planet moves, both the magnitude and direction of **R** change. Therefore, F_x and F_y are both functions of time.

where the minus signs imply that the acceleration is always toward the sun. The components of the force upon the planet are now completely specified in terms of the *x*- and *y*-components of the planet's position in the coordinate system of Figure 5.7. The components of acceleration follow by applying Newton's second law:

$$a_x = -GM_s\left(\frac{x}{R^3}\right),\tag{5.8c}$$

$$a_y = -GM_s\left(\frac{y}{R^3}\right).\tag{5.8d}$$

When expressed in standard mks units the inconveniently large numerical values of the constants and variables appearing in Equations 5.8 add considerably to the arithmetic involved in performing the orbital calculations. For instance, $G = 6.67 \times 10^{-11}$ N-m^2/kg^2, $M_s = 2 \times 10^{30}$ kg, while the orbit of Venus, for example, has a mean radius on the order of 4×10^{10} m. However, Kepler's first law is a statement about the *shapes* of planetary orbits. The absolute *sizes* of the orbits follow from the numerical values of the constants in the gravitational law and from the initial conditions assumed. For present purposes nothing is lost in selecting a set of units in which the product $GM_s = 1$. With this selection Equations 5.8 become:

$$a_x = -\left(\frac{x}{R^3}\right),\tag{5.9a}$$

$$a_y = -\left(\frac{y}{R^3}\right).\tag{5.9b}$$

The kinematic equations required to generate the solutions are the *x*- and *y*-components of the vector equations 4.27:

$$x(t + \Delta t) = x(t) + v_x\left(\frac{t + \Delta t}{2}\right)\Delta t,\tag{5.10a}$$

$$y(t + \Delta t) = y(t) + v_y\left(\frac{t + \Delta t}{2}\right)\Delta t,\tag{5.10b}$$

$$v_x\left(\frac{t + \Delta t}{2}\right) = v_x\left(\frac{t - \Delta t}{2}\right) + a_x(t)\,\Delta t,\tag{5.10c}$$

$$v_y\left(\frac{t + \Delta t}{2}\right) = v_y\left(\frac{t - \Delta t}{2}\right) + a_y(t)\,\Delta t.\tag{5.10d}$$

Special starting equations to calculate the velocity from the initial conditions over the first half interval are also required. In analogy with the spring calculation:

$$v_x\left(\frac{\Delta t}{2}\right) = v_x(0) + a_x(0)\frac{\Delta t}{2},\tag{5.10e}$$

$$v_y\left(\frac{\Delta t}{2}\right) = v_y(0) + a_y(0)\frac{\Delta t}{2}.\tag{5.10f}$$

In calculating the motion of a real planet, initial conditions (the position and velocity vector of the planet at some particular time) would be derived from astronomical observation. For this demonstration calculation a possible set of conditions expressed in a convenient set of units is:

$$x(0) = 0.500, \qquad y(0) = 0.000,$$
$$v_x(0) = 0.000, \qquad v_y(0) = 1.630.$$

The radius vector at $t = 0$ follows from the Pythagorean theorem:

$$R(0) = \sqrt{x^2(0) + y^2(0)} = 0.500,$$

while the acceleration components required in Equations 5.10 are calculated from Equations 5.9:

$$a_x(0) = -4.000,$$
$$a_y(0) = 0.000.$$

Letting the time interval $\Delta t = 0.1$, Equations 5.9e and 5.9f give the velocity components at the midpoint of the first interval of time:

$$v_x(0.05) = 0.00 - 4.000 \times 0.050 = -0.200,$$
$$v_y(0.05) = 1.63 + 0.000 \times 0.100 = 1.630,$$

and these velocities, together with Equations 5.9, give the components of the planet's position at the end of the first full time interval:

$$x(0.1) = 0.500 - 0.20 \times 0.1 = 0.480,$$
$$y(0.1) = 0.000 + 1.63 \times 0.1 = 0.163.$$

Therefore,

$$R(0.1) = \sqrt{x^2(0.1) + y^2(0.1)} = 0.507.$$

We have calculated the result of the first "hammer blow." Using the new values of the position components the acceleration at $t = 0.1$ follows from Equations 5.9:

$$a_x(0.1) = -0.480 \times 7.67 = -3.68,$$
$$a_y(0.1) = -0.163 \times 7.70 = -1.256,$$

and these accelerations can then be used to find the velocity at $t = 0.15$ and the position at $t = 0.2$. Thus the planet may be followed around its orbit step by step. Figure 5.8 shows the results of these calculations for forty-five steps with $\Delta t = 0.1$. Cross marks ($\times$) show its positions at the end of each of the intervals. It is interesting to note that the spacing between the cross marks decreases as the distance from the sun increases, in qualitative accord with Kepler's second law. Before the forty-five steps have been completed, the planet has made one complete revolution about the sun and has started to retrace its steps. Its motion is periodic with period approximately 4.20 time units. (The time of the last cross mark is $4.50 = 45 \times 0.1$. Count back to find the time the planet returns to its initial conditions.)

The shape of the orbit is certainly not circular; otherwise the planet's distance from the sun would be constant. But is the orbit an ellipse? Several criteria were mentioned briefly in Chapter 3 (see Figure 3.12, for instance), among them the requirement that the sum of the two radius vectors is constant for all points on the figure. Both foci of an ellipse lie upon its major axis and are equidistant from its center. According to Kepler's first law the sun must be at one of the foci. For the orbit in Figure 5.8, the second, empty

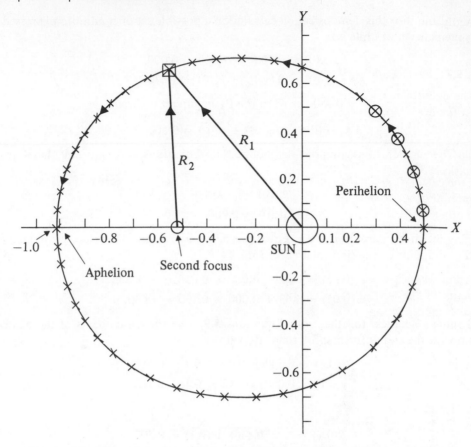

FIGURE 5.8 The orbit of a planet calculated by a series of "hammer blow" approximations. Crosses indicate its successive positions at intervals of $\Delta t = 0.1$ time units; circled crosses show these positions on its second trip about the orbit. The crowding of the crosses indicates that the orbital velocity decreases as the distance from the sun increases, in agreement with Kepler's second law. Radius vectors from the two foci to the point $x = -0.558$, $y = 0.664$ are shown. If the orbit is elliptical the sum $R_1 + R_2$ must be constant for all points on the orbit.

focus (located by the equidistant criterion) lies at the point $y = 0$, $x = -0.525$. When the planet is at perihelion (its distance of closest approach to the sun, or its position at $t = 0$), its first radius vector, R_1, is 0.005 units long, its second radius vector, R_2, $0.500 + 0.525 = 1.025$ units long. Therefore, $R_1 + R_2 = 1.525$ at perihelion. If the orbit is elliptical this sum must also be 1.525 for all of its other positions.

The point enclosed by the box in Figure 5.8 shows the position of the planet at $t = 1.1$ units. Its coordinates at that time are $x = 0.559$, $y = 0.663$. The lengths of the two radius vectors follow either by direct measurement on the graph itself or by application of the methods of Section 2.9: $R_1 = 0.867$, $R_2 = 0.663$. Then $R_1 + R_2 = 1.530$, which, given the fact that the length of the major axis and position of the second focus were read from the graph, is essentially equal to the sum at perihelion.

In order to demonstrate by this method that the orbit is really an ellipse we would have to prove that the equality is applicable to the radius vectors of every other point. Admittedly the test would be tedious. Nonetheless, if carried out it would indeed prove that the calculated orbit is in accord with Kepler's first law.

▲▲ 5.7 Generalization of Kepler's first law. Circular, elliptical, and hyperbolic orbits*

The detailed calculation in the foregoing section show that Kepler's first law follows from the law of gravitation for one particular set of initial conditions, namely:

$$x(0) = 0.500, \qquad y(0) = 0.000,$$
$$v_x(0) = 0.000, \qquad v_y(0) = 1.630.$$

But the calculation does not prove that the orbits of *all* bodies subject to the gravitational attraction of a massive, central body need be elliptical. Figure 5.9a shows the orbits of two other bodies with the same perihelion (i.e., distance of closest approach to the sun— $x(0) = 0.500$, $y(0) = 0.000$), and the same x-component of velocity at perihelion ($v_x(0) = 0.000$) as the planet of Section 5.6 whose orbit, marked 1, is shown for comparison. The calculations were made following the method of Section 5.6. The only difference between the initial conditions on three orbits is a difference in the y-components of the velocity of the respective planets at perihelion. For planets 2 and 3 these components are 1.414 and 1.750, respectively.

Yet the shapes of the three orbits are quite different. Orbit 2 is circular, Orbit 3 a greatly elongated ellipse. The differences may be understood qualitatively in analogy with the motion of terrestrial projectiles. A body thrown upward "tries" to escape the earth; the earth "tries" to bring it back and succeeds by gradually reducing its velocity to zero, then reversing its direction. The greater the body's initial, upward velocity, the farther it can travel upward before being brought to rest and starting its descent.

Similarly, we may regard the orbit of a planet as determined by two conflicting tendencies: the attempt of the planet to escape into space (its inertia), and the attempt of the sun to draw it closer via the gravitational interaction. Starting at perihelion, the sun diverts the planet from what would be its inertial course and is eventually able to make it turn about and return to its starting point. The greater the planet's velocity at perihelion, the farther it can travel before the gravitational attraction of the sun succeeds in turning it about, hence the more elongated its orbit becomes. For a given perihelion not one but rather a whole family of possible elliptical orbits follows as a consequence of the law of gravitation. The only difference between members of the family are their velocities at perihelion.

A different family of possible elliptical orbits characterized by a different set of velocities at perihelion is likewise associated with every other point in space, each of which is a conceivable perihelion for a planet. Whether or not a particular point *is* the perihelion of an existing planet is another matter. Newton's law of gravitation leads to the proper planetary orbits if the initial conditions on the orbits are specified. A great deal of additional evidence is required to determine *how* and *why* these conditions got to be what they are, and at present that problem is very far from being solved.

As the initial velocity of a body subject to the gravitational force of the sun increases, it is able to travel an increasingly greater distance before being turned about and forced to close its orbit. The gravitational attraction of the sun always diverts a body from its inertial path. But if the velocity of that body is sufficient the sun may not have time to turn

---

* This section may be omitted without serious loss of continuity.

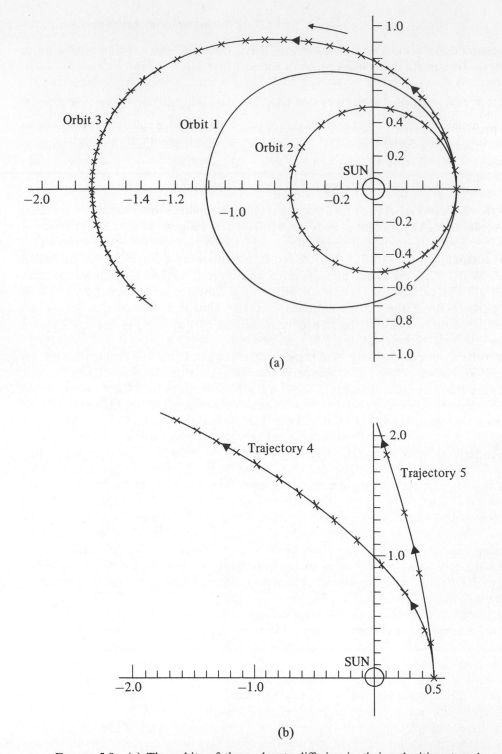

FIGURE 5.9 (a) The orbits of three planets differing in their velocities at perihelion. (Orbit 1 is reproduced from Figure 5.8.) Note the sharp decrease in the velocity of Orbit 3 near aphelion. (b) The hyperbolic trajectories of two comets differing from each other and from the planets in part a only in their velocities at perihelion.

it around and close its orbit. Curves 4 and 5 in Figure 5.9b show two such open trajectories. The *y*-components of their velocities at perihelion are 2.000 and 3.000, respectively. As their respective distances from the sun increase, the gravitational force upon them decreases and the curvatures of their orbits approach the straight line paths that would be followed if the force upon them were zero. Given the velocities of these bodies at perihelion, their motion may be traced backward in time by methods completely analogous to those of Section 5.6. This procedure yields trajectories that are symmetric about the *x*-axis, suggesting that orbits 4 and 5 represent the motion of bodies which accidentally wander into the solar system, are diverted from their inertial, linear paths by the gravitational attraction of the sun, but have sufficient velocity to avoid capture into closed orbits and are therefore able to escape once again into space.

Using advanced analytical methods which avoid the step-by-step calculations of Section 5.6, it is possible to show directly that the trajectory of any body subject only to the gravitational attraction of a massive central body must be one of the four conic sections or curves of second order: the circle, the ellipse, the parabola, and the hyperbola. The latter two curves are open, the former closed. Trajectories 4 and 5 in Figure 5.6b are hyperbolae, and represent the trajectories of those comets which occasionally stumble into the vicinity of the sun and are seen but once. There are other comets, permanent residents of the solar system, which orbit the sun in elongated elliptical orbits and are seen periodically when these orbits bring them into the vicinity of the earth. Halley's comet with its 76-year period is the most famous member of the latter class (Figure 5.10). Last seen in 1910, it is due to return briefly in 1986. Thus Newton's law of gravitation not only gives a dynamical foundation to Kepler's empirically derived law on the shapes of

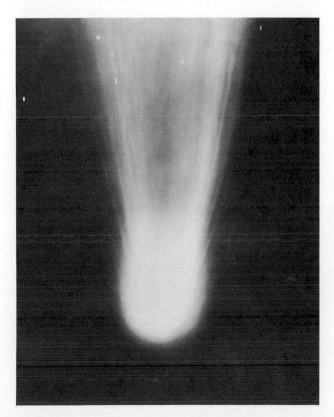

FIGURE 5.10 The head of Halley's comet photographed May 8, 1910, using a 60-in. telescope. This comet moves in a highly elongated elliptical orbit about the sun consistent with predictions based on Newton's gravitational law. (Photograph from the Mt. Wilson and Palomar Observatories.)

the planetary orbits, but also broadens the law to include the orbits of all bodies in the solar system: planets and satellites of planets, as well as comets, both permanent members of the system and one-time visitors. Indeed, it extends this law to the entire universe (Figure 5.11).

Kepler's second law is also consistent with the gravitational law but is much more general than either the first or the third laws. The force exerted upon the planets by the much more massive sun is a *central* force, since its direction is always toward a fixed point. In addition, the gravitational force is an *inverse-square* force, since its magnitude varies inversely as the square of the separation between the interacting bodies. The first and third laws of Kepler follow from the inverse square character of the force. However, it is a consequence of angular momentum conservation (a law discussed in the next chapter) that the product of the radius vector by the perpendicular component of the velocity of any body subject to the sole influence of any central force whatsoever must be constant. Thus Kepler's second law is a consequence not of the inverse square nature of the gravitational force but rather of its more general central character.

▲▲ 5.8 Deviations from Kepler's laws. The discovery of Neptune

We have seen that the laws of Kepler have their dynamical basis in Newton's law of gravitation. But the latter is considerably more general, for the validity of Kepler's laws is really only approximate. The truly universal nature of Newton's law is nowhere better manifested than in its ability to account for virtually all of the observed *deviations* from Kepler's empirically based laws, the laws from which it was originally derived. As Max Born has noted, Newton's law was the first example of a law of nature that was sufficiently flexible to encompass data that was not known at the time it was enunciated.

In our derivation of the gravitational law we assumed that only two bodies were involved: the sun and one planet, for instance, or a planet and one of its satellites. But there are more than two bodies in the solar system. There are nine planets and numerous satellites, besides various asteroids and comets. Newton's gravitational law states that *every* body exerts a gravitational force upon every other body. Because of its immense mass the greatest force upon a planet is exerted by the sun so that the attractive force of the other planets may be ignored in making approximate calculations. Nevertheless, the force exerted by the massive planet Jupiter upon a nearby planet (say Mars) may result in significant departures from the orbit the planet would have if it moved under the sole influence of the sun. As these perturbations are too small to be measured without the

1908   1915   1920

FIGURE 5.11 The double star *Krueger 60* at three different times relative to a fixed reference star. The orbit of each star about the center of mass of the two-star system is consistent with Newton's gravitational law. (Yerkes Observatory photograph.)

aid of a telescope, they were not recorded by Tycho Brahe and hence not incorporated into Kepler's laws. Nonetheless, their subsequent study led to discovery of two planets, Neptune and Pluto.

It is possible to find exact algebraic expressions for the orbit of one body moving under the sole influence of the gravitational attraction of a second without resorting to the numerical methods of Section 5.6, although the mathematics involved is beyond the scope of this text. If the massive central body is not assumed stationary (as in Section 5.6), then the two interacting bodies move in elliptical orbits with their center of mass at the focus of their respective orbits. The center of mass of the sun and any planet lies within the volume of the sun itself since it is so much more massive than any of the planets. As a result the "orbit" of the sun amounts to a wobbling relative to the stars, and there is little error in the stationary assumption.

If two moving, interacting bodies are subject to the gravitational attraction of a third *fixed* body, exact expressions for the motion of the pair may still be found, although the solution to the problem is considerably more difficult. But the general three-body problem, the calculation of the orbits of three interacting, moving bodies, is not amenable to an exact solution. During the eighteenth and nineteenth centuries, powerful analytical methods were developed to handle such problems, methods which lead to excellent, though approximate, solutions. The three-body problem may also be attacked numerically by methods that are an extension of the approach used in Section 5.6.

Figure 5.12 shows the positions of three interacting bodies at some time, $t = 0$. (These might be the sun, the earth, and the moon, for example, or the sun, Mars, and Jupiter.) The instantaneous acceleration of each is a result of the total instantaneous force upon it, the vector sum of its gravitational interaction with the other two bodies. If the velocity vectors of the three bodies are known at $t = 0$, their positions and velocities at the end of the next short time interval follow from a generalization of the method of Section 5.6, and these new conditions permit calculation of the accelerations during the next time interval, etc. The calculation proceeds exactly as in the two-body calculation, but is far more laborious, since it involves not one set of equations but three coupled sets, one for each of the three bodies. However, modern electronic computers are able to make repeated arithmetic calculations very rapidly, so that such three-body orbits may be determined to the precision desired in times on the order of a minute or less. Nothing

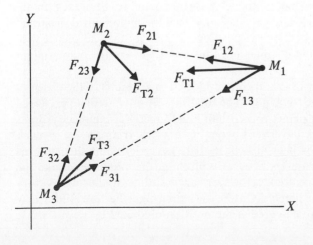

FIGURE 5.12 The gravitational interaction of a three-body system. The total force on each body is the vector sum of the forces due to the other two. Accordingly, the vector depends upon the instantaneous position of its planet relative to the other two planets.

new is involved in writing down expressions to find the orbits of four, five, six, or even more interacting bodies and letting a computer do the arithmetic.

Kepler's three simple laws were based upon the observations of Tycho Brahe, which, however, were of insufficient precision to reveal the perturbations on the basic planetary orbits caused by the influence of the other planets. Within a century of Brahe's death the telescope had been developed into a powerful scientific tool, and the perturbations observed. It is interesting to speculate on the course physics might have taken had Brahe had a good telescope, for then it would have been very difficult for Kepler to summarize his data so simply, and Newton would have had an exceedingly difficult task in trying to find the dynamic causation implied by such a complex set of kinematic laws which probably would have resembled the Copernican circles-upon-circles.

Evidently, something more than infinite precision and painstaking observation is required in the evolution of science: the ability to recognize details which are central to the problem at hand, and to ignore those which are not. An observational deviation of eight minutes of arc from the orbit of Mars predicted on the Platonic circular doctrine led Kepler to introduce his first two laws, and resulted ultimately in Newton's law of gravitation. On the other hand, deviations from Kepler's predictions which are on the order of seconds of arc are well explained by the gravitational law itself and in fact *must* be explainable in such terms if the law is to be regarded as universal. If small deviations which cannot be explained are observed, something is wrong; either the gravitational law is too crude a representation of the gravitational force, or all of the data has not been properly evaluated.

In 1781, during the course of some routine telescopic observations, William Herschel discovered a seventh planet located beyond the orbit of Saturn and having a period of eighty-four years. The new planet was ultimately named Uranus, in keeping with the mythological designation of its brothers. By 1830 measurements had revealed serious discrepancies in its orbit that could not be attributed to perturbations caused by the other known planets, particularly massive Jupiter and Saturn. One suggested rationalization given for these residual perturbations was a possible breakdown of the gravitational law at the large distances characteristic of the separation of Uranus and the sun. Another possibility was the existence of a yet undiscovered planet. This was the hypothesis favored by John C. Adams, in England, and J. J. Leverrier, in France. Working independently and unknown to each other, they set out to calculate the orbit of this hypothetical planet from the measured perturbations of Uranus. The task was horrifying in its complexity. First, it was necessary to calculate the perturbations due to the known planets, and then find the orbit of a planet of known mass that could result in the remaining discrepancies between observation and calculation. Once the hypothetical orbit had been established it was possible to calculate the position of the hypothetical planet with respect to the fixed stars as a function of time, and thus predict where the planet might be seen at any given time.

Both men completed their work in 1845 and communicated their results to the observational astronomers in their respective countries. The English were interested but preferred to make a systematic search for the planet rather than look directly at the place Adams suggested. The French applauded Leverrier's work as a fresh triumph for French mathematics, but did not search for it at all! In despair Leverrier communicated his results to the director of the Berlin observatory who promised he might undertake the search if his work schedule so permitted. However, an assistant at the observatory received permission to search immediately. On the very first night he observed a new planet at a position in the sky within a degree of the position predicted by Leverrier. It was the planet Neptune, orbiting the sun with a one hundred sixty-four year period. Its discovery was a resounding triumph not only for the young Leverrier, but for Newton's law of gravitation as well.

Again the story was repeated: Neptune's orbit showed small discrepancies that could not be attributed to perturbations due to the known planets, and it turned out that the perturbations on Uranus itself were not fully attributable to the presence of Neptune. Still another planet was suggested, and its probable orbit calculated by Percival Lowell. In 1930, following a twenty-five year search, the observatory at Flagstaff, Arizona, announced the discovery of the ninth planet, Pluto, orbiting the sun with a period of two hundred forty-eight years (Figure 5.13).

Amid all the triumphant application of the universal law of gravitation to the solar system, the planet Mercury long presented a serious embarrassment, for its orbit shows small discrepancies, unexplainable in terms of the usual perturbing influence of the other planets. The discrepancy amounts to less than one minute of arc per century, but was nonetheless regarded as intolerable in the light of the other triumphs. A satisfactory explanation was not obtained until 1916 when Einstein's general theory of relativity showed that the Newtonian law is an approximation to a more general gravitational law, an excellent approximation, but still not the final statement about the gravitational interaction.*

▲▲ 5.9   Earth satellites and interplanetary vehicles

From the discussion in this and the preceding chapters, it should be clear that keeping an artificial satellite in orbit about the earth presents no technological problems. The only problem involves establishing the orbit in the first place. Newton himself recognized

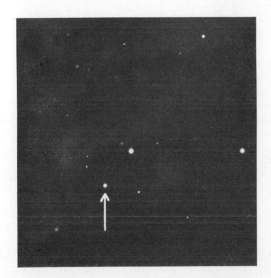 

FIGURE 5.13   The planet Pluto (indicated by the arrow) photographed on two successive nights using the 200-in. Hale telescope. (Photograph from the Mt. Wilson and Palomar Observatories.)

---

* Einstein's explanation of this discrepancy has recently (1967) been questioned by R. H. Dicke who has made very careful measurements of the sun's shape and has shown that a significant fraction of the perturbation can be attributed to the fact that the sun is spheroidal rather than spherical.

the point when he argued (Section 4.7) that a cannon ball fired from a high mountain with a sufficiently high velocity would become a satellite of the earth. Since the orbit of a satellite is completely determined if its position and velocity at one point in the orbit (say its perigee*) are set, the burden of technology lies with placing the satellite-to-be at the chosen point with the proper velocity vector. Multistage rockets with their complex of associated, computer-controlled guidance systems have been developed to do just that (Figure 5.14).

Once a vehicle has been brought to the proper position and given the proper velocity (i.e., once it is launched into its orbit) its subsequent motion is completely determined by these initial conditions and the forces upon it. To the approximation that the earth alone exerts a gravitational force upon it, and that the earth is a sphere of uniform density, the satellite will obey Kepler's laws exactly. However, these approximations are useful only if the orbital radius of the satellite is large compared to the radius of the earth. Figure 5.1b (Section 5.2) outlines the method used for calculating the total force exerted upon a particle (for instance, a satellite) by an extended, nonspherical body, and may be used to calculate the exact gravitational force exerted by the earth upon an orbiting vehicle. Given the magnitude and direction of this force at all points in the vicinity of the earth the exact orbit of the satellite follows from numerical methods similar to those of Section 5.6. The determination of this force as a function of the orientation of the satellite relative to the earth, and the computation of orbits based upon it are tasks requiring a great many calculations. Nevertheless, they are well within the capacity of modern computer technology.

Several satellites have been launched that actually take advantage of the perturbations

FIGURE 5.14 Rendezvous of Gemini VI and VII in 1965. Since an increase in the orbital velocity of a satellite changes its orbit, effecting such a rendezvous is a delicate operation. (Photograph courtesy of the National Aeronautics and Space Administration.)

---

* Point of closest approach to the earth. The apogee of an orbit is its farthest point from the earth.

caused by the nonsphericity and nonuniformity of the earth to measure these geophysical features in detail. Launched into orbits of small radii to emphasize the perturbations, the observed orbits are used to determine the force acting on the satellites as a function of their position, and the force itself used to calculate the shape and density of the earth. These investigations have revealed a number of unexpected details: that the earth is pear-shaped, for instance, bulging a few feet more at the North Pole than at the South, and that the continents are a few feet closer together than had previously been thought. Measurements to a precision of a few feet in several thousand miles by means of observed perturbations on satellite orbits suggest the precision with which such orbits can be determined and the complex gravitational effects calculated from the measurements.

The methods used to calculate the conditions required to orbit satellites about the earth may be readily extended to calculate the conditions required to launch a vehicle into an orbit that will carry it to the moon or to another planet (Figures 5.15 and 5.16). However, the latter calculations are three- and four-body problems involving the earth, the vehicle, the moon (or the planet), and usually the sun.

The calculation of an interplanetary trajectory involves the same fundamental ideas, although the basic orbit chosen is usually a solar orbit which intersects both the orbits of the earth and the planet in question rather than a terrestrial orbit that intersects the orbit of the moon. Both the trajectories of Mariner II (the Venus probe of 1962) and Mariner IV (the Martian probe of 1965) were this type of perturbed solar orbit. Having achieved their goals of probing their respective planets, they continued along their orbits as if they were small planets and presumably have now become permanent members of the solar system.

The principles involved in bringing a vehicle out of its orbit are not difficult to understand. Since the law of gravitation prescribes a precise orbital velocity for each point on a given orbit, a continuous reduction in orbital velocity implies a continuous change in orbit. The same principle may be applied in changing an orbit from one that encompasses both the earth and moon (or the earth and Mars) for instance, to orbits about the moon or about Mars itself. Deceleration, accomplished by the application of auxiliary jets,

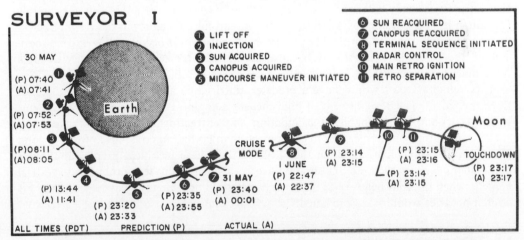

FIGURE 5.15 The trajectory of Surveyor I from the earth to its soft landing on the moon June 1, 1967. The vehicle was oriented by fixing its position relative to the sun and to the star Canopus. Actual and predicted times along the path are given. (Drawing courtesy of the Jet Propulsion Laboratory, California Institute of Technology.)

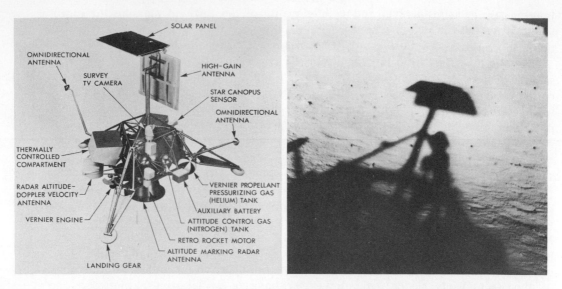

FIGURE 5.16 (a) Surveyor I, the first American vehicle to make a soft landing on the moon. (b) A photograph of the lunar landscape and its own shadow taken and transmitted by Surveyor I. (Photographs courtesy of the Jet Propulsion Laboratory, California Institute of Technology.)

results in the desired changes in velocity and therefore in an orbital contraction. A continuously applied decelerating force applied to a satellite of the earth leads to a spiral orbit that eventually ends upon the terrestrial surface. The effects of deceleration due to atmospheric drag are completely analogous.

It should be clear from these brief remarks that the foundations of the so-called Space Age were established by Newton in 1687. Implicit in his unified dynamics is the assertion that a terrestrial body will behave as a celestial body when it enters this region expressly forbidden it by the system of Aristotle. Newton and his colleagues in the Royal Society failed to launch a satellite in the late seventeenth century not because they had not considered the possibility, but simply because they lacked the technical capacity to lift a large mass from the surface of the earth, accelerate it to a high velocity, and guide it so that its velocity vector would have a predetermined value at a predetermined distance from the earth. The development of high-thrust jet engines, complex guidance systems, high-speed computers capable of calculating and correcting the course of a moving rocket, and radio communication to effect these changes had to come first. But if a good many people were surprised when they learned that these technical preparations were complete as early as 1957, no one should have been surprised to learn that this terrestrial vehicle, when in orbit, behaved as if it were a celestial body, precisely as Newton and his contemporaries would have predicted.

▲▲ 5.10 Weight, weightlessness, and the principle of equivalence

The idea of weightlessness bears investigation both because of its intrinsic interest and as a means of seeking a deeper understanding of the nature of the gravitational interaction. By definition (Equation 4.13), weight, or more properly, terrestrial weight, is the gravitational force exerted by the earth upon a gravitational mass. The generalization to lunar weight or Martian weight is obvious. Therefore, according to the strict definition a body can be weightless only if it is infinitely far from all other bodies, and quite evidently this strict condition is unlikely to apply to any space voyage that will ever occur.

That all physical and physiological aspects of strict weightlessness can be simulated in satellite orbits (and even for short times on the terrestrial surface) is a direct consequence of the equivalence of inertial and gravitational mass (Section 4.5), and has important implications for the basic nature of the gravitational interaction itself. Since the laws of physics are based upon measurement, the concept of weight cannot be separated from a measurement of, or (equivalently) from the effects of weight. The most direct consequence of terrestrial weight is free fall. However, weight cannot be measured during free fall simply because *all* bodies in free fall have the same acceleration!

If a body's weight is to be measured directly it must be at rest on a balance or some similar device. According to Newton's first law the balance (or the floor or ground upon which it rests) must exert an upward force, Mg, upon the mass to *keep* it at rest, and Newton's third law requires that the mass exert an equal downward force upon the balance. As it is this downward force that depresses the scale or balance, it is this force which is measured as the weight of the body. Then let us define the *effective weight* of a body as the force that is exerted upon the body to keep it at rest relative to its immediate environment. "Real" and effective weights are equal when a body is at rest upon the surface of the earth since the environment, floor, or balance, for instance, exerts an upward force which is equal to the downward force of terrestrial gravity.

Now let us suppose that a body rests upon the floor of an elevator which is accelerating upward at a rate a (Figure 5.17). The elevator floor must exert a force sufficient both to counteract the body's real weight, Mg, and to accelerate it upward. The magnitude of the latter force is Ma. Then according to our definition, the effective weight of the body is equal to the total force exerted upon it by the elevator floor, or is $M(g + a)$.

As another example, consider a body strapped into a centrifuge and rotated in a horizontal circle of radius R with velocity of magnitude v (Figure 5.18). The straps must exert a centripetal force to keep the body in its circular path. Therefore, it has an effective weight Mv^2/R in the horizontal direction in addition to its real weight Mg in the vertical.

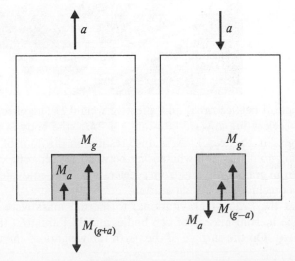

FIGURE 5.17 An object of mass M resting on the floor of an elevator accelerating upward in one case, downward in the other. In the upward accelerating elevator the force exerted on the body by the floor is $M(g + a)$, which, by definition, is the effective weight of the body. Likewise, when the elevator accelerates downward the body's effective weight is $M(g - a)$. If $a = g$ both the elevator and the body are in free fall and effectively weightless.

FIGURE 5.18 A centrifuge used to simulate effective weights up to 10 mg at NASA's Ames Research Laboratory. The photo to the right shows an astronaut strapped into the gondola at the end of the device's 30-ft arm. (Photograph courtesy of the National Aeronautics and Space Administration.)

Is there any measurable distinction between real and effective weight? The effective weight of a body in an elevator accelerating upward at a rate g is $2Mg$ (the body is said to be subject to a force of two "g's" in that case). A balance resting on the floor of the elevator will measure $2Mg$, making no distinction whatsoever between the separate contributions to the effective weight from gravitation and from acceleration. The equivalence of inertial and gravitational mass precludes such a separation.

Suppose, for the moment, that the ratio of gravitational to inertial mass were *not* constant. Let M_{i1} and M_{i2} be the inertial masses of two bodies and M_{g1} and M_{g2} their corresponding gravitational masses. On the surface of the earth the weights of the two would be $M_{g1}g$ and $M_{g2}g$, respectively, while the total force upon each in an elevator accelerating upward at a rate a would be:

$$F_1 = M_{g1}g + M_{i1}a,$$

and

$$F_2 = M_{g2}g + M_{i2}a.$$

If the gravitational mass of the first body were twice the second, the ratios of the real weights would also be two. But if the ratio of the gravitational to the inertial mass of the two were not equal, the effective weight of the first would not be twice the effective weight of the second but would, in fact, depend upon the acceleration of the elevator. A means of distinguishing between the gravitational and the acceleration components of the total force would then be available.

The equivalence of inertial and gravitational mass implies that the difference between real and effective weight is at best artificial. Since an object of mass $2M$ at rest on the surface of the earth and a body of mass M accelerating upward at a rate g have identical *effective* weights, all physical, and therefore, all physiological effects based upon weight must be identical for both. The fact that a person *knows* he is in an accelerating elevator is immaterial. The surface of the earth is taken as a standard only because it is familiar from long experience. A race of scientists born in an accelerating elevator and having no means of communication with terrestrial scientists would not necessarily conclude that their environment was accelerating upward. All the laws of physics could be consistently evolved with the assumption that the value of g in their system is greater than 9.8 m/sec² since no measurable distinction between effects due to "real" and effective weight exists.

Now let us suppose that the elevator accelerates *downward* at a rate a. The total force exerted by the floor upon a body at rest relative to it would be $M(g - a)$ so that its effective weight is smaller than its real weight. If $a = g$, that is, if the body and the elevator were in free fall, the effective weight would be zero. *No* force would be exerted to keep the body in equilibrium with its surroundings. All measurements of effective weight in free fall must necessarily be zero, and all physiological effects consistent with zero weight. Although its "real" weight remains Mg, such a body is effectively weightless.

A satellite in a stable orbit about the earth is in a state of free fall (Section 4.5). Then no force need be exerted upon any objects within the satellite to keep them in equilibrium with their environment. In this case the satellite, and all its contents are effectively weightless. If an astronaut steps outside the vehicle he will remain in orbit, or be suspended in space as far as an observer within the satellite is concerned (Figure 5.19). In fact, unless the astronaut looks earthward he will sense no motion at all. (Should he alter his orbital velocity, and the satellite's, by pushing against it, then he will go into a slightly different orbit and soon be separated from his carrier.)

The distinction between real and effective weight has its roots in nothing more profound than a prejudice for the surface of the earth as a privileged place of residence, a sort of latter-day geocentrism. The fact that all physical effects of weight, i.e., of terrestrial gravitation, can be conjured away or intensified by acceleration led Einstein to develop the idea into a theory of gravitation in his general theory of relativity.

Suppose a race of scientists lives in an elevator in free fall relative to the earth. They will be able to develop a system of physics completely consistent with the assumption that they are in a gravitation-free environment. What sort of geometry will they devise? How will they define a straight line, for instance? According to Newton's first law they know that a body experiencing no force will travel in a straight line. From their point of

FIGURE 5.19 Astronaut Edward H. White's "space walk" seen from his Gemini IV satellite. Since White as well as all objects within the satellite were themselves satellites in continuous free fall toward the earth, all were effectively weightless. (Photograph courtesy of the National Aeronautics and Space Administration.)

view no force at all is exerted upon an object thrown horizontally across the elevator. Therefore, they might use the trajectory of such an object to define the geometric idea of a straight line.

An earth-based scientist observing the experiments in progress in the elevator will disagree that the path of the object across the elevator is a straight line. He will note that the elevator is descending with an acceleration of 9.8 m/sec², and therefore see that during the time the object is moving across the elevator at constant velocity it is also falling with constant acceleration. To him the path is a parabola, the parabola that is the path of any projectile on the surface of the earth (Section 4.7).

Who is correct, the elevator scientists or the earth-based scientist? Einstein based his ideas upon the assumption that both are equally correct. Both define their geometry in terms of physical measurements. Their respective interpretations differ because their assumptions concerning their gravitational environment also differ. However, the equivalence of gravitational and inertial mass shows that there is no reason why one assumption should be considered any more basic than the other. Einstein's general theory of relativity is formulated upon this relationship between geometry and gravity (see Chapter 11).

◣◣ 5.11   The properties of matter and its interactions

Einstein's reinterpretation of gravitation in his general theory of relativity demonstrates that Newton's formulation of the problem is only one representation of the gravitational interaction, albeit a very successful one if measured by its ability to relate a variety of diverse physical phenomena to one basic idea. Nonetheless, Newton himself recognized one of the disturbing implications of his results:

> It is inconceivable that inanimate brute matter should, without the mediation of something else, which is not material, operate upon, and effect other matter without mutual contact. . . .
> That gravity should be innate, inherent, and essential to matter, so that one body may act upon another, at a distance through a vacuum, without the mediation of anything else, by and through which their action and force may be conveyed from one to another, is to me so great an absurdity, that I believe no man who has in philosophical matters a competent faculty of thinking, can ever fall into it. . . .*

In other words, how is matter to act upon matter over a great distance without intermediate contact? Is it conceivable to imagine that the "brute matter" composing the sun can reach out over ninety-three million miles and seize the earth with a force sufficient to snap a steel cable several feet thick? Newton's redefinition of natural motion and his assertion that acceleration implies the application of a force led him to postulate an interaction between the sun and earth, a force represented very well by the law of gravitation. But describing a force quantitatively is not tantamount to understanding why and how it operates. The hiatus between an apparent action at a distance and the philosophical difficulty experienced in trying to conceive it, plagued natural philosophers for more than two centuries, leading to a fundamental reformulation in terms of the field approach and eventually to a reinterpretation of the general meaning of the laws of physics themselves.

What *is* the property of matter which permits it to interact with other matter through the gravitational interaction? It has been given the name "gravitational mass," but what is gravitational mass? The most appropriate definition is simply this: gravitational mass is a property of matter that permits it to interact, through the gravitational force, with all other matter having the same property.

Far from being absurd and circular, the definition suggests a fundamental connection between the properties of matter and its interactions. Physics is concerned with the properties and behavior of matter under all conceivable conditions. It is an observational science that seeks to interpret and correlate experimentally observed physical events. But matter is never observed except in its interaction with other matter, be it only the matter of which an observer is composed. Therefore, in seeking to understand a property it is necessary to study interactions, and conversely, the interactions of an object are only comprehensible in terms of its properties. In answer to the question, "what is matter?" a physicist replies by listing a number of ways in which matter behaves, or, in other words, by listing a number of its properties. In a very real sense the properties of matter are determined by all of its possible interactions.

It is conceivable that a deeper, more fundamental theory than Newton's may redefine gravitational mass in terms of some more basic property of matter. Einstein's general

---

* Sir Isaac Newton, Letter to Richard Bentley, quoted by E. A. Burtt, *Metaphysical Foundations of Modern Science*, Humanities Press, Inc., New York, 1964.

theory of relativity is an attempt in that direction. But the general tenor of these remarks is not altered thereby. Ultimately, all properties of matter must be defined in terms of a set of interactions. The physicist, with his faith in the simplicity of nature, continues to hope that the number of interactions so required may be reduced to a minimum.

Perhaps the most basic assumption that distinguishes the Newtonian from the Aristotelian-scholastic system is the emphasis upon the universal attributes of matter rather than upon particulars, the assumption that although the universe presents a virtual infinity of different, complex physical systems, it is nevertheless possible to cut across the individual aspects of each and find common elements among them. The identification of these universals, the understanding of the role they play in the behavior of particular systems, is the foundation of what may be called, for want of a better term, "the Newtonian method."

In this context the properties of matter may be regarded as universals, and Newton's development of the law of gravitation an excellent illustration of the evolution of a universal concept such as gravitational mass from data pertinent to particular systems. Galileo's observations may be interpreted as implying that the earth interacts with all objects in its vicinity in a manner characterized by constant, free-fall acceleration. This behavior suggests that some basic interaction is involved. The next step is to learn more about the interaction and expand its area of applicability if possible. To this end, a property of all matter called gravitational mass is tentatively defined.

Further investigation, using Kepler's laws, Newton's laws of motion, and a few shrewd hypotheses, permits the formulation of an equation representing the hypothesized interaction in terms of the tentative property (Equation 5.4). Furthermore, the formulation can be turned about to provide a quantitative measure of the property called gravitational mass once some standard is selected. In other words, *the property called gravitation mass is defined for the express purpose of understanding the gravitational interaction.* If there were no gravitational interaction it would be completely meaningless to define the property!

But the assignment of gravitational mass to an object does not complete its description. It only states something about its ability to partake in the gravitational interaction. If two objects have identical gravitational masses the force between each and any other object an equal distance away will be of the same magnitude, regardless of any other differences between the objects. Equation 5.4 does not ask for the *quality* of a body M_1, whether it is a stone or an apple, for instance, but only for the quantity of gravitational mass it contains. A complete physical description of a particular apple requires a quantitative description of all its properties. One of these, but only one, is its gravitational mass, and that property serves to distinguish the apple from other objects of larger or smaller gravitational masses, but not from stones or flasks of liquid or animals with the *same* gravitational mass. Further differentiation requires a further listing of the apple's universal attributes.

The point is really not very deep. All physical systems, apples, stones, bottles of water, men, planets, stars, atoms, are qualitatively different from one another. But the Newtonian emphasis on universals implicitly assumes that each of these qualitatively different and highly complex systems can be understood in terms of universals. The complete description of even a relatively simple physical system is a task of major proportions. Therefore, in order to try to identify and understand the manifestations of these universals in a number of otherwise highly differentiated systems, it is expedient to concentrate upon a relatively small number of features of the systems. Galileo's law of falling bodies does not distinguish between apples and stones. Kepler's laws are not concerned with the differences in the surface temperatures of Mercury and Saturn. All but the features required to understand the problem at hand are ignored.

But it is abundantly clear that Galileo's law does not fully describe everything about falling bodies, nor do Kepler's laws exhaust all the possibilities of the solar system. They contain no information about the sun's heat and light, nor its chemical composition, nor its origin. They make no statement about the sizes of the planets, nor about the life that exists on (at least) one of them. The motion and interaction of the planets and the sun is an important facet in the description of the solar system. By seeking to understand that facet and by concentrating upon the general problems of motion and gravitation alone, Newton succeeded in finding a universal law applicable to far more than the motion of the bodies in the known solar system of his day. In a similar vein the sun's heat and light might best be understood, and dividends gained, by concentrating first upon the general problem of heat and light, then applying that understanding to the sun. The spirit of the Newtonian method is to investigate the universals first, then apply knowledge of all pertinent universals to particular systems. The method has been highly successful in leading to a comprehension of the nature of the physical universe and has provided fascinating insights both into the potentialities of matter and into the discipline imposed upon matter by the laws of nature.

▶▶ 5.12 The Newtonian synthesis in retrospect

Concerning the scientific revolution of the seventeenth century and the Age of the Enlightenment that was its climax, Herbert Butterfield has written:

> Since that revolution overturned the authority in science not only of the Middle Ages but of the Ancient World—since it ended not only in the eclipse of scholastic philosophy but in the destruction of Aristotelian physics—it outshines everything since the rise of Christianity and reduces the Renaissance and Reformation to the rank of mere episodes, mere internal displacements within the system of medieval Christendom. Since it changed the character of men's habitual mental operations, while transforming the whole diagram of the physical universe and the very texture of human life itself, it looms so large as the real origin both of the modern world and of the modern mentality that our customary periodisation of European history has become an anachronism and an incumbrance.[*]

The effects of that scientific revolution upon contemporary modes of thought have been so complete that many of the radical changes wrought by Newton, his colleagues, and his predecessors now seem intuitive and commonplace. As a result, the difficulty of assuming the mental posture of a pre-seventeenth-century scholar and appreciating the new directions made possible by Newton's *Principia* are considerable. To quote Butterfield again:

> But the supreme paradox of the scientific revolution is the fact that things which we find easy to instill into the boys at school, because we see that they start off on the right foot—things which would strike us as the ordinary natural way of looking at the universe, the obvious way of regarding the behavior of falling bodies, for example—defeated the greatest intellects for centuries, defeated Leonardo da Vinci and at the marginal point even Galileo, when their minds were wrestling on the very frontiers of human thought with these same problems.[†]

The scientific revolution of the seventeenth century had its basis in new approaches to old problems, in new ways of looking at long familiar phenomena, and the pivot of the

---

[*] Herbert Butterfield, *The Origins of Modern Science: 1300–1800*, G. Bell and Sons, Ltd., London, 1950, p. viii.
[†] Herbert Butterfield, *The Origins of Modern Science: 1300–1800*, p. 2.

new outlook was the change in the attitude toward motion. Aristotle's concept of motion in terms of some teleological purpose has been touched upon in Chapter 3. The roots of the new attitude date from the thirteenth century when scholars of Merton College (Oxford) and of the School of Paris dared ask, not "How can the motion of an arrow from a bow be explained in terms of the teachings of Aristotle?" but rather: "What does the motion of an arrow from a bow tell us about motion?" More than four centuries were required to bring the revolution to its climax in Newton's *Principia*, but its seeds were unknowingly sown in the thirteenth-century assumption that natural philosophy might *follow* from observation. That this observation should be quantitative and that precision should be relevant was another long but necessary step. An observed, small deviation in behavior from accepted principles had to be considered sufficiently serious to open the fundamental assumptions to question. Kepler, in trusting the precision of Tycho Brahe, but denying that the answer to the Martian problem had been given by Plato nineteen-hundred years earlier, was psychologically able to enunciate his new laws of motion.

The Newtonian concept of motion and interaction as the key to an understanding of the nature of things in the physical universe is the heart of that classical physics which grew out of Newton's *Principia*. But the ultimate logic of the Newtonian approach seems to lead to a totally mechanical model of the universe. If the nature of all things can be ultimately described in terms of the interactions of a few primary attributes, and if these attributes and interactions can be known to arbitrary precision, then all physical phenomena, and therefore, all biological and, perhaps, all psychological phenomena as well, should, in principal, be completely describable in terms of matter and motion. Knowledge of the position and the velocity vector of every body in the universe at one particular time would permit knowledge of the entire past history and the entire future fate of each body, and therefore, the entire course of the universe itself. The universe becomes a gigantic clock that, once wound, proceeds along one inevitable and predetermined course.

The limitations of this view were not fully appreciated until the early years of the present century, although a number of logical difficulties in the Newtonian scheme had been identified well before that time. Yet despite the ultimate failure of some of its basic assumptions, the great edifice of classical physics based upon the laws and the concepts of Sir Isaac Newton remains impressive in its ability to incorporate within its confines an almost incredible range of natural phenomena.

SUGGESTIONS FOR FURTHER READING ▲▲▲

The best elementary treatment of universal gravitation appears in:

GERALD HOLTON AND DUANE H. D. ROLLER, *Foundations of Modern Physical Science*, Addison-Wesley Publishing Co., Inc., Reading, Mass., 1958, Chapters 11 and 12.

An excellent discussion of gravitation and its implications for the structure of the universe is:

R. P. FEYNMAN, R. B. LEIGHTON, AND M. SANDS, *The Feynman Lectures on Physics*, Vol. 1, Addison-Wesley Publishing Co., Inc., Reading, Mass., 1963, Chapter 7.

Chapter 9 of the above reference obtains elliptical planetary orbits by a numerical method upon which the treatment in this chapter is based. One of the best nontechnical treatments of Newtonian physics from a more general viewpoint is:

ALBERT EINSTEIN AND LEOPOLD INFELD, *The Evolution of Physics*, Simon and Schuster, New York, 1961, Chapter 1.

Books and articles on the history and/or the historical consequences of the Newtonian revolution abound. Among them:

E. N. DA C. ANDRADE, *Sir Isaac Newton: His Life and Work*, Science Study Series, Doubleday and Co., Garden City, New York.

HERBERT BUTTERFIELD, *The Origins of Modern Science*, The Macmillan Co., New York, 1960, Chapters 8 and 10.

I. BERNARD COHEN, *The Birth of a New Physics*, Science Study Series, Doubleday and Co., Garden City, New York.

I. BERNARD COHEN, "Isaac Newton," *Scientific American*, Dec., 1955, p. 73.

MORTON GROSSER, *The Discovery of Neptune*, Harvard University Press, Cambridge, Mass., 1962.

The journal *Scientific American* frequently has very readable articles on gravity and contemporary exploration of the solar system, particularly using space vehicles. Some of those that appeared from January, 1955 through April, 1968 are:

W. A. HEISKANF, "The Earth's Gravity," Sept., 1955, p. 164.

O. GINGERICK, "The Solar System Beyond Neptune," April, 1959, p. 72.

J. N. JAMES, "The Voyage of Mariner II," July, 1963, p. 70.

H. M. SCHURMEIER, R. L. HEACOCK, AND A. E. WOLFE, "The Ranger Missions to the Moon," Jan., 1966, p. 52.

J. N. JAMES, "The Voyage of Mariner IV," March, 1966, p. 42.

R. B. LEIGHTON, "The Photographs from Mariner IV," April, 1966, p. 54.

R. K. SLOAN, "The Scientific Experiments of Mariner IV," May, 1966, p. 62.

PROBLEMS AND EXERCISES ▲▲▲

5.1. Two particles with masses M_1 and M_2 are separated by a distance R. How would the magnitude of the gravitational force between them and of the acceleration of M_1 toward M_2 change if:

(a) Both masses were doubled?
(b) The separation between the particles were doubled with the masses held constant?

5.2. How would the magnitude of the acceleration due to gravity on the earth's surface change if:

(a) Its radius were doubled with its mass held constant?
(b) Its radius were doubled with its *density* (mass per unit volume) held constant?

[HINT: The volume of a sphere is $\frac{4}{3} \pi R^3$].

5.3. It is stated at the beginning of Section 5.1 that the gravitational law is consistent with the approximately spherical shape of the earth. However, the earth is actually spheroidal. That is, it bulges slightly at the equator. What is the probable reason for this phenomenon?

5.4. At what distance from the earth, measured on a straight line between it and the moon, would the net gravitational force on a small body due to the two bodies be zero?

[HINT: Let x be the distance from the moon to the desired point, and $(R_{em} - x)$ the distance between the point and the earth.]

5.5. Calculate the correction to g at the equator due to the earth's rotation by comparing the weight of and the centripetal force on a 1-kg mass located there.

5.6. A 1-kg mass on the earth experiences a centripetal force due to its revolution about the sun. How does the magnitude of this force compare with the centripetal force due to the earth's rotation at the equator?

5.7. According to a footnote in Section 5.4 the difference between g at the equator and at the poles is about 0.05 m/sec². How much longer does a body require to fall 1000 m at the equator?

5.8. The mass of the moon is 0.012 times the mass of the earth, its radius is about one-fourth as large.

(a) Determine the value of g on the moon.
(b) What is the ratio of the times required for a body to fall 200 m on the earth and moon?

5.9. What is the magnitude of the gravitational force between:

(a) Two students sitting in a classroom.
(b) Two 50-ton ships 10 miles apart.
(c) The earth and the moon ($M_e = 6 \times 10^{24}$ kg, $M_m = 0.012 M_e$, $R_{em} = 3.8 \times 10^8$ m).

5.10. Given that $G = 6.67 \times 10^{-11}$ newtons-m²/kg², determine the mass of the earth. (All other necessary data appear in Appendix E.)

5.11. (a) Determine the mass of the sun from the value of G, the 1-yr period of the earth, and the 1.5×10^{11}-m radius of its orbit.
(b) What is the value of g on the surface of the sun (the radius of the sun is about one hundred times the radius of the earth)?

5.12. If a particle is located inside a sphere of radius R and at a distance r from its center, the spherical shell enclosed by the radii r and R exerts no net gravitational force upon the particle. However, the inner sphere of radius r exerts a force equal to the gravitational force that would be exerted if the entire mass of that subsphere were concentrated at its center.

Plot the gravitational force on a 1-kg mass as a function of its distance from the center of a sphere from 0 to $4R$.

5.13. The most precise method for determining G using the Cavendish apparatus is described in the text. A simpler though less accurate method is the following: when the large spheres (A and B) in Figure 5.6 are moved from their neutral positions to the positions adjacent to the small spheres, the gravitational forces exerted on the latter cause them to accelerate, rotating the bar connecting them, and deflecting the beam of light that measures the angle of rotation. G can be calculated by measuring this initial, constant acceleration of the small masses.

(a) Let the masses of the large spheres be 3 kg each, the distance between the centers of the adjacent large and small spheres 0.08 m, the length of the bar connecting the small spheres 0.08 m, and the distance from the apparatus to the scale on which the deflection of the light beam is measured 20 m. Given the following positions of the light spot on its measuring scale, calculate G:

t (sec)	x (m)
0	0.00
30	7.2×10^{-3}
60	2.86×10^{-2}
90	6.11×10^{-2}
120	11.43×10^{-2}
150	17.90×10^{-2}

(b) If measurements were continued would you expect the deflection of the light beam registered by the position of the spot on the scale to increase at the same rate? Why?

5.14. Suggest one or more methods for measuring the mass of a planet without a satellite of its own (say Venus). Which of your methods would you expect to yield the most trustworthy value? Why?

5.15. What would the period of the moon be if the strength of the earth's gravitational attraction were a constant, independent of R, and thus had the same magnitude at the moon's 3.8×10^8 m diameter as it does on the earth's surface?

[HINT: Would Kepler's third law still be valid?]

5.16. Suppose satellites orbited the earth and the moon with circular orbits of the same radius relative to the center of their parent bodies. How would their periods compare?

5.17. The periods of Jupiter's satellites (Problem 3.11) are considerably smaller than the period of Earth's moon. Why?

5.18. Are the calculated orbits of Figure 5.9a consistent with Kepler's third law?

5.19. What is the period of a satellite with perigee (closest distance to the earth) five hundred miles above the earth's surface and apogee (greatest distance from the earth) at the orbit of the moon? How long does such a satellite require to go from earth to moon? Why do you suppose the Surveyor vehicles made the trip in a somewhat shorter time?

5.20. Is it possible to launch a satellite from the earth that will go into orbit about the moon without making changes in its course when in the vicinity of the moon? Explain.

5.21. The electrostatic force between two particles bearing the respective electric charges q_1 and q_2 and separated by a distance R is:

$$F = \frac{kq_1q_2}{R^2},$$

where k is a constant (Chapter 8). The force is attractive for unlike charges. Suppose several light negatively charged particles are in orbits of various radii (not necessarily circular orbits) about a central massive positive charge of magnitude much greater than any of the others. What can you say about their orbits? Why is it important that the positive charge be so much greater than any of the negative charges? What is the comparable condition in the gravitational case?

5.22. Two satellites are in the same circular orbit about the earth, but one is 5000 m ahead of the other. In an effort to catch the leader the astronaut controlling the second satellite turns on his rear engines briefly hoping thereby to increase his orbital speed. Does his maneuver succeed? Explain.

5.23. Suppose that in the course of their motion, Venus, Earth, Mars, and Jupiter came into the position shown in the diagram relative to the sun. (The scale of the diagram is obviously incorrect.)

(a) What is the direction of the net momentum transfer to the sun during the short interval when the planets are in the configuration shown?

(b) Does Mars or Jupiter produce a larger perturbation on Earth's motion? Justify with a quantitative comparison.

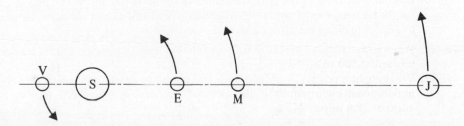

(c) Sketch the approximate configuration of the planets one earth-year later.

Data for Problem 5.23

(Orbital radii and masses are given in terms of the Earth's orbital radius and mass.)

Body	R	Mass
Venus	0.72	0.82
Earth	1.00	1.00
Mars	1.60	0.11
Jupiter	5.20	318.4
Sun		3.3×10^5

5.24. The equation for an ellipse with one focus at the origin of a Cartesian system and major axis coincident with the x-axis is:

$$\left(\frac{x+d}{a}\right)^2 + \left(\frac{y}{b}\right)^2 = 1,$$

where a is the semimajor axis of the ellipse, b its semiminor axis, and $d = \sqrt{a^2 - b^2}$ the distance between the center of the ellipse and the foci. Demonstrate that it is reasonable to call Figure 5.8 an ellipse by showing that several points on the orbit satisfy this equation for the same values of a and b.

5.25. (a) Find the center of mass of Jupiter and the sun. (Use the data of Problem 5.23.)

(b) Estimate how much the sun wobbles about the center of mass in one half a Jovian year due to its interaction with Jupiter. The sun's radius is 7×10^8 m (Jupiter's period is 11.86 yr).

(c) If a star ten light years from the earth were of a size comparable to the sun and had a planet comparable to Jupiter, what angular displacement would a telescope have to measure in order to detect the wobbling? (The velocity of light is 3×10^8 m/sec).

5.26. (a) Plot successive monthly positions of the earth and Mars for one earth-year. (Assume circular orbits and use the data of Table 3.1.)

(b) Using your graph and Kepler's third law make a rough estimate of the length of time a vehicle in a solar orbit that intersects both the orbits of earth and Mars requires to make the trip between the planets.

(c) What is the best time to launch such a vehicle from the point of view of the time required to make the trip to Mars? (That is, what relative position of the two planets is optimum for such a launching?)

5.27. (a) Using the data of Table 3.1 and Kepler's third law, plot the yearly positions of Mars and Jupiter for six years. Start at a time when the two planets are on the same side of the sun and fall along a straight line passing through the center of the sun. Assume circular orbits for simplicity.

(b) Calculate the ratio of the gravitational force on Mars due to the sun and to Jupiter for the six positions of part a. In what way would you expect the perturbations due to Jupiter to effect the orbit of Mars?

5.28. (a) What is the effective weight of a 70-kg (114-lb) man in a rocket that is accelerating upward at 100 m/sec?

(b) What might a scientist who was born and reared in an elevator conclude about his gravitational environment if the elevator accelerated downward relative to the earth at 19.6 m/sec^2?

5.29. (a) What orbital speed would need to be attained by a centrifuge of ten meter radius if the horizontal effective weight of a man strapped into it were to be double his real weight?

 (b) In order to simulate the gravitational environment of the earth on an orbiting space station, it has been proposed that the station be rotated about its axis. Suppose the station were a flat disk with a 100-m radius. What rotational velocity would be required to simulate an effective weight of magnitude Mg at its rim?

5.30. Suppose the ratio of gravitational to inertial mass were 1.00 for iron but 1.01 for aluminum.

 (a) Compare the free fall of iron and aluminum objects each having gravitational masses equal to 1 kg.

 (b) What would the effective weights of the two objects be while they were at rest on the surface of the earth? While they were on the floor of an elevator accelerating upward at 9.8 m/sec²? On the floor of the same elevator accelerating upward at five times that rate?

5.31. A hollow spherical satellite with 20-m radius is made from the iron in Problem 5.30 and a 1-m radius satellite constructed from the aluminum. The pair are launched into the same circular orbit about the earth of radius $\frac{1}{10}$ the radius of the moon's orbit and with the small satellite initially at the center of the large one. Describe the subsequent relative motion of the pair in as much detail as possible.

Symmetry principles and conservation laws

6

▲▲ 6.1   The historical idea of symmetry in physics

The human mind derives undoubted satisfaction in contemplating a principle or principles of order underlying the seemingly constant change that manifests itself throughout the universe, of believing that some things are constant, unchanging, incorruptible. Indeed, the very concept of constancy has often been used to suggest perfection itself. When Plato wedded the philosophical contemplation of perfection with the idea of geometric perfection, he arrived at his doctrine of planetary spheres, and thus laid the basis for a system of mathematical physics whose intrinsic appeal exerted a sufficient grip upon the human imagination to hold it in thrall for almost two thousand years, despite the considerable evidence that the imagined perfection of the heavens could not be interpreted in so simple and obvious a manner.

Plato conceived of geometric perfection in terms of symmetry (Chapter 3):

> . . . he made the world in the form of a globe, round as from a lathe, having its extremes in every direction equidistant from the center . . . for he considered that the like is infinitely fairer than the unlike. . . .*   *Timaeus*

But Plato did not originate the idea that symmetry implies perfection, nor was he by any means the last to use it. In art, in music, in poetry, the relationship between symmetry, constancy, and perfection is encountered so frequently that it has become a commonplace. Examples abound in other fields as well, as in the use of the balance to symbolize the impartiality of justice, for instance. Whenever it is encountered, the idea usually carries the additional implication that an object or system or concept which is symmetric is somehow understood and requires no further explanation.

The general impulse to seek constancy amid change is also one of the bases of Newtonian physics. Although we have stressed the idea of change in the foregoing chapters, the idea of constancy lies at the heart of the system. It rests first upon the law of inertia, the postulate that the *force-free* state of a particle is defined by a *constant* velocity vector, and second upon the empirically-based fact that the momentum of any isolated system of particles remains constant regardless of the interactions which are internal to it. The

---

* *The Dialogues of Plato*, 4th edition, Vol. II, trans. by B. Jowett, The Clarendon Press, Oxford, 1953, pp. 719–20.

conservation of momentum is but one of a series of conservation laws which together systemize in mathematical form the primordial human impulse to seek constancy amid the flux observed in the physical universe.

Illuminating as these conservation laws are, they remained a side issue in physics until the present century. Classical physics emphasizes change rather than constancy, and hence lays its stress initially upon forces, accelerations, velocities. The conservation laws have assumed an undisputed central role in contemporary physics, reasserting the old connection between symmetry and constancy, or invariance. But the form of the connection is new, although it recognizes, indeed, often explains, the symmetry that is expressed in the invariance of the laws with respect to a series of changing conditions.

The detailed development of these ideas is a topic of immense current interest and activity. We have already encountered several examples, although they have not been cited explicitly. The concept of symmetric laws is rarely emphasized in classical physics. Nevertheless it is profitable to review Newtonian dynamics with the basic idea in mind.

▲▲ 6.2 Symmetries of objects, systems, and physical laws

Hermann Weyl has given a definition of symmetry that applies equally well to symmetric objects (geometric symmetry), symmetric systems, and symmetric laws. According to his criterion, a thing—object, system, law—is symmetric *under a specific operation* provided its appearance is not altered by that operation. Plato explicitly used this notion in connecting perfection with sphericity: ". . . round as from a lathe. . . ." The operation of rotating a perfect sphere upon its axis does not alter the appearance of the sphere. Hence, a sphere is symmetric with respect to rotation about any axis through its center.

Weyl's criterion is easily applied to test the symmetry or lack of symmetry of other geometric figures. For instance, an equilateral triangle is symmetric under the operation of rotation through an angle of 120° about the point at its center, and is also symmetric under reflection about any one of the three perpendicular bisectors of its sides (Figure 6.1a). It is *not* symmetric under a 60° rotation about its center, but is symmetric with respect to a sequence of two such identical operations (Figure 6.1b). Similarly, an isosceles triangle is symmetric with respect to a 360° rotation about its center or under a reflection about the perpendicular bisector of its base (Figure 6.1c). Since it is symmetric with respect to a smaller set of operation, it is said to possess a lower degree of symmetry than an equilateral triangle. But although an isosceles triangle exhibits only two symmetries with respect to single operations, it has a number of other symmetries relative to *sequences* of operations. When reflected about its median, the figure reproduces itself and so is symmetric under the combined sequence of the two operations.

In its simplest form the idea that systems may be symmetric to one another derives from the geometric idea of similarity. Two triangles which have all angles equal are similar, by definition. The notion serves to classify all such triangles into a symmetric group since any member of the group may be made identical with any other by a proportionate scaling of its legs.

The planetary system of Plato possessed a symmetry based upon the rather simple and obvious geometric similarity of its constituent spheres. Kepler was loath to dispense with that symmetry, and in fact fought the necessity of using ellipses for a long time simply because those figures possess a lower degree of geometric symmetry. However, Kepler's laws imply a different, more subtle type of symmetry, a symmetry applicable to *systems*; for if the mass of Jupiter were increased to the mass of the sun, the radius vectors of its nine satellites scaled to the distances between the sun and its nine planets, and the velocity

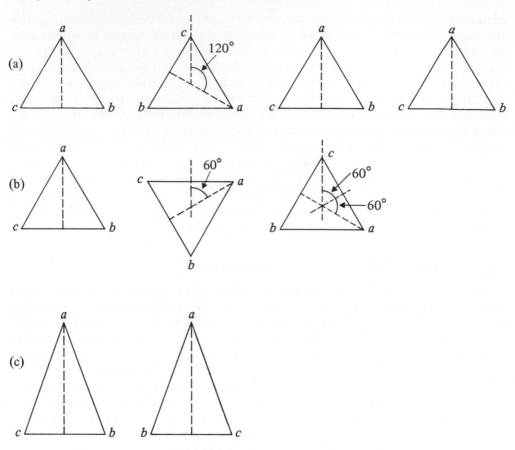

FIGURE 6.1 (a) An equilateral triangle is symmetric under a 120° rotation about its center or under reflection about the perpendicular bisectors of its sides, since neither operation alters its appearance. (b) An equilateral triangle is *not* symmetric under a 60° rotation about its center. But it is symmetric under two such operations in succession. (c) In general an isosceles triangle is symmetric only under a 360° rotation about its center or a reflection about the bisector of the angle between its equal sides.

vectors of the satellites at their perihelions set equal to the corresponding velocity vectors of the planets, then the motion of the Jovian and the solar systems would be identical. In other words, the two systems are completely symmetric under the combined sequence of operations. In a sense, the Jovian system is a scale model of the solar system, and if we do not regard the number of satellites as basic to the symmetry, it follows that all systems consisting of a massive, central body and orbiting satellites have the same symmetric relationship to each other. Furthermore, the orbits of any two satellites in the system possess a certain symmetric relationship to each other, since one may be turned into the other by a proper scaling of both distance and velocity. The importance of these symmetries is obvious from the preceding chapters; in the hands of Newton they led to a detailed understanding of the fundamental laws that underlie the order.

What is the meaning of a symmetric law? Following Feynman, let us apply Weyl's criterion as follows: we build two identical pieces of apparatus, then perform some specific operation upon one of them. If in spite of the differentiating operation the two continue to behave in the same fashion, then both they and the particular law of physics governing their behavior are symmetric with respect to the differentiating operation. If we perform the same operation on all the pairs of apparatus we can devise, we can conclude that all the laws of physics are invariant with respect to the operation we are considering. Thus Weyl's criterion permits a natural generalization from the symmetry of objects to the symmetry of systems and the symmetry of laws. But when applied to laws, the criterion involves physical measurement and observation, and any symmetry principles so devised are subject to change if some experiment is devised where results *do* depend upon the operation in question.

▲▲ 6.3 Spatial homogeneity and translational invariance

A few specific examples will clarify the meaning of Weyl's operational definition of symmetry vis-à-vis physical laws, and also point out some of the pitfalls that may be encountered in making such an application.

We assumed in Chapter 2 that motion in one dimension may be described in terms of successive displacements along a straight line relative to some arbitrary reference point called $x = 0$, but that the choice of that reference point itself could in no way alter our descriptions. In effect, we assumed that the very concept of an absolute location in space is meaningless, at least as far as our description of one-dimensional motion is concerned. This assumption defines a symmetry property of physical space which we might hope to generalize by offering experimental evidence that any two identical sets of apparatus behave in the same fundamental way regardless of their locations relative to each other. Such evidence would suggest that space is *homogeneous*, that all points in space are equivalent since no experiment can be devised to detect any fundamental difference between two points, and that the laws of physics are invariant under the operation of *translations* in space.

Is the homogeneity of space really an observed symmetry? Not at first sight, for every location upon the earth has a set of unique characteristics differentiating it from all other locations. The planets differ in size and detailed composition so that the point in space that specifies the position of Jupiter's center of mass at some specific time is certainly distinguishable from all other points in the solar system by the very fact that it *does* lie at the center of Jupiter. However, spatial homogeneity, the presumed invariance of the laws of nature relative to translations in space, does not imply that points in space cannot be differentiated from each other. Rather, it states that there is no *fundamental* difference between any two points. Thus we believe that the location of Jupiter's center of mass at any particular time is determined by the mass of the sun, the location of Jupiter's perihelion relative to the sun, and the planet's velocity at perihelion, and that these numbers are determined by the unique way in which the solar system has evolved, not by some fundamental law that determines their values uniquely. If history had been different so that Jupiter's velocity at perihelion were different, for example, then at the time in question another point in space would coincide with Jupiter's center of mass. Nevertheless, Newton's law of gravitation would still follow from a study of its orbit.

Let us apply Weyl's criterion by comparing the periods of two harmonic oscillators consisting of identical masses attached to the ends of identical springs. When placed side by side on a laboratory table and displaced equal distances from equilibrium, their oscillations are indistinguishable. To apply Weyl's criterion we must perform a specific operation on one of them and then once again compare their motion. For the present symmetry law we simply translate one in space, i.e., carry it to another location. Reviewing the analysis of Section 4.10, the period of an harmonic oscillator depends upon (1) the value of its spring constant, k, and (2) the value of the suspended inertial mass while the specific equation $T = 2\pi\sqrt{M/k}$ (Equation 4.23), assumes the validity of (3) Hooke's law, and (4) Newton's second law of motion.

Now the value of k for a specific spring (as well as the validity of Hooke's law) is determined in detail by the forces between its composite atoms, forces that we expect to be independent of the absolute location of the spring. The inertial mass of a body should also be independent of its location in space. Then if we believe in the universal validity of Newton's second law, we expect the period of any harmonic oscillator to be the same regardless of where it is. A series of experiments comparing the periods of two different springs placed at different points in space thus constitutes a test of the homogeneity of space vis-à-vis the constancy of k and M, and the validity of Hooke's and Newton's laws.

How would the periods of a pair of identical pendula compare if each were located at a different, arbitrary point in space? Assuming the validity of Newton's second law and the equality of gravitational and inertial mass (Section 4.5), the period of a pendulum (for small amplitudes),

$$T = 2\pi\sqrt{\frac{l}{g}},$$

is independent of mass and directly proportional to length (see Problems, 4.31). Therefore, we would expect the periods to be equal *if and only if* the accelerations due to gravity are also equal at the two locations. But since g varies slightly over the surface of the earth (Section 5.3), and is only about $\frac{1}{6}$ as great as at the surface of the moon, for instance, it follows that the period of a simple pendulum depends quite critically upon its location. In fact, pendulum measurements constitute one of the best methods available for determining local values of g.

Does the observed variation of g constitute a breakdown in the assumed homogeneity of space? Not in the least. According to Newton's second law and the law of gravitation, the acceleration due to gravity at any point in space depends upon the distribution of gravitational mass in its vicinity. In the simplest approximation, the value of g on the surface of the earth is

$$g = G\frac{M_e}{R_e^2}, \tag{5.5}$$

a value that must be corrected for effects due to the nonhomogeneity and nonsphericity of the earth, for altitude, and for latitude, and for centripetal acceleration (Section 5.3).

Assuming G is a universal constant whose magnitude does not depend upon the point at which it is measured, the force between two bodies calculated from Newton's gravitational law does not depend upon their *absolute* locations but only upon their relative locations, i.e., upon the distance between them. Provided the measured magnitude of the acceleration due to gravity at a point is consistent with the magnitude calculated using Newton's law of gravitation (or any other law that is independent of absolute locations in space), it follows that the results of a series of experiments with two pendula must be consistent with the homogeneity of space.

We have not applied Weyl's criterion literally in either of these examples, for we have not moved springs and pendula to different locations and compared their periods. Rather, we have invoked plausibility arguments based upon our presumed knowledge of the laws of physics to arrive at our conclusions. There is nothing particularly new in our method. Newton's gravitational law, for example, was derived from Kepler's third law, not from measurements of the gravitational force between all conceivable pairs of masses. Just as we must accept the possibility that Newton's law may not be applicable to situations not encountered as yet, so we must also impose the same cautionary proviso upon our symmetry principle.

If an experiment with two pendula were to yield results inconsistent with the assumed homogeneity of space, then the entire structure of Newtonian mechanics would be open to reconsideration. Conversely, it is not at all difficult to understand why any result that is consistent with Newtonian mechanics cannot make a fundamental distinction between two points in space: the assumption is built into the system from the beginning. We postulate the law of inertia in terms of velocity. But velocity involves the ratio of a *change* in position to a *change* in time; no absolute locations are involved. Likewise the law of momentum conservation involves changes in velocities; the definition of force involves a change in momentum. As the basic laws and concepts themselves do not incorporate the idea of absolute locations, then neither can any result that is derived from them. Therefore, the structure of Newtonian dynamics is consistent with the homogeneity of space, and any future experimental result that proves inconsistent with the principle would lead to questions regarding that fundamental structure. In the meantime the symmetry principle imposes a guideline, for it implies that equations written to describe physical events cannot change under the operation of translation in space, cannot involve the concept of an absolute location. It imposes a limitation upon the possible types of interaction we may expect to encounter in describing the physical universe.

▲▲ 6.4 Algebraic description of translational invariance

The way a particular sequence of events is described often depends upon the choice of the arbitrary reference point, $x = 0$, even though the basic laws underlying the events cannot. In Chapter 2 we described the successive positions of an automobile in terms of its distance from a toll booth. We could have selected a gasoline station five miles up the highway as the point labeled $x = 0$ with equal justification. Then when the automobile had driven one mile beyond the toll booth, it would still be four miles from the service station, its position described by the coordinate $x = 1$ relative to the toll booth but $x = -4$ relative to the station. However, we would expect no differences in the measured velocity or the acceleration of the automobile as a function of time despite the differences in the coordinate systems assigned to describe its motion.

More generally, we may conclude that a sequence of physical events is consistent with the homogeneity of space if the descriptions of the events recorded by two observers who choose their origins differently lead nonetheless to identical basic principles. In order to apply such a test we use *transformation equations* to relate the description given by one observer to the description given by the other.

Let x_A be the coordinate assigned to a particular event by observer A and x_B the coordinate assigned *to the same event* by observer B. If the two observers choose identical x-axes, the coordinate assigned an event by observer B is simply the coordinate assigned by observer A minus the distance between the respective origins. Let that distance be x (Figure 6.2). Then the transformation equation from description A to B is

$$x_B = x_A - X, \tag{6.1a}$$

while the inverse transformation from B to A is

$$x_A = x_B + X. \tag{6.2a}$$

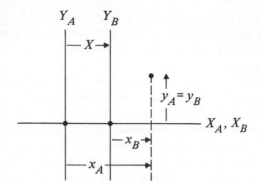

FIGURE 6.2 Relationship between the *x*-coordinates of a point in two Cartesian systems with common *x*-axes and with the origin of *B* translated a distance *X* relative to the origin of *A*.

Since our description of motion is based upon an assignment of sequential spatial positions, we may apply these equations to test the consistency of any two descriptions with our spatial homogeneity principle. In other words, the transformation equations are an algebraic statement of the principle itself. For example, suppose observer *A* measures the average velocity of a particle in his system. He records its positions $x_A(t_1)$ and $x_A(t_2)$ at times t_1 and t_2, then computes the ratio:

$$v_A = \frac{x_A(t_2) - x_A(t_1)}{t_2 - t_1}.$$

What velocity will observer *B* measure? Applying Equation 6.1a, his coordinate measures at the two times must be:

$$x_B(t_1) = x_A(t_1) - X,$$
$$x_B(t_2) = x_A(t_2) - X,$$

evidently different from the coordinates measured by observer *A*. But:

$$v_B = \frac{x_B(t_2) - x_B(t_1)}{t_2 - t_1} = \frac{(x_A(t_2) - X) - (x_A(t_1) - X)}{t_2 - t_1}$$

$$= \frac{x_A(t_2) - x_A(t_1)}{t_2 - t_1} = v_A;$$

the two observers measure the same velocities. It follows that they will also measure the same accelerations, that the momenta and the forces they calculate will be identical, and thus that they will arrive at the same basic system of dynamics.

We have applied two different types of operational consistency tests to physical laws, tests whose equivalence may not be immediately evident. In the first type of test one observer compares the results of experiments performed with two sets of apparatus whose differences he believes to be arbitrary. In the second, more mathematical test, two observers compare their descriptions of the results of an experiment with the *same apparatus*, then try to demonstrate that there is no fundamental difference in the two descriptions. A little reflection should prove the equivalence of the two types of test. For if the laws of physics are such that two identical systems behave in the same way when they are separated from each other, the coordinates used to describe their positions at any time can have no fundamental significance. Therefore, another observer can choose a different point as his $x = 0$, assign different numbers to the positions of the systems, and still reach the same basic conclusions.

Equation 6.1a assumes the two observers use a common *x*-axis. In general they will not. If they limit themselves to selecting parallel x-, y-, and z-axes and merely select different origins, they arrive at the general set of transformation equations expressing the homogeneity of space:

$$x_B = x_A - X, \tag{6.1a}$$

$$y_B = y_A - Y, \tag{6.1b}$$

$$z_B = z_A - Z. \tag{6.1c}$$

where X, Y, and Z are respectively, the x-, y-, and z-components of the vector connecting the origins of the two systems (Figure 6.3). We also have the inverse transformation from B to A:

$$x_A = x_B + X, \tag{6.2a}$$

$$y_A = y_B + Y, \tag{6.2b}$$

$$z_A = z_B + Z. \tag{6.2c}$$

We shall consider the case of two systems rotated relative to each other in Section 6.6.

▲▲ 6.5 The homogeneity of time

Just as the basic kinematic description developed in Chapter 2 is independent of the point designated as x_0, so it is independent of the time chosen as t_0, for the description involves *intervals* of time just as it involves intervals of space. Thus the assumption that time, like space, is homogeneous implies that every instant is equivalent, and that the laws of nature are invariant with respect to translations in time. The homogeneity of time does not imply that there is no way to differentiate a particular point of time from all others, but only that the particular set of circumstances that distinguish a particular "now" from all others is not determined by some unique intrinsic characteristic of that "now," but rather is the result of history. Given a different, equally probable history, that particular set of circumstances could have occurred equally well at another time.

In order to apply Weyl's test we compare the behavior of two identical sets of experimental apparatus started at two different, arbitrary times. How will the periods of two identical harmonic oscillators compare, for instance, if one is set in motion today and the other tomorrow, or next year? Unless we believe either that the interatomic forces determining the value of the spring constant, k, changes from day to day, or that inertial mass is not constant in time, or that Newton's second law is valid today but not tomorrow, we must conclude that the period of a particular harmonic oscillator does not

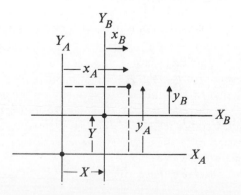

FIGURE 6.3 Relationship between the x- and y-coordinates of a point in two Cartesian coordinate systems with parallel but noncoincident axes.

depend upon when it is set into motion. Therefore, two identical harmonic oscillators started at two different times should have identical periods.

In the same way we could test the applicability of the principle to the motion of two pendula, and would expect to find that the measured periods do not depend upon the day of the week the pendula are set in motion. Of course one can think of reasons why the periods might differ slightly. For example, the surface features of the earth change considerably in times on the order of tens of thousands of years so that the local value of the acceleration due to gravity at a particular point also varies slightly. Therefore, we would expect the period of a pendulum to vary slightly over times on the order of several thousand years. But just as the expected differences in the periods of pendula located at sea level and on a mountain top do not constitute evidence against the homogeneity of space so the expected temporal variation in g is not inconsistent with the homogeneity of time, provided that variation can be derived from a fundamental law that is itself consistent with the symmetry principle. Newton's law of gravitation is such a law, for it involves only factors that are assumed to be constant with time.

Any equation used to describe a sequence of physical events can be tested for consistency with the homogeneity of time by applying an appropriate transformation equation. We consider the description of particular events given by two observers, A and B, who choose two different instants as $t = 0$. (One might have his clocks set according to Eastern Daylight time, the other according to Pacific Daylight time, for instance.) Let t_A be the time of a particular event as recorded by observer A, and t_B the time *of the same event* as recorded by observer B. If A's clock is T seconds ahead of B's, the latter observer must subtract T from each of A's measurements in order to compare them with his own. Thus the transformation equation from description A to description B is

$$t_B = t_B - T, \tag{6.3}$$

and the inverse transformation from description B to A is

$$t_A = t_B + T. \tag{6.4}$$

Let us compare the measurement of a velocity by the two observers. For simplicity assume they choose the same point as $x = 0$. (If they do not we can always apply Equations 6.1 to compare their spatial measurement, but since we already know their measurements do not depend upon their choice of their spatial origins, there is little reason to introduce the added algebraic complication.) Observer A notes that the position of an object at time t_{1A} is x_1, and that is position at a later time t_{2A} is x_2. Therefore, he calculates its velocity as:

$$v_A = \frac{x_2 - x_1}{t_{2A} - t_{1A}}.$$

Observer B finds that the same object is at the point of x_1 at time t_{1B} and at the point x_2 at the later time t_{2B}. Thus:

$$v_B = \frac{x_2 - x_1}{t_{2B} - t_{1A}}.$$

But, applying Equation 6.3,

$$t_{2B} - t_{1B} = (t_{2A} - T) - (t_{1A} - T) = t_{2A} - t_{1A},$$

and

$$v_B = \frac{x_2 - x_1}{t_{2A} - t_{2B}} = v_A.$$

The observers calculate the same velocity despite their different choices for $t = 0$. Therefore, they will arrive at precisely the same conclusions regarding the numerical values of all accelerations, momenta, and forces, and thus formulate the same basic dynamical laws. It follows that the basic structure of Newtonian mechanics is consistent with the homogeneity of time.

In the remaining sections of this chapter we shall consider other experimentally based symmetry principles that are incorporated into the structure of Newtonian mechanics. Some are more subtle than the principles of spatial and temporal homogeneity. Nonetheless, we shall approach them in a similar spirit; we first ask if any experiments performed with identical sets of apparatus lead to different basic conclusions. Failing to discover any such difference, we shall formulate the principle mathematically in terms of a set of transformation equations connecting the description of events by two observers who submit different reports only because they make different starting assumptions, starting assumptions ruled arbitrary by the symmetry principle itself.

▲▲ 6.6 Spatial isotropy and rotational invariance. The generalized idea of a vector

Just as motion can be described with reference to a Cartesian coordinate system whose origin is arbitrary, so we assumed in Chapter 2 that the directions of the three mutually perpendicular axes of that system can be chosen at will. The first assumption is justified by the verified homogeneity of physical space, the fact that all points in space are equivalent. Likewise, the second assumption can be justified by the experimental conclusions that space is *isotropic*, that all *directions* in space are equivalent as far as the fundamental laws of nature are concerned. The designation of a particular direction as "north" is entirely arbitrary, although given one such designation, the directions south, east, and west are immediately fixed.

For reasons that should be obvious to the student who has grasped the foregoing sections of this chapter, the fact that objects fall "down" does not constitute evidence against the principle. In this context "down" implies the direction toward the center of the earth and is, of course, a different direction at each point on its surface. However, an object in a freely falling elevator or an orbiting satellite does not fall at all relative to its surroundings.

In terms of Weyl's definition, spatial isotropy implies that two identical sets of apparatus rotated through some arbitrary angle relative to each other perform identically. Two harmonic oscillators of the same construction oriented with their bases perpendicular are expected to have the same period. An automobile should be equally efficient on a level superhighway running north as on the same sort of highway running west. Of course we cannot expect an apparatus whose operation depends upon the gravitational attraction of the earth to perform equally well if turned upside down, for "down" in this context refers to the gravitational attraction itself and not to a preferred direction in space. But if we were to rotate the entire Cavendish apparatus (Section 5.4) through some angle about its vertical axis we would expect a measurement of the universal gravitational constant, G, to be unaffected. Likewise, we would not expect the periods of the planets to be altered if the entire solar system, including the sun and all of the planetary orbits, were rotated through some arbitrary angle relative to the stars.

The formulation of physical laws in terms of equations involving *intervals* in space and time mirrors the respective homogeneities of space and time. In a like manner, the vector nature of the equations guarantees their consistency with spatial isotropy, for although the components of a particular vector depend upon the coordinate system in which it is specified, both its magnitude, the square root of the sum of the squares of its components, and its orientation relative to other vectors are independent of the coordinate system chosen. It follows that an equation expressed in terms of vectors is valid in all Cartesian systems if it is valid in any one, and therefore, that the choice of a particular system for a particular application is entirely arbitrary and may be dictated by convenience.

Figure 6.4a shows a rod of length l lying along the x-axis of a coordinate system established by observer A. One of its ends lies at the origin, the other at the point $x_A = l$, $y_A = 0$. Observer B chooses another coordinate system. Its origin coincides with the origin of system A, but its x- and y-axes are rotated through an angle θ relative to the respective axes of system A. In system B the end of the rod has coordinates $x_B = l \cos \theta$, $y_B = -l \sin \theta$, quite obviously different from its coordinates in system A. However, both observers must arrive at the same conclusions regarding the length of the rod, though they disagree about the individual components of length. Applying the Pythagorean theorem to observer B's measurements:

$$l_B^2 = l^2 \cos^2 \theta + l^2 \sin^2 \theta = l^2(\cos^2 \theta + \sin^2 \theta) = l^2,$$

since $\cos^2 \theta + \sin^2 \theta = 1$. Thus agreement is obtained.

Similarly, let the same rod be oriented along the y-axis of observer A's system (Figure 6.4b). In that system the coordinates of its endpoints are $x_A = 0$, $y_A = l$. Likewise, its coordinates in system B are $x_B = l \sin \theta$, $y_B = l \cos \theta$. Once again the Pythagorean theorem yields the result that the length of the rod in both systems is equal.

These considerations lead immediately to general equations transforming the description of an arbitrary point in a plane from one coordinate system to another, rotated system. As we have seen, a point with coordinates $(x_A, 0)$ in system A has coordinates $(x_A \cos \theta, -x_A \sin \theta)$ in system B, and a point with coordinates $(0, y_A)$ in system A has coordinates $(y_A \sin \theta, y_A \cos \theta)$ in system B. Therefore the transformation from A to B of an arbitrary point (x_A, y_A) is given by the equations:

$$x_B = x_A \cos \theta + y_A \sin \theta, \tag{6.5a}$$

$$y_B = -x_A \sin \theta + y_A \cos \theta, \tag{6.5b}$$

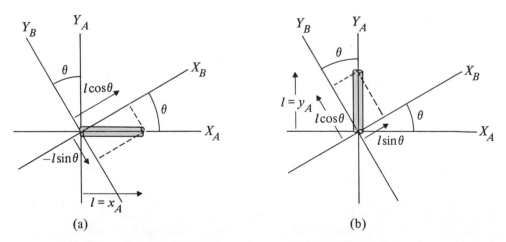

(a)   (b)

FIGURE 6.4 Two Cartesian systems with common origins rotated through an angle θ relative to each other. (a) The components $x_B = l \cos \theta$, $y_B = -l \sin \theta$ of a rod l lying along the x-axis of system A. (b) The components $x_B = l \sin \theta$, $y_B = l \cos \theta$ of the same rod lying along the y-axis of A.

while the inverse transformation from B to A is specified by the set:

$$x_A = x_B \cos \theta - y_B \sin \theta, \tag{6.6a}$$

$$y_A = x_B \sin \theta + y_A \cos \theta. \tag{6.6b}$$

Direct verification of the fact that the distance between two points is invariant under these transformations is straightforward, though it involves more algebraic manipulation than the analogous demonstrations of Sections 6.3 and 6.4. Given the invariance of length or, more generally, of displacement, the invariance of all the other vectors used in dynamics—velocity, momentum, acceleration, force—follows immediately, for all are based upon multiplication or division of this vector by one or more scalars. Velocity is defined as a displacement divided by an interval of time; momentum as the product of mass by velocity; acceleration as velocity divided by time; force as the product of acceleration by mass. Thus we arrive at general transformation equations for any vector. If the components of the vector $\mathbf{C}$ in system A are C_{ax}, C_{ay}, then, by extension of Equations 6.5, its components in the rotated system B are:

$$C_{bx} = C_{ax} \cos \theta + C_{ay} \sin \theta, \tag{6.7a}$$

$$C_{by} = -C_{bx} \sin \theta + C_{ay} \cos \theta. \tag{6.7b}$$

Again, it may be verified directly that the magnitude of a vector, defined as the square root of the sum of the squares of its components, remains invariant upon application of these transformation equations.

In general, two angles are required to specify the relative orientation of two three-dimensional coordinate systems with common origin but rotated through some angle with respect to each other. The transformation equations for this general case are only slightly more involved than Equations 6.5 through 6.7. But as we shall have no occasion to make use of them, they will not be derived here.

Chapter 2 defined vectors as quantities requiring specification of both a magnitude and a direction, in contrast with scalars which are fully specified by a magnitude alone. A more general and satisfactory, although more mathematical approach defines a vector as any triplet of related numbers whose transformation from one coordinate system into another, rotated system is given by a specific set of equations. In the special case of rotation about the z-axis the two systems are coplanar and the triplet reduces to a pair of numbers having the transformation equations 6.5 (or 6.7). This particular definition is especially useful because of the insight it gives into the mathematical structure of Newtonian physics. It suggests that vectors are constructed and used to express relationships between physical quantities principally *because* their transformation properties insure their consistency with the isotropic nature of space. We construct vectors as *triplets* of numbers simply because we base our description of physical events upon successive positions of objects in *three*-dimensional space, and believe that the physical distance between two points in space is an invariant quantity, a quantity that is independent of the way in which we choose to describe it. However, Einstein's reexamination of the properties of physical space and time leads to the conclusion that the distance between two points in space need *not* be an invariant, but in fact depends upon the velocity of the points relative to the observer. Therefore, the special theory of relativity generalizes Newtonian mechanics by reformulating physical laws in terms of related *quadruplets* of numbers which transform according to a specific mathematical prescription. Three of these four related numbers correspond to spatial components, the fourth to a temporal component. Taken together, they are called four-dimensional vectors, or, more simply, four vectors, and reflect a deeper symmetry of the physical universe implicit in Einstein's special theory of relativity (Chapter 11).

▶▶ 6.7 Reflectional invariance

If the origin and orientation of a coordinate system can be selected at will it would also seem that the choice of a particular direction as positive (leaving the other negative) should also be arbitrary. Indeed, the seemingly arbitrary nature of this choice leads to another symmetry property, called reflectional symmetry. We specified the usual directional convention in Chapter 2. Distances to the right of the origin on the x-axis are positive, distances above the origin on the y-axis (up) positive. If we rotated such a conventional coordinate system through 180° about the origin (Figure 6.5a) then all x- and all y-coordinates would change sign, and application of Equations 6.7 with $\theta = 180°$ would assure us that the rotated system is equivalent to the conventional system. However, we can also reverse the conventional direction of one axis while leaving the other unaltered. This operation corresponds to laying a mirror along one of the coordinate

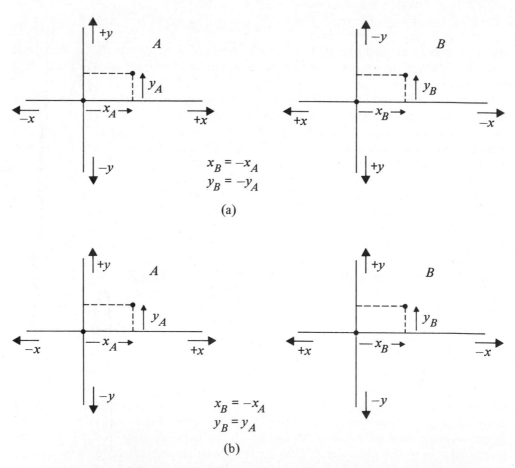

FIGURE 6.5 (a) If the Cartesian coordinate system B is rotated through 180° relative to A then *both* the x- and y-coordinates of all points in the plane reverse their signs. (b) However, if the x-axis of B is *reflected* relative to A, only the x-coordinates reverse their signs.

axes (the *y*-axis, for example), and is responsible for the name *reflectional symmetry*. It cannot be simulated by a rotation (Figure 6.5b). Thus the invariance of physical laws with respect to this particular symmetry is not automatically assured by the demonstrated isotropy of space.

The difference between the two symmetries is even more apparent in three dimensions. Suppose the plane of this page is chosen as the plane containing the *x*- and *y*-axes of a system (an arbitrary choice permitted by the isotropy of space). Then even after the directions of *x* and *y* are chosen there are still two possible ways to specify the direction of the *z*-axis: either positive in the direction out of the page or positive in the direction into the page. One choice may be transformed into the other by laying a mirror on the page, an operation that alters the direction of all *z*-components but leaves all *x*- and *y*-components unaltered (Figure 6.6a).

The conventional specification of direction is given by the famous right-hand "rule" (Figure 6.6b) which states that if the thumb, index finger, and second finger of the right hand are oriented mutually perpendicular to each other, then their directions specify the respective directions of the *x*-, *y*-, and *z*-axes. (No orientation of the hand itself is specified, an omission made possible by the isotropy of space.) Of course, if reflectional symmetry is a valid principle, then the "rule" is no rule at all, but simply a convention. The mirror image of the right hand with thumb and index finger parallel to the plane of the mirror and second finger pointing *toward* the mirror is simply the left hand with second finger pointing *out* of the mirror. No rotation of the right hand can make it identical with the left.

Thus the question of whether physical laws are symmetric with respect to reflectional symmetry reduces to the question: does nature distinguish between left and right? If the mirror image of an apparatus is built, will it perform in the same manner as the original? Feynman uses the example of a clock whose springs, gears, hands, numerals are reflections of a conventional clock. Would it mark intervals of time as a conventional clock? One might also think of the mirror image of a conventional automobile. Its steering wheel and all controls would be on the right side (as the British build their autos), but in addition it would be made with left-handed screws and left-handed gears. The numerals on its gasoline gauge and speedometer would be reversed, and the speedometer needle

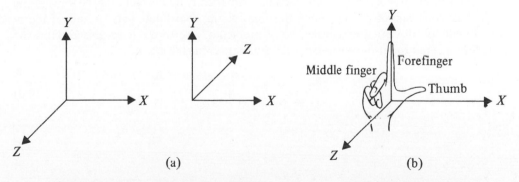

FIGURE 6.6 (a) Reflection of a coordinate system in three dimensions. Even if the positive *x*- and *y*-directions are fixed, the positive *z*-direction may be either out of or into the page. The former alternative is conventional. (b) The right-hand "rule" for determining the conventional relative directions of positive *x*-, *y*-, and *z*-axes.

would swing from right to left rather than left to right. Strange as such a car might be to operate, there is no reason to expect that it could not attain the same velocities, use the same quantity of gasoline (or petrol) per mile, and carry passengers with the same comfort as a conventional vehicle.

Nor does there seem to be any reason to doubt the principle of reflectional symmetry in more basic processes. If all directions, velocities, and accelerations are reversed in the free-fall equations, or the harmonic oscillator equations, for instance, the physical events would be correctly described. Similarly, the law of universal gravitation involves the square of the distance between the interacting bodies, and as the square of the distance is equal to the sums of the *squares* of the x-, y-, and z-components, reversal of any one cannot affect the form of the law. An orbit which is the image of a planetary orbit in a mirror passing through the sun and perpendicular to the plane of the orbit is equivalent to a reversal in the direction of the planets' motion. This in turn could be accomplished by a reversal of velocity at perihelion, a change in initial condition that has no bearing on the fundamental laws of nature.

In short, there seems no reason to question the principle of reflectional symmetry. Indeed, it is a perfectly valid principle in all of classical physics, including relativity. Hence when its violation in processes involving radioactive decay was demonstrated in 1956, the shock was considerable. We shall discuss these processes in due course (Chapter 23). However, the fact that violations of reflectional symmetry have been observed is worth mentioning at this juncture merely as a reminder that physics is an experimentally based discipline. Therefore, the symmetries we use cannot be considered valid a priori any more than Plato's spherical universe could be. We may use the symmetries as working principles only until or unless we find that they are inconsistent with experimental evidence. Those that are valid to the extent of our knowledge offer us insight into the structure of the physical universe. Those that are valid only up to a certain point can in a sense be even more tantalizing, for they raise the inevitable question: why does nature exhibit only an approximate symmetry, and what is it that must be regarded as special about the particular point at which that symmetry is broken?

▲▲ 6.8 Time reversal invariance

Spatial reflection symmetry is expressed mathematically by the fact that the form of the basic equations cannot change when the sign of one coordinate (say z) and of the z-components of all velocities, accelerations, momenta, and forces is reversed. Thus the transformational equations expressing reflectional symmetry are:

$$z_b = -z_a,$$
$$x_b = x_a, \qquad y_b = y_a, \tag{6.8}$$

and

$$C_{bz} = -C_{az},$$
$$C_{bx} = C_{ax}, \qquad C_{by} = C_{ay} \tag{6.9}$$

where $\mathbf{C}$ is any vector.

A mathematically analogous transformation is obtained when the signs of all time intervals that appear in the basic equations are reversed. However, the physical significance of the transformation is considerably different, for it implies a reversal in the conventional direction of time, a symmetry that appears at first sight to have no conceivable observational basis. On the contrary, a closer examination indicates that the symmetry of physical laws relative to time reversal is a very well-grounded principle.*

Weyl's criterion may be applied by asking whether or not a moving picture of a particular sequence of events appears fundamentally different when run backwards. For instance, would a viewer be able to decide whether a moving picture of an oscillating spring were being shown forward or backward unless the system were subject to frictional damping or the manner in which it was set into oscillation were shown? Obviously not. Similar considerations would apply to a film of a freely-falling body, as is evident from the detailed discussion of the problem in Chapter 2. It is quite easy to see that the free fall equations do not change form under the time reversal transformation:

$$t_b = -t_a. \tag{6.10}$$

We have

$$y_b = y_{b0} + v_b t_b + \tfrac{1}{2} g_b t_b^2,$$

which under the transformation $t_b = -t_a$ becomes

$$y_b = y_{b0} - v_b t_a + \tfrac{1}{2} g_b t_a^2. \tag{6.11a}$$

How do displacements, velocities, and accelerations transform under time reversal? Since displacements do not involve time, it follows that $y_b = y_a$. Velocity is defined as the ratio of a displacement to a time. Therefore, since $t_b = -t_a$:

$$v_b = -v_a, \tag{6.11b}$$

and

$$a_b = \frac{\Delta v_b}{\Delta t_b} = \frac{-\Delta v_a}{-\Delta t_a} = a_a. \tag{6.11c}$$

Substituting into the partially transformed free-fall equation:

$$y_a = y_{a0} + v_a t_a + \tfrac{1}{2} g_a t_a^2.$$

Since the form of this equation is identical to the original equation written from the point of view of observer B, it follows that free fall is invariant with respect to time reversal, consistent with the conclusions based on considering the characteristics of a filmed version of the phenomenon.

Does the motion of the planets and satellites of the solar system conform to the symmetry? A motion picture of the sun moving across the sky would, if run backwards, show the sun rising in the West and setting in the East. But the apparent direction of the sun's motion is a consequence of the direction of the earth's rotation and not of some fundamental law. Indeed, a viewer could still be misled if the film were reversed *and* shown backwards *simultaneously*.

As with the other classical principles, time reversal is implicit in the structure of Newtonian mechanics. The law of inertia does not specify a direction, but merely requires

---

* There is firm experimental evidence that time reversal may not be a valid symmetry principle in some processes involving elementary particles, although at this writing (1968) the full implications of the discovery are far from being completely understood (Chapter 23). However, the symmetry is completely valid in classical physics.

that velocity be constant. Similarly, if all the velocities, and therefore all the momenta, of a system of interacting particles were reversed, the law of momentum conservation would still retain its validity. Finally, since accelerations do not reverse their signs under the time-reversal transformation (Equation 6.11c), neither do forces.

Despite such evidence from fundamental processes, however, symmetry under time reversal appears considerably less plausible than the homogeneity of space and time or reflection in space, for example, for natural processes do seem to exhibit a preferred direction in time. To demonstrate the symmetry using a moving picture of an harmonic oscillator, for example, we specified that no damping, frictional forces be allowed. Otherwise it would be a trivial matter to discern a difference between the forward and backward run film. Even more obviously, hot and cold water, when mixed, yield tepid water, not ice and steam; oak trees do not grow backwards into acorns; human beings do not proceed from death to birth.

Actually there is no conflict between the time-reversal symmetry of fundamental processes and the unidirectional nature of time that seems to characterize virtually all complex processes, although a detailed discussion of this fascinating paradox must await a later chapter. The key lies in the distinction that must be made between improbability and impossibility, and recognition of the fact that the laws governing complex systems are laws of probability rather than laws of certainty.

For example, we shall see in Chapter 16 that the temperature of a substance is related to the mean velocity of its atoms. When hot and cold water are first mixed, the atoms of the hot water have, on the average, higher velocities than the atoms of the cold water. When two atoms collide any result consistent with the symmetry principle may occur. In general, one will gain some momentum at the other's expense, but to be consistent with time reversal we conclude that the faster atom is just as likely to gain momentum as to lose it. Otherwise a moving picture of the collision would look different when shown backward and forward. However, if the hot water were to become even hotter, then in virtually *every* collision the fast atoms would have to gain momentum at the expense of the slower atoms. While *possible*, such an occurrence is far less *probable* than the slow averaging out of the extremes, with the end result that the average velocity of the atoms in the mixture reaches a new stable value somewhere between the original extremes.

All complex biological processes, such as the growth of plants and men, are the results of long sequences of basic individual atomic processes—processes that in addition must occur in a particular sequence. Just as the probability that *all* the atoms of a sample of hot water will increase their momenta at the expense of the slower atoms is very small, so the probability that the *sequence* of chemical processes that characterizes even a simple biological process will occur in reverse order is so small that evolution from oak to acorn, while not impossible in principle, is so highly improbable that it may safely be ruled out as an occurrence likely ever to be observed during the life of this planet, or indeed of the universe.

▲▲ 6.9   Noninvariance with respect to scaling.   Existence of a fundamental size

At this juncture it is both interesting and informative to consider an imaginable symmetry that is, however, not universally valid. We have seen that nature does not distinguish between points in space and time nor (on a microscopic scale) between left and right or between forward and backward. But nature does make a distinction between "large" and "small," for not all of the laws of physics are invariant with respect to changes in scale.

Symmetry with respect to a change in scale would imply identical results with two sets of apparatus if the dimensions of one set were, say, all twice as large as the dimensions of the other. Indeed this symmetry is observed in some instances, notably those in which the gravitational interaction alone is significant. Since the period of a pendulum is $2\pi\sqrt{l/g}$, the ratio of the periods of two pendula whose lengths differ by a factor of two is $\sqrt{2}$. But in this instance the earth itself should be considered part of the apparatus and its radius therefore doubled along with the length of the pendulum. Approximating the earth as an homogeneous sphere of density d, its mass (volume times density) is given in terms of its radius by $4/3\pi R_e^3 d$, and since (Equation 5.5) $g = GM_e/R_e^2$, the value of the acceleration due to gravity is directly proportional to the radius of the earth. It follows that $T = 2\pi\sqrt{l/g}$ remains constant if the ratio of the length of the pendulum to the radius of the earth remains constant.

The gravitational interaction involves long-range forces between macroscopic bodies. However, as Galileo first discussed in detail, the strength of materials is very much a function of their dimensions and thus does vary with a change in scale. Suppose that one end of a long beam is firmly embedded in a rigid wall; the remainder is suspended above the ground. We consider a case in which the wall can barely support the weight of the beam in this manner (Figure 6.7). Then if all of its dimensions are doubled, the beam's weight, proportional to its volume, will increase by a factor of eight, whereas the strength of the joint at the wall, proportional to the cross-sectional area of the beam, will only increase by a factor of four. The scaled-up wall cannot support the scaled-up beam.

Of course we should proceed as in the pendulum example and scale up the earth as well as the beam and wall. But if we do that then the weight of the beam, Mg, increases by a factor of sixteen rather than eight so that the break will be even more decisive.

Galileo was fascinated with his discovery, and devoted considerable space to it in his

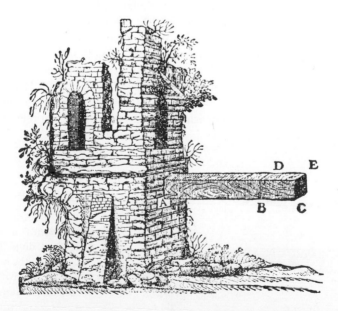

FIGURE 6.7 A sketch from Galileo's *Discourses Concerning Two New Sciences*. Suppose the wall can barely support the weight of the beam. If all dimensions are doubled, the weight of the beam increases by a factor of eight, but the strength of the joint at the wall, proportional to the cross section of the beam, increases by only a factor of four. Therefore, the scaled-up system will break.

Discourses Concerning Two New Sciences. Just as the radius of a cylinder must be more than doubled if it is to preserve its strength when its weight is doubled, so he argued that the bones of a large dog, a super dog, would have to be constructed in quite a different way than the bones of an ordinary dog (Figure 6.8). For precisely the same reason the structure of an elephant is considerably different from the structure of, say, a horse; an ant scaled up to the size of a man would be incredibly weak, in fact, it would be quite unable to support its own weight on its pipestem legs, whereas a man scaled down to the size of an ant would be the strongest of all insects.

Why do pendula scale if beams and bones do not? The fact is, we (and Galileo) have not really made a complete change of scale in any of our examples. We have assumed that the *density* of the material involved does not vary with the scale change, that iron, for instance, retains a density of 7.6×10^3 kg/m^3, water a density of 1.0×10^3 kg/m^3—in other words, that iron remains iron and water remains water. Therefore, when we increased the dimensions of the beam we increased the *number* of atoms in the beam, but not the sizes of the atoms themselves.

Then why not go all the way, perform an honest calculation with the sizes of all atoms increased by a factor of two? Simply because we cannot. The size of the earth, its distance from the sun, the size of a dog, a man, and an elephant may all be regarded as evolutionary accidents. In other words, we are at liberty to assume that these sizes could be different had history been different. Classical physics, in this sense, does not provide us with a scale. But we are *not* at liberty to assume that the sizes of atoms have the same degree of arbitrariness, although there is no classical reason why we should not. The "radius" of a hydrogen atom, of all hydrogen atoms in the universe as far as we know, is 1.08×10^{-10} m, and, as we shall learn presently, it is precisely that size because of a very fundamental principle of nature. A change in the dimensions of atoms would necessitate a change in the basic structure of the laws of nature and would imply a universe with quite a different aspect. Water would not be water nor iron iron; chemical, biological, and physical processes would all be altered. Thus the principle that Galileo discovered and discussed provides evidence for a fundamental characteristic of the universe. A symmetry that does not apply can offer as much insight, or perhaps more, than one which does. Thus, also, nature provides us with a scale of distance, for if all meter sticks were to vanish tomorrow we would still know the meaning of one meter, since we could be sure that the dimensions of the atoms were not changed by the cataclysm that destroyed the meter sticks.

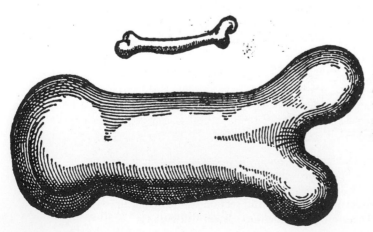

FIGURE 6.8 Galileo's sketches of the legbones of an ordinary and of a giant dog. The ratio of the thickness of the bone to its length must increase with the weight of the animal being supported.

▲▲ 6.10   Invariance principles and conservation laws

The search for links between symmetry principles and conservation laws is one of the most intriguing and satisfying aspects of contemporary physics. But it is an aspect whose full implications have only been recognized in recent years. Newtonian physics is based upon an assumption of complete determinism; its laws are laws of certainty. In contrast, contemporary physics is structured on the assumption that the laws of nature are laws of probability. In any fundamental process we can start with the assumption that all results are *possible* if not expressly forbidden. Why might a particular result be forbidden? If it proceeded in a way that would be inconsistent with one of the symmetry principles, with the homogeneity or isotropy of space, for example, or with invariance with respect to time reversal. Of course, all possible results need not, indeed will not, occur with equal probabilities, and thus detailed dynamical laws are required in addition to the symmetry principles. Nonetheless, the latter are of paramount importance in limiting the possible types of fundamental interactions. They have a restrictive or, to be more positive, a permissive rather than what we might call a directive character.

Now if we believe that a particular class of processes cannot occur, then we are saying in essence that a particular physical feature of the universe is constant. If, further, we can identify that particular feature with some constructed physical quantity, our restrictive symmetry principle can be expressed by stating that that particular quantity must in all cases remain constant. Following this line of thought, contemporary physics has arrived at the conclusion that every empirically defined conservation law follows from a particular symmetry principle, and, conversely, that to every symmetry principle there corresponds an experimentally observable conservation law. A complete specification of this presumed one-to-one correspondence is not yet available. In particular, the symmetry principles corresponding to several conservation laws formulated from observed elementary particle processes have yet to be identified. Nonetheless, the one-to-one correspondence has been demonstrated in a sufficient number of cases to make a continued search eminently worthwhile.

The law of momentum conservation which we have taken as the fundamental experimental basis of Newtonian dynamics, is a consequence of the homogeneity of space.

Consider a particle at rest on table top at some time t_0. What will happen to it at later times? To answer the questions from the viewpoint of the directive laws of Newtonian physics we would ask about the forces upon the particle. But we might proceed in a different way. If all points in its immediate vicinity are equivalent then the particle remains at rest simply because it has no reason to prefer any other point over its location at t_0. Thus the homogeneity of space alone suggests that a body at rest remains at rest. We may extend the argument to a system of interacting particles, concluding that if all points are equivalent there is no reason for the center of mass of the system to move, and therefore arrive at momentum conservation for the special case of a system whose total momentum is zero. Similarly, suppose a particle has velocity v_0 at point x_1 and we know that it is going to pass through another point x_2. What velocity will it have at that point? If x_1, x_2, and all intermediate points are equivalent, then symmetry considerations permit but one answer: it will have velocity v_0, showing that the law of inertia is consistent with the homogeneity of space.

Of course the crux of these arguments is the meaning of "equivalence." The symmetry principle does not require that there be no discernible difference. We believe that the different periods of two pendula located at sea level and on a mountain top are consistent with the principle because the difference in g at the two locations is not fundamental.

However, we arrive at that conclusion on the basis of our knowledge of Newtonian dynamics. In addition to spatial homogeneity we require some dynamical principle on which to base the decision concerning the equivalence (or nonequivalence) of all points along the path of a moving particle. As a consequence, these examples of the connection between the symmetry principle and the conservation law are illustrative and do not constitute a rigorous proof. The equivalence of momentum conservation and spatial homogeneity may be demonstrated rigorously with advanced analytical methods that are beyond the scope of this text. However, the interested student will find an excellent and highly readable discussion of the topic in *The Feynman Lectures* referred to at the end of this chapter.

▲▲ 6.11 Angular momentum and its conservation

In problems involving motion along a curve it is often more useful to deal with *angular momentum* rather than linear momentum, and just as the conservation of (linear) momentum is linked with the homogeneity of space, so the conservation of angular momentum is intimately related to isotropy.

Consider a sphere rotating about an axis with a particular velocity and with no force component applied tangent to its surface. Since by isotropy arguments there is no reason to believe that the sphere prefers to orient itself in any one particular direction, we would expect it to maintain a constant rotational velocity. Now, since the magnitude of the velocity of each point on the surface and within the interior of the sphere is in general different, and since the direction of each point changes with time, it is not immediately evident that the conservation of (linear) momentum is a particularly useful principle. But as we shall see presently, angular momentum conservation may be applied quite simply.

Angular momentum conservation may be derived from the principle of (linear) momentum conservation. Consider first the case of a particle in one-dimensional, force-free motion (Figure 6.9a). Application of linear momentum conservation is, of course, trivial since any such particle obeys the law of inertia. Let O be any arbitrary point that does not lie along the path of the particle. Then the length of the radius vector of the moving particle R (the line connecting it to the arbitrary point) sweeps out equal areas in

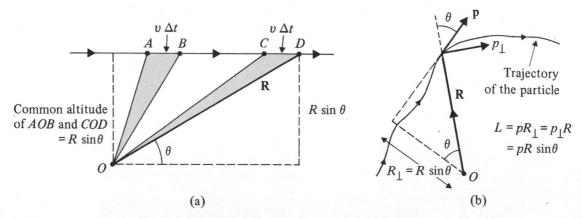

(a)　　　　　　　　　　　　　　　　　(b)

FIGURE 6.9　(a) The equal areas law (Kepler's second law) for a particle in linear, force-free motion. (b) Definition of angular momentum for a particle moving along an arbitrary trajectory.

equal times. If the distances AB and CD represent displacements in equal times, Δt, then the bases of the two triangles AOB and COD are equal. Clearly, their altitudes, the perpendicular distances from base to apex, are also equal, and since the area of a triangle is one-half the product of its base by its altitude, the equal-areas law follows immediately.

The instantaneous value of the *angular momentum* of a particle at a given point along its path is defined as the product of its (linear) momentum by the component of its radius vector in the direction *perpendicular* to the momentum at that point (Figure 6.9b). If θ is the angle between the displacement and the momentum vector of the particle, the perpendicular component of its radius vector relative to some arbitrary point is $R \sin \theta$ so that its angular momentum, L, is:

$$L = pR \sin \theta = mvR \sin \theta. \tag{6.12}$$

It is easy to see that the equal-areas law is equivalent to a statement that angular momentum is conserved, for the altitude of both triangles in Figure 6.9a is just $R \sin \theta$, and the bases $v\,\Delta t$. We may use spatial isotropy to extend the conservation law to the motion of a particle in a circle (Figure 6.10). In this case the motion is certainly not force free; on the contrary, there is a centripetal force toward the center of the circle whose magnitude is constant in time. Let us refer the angular momentum to the center of the circle, which must also be the center of force, so that the radius vector coincides with the geometric radius. Then the momentum vector and radius vector are perpendicular at all points along the path. Because of spatial isotropy we may express the components of the vectors in either coordinate system A or B, or any other rotated system. In system A the vector $\mathbf{R}$ lies along the y-axis at time t_1, the vector $\mathbf{p}$ in the x-direction. At time t_2 the vectors lie along the corresponding axes in system B. Since the two systems are equivalent and yield indistinguishable descriptions at two different times, it follows that the product of their magnitudes, by definition, the angular momentum of the particle, is constant in time. The equivalent equal-areas statement is now easily derived.

The proof of angular momentum conservation for both the force-free particle and the particle moving in a circle hinges upon the constant magnitude of the *linear* momentum vector. Referring to the definition, it is clear that this condition is not necessary or even

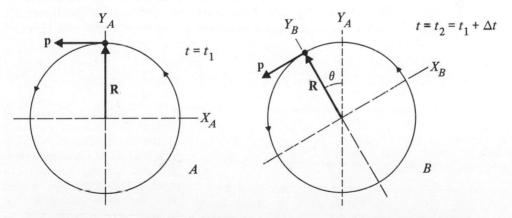

FIGURE 6.10 Proof that the angular momentum of a particle executing uniform circular motion is conserved. Diagram B, which shows the particle and the pertinent vectors describing its motion, may be obtained from A, which represents the motion at an earlier time, by rotating the latter diagram through the angle θ (see Figure 6.4).

sufficient, for the angular momentum of a particle will be constant in time if and only if the *product* of the magnitude of its momentum by the perpendicular component of its radius vector remains constant. If the magnitude of momentum changes, its angular momentum may still remain constant provided there is a compensating change in its radius vector. Conversely, if the radius vector of a particle changes, its angular momentum may change even though the magnitude of its linear momentum remains constant. In any general case the magnitudes and directions of the forces involved must be considered before one can decide whether or not a change in momentum is compensated by a change in radius vector. We shall not consider the problem at length. However, when a particle moves under the influence of a central force, that is, a force that is directed toward some specific point in space, its angular momentum about the point does remain constant in time. This is the law of angular momentum conservation for the restricted yet very broad class of central force motion. In the approximation that the planets interact only with the sun, they all move under the influence of a central force. Hence Kepler's second law follows immediately from angular momentum conservation. Proof of the law for central forces follows an argument similar to the proof for the circular case, but requires detailed application of the rotational transformation equations, Equations 6.7. A formulation of the principle in the general case involving noncentral forces will be found in any standard textbook in physics, including those listed at the end of the chapter.

Angular momentum conservation is also applicable to systems of interacting particles. For instance, if two particles interact by means of a force directed along the line between them, then regardless of the detailed nature of the force or of their motion, linear momentum conservation requires that if one loses momentum during a given time interval the other must gain an equal amount, and that the respective changes in momentum must be along the line joining them. Therefore, the product of the change in momentum of the first particle by the perpendicular component of its radius vector relative to some arbitrary point must be equal and opposite the corresponding change in the angular momentum of the second relative to the same arbitrary point. It follows that the algebraic sum of the angular momenta of the two particles will be constant (Figure 6.11). In general, the vector sum of the angular momenta of all particles in any isolated system remains constant. Application of this law in this its most general form obviously requires a discussion of the vector nature of angular momentum, and since several new concepts

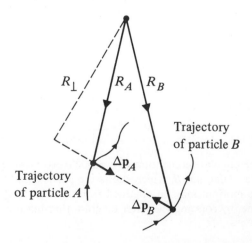

FIGURE 6.11 Angular momentum conservation for an interacting two-body system. The changes in the linear momenta of the two bodies during any time interval Δt are equal, opposite, and directed toward each other. Therefore, the bodies have the same component of radius vector perpendicular to their linear momentum changes, and it follows that the changes in their angular momenta are also equal and opposite.

are involved in that discussion, we shall not discuss it further. However, the principle is quite straightforward if we restrict our attention to motion in two dimensions, for in that case the vector sum of the angular momenta reduces to the algebraic sum exactly as with two interacting particles.

▲▲ 6.12 Inertial systems. Galilean transformations and the Newtonian principle of relativity

Each of our symmetry principles carries the implication that a specific convention we attribute to time or space for the purpose of describing physical events has no fundamental significance and is, in fact, completely arbitrary. We may choose the origin of a Cartesian coordinate system, the orientation of its axes, and their directions at will since experimental evidence indicates that nature has no preferred criteria on which to base these choices. Nature defines no absolute origin in time or space, no absolute "up," no absolute "left," no absolute direction in time. We can only define points in space *relative* to other points, directions relative to other directions. Thus the symmetry principles may also be called *relativity principles*.

Does nature provide any way to define absolute rest? The physics of Aristotle and the scholastic philosophers assumed that rest was the preferred state of all terrestrial matter, that the earth itself was at rest at the center of the universe. But the law of inertia, the fundamental postulate of Newtonian mechanics, is tantamount to a statement that rest and uniform, rectilinear motion are dynamically equivalent, and therefore, that no experiment can define a state of absolute rest. If this is true, then the law of inertia implies another symmetry principle.

Let us investigate this presumed symmetry in terms of Weyl's criterion. Critics of the Copernican hypothesis insisted that if the earth were in motion all objects on its surface would be left behind, literally swept into space. In his defense of the hypothesis Galileo argued that all objects on a moving earth, as on a moving ship, partake of its motion and, therefore, are carried along with it. In effect he was predating Weyl by three centuries, arguing that no fundamental measurement performed on a moving ship can yield a result that is different from a measurement made with identical apparatus at rest relative to the earth. If this is so, then an observer may choose a point at rest with respect to the "moving" ship as the origin of his coordinate system and, whether on the ship or not, refer all physical events to that system. Likewise, Galileo argued in effect that it is entirely consistent to select a coordinate system fixed relative to the sun for a description of planetary motion.

We may paraphrase Galileo's arguments by comparing the behavior of several basic sets of apparatus at rest relative to the earth with identical apparatus at rest relative to a jet airliner moving at 600 miles per hour. Does a passenger on such a jet have any sense of motion if its velocity is constant and he does not look out the window? He can eat a meal, read, watch a movie, sleep, walk down the aisle just as if the jet were on the ground. He is only aware of motion when the jet accelerates, a not surprising conclusion in view of the fact that our symmetry was suggested by the law of inertia. Therefore, in comparing fundamental processes, let us restrict ourselves at the outset to jets—or trains or ships—moving at constant velocities relative to the earth.

How will an object in free fall behave on the jet? We would expect it to fall straight downward with acceleration $g = 9.8$ m/sec^2. But straight downward with respect to what? With respect to the earth or the jet? Suppose a passenger drops a book on the floor from a height of 1.2 m. Since $g = 9.8$ m/sec^2, and $y = \frac{1}{2}gt^2$, the book falls in about

$\frac{1}{2}$ sec. But 600 miles/hr = 266 m/sec so that during that $\frac{1}{2}$ sec the point on the floor that was directly under the book when it started to fall has moved forward 133 m or $\frac{1}{12}$ of a mile relative to the earth. If the book is to fall to that point it must also move forward 133 m while it falls. If it fell straight downward relative to the earth it would strike the floor of the jet at the end of the aisle, if at all (Figure 6.12). It follows that the equations of free fall can be expressed relative to a moving jet just as well as relative to a moving earth, and, conversely, that free-fall experiments are consistent with a choice of a coordinate system at rest relative to the jet.

Experiments with springs and pendula lead to the same conclusion. Relative to an observer on the jet the stand supporting his pendulum or spring is fixed; relative to an observer on the earth the stand is traveling with velocity 600 miles/hr. Relative to the observer on the jet the pendulum oscillates relative to the fixed stand; relative to an observer on the earth the pendulum bob moves at a slightly higher velocity than the stand during part of a cycle, at a slightly lower velocity during another part of a cycle. However, both observers must conclude that its period, T, defined relative to the stand, is $2\pi\sqrt{l/g}$.

We have assigned the law of inertia the status of a fundamental postulate. From a somewhat different point of view it may be regarded as a necessary and sufficient test for the applicability of Newtonian dynamics, for we can envision situations in which it might not be observed. For example, if our jet accelerates relative to the earth, then all objects at rest relative to it before the acceleration will move, all objects moving at constant velocity will accelerate without the intervention of an outside force. Indeed, application of an external force will be required to keep them at rest or moving with constant velocity. Hence the law of inertia, the principle of momentum conservation, and the complete system of dynamics we have developed would not be valid with respect to a coordinate system fixed relative to the jet. We can explain away this "breakdown" in Newtonian dynamics in at least two ways: either by assuming there is some undetected force that we have not taken into account, or by assuming that it is not possible to refer physical events to the accelerating jet and still expect Newton's laws to be valid. If we adopt the second expedient we require, in effect, that the law of inertia be valid in any system to which we choose to refer our measurements. This criterion defines an *inertial system*, any system in which the law of inertia is observed to be valid.

The earth, of course, spins on its axis and revolves about the sun. Hence it is not a true inertial system. However, noninertial effects are so small that for most purposes we may regard a coordinate system fixed relative to the earth as a proper inertial system. Given one inertial system, it is quite a simple matter to define another. If our jet is moving at constant velocity, $\mathbf{u}$, relative to the earth, an object moving at constant velocity $\mathbf{v}_b$ relative to the jet has velocity $\mathbf{v}_a = \mathbf{v}_b - \mathbf{u}$ relative to the earth. Therefore, if the law of inertia is valid in a system fixed relative to the earth, it is also valid in a system fixed relative to the jet. It follows that all systems that move with constant velocity relative to any given inertial system must also be inertial systems, and our symmetry principle reduces to a statement that the laws of physics are equally valid in all inertial systems.

The transformation equations that are the mathematical expression of the symmetry principle are called the *Galilean transformations*, in recognition of Galileo's arguments regarding moving ships and the moving earth. As with all other transformation laws, these equations connect the measurement of a location of an event in space by an observer *A* relative to his chosen system of reference to the analogous measurement of the *same* event by observer *B*. The Galilean transformations assume that one observer (or more properly, his chosen system) is moving with constant velocity relative to the other, and that they relate their measurements to different inertial systems.

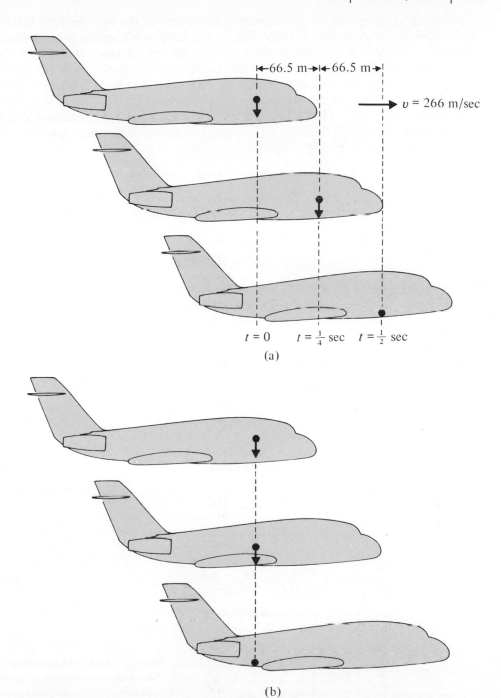

FIGURE 6.12 Free fall on a jet traveling at a constant velocity of 266 m/sec (600 miles/hr). The jet is shown in a reference frame fixed relative to the earth at three times, one-quarter second apart in both figures. In part a, a falling body falls vertically in a coordinate system moving with the jet; in part b, it falls vertically in a system fixed with respect to the earth.

For algebraic simplicity let us assume that the x-axes of the two observers coincide, that system B is moving with velocity u along the positive x-direction in the system of observer A, or, equivalently, that observer A is moving with velocity $-u$ along the x-axis of observer B (Figure 6.13). System A might be fixed relative to the earth, for instance, and system B fixed with respect to a train moving along a straight track. Let us also assume that the origins of the two systems (and therefore the three axes of the systems) coincide at time $t = 0$. Then after t seconds the origins are separated by a distance $X = ut$. Substituting into Equation 6.1a we arrive at the transformation equation for the x-coordinate of a point measured by both observers:

$$x_b = x_a - ut. \tag{6.13a}$$

Since distances in the y- and z-directions coincide in both systems (relative motion is along the x-axis only) the transformation equations for these coordinates are trivial:

$$y_b = y_a, \tag{6.13b}$$

$$z_b = z_a. \tag{6.13c}$$

Of course we could also consider relative motion in an arbitrary direction, but little would be gained by the exercise save algebraic complication. Equation 6.13a implies that a point at rest in system A moves in the negative x-direction in system B, as it must since system B (a moving train, for instance) leaves points in the earth-fixed system increasingly farther behind.

Transformation equations from B to A are obtained either by inversion of Equation 6.13a, or by recalling that if B moves with velocity $+u$ relative to A then A moves with velocity $-u$ relative to B:

$$x_a = x_b + ut, \tag{6.14a}$$

$$y_a = y_b, \tag{6.14b}$$

$$z_a = z_b. \tag{6.14c}$$

How will the two observers compare the velocity of a moving particle? According to observer A:

$$v_a = \frac{\Delta x_z}{\Delta t}.$$

Then:

$$v_b = \frac{\Delta x_b}{\Delta t} = \frac{\Delta x_a - u\,\Delta t}{\Delta t} = v_a - u, \tag{6.15a}$$

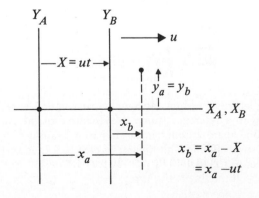

FIGURE 6.13 Relationship between the coordinates of a point measured in two inertial systems. The x-axes of the systems coincide, and B moves with constant velocity $+u$ in the x-direction relative to A.

by application of Equation 6.13a. Conversely:

$$v_a = v_b + u. \tag{6.15b}$$

As we would expect, the observed velocity differs simply by the velocity of the two systems relative to each other. A constant velocity in one system implies a different but still constant velocity in the other, as we have already concluded. Likewise, the two observers might both measure the acceleration of a particle:

$$a_a = \frac{\Delta v_a}{\Delta t},$$

and

$$a_b = \frac{\Delta v_b}{\Delta t}.$$

Applying Equation 6.15a:

$$a_b = \frac{\Delta v_a}{\Delta t} - \frac{\Delta u}{\Delta t} = a_a - \frac{\Delta u}{\Delta t}.$$

However, u is constant in time, and therefore, $a_b = a_a$. Both observers measure the same acceleration. It follows that they will define the same forces, and arrive at the same fundamental formulation of Newtonian dynamics. In other words, we have shown that the laws of Newton do not depend upon the choice of inertial system for their validity, and that the Galilean transformations are a mathematical statement of this invariant principle. This principle is called the *Newtonian principle of relativity*, since it is grounded in the observed fact that the state we choose to call rest is quite arbitrary, and therefore, that velocities are relative.

We arrived at a description of projectile motion in Chapter 4 by first considering carefully the role of initial conditions in any problem. The equivalence of free fall and projectile motion also follows directly from the Galilean transformations. Suppose a horizontal cannon mounted upon a tower of height y fires a projectile with velocity u at the same time that a stone is dropped from the tower. Relative to an observer A at rest at the base of the tower, the cannonball describes a curved trajectory, the stone falls directly downward. Relative to an observer B who moves along the level ground on a railroad flatcar with velocity u, however, the *cannonball* falls directly downward, and the stone follows a path with the reversed curvature observer A ascribes to the cannonball, in accordance with the relativity principle. If the laws of physics are to be the same in both system A and system B, the cannonball and the stone must both strike the ground at precisely the same instant. Following this line of reasoning, it becomes clear that we may separate the initial conditions of a problem from the accelerations involved simply because the symmetry principle we have developed, the Newtonian principle of relativity, is experimentally valid.

The observed equivalence of inertial systems is one of the most important and interesting of the symmetries. Part of its importance derives from the fact that for a time during the late nineteenth century its validity was seriously questioned, for it seemed to imply a logical inconsistency when applied to the electromagnetic interactions between charged particles. The principle survived, however, in a generalized, modified form as the special theory of relativity of Albert Einstein, a topic for Chapter 11.

▶▶ 6.13 Accelerated reference systems and pseudoforces

By investigating the symmetry properties of physical laws we are able to differentiate between the fundamental properties of matter and its interactions, and the purely arbitrary, mathematical properties we attribute to time and space for our convenience in understanding physical processes. The symmetry of physical laws with respect to inertial systems is especially important in this regard. However, a number of natural philosophers, notably Ernst Mach, and, later, Albert Einstein, realized that the formulation of dynamical laws relative to inertial systems still assumes the existence of a property of space for which there is no experimental evidence.

The law of inertia may be taken as a fundamental postulate or, alternately, as a precondition for the validity of Newtonian physics. The latter point of view leads us to concentrate upon inertial systems. However, how can we be sure *what* the laws of physics are in inertial systems if we have never experienced such a system? The earth is a very good approximation to such a system, but an approximation nonetheless. Its rotation, or, equivalently, its noninertial character can best be demonstrated by means of a Foucault pendulum. For simplicity we consider a long pendulum located at the North Pole (Figure 6.14). As the pendulum oscillates, its plane of oscillation is observed to rotate through one revolution per day relative to the earth. There are two possible equivalent explanations: we may say that the pendulum oscillates in a coordinate system fixed relative to the stars, and that therefore the earth completes one rotation beneath it each twenty-four hours, or that the earth is a noninertial system and therefore the pendulum is subject to a noninertial force, in this case the so-called Coriolis force. The rotation of the plane of a pendulum is also observed at other points on the earth, although it only rotates through an angle $2\pi \sin \theta$ per day, where θ is the latitude of its position on the surface.

The Foucault pendulum proves that the earth is not an inertial system, and therefore, that the law of inertia holds only approximately in a system fixed relative to it. But we postulate validity of the law of inertia in inertial systems. What do we mean by an inertial system? A system in which the law of inertia is valid! In order to escape from this circle we can assume that there is some absolute frame of reference at rest relative to the fixed stars, for instance, in which the law of inertia is truly valid. But the fixed stars are not

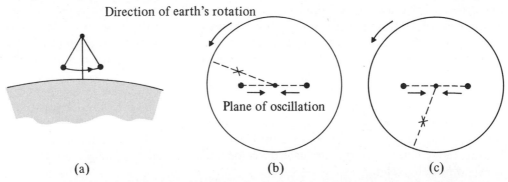

FIGURE 6.14   A Foucault pendulum at the North Pole. An observer looking down on the Pole from a refernce frame fixed with respect to the stars sees the pendulum oscillating in a fixed plane and the earth rotating beneath it (b and c). However, an observer standing at the position of the crossmark on the earth sees the plane of the pendulum rotate in the opposite direction from the rotation of the earth.

really fixed; they only appear fixed over short periods of time because of their immense distance from the earth. Ultimately we are led to postulate an inertial system that is not connected at all with matter, and such a system, as Einstein pointed out, can only be regarded as arbitrary and fictitious, since in effect it assumes the existence of absolute space unconnected with matter.

For most purposes it is possible to regard the earth as an inertial system. But Einstein argued that if we are interested in gaining insight into the fundamental nature of the physical universe, we must discard the idea of an absolute space unrelated to matter in the same manner that we have disposed of other arbitrary properties of space and time. In other words, we should develop a system of dynamics that is valid in all possible systems of reference—those that are accelerating relative to each other, for instance. However, the task is far from simple, for as we have seen, the acceleration of one system relative to another implies that the forces measured in the two systems are different. Formulation of the laws of physics relative to inertial systems is tantamount to an assumption that velocities are relative, but accelerations absolute. That is, we can give a meaning to the velocity of a particle only by referring the particle to an arbitrary co-ordinate system, but can give an absolute meaning to an acceleration in terms of the force required to produce it. The transformation equations from one inertial system to another change the velocity of a particle, but not its acceleration. To carry out Einstein's program it is necessary to assume that accelerations are also relative, having a well-defined meaning only with respect to specific coordinate systems, and that transformation equations between all such systems must be found.

For the moment let us assume that an inertial system does exist and compare physical processes in that system and an accelerated system—between the earth and an accelerated train, for instance. An object at rest on the train before it starts to accelerate will be moving at constant velocity relative to the earth so that observers on the earth and on the train will both agree that no force is acting upon it (Figure 6.15). When the train starts its forward acceleration, however, the observers will no longer reach that common conclusion. To the earth-fixed observer there is still no force upon the object—the train is merely accelerating away from it. But the train-fixed observer notes that the object rolls backwards relative to his system, and if he believes his system is valid for the for-mulation of physics, he can maintain its validity by assuming that a force of some sort is acting upon the object, accelerating it toward the rear of the train. However, the force is of a very special character, since it accelerates all objects on the train in the same direction and at the same rate. Applying Newton's second law, it is a force with magnitude pro-portional to the inertial mass of the object it accelerates. The earth-fixed observer might well view the train-fixed observer's assumption that such a force acts upon all bodies in his system as nonsense, call the force fictitious, and insist that it would be easier for the train-fixed observer to refer his observations to an inertial system. To that assertion the train-fixed observer can reply, what inertial system? Yours, the earth, may be a better approximation to what you *think* an inertial system is like, but neither of us have any direct experience in that regard.

The distinguishing feature of all noninertial, or fictitious, forces is that they act upon all objects with magnitudes proportional to the inertial mass of the objects. Some of these forces are so common that they have specific names. For example, an observer in an inertial system who observes an object fixed relative to a spinning turntable concludes that a centripetal force must be applied to the object to keep it in its circular path; when he sees an object "thrown off" the turntable he reasons that the force applied to it was insufficient. An observer who chooses a system fixed relative to the turntable admits that

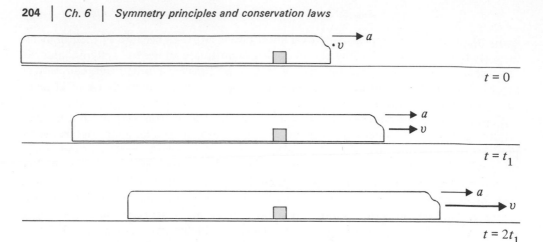

FIGURE 6.15 Origin of the pseudoforce on an object in a constantly accelerating train. The train and object are shown at three equally spaced times in a system fixed with respect to the earth, and are at rest at $t = 0$. To the earth-fixed observer, the engine of the train accelerates away from the object, while to an observer on the train the object accelerates backwards. Therefore, the latter observer invents a force acting toward the back of the train to explain his observation. Since all objects on the train accelerate backward at the same rate regardless of their inertial masses, the magnitude of the pseudoforce on a body is proportional to its inertial mass.

a force is required to keep an object at rest in his system, but concludes that that force is required not because all objects describe circular trajectories, but rather because a *centrifugal* force acts upon them. In the absence of a counter-force this centrifugal force sweeps objects off the table. Naturally, the earth-fixed observer regards this viewpoint as nonsense, and labels the centrifugal force as an invention.

Einstein was the first to make use of the curious fact that in its proportion to the inertial mass of the object upon which it acts, the gravitational force has all of the characteristics of fictitious forces, such as the centrifugal force, and that an observer in an elevator in free fall might just as well tell an earth-dweller that his gravity is fictitious as the earth-dweller tells the observer on the turntable that his centrifugal force is an invention. We have already noted (Section 5.10) that it is the equivalence of gravitational and inertial mass that permits both the earth-dweller and the observer in a freely falling elevator to assume with equal justification the validity of their systems. The equivalence of the two types of mass was recognized from the time of Galileo's free-fall experiments, of course, but in Newtonian physics it was always regarded as accidental.

Einstein, however, elevated the observed equality into a postulate of his general theory of relativity, calling it the principle of equivalence. In a sense we may regard the postulate as a manifestation of a symmetry principle that denies the special role of inertial systems, and regards acceleration, like velocity, as a relative quantity definable only with reference to a particular system which must be regarded as arbitrary. The general theory of relativity is based upon the consequences of this presumed symmetry. It first seeks transformation equations that connect the observations referred to any two arbitrary systems, then reformulates the basic equations of physics in a form that makes them independent of the system in which they are written. One immediate implication, as noted in Chapter 5, is the necessity of discarding Euclidean geometry as the preferred framework of space, and, therefore, the use of Cartesian coordinate systems. Clearly the mathematics of Einstein's general program are nontrivial, and for that reason the detailed formulation and conclusions of the general theory are beyond the competence of this text. Nevertheless, we shall try to discuss a few of its qualitative implications in Chapter 11. Even at this juncture we can appreciate something of the power and beauty of the symmetry principles of physics in permitting insight into so fundamental a manifestation of nature as the gravitational interaction of matter.

▲▲ 6.14 Symmetry concepts in physics: summary and preview

The idea that the fundamental laws of nature exhibit a set of symmetry properties will continue to appear in a number of contexts throughout the remainder of this text, for it is an idea that underlies all of physics. Chapter 7, for instance, introduces the most well known and widely applicable of the conservation laws, the conservation of energy. Although not at all obvious, this conservation law may be shown to follow as a necessary consequence of the homogeneity of time, just as momentum conservation is a consequence of the homogeneity of space. In Chapter 11 we shall deal with several consequences of Einstein's special theory of relativity which, as noted in Section 6.12, is a consequence of the symmetry of physical laws with respect to inertial systems.

But we shall make our most explicit use of the symmetry principles when we consider interactions between subatomic particles (Chapter 23), for the precise character of these interactions is not at all clear at the present writing, and hence the symmetry and conservation laws serve as guidelines in our developing search for a more specific understanding. There we shall encounter also several empirically based conservation laws whose connection with symmetry principles is tenuous at best. Nevertheless the idea of a one-to-one correspondence between conservation laws and symmetry principles is so appealing that the search for these connections is a major impetus in contemporary physics.

Like all of the principles of physics, the symmetry laws and their related conservation laws cannot be regarded as intuitively obvious, but rest upon observational evidence. For instance, although it would appear that symmetry with respect to reflections in space is an obvious property of all physical laws, that particular "obvious" law is partially violated on the subatomic level. Conversely, although the symmetry of physical laws with respect to reflections in time, time reversal invariance, would appear at first sight as a totally unwarranted assumption, there is strong evidence for its almost complete validity on the fundamental level. As exploration of the consequences of the breaking of the "obvious" space reflection symmetry on the one hand, and the at least approximate validity of the not-at-all obvious time-reversal symmetry on the other both provide considerable insight into the nature of the universe.

Again, although we now believe in the symmetry of physical laws relative to all inertial systems, that particular symmetry was questioned seriously in the late nineteenth century. In order to reestablish its validity in his special theory of relativity, Einstein had to generalize Newtonian physics, and among other things, concluded that inertial mass and energy are equivalent concepts in his famous equation $E = Mc^2$. When he went further and explored the consequences of assuming that a symmetry exists where it had been generally assumed it did not, in his rejection of a special role for inertial systems, he provided new insight into the fundamental nature of the gravitational interaction.

Thus we must always regard symmetry (and nonsymmetry) principles as empirical observational principles. Just as the human mind enjoys contemplation of symmetry in art and justice, so it regards symmetry in the universe as basic and, perhaps, as just. Only one sentence has been preserved of the writings of the Ionian philosopher Anaximander of Miletus (ca. 590 B.C.), but it is a sentence that shows the concern felt by this, the first group of natural philosophers in Western history, with the theme of constant, ordered change, a change both natural and just:

> That from which all things are born is also the cause of their coming to an end, as is meet, for they pay reparations and atonement to each other for their mutual injustice in the order of time.*

We cannot emulate Plato and assume that the symmetry of nature must coincide with what we believe a proper symmetry should be. We must let nature decide. The human mind finds symmetry pleasing; in seeking to understand the symmetries of the universe, and in seeking to understand the implications of a broken or nonexistent symmetry, it finds a means to seek a comprehension of the nature of the universe itself.

SUGGESTIONS FOR FURTHER READING ▲▲▲

The best treatment of symmetry in physics on an introductory level (though it emphasizes quantum mechanical symmetries) is:

R. P. FEYNMAN, R. B. LEIGHTON, AND M. SANDS, *The Feynman Lectures on Physics*, Vol. 1, Addison-Wesley Publishing Co., Inc., Reading, Mass., 1963, Chapter 52.

Feynman, Vol. II, Chapter 19, is devoted in its entirety to a somewhat advanced but delightful lecture on the connection between symmetry principles and the classical conservation laws.

The *Scientific American* has had occasional articles on symmetry principle, again usually quantum symmetries. Two that devote some discussion to time reversal in classical physics are:

J. M. BLATT, "Time Reversal," Aug., 1956, p. 107.

M. GARDNER, "Can Time Go Backwards?" January, 1967, p. 98.

PROBLEMS AND EXERCISES ▲▲▲

6.1. The origin of a Cartesian coordinate system B is displaced $+2$ m along the x-axis of another system A. The x-axes of the systems coincide and the y-axes are parallel.
(a) Transform the following measurements made in A to coordinate system B:

$$x = +5, \qquad y = 2;$$
$$x = +10, \qquad y = 0;$$
$$x = 0, \qquad y = 7;$$
$$x = -5, \qquad y = 2.$$

(b) Transform the following measurements made in B into the coordinate system A:

$$x = -3, \qquad y = 1;$$
$$x = 0, \qquad y = 2;$$
$$\Delta x = 7 - 1 = 6.$$

6.2. The motion of the automobile in Table 2.1 is observed from an overpass on the tollroad 1.2 miles from the tollgate. Express the position measurements in terms of this new origin, and show by direct calculation that the average speed over each interval is the same as that expressed in the table.

---

* Quoted by Giorgio de Santillana in *The Origins of Scientific Thought: From Anaximander to Proclus, 600 B.C. to A.D. 500*, Mentor Edition, New American Library, 1961, p. 22.

6.3. A rod 2 m long lies along the *x*-axis of a Cartesian coordinate system *A* with one end at the origin.

    (a) What are its components in a Cartesian system *B* whose origin coincides with the origin of *A* but whose axes are rotated through 30° relative to the original system? (Figure 6.4. sin 30° = 0.5, cos 30° = $\sqrt{3/2}$ = 0.866.)

    (b) Show by direct calculation that the length of the rod in the second system is also 2 m.

6.4. Transform the following measurements made in system *A* into system *B* (Problem 6.3):

$$x = 3, \qquad y = 2;$$
$$x = -4, \qquad y = 0;$$
$$x = 0, \qquad y = 10.$$

6.5. Show that Newton's second law and the law of universal gravitation are invariant with respect to reflections about the *x*-axis and with respect to time reversal.

6.6. Suppose you are in radio communication with a being in another galaxy who cannot see the solar system or even our local galaxy. On the basis of the symmetry principles discussed in this chapter, which of the following conventions could you instruct him about? Explain.

    (a) Your meaning of East and West.
    (b) Your definition of down.
    (c) Your number system.
    (d) Your definition of left and right.
    (e) The meaning of 1 m. Of 1 kg.

6.7. Lions and tigers are often called big cats. Determine from photographs (or memory) to what extent they really are scaled-up house cats.

6.8. Most animals from fleas to elephants can jump approximately the same height (i.e., somewhat greater than 1 ft and somewhat less than six or seven) regardless of their size. Why?

6.9. Suppose that the dimensions of and strength of the wall and beam in Figure 6.7 are such that the system is just under the breaking point. If transported to the moon how much could the system be scaled up without breaking (*g* on the moon is $\frac{1}{6}$ *g* on the earth).

6.10. A 5-kg toy safe is hoisted up by a wire and pulley system. It is found that a wire of a certain material 10^{-4}m in diameter can just do the job without breaking. What diameter cable of the same material is required to lift a 500-kg safe?

6.11. Suppose the radius of the earth and the radius of the moon's orbit were both doubled with the density of the earth remaining constant. How would *g* change at the earth's surface? How would the period of the moon change?

6.12. What are the units of angular momentum?

6.13. Calculate the angular momentum of:

    (a) A 1000-kg automobile rounding a circular, 20-m radius curve at 25 m/sec (relative to the center of the circular arc).
    (b) A 1-kg mass at the equator relative to the rotation axis of the earth.
    (c) A 1-kg mass on the earth relative to the sun.

6.14. A hoop of radius 1 m spins on its axis at two revolutions per second. How would its rotational frequency change if its radius were contracted to 0.5 m by some internal process?

6.15. A particle moves under the influence of a central force with its momentum perpendicular to its radius vector at a certain time. At a later time the magnitude of its radius vector has doubled but is again perpendicular to its momentum. How has the magnitude of the particle's linear momentum changed?

6.16. At another time the angle between the momentum and radius vector of the particle in Problem 6.15 is 30° (sin 30° = 0.5, cos 30° = 0.866). Later the angle between them is 90° once again and the magnitude of the linear momentum the same as before. How has the radius vector of the particle changed?

6.17. A hollow sphere is incident with velocity v_0 upon a similar sphere of equal radius but one-half the mass which is initially at rest. Following the collision both spheres proceed forward in the direction of the original motion. The incident sphere is initially spinning about its vertical axis in a clockwise sense. After the collision its spin velocity is in the same direction but has but one-half its former magnitude. What is the spin velocity of the second sphere?

6.18. At a particular instant the momentum of a particle is in the x-direction and its radius vector in the y-direction. How are the momentum, radius, and angular momentum affected by:

(a) Reflection about the x-axis.
(b) Reflection about the y-axis.
(c) 180° rotation about the origin.

6.19. A horizontally inclined cannon at the edge of a cliff 125 m above a level plain fires a projectile with velocity 500 m/sec. Plot the subsequent motion of the shell at 1-sec intervals seen from:

(a) An inertial system fixed relative to the earth.
(b) An inertial system moving with horizontal velocity 500 m/sec along the plain in the direction of the shell's motion.
Compare your graphs with Figure 4.12a.

6.20. The support stand of an harmonic oscillator (k = 100 N/m, M = 1 kg) moves with a constant velocity of 10 m/sec along a laboratory table. What is the period of the oscillator?

6.21. The origin of an inertial system B moves with a constant velocity of 2 m/sec along the x-axis of a system A. The x-axes of the systems coincide while the y- and z-axes are parallel (Figure 6.13). Transform the following measurements from system A to system B:

(a) x = 10 m at t = 0.
(b) x = 10 m at t = 2 sec.
(c) x = −2 m at t = 5 sec.
(d) v_x = 5 m/sec.
(e) v_x = −4 m/sec.
(f) a = 2.6 m/sec².

6.22. A particle of mass M_A is incident with velocity 12 m/sec upon a second particle with twice the mass which is initially at rest.

(a) What is the velocity of the system's center of mass?
(b) What are the velocities of the particles seen in an inertial system in which the center of mass is at rest?

6.23. Particle A in Problem 6.22 scatters from B at an angle 30° to its original direction and with a final speed of 8 m/sec.

(a) What are the x- and y-components of its final velocity? ($\sin 30° = 0.5$, $\cos 30° = 0.866$).

(b) What are the x- and y-components in an inertial system in which the center of mass of the two-body system is at rest?

(c) Using your answers to part b determine the final speed of A and the tangent of its scattering angle in the center of mass system.

6.24. In interstellar space (no gravity) at time t_0 a space ship A is moving upward with velocity 10^3 m/sec and acceleration 5 m/sec² relative to an observer B who is not accelerating. A ball in A is projected upward with initial velocity (in A) of 20 m/sec. For *each* observer what are the velocity and acceleration of the ball:

(a) Just after it leaves the projector?

(b) Just before it strikes the floor?

(c) At a time halfway between (a) and (b)?

6.25. A fast train accelerates forward at 9.8 m/sec². In order to determine the magnitude and direction of the gravitational force in this system an observer in the train hangs a plumb bob of mass M from the ceiling and notes the direction it hangs and the tension in the string from which it hangs.

(a) What is the magnitude and direction of the horizontal pseudoforce on the bob?

(b) What is the magnitude and direction of the "true" gravitational force on it?

(c) Using your answers to parts a and b, sketch the orientation of the plumb bob as seen by an observer at rest relative to the earth. What is the magnitude and direction of the total force upon it seen by an observer on the train? That is, what is the effective magnitude and direction of **g** on the train?

6.26. A train traveling at a constant speed 50 m/sec rounds a curve with radius 254 m. An observer on the train hangs a plumb bob from the ceiling in order to measure the magnitude and direction of **g** in his system. What does he conclude?

6.27. A space station in the form of a flat, 100-m radius disk rotates about its axis with constant speed. The orbital speed of a point on its rim relative to the axis is 40 m/sec.

(a) What is the pseudoforce exerted on a 10-kg object at the rim?

(b) At what distance from the axis is the pseudogravitational environment most like the earth's "real" gravitational environment?

The conservation of energy

7

▲▲ 7.1 Introduction: the energy concept in physics

The study of natural processes involves analysis of the motion of systems or, more generally, analysis of changes in these systems. Therefore, it is quite natural to concentrate at first upon identifying and measuring changes in the relevant variables of the systems, variables such as displacement, velocity, acceleration, and force. Indeed this was the approach taken by Newton and by the eighteenth-century physicists who followed him: in short, concentrate upon the way a system changes and from those changes try to deduce the basic interactions involved.

However, as indicated in Chapter 6, there is another way to approach an understanding of natural processes: to ask if anything about a system remains constant regardless of any change that may occur. This approach leads to the conservation laws which offer a new and deeper insight into the nature of physical processes in general. The laws are also indispensable in the study of systems that are too complex to be handled by the sort of detailed analytical treatment typified by the gravitational problems of Chapters 4 and 5.

For example, the experimentally established law of momentum conservation was introduced in Chapter 4 principally as a means for defining the concept of force and, with force well defined, became a side issue. However, the conservation law illuminates the momentum concept itself in a way that Newton's second law cannot since it suggests that momentum is important simply because it *is* conserved. Going one step further, it is possible to show that the conservation of momentum reflects the homogeneity of space as indicated in Chapter 6. Thus the momentum conservation law is connected with a fundamental invariance property of the physical universe.

In the late eighteenth century the French chemist Lavoisier proved experimentally that the total mass of the substances involved in any chemical reaction is the same before and after the reaction. From his research Lavoisier concluded that matter is conserved, and thereby laid an indispensable basis for the development of quantitative chemistry. No violation of the law has ever been observed, though it was generalized by Einstein in his special theory of relativity.

The law of energy conservation is one of the most important principles in physics because of its ready applicability to such seemingly diverse topics as the motion of macroscopic objects, the thermal characteristics of matter, the production, transmission,

210

and reception of light, and properties of atomic and subatomic systems. On the other hand the energy concept itself is often misunderstood by beginning students. Elementary treatments often leave the impression that energy is some type of all-permeating, elusive fluid that in the course of a physical process flows from one part of a system to another. Of course nothing of the sort is true. Like momentum, energy is a constructed quantity used to characterize the behavior of systems, a quantity that is a constant of systems and useful just for that reason. If this were a universe in which the algebraic quantity called energy were not conserved then it would be necessary, or at least useful, to find some other quantity that was.

Nevertheless, the experimentally based energy conservation law is remarkable. First enunciated and verified in the mid-nineteenth century as a means of connecting the mechanical and thermal properties of matter, it has since been generalized to cover the whole of physics. As it has managed to withstand and repulse several attacks upon its integrity in the present century it now stands as one of the most basic foundation stones upon which the edifice of physics rests.

▲▲ 7.2   The work integral.   Conservative forces

Before turning to the energy concept it is convenient to introduce the idea of work. By definition, the work performed by a force in displacing a body a distance s over a particular path is the product of the magnitude of that displacement times the component of the force *in the direction of the displacement*. The concept combines force and motion in a very special way. For instance, a force does no work upon a body unless it *moves* the body, and only its component *parallel* to the direction of motion is effective in doing work.

At least two forces act upon a body at rest on a level surface: the gravitational attraction of the earth and the upward reaction force of the surface. But as neither of these results in a displacement, neither performs work. In Figure 7.1a a body on a level surface

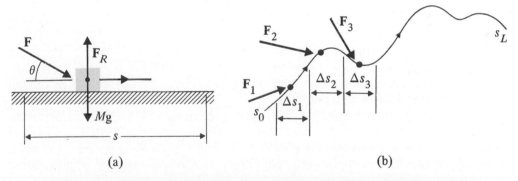

(a)   (b)

FIGURE 7.1.   (a) The work performed by a constant force **F** in displacing a body a distance s along a level surface is $(F \cos \theta)s$. The gravitational force, Mg, and the reaction force of the table, $\mathbf{F}_R$, do no work on the body. However, they enter indirectly by constraining it to remain on the table. (b) Both the magnitude of the force on a body and its direction relative to the displacement path may change as the body moves from S_0 to S_L. In such cases the work performed by the force may be approximated by breaking up the path into segments of length, Δs_1, Δs_2, Δs_3, small enough so that $F \cos \theta$ is approximately constant over each one. The total work over the entire path is the sum of the work performed over each segment.

is displaced a distance s by a constant force $\mathbf{F}$ which makes an angle θ with the surface. The parallel component of this force (i.e., the component in the direction of the displacement) is $F \cos \theta$. Therefore, it does work:

$$W = Fs \cos \theta. \tag{7.1}$$

Neither the weight of the body nor the upward reaction force of the table is *explicitly* involved since neither does any work. However, both enter indirectly in constraining the body to move along the surface.

The work performed on a body need not be constant over the entire course of its displacement since either the total force, $\mathbf{F}$, or its angle with the path may vary (Figure 7.1b). Let the displacement path be divided into many small, equal segments, $\Delta s_1, \Delta s_2, \Delta s_3, \ldots$, let $F_1, F_2, F_3, \ldots$, be the average magnitudes of the forces over each respective segment, and $\theta_1, \theta_2, \theta_3, \ldots$, the angle between each force vector and the direction of the displacement. Then the work performed over the first segment of path is approximately:

$$\Delta W_1 = F_1 \Delta s_1 \cos \theta_1,$$

over the second:

$$\Delta W_2 = F_2 \Delta s_2 \cos \theta_2,$$

etc. The total work over the entire path is the sum of these individual contributions,

$$\begin{aligned} W &= F_1 \Delta s_1 \cos \theta_1 + F_2 \Delta s_2 \cos \theta_2 + F_3 \Delta s_3 \cos \theta_3 + \cdots \\ &= (F_1 \cos \theta_1 + F_2 \cos \theta_2 + F_3 \theta_3 + \cdots) \Delta s, \end{aligned} \tag{7.2}$$

since the lengths of the segments are equal. As the lengths of the segments approach zero (and are written as ds_1, ds_2, etc.) the respective average forces attain their exact values at each point along the path.

The total work over the entire path is then expressed exactly as the integral of the parallel force component along the path (see Chapter appendix):

$$W = \int_{s_0}^{s_L} F \cos \theta \, ds. \tag{7.3}$$

The unit of work in the mks system is the *joule** (pronounced "jewel"). From the defining equation, 1 joule (J) = 1 newton-meter. Since work is the product of the component of a force times a distance it is a scalar quantity, even though work is performed over a particular displacement path.

Both Equation 7.2 and Equation 7.3, which corresponds to the limit of Equation 7.2 as $\Delta s \to 0$, may be interpreted geometrically. Figure 7.2 shows $F \cos \theta$, the parallel component of some arbitrary force plotted at all points along some path s. The work performed by the force in displacing a body from s_1 to s_2 is approximated by the product of the average parallel component of the force over that interval and the length of the interval. This is just the area of the rectangle with base $s_2 - s_1$ and height equal to the height of the curve at the midpoint of the interval, the shaded region of Figure 7.2. Referring to Equation 7.2, the total work performed between s_0 and s_L is approximated by the sum of all such rectangular areas between s_0 and s_L. As the lengths of the displacement segments decrease, the areas of the rectangles become closer approximations to the actual area under the curve. In the limit as the segments become very small, their sum is exactly

---

* Named in honor of the nineteenth-century scientist and brewer James Prescott Joule.

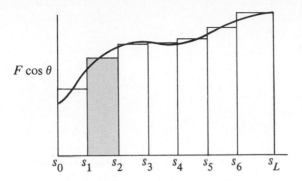

FIGURE 7.2 If the force component $F \cos \theta$ (see Figure 7.1b) is plotted as a function of s, the distance along the displacement path from s_0, the work performed by the force over the segment $\Delta s = s_2 - s_1$ is approximately $(F \cos \theta)_{\text{Av}} \Delta s$, where $(F \cos \theta)_{\text{Av}}$ is the average value of the parallel force component over that segment. This product is equal to the area of the shaded rectangle. The total work performed from s_0 to s_L is approximated by the sum of all such areas between s_0 and s_L. As the size of each interval Δs decreases, the validity of the approximation increases and in the limit as $\Delta s \to 0$ becomes exact. Therefore, the total work performed is equal to the area under the curve.

equal to the area. Therefore, Equation 7.3 implies that the total work performed in displacing a body from s_0 to s_L is equal to the total area under the curve representing the force component as a function of displacement. In general, the area must be calculated using techniques of the integral calculus, although purely geometric methods are applicable in a few cases. The finite sum, Equation 7.2, can often yield very good results provided the segments Δs are sufficiently small.

The total work performed on a body by many important forces is independent of the displacement path chosen, varying only with the locations of the end points of the path. Hence the work performed on a body in traversing *any* path between two points may be calculated once and for all by choosing the path for which the calculation is simplest. Such forces are called *conservative*.

The gravitational force is a prime example of such a conservative force. In free fall the direction of the force and the resultant displacement are in the same direction (Figure 7.3a). Therefore, if a mass M falls a distance Δy the work performed on it must be:

$$W = F \Delta y = Mg \, \Delta y. \tag{7.4a}$$

Consider the same mass sliding down a frictionless inclined plane inclined at an angle θ to the horizontal (Figure 7.3b). Only the component of the weight parallel to the surface, $Mg \sin \theta$, results in a displacement. If the length of the incline is l, the work performed in displacing the mass from top to bottom is $W = Mgl \sin \theta$. But $l \sin \theta = \Delta y$, the vertical height of the plane, so again $W = Mg \, \Delta y$. The work performed by the gravitational force in displacing a body along a frictionless inclined plane depends only upon the *vertical* component of its displacement, and is equal to the work that would have been performed in displacing the body the same *vertical* distance in free fall.

Now let us calculate the work performed by the gravitational force when a body is lifted vertically a distance Δy. In this case the directions of the displacement and

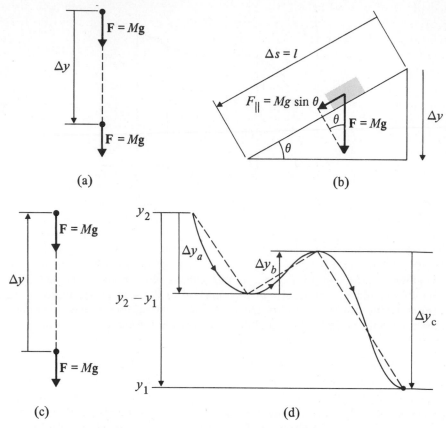

FIGURE 7.3 (a) For a body in free fall the displacement Δy is parallel to the constant gravitational force acting on it. Therefore, $W = Mg\,\Delta y$. (b) The displacement path of a body on a frictionless inclined plane is along the surface of the plane. Since the component of the gravitational force parallel to the plane performs work on the body, $W = (Mg \sin \theta)l = Mg\,\Delta y$. (c) The displacement path Δy of a body thrown straight upward is directly opposite the constant gravitational force upon it, so $W = -Mg\,\Delta y$. (d) Any arbitrary path between two points can be approximated by a series of inclines. The quantities of work performed by the gravitational force over the three inclines in the drawing are $W_a = Mg\,\Delta y_a$, $W_b = -Mg\,\Delta y_b$, and $W_c = Mg\,\Delta y_c$, respectively. Therefore, the work over the entire path is $Mg(\Delta y_a - \Delta y_b + \Delta y_c) = Mg(y_2 - y_1)$.

gravitational force are exactly opposite so that $\theta = 180°$, and $\cos \theta = -1$ in Equation 7.1. Therefore (Figure 7.3c):

$$W = -Mg\,\Delta y. \tag{7.4b}$$

The work performed by the gravitational force is *negative*. Likewise, if a mass is pushed *up* a frictionless inclined plane the component of the force parallel to the displacement must be $-Mgl \sin \theta = -Mg\,\Delta y$.

Finally, suppose a body slides down the frictionless roller coaster track shown in Figure 7.3d. What is the total work performed by the gravitational force? According to Equation 7.2 we are to determine the work along each small segment of path, then sum all of these contributions. But each segment may be approximated as a small inclined plane of vertical height Δy_i, so the work performed over each is $-Mg\,\Delta y_i$ or $+Mg\,\Delta y_i$ depending on whether the segment inclines upward or downward. It follows that the total work performed by the gravitational force is simply $Mg(y_2 - y_1)$, exactly as if the body had fallen directly over the same vertical distance. We have derived an important general result. Regardless of the displacement path between two points, the work performed by the gravitational force in carrying a mass M over that path is $\pm Mg\,\Delta y$, where Δy is the vertical distance between the points. The positive sign indicates that the vertical component of the displacement is in the direction of the force, or downward. The negative sign implies a net upward displacement.

▲▲ 7.3 Work and kinetic energy. Work performed by gravitational and linear restoring forces

A body displaced along a particular path by any force will be accelerated by that force. An expression for the resultant change in velocity for the case of free fall may be obtained by applying the proper kinematic equations from Chapter 2.

If a mass M falls from a point y_2 to y_1 the work performed by the gravitational force is

$$W = Mg(y_2 - y_1).$$

The work performed must be positive if y_2 is greater than y_1. We also know that the speed at y_1 must be smaller than at y_2 since the body accelerates as it falls. Therefore, the free-fall equations (Equations 2.12) take the form:

$$y_2 - y_1 = v_2 t + \tfrac{1}{2}gt^2,$$
$$v_1 - v_2 = gt,$$

where v_2 and v_1 are the speeds at y_2 and y_1, respectively, and t is the time required for the body to fall between the two points. From the first of these equations, $Mg(y_2 - y_1) = Mv_2 gt + \tfrac{1}{2}M(gt)^2$, and from the second, $gt = v_1 - v_2$. Thus,

$$Mg(y_2 - y_1) = Mv_2(v_1 - v_2) + \tfrac{1}{2}M(v_1 - v_2)^2,$$
$$= Mv_1 v_2 - Mv_2^2 + \tfrac{1}{2}Mv_1^2 - Mv_1 v_2 + \tfrac{1}{2}Mv_1^2,$$
$$= \tfrac{1}{2}Mv_1^2 - \tfrac{1}{2}Mv_2^2.$$

Therefore,

$$W = Mgy_2 - Mgy_1 = \tfrac{1}{2}Mv_1^2 - \tfrac{1}{2}Mv_2^2. \tag{7.5}$$

The scalar quantity $\tfrac{1}{2}Mv^2$ is called *kinetic* energy.* (*Kinetic* is derived from the Greek word for motion.) Equation 7.5 states that the work performed on a body in free fall is equal to the change in its kinetic energy. If y_2 is greater than y_1 a positive amount of work is performed, and the kinetic energy increases. As we showed in Section 7.2 the gravitational force is conservative so that the same amount of work is performed over any path between two points with the same vertical coordinates. Although it is by no means obvious, a given amount of work performed by the gravitational force *always* results in the same change in kinetic energy. Therefore, Equation 7.5 is a general result completely independent of the path taken between the end points, and v_1^2 and v_2^2 are the squares of the *total* velocity and not of any particular component. The direction of v_2 and v_1 need not be the same but in fact depend upon the particular path over which the

---

* Since work is equal to the change in kinetic energy, the latter quantity is also measured in joules.

body is displaced. For example, in free fall the velocities are both completely vertical, in motion along an incline they are parallel to the plane, whereas in motion along a roller coaster track, v_2 is in the direction tangent to the track at y_2, and v_1 in the direction tangent to the track at v_2 (Figure 7.3).

It is frequently simpler to solve problems using Equation 7.5 instead of the kinematic equations of Chapter 2. For example, suppose a body, which is initially at rest, falls to the ground from a height y_0. What is its velocity the instant before it strikes the ground? Choosing the downward direction as positive and the origin on the ground, $y_2 = +y_0$, $y_1 = 0$; also $v_2 = 0$. Therefore, $Mgy_0 = \frac{1}{2}Mv_1^2$, and $v_1 = \sqrt{2gy_0}$, a result obtained in Chapter 2 (Section 2.5) by using the free-fall kinematic equations. However, the result obtained here is much more general. Equation 7.5 is applicable over *any* path between two points with vertical coordinates y_2 and y_1. It follows that the magnitude of the velocity of a body that slides to the ground over an incline of vertical height y_0 or over a roller coaster track of maximum height y_0 is also $\sqrt{2gy_0}$. Obtaining the latter result with the methods of Chapter 2 would be particularly tedious. On the other hand we should realize that Equation 7.5 by itself does not yield complete information about motion caused by the gravitational force. It says nothing about the time required for a body to move between the end points of its path, for instance. To obtain such detailed information it is necessary to use the detailed equations of Chapter 2.

Let us calculate the change in the velocity of a body resulting from work performed on it by a linear restoring force (Section 4.9). According to Hooke's law (Equation 4.17) a spring that is stretched (or compressed) a distance x from equilibrium exerts a force $-kx$ upon an attached mass. If the force exerted by the spring displaces the mass a small distance Δx then, by definition, it performs work:

$$\Delta W = -kx\,\Delta x.$$

The minus sign indicates that the work is negative when the displacement is away from equilibrium, positive when it is toward equilibrium. Because the restoring force is not constant the work over a given displacement Δx depends upon the distance from equilibrium. Therefore, the total work performed over a large distance must be calculated by dividing the distance into small subintervals of length Δx, calculating the work performed over each, and taking the sum of all these contributions. Because the algebraic expression for the force is simple, we can carry out this calculation by using the general graphical method illustrated by Figure 7.2.

Figure 7.4 plots the force exerted by a spring as a function of its displacement from equilibrium. The total work performed by the linear restoring force of the spring in displacing a mass from x_2 to x_1 is simply the difference between the areas under the curve with the respective bases x_2 and x_1. Since the areas are triangular:

$$W = \tfrac{1}{2}kx_2^2 - \tfrac{1}{2}kx_1^2. \tag{7.6}$$

If x_2 is farther from equilibrium than x_1 the work performed is positive.

Now consider a spring stretched a distance x_0 from equilibrium and then released. The attached mass will oscillate about equilibrium with amplitude $\pm x_0$ and period $T = 2\pi\sqrt{M/k}$ (Equation 4.23), its displacement and velocity given as functions of time by Equation 4.25:

$$x = x_0 \cos\left(\frac{2\pi t}{T}\right),$$

$$v = -\frac{2\pi x_0}{T}\sin\left(\frac{2\pi t}{T}\right).$$

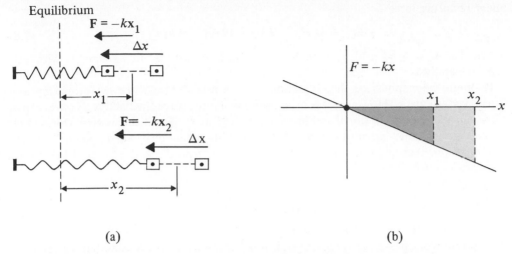

FIGURE 7.4   (a) The work performed by a linear restoring force in displacing a particle over a given path segment Δx depends on the distance of that segment from equilibrium, since the force itself is proportional to that distance. (b) The work performed by a linear restoring force in displacing a particle from x_2 to x_1 ($x_2 > x_1$) is the difference between the triangular areas with bases x_2 and x_1 under the force-vs-distance curve (see Figure 7.2). If the displacement is toward equilibrium the bases are negative and the work positive.

When the mass is at its maximum displacement, $x = \pm x_0$, its velocity is zero; one-quarter cycle later when the mass passes through the equilibrium point $x = 0$, its velocity attains its maximum magnitude, $v_{\max} = \pm 2\pi x_0/T$. Referring to Equation 7.6, the work performed by the restoring force in displacing the spring from x_0 to 0 is:

$$W = \tfrac{1}{2}kx_0^2.$$

We can express the work in terms of the maximum velocity by substituting $x_0 = \pm Tv_{\max}/2\pi$:

$$W = \frac{1}{2}k\left(\frac{T}{2\pi}\right)^2 v_{\max}^2.$$

But $T^2 = (2\pi)^2 M/k$; therefore:

$$W = \tfrac{1}{2}Mv_{\max}^2.$$

The work performed on the mass in displacing it from x_0 to equilibrium can be expressed, as in the gravitational case, in terms of a change in kinetic energy. (Since the kinetic energy of the mass is zero when $x = \pm x_0$, the work increases the kinetic energy of the mass.)

Using methods of the integral calculus it may be shown that, in general, the work performed by a force in displacing a body along a path from point 2 to point 1 is *always* equal to the difference in the body's kinetic energy at the two end points:

$$W_{21} = \tfrac{1}{2}Mv_1^2 - \tfrac{1}{2}Mv_2^2. \tag{7.7}$$

If W_{21} is positive, then v_2 must be greater than v_1. We have considered two specific examples in this section. If the force is the constant gravitational attraction of the earth, then $W_{21} = Mg(y_2 - y_1)$, and Equation 7.7 reduces to Equation 7.5. In the case of a linear restoring force,

$$W_{21} = \tfrac{1}{2}kx_2^2 - \tfrac{1}{2}kx_1^2 = \tfrac{1}{2}Mv_1^2 - \tfrac{1}{2}Mv_2^2, \tag{7.8}$$

which, for $x_2 = \pm x_0$ and $x_1 = 0$, becomes $\tfrac{1}{2}kx_0^2 = \tfrac{1}{2}Mv_{\text{max}}^2$, in agreement with our previous analysis.

It should be emphasized that Equation 7.7 is applicable to work performed by any force over any path. However, it is most useful when the force involved is a conservative force, such as the gravitational and linear restoring forces. For if the work performed by a force is path independent it can be related to another function called *potential energy*, and equations such as Equations 7.5 and 7.8 can be interpreted as examples of the energy conservation principle.

▲▲ 7.4 Potential energy. The restricted energy conservation law

The energy of a single particle or system is defined as its ability to do work. Any system that *can* do work possesses energy, even if it never makes use of its capabilities. In fact, we shall see that when a system actually *does* perform work it inevitably loses at least part of its capacity to do more.

It is not difficult to see that the expression for kinetic energy we introduced in Section 7.3 is consistent with the above definition. Suppose a body with kinetic energy $\tfrac{1}{2}Mv^2$ is brought to rest by a system which is itself displaced as it decelerates the body. The system might be a spring that compresses when struck by the moving body, or a stake driven some distance into the ground by a falling body, for instance (Figure 7.5). At each instant during the deceleration process the system and the decelerating mass exert equal and opposite forces upon each other. Since the system is displaced, work is performed on it

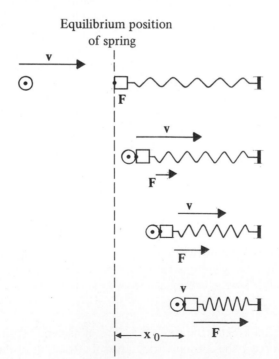

Equilibrium position
of spring

FIGURE 7.5 Proof that a moving particle has the ability to perform work. As the particle is decelerated, it exerts a force upon the spring equal and opposite to the linear restoring force of the latter. Therefore, in coming to rest the particle performs work $\tfrac{1}{2}kx_0^2$.

by the force exerted by the decelerating mass. Thus it is clear that a moving body has the ability to do work. Referring to Equation 7.7 and recalling Newton's third law it seems clear that the expression $\frac{1}{2}Mv^2$ is a reasonable measure of that capacity.*

A physical system can also have the capability of doing work by virtue of the relative positions of its components. In that case it has *potential* energy. For instance, in Figure 7.6 a mass M_A rests initially on a table top a distance y_1 from the floor, and is attached by means of a taut string and pulley to a second, smaller mass resting on the floor. No work is done while M_A remains on the table. But in falling it would exert an upward force $M_A g$ upon M_B, displacing it a total distance y_1. Therefore, while resting on the table, M_A has *capacity* to do work simply by falling to the floor. It need not do this work via a pulley system; it need do no work at all. Nonetheless it has gravitational potential energy $M_A g y_1$ relative to the floor simply because it *could* do that much work by falling.

When the mass M_A reaches the floor it can fall no farther, and hence has lost all of its potential energy. However, if the floor on which it rests is a distance y_2 above the level of a lower floor, the force exerted by M_A could do work $M_A g y_2$ by falling the additional distance. Even after it had fallen that distance it might still be able to fall to a still lower floor, a distance y_3 below, and do work $M_A g y_3$, and beyond this there might be another floor, a distance y_4 below, etc. The mass does not have an absolute gravitational potential energy, but rather a potential energy at one position relative to another position.

Generalizing from this example, if a particle is located at a point s_1 then its *gravitational potential energy* relative to some reference point s_0 is equal to the gravitation work that the gravitational force associated with it would perform when it moves from s_1 to s_0. This amount of work is equal and opposite to the work performed on the body by the gravitational force of the earth in moving it from s_0 to s_1 (Section 7.2). Thus we can also

FIGURE 7.6 The body resting on the table could perform work $M_A g y_1$ by falling to the floor (by means of the pulley arrangment shown, for example). Therefore, it has potential energy $M_A g y_1$ relative to the floor. Potential energy is always defined relative to some reference state. Thus M_A has potential energy $M_A g(y_1 + y_2)$ relative to Floor 2, $M_A g(y_1 + y_3)$ relative to Floor 3, and $M_A g(y_1 + y_4)$ relative to Floor 4. It also has negative potential energy $-M_A g y_c$ relative to the ceiling, implying that work must be performed on it to raise it to that level.

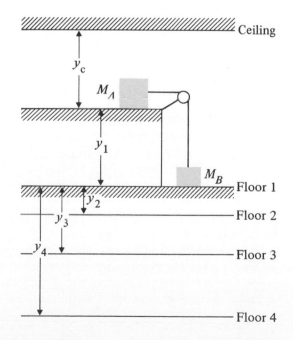

* Generally, however, not all the kinetic energy of a moving body is transferred into work performed on a decelerating system. A good deal is usually transformed into heat energy (see Section 7.8 and Chapter 16).

define the gravitational potential energy of a mass at s_0 relative to s_1 as the negative of the work that would have to be performed on it by the earth's gravitational force in carrying it from s_1 back to s_0. In either case the work performed is independent of the path between the two points. Therefore, the gravitational potential energy of a mass at s_1 cannot depend on how it got to s_1 in the first place, nor can any work that the force that displaces the body performs depend on how the body travels from s_1 to s_0. It is just this path-independent feature, valid for all conservative forces, that makes potential energy a meaningful concept.

If the gravitational force on a body is constant at all points between s_0 and s_1 (if near the earth's surface, for example) the work required to carry it between the points is given by Equation 7.4:

$$W = Mg \, \Delta y,$$

where $\Delta y = y_1 - y_0$ is the vertical component of the displacement from s_0 to s_1. For instance, the potential energy of a mass M resting on a top of an inclined plane a distance y_1 above the floor is Mgy_1 relative to the floor, since the work required to lift it a distance y_1 above the floor is independent of the path taken. If y_0 is higher than y_1 the potential energy at y_1 is negative relative to y_0, implying a negative capacity for work or the necessity of performing work on a body to displace it from y_1 to y_0.

It is worth noting that if a system has the ability to do work by virtue of the relative positions of its components it will usually do that work unless restrained. For example, in Figure 7.6 the gravitational force upon M_A would certainly perform work on M_B if M_A were not held at rest by the upward force of the table top. Therefore, if a body has potential energy then normally two forces act upon it. One of these is the force by virtue of which it has the ability to do work, the gravitational force in the present instance. The other is an equal and opposite force which restrains the body from utilizing that capacity and thus preserves its potential energy. Because two forces in equilibrium must act on a body if its potential energy is to remain constant, the concept is somewhat more subtle than kinetic energy. For a moving body has kinetic energy whether or not a force acts upon it, and the application of a single force always results in a change in its kinetic energy.

Another example of potential energy is readily available. If a spring is displaced a distance x_2 from equilibrium, the linear restoring force associated with it can perform work upon an attached mass by displacing it from x_2 to some other point, x_1. Referring to Equation 7.6, the spring-mass system has potential energy $\frac{1}{2}k(x_2^2 - x_1^2)$ at x_2 relative to x_1. But the compressed (or stretched) spring can only retain its potential energy as long as it performs no work; as soon as it does its potential energy decreases. Once again a force equal and opposite to the linear restoring force is required to keep the spring in its compressed (or stretched) state.

We can proceed from these examples to a general definition of potential energy. If a system in a state s_2 can, by virtue of the *conservative* forces associated with it, perform work W_{21} in moving to another state s_1, then the change in its potential energy between s_2 and s_1 is equal to the work it performs:

$$(PE)_2 - (PE_1) = W_{21}. \tag{7.9a}$$

If W_{21} is positive, then the potential energy at s_2 is greater than the potential energy at s_1. Usually some reference state is arbitrarily designated as the state of zero potential energy: ground level in the gravitational case, equilibrium for a spring system. If s_1 is that zero point, then

$$(PE)_2 = W_{21}. \tag{7.9b}$$

If a body falls a distance y its gravitational potential energy decreases from Mgy to zero. However, at the same time its kinetic energy increases from zero to $\frac{1}{2}Mv^2$ with (Equation 7.5) $\frac{1}{2}Mv^2 = Mgy$. Likewise, if a compressed spring displaces a mass from x_0 to equilibrium its potential energy decreases from $\frac{1}{2}kx_0^2$ to zero, but the kinetic energy of the mass increases from zero to $\frac{1}{2}Mv^2 = \frac{1}{2}kx_0^2$ (Equation 7.8). By definition, work is performed by the conservative forces associated with a system when the potential energy of the system changes (Equation 7.9). If that work is performed on the system itself (as with the falling body) or on part of the system (as with the mass-spring system), then it must result in an internal change in kinetic energy (Equation 7.7). Combining Equations 7.7 and 7.9,

$$(PE)_2 - (PE)_1 = \frac{1}{2}Mv_1^2 - \frac{1}{2}Mv_2^2, \tag{7.10a}$$

or

$$(PE)_2 + \frac{1}{2}Mv_2^2 = (PE)_1 + \frac{1}{2}Mv_1^2, \tag{7.10b}$$

or, finally,

$$(PE) + \frac{1}{2}Mv^2 = \text{const.} \tag{7.10c}$$

These equations are alternate statements of the restricted energy conservation law. *If a system (or single body) performs no external work, the sum of its potential and kinetic energies remains constant.* Such a system is called an *isolated* system, with the term having much the same connotation as the isolated systems defined in Chapter 4 in connection with the momentum conservation law.

▲▲ 7.5 Examples of energy conservation in mechanics. Potential energy diagrams

Since the restricted energy conservation principle was derived by using Newton's laws and the kinematic relations of Chapter 2, its application to a specific problem cannot yield information that is not obtainable directly from the laws themselves. However, it often yields the same results much more easily.

The simplification afforded by the principle results, in the main, from three mathematical properties of energy:

1. The potential energy of a system in a specific state is independent of its past history, i.e., how it got to that state.
2. The kinetic energy of a mass M is *always* given by the expression $\frac{1}{2}Mv^2$.
3. Energy is a scalar quantity, in contrast to force and acceleration, which are vectors.

In Figure 7.7, a body of mass M is at rest on the top of a frictionless track a distance y_2 above the baseline $y = 0$, and has potential energy Mgy_2 relative to the baseline. Presumably an external force was used to raise the mass to the point x_a, and thus to supply it with potential energy. But the details of the trip are unimportant. M has energy Mgy_2, and retains that energy as long as it does no external work.

If the body slides down the track, part of its potential energy is converted into kinetic energy; at the baseline the conversion is complete, and $\frac{1}{2}Mv^2 = Mgy_2$. To the right of the point x_b, part of the kinetic energy is converted back to potential energy. The

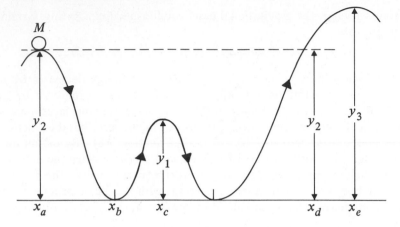

FIGURE 7.7 The mass M slides down the frictionless roller coaster track starting from rest at the point x_a, y_2, and at that point has potential energy Mgy_2 relative to the baseline, and kinetic energy zero. Therefore, its total energy is Mgy_2 throughout its motion. Clearly the particle cannot move to the right of the point x_d unless it is supplied with additional energy. It could have reached the point x_3 if it had had kinetic energy equal to $Mg(y_3 - y_2)$ at the beginning of its trip, for then its total energy would have been Mgy_3 rather than Mgy_2.

difference between the potential energy at x_a and x_c immediately gives the kinetic energy at the latter point:

$$\tfrac{1}{2}Mv^2 = Mg(y_2 - y_1).$$

To the right of x_c the potential energy is converted to kinetic, so the velocity at the second valley is equal to the velocity at the first. Beyond the second valley, kinetic energy is again converted to potential, and the velocity decreases. When $v = 0$ the potential energy is Mgy_2. The body reaches the point x_d whose height is y_2, precisely the level from which it started, since the difference in the potential energies at x_d and x_a is zero. The difference in potential energies at x_a and x_e, $Mg(y_2 - y_3)$, is a negative quantity since y_3 is greater than y_2. Thus an equivalent amount of work would have to be supplied by an external force to raise the mass to the higher level.

In applying the restricted conservation law it is imperative to define carefully the extent of the isolated system being considered, since the law requires that the system can perform no external work. A mass oscillating at the end of a spring does not constitute an energy-conserving system, but the mass and spring together do. As the mass is displaced from $\pm x_0$ to 0 the potential energy of the spring is transferred to kinetic energy of the mass; as the mass is displaced from 0 to $\pm x_0$ its kinetic energy is transferred back into potential energy of the spring.

The mass M_A in Figure 7.6 does *not* constitute an isolated system, for as it falls the gravitational force on it performs work upon M_B. But M_A and M_B together with the connecting string and pulley do. If the string is assumed weightless and the pulley both weightless and frictionless we can concentrate on the masses. Initially both are at rest so that the total kinetic energy of the system is zero. In addition, the potential energy of M_B relative to the floor is zero. Therefore the total energy of the system is $M_A gy$, the potential energy of M_A. As the mass falls its potential energy decreases, while its kinetic energy as well as both the kinetic and potential energy of M_B increase.

Just before M_A strikes the floor the total energy of the system is:

$$M_B g y_1 + \tfrac{1}{2}(M_A + M_B)v^2,$$

where the taut string assures us that the velocities of the masses are equal. But since this energy must be equal to the initial energy $M_A g y_1$ we have

$$\tfrac{1}{2}(M_B + M_B)v^2 = (M_A - M_B)g y_1,$$

or

$$v^2 = \frac{2(M_A - M_B)}{M_A + M_B} g y_1.$$

If $M_B = 0$ then we have a case of free fall, and $v = \sqrt{2gy_1}$, in agreement with our earlier conclusions.

The oscillation of a pendulum can be analyzed in terms equivalent to the motion of a particle on a frictionless track (Figure 7.8). A pendulum bob initially displaced through an angle θ_0, is a vertical distance y_1 from its vertical equilibrium level. The external force that first displaced the bob to the level y_1 supplies it with energy Mgy_1 which it retains as long as it does no work. At the equilibrium level $y = 0$, the energy is all kinetic, and $\tfrac{1}{2}Mv_0^2 = Mgy_1$, or $v_0 = \sqrt{2gy_1}$. Beyond $y = 0$ the kinetic energy is converted back to potential, and when $v = 0$ the conversion is complete. The bob comes to rest at exactly the same level as its initial vertical displacement. During its next quarter cycle the pendulum again converts its potential energy into kinetic energy, and this quarter cycle is followed in turn by a quarter cycle during which kinetic energy is transformed back to potential energy. Thus its oscillation may be represented in terms of a continuous interchange between potential and kinetic energy. If the pendulum bob does no external work its maximum amplitude at the end of each cycle remains constant, and each cycle is a faithful copy of its predecessor.

The motion of a body with known potential energy as a function of its displacement from some arbitrary point can be analyzed with the aid of a convenient graphical method.

Figure 7.9a plots the potential energy Mgy of a body on an inclined plane as a function of its horizontal distance, $x = 0$ to $x = L$, along the base of the plane. For convenience the potential energy at the base is defined as the zero point. Three horizontal lines on the same graph, E_A, E_B, and E_C, represent three possible, total energies the mass on the plane might have. Since its potential energy is always represented by the sloping line and its total energy is constant, the **kinetic** energy of the body at any point x is proportional to

FIGURE 7.8 If the initial height of a pendulum bob above its equilibrium level is known, the velocity of the bob at any other point follows from energy conservation. In particular, it is evident that the bob rises no higher then y_1 during the course of its oscillation about equilibrium.

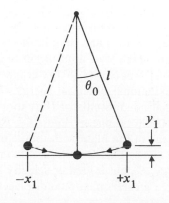

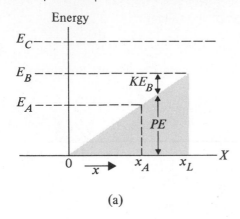
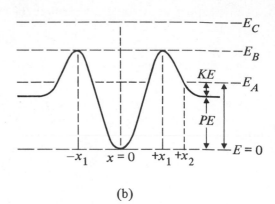

(a)   (b)

FIGURE 7.9 (a) Energy diagram for a body on an inclined plane. The potential energy as a function of x is equal to the vertical distance from the x-axis to the potential energy line, while the total energy is represented by a horizontal line. Therefore, the kinetic energy of the body is equal to the distance between the potential energy line and the appropriate total energy line. Three possible values of total energy are shown. (b) Energy diagram for a more complicated variation of potential energy with x. Again, three possible values of total energy are shown.

the length of the vertical line drawn from the plane at that point to the appropriate total energy line.

For instance, a mass that slides down the plane starting from rest at $x = L$ initially has zero kinetic energy, so its energy is represented by the line E_B. Since its kinetic energy at $x = 0$ is Mgy its kinetic energy at any other point can be determined immediately by measuring the length of the vertical line from the plane to the line E_B. If a mass with the same kinetic energy approached the plane from some negative value of x its total energy would also be E_B, and would be just sufficient to carry it to the top of the plane. A body with kinetic energy E_A approaching the plane from the bottom with kinetic energy E_C at $x = 0$ would have a velocity greater than zero at the top of the plane.

Figure 7.9b shows a more complicated graph of gravitational potential energy, and again shows three possible total energies: E_A, E_B, E_C. A body with energy E_A approaching $x = x_2$ from the outside gradually expends its kinetic energy in sliding up the slope of the hill, but stops before reaching the apex and slides back once again. A mass inside the well with the same total energy also expends its kinetic energy before reaching either apex, and thus remains trapped within the well oscillating from one side to the other. A mass with energy E_B can just surmount the barrier, while a mass with energy E_C reaches $x = x_1$ with velocity to spare. In all cases the bodies have greater velocities at the bottom of the well than on the level approaches to it.

The utility of the potential energy graphs is not limited to analysis of the motion of a body with gravitational potential energy. For instance, Figure 7.10 plots the potential energy of an harmonic oscillator (Equation 7.6) as a function of its displacement from equilibrium. The total energy lines, E_A, E_B, E_C have the same meaning as before. At $x = 0$ the energy of the mass with total energy E_A is completely kinetic, but completely potential at $x = x_0$. This is therefore its maximum displacement. A mass with greater potential energy, E_B, has a greater velocity at equilibrium than the mass with energy E_A, and therefore, a greater maximum displacement from equilibrium. If the total energy of

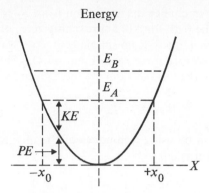

ΓIGURE 7.10   Energy diagram showing the potential energy of a simple harmonic oscillator plotted as a function of x, the distance from equilibrium, along with two possible values of total energy.

an harmonic system is known, its velocity at any displacement, x, can be found by consulting the graph.

Figure 7.10 could also be used to study the motion of a particle with total energy E_A sliding back and forth along a frictionless track with the same shape as the graph, since the graph would then represent its gravitational potential energy as a function of displacement from the origin. Such a body would attain maximum velocity at $x = 0$, would come to rest at $x = \pm x_1$, and continue to oscillate between these two points. Hence in the energy representation, the motion of an harmonic oscillator can be discussed in terms completely analogous to the motion of a particle with a particular sort of gravitational potential energy.

▲▲ 7.6   The potential energy corresponding to an inverse square force

Although we have stated that the restricted energy conservation law is valid for any potential energy that is related to a conservative force, our applications have involved only the constant gravitational force exerted by the earth near its surface and the linear restoring force typified by a spring displaced from equilibrium.

Let us now consider the potential of two particles that exert an inverse square force upon each other. Newton's law of gravitation (Equation 5.4b) is, of course, a prime example:

$$\mathbf{F} = -G\frac{M_A M_B}{R^2}\frac{\mathbf{R}}{R}.$$

Here $\mathbf{R}$ is the radius vector of M_A with M_B at the origin, and its direction defined outward from the origin so that the force is attractive. If M_A moves relative to M_B, then according to the general definition only the component of the force in the direction of the displacement does work upon the system. It follows that the gravitational force does work only if the separation R changes. No work is involved in any motion in which R remains constant, if M_A described a circular orbit about M_B, for instance.

Suppose R changes by a small amount. If the change is in the direction of the force, then according to our convention on the direction of $\mathbf{R}$ the change must be written as $-\Delta R$, and therefore, the work performed by the force over the small displacement is

$$\Delta W = G\frac{M_A M_B}{R^2}\Delta R.$$

The total work performed to change the separation from R_1 to R_2 is the sum of all such small contributions over the path for ΔW approaching zero, or the area under the curve in Figure 7.11. Unfortunately there is no simple geometric way to calculate this area as there was in the linear restoring force case (Figure 7.4). Therefore, it is necessary to perform the sum by writing the total work in the form given by Equation 7.3:

$$W_{21} = GM_A M_B \int_{R_1}^{R_2} \frac{dR}{R^2},$$

and evaluate the expression by using techniques of the integral calculus (see Appendix to Chapter 7). The result turns out to be

$$W = -GM_A M_B \left(\frac{1}{R_2} - \frac{1}{R_1} \right), \tag{7.11a}$$

which depends only upon the end points of the path since the force is conservative. The minus sign indicates that the work performed is positive when the separation between the particles decreases, i.e., when R_2 is smaller than R_1.

As an application of Equation 7.11a, consider a satellite of mass M_A in circular orbit of radius R about the earth (mass M_B). Since R remains constant it follows that the earth performs no work on the satellite. This conclusion also follows from the fact that the gravitational force on the satellite is always perpendicular to its displacement so that there is no component of force in the direction of the displacement and therefore no work performed. By definition, a satellite in any closed orbit always returns to its starting point at the end of one period. Since the change in R over the orbit is therefore zero regardless of the shape of the orbit, the total work over the orbit must be zero. During the first half period from apogee, R_2 (maximum distance from the earth) to perigee R_1 (minimum distance), the work performed on a satellite in an elliptical orbit is positive; during the half period from perigee back to apogee the work is negative but equal in magnitude to the work performed over the first half cycle. Therefore, the total work over the entire orbit must be zero.

Expressions analogous to Equation 7.11a can be obtained for more complicated forces (due to several particles for instance) by applying Equation 7.2 or 7.3. No matter how

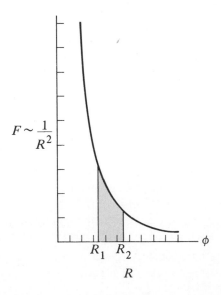

$$F \sim \frac{1}{R^2}$$

$R_1 \quad R_2$

R

FIGURE 7.11 The work performed in changing the separation of two bodies from R_1 to R_2 is proportional to the area under the force-vs-separation curve between R_1 and R_2. The appropriate graph for the inverse square force is shown. Since the gravitational force is attractive, negative work is performed when the separation increases.

complex, however, the work performed by a gravitational force to displace a particle from one point to another is always independent of the path between the points. Therefore, provided the forces involved are conservative, work can always be computed over the simplest path. In particular, the *total* work performed in one cycle about any *closed* path is always zero, since the simplest way to go from a point to the same point is simply not to move at all.

Applying the general definition of Section 7.4 (Equation 7.9), the potential energy of the two-body system with components separated by a distance R_2, relative to a separation R_1 is given by Equation 7.11a. It is convenient to choose the zero state of potential energy as the state in which the separation between M_1 and M_2 is infinite. In that case:

$$(PE)_2 = -\frac{GM_A M_B}{R_2}, \tag{7.11b}$$

which shows that the potential energy of two bodies that attract each other by means of an inverse square force is always negative.

The restricted energy conservation law for the inverse-square force is obtained by substituting Equation 7.11a into Equation 7.10a and making use of Equation 7.9a:

$$\frac{1}{2} M_A(v_{1A}^2 - v_{2A}^2) + \frac{1}{2} M_B(v_{1B}^2 - v_{2B}^2) = -GM_A M_B \left(\frac{1}{R_1} - \frac{1}{R_2}\right). \tag{7.12a}$$

If M_B is so much greater than M_A that its motion can be neglected relative to the motion of M_A, then to an excellent approximation:

$$\frac{1}{2} (v_1^2 - v_2^2) = -GM_B \left(\frac{1}{R_1} - \frac{1}{R_2}\right), \tag{7.12b}$$

where v_1 and v_2 now refer to the velocities of M_A at the separations R_1 and R_2, respectively. Equation 7.12b shows immediately that the velocity of a planet (M_A) in an elliptical orbit about the sun (M_B) decreases as its distance from the sun increases, in qualitative accord with Kepler's second law.

Escape velocity is defined as the minimum perpendicular component of velocity a particle must have at the earth's surface if it is ultimately to escape completely from the gravitational attraction of the earth. Since the gravitational force between two particles is zero only when their separation is infinite, a particle that starts at the earth's surface must have velocity greater than zero at all finite distances from the earth if it is not to be recaptured by the earth. Hence escape velocity at the earth's surface implies zero velocity at infinity. Applying Equation 7.12a with $v_2 = 0$, $R_2 = \infty$, and $R_1 = R_e$, the radius of the earth:

$$\frac{1}{2} v_1^2 = \frac{GM_e}{R_e},$$

or

$$v_1 = \sqrt{\frac{2GM_e}{R_e}},$$

But (Equation 5.5), $g = GM_e/R_e^2$, so $v_1 = \sqrt{2gR_e} = 1.1 \, (10)^4$ m/sec, or about 6.9 miles/sec.

The graphical methods introduced in Section 7.5 may be employed to good advantage in analyzing the general character of motion under the influence of an inverse-square force. Figure 7.12 plots the potential energy of a particle with mass M_A subject to the gravitational force exerted by a more massive body M_B as a function of their separation. $R = $ infinity is taken as the zero energy state in accord with Equation 7.12b. Therefore, if M_A has velocity less than escape velocity, E_A or E_B for instance, its total energy is negative although its kinetic energy can never be smaller than zero. It remains trapped in the "well." But if M_A has total energy greater than or equal to zero, such as E_C, it escapes from the well. By definition, it has velocity greater than escape velocity (or equal to escape velocity if its total energy is zero).

These conclusions can be expressed in a slightly different way by stating that a two-particle system can remain bound only if its total energy is negative. Indeed, this criterion is valid for any type of potential energy, not just the gravitational energy plotted in Figure 7.12.

The bound bodies with energies E_A and E_B in Figure 7.12 differ in the distances they are able to move from the origin before coming to rest. No planet in the solar system ever comes completely to rest, and therefore none ever attains the maximum displacement from the origin consistent with its potential energy. That would violate Kepler's second law or, equivalently, angular momentum conservation (Section 6.11). By definition, a planet with a circular orbit about the sun has a constant radius vector, R_0. It is represented by a point in Figure 7.12, has constant potential energy, and therefore constant velocity. A planet in an elliptical orbit with maximum and minimum radius vectors R_2 and R_1, respectively, has maximum potential energy at R_2 and minimum potential energy at R_1. Its periodic excursions between R_2 and R_1 may be represented as a periodic

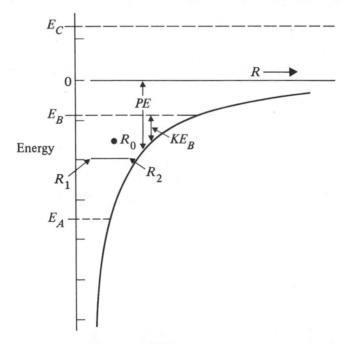

FIGURE 7.12 Energy diagram corresponding to an attractive inverse-square force. Particles with negative total energy (E_A, E_B) remain bound in the well, while a particle with total energy E_C does not. A particle in a circular orbit of radius R_0 is represented by a point on the diagram, while the line segment between R_1 and R_2 represents the total energy in an elliptical orbit with R_1 and R_2 the respective minimum and maximum distances from the force center.

interchange between potential and kinetic energy. Finally, a body approaching the origin with positive energy E_C has minimum potential energy and maximum velocity at its distance of closest approach to the sun. Because its energy remains constant, it retains the ability to escape capture in the well. Hence the orbit cannot be closed.

All these conclusions are in qualitative accord with Kepler's second law. Because the principle of energy conservation follows from Newton's laws, its application to the planetary system yields precisely the same results that were discussed in Chapter 5, but often by a much simpler route. It is worth noting that Equation 7.12b gives the velocity of a planet as a function of distance from the sun, and also leads to Kepler's laws. But like the formulation in Chapter 5, it gives no information about *why* a planet has a particular radius vector or its orbit a particular eccentricity. Equations 7.12 are based

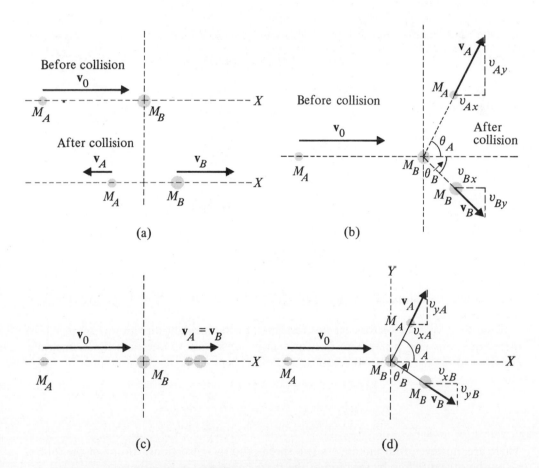

(a)

(b)

(c)

(d)

FIGURE 7.13 Two-body collisions. For the elastic collisions shown in parts a and b, kinetic energy and momentum are both conserved. In an inelastic collision (parts c and d), momentum and *total* energy are conserved, but part of the initial, linear kinetic energy is transferred into internal, potential energy of the system. If the collision is completely inelastic, part c, the bodies stick together on emerging from the collision. (In all cases shown, $M_B = 2M_A$.)

on Newton's laws. Hence they are alternate statements of the laws, and contain nothing that is fundamentally new.

▲▲ 7.7 Energy conservation in two-body collisions. Elastic and inelastic collisions

In order to apply the energy conservation law to the collision problems introduced in Chapter 4 (Section 4.2), consider the collision of two billiard balls with the respective masses M_A and M_B that together constitute an isolated system (Figure 7.13a). Before the collision M_A has speed v_0 and M_B is at rest. If we restrict ourselves to situations in which both billiard balls continue to move in the same direction following the collision, then the momentum conservation law provides one equation relating v_A and v_B, the respective speeds after collision, to the initial speed v_0:

$$M_A v_0 = M_A v_A + M_B v_B.$$

Prior to the collision the system has kinetic energy $\frac{1}{2} M v_0^2$ and no potential energy and must retain this energy during and subsequent to the collision. *If* all the energy is divided between the kinetic energy of motion of the billiard balls then:

$$\tfrac{1}{2} M_A v_0^2 = \tfrac{1}{2} M_A v_A^2 + \tfrac{1}{2} M_B v_B^2.$$

Thus momentum and energy conservation provide two equations in two unknown velocities, v_A and v_B, and the velocities are completely determined. Solving:

$$v_B = \frac{2 M_A}{M_B + M_A}\, v_0, \tag{7.13a}$$

$$v_A = \frac{M_A - M_B}{M_B + M_A}\, v_0. \tag{7.13b}$$

If M_A is larger than M_B, both proceed forward. If M_A is smaller than M_B, it recoils while the lighter mass moves forward. In the special case $M_A = M_B$,

$$v_B = v_0,$$
$$v_A = 0.$$

The incident ball stops, the struck ball takes all its momentum and energy. The two merely change roles.

If the final velocity vectors are not restricted to the incident direction (Figure 7.13b) three equations may be written: one for energy conservation, one each for momentum conservation in the x- and y-directions (Section 4.2):

$$\tfrac{1}{2} M_A v_0^2 = \tfrac{1}{2} M_A v_A^2 + \tfrac{1}{2} M_B v_B^2,$$
$$M_A v_0 = M_A v_A \cos \theta_A + M_B v_B \cos \theta_B,$$
$$0 = M_A v_A \sin \theta_A + M_B v_B \sin \theta_B.$$

There are, however, four unknowns, two speeds and two directions. If one of the four is given the others follow by solution of the three conservation equations.

An incoming mass M_A with velocity v_0 need not transfer all its energy into kinetic energy of motion, however. If the colliding spheres were deformable some of the available energy could be used to compress one or both at the time of collision, causing them to oscillate internally as well as move with respect to each other. Kinetic energy is still conserved, but shared between kinetic energy of *vibration* (internal) and kinetic energy of *translation* (motion of the body as a whole). Therefore, the conservation equation would be written:

$$\tfrac{1}{2}M_A v_0^2 = \tfrac{1}{2}M_A v_A^2 + M_B v_B^2 + X, \tag{7.14}$$

where X represents the internal kinetic energy. This equation, together with the usual momentum conservation equations suffices to determine the velocities completely if X is known, but with results that differ from those obtained previously.

Similarly, the collision could cause the balls to spin or rotate about their axes, and this motion implies that some of the initial energy of translation is transformed into *rotational* kinetic energy which contributes to the X in Equation 7.14. A collision in which $X = 0$ is called an *elastic* collision. Evidently in such a collision all energy remains translational kinetic energy. Energy is conserved in an inelastic collision, but does not all remain translational kinetic energy (Figure 7.13c and d).

▲▲ 7.8 The generalized energy conservation law

All of the specific examples of work in this chapter have involved conservative forces, forces that perform work that is independent of the path over which they displace a body. However, in applications involving the motion of real, macroscopic bodies, frictional forces are always involved, and these, by their nature, are nonconservative. For example, the total frictional force on a body moving between two points on a rough surface depends on the total length of its path, since the body moves over a greater part of the surface for a long path than for a short one (Figure 7.14). Similarly, a real falling body experiences resistance from frictional effects of the air. These effects increase with velocity and are proportional to the distance traveled. Hence the total air resistance on a projectile is greater than on a stone thrown straight upward, for both the speed and the path length of the projectile are greater.

As we shall see in Chapter 16, the energy conservation law in a more generalized form than we have been using here is applicable to both these situations if care is taken in defining the isolated system involved. For a body sliding over a rough surface the system must include the surface; for a projectile traveling in air it must include the air. In both instances the energy transfer from the moving body to the friction-producing medium results in an increase in the temperature of both the body and the medium. It is not at all self evident that the energy conservation principle should be applicable in these cases. Indeed one of the major triumphs of nineteenth-century physics was the experimental

FIGURE 7.14 Because the total frictional force on a moving body is proportional to the distance it travels, the work performed against friction in displacing a body from *a* to *c* on a rough surface is greater over the path *abc* than over the path *ac*.

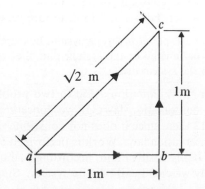

proof that heat could be considered in terms of energy and the energy concept consequently broadened to incorporate the thermal properties of matter.

The qualitative effects of frictional forces on specific systems may be analyzed by means
of the potential energy diagrams discussed in Section 7.5. For example, in Figure 7.9a
the total energy of the system, the body on an inclined plane and the plane itself, remains
constant, and the gravitational potential energy is still represented by the oblique line.
However, the vertical distance between the potential energy line and the total energy line
must now be interpreted as the sum of the kinetic energy of the body and the energy
dissipated by friction rather than as kinetic energy alone. Therefore, the velocity of a
body at any distance x along the plane will decrease as the frictional force increases.

There is an alternate and in many ways a more fruitful method of applying the energy
concept in complex situations that may involve nonconservative forces. Rather than
defining a large, isolated system it is possible to concentrate on part of the system and
incorporate the idea of energy transfer into the conservation law. Suppose that a conservative force $\mathbf{F}_A$ acts between the internal parts of a system and that another, not
necessarily conservative force $\mathbf{F}_B$ acts on the system but is external to it. For example,
$\mathbf{F}_A$ might be the gravitational force exerted by the earth on a body sliding down an inclined plane, and $\mathbf{F}_B$ the frictional force due to the rough plane. If W_A is the work performed by F_A in displacing the system from state 2 to state 1, and W_B the work associated
with $\mathbf{F}_B$ over the same path then, referring to Equation 7.7,

$$W_A + W_B = (KE)_1 - (KE)_2.$$

The work performed by the *two* forces changes the kinetic energy of the system. Now
since $\mathbf{F}_A$ is conservative we can equate W_A to the change in the potential energy
associated with $\mathbf{F}_A$ (Equation 7.9) and substitute $W_A = (PE)_2 - (PE)_1$ into the above
equation:

$$W_B + (PE)_2 - (PE)_1 = (KE)_1 - (KE)_2, \tag{7.15a}$$

or, rearranging terms,

$$W_B = (PE_1 + KE_1) - (PE_2 + KE_2). \tag{7.15b}$$

That is, the change in the total internal energy of the system is equal to work performed
upon the system by the external forces. If, in addition, the forces associated with the
system perform external work W_C, then we can write:

$$W_B = W_C + (PE_1 + KE_1) - (PE_2 + PE_1). \tag{7.15c}$$

If both W_B and W_C are zero the system is isolated, and Equation 7.15c states that its total
energy remains constant, in agreement with the restricted conservation law (Equation
7.10). However, Equation 7.15 is a more general form of the law which states:

• The work performed on a system by external forces is equal to the change in the
internal energy of the system plus the work performed by the forces associated
with the system itself.

We can apply Equation 7.15c to two problems previously analyzed by means of the
restricted conservation law. If we concentrate upon the incident billiard ball M_A in
Figure 7.13 then, since it does not constitute an isolated system, we must use the generalized conservation law. Work is performed on M_B when M_A collides with it. Therefore,
$W_B = 0$, W_C is positive and, according to Equation 7.15c, the energy of M_A decreases.
Alternately we could call M_B the system. Since work is performed on M_B at the time of

collision and M_B does no work, then $W_C = 0$, W_B is positive and the total energy of M_B increases.

As another example call the mass M_A in Figure 7.6 the system. Because of the gravitational force of the earth, work is performed on M_B when M_A drops to the floor. The work increases the potential energy of M_B from zero to $M_B gy$ and increases its kinetic energy from zero to $\frac{1}{2}M_B v_B^2$. Therefore, $W_C = \frac{1}{2}M_B v_B^2 + M_B gy$ in Equation 7.15c. In the process the kinetic energy of M_A increases from zero to $\frac{1}{2}M_A v_A^2$ while its potential energy decreases from $M_A gy$ to zero. Applying Equation 7.15c with $W_B = 0$, and noting that because the string is taut, $v_A = v_B = v$:

$$0 = \tfrac{1}{2}M_B v^2 + M_B gy - M_A gy + \tfrac{1}{2}M_A v^2,$$

or

$$v^2 = \frac{2(M_A - M_B)}{M_A + M_B} gy,$$

in agreement with the analysis of Section 7.5.

No doubt both of these problems are simpler to analyze by applying the restricted conservation law to a large isolated system than by considering the work performed upon part of that system by another. The real power of the generalized law is only apparent when nonconservative external forces such as friction or air resistance are involved. These cannot be related to potential energy, but, as we have already indicated, they can be related to temperature changes. Then the terms W_B and W_C in Equation 7.15c can be interpreted as energy transferred into and out of the system as heat, and the conservation law applied to heat transfer by means other than friction.

A complete exposition of these topics is best postponed until we develop a few ideas on the atomic and molecular properties of matter (Chapters 15–16). As we delve further into these properties we shall find that the macroscopic state of a system often changes as a result of microscopic processes, and that the energy conservation law is applicable to all of these processes as well. We shall often find it convenient to characterize such changes in the macroscopic state of a system by referring to different types of energy such as thermal, electrical, chemical, or nuclear energy. In this way we shall be able to generalize the energy conservation law to cover all natural processes.

Although the restricted conservation law that we have introduced in this chapter is exceedingly useful in the analysis of problems involving the motion of macroscopic bodies, we developed it by applying the laws of Newtonian mechanics. Therefore, the law itself is implicit in Newtonian dynamics, and it is not obvious that it should be applicable in any situation where Newtonian dynamics is not. However, like the momentum conservation law the energy conservation law has been found to be experimentally valid in every situation in which it has been tested. Therefore, we must regard the law even in its restricted form as being more basic than the laws of Newton. In fact it has the same broad status as the general symmetry principles we discussed in Chapter 6, and is a necessary consequence of the homogeneity of time (Section 6.5) even as momentum conservation follows from the homogeneity of space and angular momentum conservation from the isotropy of space. Like these laws it serves as a certain guideline when a new situation is encountered, as we shall discover when we deal with atomic, nuclear, and elementary particle processes in later chapters. In addition, as we have noted in this chapter, it is often indispensable in analyzing the behavior of complex systems where Newton's laws are valid but difficult to apply.

APPENDIX TO CHAPTER 7 | *The potential energy corresponding to an inverse square force*

The derivation of the exact expression for the work performed in changing the separation of two particles that attract each other by means of the gravitational interaction (Equation 7.11a) requires the integral calculus. The technique of evaluating an integral (or integration) follows from the fundamental theorem of the integral calculus which proves that the integration process is the inverse of differentiation (Appendix to Chapter 2). This may be seen very roughly as follows:

In defining work for an arbitrary force over an arbitrary path the first step is to divide the path into many small, equal segments of length Δs and to define the work over each as the product of the average parallel force component, F_s, by the length of the segment:

$$\Delta W = F_s \Delta s. \tag{7.16a}$$

Dividing by Δs:

$$F_s = \frac{\Delta W}{\Delta s}. \tag{7.16b}$$

That is, the average force component over a segment Δs is the ratio of the work over the segment by the length of the segment. In the limit where Δs approaches zero the force at a point on the path is equal to the derivative of the work with respect to the displacement path (Appendix to Chapter 2):

$$F_s = \frac{dW}{ds}. \tag{7.16c}$$

Therefore, if the work were known as a function of s, the parallel force component could be found at all points along the path by evaluating the derivative.

The work over a path of finite length is calculated by first allowing the segments Δs to approach zero.

$$dW = F_s \, ds, \tag{7.17}$$

which also follows by multiplying each side of Equation 7.16c by ds. The integral over the path is then defined as the sum of all such infinitesimal contributions (Equations 7.3) over the entire path:

$$W = \int_{s_0}^{s_L} dW = \int_{s_0}^{s_L} F_s \, ds, \tag{7.3}$$

where s_0 and s_L are called the limits of the integral and in this case designate the end points of the path. Equation 7.16c states that F_s is a function that may be found by evaluating the first derivative of W with respect to s. Because Equation 7.17 is the inverse of Equation 7.16c then Equation 7.3 states that W is a function whose derivative with respect to s is equal to F_s. Since the derivative depends upon the value of s at which it is evaluated, this statement is ambiguous. It may be shown, however, that W depends only upon the limits of the integral and is equal to the difference between the function whose just derivative is F_s evaluated at s_L and the same function evaluated at s_0.

In order to derive Equation 7.11, the integral

$$W = GM_AM_B \int_{R_1}^{R_2} \frac{dR}{R^2}$$

must be evaluated. Here $F_s = 1/R^2$ so W must be related to the function whose first derivative is $1/R^2$. Referring to the table in the Appendix to Chapter 2, the first derivative of the function $y = x^{n+1}/(n + 1)$ with respect to x is x^n. Letting $x = R$, $n = -2$, it follows that the first derivative of $-1/R$ must be equal to $1/R^2$. Thus to write an expression for work it is only necessary to evaluate $-1/R$ at the end points R_2 and R_1 and multiply by the constant factor GM_AM_B:

$$W = -\frac{GM_AM_B}{R_2} = -\frac{GM_AM_B}{R_1} = -GM_AM_B\left(\frac{1}{R_2} - \frac{1}{R_1}\right),$$

which is Equation 7.11a.

SUGGESTIONS FOR FURTHER READING ▲▲▲

Since the energy concept is central to physics, all introductory texts treat it in detail, for instance:

GERALD HOLTON AND DUANE H. D. ROLLER, *Foundations of Modern Physical Science*, Addison-Wesley Publishing Co., Inc., Reading, Mass., 1958, Chapter 18.

K. R. ATKINS, *Physics*, John Wiley and Sons, Inc., New York, 1965, Chapter 9.

ARNOLD B. ARONS, *Development of Concepts of Physics*. Addison-Wesley Publishing Co., Inc., Reading, Mass., 1965, Chapter 18.

R. P. FEYNMAN, R. B. LEIGHTON, AND M. SANDS, *The Feynman Lectures on Physics*, Vol. 1, Addison-Wesley Publishing Co., Inc., Reading, Mass., 1963, Chapters 13 and 14.

Chapter 16 of Arons deals with the basic integral calculus in a very understandable way.

PROBLEMS AND EXERCISES ▲▲▲

7.1. A 5-kg mass is pushed 0.5 m along a horizontal surface with constant velocity by a 30-newton force. During the first half of the trip the angle between the force and displacement vectors is 60°; thereafter the two vectors are parallel.

(a) What is the total work performed on the mass?
(b) If the angle between the force and displacement vectors remained 60° how long would the displacement path have had to be such that the total work performed would be equal to that obtained in part a?
(c) Is the surface frictionless? Explain.

7.2. A 100-kg pile driver is dropped from a height of 5 m onto a stake which it drives 0.2 m into the ground. The pile driver comes to rest with the stake.

(a) What is the velocity of the driver just before it strikes the stake?
(b) With what average force does the ground resist the stake?
(c) How far would the stake have been driven if the driver had rebounded 2 m instead of coming immediately to rest on top of the stake?

7.3. A 100-kg automobile traveling on a level highway is found to expend an energy of 6×10^4 joules/sec in order to maintain a constant speed of 30 m/sec.

(a) What is the total frictional force exerted upon the car (due chiefly to wind resistance)?
(b) Assuming the frictional forces remain constant, what additional energy is required per second if the auto maintains its constant speed traveling up a 20% grade?

7.4. A mass slides up a frictionless plane inclined at 30° to the horizontal and comes momentarily to rest at the top. If the length of the plane along the hypotenuse is 2.5 m what was the velocity of the mass at its base?

7.5. A 5-kg mass is dropped from a height of 2 m onto a vertically oriented spring whose base rests on the ground. The subsequent compression of the system is 0.5 m.

(a) What is the spring constant?
(b) What will the velocity of the oscillating system be at equilibrium?

7.6. A bow is designed in such a way that the force required to bend it is directly proportional to the distance the arrow is pulled back with the string. That is,

$$F = kx,$$

with $k = 800$ newtons/m.

(a) If the bow string is pulled back 0.75 m in order to shoot a 0.05-kg arrow straight upward how far does the arrow rise (neglecting air resistance)?
(b) Suppose the same arrow is shot at 45° to the horizontal. How high will it rise (neglecting air resistance)?

7.7. The mass of the roller coaster car in Figure 7.7 is 1000 kg, $y_3 = 25$ m, $y_2 = 20$ m, $y_1 = 4$ m. If the track is frictionless and the car starts from rest:

(a) What is its speed at the point x_b?
(b) What is its speed at x_c?
(c) What is its potential energy at x_c relative to the ground? relative to y_2?
(d) With what speed must it start from y_2 if it is to come to rest at y_3?
(e) What is its speed at x_c in this latter case?

7.8. In a variation on a roller coaster, a car of mass M slides down steeply inclined tracks, then goes through a vertical, circular loop of radius R before returning to the horizontal. What minimum velocity must the car have at the bottom of the loop if it is to stay on the tracks at the top? From what height must it slide if it is to attain this velocity?

7.9. The Roman aqueducts brought water into the city from the surrounding hills via troughs that had gentle, downward slopes.

(a) What would the minimum height of the reservoirs have had to be relative to the city if the water was to emerge with velocity 20 m/sec?
(b) How high would the reservoir have had to be if the emerging water were to have been used for a fountain with a 10 m vertical spray?

7.10. Using the energy conservation principle, derive a relation giving the maximum height of a projectile fired with muzzle velocity v from a cannon inclined at an angle θ to the horizontal.

7.11. Two masses, M_1 and M_2 (M_2 greater than M_1) are connected by a taut string which loops over a fixed pulley of negligible mass. M_2 is initially at rest on a table of height y, M_1 at rest on the floor.

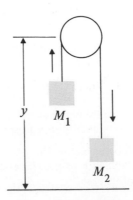

(a) What is the final velocity of the system if M_2 falls to the floor?

(b) How might the problem be solved if the pulley's mass could not be neglected?

7.12. A mass M rests on a rough but level surface of length l. When a force of magnitude F is applied parallel to the surface the body moves with constant velocity so that F must be the force required to overcome friction between the body and the surface. Show directly that this frictional force is not conservative by calculating the work performed over two different paths: the first from $x = 0$, $y = 0$ to $x = 3$, $y = 0$ and thence to $x = 3$, $y = 4$, the second directly from $x = 0$, $y = 0$ to $x = 3$, $y = 4$.

7.13. (a) Draw a potential energy diagram for the motion of a pendulum of length l, mass M, and initial angular displacement θ_0.

(b) Discuss the probable effect of air resistance on the pendulum, using your diagram as a guide.

(c) A mass M is displaced a distance s from the bottom of a smooth, spherical bowl of radius R and then released. Draw a potential energy diagram and discuss the subsequent behavior of the mass. (See sketch.)

(d) How would the behavior of the mass differ if there were friction between the bowl and the mass?

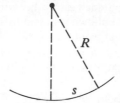

7.14. A mass M rests at the bottom of a smooth parabolic bowl whose shape is given by the equation $y = ax^2$, where a is a constant. The mass is displaced along the bowl until it is a distance y_0 above the bottom, then released.

Justify the fact that the subsequent motion of the mass is periodic about its equilibrium position at the bottom of the bowl, and find an expression for the period.

[HINT: Compare the gravitational potential energy as a function of x with the potential energy of an harmonic oscillator.]

7.15. Show that the total energy of a satellite of mass M in a circular orbit of radius R about the earth is:

$$-\frac{1}{2}\frac{GM_eM}{R},$$

if its potential energy is zero for $R = \infty$.

[HINT: Derive an expression for kinetic energy by first equating the centripetal force on the satellite to the gravitational force exerted by the earth.]

7.16. (a) Plot the gravitational potential energy for a particle of mass 1 unit interacting with another with mass such that $GM_2 = 10$ units as a function of R, from $R = 1$ to 10 units.

(b) Locate points in your potential well for circular orbits with radii 2, 4, and 8 units, respectively.

(c) Represent an elliptical orbit with total energy equal to the energy of a 5-unit radius circular orbit and with extreme distances from the force center equal to 4 and 6 units, respectively.

(d) What is the kinetic energy of the satellite in part c at the extremities of its orbit? What is the distance at which its kinetic energy is a maximum?

7.17. It is frequently stated that interplanetary space trips can be more easily launched from the moon than from the earth. Justify this statement by calculating the ratios of the escape velocities required from the earth and the moon. (The acceleration due to gravity on the moon is about $\frac{1}{6}g$ on the earth; the radius of the moon is one-fourth the radius of the earth.)

7.18. What minimum velocity would a space ship launched from earth require to escape from the solar system? (Calculate the work performed against solar gravity to go from the 1.5×10^{11} m radius orbit of the earth to infinity. The sun's mass is 2×10^{30} kg.)

7.19. An earth satellite in a circular orbit with a radius six times that of the earth's ($R_e = 6.4 \times 10^6$ m) has a 24-hr period. Therefore, if its orbital plane coincides with that of the equator, it appears suspended directly overhead. What velocity (in addition to the rotational velocity of the earth) is required to launch such a satellite from the equator?

7.20. (a) Using the principles of energy and momentum conservation show that in the direct collision of a moving billiard ball with a billiard ball of equal mass and at rest, the first stops and the second proceeds forward with the velocity of the first if and only if the collision is elastic.
(b) Can the first billiard ball come completely to rest if the collision is inelastic?

7.21. Two particles of equal mass approach each other with equal and opposite velocities and undergo an elastic collision. Following the collision their speeds are again equal to each other, equal to their initial values, and their velocity vectors are again opposite, although their axis is inclined at an angle θ to the original direction (see sketch). Does momentum or energy conservation account for the fact that the directions of the particles remain colinear? Which conservation principle accounts for the equality of the speeds of the particles following the collision? What accounts for the equality of the initial and final speeds?

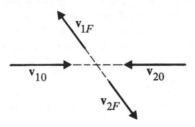

7.22. Two equal-mass particles traveling with equal and opposite velocities collide. (See sketch accompanying Problem 7.21.) Must the magnitudes of their final velocities be equal? Must they be equal to their initial values? Must their directions be opposite? Explain all three answers.

7.23. A freely falling object dropped from 125 m is observed from an elevator traveling downward with a constant speed of 10 m/sec which passes it just as it is dropped. Show that the energy, measured in the moving sytem, is conserved.

7.24. A 0.2-kg mass is incident with a speed of 20m/sec upon a second, 0.4-kg mass initially at rest.

(a) What is the initial kinetic energy of the system?
(b) What is the velocity of the inertial system in which the center of mass of the system is at rest?
(c) What are the initial energies of the particles in this inertial system?
(d) Is your answer to part c consistent with energy conservation?

7.25. A bullet of mass M_1 is fired into a block of mass M_2 which is suspended from a string of length l and therefore becomes a pendulum, rising a vertical distance y_0, then oscillating about its equilibrium position.

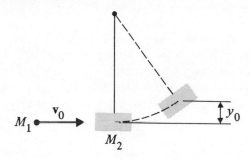

(a) Express the initial speed of the bullet in terms of the masses and the vertical displacement, y_0.

(b) How much energy does the bullet dissipate in entering the block and embedding itself there?

[HINT: Consider the problem in two steps: (1) the collision of the bullet and the block, and (2) the displacement of the block. Apply momentum and energy conservation if and where appropriate.]

Charge and its interactions: part 1

8

▲▲ 8.1 Electrostatic phenomena. The qualitative idea of charge. Charge conservation

Charge, like mass, is a fundamental property of matter. We are all familiar with a number of its more common manifestations. For example, storage batteries store charge, electric current is moving charge, a lightning bolt a dis*charge*, or spark, between two clouds or a cloud and the earth. If an amber rod is rubbed vigorously with a piece of animal fur it becomes *charged* and attracts small bits of paper to it. All of these phenomena give some feeling for the property, but do not define it. Ultimately, a satisfactory definition must be made in terms of the electromagnetic interaction, just as a satisfactory definition of gravitational mass must be made in terms of the gravitational interaction. Nevertheless, it is useful to give a general summary of several of the observed interactions between charged bodies and, on the basis of these observations, make a few hypotheses about the nature of the property called *charge* before attempting to define it quantitatively.

All of the time-honored demonstrations on the properties of charge with amber rods, animal fur, pith balls, and electroscopes are classified as *electrostatic* phenomena since they involve interactions between charges at rest. When charges move rapidly relative to one another their interaction becomes more involved, as we shall learn in the next chapter. However, provided their relative velocities are small compared with the velocity of light (3×10^8 m/sec) the dominant interaction between charges is electrostatic.

An amber rod rubbed vigorously with a piece of animal fur accelerates small objects such as bits of paper or pith balls toward it. Therefore, according to Newton's second law it exerts a force upon them. Further, since rubbing with the fur is prerequisite to observation of the force, it seems obvious that the rubbing process induces the attractive ability in the amber. By definition, the rod is said to be *charged* by the process, though the word alone does not explain the phenomenon any more than associating the word "gravity" with falling bodies explains free fall.

If only amber could be charged the effect could be discussed as a curious property of amber alone. But many other substances exhibit an analogous behavior. Rubber, for instance, also becomes charged if rubbed with cat's fur. Glass and most crystals can be charged by rubbing them with silk. All of these substances, when charged, will attract small bits of *any* material except another piece of the same material.

The amber effect was known at least as early as the sixth century B.C., but William

Gilbert's *De Magnete* (1600) contained the first systematic list of the materials that could be charged, and first reported the fact that charged objects interact with virtually any material. Gilbert called chargeable materials "electrons" (from the Greek *elektron* for amber), and was thus responsible for the name eventually given the interaction between all charged bodies. Since so many materials seem to interact through the "amber effect" then, in the spirit of Chapter 5 (Section 5.11), let us assume that the effect is a manifestation of some property of the materials, and that the forces exerted by the charged objects are manifestations of some interaction called (following Gilbert) the *electrostatic* interaction.

Although a charged amber rod attracts small bits of normally uncharged matter, it *repels* another similarly charged amber rod. Similarly two charged glass rods or two rubber rods repel each other, but a charged amber rod *attracts* a charged glass rod. The electrostatic interaction appears to manifest itself in at least two distinct ways—as an attractive or as a repulsive force. Let us assume that the interaction between charged amber or rubber or glass and another piece of charged material is related to some property induced in these materials when they are rubbed with fur or with silk, as the case may be. To be semantically consistent we shall call this property *charge*, and note that there are at least two types: amber or rubber, or type *A* charge, and glass, or type *B* charge.* The interactions between charged electrics is then summarized by the statement:

- Bodies with the same type charge *repel* each other, bodies with different type charges *attract* each other.

It does not necessarily follow that all electrostatic phenomena can be explained in terms of the single property called charge. The answer to that question must rest with experiment. However, by referring to a general result of Newtonian dynamics we can generalize our ideas about the assumed property, and devise experiments to test the validity of the generalization. We have referred to the electrostatic *interaction*, and assumed that the observed interaction between a charged amber and a charged glass rod is an interaction between their charges. Newton's third law demands that since a charged amber rod exerts a force on what we have called *uncharged* pith balls, the pith balls exert an equal and opposite force on the charged amber. Then if the force exerted on the pith balls by the amber rod is really a manifestation of the force that is exerted between charged amber and charged glass, the pith balls and all other presumably uncharged material that can be attracted to charged amber *also* have the property called charge. We emphasize that this generalization is as yet an hypothesis, for the force between charged amber and glass might well be due to quite a different property than the force between charged amber and pith balls. But assuming its validity for the moment where does the generalization lead us?

Two pith balls or two bits of paper lying beside each other on a table normally do not exert an electrostatic force on each other. In order to reconcile this observation with the hypothesis that pith and paper *do* have charge we must make the further assumption that normally a piece of material has equal amounts of type *A* and type *B* charge, and that the two types are arranged so that the effects of one type cancel the effects of the other. Then, according to the hypothesis, rubbing amber with fur either deposits some type *A*

---

* There is no a priori reason why two and only two types of charge should exist; a universe with one type or more than two is conceivable. In fact, the modern idea of charge as a basic attribute of the fundamental particles more consistently speaks of three types, the third state being neutrality or lack of charge.

charge, or removes some of type B. In either case the rod is left with an excess of type A. Similarly, rubbing glass with silk leaves an excess of type B. Apparently when charged amber is brought close to a pith ball the force exerted by the type A charge of the rod induces a rearrangement of the charge in the pith, repelling its type A, attracting its type B. The type B charge is then closer to the rod than the type A, interacts more strongly with the charge in the rod, and accelerates the ball toward it (Figure 8.1a). The opposite rearrangement is induced by a charged glass rod and as a result the pith ball is once again attracted to the rod.

Using the conventional labels positive and negative rather than A and B to designate the two types of charge has a mathematical advantage: using the symbol q to denote magnitude of charge, the *net* charge on a body is the algebraic sum, or arithmetic difference, between the two charges.* If q_1 and q_2 are the magnitudes of the positive and negative charges on a body, then its net charge is $q_1 + (-q_2) = q_1 - q_2$. Normally the magnitudes of q_1 and q_2 are equal so that the net charge on the body is zero. But by the addition of negative or the subtraction of positive charge a body acquires net negative charge, and vice versa.

Now if a pith ball actually touches a charged rod in the course of an experiment it is immediately repelled and thereafter also has the ability to attract normally uncharged objects (Figures 8.1b and c). Evidently the pith ball becomes charged when it comes in contact with the amber. We conclude that in at least some cases, charge is *mobile* and may be transferred between bodies by contact in a process called charging by *conduction*.

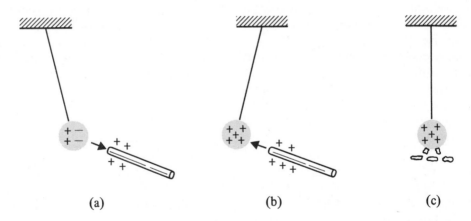

(a)   (b)   (c)

FIGURE 8.1 (a) Charged amber, with an excess of type A (positive) charge exerts an attractive force upon a neutral pith ball. The effect can be explained by assuming that the amber induces a rearrangement of the charge on the pith ball without changing the amount of its type A (positive) or type B (negative) charge. (b) If the charged amber touches the pith ball the force between the rod and ball is repulsive thereafter, suggesting that a transfer of charge has taken place and that the pith ball also has an excess positive charge. (c) The hypothesis is strengthened by the observation that the pith ball itself can now attract small bits of paper, acting, therefore, very much like the charged amber rod.

---

* It is the net charge that is generally important in electrostatic interactions and is directly measurable by experiment. Ultimately we can identify the charges on a body with the charges of the protons and electrons of which its atoms are composed. The total proton and electron charges are very large but the net charge represents a small difference between them.

Materials may be classified into two groups according to the observed mobility of charge within them. Members of one class, chiefly metals, have a high charge mobility, or conduct charge well and are known as *conductors*. Gilbert's "electrics" belong to a large class of *insulators* or *dielectrics*, which conduct charge poorly and therefore retain excess charge very well if they are not in contact with metals to which they invariably transfer such charge. Not all metals are equally good conductors, nor are all nonmetals equally good insulators. Within each class there is a considerable range of differences. But the break between the two categories is much greater than the range within each and is based upon fundamental structural differences in the materials. In Section 8.6 the conduction process in metals is discussed in more detail.

Many basic electrostatic phenomena may be studied, and most of our hypotheses about charge verified, with the aid of an electroscope, shown schematically in Figure 8.2. The heart of the instrument consists of a pair of thin gold leaves encased in a protective metal cylinder which is provided with glass end windows. The cylinder itself is insulated both from the stand on which it rests, and from the metal rod that provides both mechanical support for the gold leaves and an electrical conduction path to a metal protrusion or knob on the outside of the protecting cylinder. When charge is applied by touching charged amber or glass to the knob, for instance, the leaves repel each other, and the magnitude of their divergence gives a semiquantitative indication of the charge upon them.

When a positively charged amber rod approaches but does not touch the electroscope's knob, the gold leaves begin to diverge, and the divergence increases as the rod is brought closer to it (Figure 8.3). We can understand this behavior in terms of our charge mobility hypothesis. Initially the metallic heart of the electroscope, knob, connecting rod, and leaves, is electrically neutral, its net charge zero. The system is insulated from the protecting cylinder and from the table on which it rests, and must therefore remain neutral, since there is no way for charge to enter or leave it. Evidently the positively charged rod induces a rearrangement of the charge on the system, repelling positive charge from (or attracting negative charge to) the leaves, or both. In either case the leaves are left with an excess negative charge and repel each other. When the rod is removed the leaves converge once again, suggesting that the system as a whole does remain electrically neutral while the rod is in its proximity, as we hypothesized.

If with the rod nearby the electroscope is connected momentarily to ground* with a copper wire, or simply touched by the experimenter, its leaves collapse, showing that

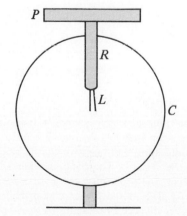

FIGURE 8.2 Essential features of a gold leaf electroscope. The metal rod (*R*) provides mechanical support for the thin gold leaves (*L*) and connects them electrically to the metal protrusion (*P*). The rod is insulated from the cylinder (*C*) which encases and protects the gold leaves.

---

* *Ground* is defined as any very large object to which a great deal of charge may be transferred.

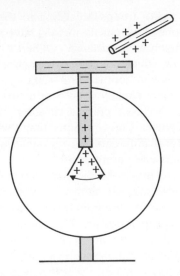

FIGURE 8.3 A positively charged rod brought near an electroscope causes the leaves to repel each other, suggesting that the rod induces a rearrangement of the charge on the instrument even as it does on the pith ball in Figure 8.1.

enough negative charge has flowed from the electroscope to ground (or positive charge from ground to the electroscope), to make the leaves electrically neutral (Figure 8.4). However, the charged rod is still nearby and must still be inducing a rearrangement of the charge on the system. Therefore, even though the leaves themselves are neutral we suspect that there is an excess negative charge at the upper end of the instrument. Indeed, when the rod is removed and the charge permitted to rearrange itself uniformly throughout the system the leaves diverge once again, showing the existence of an excess charge of one

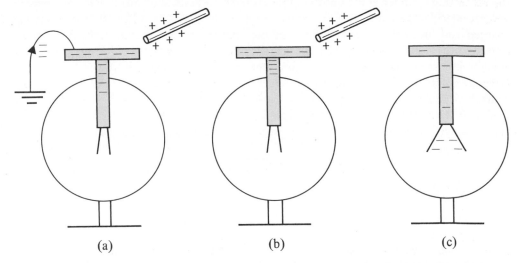

(a)   (b)   (c)

FIGURE 8.4 Charging an electroscope by induction. When a conducting path is established between the electroscope in Figure 8.3 and ground its leaves converge (part a), suggesting that negative charge has been added (or positive charge removed) from the system. The condition persists after the ground is removed (part b). However, the proximity of the charged rod implies there must still be excess negative charge at the upper end of the instrument. When the rod is removed the leaves diverge once again (part c), proving that there is now a net charge. A negatively charged rod brought near the protrusion would cause a further divergence, proving that the net charge left on the electroscope is negative.

sign or the other. The electroscope has been charged by *induction*. A second positively charged amber rod brought near the electroscope would cause the leaves to *converge*, whereas a negatively charged glass rod would lead to a further divergence. Taken together these experiments prove that the electroscope has a net positive charge, and that the signs of the charged amber and glass are opposite. By conducting a series of such experiments the validity of the major hypotheses put forward in this section may be demonstrated.

One further, fundamental property of charge is worth nothing here: its conservation. Although there are processes in which charge is created and destroyed (Chapters 20, 22, 23), extensive observation has led to the conclusion that no process ever alters the *net* charge of an isolated system. If positive charge of magnitude q is created (or destroyed) somewhere in a system, then an equivalent positive charge must be simultaneously destroyed (or created), *or* an equivalent negative charge created (or destroyed).

The net charge in an isolated system remains constant. Like the analogous principles of momentum, angular momentum, and energy conservation, charge conservation applies to all conceivable processes. Hence the limitation it imposes is a fundamental statement about the nature of the physical universe. Charge conservation follows from a symmetry principle called gauge invariance, a quantum mechanical symmetry that has no classical analogue.

◣◣ 8.2 Coulomb's law. Comparison with Newton's gravitational law

A quantitative study of the electrostatic interaction requires a quantitative definition of charge. In the late eighteenth century Charles Coulomb* carried out a definitive series of experiments measuring the strength of the electrostatic interaction between two bodies as a function of their separation and their charge. Although he had no quantitative measure of the *absolute* magnitude of net charge, he devised consistent methods for changing the net charge on particular objects by known fractional amounts, and was thus able to establish a direct proportion between the magnitude of the net charge upon one of two interacting bodies and the force between them. The variation of the force with the separation of the bodies was established in a related series of experiments and led to Coulomb's law for the electrostatic force:

- The electrostatic force between two charged particles is directly proportional to the charge upon each of them and inversely proportional to the square of their separation; the force is repulsive between like charges, attractive between unlike charges.

If two point masses have (net) charge q_1 and q_2, respectively, and are separated by a distance R, the force on a charge q_1 due to charge q_2 is given by

$$\mathbf{F} = k \frac{q_1 q_2}{R^2} \left(\frac{\mathbf{R}_{21}}{R} \right), \tag{8.1a}$$

where k is a constant of proportionality, and $\mathbf{R}_{21}$ is the radius vector from particle 2 to particle 1, and R is the magnitude of $\mathbf{R}_{21}$. The force on charge q_2 due to q_1 is given by the same expression with 1 and 2 interchanged. Thus, $\mathbf{R}_{21} = -\mathbf{R}_{12}$ (Figure 8.5). Equation 8.1a incorporates the attractive-repulsive alternatives. The product of two positive or two negative numbers is always positive so that the force between two like charges is

---

* The inverse-square nature of the electrostatic force had been demonstrated earlier in the century by Henry Cavendish, however.

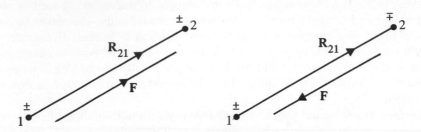

FIGURE 8.5   The radius vector **R** of charge 2 relative to 1 is outward from 1. If the charges have the same sign the electrostatic force is in the direction of **R**; if they have opposite signs it is in the opposite direction.

in the direction of the radius vector, or repulsive. However, the product of a positive and a negative number is negative. Therefore the force between unlike charges is negative, or attractive.

The unit of charge in the mks system is the *coulomb* (C), a unit defined by Coulomb's law as soon as the magnitude of the force constant k is established. For reasons that are chiefly historical, the constant is assigned the value $8.998(10)^9$ newtons-meter^2/coulomb^2, or to a very good approximation, 9×10^9 N-m^2/C^2. In the mks system the constant is usually written as $k = 1/4\pi\epsilon_0$, where ϵ_0 (called the permittivity of free space) evidently has the value:

$$\epsilon_0 = \frac{1}{4\pi k} = \frac{1}{4\pi \times 9 \times 10^9} \, \text{N} - \text{m}^2/\text{C}^2.$$

Then Coulomb's law assumes the form:

$$\mathbf{F} = \frac{1}{4\pi\epsilon_0} \frac{q_1 q_2}{R^2} \frac{\mathbf{R}_{21}}{R}.$$

Occasionally only the magnitude of the force between two charges is required, in which case the scalar equivalent of Equation 8.1a is applicable:

$$F = \frac{1}{4\pi\epsilon_0} \frac{q_1 q_2}{R^2}. \tag{8.1b}$$

It follows from Equation 8.1b that two particles each bearing a net charge of one coulomb and separated by one meter would exert a force of 9×10^9 newtons (N) upon each other. Clearly the coulomb is a very large unit. Often charge is expressed in microcoulombs (μC), or 10^{-6} C.*

Coulomb's law is a mathematical description of the electrostatic force between two particles. In that spirit it serves as an operational definition of charge just as Equations 5.4 define gravitational mass. The reasoning is not circular. There is a basic interaction

---

* The μC should not be confused with the statcoulomb, a unit based upon the cgs system *and* the choice of $k = 1$ in Coulomb's law. One coulomb = $2.998(10)^{10}$ statcoulomb. (There is no common unit of charge in the English system.) Since the mks system is used throughout this text, no further mention of the statcoulomb will be made.

observed in nature that is consistently described by assuming a property of matter called charge. Since charge and the electrostatic interaction are inseparable concepts it is completely consistent to define the property in terms of the interaction.

Equation 8.1a is not necessarily an exhaustive statement about the nature of charge, nor does it preclude other possible interactions between two charges. Rather, it is a starting point, a consistent, observational definition of the property in terms of its simplest macroscopic manifestation.* If, in the spirit of Chapter 5 (Section 5.11), we must think of matter as the sum of its properties, and if properties can only be defined in terms of interactions, then Coulomb's law is part of an answer to the question: "What is matter?"

The analogy between the mathematical forms of Coulomb's law and Newton's gravitational law (Equation 5.4a) is striking, tempting, and laden with pitfalls. Both are inverse square forces, and the dependence of Equations 5.4 upon gravitational mass is analogous to the dependence of Equations 8.1 upon charge. Indeed the similarity in *form* is so apparent that it often obscures the very real differences between the interactions. The most obvious of these is the existence of two types of electrostatic interaction, attractive and repulsive, based upon two different types of charge, positive and negative; whereas only an attractive gravitational force (and therefore only one type of gravitational mass), has ever been observed.

In addition, since $1/4\pi\epsilon_0 = 9 \times 10^9$ N-m^2/C^2 while the gravitational constant $G = 6.67 \times 10^{-11}$ N-m^2/kg^2, the relative strengths of the two interactions are quite different. If M_1, M_2, q_1, and q_2 are the respective masses and charges of two particles separated by a distance R, the ratio of the magnitudes of the electrostatic to the gravitational forces between the particles is

$$\frac{F_E}{F_G} = \frac{(1/4\pi\epsilon_0)/(q_1 q_2/R^2)}{G(M_1 M_2/R^2)} = \left(\frac{1}{4\pi\epsilon_0 G}\right)\frac{q_1 q_2}{M_1 M_2} = 1.35 \times 10^{20} \frac{q_1 q_2}{M_1 M_2}. \qquad (8.2)$$

If $M_1 = M_2 = 1$ kg, and $q_1 = q_2 = 1$ μC $= 10^{-6}$ C, then $F_E/F_G = 1.35 \times 10^8$. The electrostatic force is over one hundred million times stronger than the gravitational force between the particles. The ratio of the forces between a proton and an electron is of more basic interest. Here $M_p = 1.6 \times 10^{-27}$ kg, $M_e - 9 \times 10^{-31}$ kg, $q_p = 1.6 \times 10^{-19}$ C, and $q_e = -1.6 \times 10^{-19}$ C. Then $F_E/F_G = 2.4 = 10^{39}$. The electrostatic force dominates the gravitational force so completely that it is customary to disregard the latter in problems concerned with the interactions of elementary particles.

There are several other differences between the two forces. Charge, whatever it may be, enters the structure of matter in such a way that materials may be classified either as electrical conductors or insulators, whereas there are no analogous properties based upon gravitational mass. A most important property of gravitational mass is its equality with inertial mass (Section 4.5). No such equivalence is known for charge. Whereas the gravitational mass of a body cannot be changed without making an equal change in its inertial mass, the charge on an amber rod, for instance, can be changed by rubbing it with animal fur or touching it to a metal sphere, and neither process appreciably alters its inertial mass. Finally, Coulomb's law is but one manifestation of the interaction of charge. When the more general electromagnetic interaction is considered (Chapters 9 and 12), much of the symmetry between Equations 8.1 and 5.4 is lost.

---

* Anticipating further developments (Chapter 9) it is necessary to restrict Equation 8.1 to charges at rest with respect to each other.

▲▲ 8.3 The electric field. Electric field calculations

Newton and his contemporaries were disturbed by the implication that two gravitational masses apparently interact over vast distances without the intervention of any medium. Although there is no a priori philosophical reason why action at a distance should not be possible, the problem continued to trouble his successors. The form of Coulomb's law carries the same action-at-a-distance implications, and ultimately led Michael Faraday to propose that the presence of a charge creates or induces a condition throughout all space that in turn interacts with other charges, thus eliminating the action-at-a-distance implication. This condition is called the *electric field*.

Faraday probably thought of the electric field in the very concrete mechanical terms that were common during the mid-nineteenth century. In retrospect it is more fruitful to regard the field as an abstraction. It is an abstraction that may be harder to grasp than momentum, inertial mass, or charge, for example, since its existence rests upon more indirect measurement. Nonetheless, it cannot be regarded as any less real, for we have seen that even such "concrete" and "intuitive" concepts as momentum are defined as they are in order to make the results of observation comprehensible. The field concept is one of the most important ideas in physics. We shall find it useful at this juncture, and almost imperative in Chapter 12. Modified in modern physics by the requirements of relativity and quantum mechanics, the idea has become fundamental to our present ideas concerning the very existence of matter itself.

As in Faraday's original model let us assume that a charge creates a condition in space, the electric field, and that this condition exerts a force upon all other charge. We first seek a way to measure the strength of a field created by a charge. Because it is a force-transmitting condition, the strength of the field must be defined in terms of the force it exerts upon charge. Thus we may probe the strength of an electric field at any point by measuring the electrostatic force exerted upon a small test charge of magnitude q.*

If the force upon the charge at some point is $\mathbf{F}$ then the electric field strength vector, $\mathbf{E}$, at that point is defined as the electrostatic force per unit charge (Figure 8.6).

$$\mathbf{E} = \frac{\mathbf{F}}{q}. \tag{8.3a}$$

According to the defining equation the electric field strength is a vector whose direction is in the direction of the force upon a positive charge, opposite to the force on a negative charge, and has units newtons/coulomb. Inverting Equation 8.3a, the electrostatic force upon a charge q at a point in space with electric field strength $\mathbf{E}$ must be

$$\mathbf{F} = q\mathbf{E}, \tag{8.3b}$$

implying that the force upon a positive charge is in the direction of the field, the force upon a negative charge in the opposite direction.

In terms of the field concept we can think of the interaction of charges as a two-step process: (1) creation of the field by a charge (or group of charges); and (2) interaction of the field with another charge according to Equation 8.3b. Of course for any given situation the same force must be obtained whether it is calculated in terms of the field, or directly using Equation 8.1. This requirement permits us to find algebraic expressions for electric fields due to different charge configurations. Conversely, given the strength

---

* The charge must be small so that its interaction with the charges that create the field does not appreciably alter their positions.

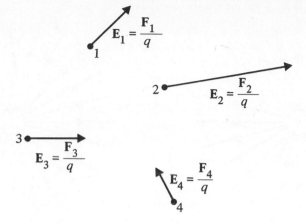

FIGURE 8.6   Mapping an electric field.   The force on a charge *q* is measured at various points in space.   The field vector at each point is then given by $\mathbf{E} = \mathbf{F}/q$.

of an electric field at all points in space, it is possible, at least in principle, to find the charge configuration that creates that field.

The simplest field to calculate is the field created by a point charge of magnitude Q_1, since the force it exerts upon a test charge *q* is (Equation 8.1):

$$\mathbf{F} = \frac{1}{4\pi\epsilon_0}\frac{qQ_1}{R^2}\frac{\mathbf{R}}{R}.$$

Applying Equation 8.3a, the electric field strength a distance *R* from the source charge Q_1 is:

$$\mathbf{E} = \frac{\mathbf{F}}{q} = \frac{1}{4\pi\epsilon_0}\frac{Q_1}{R^2}\frac{\mathbf{R}}{R}. \tag{8.4}$$

Using Equation 8.3b, the force exerted by this particular field upon another charge Q_2 is:

$$\mathbf{F} = Q_2\mathbf{E} = \frac{1}{4\pi\epsilon_0}\frac{Q_1Q_2}{R^2}\frac{\mathbf{R}}{R}$$

in agreement with Equation 8.1.

For example, the strength of the electric field created by a 2×10^{-6} C point charge is 1.8×10^4 N/C at all points 1 m from it, 1.8×10^2 N/C at all points 10 m away. If the charge is positive the field is directed away from the charge, if negative it is directed toward the charge. Such a field exerts a force of magnitude 1.8×10^{-2} N on a 10^{-6} C charge 1 m from the source, and a force of magnitude 1.8×10^{-4} N on a similar charge 10 m from the source.

Since the field created by a positive point charge is directed away from the source point and decreases inversely as the square of the distance from that point it is called an *inverse square central field*. Figure 8.7a is a useful pictorial representation of such a field. The directions of the *lines of force* diverging from the central positive charge show the directions of the electric field strength vectors, while their spacing is indicative of the magnitude of the field strength.* Figure 8.7b is an analogous representation of the field

---

* The relation can be made strictly quantitative by introducing a quantity called electric flux. However, its introduction would take us too far afield at this point.

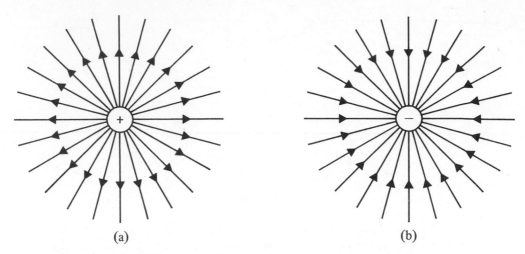

(a)   (b)

FIGURE 8.7   Electric fields of (a) a positive and (b) a negative point charge. The lines of force are in the direction of the field. Their density in any region of space is proportional to the magnitude of the field.

of a negative point charge, with the lines of force converging upon the source rather than diverging from it.

The field concept suggests a reformulated statement of Coulomb's law. In words, Equation 8.1 states that:

- Every point charge exerts a force upon every other point charge directly proportional to the product of their magnitudes and inversely proportional to the square of their separation. The force is attractive for unlike charges, repulsive for like charges.

Whereas from the point of view of the electric field:

- Every point charge creates an inverse square central field with strength directly proportional to its magnitude. The direction of the field is away from the source if the charge is positive, toward the source if it is negative. An electric field exerts a force on a charge equal to the product of the charge by the field strength vector.

Both statements lead to the same expression for the force between point charges. However, conceptually they are very different. It is entirely possible that the field formulation can suggest features of the electrostatic interaction that are not easily seen in the form given by Equation 8.1, for insight often results from the adoption of a new approach.

The field created by any number of arbitrary charges separated by arbitrary distances can be calculated by superimposing the fields created by each charge separately. Superposition is carried out in detail by vector addition of the individual forces upon test charges at all points in space. In Figure 8.8 the two charges Q_1 and Q_2 are separated by a distance D. (Q_1 and Q_2 attract or repel each other, of course, and so it must be assumed that they are held motionless by some external force.) The total force upon a test charge q is the vector sum of the force upon it due to its interaction with Q_1, and the force upon it due to its interaction with Q_2. By definition the field strength vector at that point is the total force divided by the strength of the test charge. In other words, each

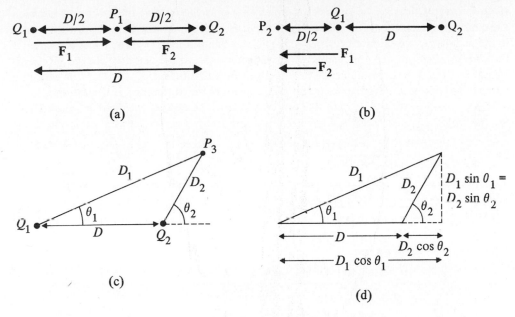

FIGURE 8.8 Geometry used to calculate the electric field due to two point charges. (a) Calculation of the field at the midpoint between the charges. (b) Calculation of the field a distance $D/2$ to the left of Q_1 (the directions of the force arrows are for positive Q_1 and Q_2). (c) Calculation of the electric field due to two charges at an arbitrary point P_3. (d) Relations between the variables D, D_1, D_2, θ_1, and θ_2.

charge creates its own field as if the other were not present. The total field vector at any point in space is the vector sum of the separate field vectors.

The components of the separate forces upon the test charge q located at P_1, a point midway between Q_1 and Q_2 (a distance $D/2$ from each) (Figure 8.8a) are:

$$F_1 = \frac{1}{4\pi\epsilon_0} \frac{Q_1}{(D/2)^2},$$

$$F_2 = -\frac{1}{4\pi\epsilon_0} \frac{Q_2}{(D/2)^2},$$

where a positive force component implies a force in the positive x-direction. If the signs of Q_1 and Q_2 are the same, the forces they exert upon q are opposite in direction, and along the line between them. Then the total force on the test charge must also be directed along the axis of the source charges, the x-axis, and given by:

$$F = F_1 + F_2 = \frac{1}{4\pi\epsilon_0} \frac{q}{(D/2)^2} (Q_1 - Q_2),$$

$$= \frac{q}{\pi\epsilon_0 D^2} (Q_1 - Q_2).$$

Using Equation 8.3a the field is also parallel to the x-axis and given by:

$$E = \frac{q}{\pi\epsilon_0 D^2} (Q_1 - Q_2). \tag{8.5a}$$

If Q_1 is greater than Q_2, E is positive, indicating that the field at the midpoint between the charges is in the positive x-direction; likewise, if Q_1 is smaller than Q_2, the field is in the negative x-direction. If $Q_1 = Q_2$, the field at the midpoint is zero; when the signs of the charges are opposite, the field is always directed toward the negative charge. Regardless of its direction, the magnitude of E is given by substituting $|Q_1 - Q_2|$, the absolute value of the charge difference, for $(Q_1 - Q_2)$, the algebraic difference, in Equation 8.5a.

If $Q_1 = +3 \times 10^{-6}$ C, $Q_2 = +2 \times 10^{-6}$ C, and $D = 4$ m, the field on the axis at the midpoint is (since $1/\pi\epsilon_0 = 4/4\pi\epsilon_0 = 4/9 \times 10^9$):

$$E = \frac{4 \times 9 \times 10^9}{16} (3 - 2) \times 10^{-6} = 2.25 \times 10^3 \text{ N/C}$$

directed toward Q_2. Therefore, the force on a charge $+10^6$ C located at P_1 will be 2.25×10^{-5} N in the direction of Q_2.

If the test charge is located at P_2 a distance $D_1 = D/2$ from Q_1 and on the axis joining the source charges (Figure 8.8b) it must be a distance $D + D/2 = 3D/2$ from Q_2. Then the separate forces on it are

$$F_1 = \frac{1}{4\pi\epsilon_0} \frac{qQ_1}{(D/2)^2} = \frac{1}{\pi\epsilon_0} \frac{qQ_1}{D^2},$$

and

$$F_2 = \frac{1}{4\pi\epsilon_0} \frac{qQ_2}{(dD/2)^2} = \frac{1}{9\pi\epsilon_0} \frac{qQ_2}{D^2}.$$

If both charges have the same sign, both forces are in the same direction and along the axis joining the charges. Therefore:

$$F = F_1 + F_2 = \frac{q}{4\pi\epsilon_0 D^2} \left(4Q_1 + \frac{4}{9} Q_2 \right),$$

and, by Equation 8.3a,

$$E = \frac{1}{4\pi\epsilon_0 D^2} \left(Q_1 + \frac{4}{9} Q_2 \right). \tag{8.5b}$$

The direction of the field is toward the charges if both are negative, away from the charges if both are positive.

As in our previous example let $Q_1 = 3 \times 10^{-6}$ C, $Q_2 = 2 \times 10^{-6}$ C, and $D = 4$ m. Then the field at P_2 is:

$$E = \frac{9 \times 10^9}{15} \left(4 \times 3 + \frac{4 \times 2}{9} \right) \times 10^{-6}$$

$$= 7.38 \times 10^{+3} \text{ N/C.}$$

But if $Q_1 = 2 \times 10^{-6}$ C, $Q_2 = 3 \times 10^{-6}$ C:

$$E = \frac{9 \times 10^9}{16} \left(4 \times 2 + \frac{4 \times 3}{9} \right) \times 10^{-6}$$

$$= 5.25 \times 10^3 \text{ N/C.}$$

Finally, let us find the field strength at a point P_3 that is not upon the axis of the charges but is located a distance D_1 from Q_1, D_2 from Q_2. In this case the forces upon the test charge are not in the same direction; each has both an x- and a y-component at P_3. If the respective angles between the x-axis and the radius vectors of q relative to Q_1 and Q_2 are θ_1 and θ_2, then (Figure 8.8c):

$$F_{1x} = F_1 \cos \theta_1, \qquad F_{2x} = F_2 \cos \theta_2,$$

$$F_{1y} = F_1 \sin \theta_1, \qquad F_{2y} = F_2 \sin \theta_2,$$

where F_1 and F_2, the magnitudes of the total forces upon q, are

$$F_1 = \frac{1}{4\pi\epsilon_0} \frac{qQ_1}{D_1^2},$$

and

$$F_2 = \frac{1}{4\pi\epsilon_0} \frac{qQ_2}{D_2^2}.$$

The components of the total force upon q are the sums of the components of the separate forces, and the components of the field derived from the total force components by Equation 8.3a:

$$E_x = \frac{1}{4\pi\epsilon_0} \left(\frac{Q_1}{D_1^2} \cos \theta_1 + \frac{Q_2}{D_2^2} \cos \theta_2 \right), \tag{8.5c}$$

$$E_y = \frac{1}{4\pi\epsilon_0} \left(\frac{Q_1}{D_1^2} \sin \theta_1 + \frac{Q_2}{D_2^2} \sin \theta_2 \right). \tag{8.5d}$$

The magnitude of the field at P_3 follows from the Pythagorean theorem (Equation 2.20a):

$$E = \sqrt{E_x^2 + E_y^2},$$

and its direction, ϕ is given by (Equation 2.20b)

$$\tan \phi = \frac{E_y}{E_x}.$$

It is not necessary to specify all of the five variables D_1, D_2, θ_1, and θ_2, and the separation D. If any three are known, the other two follow by applying trigonometric relations. For example, from Figure 8.8d it is apparent that $D_1 \sin \theta_1 = D_2 \sin \theta_2$ and $D = D_1 \cos \theta_1 - D_2 \cos \theta_2$. By substituting into Equations 8.7c and d we could express the field components in terms of D and the two angles or the two distances D_1 and D_2.

Pursuing our earlier numerical example with $Q_1 = 3 \times 10^{-6}$ C, $Q_2 = 2 \times 10^{-6}$ C, and $D_4 = 4$ m, let us choose $\theta_1 - 60°$, $\theta_2 = 120°$, so that P_3 is directly above the midpoint between the two charges. Then (see Appendix B) $\sin 60° = 0.866$, $\sin 120° = \sin (180 - 60) = 0.866$, soc $60° = 0.5$, $\cos 120° = \cos (180 - 30) = -0.5$. Also $D_1 = D_2 = (D/2) \div \cos 60° = 4$ m. Substituting into Equations 8.5c and 8.5d:

$$E_x = 9 \times 10^9 \left(\frac{3 \times 0.5}{16} + \frac{2 \times -0.5}{16} \right) \times 10^{-6}$$

$$= 0.281 \times 10^3 \text{ N/C},$$

$$E_y - 9 \times 10^9 \left(\frac{3 \times 0.866}{16} + \frac{2 \times 0.866}{16} \right) \times 10^{-6}$$

$$= 2.42 \times 10^3 \text{ N/C}.$$

The total magnitude of the field at P_3 is

$$E = \sqrt{E_x^2 + E_y^2} = 2.48 \times 10^3 \text{ N/C,}$$

with direction:

$$\tan \phi = \frac{E_y}{E_x} = \frac{2.42}{0.281} = 8.58,$$

or

$$\phi = 83.6° \text{ relative to the } x\text{-axis.}$$

Field configurations for two equal negative charges, two equal positive charges, and a negative and positive charge of equal magnitude are shown in Figure 8.9. Lines of force always diverge from the positive charge and converge on negative, implying that a positive charge is accelerated away from positive and toward a negative charge.

We have pursued this example in detail in order to show that the calculation of a two-charge field is straightforward, but that its dependence upon the geometric variables may be relatively complex. Calculations of fields of distributions involving 3, 4, 5, or more charges may be carried out in an analogous manner.

The electric field at a point in space due to a uniformly charged, extended body may be determined by first calculating the resultant force exerted upon a test charge by every small element of charge on the body, then summing each of these contributions in the same way the gravitational force due to an extended body is calculated in Figure 5.4b (Figure 8.10a). In analogy with the conclusion stated in Section 5.3, the electric field of a uniformly charged sphere at all points outside the sphere is equivalent to the field that would be created if all its charge were placed at its center (Figure 8.10b).

An electric field with constant magnitude and direction over a reasonable volume of space may be produced by using two equal and oppositely charged plane conductors with their faces parallel (Figure 8.11a). Such an arrangement is called a parallel plate *capacitor*. If one member of the pair is charged positively, for instance, it will induce a rearrangement of the charge in the second plate, with the *negative* charge of that plate on the face defining the gap.

Lines of force from each charge on the positive plate diverge in all directions, as they converge in all directions upon the charge on the negative plate. But because of the symmetry of the arrangement, the field component of each charge in the direction parallel to the plane of the gap is canceled by the field of another charge. For instance, consider two small equal areas A_1 and A_2 on the positive plate separated by a distance D. The component of the field parallel to the plate at all points along the line n, which is perpendicular to the gap between the plates and lies midway between the charges is the sum of the horizontal components due to the charge in A_1 and A_2. Since the plate is uniformly charged these components are equal and opposite and therefore cancel (Figure 8.11b). On the other hand the two components perpendicular to the plate are in the same direction. The area A_1 can be paired in the same way with all other areas on the plate such as A_3 and A_4 with the result that, except near its edges, the field component parallel to the plate created by the charge in any area is always canceled by the field component created by the charge in some other area. Therefore, the direction of the field is perpendicular to the plates. Since lines of force start on positive charge and end on negative charge, and since the plates are uniformly and equally charged, the net field in the gap must be uniform and directed from the positive to the negative plate.

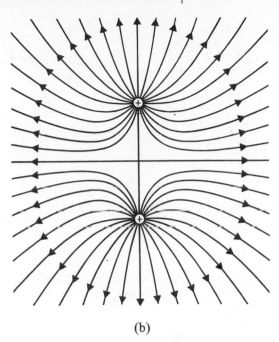

(a)

(b)

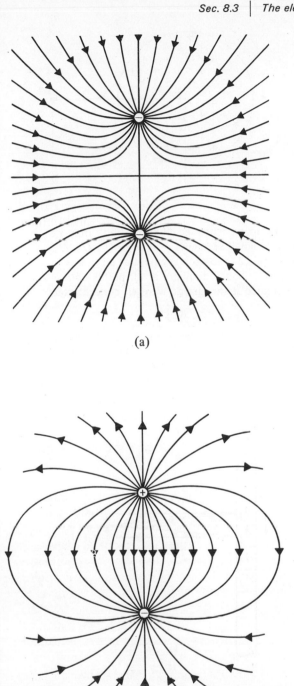

(c)

FIGURE 8.9 Electric lines of force for (a) two equal negative charges, (b) two equal positive charges, and (c) equal and opposite charges. (Adapted from David Halliday and Robert Resnick, *Physics for Students of Science and Engineering*, 2nd ed., John Wiley and Sons, Inc., © 1960.

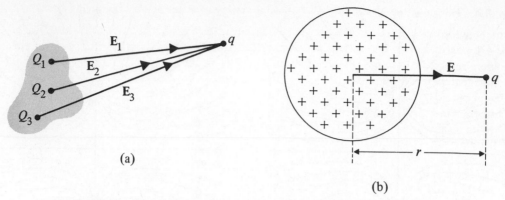

(a)

(b)

FIGURE 8.10   (a) The electric field due to an extended charged body may be determined by breaking the body up into small segments of charge Q_1, Q_2, Q_3, then calculating the vector sum of the fields due to each segment at all points in space.   (b) The electric field of a uniformly charged sphere at all points *outside* the sphere is the field that would be created if the charge were all concentrated at its center.

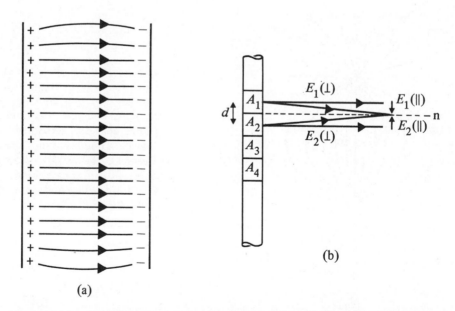

(a)

(b)

FIGURE 8.11   (a) A parallel plate capacitor and its electric field.   (b) If the two small areas A_1 and A_2 contain equal amounts of positive charge their field components parallel to the plate are equal and opposite at all points along the perpendicular n. Since each area on the plate may be paired with every other in this way it follows that the direction of the net field in the gap is as shown in part a.

▲▲ 8.4 Motion in an electric field. Potential energy of a particle in the field

In Newtonian mechanics all forces are defined in terms of their ability to accelerate inertial masses, and in this respect the electrostatic force behaves like any other. Although we have referred to charge throughout this chapter, we have never implied the existence of charge separated from inertial mass. All references to charge are really shorthand references to charged masses or charged particles.

In order to calculate the motion of a charged particle in an electric field we must first relate its acceleration to the cause of its acceleration by means of Newton's second law:

$$\mathbf{F} = M\mathbf{a},$$

and then write down the explicit form of the force:

$$\mathbf{F} = q\mathbf{E}.$$

Combining these two equations we obtain an equation relating the acceleration of a charged particle to the strength of the electric field that acts upon it:

$$q\mathbf{E} = M\mathbf{a},$$

or

$$\mathbf{a} = \left(\frac{q}{M}\right)\mathbf{E}. \tag{8.6}$$

At each point in its trajectory the acceleration of a positively charged particle is in the direction of the electric field strength vector at that point if the charge is positive, opposite to its direction if the charge is negative, and has magnitude equal to the product of the particle's charge to mass ratio times the magnitude of the field.

Equation 8.6 leads to equations of motion for charged particles in any case where $\mathbf{E}$ is known, regardless of whether or not the source of $\mathbf{E}$ is specified. If the field is constant throughout some region of space the acceleration will also be constant in that region. A free fall-like situation pertains, and therefore, Equations 2.12 can be applied with $\mathbf{a} = (q/M)\mathbf{E}$, and with the direction of the motion in the direction of $\mathbf{E}$.

For example, if a particle has a mass equal to 10^{-2} kg, a charge of -2×10^{-6} C, and is placed in a constant electric field of magnitude 2×10^4 N/C in the x-direction, its acceleration is $a = -(2 \times 10^{-6}/10^{-2}) \times 2 \times 10^4 = -4$ m/sec^2, in the negative x-direction. The x-component of its velocity and position are given as functions of time by Equations 2.12:

$$v_x = v_{0x} + at,$$
$$x = x_0 + v_0 t + \tfrac{1}{2}at^2,$$

with v_{0x} the x-component of its velocity at $t = 0$, and x_0 the x-coordinate of its position at the same time. If $x_0 = 0$, $v_{0x} = 0$, then in our example:

$$v_x = at = -4t,$$
$$x = \tfrac{1}{2}at^2 = -2t.$$

In one second the particle attains a velocity of 4 m/sec in the negative x-direction and has traveled 2 m from the origin.

By the same token a negatively charged particle traveling with sufficient speed can maintain a stable orbit about a heavy positively charged particle even as the earth orbits about the sun. Because the negative charge moves in an attractive, inverse central field its equations of motion are analogous to motion of a mass in an inverse square gravitational field. Therefore, many conclusions regarding planetary orbits should be applicable, in particular Kepler's laws. This analogy is the basis of the well-known planetary model of the atom in which a heavy positively charged nucleus plays the role of the sun and electrons the roles of the planets. But as we pointed out in Section 8.2 the electrostatic force is only part of the interaction between two charges. When charges move rapidly relative to each other a magnetic force is also present; in addition an accelerating charge radiates energy (Chapter 12). Hence the planetary analogue is not completely valid. However it is a convenient starting point for discussing internal atomic structure (Chapter 17).

Since an electric field can displace a charged particle, then by definition, it can perform work. Applying Equations 7.1 and 8.3b, the work performed by a field of strength **E** when it displaces a charge over a short distance Δs is the product of that displacement by the component of the force it exerts in the direction of that displacement (Figure 8.12):

$$\Delta W = F \Delta s \cos \theta = qE \Delta s \cos \theta. \qquad (8.7)$$

If the field varies over the displacement path between the end points s_2 and s_1 the total work performed is obtained by summing the contributions from each small segment of path over the entire length, a procedure that may be carried out either by evaluating an integral (Equation 7.3), or by finding the area under a curve, as in Figure 7.2, with $F \cos \theta$ replaced by $qE \cos \theta$. Because two types of charge exist, the work performed by a particular field over a particular path may be positive or negative. If the work performed by the field on a charge of one sign is positive over a given path it will be negative for the opposite charge over the same path.

Let us calculate the work performed by a constant 2×10^4 N/C electric field in the positive x-direction when it displaces a -2×10^{-6} C charge along a 0.5 m path parallel to the x-axis and in the positive direction (Figure 8.13a).

Since the field and displacement path are in the same direction, $\cos \theta = 1$, and, applying Equation 8.7,

$$W = -2 \times 10^{-6} \times 2 \times 10^4 \times 0.5 = -2 \times 10^{-2} \text{ J}.$$

The work is negative. Therefore, an external force would have to perform at least 2×10^{-2} joules work if the displacement were actually carried out, even as an external

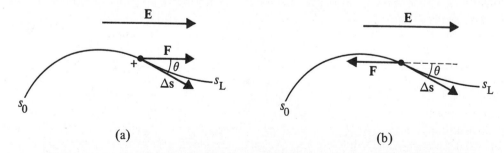

(a)   (b)

FIGURE 8.12 The work performed on a charged particle by an electric field is the product of its displacement and the parallel force component causing that displacement, $W = (F \cos \theta)\Delta s = q(E \cos \theta)\Delta s$. (a) If q is positive the force upon it is in the direction of the field. (b) If q is negative the force is in the opposite direction so that the work performed over a given path by a given field is the negative of the work performed on a positive charge of the same magnitude.

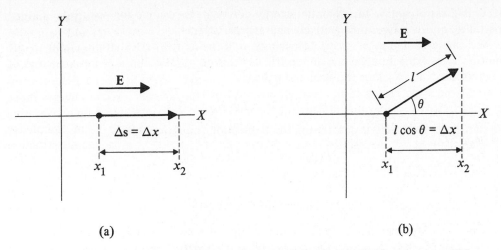

(a)   (b)

FIGURE 8.13   (a) Work performed by a constant electric field over a parallel displacement path. (b) Work performed by the same field over an inclined path of length *l*.

force is required to lift a body off the ground (Section 7.2). However, the work performed by the same field in displacing a $+2 \times 10^{-6}$ C charge over the same path is $+2 \times 10^{-2}$ joules. If no external force restrained it, this work would appear as kinetic energy of the charged body.

Now suppose a particle with charge $+2 \times 10^{-6}$ C were displaced by the same field along a straight line path of length *l* inclined at an angle θ to the *x*-axis. In this case:

$$W = qEl \cos \theta.$$

But $l \cos \theta = \Delta x$. Therefore:

$$W = qE \Delta x = 4 \times 10^{-2} \Delta x.$$

If Δx, the *x*-component of *l*, is 0.5 m then $W = 2 \times 10^{-2}$ joules, as before. That is, the work performed by the constant field is the same over all paths with the same *x*-components. In Section 7.2 we encountered a similar situation in comparing the work performed by the gravitational force on a particle in free fall with the work performed on a particle sliding down an incline or a roller coaster.

The above example suggests that the electrostatic force, like the gravitational force, is conservative. That is, the work it performs in displacing a charged particle between two points is independent of the path of the displacement, and therefore may be calculated over the simplest route available. Pursuing the analogy, a charged particle in an electric field has the ability to do work by virtue of its position in the field. Therefore, it has electrostatic potential energy relative to all other points in the field. According to the general definition (Equation 7.9a) the potential energy of a charge at the point s_2 relative to its potential energy at s_1 is equal to the work performed by the electric field in displacing the charge from s_2 to s_1. If the field is constant and in the positive *x*-direction, for instance (Figure 8.13), the potential energy difference between two points with *x*-coordinates x_2 and x_1 is (Equation 8.7):

$$PE_2 - PE_1 = qE(x_2 - x_1). \tag{8.8a}$$

If x_2 is greater than x_1 the potential energy difference is positive for positively charged particles, and negative for negatively charged particles.

We can now apply the restricted energy conservation law (Equations 7.10) to the motion of a charged particle in an electric field. If an isolated mass M has velocities of magnitude v_2 and v_1 at the points 2 and 1 then:

$$(PE)_2 - (PE)_1 = \tfrac{1}{2}Mv_1^2 - \tfrac{1}{2}Mv_2^2.$$

In particular if the field is constant in the x-direction (Equation 8.8a):

$$qE(x_2 - x_1) = \tfrac{1}{2}M(v_1^2 - v_2^2), \tag{8.8b}$$

or:

$$qEx + \tfrac{1}{2}Mv^2 = \text{const.} \tag{8.8c}$$

Again if x_2 is greater than x_1 the potential energy of a positive charge decreases so that kinetic energy must increase. On the contrary the kinetic energy of a negative charge decreases.

Referring again to our numerical example with $E = 2 \times 10^4$ N/C, $q = +2 \times 10^{-6}$ C, $M = 10^{-2}$ kg, and $x_2 - x_1 = +0.5$ m:

$$v_1^2 - v_2^2 = \frac{2qE}{M}(x_2 - x_1) = 4 \text{ m}^2/\text{sec}^2.$$

If the initial speed $v_2 = 0$, then $v_1 = 2$ m/sec. However, for a charge -2×10^{-6} C:

$$v_1^2 = -4 \text{ m}^2/\text{sec}^2,$$

or

$$v_1^2 = (v_2^2 - 4) \text{ m}^2/\text{sec}^2.$$

The initial speed must be at least 2 m/sec in the positive x-direction if the particle is to reach the end of the half-meter path without the intervention of an external force.

Potential energy graphs (see Section 7.5) are invaluable in analyzing the motion of charged particles in electric fields. Figure 8.14a shows the potential energy of a positive charge in a constant field as a function of its distance from the origin (Equation 8.8a). Potential energy is always defined relative to some arbitrary reference point at which its value is zero, and it is often convenient to choose that point as the origin as in Figure 8.14a. Figure 8.14b is an analogous graph for a negative charge in the same field. The horizontal lines E_A, E_B, and E_C represent three different possible total, constant energies. A negative charge at rest at the point x_L has total energy E_B; therefore, it would have kinetic energy E_B at the origin. Likewise, a negative charge that starts from the origin with kinetic energy E_B has just enough energy to reach x_L, whereupon it is repelled by the field back toward its starting point.

From this description it appears that the motion of a negative charge between the $x = 0$ and x_L is analogous to the motion of a mass upon an inclined plane as represented by Figure 7.9a. The charge "slides" down or up the electric plane, gaining and losing velocity as if it were a mass on a frictionless incline. A negative charge traveling toward the origin that has kinetic energy E_A at the "base" of the plane (x_0) loses all its kinetic energy by the time it reaches the point x_A. At that point it stops, and is repelled by the field, or "slides" back down the plane. However, a charge with energy E_C reaches the point x_L with velocity to spare.

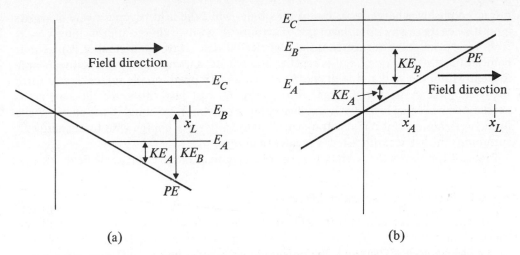

(a)   (b)

FIGURE 8.14 Energy diagrams for (a) a positive charge and (b) a negative charge of equal magnitude showing potential energy in a constant field in the x-direction.

The motion of a positive charge in the same field is represented by Figure 8.14a, and is analogous to the motion of a mass on a *negative* gravitational plane, for its potential energy is always smaller than or equal to zero. If a positive charge is at rest at the origin its total energy is zero, and remains zero. Therefore, it slides down to x_L, reaching that point with kinetic energy equal to qEx_L. Any positive charge traveling in the opposite direction can never reach the origin if its kinetic energy at x_L is less than qEx_L. But if its total energy at x_L is greater than zero it will arrive at the origin with velocity greater than zero.

Algebraic expression for the potential energy of charges in nonconstant fields are usually more involved than Equation 8.8a. Nevertheless, if the charge remains isolated in the field the sum of its potential and kinetic energies must remain constant, and its motion may be studied with the aid of a potential energy graph. Figure 8.15a shows the potential energy of a positive charge in a possible field, and is to be compared with Figure 7.9b. Evidently the field between the symmetric points $x = \pm x_1$ and $x = 0$

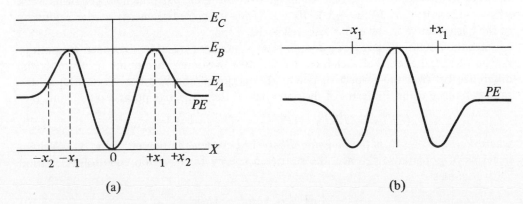

(a)   (b)

FIGURE 8.15 Energy diagrams for a nonuniform field. (a) The potential energy of a positive charge. (b) The potential energy of a negative charge of the same magnitude in the same field.

attracts a positive charge back toward the origin, while the field beyond $x = \pm x_1$ repels a positive charge away from the origin. Therefore, a positive charge approaching $x = x_1$ from the outside cannot surmount the "barrier" if its energy, E_A, is smaller than E_B. It comes to rest at $x = \pm x_2$ and is repelled toward its starting point. A positive charge located within the well and with energy E_A remains trapped, oscillating back and forth between $\pm x_A$. A positive charge with energy E_B can just surmount the barrier, is accelerated while inside the well, and then escapes once more. Should it lose energy while in the well, however, it remains trapped. Finally, a positive charge with total energy E_C surmounts the barrier with velocity greater than zero.

Figure 8.15b shows the potential energy of a negative charge in the same field.

▶▲▶ 8.5 Potential and potential difference

Because an electric field has the ability to do work upon charges, a system of field and charges contains energy. The work a field performs on a particular charge is proportional to the charge itself. Therefore, the potential energy of a given field and charge varies both with the magnitude and sign of the charge, and it becomes useful to define a quantity that measures the intrinsic capacity of a field *itself* to do work.

The *electrostatic potential*, V, of a field at a point s_2 relative to some arbitrary reference point s_0 is defined as the work the field performs on a unit positive charge in displacing it from s_2 to s_0, or:

$$V_2 = \frac{W_{20}}{q}. \tag{8.9a}$$

The unit of potential in the mks system is the *volt* (V). According to Equation 8.9a $1\text{ V} = 1\text{ J/C}$. Inverting Equation 8.9a, the *potential energy* of a charge q at s_2 relative to s_0 is qV_2, the product of the charge by the potential at s_2.

In Section 8.4 we found that a constant field of 2×10^4 N/C performs 2×10^{-2} J of work to displace a 2×10^{-6} C charge 0.5 m in the direction of the field. Therefore, the potential at the beginning of the path relative to the end is:

$$V_2 = \frac{2 \times 10^{-2}}{2 \times 10^{-6}} = 10^4 \text{ J/C} = 10^4 \text{ V}.$$

In order to displace a -2×10^{-6} C charge over the same path the field performs work $qV_2 = -2 \times 10^{-6} \times 10^4 = -2 \times 10^{-2}$ J. Thus its potential energy at the beginning of the path relative to the end is also -2×10^{-2} J.

Since the potential energy of a charge at s_2 is independent of its displacement path to s_0, the potential energy of a charge at s_2 relative to some other point s_1 is simply the difference between the respective potential energies of the points with respect to the same reference point. In terms of the potentials at the respective points:

$$(PE)_{21} = (PE)_{20} - (PE)_{10} = q(V_2 - V_1) = qV_{21}, \tag{8.9b}$$

where $V_{21} = V_2 - V_1$ is the *potential difference* between the points x_2 and x_1. Written in terms of potential difference, the restricted energy conservation equation (Equation 7.10) becomes

$$qV_{21} = \tfrac{1}{2}Mv_1^2 - \tfrac{1}{2}Mv_2^2. \tag{8.10}$$

The change in the kinetic energy of a charge moving between two points is equal to the product of the magnitude of the charge by the potential difference between the points.

In our previous numerical example we found that the potential of one end of a constant 0.5 m path (x_2) in the direction of a constant 2×10^4 N/C field relative to the other end of the path (x_0) is 10^4 m. Then the potential difference between the points is also 10^4 m, and the change in the speed of a charged particle moving across that 10^4 V potential difference is (Equation 8.10):

$$v_1^2 - v_2^2 = \frac{2qV}{M}.$$

If $q = -2 \times 10^{-6}$ C, and $M = 10^{-2}$ kg:

$$v_1^2 - v_2^2 = -4 \text{ m}^2/\text{sec}^2,$$

or

$$v_1^2 = (v_2^2 - 4) \text{ m}^2/\text{sec}^2.$$

The negative charge must have a speed greater than or equal to 2 m/sec at the beginning of the path if it is to reach the end. Again, this agrees with a conclusion of Section 8.4.

It is important to note that Equation 8.10 does not explicitly involve displacement. The potential difference between two points in a field does not uniquely specify the field itself. For example, a constant 10^4 N/C field performs 2×10^4 J work to displace a 2×10^{-6} C charge over a 1-m path in the direction of the field. Therefore, the potential difference between the end points of the path is 10^4 V, just as in our previous example with a 2×10^4 N/C field and a 0.5-m path. The potential difference between two points in a nonconstant field can also be 10^4 V. Equation 8.10 states that change in the kinetic energy of a charged particle across a given potential difference is always the same regardless of the specific field configuration involved.

If, however, the potential is known at *all* points in a region of space then the electric field in that region *can* be uniquely specified. Consider first a constant field parallel to the x-axis in some coordinate system. Applying Equation 8.9b, the potential energies of a charge q at x_2 and x_1 relative to $x = 0$ are qEx_2 and qEx_1, respectively. Therefore the potential energy at x_2 relative to x_1 is

$$PE_2 - PE_1 = -qE(x_2 - x_1) = -qE \, \Delta x_{21}. \tag{8.11a}$$

The negative sign is consistent with the fact that when an electric field does *positive* work on a *positive* charge the potential energy of the charge is reduced (see the definition of potential energy in Section 7.4). Dividing each side by q and using Equation 8.9b:

$$V_{21} = -E \, \Delta x_{21}.$$

The potential difference between two points in a constant field is equal to the negative product of the field strength times the distance between the points.

If the field is constant but *not* in the x-direction (Figure 8.16a) the work it performs to displace a charge a distance Δx in the x-direction is (Equation 8.7) $qE \, \Delta x \cos \theta$, where θ is the angle between the field direction and the x-axis. Therefore, since $E_x = E \cos \theta$ is the x-component of the field we can write:

$$V_{21} = -E_x \, \Delta x. \tag{8.11b}$$

Inverting Equation 8.11b, we obtain an expression for the x-component of a constant field in terms of the potential difference between two points on the x-axis, V_{21}, and the distance between them:

$$E_x = -\frac{V_{21}}{\Delta x}. \tag{8.11c}$$

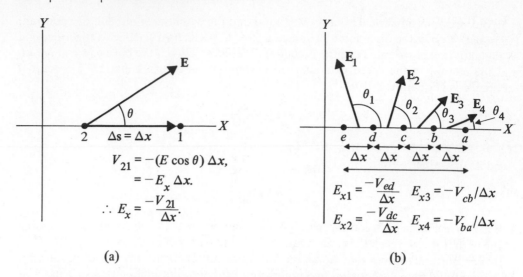

(a)   (b)

FIGURE 8.16 Relation between the potential difference between two points on the x-axis and the x-component of the electric field. (a) An electric field with constant magnitude and direction. (b) An electric field whose magnitude and direction both vary with x. In the latter case the relations are valid only if the variation in E over each interval Δx is negligible.

Even if the magnitude and/or the direction of a field is not constant it can nonetheless be expressed in terms of the potential if that potential is known as a function of the spatial coordinates. Let ΔV be the potential difference between two points very close together in an arbitrary electric field. The work performed by the field in displacing a charge over a path between the points parallel to the x-axis is (Equation 8.11b) $q\,\Delta V = qE_x\,\Delta x$, provided E_x is almost constant over the short path Δx (Figure 8.16b). This condition is always valid if Δx is sufficiently small. Therefore we can write:

$$E_x = \lim_{\Delta x \to 0} \frac{-\Delta V}{\Delta x} = -\frac{dV}{dx}. \tag{8.12a}$$

Similarly the y- and z-components of the field are

$$E_y = \lim_{\Delta y \to 0} \frac{-\Delta V}{\Delta y} = -\frac{dV}{dy}, \tag{8.12b}$$

and

$$E_z = \lim_{\Delta z \to 0} \frac{-\Delta V}{\Delta z} = -\frac{dV}{dz}. \tag{8.12c}$$

The components of the electric field at a given point are equal to the negative rates of change of the potential at that point in the appropriate directions. Thus an electric field is completely specified if its potential is known at all points in space.

For example, consider a potential given by the expression $V = ax + by$ with a and b constant. What are the corresponding expressions for the field components?

We first find an expression for the potential at the two points x_1 and $x_1 + \Delta x$ while holding y constant ($y = y_1$, for instance):

$$V(x_1) = ax_1 + by_1,$$
$$V(x_1 + \Delta x) = a(x_1 + \Delta x) + by_1 = ax_1 + a\,\Delta x + by_1.$$

Then (Equation 8.12a):

$$E_x = -\frac{V(x_1 + \Delta x) - V(x_1)}{\Delta x} = -\frac{a\,\Delta x}{\Delta x} = -a.$$

The x-component is constant and has magnitude a. By a similar argument we conclude that $E_y = -b$. Therefore, the magnitude of the field at all points in space is (Equations 2.20):

$$E = \sqrt{E_x^2 + E_y^2} = \sqrt{a^2 + b^2},$$

and its direction is given by

$$\tan \theta = \frac{b}{a},$$

where θ is the direction of the field relative to the x-axis.

As a further example let us calculate the field related to the potential $V = \frac{1}{2}ax^2$, where a is a constant (Figure 8.17a). We first note that the field must be in the x-direction since clearly the rates of change of the potential in the y- and z-directions are zero. The potentials of the field at the points x_1 and $x_1 + \Delta x$ are

$$V(x_1) = \tfrac{1}{2}ax_1^2,$$
$$V(x_1 + \Delta x) = \tfrac{1}{2}a(x_1 + \Delta x)^2 = \tfrac{1}{2}ax_1^2 + ax_1\,\Delta x + \tfrac{1}{2}a\,\Delta x^2.$$

Then:

$$\frac{\Delta V}{\Delta x} = \frac{ax_1\,\Delta x + \tfrac{1}{2}a_1\,\Delta x_1^2}{\Delta x} = ax_1 + \tfrac{1}{2}a\,\Delta x_1,$$

whose limit as $\Delta x \to 0$ is ax_1. Therefore, the magnitude of the field is given as a function of x by the expression:

$$E = -ax.$$

Finally, let us determine the field whose potential is given as a function of the distance R from the origin by (Figure 8.17c):

$$V = \frac{1}{4\pi\epsilon_0}\frac{Q}{R}, \tag{8.13a}$$

where Q is a point charge. We could write $R = \sqrt{x^2 + y^2}$ and apply Equations 8.12a and b to obtain the x- and y-components of the field. However, we have already solved a similar problem in Chapter 7 (Section 7.6). The potential energy of a charge q located at a point a distance R from the origin is

$$PE = \frac{1}{4\pi\epsilon_0}\frac{qQ}{R}, \tag{8.13b}$$

an expression which has the same form (save for the sign) as Equation 7.11b—the gravitational potential energy of a mass M_2 located a distance R from a mass M_1. Therefore, the force on q must be the Coulomb-law force due to the point charge Q, and the field related to Equation 8.13a the field of the point charge (Equation 8.4). Likewise, the potential difference between two points separated from Q by the respective distances R_1 and R_2 ($R_2 < R_1$) must be analogous to Equation 7.11a:

$$V_{21} = \frac{Q}{4\pi\epsilon_0}\left(\frac{1}{R_2} - \frac{1}{R_1}\right).$$

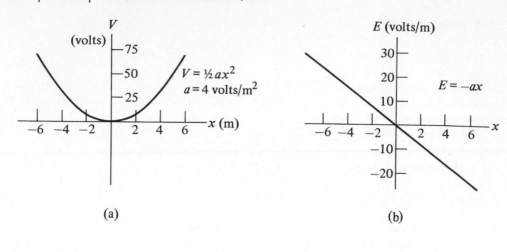

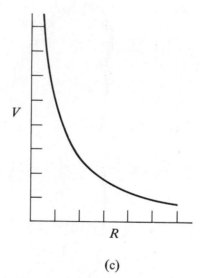

FIGURE 8.17 (a) The potential $V = \frac{1}{2}ax^2$. (b) The magnitude of the electric field corresponding to the potential plotted as a function of x for $a = 4$ volts/m². (c) Form of the potential due to a positive point charge at the origin (compare with Figure 7.12).

▲▲ 8.6 Current and conduction. Ohm's law

The difference between conductors and insulators was defined in Section 8.1 in terms of the mobility of charge in the materials. It is now known that the mobile, almost free charge in conductors is carried by electrons, elementary particles with mass equal to 9×10^{-31} kg and charge -1.6×10^{-19} C (Chapter 9). As we shall show in due course (Chapter 14 et. seq.) any atom consists of a relatively heavy, positively charged core called its *nucleus* surrounded by a sufficient number of electrons to neutralize its positive charge. Two or more atoms can interact with one another and bind themselves into the large aggregates which constitute the basis of the macroscopic matter we observe (Chapter 19). Several types of these intra-atomic bonds can be formed, depending on the nature of the interacting atoms. When atoms enter into a type of bond characteristic of an insulator their electrons are all restrained from moving any great distance from their original positions. But in one type of bond, called appropriately the metallic bond, one or more of the electrons from each atom becomes free to move about the entire aggregate, leaving a rigid positively charged lattice that contains the bulk of the mass. Normally the electrostatic attraction between the lattice and the mobile electrons prevents many of the latter from leaving the material, however, so that it remains electrically neutral.

We would expect the free negatively charged electrons in a metal to repel each other, and of course they do. However they are also attracted by the positive lattice so that unless an electric (or magnetic) field from some external source exists inside the metal, the net force on each electron is zero. Therefore, the free electrons move in all directions, suffering many collisions with other electrons and with the lattice, changing their directions almost continuously. Thus, the net displacement of an electron over even a rather long time interval is small. For present purposes we can oversimplify and regard the mobile electrons as being at rest in the metal yet free to move about.

If electrons are added to a neutral piece of metal (by touching it with a negatively charged glass rod, for instance) the net force on each free electron is no longer zero, and the electrons repel each other. Since the electrostatic force decreases with distance the excess electrons seek to move as far away from each other as they can and hence distribute themselves uniformly on the outside surface of the metal. Therefore, no excess charge can exist on the interior of a conductor. It follows from this fact and from the inverse square dependence of Coulomb's law that the electric field inside a conductor created by static charges alone is also zero.*

We can easily prove the latter assertion for the case of a metal sphere, although it is true for any shape conductor. The field at any point, P, inside the sphere (Figure 8.18) is the vector sum of the fields from the charge contained in each small area of its surface. Let us calculate the net field at P from the charge contained in the two diametrically opposite areas A_1 and A_2 subtended by a cone with vertex at P. If R_1 and R_2 are the respective distances from P to A_1 and A_2 then the area of A_1 is proportional to R_1^2 and

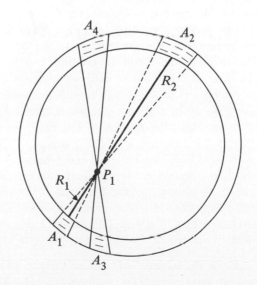

FIGURE 8.18 Geometric construction for proving that the electric field at any point P_1 within a uniformly charged spherical conducting shell is zero.

---

* The experimental fact (first noted by Cavendish) that the electric field inside a conductor really is zero serves as a confirmation of the inverse square nature of the electrostatic force.

the area of A_2 to R_2^2.* The force exerted by the charge in each of the areas upon a test charge at P is directly proportional to the charge in the area and *inversely* proportional to the square of its distance from P_1. But since the excess charge is uniformly distributed over the surface the total charge in each of the areas must be *directly* proportional to the square of the same distance.* Therefore, the net force on a test charge from the two areas is zero. Because every area on the surface can be paired in the same way with another by constructing a cone properly, it follows that no force at all would be exerted on a test charge at P or at any other point. Therefore, the electric field inside the spherical conductor is zero, as we have asserted.

If a neutral conductor is placed in an electric field (by bringing it near but not in contact with a charged amber or glass rod, for instance), then once again the net force on the mobile electrons will be different from zero, leading to a nonuniform spatial distribution of the electrons in the metal and, as a result, to an internal electric field due to the redistributed electrons themselves. Hence the net field in the metal is the vector sum of the external field and the field of the rearranged electrons. It is plausible to extend our previous result and assume that the net field is zero, and indeed this turns out to be true. The field of the rearranged electrons is equal and opposite to the external field everywhere inside the metal.

From these brief considerations we conclude that the net flow of charge in a conductor cannot be maintained for any appreciable time either by adding charge to the conductor or by placing it in an electrostatic field. The same conclusions could have been reached by applying the energy conservation law. If electrons continued to flow in one direction in a metal bar placed in an electric field they would either have to leave one end or pile up there. In both cases the potential energy of the electrons would increase, either because they would increase their separation from the positive lattice in escaping, or decrease their separation from the other electrons by piling up with them. Since the external electric field is assumed to be constant in time it cannot supply additional energy to the electrons. Therefore, their continued flow would violate the energy conservation law.

A simple mechanical analogue may help to illuminate these remarks. If a bucket of water is poured into the top of an inclined trough the water flows to the bottom of the incline and can perform work by turning a water wheel on its way. After the water reaches the bottom it cannot lift itself up to the top of the trough once again, no more than the free electrons in a metal can continue moving after they have rearranged themselves in the external field. But an external source of energy such as a mechanical pump installed at the bottom of the trough *can* lift the water back to the top of the trough so that it again flows down and turns the water wheel. Likewise an external energy source is required to maintain the motion of free electrons within a conductor. Any device which performs this function is called a source of EMF† (abbreviated $\mathscr{E}$). The most common sources of EMF are batteries and generators, although many other types exist. All perform their function by tapping their own internal sources or making use of some external source. A battery operates by means of chemical reactions that liberate some of the potential energy stored in the molecular bonds of its active substance, a generator uses the gravitational energy of a waterfall, for instance. As we have noted, sources of EMF are very much like mechanical pumps except that they "pump" charge rather than water.

---

* These statements are strictly true only as the areas become very small. Thus a rigorous proof of this proposition requires a statement about limits.

† The letters EMF stand for the outmoded term *electromotive force*. It is not only outmoded but inappropriate since EMF has the dimensions of energy rather than force.

For present purposes it is not necessary to know why a particular source of EMF functions; it is sufficient to know that such sources can be constructed. Figure 8.19 shows the basic elements of an electrical circuit which we may regard as any arrangement permitting the continuous flow of charge in a conductor (say a length of copper wire) connected to the terminals of a source of EMF. The energy delivered to the conductor by the source of EMF is unidirectional, causing the flow of mobile electrons from one of its terminals to the other and not vice versa.* By convention, the terminal from which positive charge *would* flow if it were mobile is called the positive terminal. However, as we know the mobile charge is negative. It actually flows from the negative to the positive terminal.

Let us examine the mechanism of conduction in a little more detail. For this purpose it is convenient to define a new quantity called *current* which measures the net rate at which the charge flows in a circuit. If a net charge Δq passes a particular plane surface in a conductor in a time Δt then by definition the average current through that surface is (Figure 8.20):

$$i_{av} = \frac{\Delta q}{\Delta t}. \tag{8.14a}$$

The instantaneous value of the current is the limit of the ratio when Δt approaches zero. When the net charge passing the plane is constant over an appreciable period of time then the current is constant and we may write:

$$i = \frac{q}{t}. \tag{8.14b}$$

Since charge is conserved and there is no reason to believe that it piles up at any particular point in a single wire, it follows that a constant current at one point along the wire implies the same, constant current at all other points. The unit of current is the *ampere* (A), equal by definition (Equations 8.14) to 1 C/sec.

The definition of current involves the *net* charge rather than the total magnitude of charge that crosses a given plane. The distinction is important. We have already noted

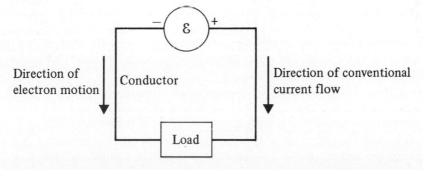

FIGURE 8.19 Basic elements of an electric circuit. The source of EMF acts very much like an electrical pump that causes electrons to flow through a conductor, through a load, and back to the source. The load is any device where electrical work is performed—a light bulb, electric motor, electronic circuit, or just an additional length of copper wire.

---

* A source of alternating EMF is no exception. The positive and negative terminals reverse many times a second. Nonetheless, at any given time one is positive, the other negative.

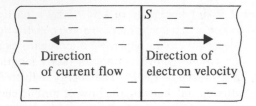

FIGURE 8.20   Current is defined in terms of the net charge that crosses a surface
S in a time Δt. If the mobile charges are electrons then the direction of current
flow is opposite the direction of the electron motion.

that in the absence of a source of EMF the free electrons in a metal move at random. At
any instant we can expect as many to be moving in one direction as in the opposite
direction. Therefore, even though a great many electrons cross a given plane in the
conductor in a time Δt the net charge across the plane will be small if not zero since
approximately the same number cross in both directions.

We have deliberately used the word *charge* rather than *electron* in defining current.
Even though we know that electrons are the mobile charges in solid conductors there is
no reason to believe that the motion of charge is restricted to the mobile negatively
charged electrons in metals. In the next chapter we shall discuss briefly the electrolysis of
water, a process in which a quantity of water is decomposed into hydrogen and oxygen
by immersing in it two copper electrodes connected to a source of EMF. There we shall
conclude that the mechanism depends on the mobility of positively charged hydrogen
ions (hydrogen atoms with one electron removed) and negatively charged oxygen ions
(oxygen atoms with two extra electrons). In a later chapter we shall discuss accelerators
such as the cyclotron which accelerates beams of electrons, as well as positively charged
protons and heavier nuclei to high energies. These high-energy beams consist of moving
charges, and can certainly be regarded as currents.

Even though we are restricting our present considerations to the motion of free
electrons in metals, it is clear that the idea of current is not confined to that process. It is
conventional to define the direction of a current as the direction in which positive charge
moves, and because many types of currents are possible we shall follow that convention
here.

If the moving charge that constitutes the current is negatively charged, as it is in a
conductor, then the direction in which the net charge actually moves is opposite to the
conventional direction of current flow.

Figure 8.21 is a somewhat idealized drawing of a section of conductor in which a steady
external electric field **E** is maintained. It might be a section of copper wire attached to a
source of EMF as shown in Figure 8.19. In any case there must be a source of EMF
present, otherwise the electric field in the conductor could not be maintained, but we need
not spell out the details. If the field were not present the mobile electrons would move
about at random. When the field is turned on the electrons are accelerated in the opposite
direction by the force it exerts on them. However, they continue to suffer collisions which
change their directions and therefore cannot move entirely in the direction opposite to
the field nor increase their speeds indefinitely as they could if accelerated in a vacuum.
Instead the field superimposes a constant coherent *drift* velocity in one direction upon
their continued random motion. Because of this coherent velocity more of them cross a
given plane in one direction than in the other and a current flows in the conductor. The
assumption that the constant force exerted by the field results in a constant velocity does

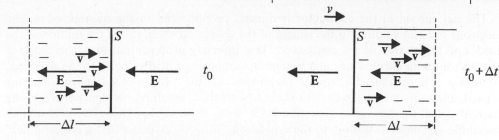

FIGURE 8.21 Idealized model of conduction. The electric field in the conductor imposes a drift velocity on the electrons in the direction opposite to the field. If the mean drift velocity is **v** then the length of the "tube" of electrons crossing the surface S in time Δt is $\Delta l = v\,\Delta t$.

not contradict Newton's second law, for it is only one of the forces on the electrons. The dominant interaction continues to arise from the collision of the electrons with one another and with the lattice. If the magnitude of the charge on each electron is e ($e = 1.6 \times 10^{-19}$ C, see Chapter 9), then the force exerted on each electron by the field is $-e\mathbf{E}$ and

$$e\mathbf{E} = -\alpha\mathbf{v}, \qquad (8.15a)$$

where α is a constant that depends on the structure of the metal in question, since it measures the effectiveness of the field in superimposing a constant drift velocity upon the random, collision-dominated motion of the electrons.

If an electron travels a net distance Δl in the direction opposite to the electric field in a time interval Δt its net velocity in that direction, or its drift velocity, is

$$v = \frac{\Delta l}{\Delta t}.$$

By definition (Equation 8.14a) the average current crossing any plane through the conductor (Figure 8.21) in that time interval is the net charge that crosses the plane divided by the length of the interval. Since we have assumed that all electrons have equal drift velocities, the amount of charge crossing any plane must be equal to the number of mobile electrons in the length Δl immediately preceding the plane times the magnitude of the charge e on each. If there are N mobile electrons per unit volume and the cross-sectional area of the conductor is A, then

$$Aq = NeA\,\Delta l,$$

and the average current across the plane is

$$i = \frac{NeA}{i}\frac{\Delta l}{\Delta t}.$$

But $\Delta l / \Delta t$ is the magnitude of the drift velocity, so

$$i = NevA. \qquad (8.15b)$$

Finally we can use Equation 8.15a to express the magnitude of the drift velocity in terms of the magnitude of the field, so that:

$$i = \frac{Ne^2EA}{\alpha}. \qquad (8.15c)$$

The net current in the conductor is directly proportional to the number of mobile electrons per unit volume, to the square of the charge on each, to the magnitude of the field, and to the area of the conductor. It is inversely proportional to α, the constant that measures the effectiveness of a field in superimposing a drift velocity on the electrons, however. A large value (Equation 8.15a) means that the field is not very effective in this regard, and implies that the current should be small. Therefore, the dependence of the current on all the factors in Equation 8.15c seems reasonable. However, it is well to recall the assumptions leading to the expression. First we assumed that a constant field can be maintained within a conductor, second that the field results in the superimposition of a constant drift velocity on the electrons. Either or both of these assumptions may not be valid in a particular circumstance. The test must rest with experiment.

Since the electric field results in a net displacement of the electrons along the length of the conductor, it performs work upon them. Therefore, a potential difference exists across a segment Δl of conductor through which current flows. Referring to Equations 8.7 and 8.9b:

$$\Delta V = -eE\,\Delta l.$$

The potential *increases* in the net drift direction of the electrons and therefore *decreases* in the conventional direction of the current. Substituting into Equation 8.15c,

$$i = \frac{NeA}{\alpha\,\Delta l}\,\Delta V,$$

or, inverting,

$$V = \frac{\alpha\,\Delta l}{NeA}\,i.$$

The *resistivity* ρ of the conductor is defined as

$$\rho = \frac{\alpha}{Ne},$$

so that

$$\Delta V = \frac{\rho\,\Delta l}{A}\,i. \tag{8.16a}$$

That is, the potential difference across a segment of conductor of length Δl and cross section A is directly proportional to Δl, inversely proportional to A, and directly proportional to the current in the segment. Finally, we define the *resistance R* of the segment:

$$R = \rho\frac{\Delta l}{A}, \tag{8.16b}$$

and substituting into Equation 8.16 we obtain:

$$\Delta V = iR. \tag{8.17}$$

The potential difference across a segment of conductor is directly proportional to the current flowing in the conductor.

Equation 8.17, known as *Ohm's law*, was first discovered experimentally by George Ohm, and turns out to be valid for metals and currents ranging from the smallest that can be detected to the largest that can be produced. Hence the assumptions used in its derivation appear to be valid for metals. However, we cannot conclude that Equation

8.17 with R constant represents a universal relation between potential difference and current. For example, the potential differences across electronic vacuum tubes or transistors do not increase in direct proportion to the current in these elements. But, we are concerned here with conduction in metals, and for this process Equation 8.17 has been amply verified.

The unit of resistance is the *ohm* (symbol Ω, the Greek capital omega) so that according to Equation 8.16b, resistivity is measured in ohm-meters. Table 8.1 lists the resis-

TABLE 8.1   *Resistivities of a Few Conductors at* 20 °C

Metal	Resistivity (ohm-meters)
Aluminum	2.83×10^{-8}
Carbon (graphite)	1000×10^{-8}
Copper	1.69×10^{-8}
Gold	2.44×10^{-8}
Iron	9.8×10^{-8}
Lead	19.8×10^{-8}
Mercury	95.8×10^{-8}
Nickel	7.04×10^{-8}
Silver	1.47×10^{-8}
Tin	11.5×10^{-8}

tivities of several materials. Since the quantity measures the work that must be performed in a conductor to cause a current to flow, a small value implies that the conductor is a good one. All conductors offer resistance to the flow of current and are also called *resistors*. The terms *conductor* and *resistor* are often used interchangeably but are not synonymous since a good conductor has a low resistance whereas a high resistance implies poor conduction properties. In addition, resistance is often attributed to current-carrying elements such as vacuum tubes and transistors that do not obey Ohm's law. Even though such elements carry currents they are usually not called conductors, for the latter term conventionally implies metallic conduction, or conduction in which the current is always directly proportional to the potential difference as described by Ohm's law.

The resistivity of a conductor increases with temperature. This is not surprising in view of the assumptions of our model. As we shall learn in a later chapter the temperature of a substance is related to the motion of its constituent atoms, and, in the case of metals, to the motion of its free electrons as well. Since the random motion of the mobile electrons in a conductor increases with temperature the superimposed drift velocity for a given field decreases, and with it the current in the conductor.

A few numerical applications of these ideas are in order. First let us find the length of 1 mm-diameter copper wire required to give a resistance of 5 ohms. Since 1 mm = 10^{-3} m, the cross section of the wire is $\pi(5 \times 10^{-4})^2 = 7.85 \times 10^{-7}$ m². Substituting into Equation 8.16b, with $\rho = 1.69 \times 10^{-8}$ ohm-meters from Table 8.1, and $R = 5$ ohms:

$$\Delta l = \frac{5 \times 7.85 \times 10^{-7}}{1.69 \times 10^{-8}} = 230 \text{ m.}$$

Then according to Ohm's law the potential difference between the ends of a 230 m-long, 1 mm-diameter copper wire carrying a current of $\frac{1}{2}$ ampere is $\Delta V = 0.5 \times 5 = 2.5$ V.

It is clear that in order to obtain reasonable resistances with relatively short lengths of material, something other than copper must be used. What is the resistance of a 0.1 mm-diameter, 1 cm-long piece of pure graphite? In this case $A = 7.85 \times 10^{-9}$ m^2, $\Delta l = 10^{-2}$ m, and using the value of ρ from Table 8.1:

$$R = \frac{10^{-5} \times 10^{-2}}{7.85 \times 10^{-9}} = 12.7 \text{ ohms.}$$

If a 100-volt potential difference is maintained across such a resistance, the current that flows is:

$$i = \frac{100}{12.7} = 7.8 \text{ amperes.}$$

Higher resistivities can be obtained by interspersing granules of an insulating material throughout a graphite lattice, thus reducing the effective cross section of the conductor.

Finally let us find the ratio of the potential differences across two conductors of the same material that are in contact if their lengths are equal and the diameter of the first twice the diameter of the second. The same current flows in each since they are in contact. According to Equation 8.16b the resistance of the second conductor is four times the resistance of the first since its cross section, which is proportional to the square of its diameter, is only one-fourth as large. Thus, using Ohm's law the potential difference across the second conductor is four times the potential difference across the first.

▲▲ 8.7   Electric circuits. EMF. Power

We have concluded that if a potential difference is maintained between the ends of a conductor a current will flow along it. According to our general ideas concerning potential difference (Section 8.5, especially Equation 8.10), the moving electrons that constitute the current should gain kinetic energy as their potential energy decreases. Yet we have assumed that their drift velocity remains constant, and in view of the experimental validity of Ohm's law that assumption seems justified.

There is really no contradiction between the constant drift-velocity assumption and the energy conservation law provided we realize that the general and not the restricted conservation principle is applicable. The restricted law is applicable only to isolated systems. But an electron in a conductor which makes frequent collisions with other electrons and with the lattice is certainly not isolated. After each collision the electric field in the conductor accelerates the electron. However, it cannot travel far before suffering another collision and changing both the magnitude and direction of its velocity. Again the electron is accelerated slightly, again it suffers a collision. Since each electron makes many collisions in even a short time interval we expect its average drift velocity to be constant. However, since there is no long-term increase in kinetic energy despite the work performed on the electrons by the field we must conclude that energy is transferred to the conductor by the electrons, an energy that manifests itself as an increase in temperature.

If a potential difference is required to maintain the flow of current in a resistance, and if as a result of that current flow energy is transferred to it, then we require an external energy source to maintain the potential difference. This is the role of the source of EMF. We can now better understand the elements of the basic circuit shown in Figure 8.19. The source of EMF, which we originally likened to a water pump, is able to maintain a potential difference between its terminals. It does so by utilizing its own internal energy, chemical energy in the case of a battery, mechanical energy in the case of a generator, for instance. Current flows in the circuit and work is performed as a result of the potential difference. Therefore, we may regard an electric circuit as an arrangement whereby energy provided by a source of EMF is transferred to one or more resistances in a circuit through the medium of an electric current which flows as a result of a potential difference maintained by the EMF. Because the source of EMF maintains a potential difference between the ends of the circuit connected to its terminals, EMF is measured in *volts*, the same units used to measure potential difference.

Figure 8.22a shows a generalized electric circuit consisting, as before (Figure 8.19), of a source of EMF, a conductor to carry current between its terminals, and in addition a load which we define as any device to which energy can be transferred by a current. Since the load draws current and receives energy there must be a potential difference between its input and output terminals, and we can define its resistance, r, as the ratio of that potential difference to the current flowing into it:

$$r = \frac{\Delta V}{i}. \tag{8.18}$$

The resistance so defined need not be a constant, but may (in fact usually does) vary with the current. Therefore, it should not be assumed that all (or even any) electrical devices such as light bulbs, motors, or electronic circuits, obey Ohm's law in the sense that r is constant. But for some purposes we can replace the load in a circuit with an equivalent resistor, symbolized by the jagged line (R) in Figure 8.22b, and for this reason the generalization is very useful. If, for instance, we know that the resistance of a particular light bulb is 240 ohms and is connected across a 120-volt line with copper leads whose resistance can be neglected, then using Equation 8.18 we find that the bulb will draw a current of $120/240 = 0.5$ amperes.

An electric circuit rarely consists of a single conduction path between the terminals of a source of EMF. Rather, it usually has several branches and loops (Figure 8.22c), most or all of which in combination constitute the load. In analyzing the behavior of such a circuit it is necessary to know the currents flowing in the different branches and the potential differences across them. Such an analysis is facilitated by replacing a network of resistors between two points in a circuit by a single equivalent resistor that draws the same current as the network and has the same potential difference.

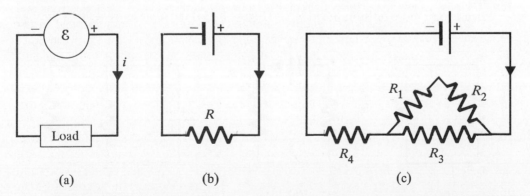

(a)   (b)   (c)

FIGURE 8.22 (a) Semipictorial representation of a circuit (Figure 8.19). (b) Standard representation of a circuit with the EMF shown by the symbol ⊣⊢ and the load by a resistor —⌁⌁⌁—. (The resistance of the leads is assumed negligible compared with the load resistance.) (c) A network of resistors.

There are two distinct ways in which resistors may be connected together across a source of EMF. If the resistors are in *series* there is only one conduction path through the combination (Figure 8.23a); if they are in *parallel* there are as many conduction paths as resistors (Figure 8.23b). It is often necessary to specify where a source of EMF is

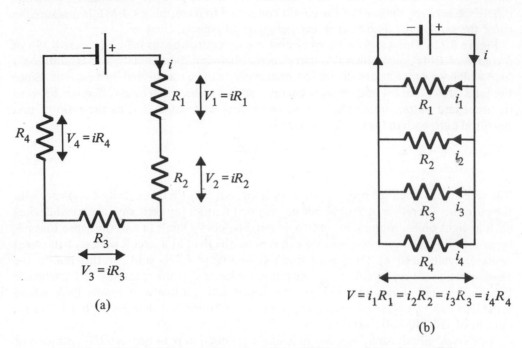

FIGURE 8.23 (a) Four resistors in series. (b) Four resistors in parallel.

placed before we can decide whether a particular set of resistors is a series combination, a parallel combination, or a mixture of both. Figure 8.24 illustrates the point. If a source of EMF is placed between the points *a* and *b*, there is but one conduction path between its terminals and the resistors are in series (Figure 8.24b). But if it is placed between the points *a* and *c* (Figure 8.24c) there are two conduction paths and the resistors are in parallel.

When two or more resistors are in series (Figure 8.23a) the same current flows through

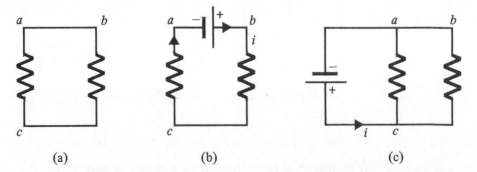

FIGURE 8.24 (a) Two resistors connected together without a source of EMF. The same pair of resistors connected (b) in series and (c) in parallel across a source of EMF.

each of them since charge does not pile up anywhere in the circuit. The potential difference V across the entire combination is the sum of the potential differences across each element:

$$V = V_1 + V_2 + V_3 + V_4.$$

Substituting $V_1 = iR_1$, $V_2 = iR_2$, etc.,

$$V = i(R_1 + R_2 + R_3 + R_4).$$

The total resistance of the combination R is the resistance that would draw the same current for the same total potential difference, or

$$iR = i(R_1 + R_2 + R_3 + R_4).$$

Therefore:

$$R = R_1 + R_2 + R_3 + R_4. \tag{8.19a}$$

The total resistance of a combination of resistors in series is the sum of the separate resistances.

If several resistors are connected in parallel a different current will flow through each unless their resistances are equal. But since charge is conserved, the total current flowing into the combination is equal to the sum of the currents in the separate elements:

$$i = i_1 + i_2 + i_3 + i_4.$$

Because the same potential difference exists across each resistor we have:

$$i = \frac{V}{R_1} + \frac{V}{R_2} + \frac{V}{R_3} + \frac{V}{R_4}.$$

The total resistance of the combination must draw the same total current for the same potential difference. Since $i = V/R$:

$$\frac{V}{R} = \frac{V}{R_1} + \frac{V}{R_2} + \frac{V}{R_3} + \frac{V}{R_4},$$

or

$$\frac{1}{R} = \frac{1}{R_1} + \frac{1}{R_2} + \frac{1}{R_3} + \frac{1}{R_4}. \tag{8.19b}$$

Therefore, the reciprocal of the total resistance of a parallel circuit is the sum of the reciprocals of the separate resistances. Since there is more than one conduction path in such a circuit its total resistance is always *smaller* than any of the constituent resistances.

Let us consider some numerical examples. Two and three ohm resistors are connected in series across a 10-volt source of EMF. What is the potential difference across each resistor and what currents do they draw?

Since there is one conduction path across the source of EMF, the same current flows in both resistors. Referring to Equation 8.19a, the total resistance of the circuit $R = 2 + 3 = 5$ ohms. Then (Equation 8.18) $i = 10/5 = 2$ amperes. Using Equation 8.17, the potential differences across the resistors are $V_1 = 2 \times 2 = 4$ volts and $V_2 = 2 \times 3 = 6$ volts, and their sum is 10 volts, as it must be.

If the same combination is connected in parallel across the 10-volt source of EMF then (Equation 8.19b) $1/R = \frac{1}{2} + \frac{1}{3} = \frac{5}{6}$, $R = \frac{6}{5} = 1.2$ ohms, and the total current in the circuit is $10/1.2 = 8\frac{1}{3}$ amperes. The separate currents are $i_1 = 10/2 = 5$ amperes,

$i_2 = 10/3 = 3\frac{1}{3}$ amperes, and their sum, $5 + 3\frac{1}{3} = 8\frac{1}{3}$ amperes, is equal to the total current calculated by using the total resistance.

More complicated networks can often be broken down into subsets of series and parallel combinations. For instance, in Figure 8.25 the parallel combination R_1 and R_2 is in series with R_3. The total resistance of R_1 and R_2 follows from Equation 8.19b:

$$\frac{1}{R_P} = \frac{1}{R_1} + \frac{1}{R_2},$$

or

$$R_P = \frac{R_1 R_2}{R_1 + R_2},$$

so that the total resistance of the circuit is (Equation 8.19a):

$$R = R_3 + \frac{R_1 R_2}{R_1 + R_2}.$$

If $R_1 = 200$ ohms, $R_2 = 300$ ohms, $R_3 = 80$ ohms, and the network is connected across the terminals of a 50-volt battery then:

$$R_P = \frac{200 \times 300}{200 + 300} = 120 \text{ ohms},$$

and

$$R = 80 + 120 = 200 \text{ ohms}.$$

The total current in the network is $i = 50/200 = 0.25$ amperes, which is also the current in R_3 so that $V_3 = 0.25 \times 80 = 20$ volts, and the potential difference across the parallel combination is $50 - 20 = 30$ volts. Therefore, $i_1 = 30/200 = 0.15$ amperes, $i_2 = 30/300 = 0.1$ ampere, and $i_1 + i_2 = 0.25$ amperes, the total current in the circuit.

The energy delivered to any part of an electric circuit can be expressed in terms of the current that flows in it and the potential difference across it. From Equation 8.9b, the work performed on a charge Δq in moving it across a potential difference V is $\Delta q V$. If V is the potential difference across a circuit element then in view of our earlier discussion the energy transferred to the element is equal to the work performed on the charge by the source of EMF so that:

$$\text{Energy} = V \Delta q.$$

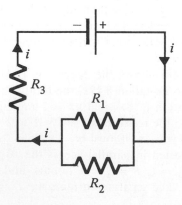

FIGURE 8.25 A parallel combination of resistors, R_1 and R_2, in series with the single resistor, R_3.

The *power* of any system (electrical or otherwise) is defined as the rate at which the system performs work, or, equivalently, the rate at which its energy changes:

$$P = \frac{\Delta(\text{Energy})}{\Delta t}.$$ (8.20)

Power is measured in *watts* (W), with 1 W equal to 1 J/sec. Evidently the power delivered to an electrical element is

$$P = V\frac{\Delta q}{\Delta t},$$

or, from Equation 8.14,

$$P = Vi, \cdot$$ (8.21a)

where i is the current through the element and V the potential difference across it. If the equivalent resistance of the circuit element is r, then Equations 8.18 and 8.21a may be combined to obtain an alternate expression for the power delivered to it:

$$P = (ir)i = i^2r.$$ (8.21b)

For example, suppose an electric pump is designed to lift water to a height of 5 m at a rate of 10 kg/sec, and is to be operated from a 100-volt source of EMF. What minimum current will the pump draw? The work required to lift 10 kg to a height of 5 m is

$$W = Mgy = 10 \times 9.8 \times 5 = 490 \text{ joules.}$$

Therefore, the pump expends 490 J/sec or 490 W, and this power must be delivered by the source of EMF. Suppose the resistances of the leads connecting the pump to the 100 volt source of EMF are negligible. Then (Equation 8.21a):

$$i = \frac{490}{100} = 4.9 \text{ amperes}$$

is the *minimum* current the pump draws. Actually it will always draw more than that, partly because the source cannot deliver its full EMF, but, more important, because not all the energy transferred to the pump can be utilized to perform useful mechanical work. Some of it is always dissipated as heat in the windings of its motor.

It is worthwhile pointing out a feature of any electrical circuit which has thus far been ignored. We have noted that an equivalent resistance r can be attributed to any circuit element in which a current performs work. Current certainly flows through the source of EMF in a circuit (Figure 8.22), and, furthermore, does some work in the source itself. Thus in order to be consistent an internal resistance should also be attributed to the source.

The circuit shown in Figure 8.26 incorporates the internal resistance of the source. Here $\mathscr{E}$ represents the source without the resistance, R_L is the equivalent resistance of the load, and R the resistance of the leads connecting the load to the terminals of the source. The potential difference across the terminals is taken between the points a and b and excludes the internal resistance represented by r. The current in the circuit is given by Equation 8.18:

$$i = \frac{\mathscr{E}}{(r + R + R_L)},$$

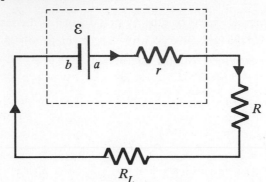

FIGURE 8.26 A circuit showing the internal resistance of the source of EMF (r) and the resistance of the conducting leads (R) as well as the load resistance (R_L). The dashed line encloses the source of EMF shown in the other circuit diagrams.

and the potential difference across the terminals is

$$V = i(R + R_L),$$

or, eliminating i,

$$V = \left(\frac{R + R_L}{r + R + R_L}\right)\mathscr{E}.$$

Therefore, the potential difference across a circuit is always less than the rated EMF of the source. Since r usually increases with current so does the difference between V and $\mathscr{E}$. The relation implies that a part of the capacity of the source to perform work is dissipated in the source itself, which is reasonable.

SUGGESTIONS FOR FURTHER READING ▲▲▲

Among the many physics texts dealing with static and current electricity are:

GERALD HOLTON AND DUANE H. D. ROLLER, *Foundations of Modern Physics Science*, Addison-Wesley Publishing Co., Inc., Reading, Mass., 1958, Chapters 26 and 27.

JAY OREAR, *Fundamental Physics*, John Wiley and Sons, Inc., New York, 1961, Chapter 7.

K. R. ATKINS, *Physics*, John Wiley and Sons, Inc., New York, 1965, Chapters 14, 15, and 16.

Holton's approach is historical, and occasionally confusing. Orear's is terse and to the point. Atkins' is probably the most similar to this chapter of the three.

PROBLEMS AND EXERCISES ▲▲▲

8.1. Two equal positive charges are separated by a distance R. How does the magnitude of the electrostatic force between them change if:

(a) The magnitude of one charge is doubled.
(b) The magnitudes of both are doubled.
(c) The distance between them is doubled.

8.2. A positive charge A a distance R from another equal positive charge B creates an electrostatic field which exerts a force on B. How does the field at B change if:

(a) The magnitude of A is doubled.
(b) The magnitude of B is doubled.

(c) The distance between A and B is doubled.

(d) The sign of A is changed from positive to negative.

(e) The sign of B is changed from positive to negative.

Are your answers consistent with the answers to Problem 8.1? Explain.

8.3. Two charges, $q_A = +2 \times 10^{-6}$ C and $q_B = +10^{-6}$ C, are located on the x-axis of a Cartesian coordinate system at $x = -0.5$ m and $x = +0.5$ m, respectively. What is the electric field (magnitude and direction) at:

(a) The origin.

(b) $x = 0$, $y = +0.5$ m.

(c) What is the force exerted on a $+2 \times 10^{-6}$ C charge located at points (a) and (b)?

(d) What is the force exerted on a -3×10^{-6} C charge at these same points?

8.4. Repeat Problem 8.3 for $q_B = -10^{-6}$ C and all other conditions unaltered.

8.5. Four charges of equal magnitude q are located at the corners of a square with sides d. The charges at the upper left and lower right hand corners are positive, the other two are negative. Determine the magnitude and direction of the electric field at:

(a) The center of the square.

(b) The centers of each side.

8.6. A particle with charge $+2 \times 10^{-6}$ C and mass 10^{-3} kg is placed in a uniform electric field. The magnitude of the field is adjusted until the gravitational and electrostatic forces upon it balance so that it remains motionless.

(a) What is the magnitude and direction of the electric field?

(b) The particle is now replaced by another particle of equal mass and charge $q = -2 \times 10^{-6}$ C. Find its acceleration vector.

8.7. A particle with mass 10^{-3} kg and charge $+2 \times 10^{-6}$ C is given an initial, horizontal velocity $v_0 = 0.5$ m/sec at point 1 near the upper plate of the parallel plate capacitor shown in the accompanying figure. The field in the capacitor is uniform, downward, and of magnitude 10^3 N/C.

(a) When does the particle strike the bottom plate?

(b) At what horizontal distance from its starting point does it do so? Assume gravitational effects are negligible.

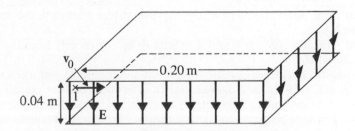

8.8. (a) Referring to Problem 8.7, what is the initial horizontal velocity of the particle such that it just misses hitting the lower plate?

(b) Sketch its path after it emerges from the capacitor. At what angle to the horizontal does it emerge?

Assume gravitational effects are negligible.

8.9. Two 10^{-3} kg mass particles, the first with charge $+2 \times 10^{-6}$ C, the second with $q = +10^{-6}$ C, are both given initial horizontal velocities of 1.0 m/sec at point 1 in the uniform 10^3 N/C field of the diagram.

(a) What is the vertical separation between their trajectories at the end of the capacitor?

(b) The apparatus provides a means for separating particles with the same mass and velocity but different charges. Could an analogous device be built to effect the gravitational separation of particles with different masses? Explain.

8.10. A gravitational field due to a gravitational mass or mass distribution can be defined, in analogy with the electric field, as the gravitational force exerted on a 1-kg mass.

(a) Express Newton's law of gravitation in terms of the gravitational field.
(b) What is the magnitude and direction of the earth's gravitational field at its surface? At the orbit of the moon?

8.11. In order to appreciate the unique aspect of the principle of equivalence discussed in Chapters 5 and 6 (the principle stating that the ratio of inertial to gravitational mass is equal for all bodies) it is useful to contrast the gravitational force with the electrostatic force, for no such principle has ever been discovered for the latter. Thus, suppose that an elevator is in free fall.

(a) What is the "true" force on a particle in the elevator with mass 2×10^{-2} kg? On another with twice the mass? Describe their motion relative to the elevator.
(b) While the elevator is falling, a constant electric field is turned on in the shaft and the first particle given a $+2 \times 10^{-4}$ C charge. What is the magnitude and direction of the field if the acceleration of the particle relative to the elevator is 9.8 m/sec^2 toward the floor?
(c) Can an experiment be devised to test whether the acceleration of the particle relative to the elevator is the result of a gravitational or an electric force? Explain.
(d) How does this problem illustrate the uniqueness of the principle of equivalence in gravitational interactions?

8.12. (a) What is the potential difference between the capacitor plates in Problem 8.7?
(b) A 10^{-3} kg particle with charge $+2 \times 10^{-6}$ C is initially at rest at point 1 near the upper plate. What is its velocity just before striking the lower plate?
(c) A particle with the same mass but with charge $-2 = 10^{-6}$ C is projected straight upward from the bottom plate. What is its velocity if it just reaches the top plate before stopping?
Neglect the gravitational force in both parts b and c.

8.13. A particle with mass 10^{-3} kg and charge -2×10^{-6} C is momentarily at rest 1.8×10^{-2} m away from a massive particle with charge $+8 \times 10^{-6}$ C.

(a) What is the potential energy of the negative charge relative to the attractive force center?
(b) What minimum velocity would it require to escape entirely from the attraction of the central charge?
(c) The negatively charged particle is removed and a particle with the same mass but charge $+2 \times 10^{-6}$ C is projected straight toward the massive central particle from a great distance, coming momentarily to rest at the former position of the negatively charged particle before reversing its direction. What was its initial velocity?

8.14. (a) Suppose the negative charge in Problem 8.13 was not at rest relative to the force center but instead orbited about it. What could you say about its orbit?
(b) Another particle with the same mass and charge orbits the central particle at twice the distance. How does the period of its orbit compare with that of the first?
(c) The original particle is now given twice the negative charge. By how much must its velocity change if it is to maintain the same circular orbit?

8.15. Two identical particles with mass 5×10^{-3} kg and charge $\frac{1}{3} \times 10^{-6}$ C with initial velocities of magnitude 20 m/sec approach each other as shown in the sketch.

(a) What is the total kinetic energy of the two-particle system?
(b) What is their distance of closest approach?

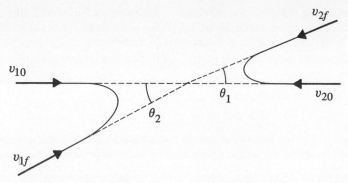

(c) After the particles have arrived at their minimum separation they recede from each other as shown in the sketch. When they are separated by a great distance it is noted that $v_{1f} = 20$ m/sec and $\theta_1 = 30°$. What are v_{2f} and θ_2? Why?

8.16. The trajectories of the two positively charged particles of Problem 8.15 are hyperbolae. Is this reasonable? Why?

8.17. The potential difference in a certain region of space is given as a function of distance from the origin by $V = \frac{1}{2}kx^2$.

(a) Sketch potential energy diagrams for a negatively and a positively charged particle in the field.

(b) Show that the motion of a negative particle initially at rest on the x-axis ($x_0 \neq 0$) is periodic about the origin.

(c) If the particle's mass and charge are 2×10^{-3} kg and -10^{-6} C, respectively, and $k = 10^4$ V/m², what is the period of its oscillation?

8.18. The electric fields in the accompanying sketch have magnitudes $E_1 = 10^6$ N/C and $E_2 = 1.5 \times 10^6$ N/C, respectively. Distances between the plates are in meters.

(a) What is the potential of plate B relative to plate A (in volts)? of C relative to B? of C relative to A?

(b) An electron (mass about 10^{-31} kg, charge -1.6×10^{-19} C) is projected through a small hole toward plate B. What minimum velocity must it have to reach B? If it starts from A with this velocity what is its velocity at C?

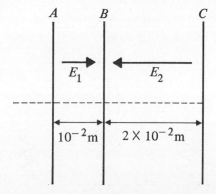

8.19 In a 10^{-4} m radius conductor, 2×10^{13} electrons, each with charge -1.6×10^{-19} C and moving in the positive x-direction, cross a certain plane in 10^{-3} sec. During the same time interval 1.5×10^{13} electrons cross the plane moving in the opposite direction. What is the average current across the plane in amperes? In what direction does it flow?

8.20. The Alternating Gradient Synchrotron at Brookhaven National Laboratory produces an external beam containing about 10^{12} protons (charge $+1.6 \times 10^{-19}$ C) once every $2\frac{1}{2}$ sec. What is the average beam current in amperes?

8.21. A copper wire of radius 10^{-3} m (1 mm) carries a steady 5-ampere current.

(a) What is the net number of electrons that cross a plane surface perpendicular to the wire each second (charge $= -1.6 \times 10^{-19}$ C)?

(b) Copper contains about 8.4×10^{28} mobile electrons/cm³. What is the mean drift velocity of the electrons in the conductor?

(c) How can you reconcile your answer to part b with the fact that a lamp, connected to a wall socket by a 1-m cord, lights up virtually instantaneously when turned on?

8.22. A 100-m long, 10^{-3} m radius copper wire is welded to the end of an aluminum wire of equal length and radius. The free ends of the wires are connected across the terminals of a source of EMF. A 10-ampere current flows in the copper wire.

(a) What current flows in the aluminum wire?

(b) What voltage is delivered by the source of EMF?

8.23. You are given a piece of copper sufficient to make a thin wire 200 m long or a thicker one 50 m long but with the same total mass. How would the resistances of the wires compare?

8.24. A 30-, a 15-, and a 5-ohm resistor are connected in series across a 25-volt battery.

(a) How much current is drawn from the battery?

(b) What is the potential drop across each resistor?

(c) How much power is dissipated in each? in the entire circuit?

8.25. The 30-, 15-, and 5-ohm resistors of Problem 8.24 are connected in parallel across the same battery.

(a) What is the total equivalent resistance across the battery terminals?

(b) How much current flows in each resistor?

(c) What power is dissipated in each resistor? in the entire circuit?

8.26. If the battery of Problem 8.25 has $\frac{2}{3}$ ohms internal resistance what are the answers to parts a and b? What is the external potential difference between the battery terminals?

8.27. You are given two equal resistors and a battery with negligible internal resistance and want to design a circuit that dissipates the smallest possible power. Should the resistors be connected in series or in parallel across the battery terminals?

8.28. In the circuit shown:

(a) What is the total resistance across the battery terminals? (Resistances shown are in ohms.)

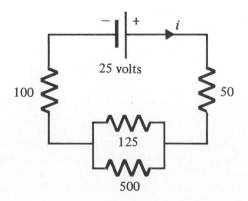

(b) What current flows from the battery?

(c) What is the potential difference across each resistor?

(d) What current flows in each resistor?

8.29. How much current is drawn by a 110-volt, 100-watt light bulb? What is the resistance of such a bulb?

8.30. How much power is required to lift a 1000-kg elevator 20 m in 5 sec? If the power is supplied by a 2000-volt source, what minimum current does the motor draw?

8.31. One horsepower is a unit of power equal to about 7.5×10^2 watts. Suppose a 50-horsepower electric car were designed to operate with a 500-volt battery. What current would be drawn?

Charge and its interactions: part 2

9

▲▲ 9.1 Permanent magnets. The magnetic field. Magnetic dipoles

The natural magnetism of several iron-bearing minerals was known in antiquity and the subject of magnetism first discussed systematically in 1600 by William Gilbert in his *De Magnete*. In the Newtonian context the rather well-known magnetic phenomena should be classed as manifestations of an interaction; for permanent magnets attract bits of iron, and therefore exert forces upon them. We can label the interaction between a permanent magnet and iron "magnetic."

At first glance the magnetic and electrostatic interactions appear quite analogous. Only the ends of a bar, horseshoe, or other type magnet have the ability to attract iron. These ends are called magnetic *poles*. A tentative, phenomenological theory of magnetism can be based on the assumption that the poles are responsible for the interaction, just as charge is responsible for the electrostatic interaction. The similarity is emphasized by the observations that pole strengths differ from magnet to magnet, that the attraction exerted by a pole upon a piece of iron varies inversely with the square of the distance from the pole, and that two distinct types of magnetic force exist. That is, two magnets will either attract or repel each other according to which of their respective poles are adjacent. Accordingly the two opposite poles of all magnets can be designated respectively as positive and negative (or north and south), and a repulsive-attractive law stated:

- Like poles repel, unlike poles attract.

If one pole of a particular, long bar magnet is chosen as a standard, positive unit pole, then pole strengths can be measured for all magnets, and Coulomb's magnetic force law stated:

- The magnetic force between two point poles is directly proportional to the strengths of the poles and inversely proportional to their separation. The force is repulsive between like poles and attractive between unlike poles.

If M_1 and M_2 are the strengths of two poles then we can write an equation for Coulomb's magnetic law in analogy with the electrostatic law (Equation 8.1):

$$\mathbf{F} = a \frac{M_1 M_2}{R^2} \frac{\mathbf{R}_{21}}{R},$$ (9.1)

where a is a constant whose magnitude can be determined experimentally as soon as the unit of pole strength is defined, $\mathbf{R}_{21}$ is the radius vector from M_2 to M_1, and R is its magnitude. As we shall see in the next sections, a magnetic force exists between two currents as well as between two permanent magnetic poles. In fact the existence of poles can be directly attributed to atomic currents in iron. Therefore, the current-current inter-action is really more fundamental than the pole-pole interaction, and we can best define the constant a in terms of that interaction. Thus for the present we measure M in pole strength units and leave a undefined.

The analogy between charges and poles breaks down in the face of a number of dif-ferences between the electrostatic and magnetic forces. Charged amber attracts virtually all small objects, magnetized iron attracts iron alone. A neutral piece of iron can be magnetized by contact with a permanent magnet, but no magnetic property analogous to electric conduction has ever been observed. Rubbing with animal fur, silk, or any other material fails to enhance the magnetic properties of iron, though a high temperature or a few hard blows with a hammer can destroy it. Most important, free magnetic poles have never been observed.* Permanent magnets always have equal and opposite poles on opposite ends. Cutting a long bar magnet in two does not separate the poles from each other, but instead creates two new opposite poles at the cut leaving two shorter magnets where there had been only one (Figure 9.1). Continued cutting merely multiplies the number of poles. If a long bar magnet is cut into ten pieces then ten short magnets with positive and negative poles equal to the original pole strengths are created. Appar-ently the two pole types cannot be separated. The further observation that the two oppositely magnetized poles at the ends of a magnet have the same strength would appear to be related to their inseparability.

A small test pole can be used to define a magnetic field in complete analogy with the way an electric field is defined by a test charge. Since free poles do not exist in nature such a test pole must be the positive end of a bar magnet so long that each pole can be considered virtually free of its twin. If M is the strength of the pole and the magnetic force upon it at some point in space is $\mathbf{F}$, then the magnetic field strength vector $\mathbf{B}$ is defined as

$$\mathbf{B} = \frac{\mathbf{F}}{M}. \tag{9.2a}$$

Therefore, the force exerted on a pole of strength M by a field $\mathbf{B}$ is

$$\mathbf{F} = M\mathbf{B}. \tag{9.2b}$$

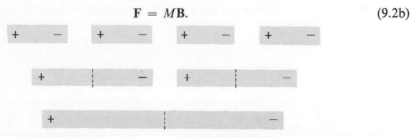

FIGURE 9.1 Free, single magnetic poles have never been observed. If a long bar magnet is cut in half in an attempt to separate its positive and negative poles, two bar magnets result instead. Continued cutting merely multiplies the number of magnets.

---

* The existence of free magnetic poles (or monopoles) was predicted in the 1930's by P. A. M. Dirac. A number of experiments to search for such monopoles have been performed in recent years, but the results of all of them have been negative.

The unit of magnetic field in the mks system is the weber/meter^2.* A field of 1 weber/meter^2 is quite intense. Large electromagnets usually can produce fields no greater than about twice that value, although fields on the order of 10 to 20 webers/meter^2 have been attained by using special techniques. The fields near the permanent magnets commonly found in laboratories are at most a few hundredths of a weber/meter^2, whereas the earth's field is less than 10^{-3} webers/meter^2.

The analogy between Equations 9.2 and 8.3a can be used to determine magnetic field configurations produced by particular pole distributions. Since free poles do not seem to exist in nature, neither do magnetic fields created by single poles. However the field due to two equal and opposite poles separated by a distance D is frequently encountered. Such an arrangement, typified by a bar magnet or a compass needle, is called a *magnetic dipole* (Figure 9.2). Algebraic expressions for the field created by a magnetic dipole at a particular point in space can be derived by first calculating the field at the point due to each of the separate poles by means of Equations 9.1 and 9.2, then taking the vector sum of the two fields at that point. In Section 8.3 we followed an analogous procedure to calculate the electric field of two charges separated by a distance D (Equations 8.5).

If $Q_1 = -Q_2$ such an arrangement would be called an *electric dipole*. Therefore, in order to find expressions for the field of a *magnetic* dipole we have only to substitute M for Q_1, $-M$ for Q_2, and a for $1/4\pi\epsilon_0$ in Equations 8.5. In this way we find that the magnetic field components at a point P a distance D_1 from one pole, and D_2 from the other are (Equations 8.5c and 8.5d):

$$B_x = aM\left(\frac{\cos\theta_1}{D_1^2} - \frac{\cos\theta_2}{D_2^2}\right),$$

$$B_y = aM\left(\frac{\sin\theta_1}{D_1^2} - \frac{\sin\theta_2}{D_2^2}\right),$$

where θ_1 and θ_2 are the angles between the directions of the radius vectors $\mathbf{D}_1$ and $\mathbf{D}_2$ and the dipole axis which is oriented in the x-direction (Figure 9.3). The magnitude and direction of the resultant field is then obtained by using Equations 2.20:

$$B = \sqrt{B_x^2 + B_y^2},$$

$$\tan\phi = \frac{B_y}{B_x}.$$

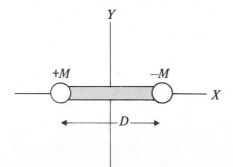

FIGURE 9.2 A magnetic dipole oriented along the x-axis. (Compare with Figure 8.7.)

---

* The reasons for the hybrid nature of the unit are chiefly historical. The gauss, equal to 10^4 weber/meter^2, is also used, although it is a cgs unit.

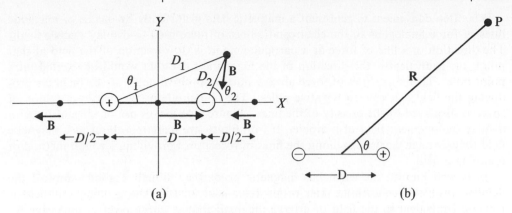

FIGURE 9.3 (a) Relative magnitudes and directions of the field due to a magnetic dipole at four points. (b) The variables **R** and θ appearing in the expression for the field of a dipole at distance large compared to its length.

It is customary to define the *magnetic dipole moment*, or simply the *magnetic moment*, μ, as the product of the pole strength by the dipole length:

$$\mu = MD. \tag{9.3}$$

Expressed in terms of the magnetic moment of a dipole the field components at the point P in Figure 9.3a are

$$B_x = \frac{a\mu}{D}\left(\frac{\cos\theta_1}{D_1^2} - \frac{\cos\theta_2}{D_2^2}\right), \tag{9.4a}$$

$$B_y = \frac{a\mu}{D}\left(\frac{\sin\theta_1}{D_1^2} - \frac{\sin\theta_2}{D_1^2}\right). \tag{9.4b}$$

It is not necessary to know all five variables D, D_1, D_2, θ_1, and θ_2 in order to find the field at the point P given by Equations 9.4a and 9.4b, for trigonometric relations permit us to eliminate two of the five. For instance, we could express the field components in terms of D and the distances D_1 and D_2 or D, θ_1, and θ_2 alone. (See Figure 8.8d and the remarks following Equation 8.5d.) However, the resultant expressions are rather involved and we shall not write them down here.

If the distance R from the midpoint of a dipole to the field point P is very large compared with the length of the dipole D (Figure 9.3b), then D_1 and D_2 are almost equal, as are the angles θ_1 and θ_2, and it may be shown that to a very good approximation the field components are given by

$$B_x = \frac{\mu(3\cos^2\theta - 1)}{R^3}, \tag{9.4c}$$

$$B_y = \frac{3\mu\sin\theta\cos\theta}{R^3}, \tag{9.4d}$$

where θ is the angle between the radius vector **R** from the center of the dipole to the field point. This situation is particularly interesting since, as we shall note in a later section, magnetic dipole moments may be attributed to atoms, and the external field of a permanent magnet is, in fact, the vector sum of the fields created by these dipoles.

It is often convenient to represent a magnetic field graphically by means of magnetic lines of force analogous to the electrostatic lines of force used to display electric fields. The direction of a line of force at a particular point is the direction of the field at that point, or, equivalently, the direction of the magnetic force that would be exerted on a point pole. Therefore, lines of force always start on positive poles of the magnets producing the field and end on negative poles. The magnitude of the field in a region of space is displayed by the density of the lines. Figure 9.4a makes use of lines of force to display the magnetic field of a dipole. If iron filings are scattered about in a magnetic field they arrange themselves along the lines of force, thus providing a rough method of mapping a field.

As is well known, the earth has magnetic properties, though a good many of the detailed problems concerning their origin remain unsolved. The geomagnetic field is roughly equivalent to the field of a large magnetic dipole whose positive and negative poles are near the respective North and South Poles of the earth. Because of the well-known existence of the geomagnetic field the positive pole of any permanent magnet is often called its north pole, the negative pole its south pole.

Equations 9.4 give the magnetic field at any point in space created by a dipole as a function of its magnetic moment, its length and the position of the point in question relative to the dipole. It is also useful to know the effect of an external magnetic field on a magnetic dipole.

Figure 9.5a shows a dipole of pole strength M and length D oriented at an angle θ relative to a uniform magnetic field whose direction is parallel to the x-axis. Referring to Equation 9.2 the field exerts a force of magnitude MB on the positive pole and an equal and opposite force on the negative pole. Each force can be resolved into equal and opposite components parallel and perpendicular to the dipole axis. The opposite vertical

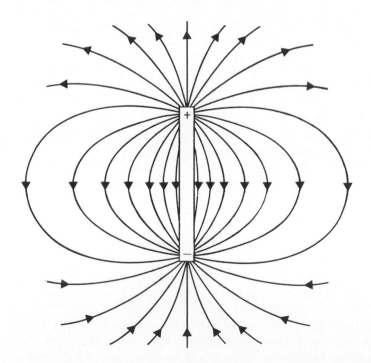

FIGURE 9.4   Lines of force of a magnetic dipole. (Compare with Figure 8.9c.)

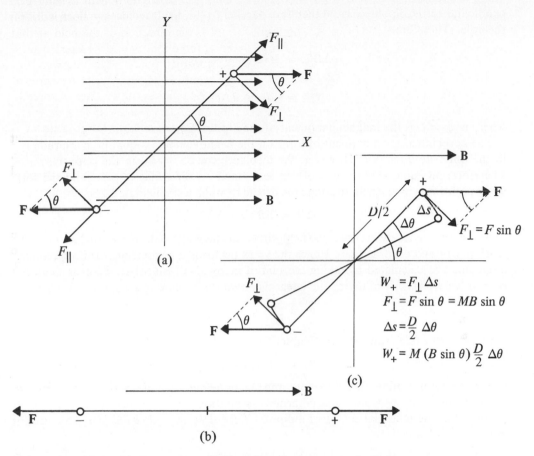

FIGURE 9.5 (a) Forces on a dipole oriented at an angle θ relative to a constant magnetic field. (b) A dipole oriented parallel to the field. (c) Calculation of the work performed by the field in rotating the dipole through a small angle $\Delta\theta$.

components tend to separate the poles, and, assuming they are the opposite poles of a rigid bar, these components have no appreciable effect. However, the perpendicular components tend to rotate the dipole about the midpoint of its axis. If the dipole is parallel to the field direction (Figure 9.5b) the perpendicular components are zero and the dipole is in equilibrium with the field. Evidently equal and opposite external forces must be applied to the poles of a dipole in order to keep it at a nonzero angle relative to a constant magnetic field. If both forces are removed, the magnetic field performs work by rotating the dipole through an angle θ. Therefore, a magnetic dipole whose axis makes an angle θ relative to a magnetic field has potential energy of orientation relative to its equilibrium position, even as a positive point charge located in a region of high electrostatic potential has potential energy relative to a region of lower potential.

An expression for the orientation energy of a magnetic dipole can be derived by referring to Figure 9.5 and using Equation 9.2 and the general definition of work (Equations 7.1 to 7.3). Consider first the work performed on the positive pole. When the dipole rotates through a small angle $\Delta\theta$ (measured in radians) the positive pole is displaced along a circular arc of length $\Delta s = (D/2)\,\Delta\theta$. Only the field component $B \sin \theta$ perpendicular to the dipole axis and therefore parallel to the displacement arc does work on the pole. Therefore:

$$\Delta W_+ = M(B \sin \theta)\frac{D}{2}\,\Delta\theta$$

$$= \frac{\mu}{2} B \sin \theta\,\Delta\theta,$$

where $\mu = MD$ is the magnetic moment of the dipole (Equation 9.3).

The perpendicular component of force on the negative pole is equal in magnitude but in the opposite direction. However, the displacement Δs is also in the opposite sense. Therefore, an equal amount of work is performed on the negative pole, and the total work performed by the field to rotate the dipole through a small angle $\Delta\theta$ is

$$\Delta W = \mu B \sin \theta\,\Delta\theta.$$

As the dipole rotates toward the field direction the angle θ decreases and so does the work performed per small $\Delta\theta$. Hence the work performed in rotating it through a large angle must be calculated by taking the sum of many small contributions over small $\Delta\theta$, or in other words by evaluating the integral (Equation 7.3):

$$W = \int_\theta^0 \mu B \sin \theta\,d\theta,$$

with the result (see Appendix to Chapter 7):

$$W = -\mu B \cos \theta,$$

where the minus sign implies that work must be done *against* a magnetic field in order to rotate a dipole away from its equilibrium orientation, i.e., in order to increase θ. It follows that the potential energy of a dipole oriented at an angle θ relative to a constant magnetic field is

$$PE_\theta = -\mu B \cos \theta. \tag{9.5}$$

Our derivation of Equation 9.5 assumes a magnetic field that is constant in both magnitude and direction over the length of the dipole. If the field has a constant direction but a magnitude that varies uniformly with distance as in Figure 9.5c, Equation 9.5 remains valid provided B is taken as the field strength at the dipole's equilibrium orientation. For more complex field configurations in which both the magnitude and direction of $\mathbf{B}$ vary appreciably over the dipole length there may be no orientation at which the field direction is simultaneously parallel to both its ends. However, there is always some orientation for which the perpendicular forces on the two ends are equal and opposite. Therefore, the dipole will always be rotated into equilibrium position, and if not at that position will have potential energy relative to the field.

In Equation 9.2 we defined the magnetic field strength vector in terms of the magnetic force upon a point pole. But since single poles apparently do not exist in nature such a measurement cannot really be carried out. However, a magnetic field may be mapped by using a small dipole such as a compass needle. If the dipole is sufficiently small the variation of the field over its length will be negligible. Therefore, when placed at various points in space it will always assume an alignment parallel to the field, along a line of force. Because the force on the dipole at equilibrium is parallel to its axis the magnitude of the field strength is more difficult to measure. The average field at the center of the dipole axis could be determined by measuring the work performed by an external force in rotating it through an angle θ at constant velocity (so that its kinetic energy remains constant) and then applying Equation 9.5. However, such a measurement would give rather imprecise results. It is preferable to determine the magnitude of a field by measuring the force it exerts on a current, as we shall see in the next sections.

▲▲ 9.2 Magnetic fields of currents. Electromagnets

The superficial similarities between electrostatic and magnetic phenomena are so striking that it is tempting to seek some relationship between the two forces. Alas, the connection is elusive. Permanent magnets neither attract nor repel charged pith balls; the force exerted by charged amber upon magnetized bits of iron is no greater than the force exerted by the amber upon other, comparable bits of material.

In 1820 Hans Oersted noticed that a current-carrying wire causes the deflection of a magnetized compass needle, suggesting that the current exerts a magnetic force upon the needle, or, equivalently, that the current creates a magnetic field. Upon hearing of Oersted's discovery André Ampère carried out a series of experiments and found that two current-carrying conductors either attract or repel each other depending upon the relative directions of their currents. Combining his results with Oersted's, he argued that the magnetic field established by the current in one conductor exerts a force upon the current in the other, and vice versa, as Newton's third law requires.

Figure 9.6a shows a somewhat idealized arrangement for measuring the force between two currents in a rather special case. The *short, straight* segments of conductor, Δs_1 and Δs_2, carry currents i_1 and i_2, respectively, are parallel to each other, and are separated by a distance R. In addition, the radius vector **R** is *perpendicular* to both segments. If the currents flow in the same direction the conductors attract each other; if they flow in the opposite direction the force is repulsive. In either case the magnitude of the force is directly proportional to the currents and to the lengths of the two segments, and inversely proportional to the square of the distance between them:

$$F = k \frac{i_1 \, \Delta s_1 i_2 \, \Delta s_2}{R^2}. \tag{9.6a}$$

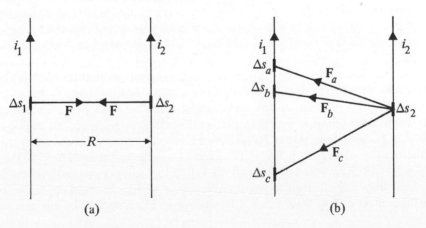

(a)   (b)

FIGURE 9.6 (a) Magnetic force between two very short current-carrying segments. (b) Magnetic force vectors on a short current-carrying segment due to the various segments of a long, straight, current-carrying wire.

In the mks system the constant k is written as $k = \mu_0/4\pi$, with μ_0 called the permeability of free space. Thus we have

$$F = \frac{\mu_0}{4\pi} \frac{i_1 \, \Delta s_1 i_2 \, \Delta s_2}{R^2}. \qquad (9.6b)$$

The experimentally determined value of $\mu_0/4\pi$ is 10^{-7} newtons/ampere^2, which indicates that the force between two current-carrying conductors is also small. For example, the force between two 0.01-m long copper wires 0.1 m apart each carrying 10 A is only 10^{-7} N. This is roughly equal to the gravitational force between two 25 kg spheres with their centers separated by 0.1 m, or to the electrostatic force between two point charges separated by the same distance with magnitudes 3.5×10^{-10} C!

It is important to note that Equation 9.6 is quantitatively correct *only* if the lengths of the two segments are small relative to the distance between them, *and if* they are parallel to each other. That is, the distance from a point on one segment to any point on the other (R in Equation 9.6) must be (virtually) constant. Figure 9.6b suggests the primary reason for these restrictions. The distance between the short current-carrying segment Δs_2 and each segment of the long wire s_1 depends upon which segment of the latter is chosen. However the force on Δs_2 not only decreases as the inverse square of the distance to a particular segment of s_1, but, as we shall note in due course, varies as well with the angle between s_1 and the line joining the segment to Δs_2. Therefore, the total force on the latter must be found by summing the varying contributions due to each small segment of the long wire. The general situation is analogous to the procedure following in finding the gravitational or electrostatic forces exerted by extended objects, although the additional angular dependence of the force between two currents usually complicates the detailed calculations.

Although we have written a relation for the force between two short current-carrying segments we have presented no evidence to support Ampère's contention that the force is magnetic. Such evidence will be discussed presently. However, it is easy to prove that the force cannot be electrostatic. The interior of a conducting wire contains a fixed lattice of positive charge and mobile, almost free electrons whose motion constitutes the current that flows in the wire (see Section 8.6). Since the conductor is electrically neutral, then at any given time each section of the wire contains an equal amount of positive and negative charge, even though the existence of a current implies that at a later time different specific electrons will be associated with a given segment of positive lattice. Hence the electrostatic fields of the positive and negative charges cancel each other outside the conductor.

However, suppose the positive charge were stripped away so that the mobile electrons that constitute the current would in effect move along a neutral tube. In the absence of the neutralizing positive lattice the electrostatic force between two such columns of current would be enormous. For example, a cylindrical copper wire 0.01 m (1 cm) long and 10^{-3} m (1 mm) in diameter has a volume $\pi r^2 l$, or approximately 7.5×10^{-7} m^3. Since the density of copper is 8.9×10^3 kg/m^3 the wire has mass $8.9 \times 10^3 \times 7.5 \times 10^{-9} = 6.7 \times 10^{-5}$ kg and contains about 6.3×10^{20} copper atoms.* If each atom would contribute one electron to the mobile charge in a real wire then our equivalent hollow tubes must each contain 6.3×10^{20} electrons. The charge of an electron (Section

---

*In Chapter 14 we show that 63 kg of copper contain 6×10^{26} atoms. Therefore, there must be $(6.7 \times 10^{-5} \div 63) \times 6 \times 10^{26} = 6.3 \times 10^{20}$ atoms in 6.7×10^{-5} kg of the metal.

9.7) is -1.6×10^{-19} C; therefore, the tubes each carry a total charge of $-1.6 \times 10^{-19} \times 6.3 \times 10^{20} = 100$ C. From Equation 8.1 it follows that in the absence of the neutralizing positive charge the electrostatic force between two such wires separated by 0.1 m would be on the order of 10^{16} N! This number is to be compared with the observed 10^{-7} N force between two equivalent wires each carrying 10 A current. Clearly the electrostatic force has an intrinsic magnitude far greater than the magnetic force between currents of several amperes in conventional conductors. But as we shall note in Section 9.6 the magnetic force between two very rapidly moving charges can be comparable in magnitude to the electrostatic force between them.

In order to prove that the force between a pair of current-carrying wires is magnetic we must demonstrate first that a single current-carrying wire exerts a force upon a permanent magnetic dipole, and second that a permanent magnet exerts a force upon a current-carrying wire. The first set of experiments, in essence a repetition of Oersted's original observations, prove that a current-carrying wire creates a magnetic field, the second that a magnetic field exerts a force upon a current-carrying wire.

In view of our allusion to Oersted's discovery it is not surprising that the first of the proposed tests on the nature of the current-current interaction yields positive results. Figure 9.7 shows a small magnetic dipole (a compass needle, for instance) in the proximity of a long wire. The dipole is completely free to rotate and, according to the analysis in Section 9.1, will therefore orient itself along magnetic lines of force. If there is no current in the wire the negative pole of the needle points toward the earth's magnetic north pole (Figure 9.7a). But when current flows the dipole orients itself in a direction perpendicular to the wire, and maintains a perpendicular orientation when it is moved about in the vicinity of the wire.* The magnitude of the field at any point can be determined by carefully measuring the external force required to rotate the dipole through a particular angle while the current flows (see derivation of Equation 9.5), and turns out to be the same at all points equidistant from the wire. Not unexpectedly the magnitude of the field decreases as the distance from the wire increases. From these observations we conclude that the magnetic lines of force that represent the field are concentric circles lying in planes perpendicular to and centered upon the current (Figure 9.8a). Their direction may be expressed in terms of the so-called right-hand screw convention (Figure 9.8b). That is, when the thumb of the right hand points in the conventional direction of the current (*opposite* the direction electrons actually flow in the conductor) then the fingers, curving about the thumb as an axis, point in the field direction. The convention implies that the direction of the field reverses when the current reverses, a prediction easily verified with the compass needle (Figure 9.7c).

It is interesting to compare these magnetic field configurations with the *electrostatic* field of a long positively charged rod (Figure 9.9). Since the electrostatic force between two charges is in the direction of the line joining them the electrostatic lines of force in a plane perpendicular to the rod radiate outward from the center, in evident contrast with the magnetic case.

As we have noted the magnitude of the field of a long wire can be measured as a function of distance from the wire by placing a dipole at various points and determining the external force required to rotate it against the field. But the wire is an extended body so that the force it exerts must be regarded as the sum of the forces exerted by each of its

---

* Actually the earth's magnetic field causes small departures from exact perpendicularity. But if the wire carries a high current (a few amperes) this perturbing effect is small.

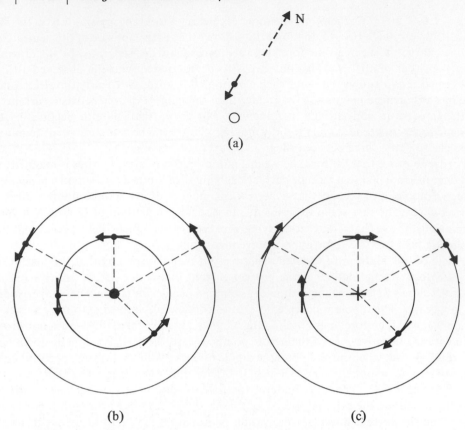

FIGURE 9.7   Finding the direction of the magnetic field of a long current-carrying wire (oriented perpendicular to the page) by using a compass needle (short
arrow). (a) When no current flows in the wire the positive pole of the dipole
orients itself opposite the direction of the geomagnetic field. (b) When current
flows out of the page the dipole orients itself perpendicular to the direction of
current flow regardless of where it is placed. (c) When the current flow is into
the page the direction of the dipole reverses itself but remains perpendicular to
the wire.

segments (Figure 9.6b). It is more appropriate to give a relation for the field at a distance
R from a very short segment of wire of length Δs carrying a current i:

$$B = C \frac{i\,\Delta s}{R^2} \sin\,\theta, \tag{9.7}$$

where θ is the angle between the direction of the current flowing in Δs and the line joining
Δs to the point a distance R away (Figure 9.10b), and C is a constant whose magnitude is
as yet undetermined. The *direction* of the field is perpendicular to the plane containing
the segment Δs and the radius vector **R**. If this plane is chosen as the xy-plane of a Cartesian coordinate system, then B points in the z-direction.

   Figure 9.11 illustrates the procedure used to calculate the magnetic field at a point P
a distance D from a long straight wire. Consider a short segment Δs located a vertical
distance s below the point in question. Then the total distance R from Δs to P, given by

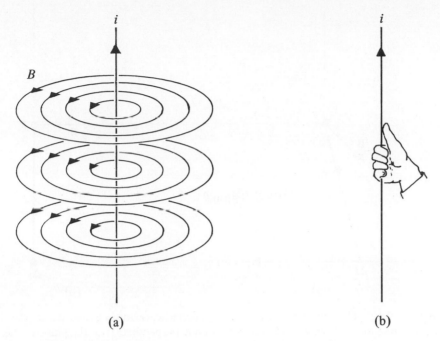

FIGURE 9.8 (a) Magnetic lines of force around a straight, current-carrying wire. (b) Right-hand screw convention for determining the direction of the magnetic lines of force.

FIGURE 9.9 (a) Magnetic lines of force of a wire whose current flows out of the page. (b) Electric lines of force of a positively charged rod (compare with Figure 8.7a).

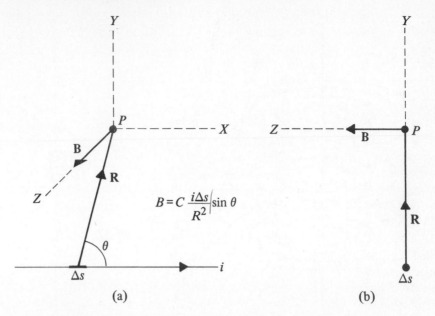

$$B = C \frac{i\Delta s}{R^2} \Big| \sin \theta$$

(a)   (b)

FIGURE 9.10   The field created by a short current-carrying segment Δs at point P, is a function of i, Δs, R, and θ; its direction is perpendicular to the plane of the segment and the radius vector **R**. In part a Δs and **R** lie in the plane of the page, while **B** is perpendicular to it and outward; in part b the current is perpendicular to the page and outward.

the Pythagorean theorem, is $\sqrt{s^2 + D^2}$. Likewise, $\sin \theta = D/\sqrt{s^2 + D^2}$ so that the contribution to the field at P from the segment is (Equation 9.7):

$$\Delta B = Ci \frac{D \, \Delta s}{(s^2 + D^2)^{3/2}}.$$

Evidently the field contributions from segments of equal length vary with s in a non-trivial manner. In order to find the total field at P we sum over the contributions from all these segments by using the integral calculus. If P is far from both ends of the wire

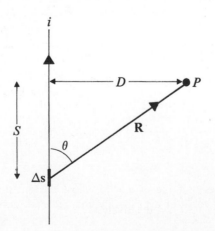

FIGURE 9.11   Calculation of the magnitude of the magnetic field at a point P due to a long, straight, current-carrying wire.

(i.e., if D is small relative to its length) then variable s can be assumed to go from $-\infty$ to $+\infty$ and:

$$B = Ci \int_{-\infty}^{\infty} \frac{D}{(s^2 + D^2)^{3/2}} \, ds.$$

It can be shown that on performing the integration:

$$B = \frac{2Ci}{D}. \tag{9.8}$$

The field is inversely proportional to the distance D, *not* to its square, as in the case of a short segment.

The direction of the field due to each segment is mutually perpendicular to the segment and the radius vector **R**. Since Δs and **R** lie in the same plane for all segments it follows that the total field at P must be perpendicular to the wire, in accord with the compass needle experiments we discussed earlier in this section, and the right-hand screw convention.

In order to evaluate the constant C appearing in Equation 9.7 (and in Equation 9.8), let us first write an expression for the field a *perpendicular* distance R from a short current-carrying segment. Since $\sin 90° = 1$, then:

$$B = C \frac{i \, \Delta s}{R^2}.$$

Now if another short segment Δs_2 carrying current i_2 were placed at the same perpendicular distance we know that there would be a force between the wires (Equation 9.6, Figure 9.6). Using the subscript 1 to label the original current and segment:

$$F = \frac{\mu_0}{4\pi} \left(\frac{i_1 \Delta s_1}{R^2} \right) i_2 \, \Delta s_2.$$

A comparison of these equations suggests that but for the differences between the constants C and $\mu_0/4\pi$ the force upon the second segment is the product of the field created by the first times $i_2 \, \Delta s_2$. If we adopt the view that the current-current interaction is more fundamental than the forces between permanent magnetic poles we can base the unit of field strength upon these two equations by letting $C = \mu_0/4\pi = 10^{-7}$ N/A². Then for the field of a short segment (Equation 9.7):

$$B = \frac{\mu_0}{4\pi} \frac{i \, \Delta s}{R^2} \sin \theta, \tag{9.9a}$$

while for the field a distance D from a very long wire (Equation 9.8):

$$B = \frac{\mu_0}{4\pi} \frac{i}{D}. \tag{9.9b}$$

A means for defining a standard for magnetic field measurements is now available, since according to Equation 9.9b the magnitude of the field strength 1 m from a very long wire carrying a current of 1 A is 2×10^{-7} webers/m². Given this standard for magnetic field strength we can also define the unit of permanent pole strength as that pole strength upon which a 1-weber/m² field exerts a force of 1 N (Equation 9.2). Finally, we could use this unit of pole strength to evaluate the value of the proportionality constant appearing in Equation 9.1. We shall not do this in detail, but shall merely refer to the unit of pole strength as mks pole units.

We can get a better idea about the magnitude of the magnetic force due to a current by performing a numerical calculation. Suppose a 0.01 m dipole of pole strength 2000 mks pole units is placed 0.05 m from a long straight wire carrying a 10-A current. What is the force upon its two poles when they are equidistant from the wire?

From Equation 9.9b the field at the dipole is

$$B = \frac{2 \times 10^{-7} \times 10}{0.05} = 4 \times 10^{-5} \text{ Wb/m}^2.$$

Therefore (Equation 9.2) the force on either pole is:

$$F = 2 \times 10^3 \times 4 \times 10^{-5} = 0.08 \text{ N}.$$

The magnetic moment of the dipole is (Equation 9.3):

$$\mu = 2 \times 10^3 \times 10^{-2} = 20 \text{ J/Wb/m}^2.$$

Therefore, if it is externally constrained at an angle 90° to its equilibrium orientation along the field direction, the dipole has potential energy given by Equation 9.5:

$$PE = 2 \times 4 \times 10^{-5} = 8 \times 10^{-4} \text{ J}.$$

As we have pointed out before, and as this example emphasizes, the magnetic force exerted by currents of normal magnitude is quite small. In order to obtain greater field strengths a bundle of wires each carrying a high current can be used, since the field created thereby is simply the vector sum of the fields due to each wire. For instance, a bundle of fifty wires each carrying 1000 A in the same direction would produce a magnetic field $50 \times 1000 = 5 \times 10^4$ times the field in the previous example, or 2 webers/m² at a point 0.05 m away. Whenever a current flows through a conductor of resistance R it dissipates energy i^2R per second, energy which appears in the form of heat (Equation 8.21a). For example, one-half million joules per second is dissipated by a 1000-ampere current in a $\frac{1}{2}$-ohm resistor. Unless the heat produced is carried away continually (by flowing water, for example) the conductor will be destroyed in a very short time. For this reason magnetic field strengths are usually limited to about 5 webers/m² or less. However, a few special alloys exist whose resistance virtually disappears when they are cooled to temperatures a few degrees above absolute zero (Chapter 14). Consequently they can carry high currents and suffer very little heating. Field strengths up to about 20 webers/m² have been produced by using these alloys as conductors.

Field configurations differing from the field of a straight wire (Figure 9.9) can be obtained by using conductors of varying shapes. Figure 9.12a shows a single circular wire loop of radius r. Each segment Δs is equidistant from the center and makes an angle of 90° with the radius vector. By using the right-hand screw convention (Figure 9.8b) at different segments it follows that the direction of all contributions, and thus the direction of the total field, is perpendicular to the plane of the page, upward if the current flow is counterclockwise, downward if clockwise. Therefore, the contribution of each segment to the field at the center is $(\mu_0/4\pi)/(i\,\Delta s/r^2)$ (Equation 9.9a), and the total field at that point is the sum of the individual contributions. Since the sum of the Δs is simply the circumference $2\pi r$ then the magnitude of the field at the *center* of the circular wire loop is

$$B = \frac{\mu_0}{2} \frac{i}{r} \qquad \text{(Field at center of single circular loop).} \qquad (9.10)$$

At other points both inside and outside the loop, the contributions from the segments remain perpendicular to the page. However, they differ in magnitude since neither r

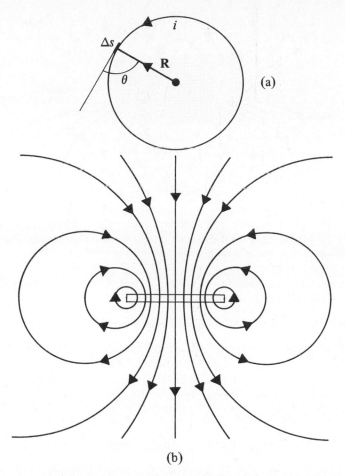

FIGURE 9.12   Magnetic field due to a single circular current-carrying loop.
(a) Calculation of the field at the center of the loop. (b) Sketch of the loop and
its field lines seen from the side.

nor θ remains constant for each segment, so that the integral calculus is required to
determine the field strength at points other than the center. Figure 9.12b is a sketch of
the circular loop and its magnetic field lines seen from the side.

Figure 9.13 shows a long, closely packed helical coil of wire often called a *solenoid*.
The field at any point inside or outside the coil is, as usual, the vector sum of contributions from each small current-carrying segment. Using the right-hand screw convention
we can see that all contributions are parallel to the axis of the solenoid. Currents in any
two diametrically opposite segments flow in the opposite direction. Therefore, inside the
coil their fields are in the same direction, or toward the top of the page if the current flows
into the page on the right side. It follows that the total field inside the solenoid is also
in this direction. Outside the coils the fields of any two diametrically opposite segments
are in the opposite direction and therefore partially cancel each other.

Although it is not at all obvious, the contributions from all segments add to produce a
uniform field at all points inside the coil but not too near the ends. If the coil had n turns

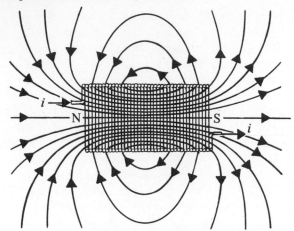

FIGURE 9.13 The magnetic field due to a solenoid. (From David Halliday and Robert Resnick, *Physics for Students of Science and Engineering*, 2nd edition, John Wiley and Son, Inc., New York © 1960.)

of wire per meter, carries a current i, and has a radius that is small compared with its length, then a detailed calculation shows that the inside field is

$$B = \mu_0 n i \qquad \text{(Field inside a solenoid)} \qquad (9.11)$$

independent of its radius. At the ends of the coil the lines of force diverge, as shown in Figure 9.13.

By using several layers of wire it is possible to wind a coil with 10,000 turns per meter. If such a coil carries 5 A current then since $\mu_0 = 4\pi(\mu_0/4\pi) = 4\pi \times 10^{-7}$:

$$B = 4 \times 3.14 \times 10^{-7} \times 10^4 \times 5 = 0.05 \text{ Wb/m}^2.$$

For comparison, the field 0.02 m from a long wire carrying the same current is (Equation 9.9b):

$$B = \frac{2 \times 10^{-7} \times 5}{2 \times 10^{-2}} = 5 \times 10^{-5} \text{ Wb/m}^2.$$

Thus a bundle of 1200 such wires is required to produce the same field as the solenoid at that point. Since in addition the solenoid's field is uniform within the coil it is clear why it is often preferred to the straight wire as a field source.

Earlier in this section we assumed that the magnetic force between currents (or more generally the force between two moving charges—Section 9.5) is more fundamental than the forces between permanent poles. It is now known that the very existence of permanent poles can be attributed partially to the fact that electrons in atoms orbit about their nuclei and therefore constitute microscopic current loops in matter, and partially to the fact that the electrons themselves have intrinsic spin angular momenta (Chapter 19). Normally the orientation of the atomic currents in matter is random so that the vector sum of the magnetic fields they produce is zero.

But an external magnetic field exerts a force on any current loop which, as we shall see in Section 9.3, tends to orient its plane perpendicular or toward the field direction. Therefore, if a sample of material is placed in such a field the small magnetic fields produced by its atomic current loops add to produce a nonzero field in the material (Figure 9.14b). The relative magnitude of this induced field depends on the types of atoms involved, or more specifically upon the nature of the forces between them. It is usually quite small relative to the external field. However, in a very few materials, notably iron, nickel, and a few special alloys, the induced magnetic field can be very large and enhances the original external field. These materials are called *ferromagnetic*.

For example, if a soft iron cylinder is placed inside a solenoid the lines of force of the current become concentrated along the axis of the iron, appearing to enter at one end and leave at the other (Figure 9.15). Therefore, a positive magnetic pole would attract to the first end but be repelled from the other, so that in essence the ends may be regarded as poles of the opposite type. Such a system is called an *electromagnet*. If two identical iron-core coils are arranged in series the opposite poles are adjacent, and the lines of force across the intervening air gap are continuous and the field constant. Indeed, this method is commonly used to produce magnetic fields with constant magnitude and direction over appreciable regions of space (Figure 9.16).

When a sample of ferromagnetic material such as iron is placed in an external field and then removed from it the alignment of its internal current loops does not entirely disappear, and the sample becomes a permanent magnet. Presumably the natural magnetism of iron-bearing minerals was induced in much the same way by the magnetic field of the earth.

We have stated that virtually all magnetic phenomena are manifestations of the interaction of moving charges. The exceptions are found in the subatomic domain, for many of the elementary particles have intrinsic dipole moments that cannot be attributed to moving charges, in any simple way. The dipole moments of the electron, proton, and neutron contribute to the structure of all atoms and therefore to the properties of macroscopic matter. We shall return to this point in Chapter 19.

▶▶ 9.3 Magnetic force on a current. Current loops as magnetic dipoles. The galvanometer. Electric motors

In the foregoing section we centered our attention upon the magnetic fields produced by currents, and discussed briefly the forces exerted by these fields upon permanent magnetic

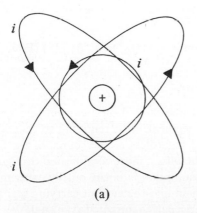
(a)

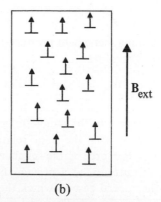
(b)

FIGURE 9.14 (a) The electrons that orbit the nucleus of an atom give rise to microscopic current loops. When placed in an external magnetic field these currents tend to orient themselves perpendicularly to the field. (b) In some materials, such as iron and nickel, the microscopic fields (small arrows) produced by these loops add vectorially to produce an appreciable internal field in the direction of the external field.

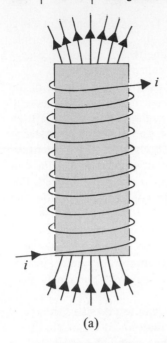

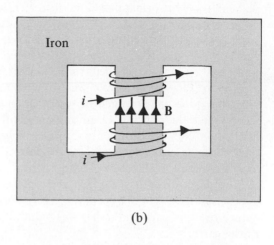

(b)

(a)

FIGURE 9.15　(a) A single electromagnet consisting of an iron cylinder surrounded by a solenoid. (b) An electromagnet that produces an intense, uniform field across the gap between its pole faces.

dipoles. Let us now turn to the second aspect of the current-current interaction by considering the forces exerted *on* currents by magnetic fields.

Referring to Equation 9.6 the magnitude of the force between two short current-carrying segments in the special case where both lie in the same plane and are perpendicular to the line connecting them is (Figure 9.6a):

$$F = \frac{\mu_0}{4\pi}\left(\frac{i_1\,\Delta s_1}{R^2}\right)i_2\,\Delta s_2.$$

But the magnetic field produced by i_1 at the position of i_2 is $(\mu_0/4\pi)(i_1\,\Delta s_1/R^2)$ (Equation 9.9a). Therefore:

$$F = Bi_2\,\Delta s_2.$$

We conclude that at least in this special case the force exerted on a current segment is proportional to the magnetic field strength at the segment. It is tempting to generalize and assume that the same relation would be valid regardless of the source of the field exerting the force on the segment, whether a straight wire, a more complicated configuration of currents, or a permanent magnet. This assumption is borne out by experiment for the special case in which the direction of the field and the current-carrying segment are perpendicular. The magnitude of the force upon a current oriented at an angle θ to the field (Figure 9.17) is given by the more general expression:

$$F = iB\,\Delta s\,\sin\theta. \tag{9.12}$$

The magnetic force exerted on an extended current such as a long, straight wire may be obtained by dividing it into short segments. Use Equation 9.12 to calculate the force on

(a)

FIGURE 9.16 (a) An electro-magnet, constructed by the American physicist Joseph Henry in 1832, which could lift over 3000 lb of iron. (Photograph courtesy of the Smithsonian Institution.) (b) A "bending" magnet used to deflect high-energy charged particles (Section 9.4) capable of producing an upward (or downward) field of almost 2 Wb/m across its gap when 2000 A flow in its coils. The magnet is constructed according to the design shown in Figure 9.15b. Because the coils carry such high currents, water flows through them continuously to carry off the heat generated in the process. The coils are brought out beyond the iron to facilitate the necessary connections to the electric power supply and the water circulating system. (Photograph courtesy of Brookhaven National Laboratory.)

(b)

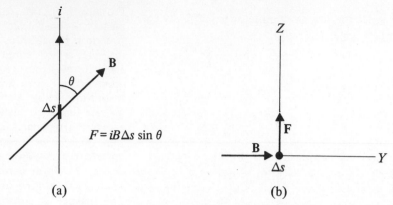

FIGURE 9.17   Magnetic force on a current-carrying segment.   (a) Geometric quantities defined.   (b) Direction of the force relative to the current direction (perpendicular to the page and outward) and the field direction.

each, then take the vector sum of these forces. The forces upon each segment of a long straight wire inclined at an angle θ to a uniform magnetic field are equal, for instance. Therefore the total force is simply $iBl \sin \theta$, while the force per unit length is $iB \sin \theta$.

We are now in a position to find the magnitude of the force between two long, parallel current-carrying conductors (Figure 9.18a). The magnetic field at a distance R from the first is (Equation 9.9b):

$$B = \frac{\mu_0}{2\pi} \frac{i_1}{R}.$$

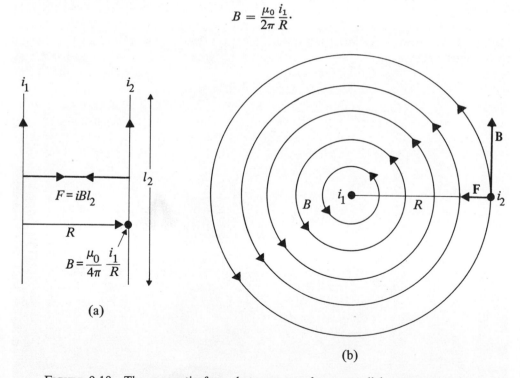

FIGURE 9.18   The magnetic force between two long, parallel current-carrying conductors. In part b the direction of both currents is perpendicular to the page and outward.

Therefore, since the second conductor is perpendicular to the field produced by the first, the force upon it per meter is:

$$\frac{F}{l_2} = i_2 B = \frac{\mu_0}{2\pi} \frac{i_1 i_2}{R}. \tag{9.13}$$

If, for example, the wires are 0.05 m apart and carry 10 A current each:

$$\frac{F}{l_2} = \frac{2 \times 10^{-7} \times 10^2}{5 \times 10^{-2}} = 4 \times 10^{-4} \text{ N/m}.$$

Note that the force is proportional to the currents in *both* segments, implying that each current exerts a force of the same magnitude on the other.

We have not yet considered the *direction* of the force exerted on a current by a magnetic field. However, reference to Figure 9.18b indicates that it is *not* in the direction of the field. As Ampère first noted, the direction of the force between two parallel straight wires is perpendicular to both wires and directed along a line joining them. But we know that the direction of the magnetic field produced by the first current may be represented by a series of concentric circles centered upon the source. In Figure 9.18b the planes of these circles are perpendicular to the plane of the page, so that to the left of the first wire the direction of the field is out of the page and represented by an emerging arrow head (·), and into the page to the right of the wire and represented by the tail of a receding arrow (+). *Therefore, the direction of the force on the second wire must be perpendicular both to the direction of the field and to the direction of the current.*

Since the currents in Figure 9.18 are in the same direction and since we know that the force between the wires is attractive, we can immediately establish a relationship between the direction of the magnetic force on a current, the direction of the field that exerts that force, and the direction of the current itself. In fact, the three directions are related by the famous right-hand rule (Figure 9.19; see also Figure 6.6). If the thumb of the right hand points in the direction of the current (*opposite* the direction the electrons flow) and the index finger in the direction of the field, then if the second finger is mutually perpendicular to both thumb and index finger it designates the direction of the force on the current. The rule is clearly applicable in Figure 9.18, and is also consistent with the observed fact that the force between two currents in the same direction is attractive while the force between two currents in the opposite direction is repulsive.

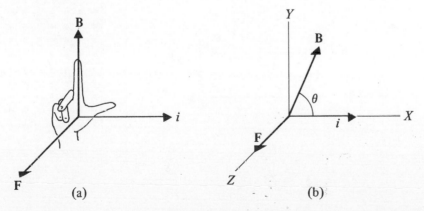

FIGURE 9.19 (a) Use of the right-hand rule for determining the relative directions of current flow, field, and force. (b) The directions of current, field, and force relative to a three-dimensional Cartesian coordinate system.

(Equivalently, if the current and field lie in the *xy*-plane and have components in the positive *x*- and *y*-directions of a Cartesian coordinate system, the force on the current is in the positive *z*-direction. See Figure 9.19b.)

It is worthwhile pausing momentarily to compare Figures 9.10 and 9.11 with Figures 9.18 and 9.19. The former indicate that the field produced *by* a current segment at any point in space is perpendicular to the plane containing the segment and the line joining it to the point. The latter shows that the force *on* a current is perpendicular to the plane of the field and current. Many beginning students find both of these directional relations, and especially the second, somewhat troublesome. The root of the difficulty probably lies in the implicit but incorrect notion that a force must be in the direction of a field. Indeed this is the case for the electrostatic force on a positive charge, or for the magnetic force on a positive permanent pole. But as we have shown in these two sections it is simply not true for magnetic forces on currents. Since the search for a consistent description of natural phenomena is a primary objective of physics, we must accept the experimentally determined relations between the direction of the magnetic field, its source, and the currents it acts upon if we are to include the magnetic field concept in that description.

Let us consider briefly the effect of a magnetic field upon the current in a conductor other than a long straight wire. Figure 9.20 shows two views of a rectangular current-carrying loop with sides of length *x* and *y*. The perpendicular to the plane of the loop is oriented at an angle θ to a constant magnetic field of magnitude *B*. The forces upon each pair of opposite sides are equal and opposite. Hence those upon the two sides of length *y* merely tend to compress (or stretch) the loop. However, the equal and opposite forces on the other two sides tend to rotate it toward the direction perpendicular to the field. Referring to Equation 9.12 each of these latter forces has magnitude

$$F = iBx.$$

When the field has rotated the loop into a perpendicular orientation then the forces on the sides of length *x* also do nothing more than expand it. But the field has performed

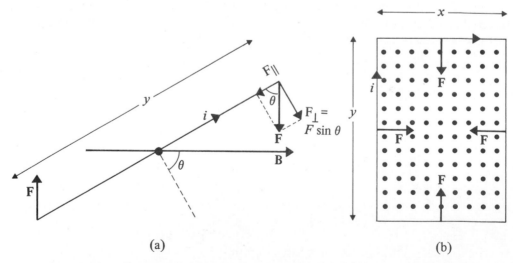

(a) (b)

FIGURE 9.20 The magnetic force on a rectangular, current-carrying loop. In part a, the current flows into the page at the top of the loop, out of the page at the bottom. The magnetic field in part b is out of the page.

work in the course of the rotation. When the loop rotates through a small angle $\Delta\theta$ its upper end is displaced a distance $\Delta s = (y/2)\Delta\theta$. Since only the component of the magnetic force parallel to Δs performs work then:

$$\Delta W = (F \sin\theta)\Delta s = ix\frac{y}{2} B \sin\theta \Delta\theta.$$

The equal and opposite force on the lower side causes an equal displacement in the opposite direction so that the total work over the angular displacement $\Delta\theta$ is

$$\Delta W = ixyB \sin\theta \Delta\theta,$$
$$= iAB \sin\theta \Delta\theta,$$

where $A = xy$ is the area of the rectangular loop. This relation is very similar to the one we derived in Section 9.1 for the work performed on a permanent magnetic dipole. As the loop swings toward its final, perpendicular position the angle θ changes, and so does the work performed for equal $\Delta\theta$. To find the total work performed by the field the sum of all these small contributions must be taken by evaluating the integral:

$$W = iAB \int_\theta^0 \sin\theta \, d\theta,$$

with the result:

$$W = -iAB \cos\theta.$$

It follows that a rectangular current-carrying loop whose *perpendicular* is oriented at an angle θ to a magnetic field has potential energy of orientation $-iAB \cos\theta$. Although it is not obvious, a flat, single-turn loop of *any* shape has the same potential energy in a magnetic field.

This result is very similar to Equation 9.5, the orientation energy of a permanent magnetic dipole in a uniform field. But there is an important difference. A permanent dipole orients itself *parallel* to a uniform field while a current loop orients itself with its plane *perpendicular* to the field. If we think of the magnetic moment of a permanent dipole as a *vector* whose direction is along its axis then we can state that a magnetic field rotates that vector into an orientation parallel to itself. In view of the foregoing results we can characterize the effect of a field on a current loop by attributing to the loop a magnetic dipole moment of magnitude:

$$\mu = iA, \tag{9.14}$$

provided we agree that the direction of its dipole moment is *perpendicular* to its plane. This characterization is especially useful in dealing with the magnetic forces on the atomic-loop currents in matter.

Suppose a flat, circular loop of radius 0.02 m with ten turns of wire carrying a 5 A current is constrained with its plane parallel to a uniform, 1.5 Wb/m² magnetic field. How much work will the field perform on the loop if the external constraint is removed?

The area of the loop is πr^2. Since the field exerts the same force on each of the ten turns the dipole moment of the loop is ten times the dipole moment of each turn so:

$$\mu = 10 \times (5 \times \pi \times 0.02^2),$$
$$= 6.28 \times 10^{-2} \text{ J/Wb/m}^2.$$

(In view of Equation 9.14 the unit of dipole moment can also be written as amperes-meter^2, which is the usual convention.) Then the work performed by the field is:

$$W = PE_i - PE_f = -iAB \cos 90° - (-iAB \cos 0°)$$
$$= iAB = 6.28 \times 10^{-2} \times 1.5 = 0.094 \text{ J.}$$

A loop of wire suspended in a permanent magnetic field can be used as a current-measuring instrument known as a *galvanometer* (Figure 9.21). The loop is suspended vertically from a fine wire that twists as the loop turns and in so doing exerts a restoring force proportional to the angle through which the loop has rotated. The system is arranged in such a way that if no current flows in the loop its plane is oriented parallel to the permanent magnetic field and there is no twisting of the suspension wire. The magnetic field exerts equal and opposite forces on two sides of the loop proportional to a current flowing in it, and thus rotates the loop toward a direction perpendicular to the field. As it does, the twisted suspension tends to rotate the loop back toward its parallel orientation. Eventually an equilibrium is established between these two counter rotations and the loop comes to rest with its plane oriented at an angle θ to the field direction. Since the forces exerted on the ends of the loop by the field are proportional to the current in the loop its angle of deflection is a measure of the current flowing through it. Usually the permanent poles used to create the field are shaped so that the magnitude of the field in which the loop finds itself is the same regardless of its orientation. In that case its angle of deflection is directly proportional to the current.

Figure 9.22a shows a galvanometer used as an *ammeter* to measure the current flowing in an electric circuit. The instrument is in series with the circuit resistance R and has its own internal resistance r which includes the resistance of the moving loop. In the absence of the ammeter a current $i = \mathscr{E}/R$ would flow in the circuit. But because of the additional resistance the actual current is $i' = \mathscr{E}/(R + r)$. Since it is desirable to arrange the circuit so that the introduction of the meter alters the current as little as possible it is clear that r must be very small relative to R.

In Figure 9.22b a galvanometer is used as a *voltmeter* to measure the potential difference across a circuit resistance R. If a constant current flows in the circuit the potential difference in the absence of the voltmeter is $V = iR$. However, the internal resistance of the instrument provides an alternative path for the current. The actual resistance between the two points at which it is connected is $R' = rR/(r + R)$ (Equation 8.19a), and the potential difference $V' = iR'$. Therefore, in order to minimize its effect on a circuit the internal resistance of a voltmeter should be very *large* relative to the circuit resistance.

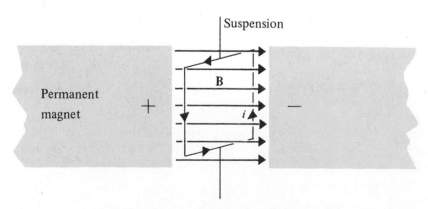

FIGURE 9.21 Essential features of a galvanometer.

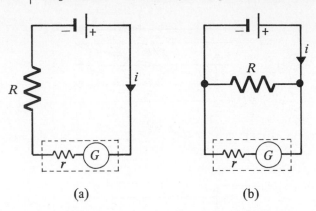

(a)   (b)

FIGURE 9.22   A galvanometer used as (a) an ammeter, and (b) a voltmeter.   In each case a dashed line surrounds the instrument in question.

A current-carrying loop also constitutes the basic element of an electric motor (Figure 9.23). If the loop is originally parallel to a magnetic field it will rotate toward a perpendicular orientation, and as it turns can perform work if coupled to an external system. Because the loop has nonzero velocity when it arrives at the latter equilibrium orientation, it normally rotates through equilibrium to the point where the magnetic force, which always tries to orient it in the perpendicular direction, brings it to rest and starts to swing it back again. Hence the loop oscillates about equilibrium *unless* the direction of its current is reversed at the equilibrium position. In that case the forces will be in the proper direction to continue rotating it toward a new equilibrium position again perpendicular to the field but turned through 180°. If the current continues to change direction each time the loop reaches its perpendicular orientation, the unidirectional rotation will also continue.

The power delivered by an electric motor can be increased by using many turns of wire in place of a single loop, and by arranging several such coils about a single core so that when one coil is parallel to the field another is at an angle of 60°, a third at 120°, for instance (Figure 9.23c). Of course the current in each coil must be reversed when that coil is in the appropriate, perpendicular position.

Consider a motor consisting of three 100-turn rectangular coils with dimensions 0.05×0.10 m oriented at 60° to one another. If each coil carries 3 A and the coil moves in a 0.2 Wb/m² field, what is the maximum work it can perform per revolution? If the current in the coil alternates at 60 cycles/sec what maximum power can the motor deliver?

The area of each loop is $0.05 \times 0.10 = 5 \times 10^{-3}$ m³. Since each loop has one hundred turns and carries 3 A then its dipole moment is (Equation 9.14):

$$\mu = 100 \times 3 \times 5 \times 10^{-3} = 1.5 \text{ A-m}^2.$$

In turning through 90° each coil performs maximum work (Equation 9.5):

$$W = -\mu B \cos(90°) - (-\mu B \cos 0°) = \mu B,$$
$$= 1.5 \times 0.2 = 0.3 \text{ J},$$

and four times this amount in one 360° revolution. Since in addition there are three coils:

$$W = 4 \times 3 \times 0.3 = 3.6 \text{ J per revolution.}$$

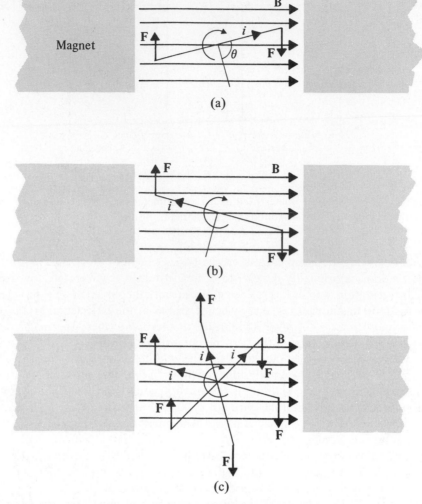

FIGURE 9.23   A simple electric motor constructed by placing a rectangular current-carrying loop in a magnetic field.   If the current direction reverses each time the plane of the loop is parallel to the field (b) the loop continues to rotate. (c) A more efficient motor can be devised by using several loops of wire.

This is the maximum work the motor can perform. Part of its energy will doubtless be dissipated as friction.

If the current alternates sixty times per second the motor rotates once in $\frac{1}{60}$ seconds. Referring to Equation 8.20, its maximum power is:

$$P = \frac{3.6}{1/60} = 216 \text{ W.}$$

▲▲ 9.4   The magnetic force on a moving charge.   Motion of a charge in a magnetic field. The cyclotron.   Atomic dipole moments

Although we have formulated the magnetic force as an interaction between current-carrying conductors, we should remember that current is nothing more than moving

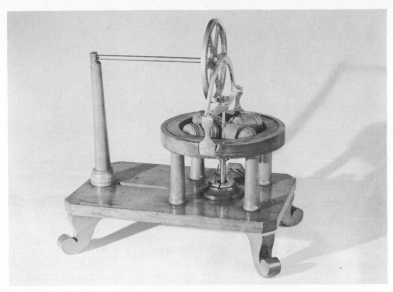

FIGURE 9.24 The first patented electric motor built by John Davenport, a Vermont blacksmith, in 1837. Davenport built an electromagnet and ultimately invented this motor after becoming fascinated by accounts of Joseph Henry's experiments with the electromagnet shown in Figure 9.16a. (Courtesy of the Smithsonian Institution.)

charge, and an electric circuit, fundamentally, a system for maintaining the motion of a rather appreciable quantity of charge. Hence on a more basic level the magnetic force is an interaction between charges in motion. Therefore, we expect that a free, moving charge should produce a magnetic field, and, conversely, that a magnetic field should exert a force upon a moving charge.

By definition (Equation 8.14) if a net charge Δt crosses a given surface in a time Δt then the average current flowing across that surface during that time interval is

$$i = \frac{\Delta q}{\Delta t}.$$

Suppose that an assembly of n charges each of magnitude q_i spread over a distance Δs all move along common trajectory with velocity v (Figure 9.25). [These charges might be the mobile electrons in a short segment of conductor, for instance (Figure 8.21). However, for present purposes it is not desirable to confine our attention to that special case.] If a time Δt is required for all the charges in the group to cross a particular surface, then during that time interval the average current flowing across the surface is

$$i = \frac{nq_i}{\Delta t}.$$

The average speed of the charges is

$$v = \frac{\Delta s}{\Delta t}.$$

Therefore, we obtain the relation:

$$i \, \Delta s = nq_i v.$$

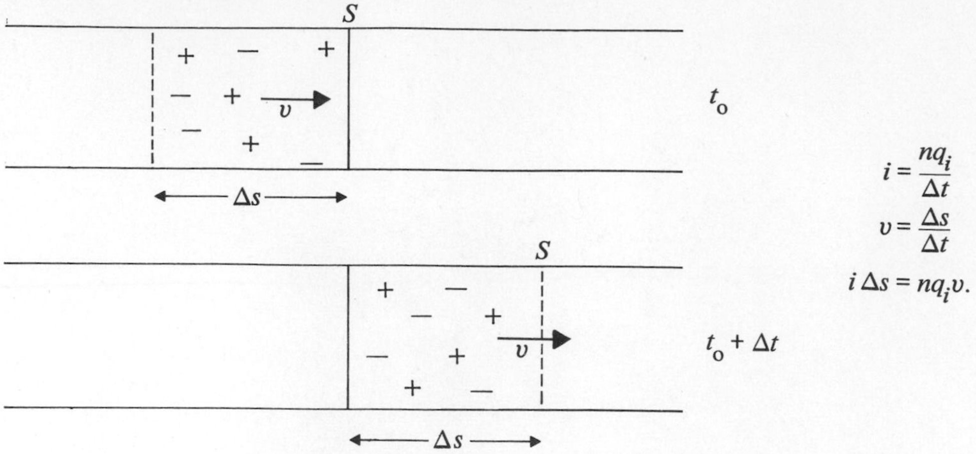

FIGURE 9.25 The current due to the motion of a group of charges traveling with velocity v across a surface S in time Δt.

A similar equation was obtained in our discussion of the conduction process in Section 8.6. It is valid even if we confine our attention to a single charged particle; for its average speed during the time Δt is the ratio of Δs, the distance it travels in that time, to the length of the interval and if but one charge crosses a given surface in the time Δt, the average current is still $q/\Delta t$.

We can now easily write down an expression for the magnitude of the magnetic field produced at a distance R from a charge q moving with speed v by substituting $i\,\Delta s = qv$ into Equation 9.9a:

$$B = \frac{\mu_0}{4\pi}\frac{qv}{R^2}\sin\theta, \tag{9.15}$$

where θ is the angle between the velocity vector $\mathbf{v}$ and the radius vector $\mathbf{R}$ from the charge to the point P at which the field is measured (compare Figure 9.10a and 9.26a).*

The derivation of the relation $i\,\Delta s = qv$ was made in terms of an average current and an average speed. But since Δs, R, and θ approach their instantaneous values simultaneously, Equation 9.15 gives the instantaneous value of the magnetic field at a point in terms of the instantaneous values of the vectors $\mathbf{v}$ and $\mathbf{R}$. The direction of the velocity vector is the direction of the equivalent current segment. Hence the field at any point P is perpendicular to the plane of $\mathbf{v}$ and $\mathbf{R}$ (compare Figures 9.10b and 9.26b) and oriented according to the right-hand rule with the thumb and index finger pointing respectively along the velocity and radius vectors, and the third finger in the directions of the field.

The magnitude of the instantaneous force exerted *on* a moving charge can be obtained in the same way by substituting $i\,\Delta s = qv$ into Equation 9.12:

$$F = qvB\sin\theta, \tag{9.16}$$

with θ the angle between the velocity and field vectors (compare Figures 9.17a and 9.27a). From Figure 9.17b the direction of the force is perpendicular to the plane of $\mathbf{v}$ and $\mathbf{B}$, and

---

*Equation 9.15 is valid only if the velocity of the charge is constant. If the charge accelerates then it radiates energy, and another term must be added to the equation. However, for small accelerations the additional term can usually be neglected.

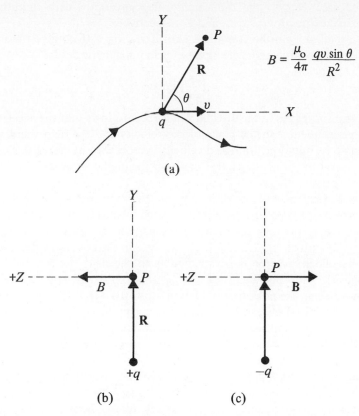

(a)

$$B = \frac{\mu_\text{o}}{4\pi} \frac{qv \sin \theta}{R^2}$$

(b)   (c)

FIGURE 9.26 (a) The field created by a moving charge at the point P in terms of the instantaneous value of its velocity vector and the angle between that vector and the radius vector of the point P. (b) Direction of the field of a positive charge with instantaneous velocity out of the page. (c) Direction of the field of a negative charge with the same velocity vector.

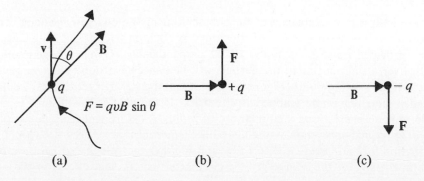

$$F = qvB \sin \theta$$

(a)   (b)   (c)

FIGURE 9.27 The force exerted on a moving charge by a magnetic field. In part b the charge is positive and its velocity vector out of the page; in part c the charge is negative with velocity vector the same as in part b.

again oriented according to the right-hand rule convention with thumb, index, and middle finger in the direction of **v**, **B**, and **F**, respectively.

Newton's second law can be combined with Equation 9.16 to give the magnitude of the acceleration of a charged particle of mass M in a magnetic field:

$$a = \left(\frac{q}{M}\right) vB \sin \theta. \tag{9.17}$$

Since acceleration is always in the direction of force it follows that the acceleration is and must *remain* perpendicular to the plane of the velocity and the field vectors. Given the acceleration and the initial position and velocity vectors for any particular case, both the velocity and displacement of the charge can in principle be determined as a function of time by applying the methods of Chapter 4.

In Figure 9.28 the magnetic field is constant over an appreciable volume of space, perpendicular to the plane of the page, and directed inward. Letting the z-axis define the field direction, the xy-plane is the plane of the page with positive y- downward. Now suppose a mass M with charge q and initial velocity v in the positive x-direction enters the field. Since its velocity vector is perpendicular to the field the force exerted upon it results in an acceleration of magnitude $a = (q/M)vB$ in the positive y-direction (downward) if q is positive, in the negative y-direction (upward) if it is negative. In the language of Section 4.6, the initial effect of the field is a sharp hammer blow in the y-direction, giving the particle a y-component of velocity in addition to its initial x-component, but leaving the magnitude of the velocity unchanged. In other words, the mass is deflected from its former linear trajectory.

Now the magnetic force upon a moving charge is *always* perpendicular to the plane containing the field and velocity vectors. Therefore, as the direction of the particle's velocity changes, so does the direction of its acceleration. Because the force is constant in magnitude and perpendicular to the velocity it can never change the magnitude of the velocity, but can only alter its direction. Hence the force and velocity are *centripetal* and we may substitute $a = v^2/R$ into Equation 9.17 to yield:

$$\frac{v^2}{R} = \left(\frac{q}{M}\right)vB,$$

or, rearranging factors:

$$R = \frac{Mv}{qB} = \frac{p}{qB}, \tag{9.18}$$

where $p = Mv$ is the magnitude of the momentum of the charged particle. This is a significant result. The trajectory of a charged particle in a constant magnetic field is circular, provided **v** and **B** (or **p** and **B**) are perpendicular. Given a large enough field strength over a sufficient area, the particle will be deflected around the complete circle and back to its starting point (Figure 9.28b). It will thenceforth retrace its circular path repeatedly, thus remaining trapped in the field. If the field is insufficient to trap the particle, it is deflected along a circular arc of radius R before emerging into a field-free region of space and once again assuming its linear, inertial course (Figure 9.28c). Examining Equation 9.18 it is evident that a reversal of either the velocity or field vectors or a change in the sign of the charge gives a circular trajectory that curves in the opposite direction.

The momenta of charged particles participating in nuclear or elementary particle interactions are frequently determined by measuring their curvatures in a constant

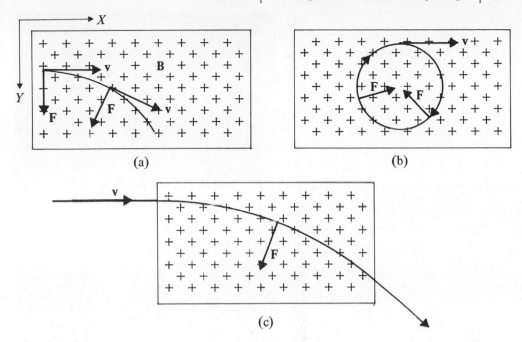

FIGURE 9.28   Trajectory of a positively charged particle in a uniform magnetic field perpendicular to the page and inward. (a) Initial orientation of the vectors. (b) Circular trajectory of a slow particle. (c) Circular arc of a faster particle. The trajectories of charged particles through the bending magnet shown in Figure 9.16b resemble part c.

magnetic field of known magnitude and direction. Figure 9.29 shows the tracks of several particles in a bubble chamber (Chapter 21), placed in a magnetic field whose direction is perpendicular to the plane of the page. Since the tracks curve in both the clockwise and counterclockwise directions it is evident that both positively and negatively charged particles are present. The fact that the tracks have different degrees of curvature indicates that the charge to mass ratios and/or the momenta of the particles that produced them also differ. Another set of measurements is required to decide between these alternate possibilities (Chapter 21).

As a numerical example suppose a proton with mass 1.6×10^{-27} kg and charge $+1.6 \times 10^{-19}$ C is observed to follow a trajectory of radius 1.2 m in a plane perpendicular to a uniform magnetic field of 0.05 Wb/m². What is its velocity?

The charge to mass ratio of the particle is:

$$\frac{q}{M} = \frac{1.6 \times 10^{-19}}{1.6 \times 10^{-27}} = 10^8 \text{ C/kg.}$$

Substituting into Equation 9.18:

$$v = \left(\frac{q}{M}\right) BR = 10^8 \times 5 \times 10^{-2} \times 1.2$$

$$= 6 \times 10^6 \text{ m/sec.}$$

What is the radius of curvature of an α-particle (nucleus of the helium atom) with the same velocity in the same field?

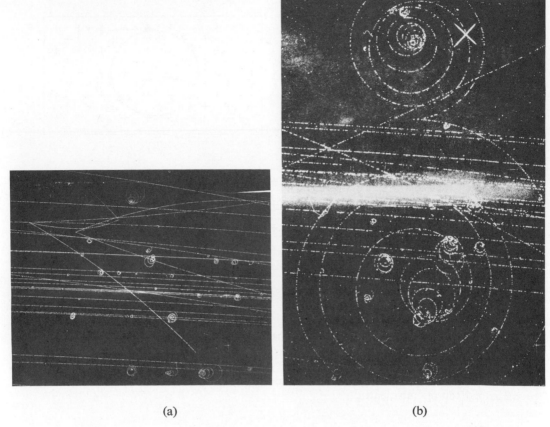

(a)   (b)

FIGURE 9.29   Charged particle tracks in a liquid hydrogen bubble chamber.
(a) High energy, negatively charged antiprotons pass through the chamber from
left to right, curving slightly toward the bottom of the page. Tracks of secondary
particles produced in the interactions of the antiprotons with the protons in the
hydrogen have larger curvatures, indicating that their momenta are smaller than
the incident momentum. (b) Enlarged portion of a bubble chamber photograph
showing the opposite directions of curvature of a negatively and a positively
charged electron (a positron) produced in the chamber by a high energy γ-ray.
(The γ-ray, which is neutral, does not produce a track.) The spiral tracks indicate
that the particles lose energy along their paths through interactions with the
liquid hydrogen (Chapter 20). (Photographs courtesy of Brookhaven National
Laboratory.)

The α-particle has twice the positive charge as the proton and approximately four times
its mass. Therefore:

$$\frac{q}{M} = 5 \times 10^7 \text{ C/kg},$$

and

$$R = \frac{6 \times 10^6}{5 \times 10^7 \times 5 \times 10^{-2}} = 2.4 \text{ m}.$$

Equation 9.18 may be written in a form that serves to illustrate the basic operating
principle of the cyclotron, the best-known particle accelerator as well as the progenitor
of the most energetic present-day accelerators whose purpose and operation are discussed

in Chapter 21. The period of a particle moving with speed v in a circular trajectory of radius R is the ratio of the circumference of the circle to the speed:

$$T = \frac{2\pi R}{v}.$$

Therefore, the period of a particle of charge to mass ratio q/M in a magnetic field B is (Equation 9.18):

$$T = \frac{2\pi R}{v} = \frac{2\pi M}{eB}.$$

The frequency of the particle, f, is the reciprocal of its period, or the number of times it revolves about the circle per second. Thus:

$$f = \frac{1}{T} = \frac{q}{M}\frac{B}{2\pi}, \tag{9.19}$$

a relation which states that the frequency of the particle is independent of *both* its speed and the radius of its circular trajectory. This result follows from the fact that its radius is directly proportional to its speed. Therefore, a rapidly moving particle requires the same length of time to traverse a greater path length in a fixed field as a slower particle takes to complete its shorter characteristic trajectory.

Figure 9.30 shows a cyclotron in cross section. Two hollow, semicircular conductors called "dees" because they are shaped like the letter "D," are located between the poles of an electromagnet. A periodically-varying high voltage applied to the dees makes one of them positive with respect to the other during half of each cycle, and negative during the other half cycle. Therefore, the direction in which a charged particle in the gap between them is accelerated reverses direction during each half cycle. Protons (or other charged particles), produced by ionizing gas at an electric arc placed in the gap at the center of the dees, are initially accelerated toward and into the member of the pair that happens to be negative at that moment. While they remain inside these conductors the protons are shielded from the time-varying electric field (Section 8.6), but not from the constant magnetic field. Because that field is perpendicular to the plane of the conductors, the protons enter circular trajectories from the moment they are produced, describe semicircular arcs, and return once more to the accelerating gap. The potential difference between the conductors changes all the while. Hence some of the protons complete their first semicircular excursions during the time the second dee is negative. These protons will be accelerated back across the gap and into that negative dee. Because their velocities have increased during their transit across the gap their orbits now have larger radii than they had during their first excursion into a dee. However (Equation 9.19), they still require the same time to complete their larger semicircular orbits. If the frequency of the alternating potential across the dees is equal to the orbital frequency of the protons in the magnetic field (Equation 9.19), then the electric field *always* reverses its direction during the time the proton is making one of its semicircular turns through a dee. Hence all protons that arrive *once* at the gap at the proper moment for acceleration *always return* at exactly the right moment, even though their velocities have increased in the meantime. With each successive acceleration their velocities increase, but so do their orbital radii. Therefore, the accelerating particles move in a spiral trajectory and ultimately reach the periphery of the dees. Here a constant, negative potential ejects them from the system so that they may coast along with constant velocity toward an experimental target.

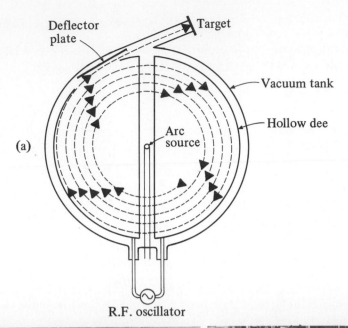

(a)

R.F. oscillator

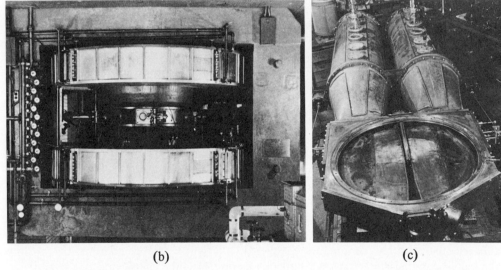

(b)   (c)

FIGURE 9.30   (a) Principle of the cyclotron.   Protons or other positively charged
particles, produced by stripping the electrons from neutral atoms at the arc
source, are accelerated by an electric field across the gap between the two semicircular dees.   The electric field alternates its direction with a frequency equal
to the orbital frequency of the particles in the magnetic field, which is perpendicular to the plane of the page.   Therefore, whenever the particles arrive at the
gap the field is in the proper direction to accelerate them, and they describe spiral
trajectories of increasing radius.   (Compare with the spirals of decreasing radius
in Figure 9.29b).   Finally, an electric field at the deflector plate ejects them from
the field.   (From Derek L. Livesey, *Atomic and Nuclear Physics*, Blaisdell Publishing Co., Waltham, Mass., 1966.)   (b) General view of the magnet and chamber
enclosing the dees of the cyclotron designed and built by M.S. Livingston at
MIT 1938–40.   (c) Arc source, dees, and power supply lines for the MIT cyclotron.   This cyclotron accelerated deuterons (the nuclei of heavy hydrogen, $M =
3.2 \times 10^{-27}$ kg) to 2.7×10^{-12} J (18 MeV — see Chapter 10).   (Photographs
courtesy of M.S. Livingston.)

The velocity attained by the protons accelerated in a cyclotron is proportional to their maximum radius of curvature (Equation 9.18):

$$V_{max} = \frac{q}{M} BR_{max},$$ (9.20a)

and so

$$E_{kin} = \frac{1}{2} Mv^2 = \frac{e^2}{2M} (BR_{max})^2.$$ (9.20b)

That is the energy of the emergent beam is determined by the magnitude of the field B, and limited only by the size of the electromagnet used to produce that field.

For example, let us find the radius of the electromagnet required in a cyclotron that is to accelerate protons to speeds of 2×10^7 m/sec if the strength of the magnetic field is 0.5 Wb/m². We have:

$$\frac{q}{M} = 10^8 \text{ C/kg.}$$

Substituting into Equation 9.20a,

$$R_{max} = \frac{2 \times 10^7}{10^8 \times 0.5} = 0.4 \text{ m.}$$

The frequency of the alternating potential difference that must be maintained across the gap is obtained from Equation 9.19:

$$f = \frac{10^8 \times 0.5}{2 \times 3.14} = 7.95 \times 10^6 \text{ cycles/sec.}$$

The applicability of the simple cyclotron principle is limited to velocities smaller than about 10% the speed of light (3×10^8 m/sec) by an effect predicted by Einstein in 1905 and verified repeatedly since that time. When a particle moves with speed v its inertial mass, M, increases over the value M_0 of its inertial mass at rest. If c is the speed of light, then, as we shall show in Chapter 11 (Equation 11.19):

$$M = \frac{M_0}{\sqrt{1 - v^2/c^2}}.$$

The increase in mass only becomes appreciable at high speeds. For instance, it amounts to about 3% for $v = 3 \times 10^7$ m/sec, or 0.1 c. But since the mass of a particle accelerated in a cyclotron does increase significantly at higher speeds, then according to Equation 9.19 there is a proportionate decrease in its frequency of revolution. When this frequency change becomes appreciable the accelerated particles arrive at the gap between the dees well after the time at which the direction of the potential difference has changed. As a result they are too late to receive the optimum acceleration. In fact, they will be decelerated if they are more than one-half cycle late.

Two different methods are used to overcome this limitation. In a *synchrocyclotron* the magnetic field strength increases toward the periphery of the particle orbit so that the ratio (B/M), and therefore, from Equation 9.19, the orbital frequency of the particles, remains constant as their speeds increase. In the *FM (frequency-modulated) cyclotron* the frequency of the alternating potential across the gap between the dees is decreased so that it remains equal to the decreasing orbital frequency of the accelerated particles. In Chapter 21 we shall discuss these and other modifications of the cyclotron principle that have permitted the construction of the very high energy accelerators that are indispensable tools in contemporary elementary particle research.

The trajectory of a particle in a magnetic field whose magnitude and/or direction varies from point to point is generally more involved than the circular trajectory characteristic of a constant field, but in principle is no more difficult to calculate than the trajectory of a particle subject to any other kind of force. We require only a knowledge of the initial position and velocity vector of a charged particle and a map of the field at all points in space. Given these data we can use Equation 9.17 to determine the magnitude and direction of the "hammer blow" inflicted by the field at the initial position. Then with the aid of the general kinematic apparatus of Chapter 2 we can find out where the particle goes as a result of that blow, and given the field at that new position can calculate the magnitude and direction of the next "hammer blow," etc. Detailed calculations of this sort were carried out for an harmonic oscillator in Chapter 4, and for planetary motion in Chapter 5. The magnetic force is neither a Hooke's law force nor a gravitational force. Nonetheless, it is a force that acts upon a moving mass. Hence Newton's laws and the particle kinematics of Chapter 2 are equally applicable.

The foregoing discussion of particle orbits assumes that save for the magnetic force the particles in question are completely free. Naturally, if a magnetic field acts upon a particle which is also subject to another force the resultant motion may be considerably more involved. There is one such case of particular interest. Figure 9.31 is a diagram of the familiar planetary model of a hydrogen atom which, though oversimplified, is sufficient for our present purposes. An electron of mass $M_e = 9 \times 10^{-31}$ kg and charge -1.6×10^{-19} C orbits about a proton of mass 1.6×10^{-27} kg and charge $+1.6 \times 10^{-19}$ C. The primary interaction between the particles, the interaction that keeps the electron in orbit, is electrostatic. Using the symbol e to represent the magnitude of the fundamental charge 1.6×10^{-19} C (Section 9.7), and referring to Equation 8.1 we can write:

$$F = \frac{1}{4\pi\epsilon_0} \frac{e^2}{R^2}.$$

If the orbit is circular the result of the electrostatic interaction is to supply a centripetal force so that

$$\frac{M_e v^2}{R} = \frac{1}{4\pi\epsilon_0} \frac{e^2}{R^2},$$

or, solving for the orbital speed:

$$v = \sqrt{(1/4\pi\epsilon_0)(e^2/M_e R)}.$$

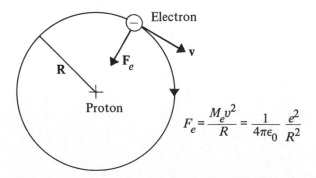

$$F_e = \frac{M_e v^2}{R} = \frac{1}{4\pi\epsilon_0} \frac{e^2}{R^2}$$

FIGURE 9.31   Planetary model of the hydrogen atom.

Since the electron is a charge in motion it can be regarded as a current loop, and therefore, has an equivalent magnetic dipole moment $\mu = iA$. The average loop current is equal to the charge e divided by its period $T = 2\pi R/v$, the time the electron requires to complete one orbit:

$$i = \frac{e}{T} = \frac{ev}{2\pi R} = \sqrt{e^4/[(4\pi\epsilon_0)4\pi^2 MR^3]}.$$

The loop area $A = \pi R^2$. Therefore:

$$\mu = iA = \sqrt{e^4 R/[(4\pi\epsilon_0)4M_e]} = \frac{e^2}{2} \sqrt{R/4\pi\epsilon_0 M_e}. \tag{9.21a}$$

The radius of the electron's orbit in the normal ground state of hydrogen is 5×10^{-11} m. Substituting into Equation 9.21a,

$$\mu = \frac{(1.6 \times 10^{-19})^2}{2} \sqrt{\frac{9 \times 10^9 \times 5 \times 10^{-11}}{9 \times 10^{-31}}} = 9 \times 10^{-24} \text{ A-m}^2.$$

Equation 9.21a can be expressed in a more general and convenient form by writing it in terms of the electron's orbital angular momentum (Equation 6.12):

$$L = M_e vR = \sqrt{e^2 MR/4\pi\epsilon_0}.$$

Dividing Equation 9.21a by this expression and multiplying both sides by L:

$$\mu = \left(\frac{e}{2M_e}\right)L. \tag{9.21b}$$

Thus the orbital magnetic moment of the electron orbit is proportional to the particle's charge to mass ratio and to its orbital angular momentum. Although we have derived Equation 9.21b for the special case of a circular orbit, it is valid for any electron orbit in which the electrostatic attraction of the atomic nucleus is the dominant force on the particle.

▶▶ 9.5 Electromagnetic induction

When a conductor moves with velocity **v** through a magnetic field **B** it obviously carries its mobile electrons along with it. Therefore, the field exerts a force upon each electron with magnitude given by Equation 9.16. If the moving conductor forms all or part of a continuous loop then the force imparts a drift velocity to the electrons, and given proper cirumstances, a current may flow around the loop.

Figure 9.32 shows one possible arrangement for demonstrating this effect. A metal bar of length z moves with velocity **v** in the positive x-direction upon (and perpendicular to) metal tracks connected at their far end through a sensitive galvanometer which completes the closed loop. The entire system is in a uniform magnetic field which emerges from the page but makes an angle θ to the positive y-direction, perpendicularly outward from the plane of the page. Therefore, the angle between **v** and **B** is $(90 - \theta)$, and the magnitude of the force on each electron (Equation 9.16):

$$F = evB \sin(90 - \theta),$$
$$= evB \cos\theta,$$

where the conventional symbol e is used to denote the magnitude of the electron's charge. Applying the right-hand rule, the magnetic force, perpendicular to the plane of **v** and **B**, is along the moving bar and in the *upward* direction on the negative electrons. Therefore,

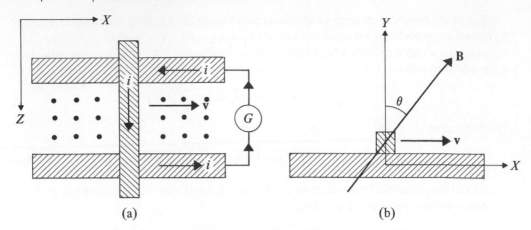

FIGURE 9.32 Arrangement demonstrating the induction of a current in a conductor moving relative to a magnetic field. (a) Top view, (b) Side view.

the conventional current direction must be downward along the bar, or counterclockwise about the loop. If the experiment is actually performed the galvanometer deflects in the direction indicating the predicted direction of current flow. When the bar moves with equal speed in the negative *x*-direction an equal and opposite galvanometer deflection is observed, showing that the current direction has reversed in accord with the right-hand rule. The same change is noted if the direction of **B** is reversed without changing **v**.

Since current flows in a counterclockwise direction around the loop when the direction of the field and velocity are as shown in Figure 9.32 there must be an EMF around the loop which causes current to flow in the direction indicated in the diagram. The magnitude of the force on each electron is

$$F = evB \cos \theta,$$

which, in displacing an electron the length of the bar performs work,

$$W = Fz = evzB \cos \theta.$$

Hence the work per unit charge, equal to the EMF induced by the motion, is:

$$\mathscr{E} = \frac{W}{e} = vzB \cos \theta.$$

But $v = \Delta x/\Delta t$, so:

$$\mathscr{E} = \frac{\Delta x}{\Delta t} zB \cos \theta.$$

The product $\Delta xz/\Delta t = \Delta A/\Delta t$, the change in the area $A = xz$ of the loop. If the *y*-axis of the coordinate system is perpendicular to the plane of the page and outward then the counterclockwise direction around the loop, the direction of the current when the area *decreases*, is the conventional positive direction of rotation.* Therefore we may write:

$$\mathscr{E} = -\frac{\Delta A}{\Delta t} B \cos \theta. \tag{9.22}$$

---

* The conventional positive direction of rotation is a Cartesian system and is defined by the right-hand screw convention as counterclockwise (Figure 9.9b) even as the relative orientation of the axes is defined by the right-hand rule (Figure 9.19b).

On the other hand, if the area of the loop increases or if B is reversed then the current flows in the opposite sense.

If the cross bar in Figure 9.32 is 0.1 m long and moves at a rate of 5 m/sec through a 0.04 Wb/m^2 magnetic field in the y-direction, what is the magnitude of the induced EMF around the loop? Here $\theta = 0$, so:

$$\frac{\Delta A}{\Delta t} = -z \frac{\Delta x}{\Delta t} = -zv = -5 \times 0.1 = -5 \times 10^{-1} \, \text{m}^2/\text{sec}$$

$$\mathscr{E} = 5 \times 10^{-1} \times 4 \times 10^{-2} = 2 \times 10^{-2} \, \text{V}.$$

If the resistance of the entire circuit is 0.1 ohms, the current that flows must be

$$i = \frac{\mathscr{E}}{R} = 0.2 \, \text{A}$$

in the counterclockwise direction, since $\mathscr{E}$ is positive.

Figure 9.33 shows another situation in which an EMF is induced in a conductor by virtue of its motion relative to a magnetic field. A rectangular loop rotates with constant frequency f about an axis which bisects the sides 1 and 3 (each of length b) and is perpendicular to them. As the loop rotates, the angle θ between the perpendicular to its plane and the direction of the magnetic field **B** changes at a constant rate. Applying the right-hand rule, it is clear that the magnetic forces on the mobile electrons in sides 2 and 4 are along the direction of the two sides, and must be equal and opposite, since the velocity vectors of the two sides are always equal and opposite. Therefore, current flows around the loop in the direction indicated in the diagram. If θ is the instantaneous angle between the plane of the loop and the field, the magnitude of the force on each electron is:

$$F = evB \sin \theta,$$

and in the opposite direction in the two sides since their velocity vectors are also in the opposite direction. A current flows around the loop, indicating that an EMF is induced by the rotation.

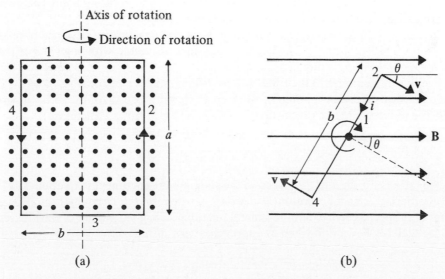

FIGURE 9.33 Current induced in a loop rotating in a magnetic field. (a) Side view showing field lines emerging from the page. (b) Top view.

The speed of each of the two sides is equal to the ratio of the circumference of its circular path to its period of revolution:

$$v = \frac{2\pi(b/2)}{T} = \pi b f,$$

since $f = 1/T$. Therefore the magnitude of the work performed on an electron displaced over the length a is

$$W = Fa = e\pi fabB \sin \theta.$$

Because the magnetic field exerts a force upon the electrons in both sides 2 and 4, the induced EMF, equal to the work per unit charge, is

$$\mathscr{E} = 2\pi fAB \sin \theta,$$

where $A = ab$ is the area of the loop.

The instantaneous angle θ can also be expressed as a function of frequency. Sides 2 and 4 travel a distance $s = vt$ from the orientation at which $\theta = 0$ in time t, so $\theta = s/R = (v/R)t = 2\pi ft$, $v = 2\pi Rf$, and

$$\mathscr{E} = 2\pi fAB \sin 2\pi ft. \tag{9.23}$$

Figure 9.34a plots the magnitude of the EMF around the loop as a function of t. At $t = 0$ ($\theta = 0$) the velocity vectors of sides 2 and 4 are parallel to **B**, and the current and EMF both zero. One-quarter cycle later at $t = T/4 = 1/4f$ ($\theta = \pi/2$ radians), they are perpendicular to the field, and both current and EMF have attained their maxima. Thereafter they decrease to zero at $t = 1/2f$ ($\theta = \pi$ radians). During the next half-cycle the roles of sides 2 and 4 are interchanged so that both the current and EMF reverse their directions around the loop, decrease to their minimum values at $t = 3/4f$, and increase again to zero at $t = 1/f = T$. If the loop is attached to a pair of conductors which are the input leads of an external circuit (Figure 9.33b), a sinusoidally varying current flows in the circuit, reversing itself every half-cycle. Hence the rotating loop becomes an alternating current generator.

For example, suppose a sixty-cycle alternating current generator is designed to produce a maximum EMF of 120 V. The coil is a fifty-turn rectangle with sides 0.3×0.4 m. What magnetic field is required?

Referring to Equation 9.23 the EMF attains its maximum value for $\sin 2\pi ft = 1$. Since the field performs the same amount of work on an electron in each of the turns of wire on the coil the induced EMF is proportional to the number of turns. Therefore:

$$B = \frac{\mathscr{E}}{2\pi fnA} = \frac{120}{2 \times 3.14 \times 60 \times 50 \times 0.3 \times 0.2} = 0.054 \text{ Wb/m}^2.$$

The equations for the EMF induced in the sliding bar experiment (Equation 9.22) and in the alternating current generator (Equation 9.23) are rather different in form. However, they are both special cases of a more general relation. Using techniques of the differential calculus it can be shown that when Δt approaches zero then:

$$\lim_{\Delta t \to 0} \frac{\Delta(\cos 2\pi ft)}{\Delta t} = -2\pi f \sin 2\pi ft.$$

(That is, $-2\pi f \sin 2\pi ft$ is the instantaneous rate of change of $\cos (2\pi ft)$, or its first

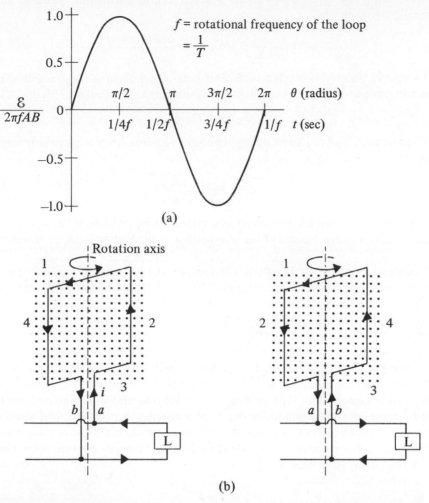

FIGURE 9.34   (a) The EMF induced in the rotating loop of Figure 9.33 plotted as a function of θ and of time ($\theta = 2\pi ft$ radians). (b) The rotating loop at two points in its cycle one-half period apart. The leads a and b change roles twice per cycle. If connected to an external circuit via a slip ring device of some type (to avoid twisting the leads) the loop constitutes a simple alternating current generator.

derivative with respect to time. See Appendix to Chapter 2). Therefore, we can write Equation 9.23 as

$$\mathscr{E} = \lim_{\Delta t \to 0} - BA \frac{\Delta(\cos 2\pi ft)}{\Delta t} = \lim_{\Delta t \to 0} - BA \frac{\Delta(\cos \theta)}{\Delta t},$$

since $\theta = 2\pi ft$. Because B and A are constant this is entirely equivalent to:

$$\mathscr{E} = \lim_{\Delta t \to 0} - \frac{\Delta(BA \cos \theta)}{\Delta t}.$$

In the sliding bar experiment (Figure 9.32) A changes with time while B and θ are constant. There again:

$$\mathscr{E} = -\frac{\Delta A}{\Delta t} B \cos \theta = -\frac{\Delta(BA \cos \theta)}{\Delta t}.$$

The *magnetic flux* Φ_B through a surface of area A is defined as the product of the area by the component of the magnetic field perpendicular to the surface (Figure 9.35):

$$\Phi_B = AB \cos \theta. \tag{9.24}$$

Hence the results of both the moving wire and rotating loop experiments can be expressed as

$$\mathscr{E} = \lim_{\Delta t \to 0} -\frac{\Delta \Phi_B}{\Delta t}. \tag{9.25}$$

The instantaneous value EMF induced in a circuit due to its motion in a magnetic field is equal to the negative change of the magnetic flux through the surface with respect to time.

Although we have derived Equation 9.25 for two special cases it is applicable to circuits of any shape and to all conceivable types of motion. In 1831 Michael Faraday (Figure 9.36) discovered that an EMF is also induced in a circuit if there is a magnetic flux change due to a change in magnetic field even when there is no physical motion of the conductor relative to the field, and that Equation 9.25 is applicable in this case as well. For this reason Equation 9.25 is called Faraday's law of electromagnetic induction.*

For example, Figure 9.37 shows two parallel wire loops. Initially, a constant current maintained by an EMF flows in the first loop creating a magnetic field which is constant in time. The magnetic flux through the second loop is also constant and no EMF is induced. But when the current in the first loop increases, its magnetic field also increases and *a current is observed to flow in the second loop as long as the primary current continues to increase.* If R is the radius of the secondary loop and $\Delta B_1/\Delta t$ the rate of change of the primary field, then (Equation 9.25):

$$\mathscr{E}_2 = -\pi R^2 \frac{\Delta B_1}{\Delta t}.$$

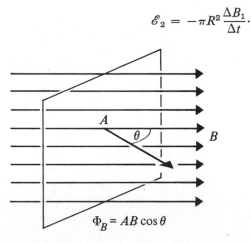

$$\Phi_B = AB \cos \theta$$

FIGURE 9.35 The magnetic flux through a surface of area A is defined as $\Phi_B = AB \cos \theta$, with θ the angle between the perpendicular to the surface and the field direction.

---

*It is worth noting that it was not known in 1831 that electrons constitute the mobile charge in a conductor, so that Equation 9.25 could not have been derived by considering the force upon this mobile charge. Hence, Faraday's law was completely original.

FIGURE 9.36 Michael Faraday conducting a lecture-demonstration. (Original photograph in the Burndy Library, Norwalk, Connecticut.)

FIGURE 9.37 The changing magnetic field created by the changing current in one loop induces a current in the other even though the loops do not move relative to each other. (The direction of the induced current in Loop 2 indicates that $\mathbf{B}_1$ is increasing.)

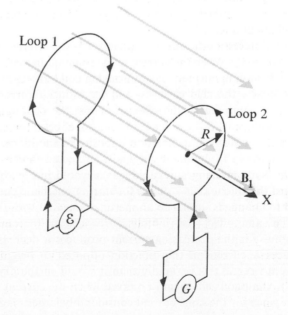

This equation predicts that the induced EMF is proportional to the *rate* at which B_1 increases rather than to the magnitude of B_1 itself, and that the direction of the induced current reverses when the primary field decreases. Both predictions have been verified experimentally.

Equation 9.25 can only be derived from the magnetic force law in cases where conductors move relative to a magnetic field. But because Faraday's law has a much wider range of applicability, it is at least in part an independent experimental law with the same status as Coulomb's law for the interaction of charges at rest, or the magnetic force law between current-carrying conductors. Since a constant current inducing a constant magnetic field is equivalent to charge moving with constant velocity, accelerating charges produce a time-varying magnetic field. Therefore, Faraday's law can be regarded as a force law involving *accelerating* charge, a point we shall pursue in Chapter 12.

Like any other current, the current induced in a coil by a change in the external magnetic flux through it produces in turn another magnetic field. We may use this fact to state a rule, known as Lenz's law, which relates the direction of the change in the external flux to the direction of the induced current. The direction of the magnetic field produced by an induced current is always *opposed* to the *change* in the field that induces it. The change may be either in magnitude or direction or both. This is the meaning of the minus sign in Equation 9.25.

Thus in Figure 9.37 the magnetic field through the second coil is in the positive *x*-direction. When the field increases it also *changes* in the positive *x*-direction so that according to Lenz's law the field of the *induced* current is in the negative *x*-direction. Applying the right-hand screw convention we conclude that the direction of the induced current must be clockwise around the second loop. On the other hand, when the primary field decreases, its *change* is in the *negative x*-direction, the field of the induced current in the *positive x*-direction, so that the induced current must flow about the loop in the counterclockwise direction. Likewise, in Figure 9.33 the direction of the field through the rotating coil increases in the *counter*clockwise direction as θ changes from 0 to 90°, and Lenz's law requires that the field of the induced current must be in the *clock*wise direction. The right-hand screw convention then yields a current flow direction consistent with the direction obtained by considering the force on the moving mobile electrons in the moving conductor.

It is interesting to apply Faraday's law to a long cylindrical coil of wire, a solenoid (Section 9.3). When the current in the solenoid increases, its magnetic field also increases. But a changing magnetic field through a coil induces an EMF in the coil *regardless* of the reason why the field changes, and the induced current in turn produces a field in the direction opposed to the change. Thus, the changing field in the solenoid induces a countercurrent in the solenoid itself, an effect known as self-induction. The induced current is always in a direction opposite to the increasing current that induces it. The net effect is to inhibit the originally projected increase in the current, and thus in the field. Neither changes as rapidly as it would in the absence of the self-induction. If we regard the solenoid as a device for storing magnetic energy, then the "reluctance" of the field to change is similar to an inertia associated with that stored energy.

The same effect also inhibits a decrease in the current, and for precisely the same reasons, for the decreasing current produces a decreasing magnetic field which in turn induces a current in the direction opposed to original decreasing current. Thus the current decreases less rapidly than it would in the absence of the self-induction of the coil. Analogous effects are observed when the current in any conductor changes. However, since for the same current considerably larger magnetic fields may be produced with a solenoid than with a straight wire, for example, self-induction is also more noticeable in the former case. Solenoids used to control and/or limit current changes in electric circuits are called *inductance* coils.

▲▲ 9.6 Total force between moving charges. Noninvariance of the total force with respect to the Galilean transformations

The primary emphasis of this chapter has been upon the creation of magnetic fields by currents and the effects of these fields upon moving charges. But although it is usually convenient to separate the source of a magnetic field from its effect, it is also necessary to emphasize on occasion that virtually all magnetic interactions begin and end with moving charges. Hence we can write an expression for the magnetic force between two moving charged particles that does not involve the mediation of a magnetic field, even as we previously wrote an analogous, experimentally-determined equation for the force between two current-carrying segments (Equation 9.6). In the special case in which two charges q_1 and q_2 have constant, parallel velocity vectors (Figure 9.38), the required magnitude of the force follows directly by substituting $i_1 \Delta s_1 = q_1 v_1$ and $i_2 \Delta s_2 = q_2 v_2$ into Equation 9.6 (with $\theta = 90°$):

$$F = \frac{\mu_0}{4\pi} \frac{q_1 q_2 v_1 v_2}{R^2}. \tag{9.26}$$

The direction of the force is along the line joining the charges, and the force is attractive if the velocities are in the same direction and the two charges have the same signs. Of course there is also an *electrostatic* force between the charges that is independent of their velocities (Equation 8.1). Both forces vary directly with the product of the magnitude of the charges and inversely with the square of their separation. Therefore, the ratio of their magnitudes is given by a particularly simple expression:

$$\frac{F_m}{F_e} = -(\mu_0 \epsilon_0) v_1 v_2,$$

where the negative sign indicates that the forces are in the opposite directions if the velocities are in the same direction.

How large is the ratio of the measured proportionality constants? Since $1/4\pi\epsilon_0 = 9 \times 10^9$ N-m^2/C^2 and $\mu_0/4\pi = 10^{-7}$ N/A^2 then:

$$\frac{1}{\mu_0 \epsilon_0} = \frac{1/4\pi\epsilon_0}{\mu_0/4\pi} = 9 \times 10^{16} \left(\frac{\text{A}^2\text{-m}^2}{\text{C}^2}\right).$$

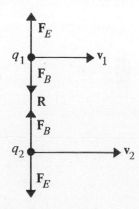

FIGURE 9.38 The electrostatic and magnetic forces between two charges with the same polarity moving with constant, parallel velocities.

But 1 A = 1 C/sec, so we can write:

$$\frac{1}{\mu_0\epsilon_0} = 9 \times 10^{16}\left(\frac{C^2\text{-m}^2/\text{sec}^2}{C^2}\right) = 9 \times 10^{16} \text{ m}^2/\text{sec}^2.$$

Thus $\mu_0\epsilon_0$ has the dimensions of an inverse velocity squared, as it must if the force ratio is to be dimensionless. By convention the inverse square root of the ratio $1/\sqrt{\mu_0\epsilon_0}$ is designated with the letter c. That is:

$$c = \frac{1}{\sqrt{\mu_0\epsilon_0}} = 3 \times 10^8 \text{ m/sec.} \tag{9.27}$$

With this substitution the ratio of the forces becomes:

$$\frac{F_m}{F_e} = -\frac{v_1 v_2}{c^2}. \tag{9.28}$$

Thus the magnetic force between two charges is small relative to the electrostatic force, provided their speeds are small relative to the very large speed $c = 3 \times 10^8$ m/sec.

Does the speed c have any significance in itself or is it only the square root of the ratio of two experimentally determined constants? It has, in fact, a totally unanticipated significance, for it is precisely equal to the measured speed of light in vacuum. It would be surprising if that equality were accidental.

Equation 9.28 has a further unexpected and rather disturbing implication. If two charges are at rest relative to an observer B, he measures only an electrostatic force between them of magnitude

$$F_B = \frac{1}{4\pi\epsilon_0} \frac{q_1 q_2}{R^2}.$$

However, from the viewpoint of another observer A (Figure 9.39) traveling with constant

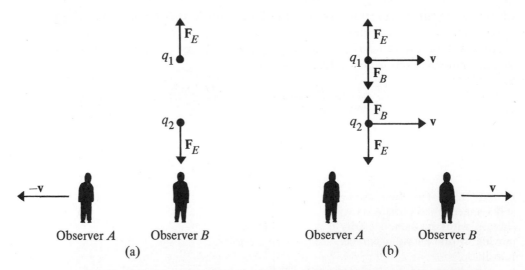

FIGURE 9.39 The forces between two charges with the same polarity measured by (a) Observer B at rest relative to the charges, and (b) Observer A moving with velocity $-\mathbf{v}$ relative to them. From Observer A's point of view both Observer B and the charges move with velocity $+\mathbf{v}$.

velocity $-v$ relative to observer A, the two charges both travel with velocities $+v$ so that he also notes a magnetic force between them and writes the total force as

$$F_A = F_e + F_m = F_e\left(1 + \frac{F_m}{F_e}\right) = \frac{1}{4\pi\epsilon_0}\frac{q_1 q_2}{R^2}\left(1 + \frac{F_m}{F_e}\right),$$

or, using Equation 9.28,

$$F_A = \frac{1}{4\pi\epsilon_0}\frac{q_1 q_2}{R^2}\left(1 - \frac{v^2}{c^2}\right) = F_B\left(1 - \frac{v^2}{c^2}\right). \tag{9.29}$$

Equation 9.29 states that the measured force between two charges depends on their velocities relative to an observer. This directly contradicts one of the symmetry principles of Chapter 6 (Section 6.12) which states that the laws of physics are the same for all observers moving with constant velocity relative to one another. Either this symmetry principle is in error or our formulation of the forces between moving charges is still incomplete. It is not hard to understand how the latter situation might arise. The equations describing the magnetic interactions are based on laboratory experiments involving speeds much smaller than the speed of light. As Equations 9.28 and 9.29 suggest, any deviations from these experimental laws probably would not be readily apparent at such small speeds. For instance, if $v = 10^3$ m/sec in Equation 9.29, then $(v/c) = \frac{1}{9} \times 10^{-7}$, and the ratio F_A/F_B differs from unity by only about ten parts per billion. In any event it seems clear that there may well be an important connection between the interaction of charges and the nature of light, a connection we shall investigate in the following chapters.

◣◣ 9.7 The charge structure of matter. The fundamental charge

The assumption that the fundamental properties of matter can in principle be understood in terms of the properties and interactions of a set of elementary particles is basic in contemporary physics. It is to be noted that the validity of this assumption has by no means been completely verified experimentally. Indeed, the number of elementary particles that exist is unknown, and even the significance of the word *elementary* when used in this context is debatable. We shall discuss the problem of the "elementary" particles in Chapters 22 and 23. At this juncture it is sufficient to state that their ability to participate in electrostatic and magnetic interactions is among their important properties. By definition their charges are determined by observing the way they participate. It is significant that all of the elementary particles exhibit one of three charge states: positive with magnitude 1.6×10^{-19} C, negative with the same magnitude, and zero.* The proton, the electron, and the neutron, the most well known of the elementary particles which together form the basic constituents of atoms, each exhibit a different one of these states. The proton's charge is positive, the electron's negative, the neutron's zero. Since *all* of the elementary particles have either zero charge, or positive or negative charge of the same magnitude, it follows that charge may be added or subtracted from a macroscopic body only in units $e = 1.6 \times 10^{-19}$ C. Hence charge is quantized, and not continuous. The only observed charge with magnitude smaller than $\pm e$ is zero!

Most of the properties of the electrostatic and magnetic interactions discussed in this and the previous chapters do not distinguish between continuous and quantized charge. It is conceivable that charge might enter matter as a disembodied massless fluid of some

---

* There have been suggestions that particles with charges $\frac{1}{3}$ and $\frac{2}{3}$ this magnitude may exist, but none have been found at this writing (see Section 23.4).

sort that would easily flow through metals and attach itself to insulators. A free charge would then be a drop of that fluid. Indeed this idea was quite popular in the late eighteenth and early nineteenth century. However, toward the middle of the nineteenth century the quantized theory began to evolve from attempts to find consistent explanations for observations of current conduction in liquids, metals, and gases.

If two metallic electrodes are connected across the terminals of a source of EMF such as a storage battery and immersed in water mixed with a small amount of sulphuric acid, then the water, normally an insulator, becomes a conductor. Current flows between the electrodes and is accompanied by dissociation of the water into its components. Hydrogen is liberated at the negative electrode (or *cathode*), oxygen at the positive electrode (or *anode*) (Figure 9.40).

The electrolysis of water was investigated thoroughly by Svante Arrhenius (who in 1882 established the basic ionic dissociation mechanism involved) as well as by others, most notably Michael Faraday. The phenomenon is intimately bound up with the molecular structure of matter and is an excellent example of the charge conservation principle. By definition, the current in the water consists of moving charge. The dissociation linked with the current flow implies that normally neutral water molecules are broken up into charged components called *ions*, that the positive hydrogen ions migrate to the cathode and the negative oxygen ions to the anode. But since *neutral* hydrogen is liberated at the negative electrode it follows that the positive ions must each receive a negative charge there and become neutral hydrogen atoms, and it is reasonable to assume that they receive the negative units from the electrode itself and thus ultimately from the storage battery. If current is to flow continuously an equal amount of negative charge must be returned to the battery. This will happen if the negative ions at the anode give up negative charge and become neutral oxygen atoms, which they apparently do.

Faraday showed that the mass of hydrogen and oxygen liberated at the electrodes is related to the current supplied by the battery and to the number of atoms per unit mass of the respective gases. If these latter numbers are known, then measurement of the mass of gas that is liberated when a particular current flows in the treated water leads to the magnitude of the fundamental (hypothesized) unit of charge supplied to each ion by the storage battery. In the late nineteenth century it was proposed that this unit be called the *electron*. Its magnitude, based on modern electrolytic measurements, is approximately 1.6×10^{-19} C.

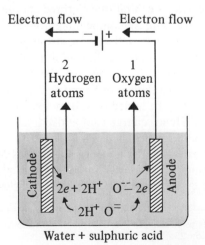

FIGURE 9.40 The electrolysis of water.

Electrolysis measurements provided the first suggestion that the charge flowing in a conductor attached to a source of EMF is a negative electron current moving from the negative to positive terminal, or opposite the conventional direction of the current flow between the terminals. Additional evidence came from the observation first made by Thomas Edison that a hot current-carrying filament in a vacuum emits negative charge. Apparently some of the electrons in the wire receive enough energy to escape the attraction of the positive lattice and quite literally boil off. When such a filament is sealed into an evacuated glass tube with another electrode maintained at a positive potential relative to the filament, then the negative charge from the filament is accelerated toward the positive anode (Figure 9.41a). A small amount of residual gas in the tube will glow under these circumstances, delineating the paths of the negative charge, or "cathode rays" streaming from the cathode. Likewise, a zinc sulfide screen at the anode will phosphoresce at the charge's point of impact, defining the termination of the accelerated charge (and, incidentally, providing the basis for the modern cathode ray tube).

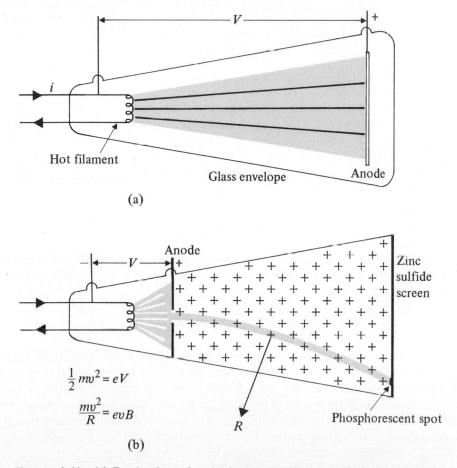

FIGURE 9.41 (a) Production of cathode rays by electrons "boiled" off a hot filament and accelerated by a positive potential difference. The sealed glass tube contains a small amount of residual gas which glows along the electron paths. (b) Measurement of the charge to mass ratio of the electrons. The magnetic field is perpendicular to the page and inward.

Since cathode rays define the path of moving negative charge they are deflected by a magnetic field. A bar magnet held near a cathode ray tube moves the phosphorescent spot on the zinc sulfide screen in a direction characteristic of current flow along the axis of the tube, suggesting that negatively charged rays consist of a great number of negatively charged masses. J. J. Thomson made the not unnatural assumption that each had a fundamental (then unmeasured) unit of charge, and that each was therefore a free electron. In 1897 he measured the charge to mass ratio of the so-called cathode ray particles and thus is credited with the discovery of the electron.

A method similar to his is illustrated in Figure 9.41b. The hypothesized electrons boil off a hot filament* and are accelerated by a positive potential difference V to an anode whose special construction permits them to pass through it and travel a reasonable distance in a region with no electric field before striking a zinc sulfide screen. If the initial velocity of the electrons at the filament is zero then they arrive at the anode with kinetic energy (Equation 8.17):

$$\tfrac{1}{2}Mv^2 = eV,$$

so

$$v = \sqrt{2(e/M)V},$$

where e is the charge of each of the hypothesized electrons.

After passing through the anode the speed of the "electrons" remains constant, with a phosphorescent spot on the zinc sulfide screen defining their termination point. The introduction of a magnetic field between the anode and screen and perpendicular to the path of the particles results in the deflection of the spot, a deflection related to the tube dimensions and the radius of curvature of the electrons in the field. The speed of the electrons may be written in terms of the field strength, the curvature of their trajectories, and their charge to mass ratio, by means of Equation 9.17:

$$v = \frac{e}{M}\,BR.$$

The elimination of v between the two derived equations gives e/M in terms of measurable fields and tube dimensions. The best modern value of the ratio, measured by a method analogous to Thomson's is:

$$\frac{e}{M} = -1.75886 \times 10^{11}\ \text{C/kg}.$$

Thomson's experiment shows that the charge to mass ratio of all the charged cathode ray particles is identical. If this were not so then each would be deflected through a different radius in the magnetic field and a diffuse glow rather than a small spot would appear on the screen. If the *masses* of the particles are also equal then their charges must also be the same, and we may assume that the particles are free electrons each bearing a fundamental, negative unit of charge. On this hypothesis neutral, macroscopic matter consists of a number of negatively charged electrons bound in some sort of positive, stationary charge matrix.

---

* Actually Thomson's electrons were not derived from a hot filament but from the bombardment of a cathode with positive ions. Figure 9.38b illustrates a more modern method of measurement whose principle, however, is the same as Thomson's.

Thomson's crude model is a start toward a theory of the structure of matter. But his crucial assumption that cathode ray particles have equal mass, while reasonable, remains an assumption. His measurements show only that the ratio e/M is the same for all of them. Proof of *charge* quantization based on Thomson's experiments rests on the assumption of *mass* quantization. Between 1909 and 1911 R. A. Millikan carried out a series of measurements that proved charge quantization directly, and therefore (by inversion), Thomson's mass quantization as well. In so doing he also made the first precise measurement of the fundamental unit of charge. His method is illustrated in Figure 9.42.

Oil sprayed into the region between the plates of a parallel plate capacitor forms into droplets which pick up some of the free charge that always exists in small density in the atmosphere. A uniform electric field **E** across the gap accelerates the charged droplets upward. If the magnitude of the field is adjustable a particular drop of mass M and charge q may be suspended motionless provided its upward, electrostatic acceleration exactly balances the downward acceleration due to gravity. For that particular value of the field,

$$Mg = qE.$$

If the drop's net charge is due to the fact that it has picked up n free electrons each with charge e, then

$$ne = q = \left(\frac{M}{E}\right)g. \tag{9.30}$$

On the basis of this assumed quantization the fundamental unit of charge can be determined in terms of M, e, and g, *if* the number of electrons on the observed drop is known. A sufficiently small drop will have very few free electrons, 3, 4, 8, or 10, for instance. If observations are made on a great many drops, the ratio M/E for each will be an integral multiple of some least common divisor. According to Equation 9.30, that least common divisor is the basic unit e, and the integral multiplier for each drop the number of free electrons it has picked up. Finding such a least common divisor for all the drops is the key to the proof that charge is quantized. If it were not, then Equation 9.30 would not be applicable, and no common divisor could be found among the data. An unambiguous proof of quantization, as well as a precise determination of e, requires that the number of charges on each drop be small. Otherwise, inevitable experimental uncertainties make it difficult to determine a least common denominator, or indeed even to prove that one exists.

Millikan worked two years on his definitive experiments and proved quantization beyond a doubt. The best modern measurement of the magnitude of the electron's charge is

$$e = 1.60208 \times 10^{-19} \text{ C},$$

FIGURE 9.42 Essential features of Millikan's apparatus for measuring the charge of the electron.

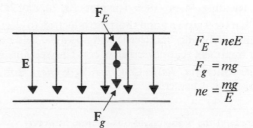

a value equal to the magnitude of the charge on the proton, although of course, the signs of the charges are equal. Significantly, Millikan's value is in agreement with measurements based on electrolysis, emphasizing the fundamental role played by the electron in the basic structure of matter.

Because the motionless suspension of a small drop between gravitational and electric fields is difficult, the Millikan method actually differs in detail but not in principle from the simple scheme suggested above. The motion of a drop between the capacitor plates depends upon its mass, its charge, and the field magnitude. If E is adjusted so that the drop moves slowly upward then its velocity can be accurately determined by observing the length of time it requires to cover a specific distance. By reversing the field direction but keeping its magnitude constant, the drop is made to move downward with a velocity that depends upon the sum of the electrostatic and gravitational forces rather than their differences. A number of experimental uncertainties are canceled out by comparing the two velocities, and the drop may be followed for a great number of round trips thus permitting a more precise determination of its average velocity.

In the absence of an electric field across the capacitor gap a drop will not fall with acceleration g; air resistance to its small mass makes it behave like a man with a parachute and drift downward at a constant velocity whose magnitude depends on its mass. Measurement of the downward velocity in the absence of an electric field is an excellent way to determine the mass of a drop, a quantity that is necessary if Equation 9.30 is used to find its net charge.

One may argue that the combined results of Thomson and Millikan do not exclude the possibility that a smaller, nonzero charge *could* exist. But none has been found.* Despite the great variation among the masses of the elementary particles, ranging from zero to more than twice the proton mass, only three charge states have ever been observed: $+e, 0, -e$. This statement is, of course, limited to the experimental accuracy with which the magnitudes of charges have been measured, and is subject to change if better measurements were to reveal small variations among the charges. That possibility cannot be excluded a priori. However, a very precise comparison of the electron and proton charges made as late as 1959 indicated that the magnitude of the proton and electron charge are equal within the limits of presently attainable experimental accuracy.

SUGGESTIONS FOR FURTHER READING ▶▶▶

Among the many introductory texts treating current electricity and magnetism are:

GERALD HOLTON AND DUANE H. D. ROLLER, *Foundations of Modern Physical Science*, Addison-Wesley Publishing Co., Inc., Reading, Mass., 1958, Chapter 28.

JAY OREAR, *Fundamental Physics*, John Wiley and Sons, Inc., New York, 1961, Chapters 8 and 9.

K. R. ATKINS, *Physics*, John Wiley and Sons, Inc., New York, 1965, Chapter 17.

ARNOLD B. ARONS, *Development of Concepts of Physics*, Addison-Wesley Publishing Co., Inc., Reading, Mass., 1965, Chapters 23, 24, and 25.

Orear's Chapter 9 gives a good short introduction to electrical applications; Aron's Chapter 23 deals qualitatively with the electric and magnetic field concepts simultaneously. An excellent advanced treatment that nevertheless contains sections suitable for beginning students is:

CHALMER SHERWIN, *Basic Concepts of Physics*, Holt, Rinehart, and Winston, Inc., New York, 1961, Chapter 5.

---

* See footnote at the beginning of this section, however.

DAVID L. ANDERSON, *The Discovery of the Electron*, Momentum Series, D. Van Nostrand and Co., Princeton, N.J, 1964.

Anderson presents a very readable account of the subject. There are two paperback books available which explore the subject of magnetism considerably further than in this chapter:

FRANCIS BITTER, *Magnets: The Education of a Physicist*, Science Study Series, Doubleday and Co., Garden City, N.Y, 1959.

L. W. McKEEHAN, *Magnets*, Momentum Series, D. Van Nostrand and Co., Princeton, N.J.

There have also been several articles on magnetism in the *Scientific American* in recent years.

S. K. RUNCORN, "The Earth's Magnetism," September, 1955, p. 152.

H. P. FURTH, "Strong Magnetic Fields," February, 1958, p. 28.

H. H. KOLM AND A. J. FREEMAN, "Intense Magnetic Fields", April, 1965, p. 66.

A. COX, "Reversals of the Earth's Magnetic Field," February, 1967, p. 44.

W. B. SAMPSON, "Advances in Superconducting Magnets," March, 1967, p. 114.

PROBLEMS AND EXERCISES ▲▲▲

9.1. (a) A tight bundle of ten, 5-m long insulated copper wires, each carrying an equal current, produces a 10^{-3} Wb/m² field at a perpendicular distance 0.1 m from their centers. What current does each of them carry?
(b) Sketch their field configuration.
(c) If the resistance of each of the wires is 1 ohm, what total power is dissipated in creating the field?

9.2. (a) What is the magnitude and direction of the field produced by the wires in Problem 9.1 at twice the perpendicular distance from the bundle of wires?
(b) How does the field at 0.1 m change if the current in each wire doubles? How does the power dissipated change?
(c) How is the field affected by a reversal of the current in all the wires? By a reversal of the current in half of them?

9.3. You have a very long insulated wire of length l and a battery with a fixed EMF and negligible internal resistance. Will the field at a given perpendicular distance from the wire be greater if you cut it in half, twist the pieces together, and connect them in parallel across the battery or if you simply connect the two ends of the long wire to the terminals? Answer the question by giving a quantitative comparison. What is the ratio of the power dissipated in the two cases?

9.4. A $\frac{1}{2}$-m long, 0.06-m diameter solenoid is evenly wound with 6000 turns of copper wire and carries a current of 1 A.

(a) What is the magnetic field at its center?
(b) What current would a 1-m long wire carry if it produced a field of the same magnitude at the same distance (0.03 m)?
(c) What is the ratio of the power dissipated in the two cases? (Assume the cross sections of the wires are equal.)

9.5. A dipole of length l, mass M, and dipole moment μ, oriented parallel to a constant magnetic field B, is rotated through a small angle θ, then released.

(a) Show that the dipole describes simple harmonic rotational oscillations about the direction of the field.
(b) What is its period?

Assume that half the mass of the dipole is concentrated at each pole.

[HINT: First show that the force on each pole is proportional to θ if θ is small.]

9.6. A long, straight wire parallel to the x-axis carrying a 5 A current which flows in the positive x-direction is placed in a 0.6 Wb/m² constant magnetic field which is in the positive y-direction.

(a) Calculate the magnitude of the force on the wire per unit length and make a sketch indicating its direction.

How is the force on the wire affected if each of the following changes is made one at a time, with all other conditions remaining as given above:

(b) The field direction is reversed.
(c) The current is reversed.
(d) The angle between the field direction and the x-axis is changed to 30°.
(e) The field direction is made parallel to the x-axis.

9.7. Two horizontal 1-m wires carrying currents of equal magnitude are oriented so that one of the wires is located 0.05 m directly above the other. The lower wire lies on a table top. However, the upper one is suspended by the magnetic force upon it.

(a) If the mass of each wire is 0.01 kg, what is the magnitude of the current flowing in each?
(b) Are the current directions the same or opposite?
(c) If, in part a, the wires were originally adjacent, how much work would the magnetic field have performed in lifting one wire 0.05 m above the other?

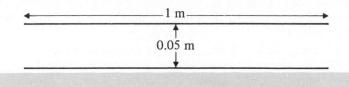

9.8. A sensitive device for measuring currents is shown in the sketch. The lower part of a rectangular loop, suspended in a magnetic field, constitutes one-half of a balance. A pan is suspended from the other half of the beam. With no current flowing, weights are added to the pan until its total weight balances that of the loop. The current is then turned on and more weights added until balance is again achieved.

(a) If the magnetic field strength is 0.1 Wb/m², and 5×10^{-3} kg must be added to the pan to achieve balance after the current is turned on, how much current flows in the loop? Assume the dimensions shown in the sketch.
(b) Why isn't the entire loop suspended in the field?

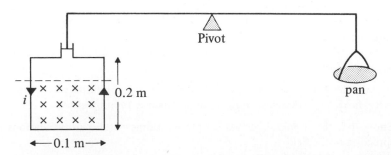

9.9. A rectangular loop of wire with dimensions 0.1×0.05 m carrying a 5 A current is in equilibrium in a constant 0.5 Wb/m² magnetic field. The forces are in the direction tending to expand the loop.

(a) Sketch the relative orientation of the loop and the field, showing the direction of current flow.

(b) What is the dipole moment of the loop (magnitude and direction)?

(c) How much work must be performed if the loop is rotated 180° about an axis bisecting the two short sides and perpendicular to them?

(d) How much work is performed in rotating the loop 180° about an axis along one of its diagonals?

9.10. (a) Suppose the material from which the loop in Problem 9.9 is constructed is somewhat elastic so that each dimension increases by 5% when the field is turned on (with the plane of the loop in equilibrium with the field). How much work would the field perform in stretching the loop?

(b) How would the loop behave if the field were suddenly turned off? Answer as completely as possible.

9.11. The kinetic energy of the electron in hydrogen in its normal state is about 4.4×10^{-18} J.

(a) Assuming the planetary model has some validity, calculate the corresponding orbital velocity of the electron. ($M_e = 9 \times 10^{-31}$ kg, charge $= -e = -1.6 \times 10^{-19}$ C.)

(b) The "radius" of the electron orbit in hydrogen is about 10^{-10} m. What is the magnetic moment corresponding to the circulating electron current?

(c) A hydrogen atom is placed in a 2.0 Wb/m² external magnetic field whose direction is 30° to the perpendicular to its orbit. How much work does the field perform in orienting the atom so that its perpendicular coincides with the field direction?

9.12. Use the data in Problem 9.11 to calculate the magnetic field created by the circulating electron at the center of the atom.

9.13. An ammeter with a 2-ohm internal resistance is connected in series with a battery and a 100-ohm resistance.

(a) What percentage error is made in measuring the current through the external resistor?

(b) What error would be made if the meter were connected in series with 1000 ohms?

9.14. A voltmeter with 10,000 ohms internal resistance is connected across a 100-ohm resistor in series with a battery. What percentage error is made in measuring the potential drop across the resistor? What error would be made in measuring the potential drop across a 1000-ohm resistor?

9.15. A particle with charge -2×10^{-6} C and mass 10^{-3} kg travels with velocity 10^5 m/sec in the positive x-direction in a constant magnetic field of strength 0.5 Wb/m² in the positive y-direction.

(a) What are the magnitude and direction of the instantaneous force on the particle? What are the magnitude and direction of its instantaneous acceleration?

(b) How will the force change if the direction of the particle's velocity is reversed?

(c) If the sign of the charge is reversed?

(d) If the direction of the field is inclined 30° to the y-axis?

9.16. A charge with magnitude $+10^{-6}$ C travels with velocity 2×10^0 m/sec in the positive x-direction in a constant 100 N/C electric field in the y-direction. A magnetic field in the region is adjusted until the particle travels in a straight line.

(a) What are the magnitude and direction of the magnetic field?

(b) What would be the net force on a -10^{-9} C particle in the same fields?

9.17. A particle with mass 10^{-3} kg and charge $+10^{-6}$ C travels with velocity 2×10^6 m/sec in the positive x-direction. What are the magnitude and direction of the magnetic field that exactly negates the gravitational force upon it?

9.18. An α-particle with kinetic energy 10^{-18} J, mass 6.4×10^{-27} kg, and charge $2e = 3.2 \times 10^{-19}$ C, traveling in the positive x-direction, enters a constant magnetic field of magnitude 10^{-2} Wb/m^2 in the positive z-direction.

(a) What is the radius of curvature of its trajectory? In what direction is it deflected?
(b) What is the radius of curvature of a proton of the same energy in the same field?
   ($M_p = 1.6 \times 10^{-27}$ kg, $q = e = 1.6 \times 10^{-19}$ C.)

9.19. A high-energy proton with momentum 3×10^{-18} kg-m/sec enters a bubble chamber and travels in a direction perpendicular to a constant 1.5 Wb/m^2 magnetic field. What is the magnitude of its radius of curvature?

9.20. Show that a magnetic field performs no work on a charged particle that is subject to no other forces. Is your answer consistent with the fact that work *is* performed on a current loop? Why?

9.21. A charged particle enters a constant magnetic field with its initial velocity vector inclined at an angle θ to the field. Show that its trajectory is a helix with radius

$$R = \frac{Mv \sin \theta}{qB} \qquad \text{and} \qquad \text{pitch} = \frac{2\pi Mv \sin \theta \cos \theta}{qB}.$$

9.22. A cyclotron, whose pole pieces are 1 m in diameter and produce a 1.0 Wb/m^2 uniform magnetic field, is designed to accelerate protons ($M_p = 1.6 \times 10^{-27}$ kg, $q = e = +1.6 \times 10^{-19}$ C).

(a) What must the frequency of the alternating potential across the "dees" be?
(b) What is the maximum energy attained?
(c) If the magnitude of the accelerating potential is 5×10^4 V, how many times does each proton cross the gap between the dees?

9.23. Design a cyclotron capable of accelerating deuterons (the nuclei of heavy hydrogen, $M = 3.2 \times 10^{-27}$ kg, $q = e = 1.6 \times 10^{-19}$ C) to 10^{-12} J, given these limitations: (1) a magnetic field no greater than 1.5 Wb/m^2, (2) pole pieces no greater than 1.0 m in radius, and (3) an alternating voltage of frequency no greater than 5×10^6/sec.

9.24. A 1-m wire parallel to the z-direction of a Cartesian coordinate system moves with velocity 100 m/sec in the positive x-direction in a 1.0 Wb/m^2 magnetic field in the positive y-direction.

(a) What is the magnitude of the EMF induced between its ends?
(b) If the wire forms part of a complete circuit with a total resistance of 5 ohms, what current flows? What is its direction?

9.25. An alternating current generator consists of a one-hundred turn loop of wire wound on a 0.1×0.2 m rectangular frame rotating in a 0.5 Wb/m^2 magnetic field at a frequency of 60 cycles/sec.

(a) What maximum EMF is generated?
(b) If the resistance of the loop is 100 ohms, what maximum current flows?
(c) What maximum power is dissipated in the loop?

9.26. Design an alternating current generator that can deliver 110 V at 60 cycles/sec. Restrict yourself to magnetic fields smaller than 1.0 Wb/m^2.

9.27 A long solenoid of diameter 0.10 m wound with 5000 turns of insulated copper wire is concentric with and encloses completely another solenoid with a 10-ohm resistance.

(a) If the current in the larger solenoid rises from 0 to 5 A in $\frac{1}{2}$ sec, what current is induced in the smaller one?

(b) What current is induced in the small solenoid if the current in the larger one rises from 0 to 1 A in 0.05 sec?

9.28. Find the magnitude and direction of the *total* force and the ratio of the magnetic to the electrostatic forces between two electrons (charge $= e = -1.6 \times 10^{-19}$ C) 0.01 m apart traveling with velocities 10^6 m/sec. 10^7 m/sec. 10^8 m/sec. At rest.

9.29. Electrons, boiled off a hot filament, are accelerated by a 1000-V positive potential difference then deflected by a constant magnetic field into a circular trajectory of radius 0.12 m. Using the charge to mass ratio given in the text, calculate the magnitude of the field.

The nature and properties of light

10

▲▲ 10.1 **Rectilinear propagation, reflection, refraction, and dispersion of light**

Since Newton's laws are concerned with the connection between the motion of particles resulting from the forces upon them, they are most readily applicable to physical processes that clearly involve particle motion. Therefore, it is not immediately obvious that a study of the nature and properties of light can be approached from the Newtonian viewpoint, for neither a readily apparent particle structure nor indeed any obvious motion at all is involved. Nevertheless, common experience does suggest that light, whatever it may be, interacts with matter. It is reflected by certain materials, transmitted (though refracted) by other types, absorbed by still others. Light is detected by its effects upon the retina of the eye or the chemicals suspended in the emulsion of photographic films. It is produced by the massive, material sun, by a current-carrying tungsten filament, or by an electrical discharge in a tube containing a small amount of residual gas. Indeed, these last examples suggest a possible connection between light and the electromagnetic interaction. If the production of light is connected in some way with the electromagnetic interaction, its reflection, refraction, absorption, and detection might well be connected in some fundamental way with the charge structure of matter. Therefore, it is tempting to seek an understanding of the nature and properties of light in terms of our general, developing picture of matter and its interactions, even if we must broaden or modify the basic Newtonian formulation to do so.

Our approach will be experimental. Starting with a few simple, common observations we shall reach some tentative conclusions about the nature of light. More refined observations will permit us to sharpen our ideas and actually lead us to try incorporating light into the Newtonian framework. However, more sophisticated investigations will reveal serious inconsistencies in all attempts at such a formulation and force us to reexamine the entire logical basis of Newtonian physics. Ultimately, this reexamination will lead us both to Einstein's special theory of relativity and to quantum mechanics, the two major modifications of Newtonian physics that have been made in this century, and give us a far more profound insight into the basic unity of the physical universe than classical physics could ever offer.

The simplest of these observations are all related to the gross interactions of light with matter: its reflection from polished metallic surfaces, its absorption by opaque objects, and its refraction (or bending) upon passage from one transparent medium to another with the dispersion (separation into the colors of the rainbow) that always accompanies such refraction.

In all of these interactions light behaves as if it were propagated from its source in straight lines. In fact, this property of rectilinear propagation is probably the simplest experimental conclusion one can reach regarding its nature (Figure 10.1). The light emerging from a small circular aperture cut in a piece of heavy black paper seems to come from an approximate point source. If this source is placed well behind a rectangular slit of moderate dimensions, say a few millimeters wide, we observe that all light originating at the source and passing through and beyond the slit is confined to the so-called "shadow region" which is bounded by the straight lines drawn tangent to the edges of the slit and intersecting at the source. We conclude that light is propagated in straight lines in all directions from a source and that those rays which pass through the slit continue to propagate in straight lines in the region beyond.

Rays of light may change their directions by means of two distinct types of interaction with matter: reflection and refraction. The angle of incidence of a ray on a reflecting

(a)

(b)

FIGURE 10.1 The rectilinear propagation of light. (a) Light from a source passing through an aperture of moderate dimensions appears to propagate as a bundle of rays. (b) Introduction of a second aperture produces an approximately parallel beam. (From *PSSC Physics*, D. C. Heath and Company, Boston, © 1965.)

surface is defined as the angle between the incoming ray and the perpendicular to the surface at the point of incidence, while the angle of reflection is the angle between the reflected ray and the same perpendicular. By observation these two angles are always equal (Figure 10.2a):

$$\theta_i = \theta_r. \tag{10.1}$$

When a ray of light in air passes into another transparent medium (say water or glass) it does not maintain its original direction but is bent toward the direction of the perpendicular to the surface. On reemerging into air it is bent away from the perpendicular (Figure 10.2b). As in the case of reflection, the angle of incidence is defined as the angle between the incoming ray in air and the perpendicular at the interface between the media, whereas the angle of refraction is the angle between the ray and the perpendicular in the refracting material. Regardless of the magnitude of the incoming angle, the ratio of the sines of the angles of incidence and refraction is a constant which is characteristic of the material and called its *index of refraction*:

$$\frac{\sin \theta_1}{\sin \theta_2} = n_2,$$

or

$$\sin \theta_1 = n_2 \sin \theta_2.$$

The experiment should more properly be performed with light passing from a vacuum into the second medium since, by definition, the vacuum has unit index of refraction. However, the indices for all gases are very close to unity—1.0003 for air at room temperature, for instance. Water has a refractive index 1.33; glasses differ in their indices according to their composition and range from about 1.4 to 1.75. In general, if a ray of light passes from a material of index n_1 into a material of index n_2, then

$$n_1 \sin \theta_1 = n_2 \sin \theta_2, \tag{10.2}$$

where the subscripts label the angles of incidence and refraction, respectively. According to Equation 10.2 rays are bent toward the perpendicular as they pass into a medium with larger refractive index and away from the perpendicular if the second medium has a lower index.

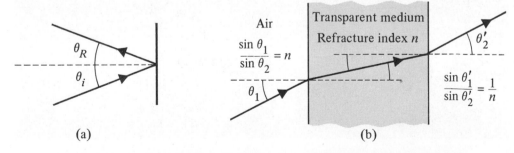

(a)   (b)

FIGURE 10.2   (a) The law of reflection: $\theta_i = \theta_R$. (b) The law of refraction. Light is bent at the interface between two transparent media. If a ray passes from a medium with refractive index n_1 into a medium with refractive index n_2 then $\sin \theta_1/\sin \theta_2 = n_2/n_1$. Since n is very nearly 1 for air, then in passing from air into another transparent medium, the angles of incidence and refraction are related by $\sin \theta_2/\sin \theta_1 = n_2/1 = n_2$.

Equations 10.1 and 10.2 are the basis of lens and mirror optics. Perpendiculars to a curved surface are not parallel to each other, but vary in direction according to their intersection points with the surface. Hence reflection or refraction angles depend upon the point at which a ray is incident. Properly shaped spherical lenses and mirrors are therefore able to focus large bundles of rays to a point.

Newton first observed the dispersion that always accompanies the refraction of white light. Figure 10.3 shows a narrow bundle of parallel rays of white light incident upon a glass prism. The emergent light consists of a divergent, multicolored beam ranging over

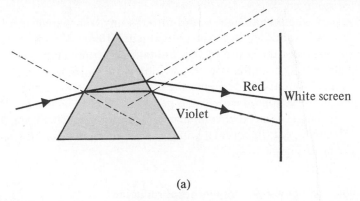

(a)

(b)

FIGURE 10.3 (a) Diagram showing the refraction and dispersion of white light by a prism. The dashed lines are perpendicular to the entrance and exit faces. (b) Photograph of refraction and dispersion of several narrow beams of light entering a prism from the lower left. The two beams nearest the bottom are totally reflected from the second glass-air interface. (See Problem 10.3.) (Photograph from *PSSC Physics*, D. C. Heath and Co., Boston, © 1965.)

the entire spectrum from violet at one edge through blue, green, and yellow, to orange and finally red at the other. We can understand the phenomenon on the hypothesis that white light is a mixture of several colored components and that the index of refraction for a given material is slightly different for each. In most common materials the index for violet and blue light is greater than the index for red, while the index for yellow light has an intermediate value. (For example, the index of refraction in crown glass is 1.532 for blue light, 1.517 for yellow, and 1.512 for red). It follows from Equation 10.2 that the refraction angle for light passing from air into a transparent medium is usually greater for blue than for red light.

Dispersion occurs when white light passes through any transparent medium (such as the sheet of glass with parallel faces shown in Figure 10.4). However, the geometric form of a prism enhances the width of the resultant spectrum simply because the perpendiculars to its entrance and exit faces are not parallel. Since each component is refracted through a different angle on entering the prism and travels a different distance through the glass, its direction on emerging is parallel neither to its incident direction nor to the emergent direction of the other components (Figure 10.3). Therefore, the emergent, dispersed beam is divergent, in contrast with the broadened but parallel emergent beam from the glass plate in Figure 10.4.

▲▲ 10.2 Visible and nonvisible components of radiation

As we have noted, the dispersion of white light is understandable on the assumption that it is really a mixture of several components. By examining dispersion in more detail we shall be led to the conclusion that the light from an incandescent source such as a carbon arc, a tungsten filament, or the sun is accompanied by components that have virtually the same properties as the visible radiation except for the fact that they cannot be detected by the human eye.

Figure 10.5 shows four wedge spectrograms, photographs of a calibrated grid which is illuminated by white light dispersed by a specially constructed prism. (The grid occupies the position of the screen in Figure 10.3a.) Dispersion is in the horizontal direction so that violet light falls in a band extended from about 38 to 41 or 42, yellow is centered about 60, red extends from the low 70's to about 78.* The vertical scale is proportional

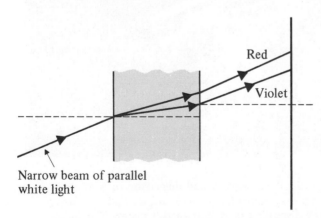

FIGURE 10.4 Refraction and dispersion by a glass sheet with plane, parallel faces.

---

*These numbers are proportional to the wavelengths associated with each component. Thus 56 implies 5.6×10^{-7} m, etc. (See Chapter 13.)

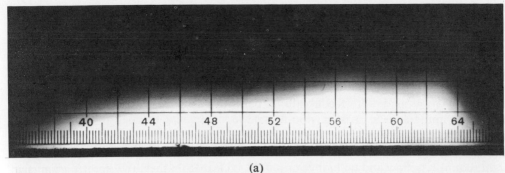

(a)

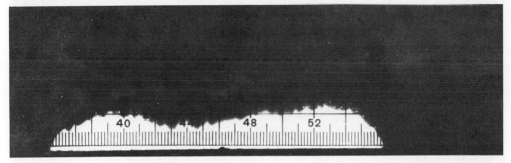

(b)

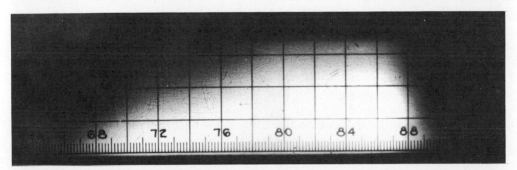

(c)

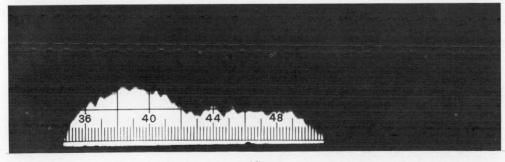

(d)

FIGURE 10.5   Wedge spectrograms made with (a) Panchromatic film (Kodak Plus X sheet film). (b) Orthochromatic film. (c) High speed infrared film. (d) Blue sensitive film. (Courtesy of the Eastman Kodak Company.)

to the sensitivity of the film used to photograph the grid. Thus the spectrograms automatically plot film sensitivity as a function of color.

If the illuminated grid were seen by a person with average vision he would conclude that the illuminated portion extends from about 38 to 78, thus defining the sensitivity of the average human eye. However, it is clear from the four spectrograms that a given type of film "sees" in a way that is different both from other types and from human beings. Figure 10.5a was made with Kodak Plus-X panchromatic film, a type frequently used by amateur photographers. It is obviously able to detect violet, blue, green, and yellow light, but cuts off somewhere in the region where orange merges into red. Figure 10.5b is a photograph made with orthochromatic film which "sees" violet, blue, and green light, but little yellow and no orange or red. It is clear from these two spectrograms that the extent of an observed spectrum depends on the means used to observe it. Since the human eye is sensitive to colors that neither the panchromatic nor the orthochromatic film can detect, we might suspect that, conversely, white light might be accompanied by components that neither the eye *nor* the panchromatic and orthochromatic film can detect, but which could be detected by using a different technique.

Figure 10.5c, taken with high speed infrared film, shows that this supposition is correct, for it indicates a sensitivity far beyond the limits of human detection (about 78). This is the first indication we have had that the radiation from a source of white light contains nonvisible as well as visible components. Those beyond the red end of the visible spectrum are called infrared (below red). The limit "seen" by the film in Figure 10.5c does not represent the upper limit of these components. Rather, it represents the limit of the film's ability to "see." In addition, the glass of the prism is opaque to rays that are well beyond the red. But the detected spectrum may be extended still farther by using a rock salt prism and nonphotographic detection methods. As we shall see in a later chapter these infrared components manifest themselves as heat when they interact with matter.

Finally, Figure 10.5d is a photograph made with a type of blue-sensitive film commonly used for copying line drawings. As its name implies, its sensitivity does not extend beyond the blue regions of the spectrum. However, it reveals the existence of components *below* those that the human eye can detect (about 38). These are called ultraviolet components (below violet). Ordinary glass becomes opaque at about the limit shown. But a quartz prism used with special film would show that the spectrum extends beyond the cutoff shown in Figure 10.5d.

Light has been defined in terms of the visible components of a dispersion spectrum. But since both infrared and ultraviolet radiation are also dispersed by a prism and also recorded on film of some type we conclude that the differences between the way we sense ultraviolet, infrared, and visible components have to do with the way the nerve endings in the retinas of our eyes are constructed or with the type of film in our cameras. In other words, there seems to be no qualitative difference between the way the visible and nonvisible components are propagated and dispersed. As we shall learn in this and the succeeding chapters there is also no qualitative difference between the production of the two types of components or in the way they interact with matter. Therefore, when we seek to answer the question, "What is light?" it seems clear that our study must also include infrared and ultraviolet radiation, and indeed any other yet unnamed types of components that are experimentally related to light. Therefore, let us tentatively define *light* in terms of any component radiated from a source that can be dispersed by a prism and recorded on some type of film. As we shall see presently, that definition will have to be broadened as we extend our knowledge of the spectrum beyond the two limits shown in Figures 10.5c and 10.5d.

▲▲ 10.3 The photoelectric effect and the photon concept

We now seek some way to assign a fundamental, quantitative meaning to the idea of color. A tentative assignment might be made in terms of the indices of refraction of some standard material. For example, crown glass has index 1.532 for blue light, 1.517 for yellow, and 1.512 for red. Indices of refraction for ultraviolet components transmitted by crown glass are greater than 1.532, and for the infrared, less than 1.512. Thus the identification with a refractive index permits a natural extrapolation to nonvisible "colors." However, it is unsatisfactory for at least two reasons. First, no material is transparent over the entire spectrum from far ultraviolet to far infrared. Second, and more important, the identification of color with the refractive properties of matter cannot tell us anything about the basic nature of light since we do not know why the interaction of light of a particular color with glass of a particular composition manifests itself as a particular index of refraction.

The most satisfactory way to characterize color is in terms of energy. This characterization has the added advantage of providing a link with the system of Newtonian mechanics developed in the preceding chapters. Energy is defined as the ability to do work, therefore, energy may be attributed to light if and only if we can justify the hypothesis that light does work.

Photographic film consists of certain light-sensitive chemical compounds suspended in a transparent base. Chemical reactions are induced when light is incident upon these compounds, reactions which are intensified when the film is developed. In Chapters 14 and 16 we shall consider chemical reaction mechanisms in more detail. For the present it is sufficient to state that all such reactions involve atomic rearrangements accompanied by changes in the internal energy of the molecules involved. Therefore, since light induces chemical reactions in photographic film let us make the tentative hypothesis that the propagation of light involves the propagation of energy, and that the absorption of light by matter is to be understood in terms of some sort of energy transfer mechanism. In order to make a more quantitative statement about the basis of photochemical processes we would have to have more details on the specific reactions involved. However, if the identification of light with energy is consistent, the transfer mechanism should also be manifest in its other interactions with matter.

In the *photoelectric effect* light incident upon a metallic surface causes the ejection of electrons from the metal. Figure 10.6 shows a simple means of observing the effect. A clean piece of metal (zinc or magnesium, for example) is placed in contact with a positively charged electroscope. When white light from a carbon arc is incident upon the metal the leaves of the electroscope converge, indicating that their net positive charge is decreasing. This would occur if electrons were being ejected from the metal. Now normally an electron remains bound within a metal so that its total energy relative to the surface must be negative; if ejected it has kinetic energy greater than zero. Since the electroscope leaves converge only when light is incident upon the metal we conclude that the light itself must be the source of the additional energy the bound electrons require to escape.

If a piece of opaque material is interposed between the light source and metal the electroscope leaves stop converging, an observation that is not surprising. However, the leaves also stop converging if a transparent glass plate is interposed, and this is unexpected in view of our conclusion that it is the light incident upon the metal which leads to the ejection of the electrons (Figure 10.6b). We must conclude that not all components of white light are effective in inducing the photoelectric process, and, in fact, those that *are* effective must be among the nonvisible components absorbed by the glass. This

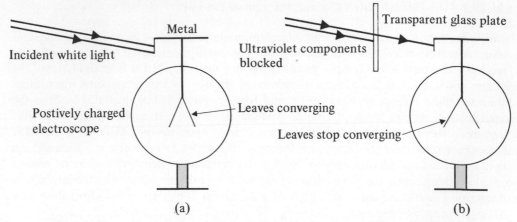

FIGURE 10.6 Demonstration of the photoelectric effect on zinc or magnesium. (a) White light incident on the metallic surface in contact with a positively charged electroscope causes its leaves to converge, indicating that their net charge is decreasing. (b) A transparent glass plate interposed in the beam of light causes the leaves to stop converging. Since ordinary glass does not transmit ultraviolet radiation, this suggests that these are the components responsible for the effect.

conclusion is confirmed by observing that the leaves *do* converge if the ordinary glass plate between source and metal is replaced by a plate of transparent, fused quartz. Since quartz transmits ultraviolet components while ordinary glass does not, we conclude that it is the ultraviolet components which are able to induce the photoelectric effect in common metals such as copper and zinc.

Figure 10.7 is a schematic diagram of an apparatus used by R. A. Millikan in his systematic investigations of the photoelectric effect in 1916. Light incident upon one of

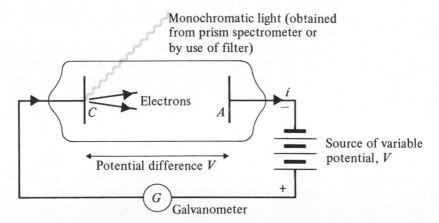

FIGURE 10.7 Millikan's apparatus for studying the photoelectric effect. Monochromatic light incident upon the electrode C causes the emission of electrons. When the negative potential difference between the electrodes is just sufficient to stop all electrons before they reach A then the potential energy of these electrons at A must be smaller than eV, and hence their kinetic energy at C also smaller than eV.

a pair of metallic electrodes (C) results in the ejection of electrons, some of which travel to the other electrode (A) and thence flow through a current-measuring meter such as a sensitive galvanometer placed in an external circuit connecting the electrodes. If there is a negative potential difference V between A and C, then an electron that leaves C with kinetic energy less than eV (e the charge on the electron) cannot reach A and register in the external circuit. Therefore, a measurement of the current in the circuit as a function of the retarding potential between the electrodes measures the relative number of electrons ejected from C as a function of their kinetic energy upon ejection. The electrodes are sealed in an evacuated, transparent quartz envelope to inhibit corrosion of the metallic surfaces by the atmosphere and to prevent the electrons from losing energy by collisions with air molecules. An arrangement of prisms and/or filters placed outside the tube can be used to insure that the light incident upon C is of but one color (i.e., is monochromatic).

Measurements are made by observing the galvanometer current as a function of the retarding potential when light of a particular color falls upon the photocathode, C. To be explicit, let the incident light be well in the ultraviolet region of the spectrum and let the photocathode material be copper. The current in the external circuit decreases as the potential difference between the electrodes is increased. At some particular retarding potential, V_1, the current ceases to flow entirely, remaining zero for all higher potential differences. It follows that no electron leaves C with kinetic energy greater than eV_1, and we conclude that this energy is related to the maximum energy an electron can absorb from the light incident upon the photocathode.

If the experiment is repeated using light of the same color but of a higher intensity, then at any given setting of potential difference between the electrodes, the number of electrons reacing the anode per second will be greater than with the weaker source, but the value of the potential at which the current goes to zero remains V_1 as before. *The maximum energy that a single electron can absorb from the incident beam does not depend on the intensity of the incident light.* This is a most significant conclusion, for it suggests that light consists of discrete, energy-carrying packets or quanta called *photons*, and permits us to think of the photoelectric effect in terms of the absorption of these photons by the bound electrons in the metal. The *total* kinetic energy ejected from C per second is equal to the product of the kinetic energy of a single electron by the number of electrons ejected. Therefore, the observed increase in the *number* of electrons reaching A as the incident intensity increases implies that the *number* of photons in a beam of light increases with the intensity of the light. *If* the maximum energy of a single electron also increased with the intensity of the incident light we might conclude that an electron could absorb any amount of energy whatsoever from the beam. But as this is not the case the photon representation is inescapable.

As we have suggested, the electrons within a metal must all have negative potential energies relative to a free electron at the surface. Otherwise they would not be bound. (See Section 7.5 for a discussion of negative potential energy wells.) It is reasonable to suppose that the negative energy of a bound electron, which is equal in magnitude to the energy required to free itself from the metal, should vary with its depth in the metal and be greatest for electrons near the surface (Figure 10.8a) When a bound electron within a metal absorbs a photon with energy numerically greater than its binding energy it is able to free itself.* The kinetic energy of the emerging electron is the difference between

---

* The binding energy is here defined as a positive quantity and hence is the negative of the electron energy on the usual scale for which the zero represents a free electron at rest.

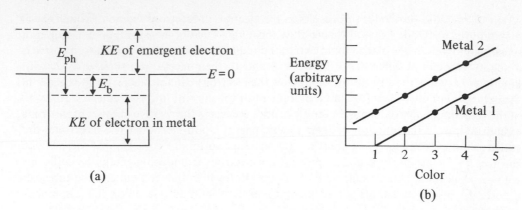

(a)

(b)

FIGURE 10.8   (a) Energy diagram for the photoelectric effect. Electrons bound in the metal have negative total energies relative to a free electron with zero velocity at the surface. If E_b is the energy that must be supplied to an electron to free it from the well then an electron that absorbs a photon with energy E_{ph} emerges with kinetic energy $E_{ph} - E_b$. (Since E_b, the binding energy, is the energy required to free an electron it is therefore the negative of the total electron energy in the metal.) (b) The kinetic energy of electrons emerging from two metals as a function of the color of the light incident upon them. The color scale is calibrated using metal 1 in such a way that the emergent electron energy for color 3 is twice the emergent electron energy for color 2, the electron energy for color 4 twice that for color 3, etc. Electron energies are then measured for the same colors incident upon metal 2. The fact that the lines for the two metals are parallel confirms the Einstein relation $KE = E_{ph} - E_b$ which is represented by part a.

the energy of the absorbed photon and the electron's binding energy. If we assume light of a particular color consists of photons all of which carry the same energy, then the differences in the kinetic energies of the electrons leaving a metal reflect the differences in electron binding energies, the electrons with the maximum kinetic energy being those that had the minimum (binding) energy in the metal. Let E_{ph} be the energy of an incident photon and E_b the minimum binding energy of an electron in the metal. Then on the supposition that color is to be identified solely with photon energy and that the energy conservation principle is valid for the photon absorption process, the maximum kinetic energy of an emergent electron is

$$KE = E_{ph} - E_b. \tag{10.3}$$

This is the essence of Einstein's theory of the photoelectric effect, first proposed in 1905. It can be tested by changing the color of the light incident upon the electrode C in Figure 10.8a, and repeating the measurement of current vs potential difference. If the new color chosen is still in the ultraviolet but closer to the visible spectrum, the cut-off potential, V_1, and thus the maximum electron energy, will be smaller than before. Assuming the validity of Equation 10.3, a lower photon energy is thereby implied. The measurements could be repeated for colors still closer to the visible spectrum. Eventually a color is reached for which no electrons are emitted from the metal. According to Equation 10.3 the photon energy corresponding to this threshold color must be equal to the minimum electron binding energy in the metal. For copper this color is well in to the ultraviolet region and corresponds to a binding energy of 6.9×10^{-19} J.

A single set of observations of kinetic energy vs color does not verify completely the hypothesis that the property can be identified with photon energy. To test Equation 10.3 further the measurements must be repeated using other metals at the photocathode. Since in general metals should differ in their minimum electron binding energies, the maximum energy of the electrons ejected for a particular incident color will depend on the metal used as well as the color. However, Equation 10.3 and the hypothesis leading to it can be tested by comparing maximum kinetic energies from two metals at several different colors. Call the metals A and B and measure at the two colors, designated as 1 and 2. Then for metal A:

$$E_{ph}(1) = (KE)_{A_1} - E_b(A),$$
$$E_{ph}(2) = (KE)_{A_2} - E_b(A),$$

so that

$$E_{ph}(1) - E_{ph}(2) = (KE)_{A_1} - (KE)_{A_2}.$$

Now if photon energy completely determines the color of light, then also for metal B:

$$E_{ph}(1) - E_{ph}(2) = (KE)_{B_1} - (KE)_{B_2},$$

or

$$(KE)_{B_1} - (KE)_{B_2} = (KE)_{A_1} - (KE)_{A_2},$$
$$\Delta KE_B = \Delta KE_A.$$

The *differences* between the maximum kinetic energies at the two colors must be equal for all metals. That is, if maximum kinetic energy is plotted against some arbitrary color scale (for example, a scale based on indices of refraction in quartz) the graphs for all metals should be parallel straight lines (Figure 10.8b). This turns out to be the case. Therefore, we may summarize our experimentally based conclusions as follows:

1. Light of a particular color consists of discrete, energy carrying entities called *photons*, all of which have the same energy.
2. Photons of ultraviolet light have higher energies than photons of visible light, while photons of infrared light have lower energies. In the visible region photons of violet light have the highest energies, photons of red light the lowest energies.
3. The *total* energy in a beam of light is the product of the number of photons times their individual energies. Therefore, the number of photons in a beam increases with the intensity of the light. However, electrons in a metal absorb individual photons completely. An electron *cannot* absorb a fraction of a photon.

Because photon energies, electron binding energies, indeed all of the energies that characterize atomic and nuclear processes are microscopic compared with the energies that characterize falling bodies and automobiles, for instance, it is convenient to introduce a new energy unit, the electron volt. One electron volt (eV) is defined as the energy gained by a particle bearing the fundamental charge e when it is accelerated by a potential difference of one volt. Since $e = 1.6 \times 10^{-19}$ C:

$$1 \text{ eV} = eV = 1.6 \times 10^{-19} \times 1 = 1.6 \times 10^{-19} \text{ J.} \tag{10.4}$$

Photon energies may be measured by using the photoelectric effect. Those at the extreme blue end of the visible spectrum have energies on the order of 3.1 eV. The energy of photons in the yellow region are about 2.0 eV, while the energy at the extreme red end of the spectrum is about 1.6 eV. The minimum electron binding energy in copper is 4.30.

As most common metals also have binding energies of this order only ultraviolet photons result in the ejection of electrons from them. (For instance, the binding energies in magnesium and zinc are 3.46 and 3.74, respectively.) However, the alkali metals, sodium, potassium, and cesium, have binding energies ranging down to 2.0 eV. Therefore, electrons are ejected from these metals even for incident light in the visible region of the spectrum.

▲▲ 10.4 X-rays

In addition to suggesting that light can be represented in terms of photons, the photoelectric effect implies a further connection with the electromagnetic interaction, for some facet of this interaction presumably explains the ability of electrons to absorb photons.

Matter is composed of atoms each of which consists of negatively charged electrons bound to a positive nucleus primarily by the electrostatic force. We may think of these systems as having internal, electrical potential energies given in terms of the separations of their charged components, even as the potential energy of the sun and a planet varies with the separation of the two bodies (Section 7.6). Hence it is conceivable that atoms might be able to decrease their internal energies through internal, structural rearrangements, and that photons might be created to carry off the excess energy involved in such processes. Since the photon energies we have encountered are on the order of several electron volts we would also expect the energies characterizing atomic processes to be of this order.

Although the outlines of this conjecture (Chapters 16 and 17) are correct, at the moment it remains a conjecture. Still, the hypothesis that photons are created in electromagnetic interactions can be investigated by stopping a high-velocity electron beam in a piece of metal and looking for the emission of photons. Since the object of the experiment is to search for light emitted as a result of the bombardment of matter by electrons, the process studied is just the inverse of the photoelectric effect.

Figure 10.9 shows the apparatus involved. Electrons are "boiled off" a hot, current-

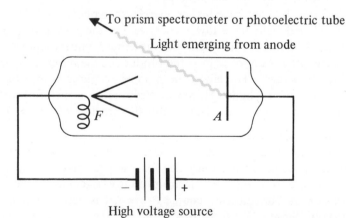

FIGURE 10.9   An x-ray tube. Electrons are boiled off a hot filament and accelerated by a potential difference of several thousand volts to the anode *A* where they stop and are observed to emit a broad spectrum of light. The characteristics of the spectrum may be studied by using a prism spectrometer or, for the higher energy photons, by permitting the light to fall upon the photocathode, *C*, of the Millikan photoelectric tube (Figure 10.7).

carrying filament (F) and accelerated to the metallic anode (A) by a positive potential difference, V. Both electrodes are sealed inside a thin, evacuated quartz envelope. (The tube is very similar in design to the one shown in Figure 9.41 used to measure the charge to mass ratio of the electron.) Upon reaching the anode the electrons interact with its atoms, transfer their kinetic energies to them, and eventually come to rest. If the number of electrons emitted by the filament is sufficiently high and the potential difference between the electrodes on the order of a few thousand volts, the anode becomes hot and glows, suggesting that most of the incident electron energy is transformed into thermal agitation of the anode atoms. Presumably most of the electrons do not stop suddenly at the anode surface, but penetrate a short distance, lose a small fraction of their energy in each interaction with an atom, and eventually come to rest or, more properly, have their speeds reduced to the speeds of the mobile conduction electrons in the metal.

A prism spectrometer used to analyze the components of the light emitted from the anode (Figure 10.9) shows that the photons range in energy from the infrared to the region in the ultraviolet at which the quartz ceases to be transparent. However, there is no reason to believe that this limit represents the maximum photon energy emitted at the anode, for those with higher energies would be absorbed by the quartz. If the potential difference between the electrodes is on the order of 10,000 V, a few of the 10,000 eV electrons should stop after making two or three large energy-loss interactions rather than after many interactions with losses on the order of a few eV. These interactions should result in the emission of photons with energies of several hundred or several thousand electron volts.

William Conrad Roentgen first observed these high energy components of "light" in 1895. Since he did not at first recognize their qualitative similarity with visible light, he called them x-rays, and so they are still designated. Even quartz is opaque to ultraviolet light whose photons have energies above about 10 eV. But thin quartz and ordinary glass become transparent once again for photons with energies in the several hundred eV region. In fact, these photons are able to penetrate thin pieces of any material (including human flesh), and their penetrating ability increases with their energy. Photographic film wrapped in black paper would be fogged if left in the vicinity of the x-ray tube shown in Figure 10.9.

The energy spectrum of the x-ray photons may be studied by replacing the prism spectrometer with a tube similar to the one used to study the photoelectric effect (Figure 10.7) and collimating the beam with a slit cut in a thick lead block. X-ray photons incident upon the photocathode of the tube should emit electrons whose kinetic energies can be measured by increasing the retarding potential of the tube to the cutoff point. As expected, the spectrum of these x-rays extends almost up to an energy eV, where V is the accelerating potential of the x-ray tube, and e the charge of the electron, that is, almost to the maximum energy of the accelerated electrons.

These experiments not only confirm the suggestion that light is produced by means of the electromagnetic interaction; they also extend the spectrum into the 10,000 electron-volt range. There is no reason to believe it could not be extended indefinitely, given the technology to accelerate electrons to sufficiently high energies. X-ray tubes such as the one shown in Figure 10.9 extend into the 100,000 volt region. The attainment of electron energies in the million electron volt (MeV) and billion electron volt (BeV) region requires the use of the particle acceleration techniques of nuclear physics. Components of the light obtained by stopping electrons of these energies are usually called γ-rays rather than x-rays and are important in nuclear and elementary particle research. Photons with energies up to 10 BeV (billion electron volts) are obtained from the 10 BeV electron synchrotron located at Cornell University, which operates on a variation of the cyclotron principle discussed in Section 9.4. The highest energy photons presently available are produced at the 20 BeV Stanford University linear accelerator (Section 21.2).

▲▲ 10.5 Compton scattering of x-rays by electrons

In 1923 A. H. Compton used an x-ray beam in a series of experiments demonstrating that photons carry momentum as well as energy, and that they may transfer part of their momentum to electrons and be scattered in a process analogous to the collision and subsequent scattering of billiard balls (Chapter 4).

A quantitative discussion of Compton scattering requires the use of special relativity and hence must be postponed to Chapter 11 (Section 11.11). But the essential features of the experiment are shown in Figure 10.10. If a photon of energy E_{ph} "collides" with an electron in matter, and if the incident photon carries momentum as well as energy, then energy and momentum conservation equations (generalized by the special theory of relativity) should relate the energy of the scattered photon and electron to their scattering angles and to the incident photon energy. Using these conservation equations it is shown in Chapter 11 that to a very good approximation the decrease ΔE in the photon energy resulting from such a collision is given as a function of its scattering angle θ and initial energy E by

$$\frac{\Delta E}{E} = -\frac{E}{M_e c^2}(1 - \cos \theta), \qquad (10.5)$$

where M_e is the mass of the electron and c the velocity of light. The term $M_e c^2$ is called the *rest energy** of the electron and is equal to 5.1×10^5 eV or 510 keV (1 keV $= 10^3$ eV).

The expected fractional energy loss for a 1 eV incident photon (in the visible region) scattered through 90° (cos $\theta = 0$) is

$$\frac{\Delta E}{E} = \frac{1}{5.1 \times 10^5} = 1.95 \times 10^{-6},$$

so that

$$\Delta E = 1 \times 1.95 \times 10^{-6} = 1.95 \times 10^{-6} \text{ eV}.$$

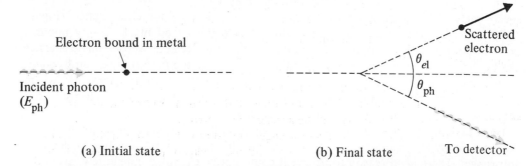

Electron bound in metal

Incident photon
(E_{ph})

Scattered electron

θ_{el}

θ_{ph}

(a) Initial state

(b) Final state

To detector

FIGURE 10.10 Kinematics of Compton scattering. A photon with energy E_{ph} is incident upon a bound electron. The photon scatters at an angle θ_{ph}. The amount of energy lost by the scattered photon is consistent with the assumption that the interaction may be regarded as a generalization of the billiard ball collisions of Chapter 4.

* Rest energy is discussed in Section 11.9.

While for a 5000 eV x-ray photon scattered through the same angle:

$$\frac{\Delta E}{E} = \frac{5 \times 10^3}{5.1 \times 10^5} = 9.7 \times 10^{-3},$$

$$\Delta E = 5 \times 10^3 \times 9.7 \times 10^{-3} = 49.7 \text{ eV.}$$

For a number of reasons, mostly experimental, it is impossible to produce a photon beam of one single well-defined energy. Rather, such a beam will have a spread of energies about the central, nominal value. In order to observe the expected energy shift resulting from Compton scattering, the spread in the incident photon energy must be smaller than the magnitude of the expected shift. A laser would be required to produce a beam of visible light with a spread of less than two parts per million, as required (see above example). But Compton worked in 1923, almost forty years before their invention, and so used x-ray photons in the keV or thousand eV region where much larger percentage charges are anticipated. He measured the energy losses of the scattered photons as functions of their scattering angles and incident energies. Since his results were in complete accord with Equation 10.4, he concluded that photons carry both energy and momentum and are able to interact with electrons in matter almost as if they were particles (Figure 10.11).

▲▲ 10.6 Diffraction and interference

It is tempting to conclude that photons *are* particles and attribute to them all the implied properties of baseballs and falling stones. But lacking further evidence it would be unwise to yield to that temptation, for photons have properties that are not shared by these macroscopic objects. We have spoken of their absorption and creation, for example,

FIGURE 10.11 Analysis of x-rays with 18×10^3 eV incident energy scattered by carbon at various angles to show the Compton effect. The apparatus detects those x-rays which pass through the carbon without scattering and therefore retain their incident energy, as well as those scattered through a particular angle. The separation between the incident and scattered peaks increases with increasing scattering angle, as predicted by the Compton effect equation. (Note that the energy scale *decreases* from the origin outward.)

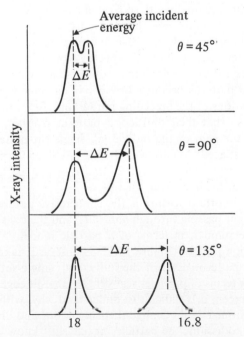

Energy in keV (thousand electron volts)

and of their dispersion by a prism. But the critical difference between photons and base-balls lies in their relation to common experience. We can see a baseball and record its trajectory by means of high-speed, multiple-exposure photography. But we deduce the existence of photons only as a result of the interaction of light with rather involved apparatus.

What, after all, *is* a particle? Our minds want a picture, and instinctively turn to grains of sand or salt in an effort to form one. But sand and salt have color, salt has taste. Surely these attributes are not shared by photons, nor are they necessary attributes of classical particles. Used in the sense of Chapters 2 to 9, a particle is an entity whose trajectory can be described at all times by a single, time-varying position vector. The term implies localization in space. To the extent that photons can be so described they qualify as classical particles. Surely a photon is localized in space when it is absorbed or scattered by an electron in the photoelectric or in the Compton effects. But can it be localized at other times?

Let us return to Figure 10.1 which shows a simple apparatus for demonstrating the rectilinear propagation of light. When photons pass through the slit, their locations in the direction parallel to the slit is uncertain because the slit is several millimeters wide. We can try to decrease the uncertainty by decreasing the width of the slit, but if we do, something quite unexpected occurs: the beam of light in the "shadow" region beyond the slit decreases as expected until the slit is about a millimeter wide. Thereupon it grows broader again, spills out of the "shadow," and continues to grow broader as the slit width decreases! The rectilinear assumption breaks down if the confining slit becomes too narrow, suggesting that light bends around the corners or is *diffracted* by the slit (Figure 10.12).

In order to understand better the implications of this result for the photon model consider the experimental arrangement shown in Figure 10.13. A beam of visible, mono-chromatic light from a small source is incident upon an opaque screen with two rectangular slits of equal width separated by a distance d. The light that passes through the slits falls upon a white screen located a distance S_0 from the pair of slits. When the slits are a few millimeters wide and several centimeters apart the pattern on the white screen is just the pattern that would be expected from the rectilinear propagation assumption: light from each slit is confined to its own "shadow region." As the slits are narrowed each of the two patterns becomes broader in agreement with the narrow, single-slit diffraction observations of the preceding paragraph. But if in addition the slits are moved closer together so that their diffraction patterns overlap, the resultant intensity pattern is not simply the sum of the individual, single-slit patterns but consists rather of a series of equally spaced, equally wide bands of color alternating with black bands. This characteristic phenomenon is called *interference* since light from one slit interferes with the pattern of the light from the other.

The important feature is the cooperative nature of the phenomenon, its dependence upon light passing through *both* slits, and the consequent difficulty experienced in trying to understand it in terms of a particle model. When either of the slits is blocked, a diffraction pattern (Figure 10.12) is observed; taken together the slits produce an interference pattern. Even if the individual, single-slit diffraction patterns could be understood in terms of particles scattering at the slit edges and producing a broad smear on the white screen, it is difficult to understand why, with both slits open, the particles passing through one should change their directions and arrive at different points on the screen. Are we to assume the particles at one slit "know" whether or not the other is open?

To be more explicit, let us concentrate upon one of the dark bands near the center of

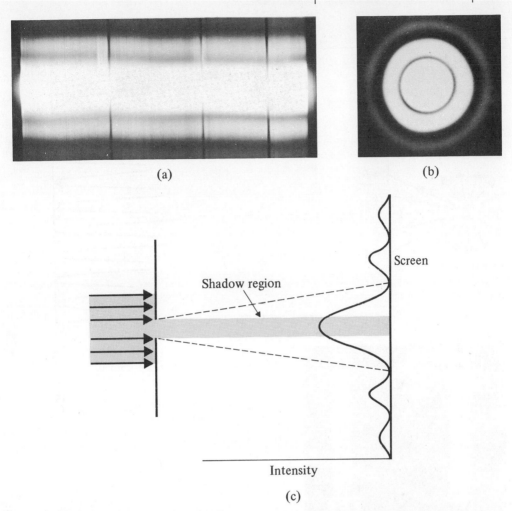

FIGURE 10.12 (a) The diffraction of light from a thin filament viewed through a narrow slit. Part c shows the experimental arrangement used to produce the pattern. (The horizontal black lines are supports holding the filament.) (b) The diffraction of light passing through a small circular hole. (c) Experimental arrangement for producing a diffraction pattern. (Photographs from *PSSC Physics*, D. C. Heath and Co., Boston, © 1965.)

the two-slit pattern (x_0 in Figure 10.13a). If we were to try explaining the pattern in terms of a particle model we would say that no particles reach the screen at the position of this band, hence no energy is transferred to the screen. But if either of the slits is closed, a nonzero intensity is observed at that point on the screen, indicating that energy arrives via either of the one-slit routes but *not* via the two-slit route. It is quite impossible to understand this result in terms of a classical particle model without attributing some exotic, teleological property to photons. For if one particle were to arrive at the same point on the screen from each slit the resultant intensity would be equal to the energy carried by the two particles, not zero!

Furthermore, the two-slit interference pattern violates the minimal localizability

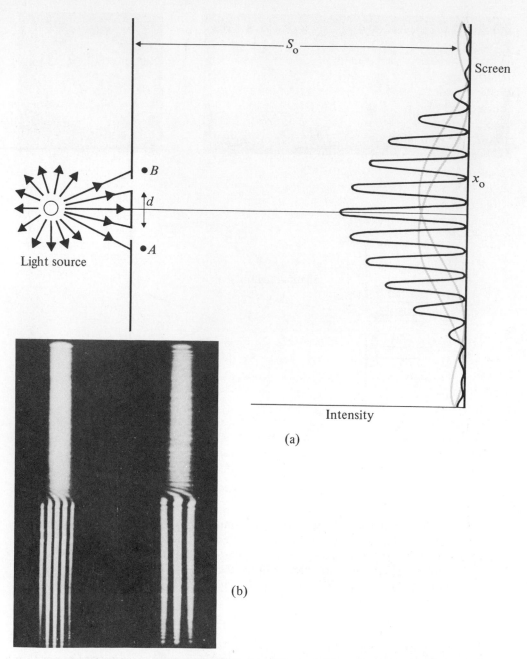

(a)

(b)

FIGURE 10.13   (a) Arrangement for observing the interference of light from two
narrow, closely spaced slits. The heavier curves sketch the intensity patterns produced if each of the two slits is alternately closed. (b) Interference and diffraction
compared. The fine lines in the lower part of each photograph are interference
lines produced by light passing through two slits. The slit separation is greater
in the photograph at the left. The broad bands above show diffraction from
single slits. (Photograph from Francis W. Sears and Mark W. Zemansky, *University Physics*, 2nd edition, Addison-Wesley Publishing Co., Inc., Reading,
Mass., © 1949, 1955.)

criterion demanded of all classical particles since there is no way to determine which of the two possible routes a photon from the source takes on its way to the screen. If we try to make such a determination by closing one slit so that the photons are certainly localized at the other, the interference pattern is replaced by a diffraction pattern. The attempt to localize the photons results in the disappearance of the very effect we seek to understand! Yet we cannot doubt that photons *do* pass through the slits for if we were to replace the white screen with a photoelectric detector we would reach all the conclusions of Section 10.3.

All attempts to explain interference in terms of photons having purely classical particle properties are doomed to failure. Therefore, let us adopt an experimental approach and see if the characteristics of the two-slit interference pattern can be related to the energy of the photons in the incident beam of light. If the interference pattern is studied as a function of the slit separation and the incident beam energy, the following conclusions are reached:

1. The widths of the characteristic light and dark interference bands and the spacing between the centers of adjacent bands *increase* as the slit separation *decreases*.
2. The widths of the bands and their spacing also increase when the incident photon energy decreases.

We can relate the widths of the bands to the slit separation in terms of a geometric construction (Figure 10.14a). Let d be the separation between the centers of the slits, labeled A and B, and let S_0 be the distance from the slits to the white screen. Call the central bright fringe 0, the succeeding bright fringes to the left of the central fringe $1, 2, 3, 4, \ldots, n$, and the distance from the central fringe to the nth bright fringe x_n. Finally, let $S_A(n)$ and $S_B(n)$ be the respective distances from slits A and B to fringe n, and the differences between the distances Δ_n. Since the fringes are equally spaced and S_0 is very much larger than d (S_0 is usually a few tenths of a meter while d is a few tenths of a millimeter), we can show that the differences between these Δ's for any pair of adjacent fringes are approximately equal.

Let us concentrate upon two such Δ's, labeled Δ_{n+1} and Δ_n, respectively. Then, referring to Figure 10.14b,

$$\tan \theta_{An} = \frac{x_n + d/2}{S_0},$$

$$\tan \theta_{Bn} = \frac{x_n - d/2}{S_0}.$$

Since the angles are very small we can equate θ to $\tan \theta$ in each case (see Appendix B to text). Also from Figure 10.14b,

$$S_A = \frac{S_0}{\cos \theta_{An}}, \qquad S_B = \frac{S_0}{\cos \theta_{Bn}}.$$

So:

$$\Delta_n = S_{An} - S_{Bn} = S_0 \left(\frac{\cos \theta_{Bn} - \cos \theta_{An}}{\cos \theta_{An} \cos \theta_{Bn}} \right).$$

Again because the angles are small the denominator of this expression is approximately

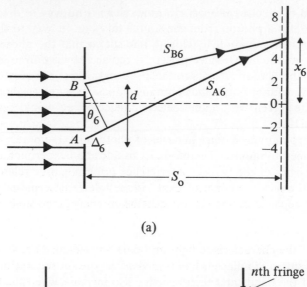

(a)

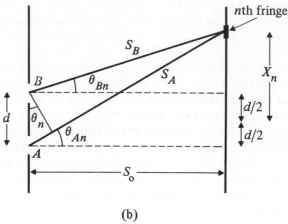

(b)

FIGURE 10.14 (a) Geometric construction for determining the positions of the maxima and minima of the double-slit interference pattern. (The construction is shown explicitly for the sixth maximum.) (b) Details of the construction.

equal to one, and we can express the numerator in terms of the approximate equations for $\cos \theta$ given in Appendix B:

$$\cos \theta_{An} = 1 - \frac{\theta_{An}^2}{2},$$

$$\cos \theta_{Bn} = 1 - \frac{\theta_{Bn}^2}{2}.$$

Therefore, to an excellent approximation:

$$\Delta_n = \frac{S_0}{2} (\theta_{An}^2 - \theta_{Bn}^2),$$

or, substituting expressions for the angles in terms of the distances:

$$\theta_{An}^2 - \theta_{Bn}^2 = \frac{1}{S_0^2}\left(x_n + \frac{d}{2}\right)^2 - \frac{1}{S_0^2}\left(x_n - \frac{d}{2}\right)^2$$

$$= \frac{2d}{S_0^2}\, x_n,$$

and

$$\Delta_n = \frac{d}{S_0}\, x_n.$$

We could derive a similar expression for Δ_{n+1}. Therefore:

$$\Delta_{n+1} - \Delta_n = \frac{d}{S_0}\,(x_{n+1} - x_n).$$

That is, the difference between two succeeding Δ's is proportional to the distance between their adjacent fringes. Since the fringes are equally spaced it follows that to the extent that the small angle approximation is valid the differences between all pairs of Δ's corresponding to adjacent fringes are equal. That is:

$$\Delta_1 - \Delta_0 = \Delta_2 - \Delta_1 = \Delta_3 - \Delta_2 = \Delta_4 - \Delta_3 = \cdots = \Delta_{n+1} - \Delta_n.$$

It is useful to assign a special symbol, λ (Greek *lambda*), to this constant difference:

$$\Delta_{n+1} - \Delta_n = \lambda. \tag{10.6a}$$

It also follows from the foregoing that the difference between the Δ's for two nonadjacent fringes is equal to the product of λ by the difference between the indices, n, of the pair. Thus for the fourth and first fringes,

$$\Delta_4 - \Delta_1 = 3\lambda,$$

or more generally,

$$\Delta_m - \Delta_n = (m - n)\lambda.$$

But since the distances from A and B to the central fringe is zero, then $\Delta_0 = 0$, and

$$\Delta_n = n\lambda. \tag{10.6b}$$

The magnitude of difference Δ_n may be related to the slit separation d by referring to Figure 10.14a. The distances x_n and S_0, and Δ_n and d are corresponding legs of similar triangles so that

$$\frac{\Delta_n}{d} = \frac{x_n}{S_0},$$

or

$$\Delta_n = d\left(\frac{x_n}{S_0}\right).$$

Substituting into Equation 10.6b,

$$d\left(\frac{x_n}{S_0}\right) = n\lambda,$$

or

$$x_n = n\lambda\left(\frac{S_0}{d}\right). \tag{10.7a}$$

where $n = 0, 1, 2, 3, \ldots$, which gives the position of the nth bright fringe on the screen. Since the centers of the dark fringes are midway between adjacent bright fringes, then by similar reasoning the positions of the dark fringes are given by

$$x_n = \left(n + \frac{1}{2}\right)\lambda\left(\frac{S_0}{d}\right), \tag{10.7b}$$

where $n = 0, 1, 2, \ldots$. Alternately, the equations may be written in terms of the angle θ_n in Figure 10.14a by using the relation $x_n/S_0 = \tan\theta_n$. Both equations show the inverse dependence of the width of the pattern on the slit separation since x_n increases with decreasing d.

The length λ which characterizes the interference pattern may be related to the energy of the incident photons by measuring the change in x_n as the color of the incident light is varied while d is kept constant. Since the pattern broadens with decreasing energy it follows that λ must vary inversely as the energy. A careful series of such measurements yields the result:

$$\lambda = \frac{1.23 \times 10^{-6}}{E_{\text{ph}}}\text{ m}, \tag{10.8}$$

if E_{ph} is expressed in electron-volts. (For E_{ph} in joules the value of the numerical constant is 1.8×10^{-25}.) This constant evidently is characteristic of the nature of light itself. As we shall ultimately learn it is the product of Planck's constant, h, the fundamental constant of quantum mechanics, and the velocity of light, c, the fundamental constant of relativity.

A numerical example will clarify these ideas. Suppose a monochromatic beam of yellow light whose photons have 2.0 eV energy is incident upon a double-slit apparatus in which $d = 0.5$ mm (5×10^{-4} m) and $S_0 = 0.8$ m. What is the spacing between successive bright fringes in the resultant interference pattern?

Referring to Equation 10.8:

$$\lambda = \frac{1.23 \times 10^{-6}}{2.0} = 6.15 \times 10^{-7}\text{ m}.$$

The distance between two successive bright fringes is

$$x_{n+1} - x_n = (n + 1)\lambda\left(\frac{S_0}{d}\right) - n\lambda\left(\frac{S_0}{d}\right),$$

$$= \lambda\left(\frac{S_0}{d}\right) = 6.15 \times 10^{-7} \times \left(\frac{8 \times 10^{-1}}{5 \times 10^{-4}}\right),$$

$$= 9.8 \times 10^{-4}\text{ m} = 0.98\text{ mm}.$$

If 20 eV photons were incident on the same pair of slits, then

$$\lambda = 6.15 \times 10^{-8}\text{ m},$$

and

$$x_{n+1} - x_n = 0.098\text{ mm}.$$

It is apparent that if a double-slit fringe pattern is to be observed then the slit separation cannot be more than a few thousand times the value of λ characteristic of the incident photons. A detailed analysis of diffraction by a single slit (Chapter 13) also yields the result that the spreading of light into the shadow region is negligible if the slit width is more than a few thousand times λ. *Hence we may think of λ as a characteristic number* *whose value relative to the dimensions of any experimental apparatus determines the degree to which the approximation that light travels in straight lines (Figure 10.7) is applicable in that instance.*

It is useful to use the *angstrom unit* (abbreviated Å) as a measure of λ in the visible, ultraviolet, and x-ray regions of the spectrum. By definition:

$$1 \text{ Å} = 10^{-10} \text{ m}. \tag{10.9}$$

The visible region of the spectrum extends from about 4000 to 8000 Å. Referring to our previous example, $\lambda = 6150$ Å for 2 eV photons. The x-ray region extends from a few tenths to tens of angstroms. For instance if $E_{ph} = 5000$ volts then (Equation 10.8):

$$\lambda = \frac{1.23 \times 10^{-6}}{5 \times 10^3} = 2.46 \times 10^{-10} \text{ m} = 2.46 \text{ Å}.$$

It is possible to begin a study of the nature of light by discussing interference by a double slit before the photoelectric and Compton effects. Had we done so we would probably have concluded initially that light can be represented completely in terms of classical waves (Chapter 13). We would then have designated λ as the *wavelength* of light and characterized color in terms of wavelength rather than energy. However, even as the classical particle model, which implies that light is transmitted in packets, cannot explain observed interference and diffraction effects, so the classical wave model, which carries the implication that the transmission of light is continuous, fails to explain the photoelectric effect. In fact, *all* attempts to reconcile the observed properties of light with classical ideas fail. A satisfactory comprehension requires a reformulation of the basic foundations of physics in terms of quantum mechanics. But before turning to quantum mechanics, it is necessary to examine the basic ideas of classical probability and statistics and their application to the molecular theory of matter. These topics constitute the subject matter of Chapter 15.

However, the present topic, light, has not yet been exhausted, nor all of its nonclassical features explored. We have concentrated upon its interaction with matter. Let us now consider its propagation, more specifically, its velocity of propagation.

▲▲ 10.7 The speed of light

Galileo made one of the first suggestions of a method to measure the speed of light. One member of a team, stationed on a hilltop, was to fire a cannon and simultaneously uncover a lantern. An observer on another, distant hilltop would have been instructed to record the time interval between the arrival of the sound from the cannon and light from a lantern, and to compute from this datum and the known separation of the hilltops the differences in the velocities of sound and light. After making several attempts in this vein, followers of Galileo could only conclude that the speed of light was far too great to be measured by this method.

Galileo's method failed because the time required for light to traverse the relatively short distance between hilltops is infinitesimal compared with the reaction time involved in manipulating cannons and lanterns. Lacking a precise measure of very short intervals, very long distances are required to obtain accurate measurements of high velocities. In 1650 Olaf Römer made the first successful measurement of the velocity of light by determining the time required for its propagation across the earth's orbit.

Since astronomical events are not observed until the light they produce is received by an earth-fixed telescope, the elapsed time between the event and its observation varies with the distance between the event and the earth. In addition, the time intervals between a series of events depend upon the velocity of the earth relative to the place where the events occur. Consider, for example, a light on Jupiter that flashed briefly once per minute, a signal that would require several minutes to reach the earth. If the velocity of the earth relative to Jupiter were zero, the *interval* between the reception of successive signals would still be one minute. But since the separation between the planets changes with time, then each successive light pulse would take slightly a longer time to travel to the earth if the distance were increasing and consequently the observed *interval* between pulses would be longer than the actual interval. Likewise, if the separation were decreasing, the observed interval would be shorter than the actual interval.

Lacking a periodic, flashing light on Jupiter, Römer substituted the period of revolution of one of its innermost satellites. According to Kepler's laws the satellite's period must be constant and can be measured by observing the elapsed time between its successive disappearances behind the planet. The relative velocity of Earth and Jupiter varies depending upon the respective orbital positions of the planets, the greatest time lag between event and reception occurring when the separation between the planets is a maximum, the smallest when it is a minimum (Figure 10.15). Observation of the satellite's period over the course of an earth year permits calculation of the time light requires to cross the earth's orbit. According to analogous contemporary measurements, the length of this interval is about seventeen minutes, or one thousand seconds, and the diameter of the earth's orbit about 186 million miles, or 3×10^{11} m. Therefore, the velocity of light in vacuum is about 3×10^8 m/sec. Since light requires but 10^{-8} sec to traverse three kilometers (roughly two miles) and human reaction times are measured in

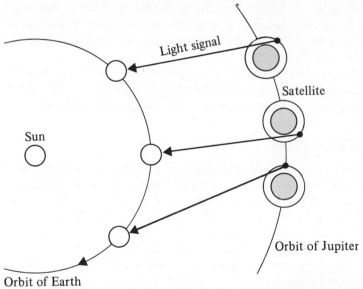

FIGURE 10.15 Römer's measurement of the speed of light. The successive disappearances of the innermost satellite of Jupiter may be regarded as a light signal transmitted to earth. Since in the figure the distance between the planets is increasing, so also is the time interval each successive signal requires to reach the earth. Thus the observed period of the satellite is longer than the actual period, determined by using Kepler's third law. Measurement of the discrepancy together with data on the relative velocities of earth and Jupiter can then be used to determine the speed of light.

tenths of seconds, it is small wonder that Galileo's suggested measurements were totally inconclusive.

In the late nineteenth and early twentieth centuries the American physicist A. A. Michelson devoted many years to a study of the propagation of light, perfecting a series of methods for making precise measurements of its velocity (Figure 10.16). Terrestrial measurements invariably use a system of mirrors to reflect light over a precisely determined path length and back again to its source, thus permitting accurate comparison of departure and arrival times. Figure 10.17 shows a rather simplified version of such a system. A mirror M_1 rotates at high speed about an axis perpendicular to the page. When the perpendicular to M_1 makes a 45° angle with light incident from the slit S_1 then, according to Equation 10.1, the mirror reflects the light in a direction perpendicular to its

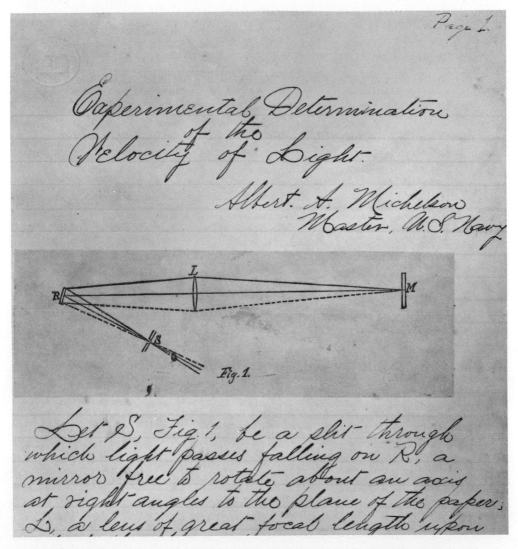

FIGURE 10.16 First page of the notebook kept by A. A. Michelson, then an instructor at the U.S. Naval Academy, during his first measurement of the speed of light in 1878. (Original notebook in the library of the U.S. Naval Observatory, Washington, D.C.)

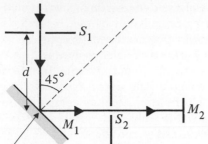

Rotation axis perpendicular
to the plane of the page.

(a)

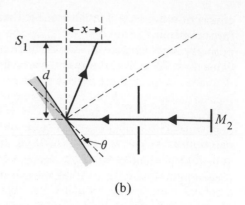

(b)

FIGURE 10.17 Schematic diagram of the rotating mirror measurement of the
velocity of light. In (a) light from slit S_1 is incident upon the rotating mirror M_1
at an angle of 45° to its perpendicular and is therefore reflected through the slit
S_2 to the stationary mirror M_2. By the time the light returns to M_1, however
(b) the latter has rotated through an angle θ so that it does not reflect the light
back through S_1 but rather to a point a distance x away. The distances x and d
yield the angle the mirror has rotated during the light's round trip time from M_1
to M_2 and back again; the velocity of light follows from this angle, the rotation
period of the mirror, and the distance from M_1 to M_2 and back.

original direction. The ray passes through the aperture S_2, and is reflected back to the
rotating mirror by the stationary mirror M_2. But if M_1 is rotating, its direction relative
to the returning light will not be 45°, and thus it will no longer reflect the light to slit S_1
but rather to some other position on the screen.

Let T be the rotational period of the mirror and θ the angle through which it rotates
during the time required for the light to make a round trip from M_1. Then

$$\frac{\theta}{2\pi} = \frac{t}{T},$$

or

$$t = T\left(\frac{\theta}{2\pi}\right).$$

The deflection angle θ may be calculated from a knowledge of x, the observed deflection
distance of the light on the screen:

$$\tan\left(\frac{\theta}{2}\right) = \frac{x}{d},$$

or, since θ will always be a small angle, $\theta \cong 2x/d$. Then if the round trip distance is
known, the velocity of light follows from the round trip time, t.

The symbol c is conventionally used to designate the velocity of light in vacuum. Its
most precise measured value is $c = 2.997925 \times 10^8$ m/sec, enormously larger than
any commonly experienced velocity. For instance, it is one million times greater than
the speed of sound in air, or ten thousand times the speed of the earth in its orbit about the
sun. Light travels the distance from the sun to the earth in eight minutes, from the moon
to the earth in one and one-quarter seconds, and a distance equal to the earth's 8000-mile
diameter in less than one-twentieth of a second. We have already noted an interesting

connection between the speed of light and the ratio of the electrostatic to the magnetic force constants (Equation 9.27). In the next chapter we shall see why the constant c is properly regarded as a fundamental constant of the physical universe. Its approximate value, 3×10^8 m/sec, is one of the very few numbers worth committing to memory.

10.8 The speed of light and the Newtonian principle of relativity

Because Newton's laws and the assumptions on which they are based lead to excellent descriptions of phenomena such as the motion of falling bodies, of planets and satellites, and of oscillating springs, there is a very natural temptation to believe that *all* possible phenomena can be represented in terms of visualizable scale models or, equivalently, that identical mathematical statements must necessarily imply precisely identical physical pictures. We have already touched upon the inconsistency of these assumptions in regard to the photoelectric effect. Photons carry far smaller energies than any macroscopic objects with which we have any direct experience. Therefore, we should not be surprised or alarmed by the fact that their behavior in interference experiments violates our intuitive notions about the way particles *should* behave.

Similarly, since nothing in our common experience gives us any feeling for a velocity of 3×10^8 m/sec, there is no reason to believe that we are justified in thinking about a beam of photons as having any analogy whatsoever with say a stream of bullets. In developing the velocity concept in Chapter 2 we made explicit use of the idea that we could measure the position of a moving body at any time we wished. But measurements of the velocity of light by the methods outlined in Section 10.7 imply no more than that a finite time interval elapses between the emission of a photon at a source and its absorption at a detector, and that the ratio of the distance between source and detector and that time interval is 3×10^8 m/sec. Attempts to detect a beam of light at intermediate points along its path result in at least its partial destruction. Hence, although it may be *useful* to represent the probable behavior of light between source and detector in terms of some mechanical model, no such model can be completely and directly justified by experiment in the same way that the model of an oscillating spring can, for instance.

In particular, it is useful to ask *why* the velocity of light in vacuum is 3×10^8 m/sec. The velocity of a rifle bullet depends upon the momentum imparted by the rifle; the velocity of sound in air depends in part upon the density of the air through which it propagates (Chapter 13). We know that photons are emitted when electrons are brought to rest in matter (Section 10.4). But since the velocity of a photon is independent of its energy, that velocity cannot depend upon the details by which the electrons are brought to rest. Therefore, the rifle-bullet analogy is not applicable. Neither can the velocity of light be understood in complete analogy with the velocity of sound, since photons are propagated in the vacuum, whereas sound is not.

During the 1860's, James Clerk Maxwell demonstrated mathematically that light is a fundamental manifestation of the electromagnetic interaction, and that it can be regarded as a mechanism of energy transfer between systems of accelerating charged particles (Sections 12.3–4, 13.9–10). He also showed that the velocity of light is intimately connected with the basic properties of the interaction itself, and therefore cannot depend upon such details as why a particular system of charges loses energy. We have already had an intimation of this fundamental connection in Chapter 9 where it was shown (Equation 9.27) that the measured velocity of light is related to the numerical values of the electrostatic and magnetic force constants by $c^2 = 1/\mu_0\epsilon_0$. We shall discuss the connection more fully in Chapters 12 and 13. It is, in fact, a connection that has been confirmed experimentally many times since 1870. However, it leads to a serious paradox vis-à-vis our intuition and our formulation of a basic symmetry principle. The law of inertia states that rest and uniform velocity may be regarded as dynamically equivalent, implying (see Section 6.12) that the concepts of absolute velocity and absolute rest have no validity in Newtonian mechanics. The symmetry principle based upon this equivalence is expressed by the Galilean transformations (Equations 6.13 and 6.14), and reflects the observationally-based conviction that no experiment performed on a jet traveling at a constant 600 mile/hr velocity relative to the earth can lead a passenger to the conclusion that he is in motion and the earth at rest. Falling bodies fall vertically relative to the jet, for instance, and therefore describe shallow parabolic trajectories relative to the earth. Pendula and springs behave in the same way relative to the jet as they do when at rest relative to an earth-fixed laboratory.

The classical velocity composition equations (Equation 6.15) are derived directly from the Galilean transformation equations, and are an important corollary statement of the symmetry principle: if observer B travels with constant velocity $\mathbf{u}$ relative to observer A, and if the x-axes of their respective coordinate systems are parallel, then the x-components of the velocities measured by the observers are related by Equation 6.15:

$$v_B = v_A - u,$$

or

$$v_A = v_B + u.$$

There is nothing in the structure of Newtonian dynamics that would lead us to believe that our conclusions relative to experiments on the 600 mile/hr jet are not equally valid relative to an interstellar rocket receding from the solar system with velocity $u = 2 \times 10^8$ m/sec. Since our investigations of the electric and magnetic interactions and also of the nature of light have been based upon the general Newtonian framework, we should be able to incorporate electrostatic and magnetic interactions into our statement of the symmetry principle, and conclude that no electrostatic or magnetic phenomenon can be used to detect a state of absolute motion or absolute rest.

However, in Section 9.6 we noted an apparent conflict between the symmetry principle and two interactions, for the magnitude of the total force between two charges seems to depend upon their velocities relative to an observer (Equation 9.29). In addition, Maxwell's conclusions imply that the speed of light in *vacuo* is equal to $1/\sqrt{\mu_0 \epsilon_0}$ (Equation 9.27), where the two constants are determined in the laboratory by measuring forces between charges and currents. Therefore, unless we abandon our symmetry principle for the interaction of charges, we are forced to conclude that an observer on an interstellar rocket traveling with velocity 2×10^8 m/sec relative to the solar system must measure the velocity of light as 3×10^8 m/sec *regardless of whether the source of that light is on the rocket or in the solar system*. Any other answer would imply that the relative strength of the electrostatic and magnetic forces between two charges depends upon the absolute motion of the observer, in violation of our assumed symmetry principle, a principle based upon the law of inertia itself. Yet if a projectile were fired from the earth past the rocket with velocity 3×10^8 m/sec, both our intuition as well as the velocity composition laws (Equations 6.15) lead to the conclusion that a passenger would measure its velocity as 10^8 m/sec. Why shouldn't he reach the same conclusion if he measured the velocity of light from the sun? But if he *did* conclude that light from the sun traveled past him with a reduced velocity he would also have to conclude that the laws of electricity and magnetism, the interaction between charged particles, differ in a basic way on the earth and in his vehicle. Hence, he would know he was in motion, in violation of the symmetry principle.

We must conclude that either the basic interaction between charges *does* distinguish between rest and constant velocity (i.e., that Equation 9.27 is valid), or that there is a fault in our intuition about relative velocities, and hence in the Galilean transformations which we have hitherto regarded as a correct mathematical expression of that symmetry. Indeed, we have had good reason to make the latter assumption, since it works so well with falling bodies and oscillating springs. Einstein chose to preserve the symmetry principle, and based his theory of relativity upon the assumption that the Galilean transformations are not necessarily applicable in all circumstances.

No one has experience with projectiles traveling at velocities approaching 3×10^8 m/sec. Hence, arguments based upon presumed analogies between photons and such high-velocity objects cannot be trusted. Suppose that the interstellar rocket itself were traveling at the velocity of light. In that case the projectile would appear to be at rest, and pursuing the analogy, so would the photons in light from the sun. We have experience with projectiles at rest. We have none at all with photons at rest. In fact, the idea makes no sense whatsoever. All of our knowledge of the properties of photons is experimental knowledge, and one of the fundamental experimental conclusions is that light travels with velocity equal to 3×10^8 m/sec in vacuo. It is useless to speculate about the properties light would have if its velocity in vacuo were variable because it simply is *not* variable.

The statement that the velocity of light is measured as 3×10^8 m/sec implies that a finite time interval elapses between the emission of light and its detection at a distant source; to state that this measured velocity is independent of the relative velocity of the source and the detector is to imply that the ratio of the distance light travels in a given time interval to the length of that time interval is independent of whether source and detector are moving relative to each other or not. The measurement of any velocity, material projectiles as well as light, is intimately connected with the measurement of time intervals and of distance. Einstein laid the basis for his special theory of relativity by pointing out some fundamental inconsistencies between the Newtonian concepts of space and time and a number of experimental results that had subsequently been noted, in particular, the relationship between the electrostatic and magnetic forces and their connection with the speed of light.

SUGGESTIONS FOR FURTHER READING ▲▲▲

For a more detailed account of geometric (ray) optics, including the principles of optical instruments, see:

FRANCIS W. SEARS AND MARK W. ZEMANSKY, *University Physics*, Addison-Wesley Publishing Co., Inc., Reading, Mass., 1955, Chapters 40–43.

PSSC College Physics, Raytheon Education Co., Boston, 1968, Chapter 10.

Most texts treat light from the wave viewpoint from the beginning. One that does not is:

PSSC College Physics, Raytheon Education Co., Boston, 1968, Chapter 5.

Another good introduction to the nature of light is:

ARNOLD B. ARONS, *Development of Concepts of Physics*, Addison-Wesley Publishing Co., Inc., Reading, Mass., 1965, Chapter 26.

A fascinating discussion of human vision is found in:

R. P. FEYNMAN, R. B. LEIGHTON, AND M. SANDS, *The Feynman Lectures on Physics*, Vol. 1, Addison-Wesley Publishing Co., Inc., Reading, Mass., 1963, Chapters 26 and 27.

Measurements of the speed of light are discussed in:

BERNARD JAFFE, *Michelson and the Speed of Light*, Science Study Series, Doubleday and Co., Garden City, N.Y., 1966.

J. H. RUSH, "The Speed of Light," *Scientific American*, August, 1955, p. 62.

The entire issue of *Scientific American* for September 1968 is devoted to the subject of light.

PROBLEMS AND EXERCISES* ▲▲▲

10.1. Three narrow beams of light are incident upon a plane glass surface at angles of 30°, 45°, and 60°, respectively, to its perpendicular. The refractive index of the glass is 1.5. With what angles to the perpendicular do the beams travel inside the glass?

10.2. A ray of light is incident upon one type of glass with index of refraction 1.5, another type with index 1.7, and water with index 1.33. Its angle of incidence in each case is 30°. Find its angle of refraction for each of the three cases.

10.3. When light passes from a medium with a large index of refraction to a medium with a smaller one, Snell's law (the refractive law) shows that it is bent *away* from the perpendicular to the interface between the media.

   For a particular angle of incidence, called the *critical angle*, the angle of refraction is 90°, indicating that the refracted ray is parallel to the interface. For all larger angles of incidence the sine of the refracted angle calculated by using Snell's law is greater than 1. Since the sine of a physical angle is never greater than 1 this indicates that refraction no longer occurs. Rather, the ray at the interface is reflected back into the original, high-index medium. This phenomenon is called *total reflection*.

   (a) Find the critical angle for glass with refractive index 1.4, glass with refractive index 1.7, and water with refractive index 1.33, by finding the angle of incidence in each case corresponding to a refractive angle of 90°.

   (b) Can total reflection occur as a ray of light passes into a medium of higher refractive index? Explain.

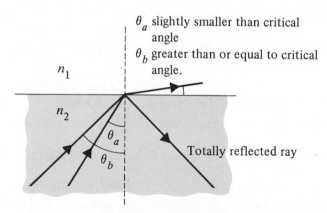

10.4. The refractive index of air relative to the vacuum is 1.003 at atmospheric pressure and normal temperatures, about 1.0015 at one-half atmospheric pressure. Estimate the angular deflection θ and the linear deflection δ (see sketch) of a ray of light from a star

---

* N.B.   Tables of trigonometric functions, required in number of problems, are available in any standard compilation of mathematical tables, *the Handbook of Chemistry and Physics*, for instance. Graphs of the functions appear in Appendix B.

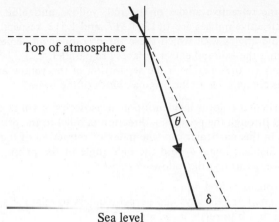

Top of atmosphere

Sea level

due to atmospheric diffraction by assuming the atmosphere is 30,000 m thick, that its pressure is constant and equal to one-half its sea-level value, and that the boundary between the atmosphere and the vacuum at the top is sharp. Let the angle of incidence be 45°. Repeat for a 60° angle of incidence. How might these estimates be improved?

10.5. A ray of white light is incident upon a 0.5 m thick glass plate with parallel faces at an angle 30° to the perpendicular. The indices of refraction for blue and red light are 1.532 and 1.512, repectively. Calculate:

(a) The refractive angles of the blue and red components at the first interface.
(b) Their linear separation on leaving the plate.

10.6. A ray of white light is incident at 60° to the perpendicular to one face of a prism whose cross section is an equilateral triangle (see sketch). The base of the prism is 0.05 m long and the point of incidence is halfway from base to apex measured along the face.

(a) What is the refractive angle at the interface for blue light (refractive index = 1.532)?
(b) What is the angle of incidence of the blue light at the second interface?
(c) What is the angle of refraction at the second interface?
(d) What is the total deviation angle for blue light passing through the prism?

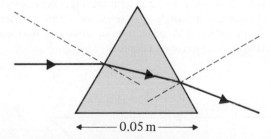

—— 0.05 m ——

10.7. Repeat Problem 10.6 for red light incident at 60° (refractive index = 1.512). Determine the approximate linear separation of the red and blue components as they leave the prism (assume equal path lengths in the prism) and after the rays have traveled 0.5 m farther in air.

N.B.: Preparation of a good sketch will facilitate the solution to Problems 10.6 and 10.7 since the geometry involved is somewhat complicated.

10.8. A beam of white light 2 mm wide is incident upon the surface of a thick piece of crown glass at an angle of 30°.

(a) Calculate the refractive angles of the red, yellow, and blue components of the beam. (Refractive indices are 1.512, 1.517, and 1.512, respectively.)

(b) Calculate the angles with which these three components emerge from the plate, assuming that the exit and entrance faces are parallel.

(c) How thick must the plate be if the separation of the yellow and red components upon exit is comparable to the original width of the beam?

10.9. If light of a particular color is incident upon an isosceles prism at one particular angle θ_1, it will travel through the prism in a direction parallel to the prism base and emerge with $\theta_2' = \theta_1$. In this particular case the index of refraction of the prism, n, is simply related to the incident angle θ_1 and the half-angle of the prism, $A/2$. Find this relationship by going through the following steps:

(a) Relate the angles θ_1 and θ_2.

(b) Use the geometry of the rays and perpendiculars to relate A and θ_2.

(c) Use parts a and b to relate θ_1, n, and $A/2$.

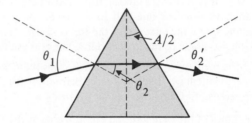

10.10. The accompanying diagram shows a ray of light incident upon a concave mirror of radius R. The ray is parallel to the mirror axis and incident at a distance y from the vertex. After reflection the ray intersects the mirror axis a distance f from the vertex. Use the diagram to show that the mirror focuses all such parallel rays to the same point regardless of their y-distance from the axis, provided these y-distances are small compared with the radius of curvature, R. Answers to each step appear below. If you cannot complete a particular step look at the answer to that step only.

(a) Write an expression for the distance y in terms of the angle ϕ and the distance $(R - x)$ and another in terms of the angle B and the distance $(f - x)$.

(b) Relate $(f - x)$ to $(R - x)$, B, and ϕ by eliminating y between your two expressions.

(c) Write an expression for the angle B in terms of ϕ and θ_R, then by first expressing both ϕ and θ_R in terms of θ_i convert your equation derived in part b into an equation relating $(f - x)$ to $(R - x)$ and θ_i.

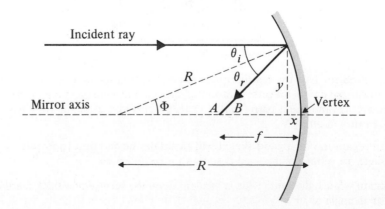

(d) If y is much smaller than R it follows that θ_i is also small. Use this assumption to simplify the relationship between $(f - x)$, $(R - x)$, and θ_i.

(e) If y is much smaller than R then so is x. If x is set equal to zero, your equation should now be $f = \frac{1}{2}R$. Why does this demonstrate the focal properties of the mirror for small y?

(f) Estimate the error made in your approximations for $y/R = 0.01$; for $y/R = 0.1$.

Answers to Problem 10.10

(a) $y = (f - x) \tan B$, $y = (R - x) \tan \phi$.

(b) Therefore, $(f - x) = (R - x) \tan \phi/\tan B$.

(c) $B = 180 - A$, but $A = 180 - (\phi + \theta_i)$. So $B = \phi + \theta_R$. However, $\theta_i = \phi$ and $\theta_i = \theta_R$. Therefore, $B = 2\theta_i$ and $(f - x) = (R - x) \tan \theta_i/\tan 2\theta_i$.

(d) If θ_i is small then $\tan \theta_i = \theta_i$ and $(f - x) = (R - x)/2$ (θ in radians).

(e) Since f is a constant independent of y (provided y is sufficiently small) then all parallel rays incident on the mirror and not too far from its axis are reflected back through the same point on the axis. This point, $f = R/2$, is called the *focal point* of the mirror.

10.11. (a) An electron is accelerated by a potential difference of 2500 eV. What energy does it gain in electron volts? In joules? How much does its velocity increase?

(b) Repeat part a for a proton accelerated by a 2500-volt potential difference. ($M_e = 9 \times 10^{-31}$ kg, $M_p = 1.6 \times 10^{-27}$ kg, $e = 1.6 \times 10^{-19}$ C.)

10.12. Protons are accelerated by a cyclotron whose 0.4 m radius pole pieces produce a constant 1.5 Wb/m² magnetic field. What is their maximum energy in electron volts? What potential difference could produce the same acceleration in a single stage?

10.13. The binding energy of the electron in a hydrogen atom is -13.6 eV. What is the binding energy in joules? What is the significance of the negative sign?

10.14. The human eye can just detect a beam of yellow light incident upon the retina with a power of 1.7×10^{-18} watts. How many photons per second fall on the retina in this case? (A photon of yellow light has about 2.0 eV energy.)

10.15. The intensity of a beam of light may be rated in terms of the energy it transfers to a surface area per unit time. For example, a new 100 watt incandescent bulb delivers 7.2×10^{-9} J/sec to a surface area of one square meter located a distance of one meter from the bulb. (The "wattage" of a bulb refers to its input power consumption and not to its output power.) The peak intensity of such a bulb falls in the yellow region of the spectrum.

(a) Estimate the number of photons per second falling on a one square meter surface area one meter from such a source.

(b) Suppose the surface is an alkali metal (sodium, potassium, cesium, lithium, rubidium) and that 5% of the incident photons are effective in causing the emission of electrons via the photoelectric effect. How many electrons are emitted per second? To what current does this correspond?

In parts a and b assume that the average energy of a photon in the beam is equal to the energy of a photon of yellow light.

10.16. (a) Ten electron-volt photons, 100 electron-volt photons, and 1000 electron-volt photons Compton scatter from electrons through 90°. What is the energy change in each case?

(b) Calculate the energy change for photons with the above incident energies scattered through 180°.

10.17. A beam of photons with nominal energy E_{ph} actually contains photons whose energies range from values 1% lower to 1% higher than the nominal value. When the photons in the beam Compton scatter from electrons through 90° the effect is barely discernible. That is, the energy shift due to scattering is equal to the uncertainty in the incident energy. What is the nominal, central energy of the incident beam?

10.18. Why isn't the binding energy of the electron in matter (usually on the order of a few eV) considered in the expression for the energy shift in Compton scattering?

[HINT: Consider the results of Problems 10.16 and 10.17.]

10.19. In the nuclear Compton effect, photons are scattered by the nuclei in matter rather than by the electrons. What incident photon energy is required if a $\frac{1}{2}\%$ energy shift is to be measured for 90° Compton scattering from hydrogen? A 5% shift?

10.20. To what wavelengths in meters and angstroms do the following photon energies correspond?

(a) 0.01 eV.
(b) 1.5 eV.
(c) 20 eV.
(d) 5000 eV.

10.21. What is the longest wavelength for which the photoelectric effect is observable on copper (binding energy 4.3 eV)? On sodium (binding energy 2.4 eV)? To what colors do these wavelengths correspond?

10.22. A two-slit interference apparatus may be used to assign the wavelengths 6×10^{-7} m and 4×10^{-7} m, respectively, to yellow and blue light.

What retarding potential must be applied between a cesium electrode C and the anode A of the Millikan apparatus in order to stop all photoelectrons produced on the cesium with incident blue light? With incident yellow light? With ultraviolet "light" of wavelength 3×10^{-7} m?

10.23. (a) What slit separation leads to an interference pattern for blue light ($\lambda = 4000$ Å) with the centers of adjacent bright fringes spaced 0.5 mm apart on a screen 1 m away?
(b) Given this slit separation, what fringe spacing will be observed with red light? ($\lambda = 7800$ Å.)
(c) What type of interference pattern would you expect if white light were incident upon the slits?

10.24. (a) What slit spacing is required to observe a 0.1 mm fringe separation for 1000 eV x-rays?
(b) In view of your answer to part a why can x-rays be regarded as "rays" for ordinary purposes? (Explain your interpretation of the word *ordinary*.)
(c) Typical nuclear dimensions are on the order of 10^{-15} m. What photon energy would lead to interference-type phenomena in their interaction with nuclei? (Think of the nucleus as a slit system.)

10.25. The width of a single-slit diffraction pattern upon a screen located a distance S_0 from a slit of width a may be calculated by assuming a relationship between the interference

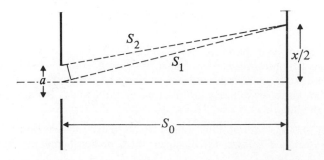

and the diffraction phenomena. Let $x/2$ be the half-width of the pattern upon the screen (i.e., the distance from the center of the pattern to the point on the screen where the intensity falls to zero), and think of the slit as being divided into a great number of bands or subslits of width Δs each of which acts as an interference slit. Go through the following steps in the derivation. If you have difficulty with a particular step refer to the answers up to and including that step only.

(a) If light from the uppermost subslit interferes completely destructively with light from the subslit just above the center of the main slit a how are the distances S_1 and S_2 related?

[HINT: Think of $x/2$ as the distance to the first interference minimum for the subslits.]

(b) Write an expression relating the difference between S_2 and S_1 to the slit width a, the pattern width x, and the slit to screen distance S_0.

(c) You should be able to convince yourself that each subslit in the upper half of the main slit pairs off with another subslit in the lower half to produce an interference minimum, and that for S_0 much greater than a the distances between the corresponding slits and the minimum is the same for each pair. With this in mind write an expression for the width of the pattern, x, in terms of the wavelength of the incident light, λ, a, and S_0.

(d) Suppose a parallel beam of yellow light (wavelength 6×10^{-7} m) is incident upon the slit. For what slit width a will the width of the "shadow region" be equal to the width of the diffraction pattern? That is, how small must the slit be to observe diffraction? (Let S_0 be 1 m.)

(e) What is the width of the diffraction pattern produced by a slit ten times narrower than the slit in part d?

Answers to Problem 10.25

(a) If the two subslits were actually slits in a double-slit interference apparatus; and if their first minimum were located at $x/2$, then

$$\Delta = S_2 - S_1 = \frac{\lambda}{2},$$

where λ is the wavelength of the incident light.

(b) By studying the similar triangles:

$$\frac{\Delta}{a/2} = \frac{x/2}{S_0}.$$

Therefore, $\Delta = ax/4S_0$.

(c) Since $ax/4S_0 = \lambda/2$, it follows that $x = 2\lambda(S_0/a)$.

(d) For parallel light incident upon the slit, the width of the shadow region is equal to the width of the slit itself. Then $x = a$ and we have

$$a = 2\lambda(S_0/a),$$

$$a = \sqrt{2\lambda S_0} = \sqrt{12 \times 10^{-7}} = 1.1 \times 10^{-3} \text{ m} \ (= 1.1 \text{ mm}).$$

(e) For $a = 1.1 \times 10^{-4}$ m, $x = 12 \times 10^{-7}/1.1 \times 10^{-4} = 1.1 \times 10^{-2}$ m $(= 1.1$ cm).

10.26. In a measurement of the speed of light made using the Michelson method (Section 10.7, Figure 10.17), the stationary mirror M_2 is placed 75 m away from the rotating mirror M_1. When the latter attains a certain rotational frequency f_0 the deflection of the returning light (x) on a screen 1 m away (d) is 5.3 mm $(5.3 \times 10^{-3}$ m).
What is the rotational frequency of M_1?

The special theory of relativity
11

▲▲ 11.1 Historical introduction

Our attempt to incorporate light into the framework of Newtonian mechanics has encountered two distinct classes of difficulty. First, the assumption that a beam of light consists of discrete, energy-carrying entities called *photons* that can be treated very much like classical particles is inconsistent with the double-slit interference experiment. The second difficulty arises from assumption that light is a fundamental manifestation of the interaction between charges and, thus, that its velocity in vacuum is constant. For we must choose between a presumed basic symmetry of the physical universe vis-à-vis observers moving with constant velocity relative to each other, and the Galilean transformations (Equations 6.13) which we have taken as a mathematical statement of that symmetry.

Historically, the second of these difficulties was encountered earlier than the first. Maxwell's brilliant demonstration of the connection between the interaction of charges and the propagation of light predates the introduction of the photon concept by four decades. He and his contemporaries had no doubt that light was propagated as a wave, for interference effects were well known whereas the photoelectric effect had not yet been discovered. They were more concerned with the apparent difficulty encountered in trying to imagine the propagation of a wave in a vacuum, and had invented a medium called the ether for that express purpose. The fact that light seemed to travel through that presumed medium with a very high speed independent of the motion of both source and observer engendered a considerable array of conceptual problems. Many of these did not disappear until Albert Einstein showed that Maxwell's synthesis had really disposed of all need for the ether.

Although the ether controversy is of considerable historical interest, it need not concern us here. In fact, for a time, the presumed problem of the ether masked the more fundamental paradox concerning the invariance of the velocity of light and the fundamental symmetry implicit in the law of inertia. Given the benefit of hindsight, the nature of that paradox is really much clearer to us now. Whatever the nature of light, whether classical particle, classical wave, or neither, we must reconcile two apparently contradictory pieces of experimental evidence. First, there is no doubt that since the speed of light is a manifestation of the fundamental interaction between charges, it has the value 3×10^8 m/sec (in vacuum) independent of the relative velocity of source and observer. Second, no

380

FIGURE 11.1   Albert Einstein, 1879–1955. (Photograph courtesy of the American Institute of Physics, Center for the History and Philosophy of Physics.)

experimental test can be devised that differentiates between rest and constant velocity motion. The reconciliation of these two facts requires that we modify certain features of the Newtonian system which are in fact less fundamental. We have assumed implicitly that intervals of length and time are invariant quantities, that a particular time interval or a particular length has the same meaning for all observers. By abandoning these seemingly obvious assumptions we shall not only preserve our symmetry principle, but at the same time broaden it to accommodate the velocity of light and the fundamental interaction between charges.

▲▲ 11.2 Noninvariance of moving time and length standards

In Section 6.12 we defined inertial systems as reference systems in which the law of inertia is valid, and showed that all systems moving with constant velocity relative to a given inertial system are also inertial systems. A reference system fixed relative to the earth is a reasonable approximation. Therefore, so is any system fixed relative to a ship, a train, a jet, or a rocket moving with constant velocity relative to the earth. Our symmetry principle requires the laws of physics to be equally valid in all such systems. We must try to reconcile that principle with the requirement that the velocity of light in vacuum is constant regardless of the relative velocity of source and detector. In other words, we *also* require that the velocity of light have the invariant magnitude $c = 3 \times 10^8$ m/sec in all inertial systems.

Figure 11.2a shows a light clock, an idealized arrangement for measuring time intervals in terms of the speed of light. A short pulse of light emitted at the lower mirror M_1 travels to the upper mirror M_2 and is reflected back again. If Δy is the distance between the mirrors, the time interval required for the round trip from M_1 to M_2 and back again is

$$t = \frac{2 \, \Delta y}{c}.$$

Now suppose two observers, A and B, are each at rest relative to identical light clocks, but that both observer B and his clock are traveling in the x-direction with velocity $+u$ relative to observer A. Let $\Delta t_A(a)$ be a time interval measured by observer A using clock

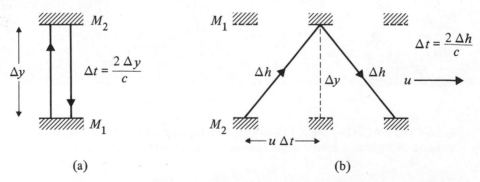

FIGURE 11.2   Measurement of a time interval with (a) a stationary light clock, and (b) a light clock moving with relative velocity $+u$ perpendicular to its length.

A, $\Delta t_A(b)$ a time interval measured by the same observer using clock B, etc. In view of the foregoing:

$$\Delta t_A(a) = \frac{2\,\Delta y}{c},$$

$$\Delta t_B(b) = \frac{2\,\Delta y}{c}.$$

That is, since the clocks are identical, each observer measures the same time interval for a round trip journey of a light ray using a clock relative to which he is at rest.

However, it does *not* follow that observer A measures the same time interval using clock B. He notes that that clock moves a distance $u\,\Delta t_A(b)$ while the light travels from M_1 to M_2 and back again. Further, as he sees it the light ray cannot travel along paths perpendicular to mirrors (Figure 11.2b), and during the round trip must have traveled a distance $2\,\Delta h$ rather than $2\,\Delta y$. Therefore, the time interval for a round trip measured by observer A using clock B which travels with constant speed $+u$ relative to him is

$$t_A(b) = \frac{2\,\Delta h}{c}.$$

If we want to retain the implicit Newtonian assumption that the length of a time interval measured by any clock has the same meaning for all observers, then $\Delta t_A(b) = \Delta t_B(b)$. Since Δh is greater than Δy, this can be true only if c is greater in system A in which observer A is at rest than in system B. On the other hand if we require that the speed of light must have the same magnitude in all inertial systems then the interval $\Delta t_A(b)$ measured with a moving clock must be greater than the interval $\Delta t_B(b)$, or $\Delta t_A(a)$, measured with clocks at rest.

Let us calculate the time interval measured by the moving clock as a function of its velocity relative to observer A, that is, $\Delta t_A(b)$. Referring to Figure 11.2b, the length of the round-trip light path seen by A is twice the length hypotenuse of the triangle whose legs have lengths $u\,\Delta t_A(b)/2$ and Δy. Therefore, from the Pythagorean theorem:

$$\Delta h^2 = \Delta y^2 + \left(\frac{u\,\Delta t_A(b)}{2}\right)^2;$$

also,

$$\Delta h = \frac{c\,\Delta t_A(b)}{2};$$

so

$$\left(\frac{c\,\Delta t_A(b)}{2}\right)^2 = \Delta y^2 + \left(\frac{u\,\Delta t_A(b)}{2}\right)^2.$$

Rearranging terms,

$$\Delta t_A^2(b)(c^2 - u^2) = 4\,\Delta y^2,$$

and solving for $\Delta t_A(b)$,

$$\Delta t_A(b) = \frac{2\,\Delta y}{c}\,\frac{1}{\sqrt{1 - u^2/c^2}}.$$

But $2\,\Delta y/c = \Delta t_B(b)$ and also $\Delta t_A(a)$, the times measured by the observers with their own, stationary clocks. Therefore:

$$\Delta t_A(b) = \frac{\Delta t_A(a)}{\sqrt{1 - u^2/c^2}}. \tag{11.1}$$

Since the denominator is never greater than unity the time required for the light to make one round trip between the mirrors in the moving clock (by definition the standard time interval measured with that clock) is greater than the time interval recorded with the stationary clock, and the discrepancy increases with increasing relative velocity. In other words, time seems stretched out or dilated in the moving system, a conclusion frequently summarized by the somewhat misleading statement that moving clocks slow down.

Since the basic symmetry principle we seek to preserve requires that *no* test can determine a state of absolute rest, it follows that a clock which is "moving" from the viewpoint of one observer is at rest from the viewpoint of another. If observers *A* and *B* have identical clocks in their chosen inertial systems and observer *A* compares a time interval measured with his clock to a time interval measured with *B*'s clock (the "moving" clock), he concludes that *B*'s clock runs more slowly than his own. Observer *B*, on the contrary, finds nothing wrong with his clock, for as far as he is concerned *A*'s clock is "moving," and therefore *A*'s clock must be the slow one!

In view of Equation 11.1 why was it ever assumed that a particular time interval *could* have the same meaning to observers in motion relative to each other? Simply because the time dilation required by the constancy of *c* is so small for velocities of the magnitude we commonly experience that it can usually be neglected. For example, the velocity of the earth in its orbit is about 3×10^4 m/sec, so $(u/c)^2 = 10^{-8}$, and $1/\sqrt{1 - u^2/c^2} = 1.000000005$. Thus a clock that measured exactly 1 sec in its own reference frame would seem to measure $1/\sqrt{1 - u^2/c^2} = 1.000000005$ sec if it moved with speed 3×10^4 m/sec relative to an observer. Even for $u = 0.1\ c$, Equation 11.1 states that a clock is but 0.5% slow.

Although the time dilation equation (Equation 11.1) predicts small effects even for very high speeds there is no doubt at all regarding its validity. For example, muons (designated μ) are elementary particles with mass about 207 electron masses, produced in the decay of π- and K-mesons. These latter particles are produced when very high energy protons interact with the protons and neutrons in the atoms of ordinary matter. Muons are themselves unstable, decaying on the average 2.2×10^{-6} sec after being produced. However, their lifetimes are one hundred times longer than the π- and K-meson lifetimes. (Chapters 22 and 23 contain a more detailed discussion of elementary particle processes.)

Muons were first observed in the 1930's as one component of the cosmic rays that continuously bombard the earth. Their production was ultimately traced in turn to the interaction between high energy, primary cosmic ray protons from outerspace and the gases in the upper atmosphere of the earth. Suppose that muons are produced at an altitude of 100,000 ft, or 3×10^4 m. If they are traveling near the speed of light they should reach sea level altitudes in about 10^{-4} sec. But as the mean lifetime of a muon is but 2.2×10^{-6} sec, almost none of them should survive for a sufficient time to be observed at sea level, *unless* we concede that their lifetimes, which may be used to measure time intervals and can therefore be regarded as clocks, are 2.2×10^6 sec only when the particles are at rest. Relative to clocks at rest on the earth the muon decay rate slows down. Therefore, the moving particles should have longer lifetimes than the same particles at rest. Given a sufficient velocity, many should reach sea level altitudes before decaying (Figure 11.3). Furthermore, if Equation 11.1 is applicable, the number surviving the trip should be an increasing function of velocity. Measurements on the decay rate of cosmic ray muons, as well as on the decay of shorter lived particles produced by high energy accelerators, leave no doubt that Equation 11.1 is a completely valid statement.

The comparison of time intervals in the foregoing example involves the propagation of

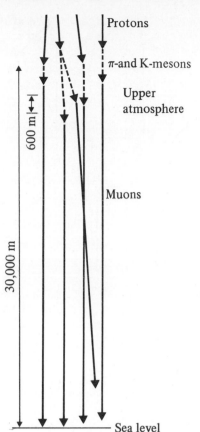

FIGURE 11.3 Time dilation and muon decay. Some of the muons produced as decay products of π- and K-mesons in the upper atmosphere are observed at sea level, indicating that they have traveled 30,000 m or so. Since the mean lifetime of a muon in its rest frame is 2×10^{-6} sec, they must decay at a slower rate when in motion relative to an earth-fixed observer. Otherwise they would travel only about 600 m, before decaying.

light rays over paths perpendicular to the direction of relative motion of two inertial systems. We were able to reconcile the constancy of c and the symmetry of physical laws relative to inertial systems by giving up the idea that time intervals have the same meaning in all such systems. It is worth asking whether we might also have achieved the required reconciliation by assuming a change in the length Δy_B of the moving system when measured by an observer at rest in system A. But in fact it is not difficult to show that a length *perpendicular* to the direction of its motion relative to an observer must appear equal both to that observer and another observer at rest relative to it.

Consider the experiment illustrated in Figure 11.4a. Two observers, A and B, are at rest at the bases of identical rods of length Δy oriented perpendicular to the direction of their relative motion. A small light pulser that can be actuated from the base is located on top of each rod. As before, observer B and his apparatus move with constant velocity $+u$ relative to A. The apparatus is arranged so that a short light pulse is emitted from the top of each rod when their bases are in coincidence. (Since it takes a finite time for the signal actuating the pulses to travel up the rods they must begin their journeys before the bases actually coincide.) Light from the pulsers then travels outward in all directions with constant speed.

Suppose that as a result of the relative motion observer A finds that the length of the moving rod, $\Delta y_A(b)$, has become shorter than his stationary rod, $\Delta y_A(a)$. (As before, $\Delta y_A(b)$ means the length of the rod at rest relative to B when measured by observer A, etc.) In that case light from his own rod would have traveled a greater distance than light

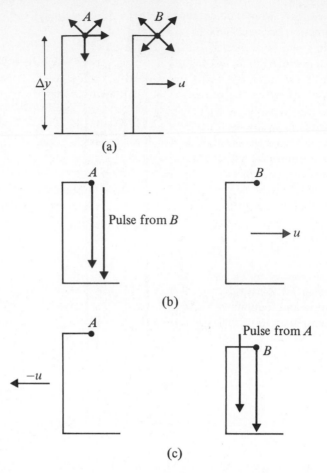

FIGURE 11.4 (a) At the moment two identical rods coincide, a light pulse is emitted from the top of each. (b) *If A* sees *B*'s rod contract,then the pulse from *B* arrives before his own pulse. (c) Since the arrival of a pulse is a physical event, then *B also* sees his own pulse arrive first and *also* concludes his own *stationary* rod contracts. Since this contradicts the invariance of physical laws with respect to inertial systems we conclude that neither of the rods contracts in a direction perpendicular to its motion.

from the moving rod in order to reach him. Therefore he would see the latter pulse first (Figure 11.4b). He would conclude that the pulse from the top of his rod must have traveled farther to reach the base of the moving rod than the pulse from the moving rod itself (Figure 11.4c),

What does observer *B* conclude about the order in which the pulses arrive? Since each arrival qualifies as a physical event he also sees the pulse from his own rod before the pulse from the rod at rest relative to *A*, and also concludes that his own rod is the shorter. But this conclusion is contrary to the requirement that physical laws must be the same in all inertial systems. From *B*'s point of view the rod at rest relative to observer *A* is in motion. Whereas *A* concludes that lengths *contract* in the direction perpendicular to their motion, *B* concludes that such lengths *expand*. Since the conclusions are contradictory the original assumption that *A* measures different lengths for the two rods must be wrong. Therefore, we conclude that a length is *not* changed by constant velocity motion in a direction *perpendicular* to its orientation.

However, there will be a change in a length moving *parallel* to itself. In Figure 11.5a observers A and B are again at rest relative to their respective light clocks which are now turned parallel to the common x-axis. We specify that the clocks are identical. Therefore, the distances between the mirrors as measured by the observer at rest relative to each clock must be the same, or $\Delta x_A(a) = \Delta x_B(b)$. As before, observer B and his apparatus move with constant velocity $+u$ along the x-axis relative to observer A.

Figure 11.5b shows a method observer B might use to measure the length of his apparatus. He is equipped with a stationary clock that has been synchronized to agree with his standard light clock. From his point of view a specified point on the x-axis of A's reference system moves in the negative direction with constant velocity $-u$. When the leading end of his apparatus coincides with that reference point he starts his clock, and stops it when the trailing edge coincides with the same point. If the time interval he measures is $\Delta t_B(b)$, then

$$\Delta x_B(b) = u\,\Delta t_B(b).$$

Meanwhile observer A measures the length of B's apparatus using the same procedure, starting *his* stationary clock when the leading edge coincides with the reference point and stopping it when the trailing edge goes by. But of course he sees B's apparatus moving

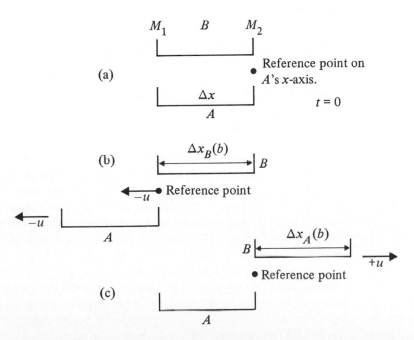

FIGURE 11.5   The Lorentz contraction. Observers A and B both determine the distance between M_1 and M_2 in system B by measuring the time intervals between the coincidence of the ends of the length with a reference point on the x-axis in system A. The relative velocity is parallel to the length being measured. From B's point of view (b) the reference point moves with velocity $-u$; from A's point of view the reference point is at rest and B in motion with relative velocity $+u$. Since the observers have already agreed to disagree about the measurement of time intervals, they also disagree about the measurement of the length Δx.

and the reference point at rest. Further, we know that to observer A the moving clock fixed relative to B runs more slowly than his own stationary clock. Hence A finds that a *shorter* interval elapses between the times the ends of the apparatus coincide than B found. Since A measures the length as $u\,\Delta t_A(b)$, he finds that the moving length *contracts*. Referring to Equation 11.1 the amount of contraction is specified by the factor $\sqrt{1 - u^2/c^2}$ which measures the discrepancy between the moving and fixed clocks. If $\Delta x_A(b)$ is the length of apparatus B as measured by A, then

$$\Delta x_A(b) = \Delta x_B(b)\sqrt{1 - u^2/c^2},$$

or, since $\Delta x_A(a) = \Delta x_B(b)$,

$$\Delta x_A(b) = \Delta x_A(a)\sqrt{1 - u^2/c^2}. \tag{11.2}$$

Like time dilation the contraction of a length in the direction of its motion, called the Lorentz contraction, has received undoubted experimental confirmation. In fact, we may analyze the muon decay problem in terms of Equation 11.2 rather than Equation 11.1, for the 30,000 m such a particle must travel is 30,000 m only when measured by an observer at rest on the earth (Figure 11.2). A muon traveling with virtually the velocity of light "sees" a much shorter length, and hence must traverse a much smaller distance in its 2.2×10^{-6} sec lifetime. If its velocity is sufficiently high it will make the journey with time to spare.

▶▶ 11.3 Einstein's definition of simultaneity

By assuming that neither time intervals nor lengths need have the same invariant meaning to observers in relative motion to each other we have made a start toward reconciling the constant speed of light in vacuum with the requirement that physical laws be identical in all inertial systems. In the late nineteenth century H. A. Lorentz arrived at similar conclusions, although he based his reasoning on the apparent existence of discrepancies between the observed interaction between charges and the requirement of symmetry vis-à-vis inertial systems similar to those we noted in Chapter 9. The undoubted experimental validity of Equations 11.1 and 11.2 as proved later by the existence of cosmic-ray muons at sea level, for example, suggests that the paradox presented by the requirement that c be constant in all inertial systems has been resolved, and that we can now examine the further consequences of time dilation and Lorentz contraction. Nonetheless, perhaps it is natural to feel somewhat unhappy about a reconciliation achieved by incorporating two seemingly arbitrary assumptions into the Newtonian system. Without doubting the validity of Equations 11.1 and 11.2, we might hope to base them upon more fundamental considerations.

Albert Einstein made his initial contribution to this problem in 1905, deriving the same results as Lorentz. However, he started from a much more basic point, examining first the fundamental meaning of time as used in physics. The insight he gained during his investigations led him to his special theory of relativity, which must be regarded as a full-scale modification of the Newtonian system. (The word *special* is used to denote the restriction of the theory to the description of events in inertial systems.)

The physical concept of time, as distinct from any abstract, philosophical overtones it may have, is really quite simple. In fact, the recognition of its true simplicity was one of Einstein's first contributions to our understanding. None of the equations we have encountered ask what time *is*. Rather, they ask for the time *at which* an event occurs, or for the time interval separating two or more events. Physical time is really nothing more than a convenient means for labeling and for ordering physical occurences. Then how do we assign times to events?

Let us refer to Einstein's formulation of the problem:

> If we wish to describe the *motion* of a material point, we give the values of its coordinates as a function of the time. Now we must bear carefully in mind that a mathematical description of this kind has no physical meaning unless we are quite clear as to what we understand by "time." We have to take into account that all our judgements in which time plays a part are always judgements of *simultaneous events*. If, for instance, I say, "That train arrives here at 7 o'clock," I mean something like this: "The pointing of the small hand of my watch to 7 and the arrival of the train are simultaneous events."*

The algebraic description of motion developed in Chapter 2 requires that the *time* at which a moving body is at a particular *point* in space be specified over the entire course of its motion. We can specify the position of a particle at any time in terms of three numbers, its *x*-, *y*-, and *z*-coordinates relative to some Cartesian system. We may regard a Cartesian system as an imaginary three-dimensional grid spanning all space. Suppose observers with identical clocks are stationed at each intersection point of the grid (Figure 11.6), and that a particle moves along some trajectory through the grid. Each observer is instructed to note the reading on his clock if and when the particle coincides with his grid point. Let us refer to each of these spatial coincidences between the particle and a grid point as an *event* (Section 2.2), and define the time reported by the observer at that point as the *local time* of the event. Then each event is described by a set of four correlated numbers: the spatial components of the appropriate grid point and the local time, and we obtain a complete description of a particle's motion by compiling all these sets of correlated spatial and temporal coincidences.

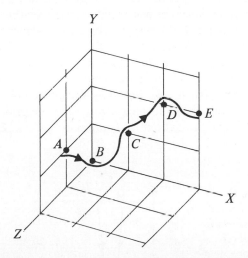

FIGURE 11.6 Description of a process (in this case the motion of a particle) in terms of a set of local events. Observers at the intersection points of a three-dimensional Cartesian grid are equipped with identical clocks. Each event consists of a report by a local observer giving the three Cartesian coordinates of his station and the time at which the particle coincides with it.

---

* A. Einstein, "On the Electrodynamics of Moving Bodies," trans. by W. Perrett and G. B. Jeffery for *The Principle of Relativity*, Dover Publications, Inc., New York, 1923, pp. 38–9.

In arriving at the final step of this procedure, the compilation of the reports of all observers, we have made the implicit assumption that a particular time has the same meaning at *all* points in space. But we have defined time measurements in terms of local simultaneity, in terms of the reading on a clock made by a local observer. In order to define time throughout all space we must devise a procedure for synchronizing all the clocks, and this implies communication between the various observers. An observer at one of the grid points might telephone another, distant observer, ask for the reading on his clock, set his own accordingly, and thereafter assume that he knows the meaning of "7 A.M." at the second observer's point. To be completely consistent he must realize that telephone messages are not transmitted instantaneously. For instance, it might require 10^{-4} sec for transmission of the second observer's voice. Then if the first observer hears that voice say "my clock reads 7 A.M." he must set *his* clock at 7 A.M. plus 10^{-4} sec. Otherwise his clock will lag behind the other by the transmission time of the telephone message.

Clearly the synchronization of clocks requires knowledge of the transmission time of a signal between nonlocal observers. But this suggests a paradox. Since nonlocal time can only be defined in terms of synchronized clocks, communication times cannot be measured until clocks are synchronized, and clocks cannot be synchronized until communication time is known.

Einstein resolved the ambiguity by appealing to the known constancy of the speed of light in vacuo. He *defined* the time interval required for light to travel between two points as the distance between the points divided by the constant c, and thus promoted the speed of light to the role of fundamental arbiter in the definition of time intervals. If the distance between two points is defined in terms of a standard meter stick, Einstein's definition becomes completely unambiguous. But as a consequence time becomes intimately tied to distance, or space, and distance itself related to the *measurement* of distance.

If an experimenter at a point A observes a clock located d meters away at point B (he may use a telescope if necessary) then following Einstein's prescription he concludes that he is actually observing a reading on that clock $\Delta t = d/c$ sec in the past (Figure 11.7). Using that information he can also determine the present reading on B's clock, and can synchronize his own clock with it. By repeating the procedure he can determine the present reading on all distant clocks located throughout the grid, and thus arrives at a satisfactory definition of time throughout his coordinate system. Einstein's synchroniza-

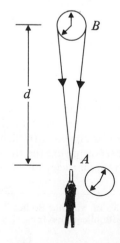

FIGURE 11.7 The synchronization of clocks. Observer A, equipped with a telescope, synchronizes his clock with B by noting the reading on it. In order to carry out the operation correctly he must take the transit time of light from B into account.

tion procedure, his promotion of the speed of light to the role of fundamental arbiter among the clocks, permits us to generalize the purely local, semi-intuitive notion of simultaneity by giving it a unique meaning throughout all space.

If we compare Figures 11.7 and 11.1, it becomes apparent that the synchronization procedure could be carried out using a light clock with one mirror at point A, the other at B. It follows that these light clocks are not simply one of many equivalent types of clock but, in fact, embody Einstein's concepts of simultaneity and synchronization. They must be regarded as *standard* clocks against which the relative precision of all other clocks must be measured.

By using identical light clocks as time standards we can show that the way in which clocks are synchronized depends upon their motion relative to the experimenter who synchronizes them. In Figure 11.8 observer A attempts to use a "moving" light clock oriented parallel to his y-axis to synchronize two identical, conventional clocks at rest in his coordinate system. The first is located at the point on the x-axis coincident with the lower mirror when it emits a flash of light, the second at the point coincident with its return. He calculates the time interval measured by the light pulse's round trip between the mirrors and synchronizes his clocks accordingly. However, observer B is at rest relative to the light clock, and so measures a difficult round trip transit time for the light. Thus he would say that observer A did *not* synchronize the clocks correctly.

Alternately, observer A might synchronize his clocks by observing the reading on one of them with a telescope and then calculating the direct transit time of light from one to the other. But to observer B the two clocks are in effect a light clock moving in the negative x-direction, and so he believes that their separation is contracted. Again he calculates a different transit time, and again he disagrees with observer A's procedure.

We have agreed that the time interval between a pair of events that occur at two widely separated points must be determined by measuring the time at which each event occurs using a clock located at the point of its occurrence. If the clocks are synchronized the required time interval can be determined from the two separate readings. But we have just seen that any judgment regarding synchronization depends upon the motion of the clocks relative to an observer. Therefore, while the time interval between two events is the same throughout any inertial system, it will *not* be the same in different inertial systems. In order to avoid ambiguities we must specify that the time assigned to a physical event be assigned by using a clock at rest relative to the observer, and that the time interval between two events be determined by synchronized clocks at rest relative to each other.

It is worthwhile to consider the meaning of Equation 11.2, the Lorentz contraction, in terms of these ideas. In order to measure the length of an object (a meter stick, for

FIGURE 11.8 An attempt to synchronize two stationary clocks by using a moving light clock. Since an observer B at rest relative to the light clock measures a different interval with it than observer A, who sees it as a moving clock, then B claims that A could not have carried out the synchronization procedure properly.

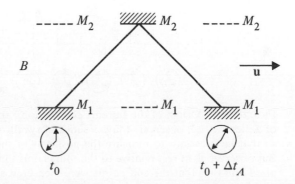

instance) moving with constant velocity along the *x*-axis we record *simultaneously* the positions of its end points, x_2 and x_1, and call its length $\Delta x = x_2 - x_1$ (Figure 11.9). The measurement is particularly simple for an observer at rest relative to the rod since the positions of the end points remain constant in time. However, observer *A* sees the rod moving along his *x*-axis. In order to be certain that he measures the positions of its end points *simultaneously*, he first lays a series of synchronized clocks along the *x*-axis. To observer *B* these clocks are moving in the negative *x*-direction. He does *not* regard their synchronization as correct, and hence concludes that observer *A* does *not* measure the end points simultaneously. Since the observers disagree about the meaning of time in their respective systems it follows that they also disagree about the measurement of length in the direction parallel to their relative motion.

At this juncture it is tempting to ask if moving clocks *really* slow down, if lengths *really* contract. In other words, must we regard the properties of time and space as properties that depend upon motion relative to an observer? Newton conceived of absolute space and absolute time existing by themselves quite apart from physical events. In a sense, absolute space and time were a passive backdrop against which all processes occurred. But in Chapter 6 we concluded that virtually all of the properties we might possibly attribute to space and time such as absolute locations, orientations, directions, are, in fact, only conventions. Hence it appears that physical space and time have no meaning that can be separated from physical processes. They are constructs we devise to order our sense impressions, our observations of such processes. Since the properties of space and time rest upon the measurements of physical events, there is no a priori reason why they should not depend upon the state of motion of the observer who undertakes the measurements. As we have seen, the measurements of time and space are intertwined in relativity. Since both are basically ordering concepts for our sense impressions there is really no reason why they *ever* should have been regarded as separable. From this point of view Einstein's system is really more in accord with "common sense" than Newton's!

◣◣ 11.4 The Lorentz transformations

In Chapter 6 we took the Galilean transformations (Equation 6.13) as the mathematical statement of the symmetry of physical laws with respect to inertial systems. We know now that they cannot be. In the first place, their application to the velocity of light leads to results that are inconsistent with the measured invariance of its magnitude in all inertial systems (Section 10.8). In the second place, the Galilean transformations implicitly assume that time intervals between events have the same magnitude in all inertial systems. Therefore, we must find a set of transformation equations consistent with the

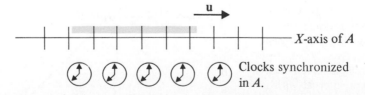

FIGURE 11.9   Origin of the Lorentz contraction. In order to measure the length of a moving rod, observer *A* lays a series of synchronized clocks along his *x*-axis so that he is certain to measure the positions of the end points simultaneously. But observer *B*, at rest relative to the rod, claims that *A*'s clocks are not synchronized and thus that the end points were measured at different times.

invariant magnitude of c. These transformations, called the Lorentz transformations in honor of H. A. Lorentz, become the revised mathematical statement of the symmetry of physical laws with respect to inertial systems.

As in our derivation of the Galilean transformations, let inertial system B have constant velocity $+u$ relative to inertial system A, and let the direction of relative motion be along the common x-axes of the two systems (Figure 11.10). Let clocks at the origins of the two systems each be set at $t = 0$ at the instant these origins coincide. This can be done by placing an experimenter with a clock at the origin of each system. When the origins coincide the reading on clock A is a local event to the observer at the origin of system B, and vice versa. Therefore, at that moment the observers encounter no ambiguity in synchronizing their clocks at $t = 0$.

Now an observer at rest in system A assigns spatial coordinates x_a, y_a, and z_a and the time coordinate t_a to some event. Similarly, an observer at rest in B assigns spatial coordinates x_b, y_b, z_b, and *his* time coordinate t_b to the same event. The Lorentz transformations relate the two sets of measurements in a way that is consistent with the requirement that both observers must measure $c = 3 \times 10^8$ m/sec in vacuo. Suppose that from A's viewpoint a beam of light is emitted from x_{1a} at time t_{1a} and detected at x_{2a} at time t_{2a}. The observer writes:

$$x_{2a} - x_{1a} = c(t_{2a} - t_{1a}),$$

or

$$\Delta x_a = c\,\Delta t_a. \tag{11.3a}$$

Observer B measuring the emission and detection of the *same* light writes:

$$x_{2b} - x_{1b} = c(t_{2b} - t_{2a}),$$

or

$$\Delta x_b = c\,\Delta t_b. \tag{11.3b}$$

If the Lorentz transformations are used to express x_{1b}, x_{2b}, t_{1b}, and t_{1a} as functions of x_{1a}, x_{2a}, t_{1a}, t_{2a}, y_{1a}, z_{1a}, and the relative velocity, u, and if the expressions so obtained are substituted into Equation 11.3b, the resulting equation must reduce to Equation 11.3a. This is consistent with the general meaning of transformation equations as we

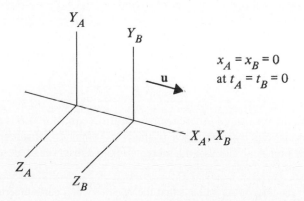

FIGURE 11.10 The two inertial systems used in the derivation of the Lorentz transformations.

defined them in Chapter 6. If we express the transformation equations in terms of general functional notation:

$$x_b = F(x_a, y_a, z_a, t_a, u),$$ (11.4a)

$$t_b = G(x_a, y_a, z_a, t_a, u),$$ (11.4b)

then, substituting into Equation 11.3b we have:

$$\Delta F(x_a, y_a, z_a, t_a, u) = c\,\Delta G(x_a, y_a, z_a, t_a, u),$$

which must reduce to Equation 11.3a:

$$\Delta x_a = c\,\Delta t_a.$$

This requirement is not quite sufficient to determine the explicit forms of F and G. In addition we must assume that the functions do not have terms proportional to the products of the coordinates nor to any coordinate raised to any power higher than the first. That is, they must be *linear* in the coordinates:

$$F(x_a, y_a, z_a, t_a, u) = f_1 x_a + f_2 y_a + f_3 z_a + f_4 t_a,$$

where the four coefficients f_1, f_2, f_3, and f_4 may be functions of u. All of the transformation equations of Chapter 6 are linear. In particular consider the Galilean transformations:

$$x_b = x_a - u t_a.$$

Here $f_1 = 1$, $f_2 = f_3 = 0$, and $f_4 = -u$. Since we expect these transformations to be good approximations to the Lorentz transformations when the relative velocity is small, it seems reasonable to assume the Lorentz transformations will also be linear in form.* The test of the assumption must, of course, rest with experiment. We can simplify even more by noting that since lengths perpendicular to the direction of relative motion are the same in the two systems (Section 11.2) the transformations will not involve y_a and z_a. In other words, $f_2 = f_3 = 0$. Similar considerations apply to the function G in Equation 11.4b.

The detailed algebraic manipulations leading from these arguments to the transformations are given in the appendix to this chapter and yield:

$$x_b = \frac{x_a - u t_a}{\sqrt{1 - u^2/c^2}},$$ (11.5a)

$$y_b = y_a,$$ (11.5b)

$$z_b = z_a,$$ (11.5c)

$$t_b = \frac{t_a - [(u/c^2)x_a]}{\sqrt{1 - u^2/c^2}}.$$ (11.5d)

Let us reemphasize the meaning of these transformation equations: B is an inertial system moving with constant velocity $+u$ relative to inertial system A. Observers in both systems are equipped with identical clocks and meter sticks. Observer A describes a series of

---

*Another reason for the linear assumption is that the symmetry of a pair of inertial systems requires that the inverse transformations must be of the same form as the direct transformations when $-u$ is substituted for u. (Compare Equations 11.5 and 11.6). Linear transformations have this property. Few (if any) other types of transformation equations do.

events, say the trajectory of a particle, by assigning it a series of space-time coordinates, x_a, y_a, z_a, t_a relative to his system. Observer B describes the *same* events by assigning a series of space-time coordinates, x_b, y_b, a_b, t_b relative to *his* system. According to the Principle of Relativity, the symmetry principle requiring the invariance of physical laws relative to inertial systems, the basic laws underlying the particle trajectory must be written so that the descriptions of the motion in systems A and B are connected by Equation 11.5.

The most obvious difference between the Lorentz and Galilean transformations is the time transformation, Equation 11.5d. The time of an event measured in system B differs from its time measured in A, as we anticipated. It is a function not only of t_a but also of the relative velocity u *and* the local point in A (i.e., x_a) where the local time t_a is measured.

The transformation of the x-coordinates is also a function of relative velocity, as in the Galilean transformations, and of the time of the event in system A. As with Galilean transformations the coordinates of the event in the two directions perpendicular to the direction of relative motion are identical.

Equations 11.5 relate the four coordinates of an event in A to its coordinates in B; the inverse Lorentz transformations state the inverse relation. Since A has velocity $-u$ relative to B, they can be derived from the direct transformation equations simply by substituting $-u$ for u and interchanging the subscripts a and b. They also follow by a direct algebraic inversion:

$$x_a = \frac{x_a + ut_b}{\sqrt{1 - u^2/c^2}}, \tag{11.6a}$$

$$y_a = y_b, \tag{11.6b}$$

$$z_a = z_b, \tag{11.6c}$$

$$t_a = \frac{t_b + [(u/c^2)x_a]}{\sqrt{1 - u^2/c^2}}. \tag{11.6d}$$

Let us use the transformations to relate the propagation of light measured in two inertial systems. In B we have (Equation 11.3b):

$$(x_{2b} - x_{1b}) = c(t_{2b} - t_{1b}).$$

Applying Equation 11.5 to transform the source coordinates in $A(x_{1a}$ and $t_{1a})$ to the source coordinates in B:

$$x_{1a} = \frac{x_{1a} - ut_{1a}}{\sqrt{1 - u^2/c^2}} \quad \text{and} \quad t_{1b} = \frac{t_{1a} - (u/c^2)x_{1a}}{\sqrt{1 - u^2/c^2}},$$

with analogous expressions for the detector coordinates. Therefore:

$$\Delta x_b = \frac{\Delta x_a - u\,\Delta t_a}{\sqrt{1 - u_2/c^2}} \quad \text{and} \quad \Delta t_b = \frac{\Delta t_a - (u/c^2)\,\Delta t_a}{\sqrt{1 - u^2/c^2}}.$$

Substituting into Equation 11.3b,

$$\frac{(\Delta x_a - u\,\Delta t_a)}{\sqrt{1 - u^2/c^2}} = \frac{c[\Delta t_a - (u/c^2)\,\Delta t_a]}{\sqrt{1 - u^2/c^2}}.$$

Canceling the square root in the denominator and collecting terms,

$$\Delta x_a\left(1 + \frac{u}{c}\right) = c\,\Delta t_a\left(1 + \frac{u}{c}\right).$$

Or, finally, $\Delta x_a = c\,\Delta t_a$, the result obtained directly in Equation 11.3a. Thus we have shown that the Lorentz transformations are indeed consistent with the required invariance of c.

◢◣ 11.5 Einstein's velocity addition law. The ultimate speed. Causality in relativity

Equations 11.5 and 11.6 deal with the transformations of points, displacements, and time intervals. Let us now turn to the measurement of velocity in two inertial systems which are themselves in relative motion. By definition the velocity of a particle measured in the system B is

$$v_b = \frac{\Delta x_b}{\Delta t_B}.$$

Using Equations 11.5,

$$v_b = \frac{\Delta x_a - u\,\Delta t_a}{\Delta t_a - (u/c^2)\,\Delta x_a}.$$

Dividing numerator and denominator by Δt_a,

$$v_a = \frac{(\Delta x_a/\Delta t_a) - u}{1 - (u/c^2)(\Delta x_a/\Delta t_a)} = \frac{v_a - u}{1 - uv_a/c^2}, \tag{11.7}$$

since $v_a = \Delta x_a/\Delta t_a$. Equation 11.7 is the relativistic equation for the composition of velocities replacing the Galilean addition law, Equation 6.15. The inverse law merely replaces u by $-u$ and interchanges the subscripts. If $v_a = c$,

$$v_b = \frac{c - u}{1 - uc/c^2} = \frac{c(1 - u/c)}{1 - u/c} = c.$$

That is, the measured velocity of light is the same in the two systems, as it must be.

Two velocities that are each less than c cannot add to give a resultant velocity greater than c, as they would if the Galilean transformations were valid. Suppose a rocket traveling with velocity $+u = 0.9\,c$ relative to the earth fires another rocket forward in its own system with velocity $v_b = +0.9\,c$ (Figure 11.11). According to the Galilean velocity composition equation (Equation 6.15) the velocity of the second rocket relative to the earth-fixed system would be $1.8\,c$. But using the inverse of Equation 11.7 (i.e., setting $u = -u$ and interchanging the subscripts):

$$v_a = \frac{0.9\,c + 0.9\,c}{1 + 0.81\,c^2/c^2} = \frac{1.8}{1.81}\,c,$$

which is smaller than c.

The Lorentz transformations for x and t as well as the time dilation and Lorentz contraction equations all involve the factor $\sqrt{1 - u^2/c^2}$, a factor that becomes imaginary for relative velocities u greater than c. Thus we conclude that such velocities have no meaning in our system, or, in other words, that the velocity of a *material* object cannot exceed the velocity of light. We can reach the same conclusion by examining the relativistic velocity addition equation (Equation 11.7). More basically, the limitation follows from

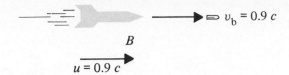

$$v_a = \frac{u + v_b}{1 + \frac{uv_b}{c^2}} = \frac{1.8}{1.81}\, c$$

Observer A

FIGURE 11.11 The relativistic addition of velocities. A rocket (system B) travel-ing with velocity $u = +0.9\ c$ relative to a stationary observer (A) fires a pro-jectile with velocity $0.9\ c$ relative to B. The velocity of the projectile relative to A is $(1.8/1.81)c$.

the experimental fact of the invariant magnitude of c in all inertial systems which permits it to assume the role of fundamental arbiter of time. It is an observed *fact* that the interaction between two charges separated by a distance d is transmitted in time $\Delta t = d/c$, and that the constant c characterizing the transmission time is independent of the relative motion of the charges. As a consequence we conclude that the structure of physical time and space places the limit c upon *all* physical velocities.

The velocity of light is built into our kinematic system from the beginning, and thus plays a more fundamental role than any constant in Newtonian physics. If for instance, the magnitude of G (the universal gravitational constant) were changed, the forces between all masses would also change. As a consequence the appearance of the universe would certainly be different, but Newtonian dynamics would remain unaltered. For example, the algebraic form of the universal gravitational law would not change. In contrast, the constant c determines the very structure of time and space in physics. If its value were altered then we would have a different view of time and space themselves.

In view of the form of the Lorentz transformations it is not at all surprising that the Galilean transformations seem to describe correctly the motion of projectiles, or even of the earth in its orbit about the sun. Suppose $u/c = 0.01$ (recall that the orbital velocity of the earth relative to the sun is 3×10^4 m/sec, or $u/c = 10^{-4}$). Substituting $u/c = 0.01$ into Equations 11.5a and 11.5d,

$$x_b = \frac{x_a - ut_a}{\sqrt{1 - 0.0001}} = 1.0005(x_a - ut_a),$$

$$t_b = 1.0005\left(t_a - \frac{0.01x_a}{c}\right) = 1.0005\left(t_a - \frac{x_a \times 10^{-10}}{3}\right).$$

The derivations from the Galilean transformations are less than 0.05%. At "ordinary" velocities the Galilean transformations are satisfactory approximations to the Lorentz transformations. Special relativity generalizes rather than replaces Newtonian physics. In other words, the Newtonian system is a special, low-velocity approximation to the relativistic system.

The Lorentz transformation for time also leads to an important conclusion regarding the causal relation between physical events. Let the time interval between two events in system A be $\Delta t_a = t_{2a} - t_{1a}$. When Δt_a is positive, then t_{1a} is smaller than t_{2a}, implying event 1 takes place before event 2. If in another system, *B*, the interval $t_{2b} - t_{1b}$ were *negative*, the order of the time events in that system would be reversed. Suppose observer *A* concludes that event 1 is the cause of event 2. If observer *B* sees the time order reversed he would then conclude that the *effect* follows the *cause*, which is absurd, for a cause-effect sequence cannot depend upon the choice of inertial system. Therefore, two events *cannot* be causally connected unless the time interval between them has the same sign in *all* inertial systems.

Let the time interval between two events in system *A* be Δt_a. In system *B*, Equation 11.5d gives:

$$\Delta t_b = \frac{\Delta t_a - u/c^2 \, \Delta x_a}{\sqrt{1 - u^2/c^2}}.$$

Now suppose the spatial separation between the events, Δx_a, is equal to the distance light travels between them in the interval Δt_a. Then $\Delta x_a = c \, \Delta t_a$ and

$$\Delta t_b = \frac{\Delta t_a (1 - u/c)}{\sqrt{1 - u^2/c^2}}.$$

Since u/c is always smaller than 1, Δt_b and Δt_a have the same sign regardless of the relative velocity of the systems, and causality is preserved. But if Δx_a is greater than $c \, \Delta t_a$, it is possible to select a system, *B*, whose velocity relative to *A* is sufficient to reverse the sign of Δt_b, and therefore the casual order of the events. Therefore, *if* the spatial separation between two events in one system is so large that light cannot travel from one to the other during the time interval between them, their time order can be reversed in *some* system and therefore they can have no causal connection in *any* system. This result also follows from the fact that the velocity of light is the ultimate physical velocity. Physical causality implies physical communication, and therefore, one event cannot influence another unless at least enough time elapses for light to be propagated between them.

▲▲ 11.6 The twin paradox

It is worth considering one final kinematic implication of Equations 11.1 and 11.2: the rather famous twin paradox.

Suppose that one of a pair of 30 year-old twins (call him *A*) watches his brother *B* depart on a round-trip voyage to a star ten light years* away in a rocket ship whose velocity relative to the earth is 99% the velocity of light (Figure 11.12). Seen from the earth, twin *B* reaches his destination in $l/u = 10 \, c/0.99 \, c = 10.1$ years. Therefore, 20.2 years have elapsed by the time *B* returns. At that time his brother is 50.2 years old.

However, the earth-bound brother, *A*, notes that during the course of the voyage *all* clocks on the rocket run more slowly than clocks on the earth. Hence *B*'s biological processes are retarded and he ages less rapidly than the people on earth. From Equation 11.1 with $\sqrt{1 - (u/c)^2} = \sqrt{1 - (0.99)^2} = 0.141$ we find that during 20.2 years of earth-time the clocks on the rocket advance only 2.84 years. The 50.2-year-old, stay-at-home twin greets a returning brother who has yet to celebrate his thirty-third birthday!

But how does twin *B* analyze the trip? As far as he is concerned nothing extraordinary happens to his biological processes except during acceleration at the beginning, middle,

---

* One light year is the distance light travels in one year, or about 3.14×10^7 sec. Since $c = 3 \times 10^8$ m/sec, a light year is about 9.4×10^{15} m, or roughly 6×10^{12} miles.

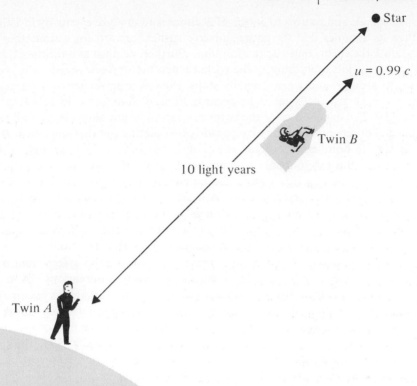

FIGURE 11.12   The twin paradox.   Twin *B* makes a round trip journey to a star
ten light years away.   On his return *both* he and his brother agree that as a result
of the journey *B* has aged less than *A*.

and end of his journey.   His heartbeat and breathing cycle can be regarded as clocks at
rest in his reference system, and he considers his aging process as entirely normal.   However, seen from the rocket, the distance from the earth to the destination is contracted,
for it is ten light years only in the rest system of the earth.   Applying Equation 11.2 with
$\sqrt{1 - (u/c)^2} = 0.141$, twin *B* measures the distance as 1.41 light years and so completes
the round trip in $2 \times 1.41\ c/0.89\ c = 2.84$ yr.   Therefore, even from *his* point of view he
is 32.84 years old at its conclusion.   From the viewpoint of *both* observers the returning
twin is the younger.   Yet our extensive reanalysis of time and space was motivated by the
conviction that the laws of physics should be the same in all inertial systems.   Here is an
asymmetric result.   Twin *A* ages 20.2 years, twin *B* only 2.84 years.

However, the experiences of the twins are *not* identical, hence their conclusions need
not be symmetric.   The analysis of time intervals using light clocks assumes that observer
A can adopt the viewpoint that *B* and his clock are moving with velocity $+u$, or that *B*
can equally well believe that *A* is moving with velocity $-u$.   We also assume that the
relative velocity of the observers remains constant during the time they compare their
clocks.   But in the twin problem, it is perfectly clear that one makes the space voyage
while the other stays behind.   Initially, they are both in the earth-fixed system.   Later *B*
accelerates into an inertial system moving with velocity $+0.99\ c$ m/sec relative to system
A; on his return trip he is in still another inertial system moving with velocity $-0.99\ c$
m/sec relative to the earth.   Finally, at the end of the voyage he decelerates once again
into the earth-fixed system.   From *A*'s point of view one lone rocket goes to a distant

star, turns around, and returns to earth. If B chooses to analyze events by insisting he is at rest then he assumes that the entire universe rushes forward for a time, then rushes backward until the earth comes up to meet him. Further, he must assume the existence of pseudoforces that jolt everything in the rocket when the universe starts to move away, when it turns around, and when it finally stops, even as a passenger on an accelerating train must invoke pseudoforces if he regards himself and the train as being at rest (Section 6.13). The experiences of the twins are certainly not equivalent in all respects.

Einstein and others resolved the twin paradox by pointing out that since twin B spends part of his time in noninertial systems, the analysis of Sections 11.1 through 11.4 is not completely valid. But this loophole need not be invoked. It is possible to envision a trip so long that the time required during the acceleration and deceleration is negligible compared with the total round trip time. A more satisfactory resolution recognizes the asymmetric experiences of the twins, specifically, the fact that twin B spends time in several different inertial systems during the course of his voyage, while twin A remains in the same system. The simple time dilation equation (Equation 11.1) was derived on the assumption that observers A and B each remain in one inertial system and that the observations they make of each other's clocks are local observations. A complete analysis of the twin problem involves several inertial systems, as well as events that are clearly nonlocal, and requires use of the full Lorentz transformation equations. (The interested student is referred to a collection of papers cited at the end of the chapter.) The results of the detailed analysis for a twenty-light-year voyage at 99% the speed of light are precisely the results of our simple analysis. When the 32.84-year-old space traveler returns to earth he greets a 50.2-year-old twin brother!

The whole paradox of the twins arises from a misunderstanding of the meaning of symmetry principles. To claim that the asymmetric aging of the twins invalidates the equivalence of physical laws in all inertial systems is equivalent to claiming that two identical pendula must have identical periods throughout all space if the homogeneity of space is a valid principle. The symmetry principles imply only that the basic laws are the same under a given set of operations. Given two completely equivalent situations, the symmetric *application* of those laws leads to indistinguishable results.

▲▲ 11.7 The invariant separation between events in space-time

The time dilation and Lorentz contraction equations as well as the more general equations of the Lorentz transformations (Equations 11.5 and 11.6) insure the constancy of c in all inertial systems. But they also imply that the laws of physics in their Newtonian forms do *not* satisfy the symmetry principle we seek to preserve. Let us consider the momentum conservation principle, for example. A billiard ball of mass M_1 traveling along the x-axis with velocity v_0 collides with another billiard ball of mass M_2 initially at rest at the origin (Figure 11.13a). The momentum of the system before the collision is M_1v_0. If both balls continue along the x-axis after collision their respective final velocities, v_{1f} and v_{2f}, are related to v_0 by the momentum conservation law (see Section 4.2):

$$M_1v_0 = M_1v_{1f} + M_2v_{2f}.$$

Now let us consider the collision from the viewpoint of an observer moving parallel to the x-axis with velocity $+u$ (Figure 11.13b). Using the *classical* velocity addition equation (Equation 6.15), M_1 has velocity $v_0 - u$ in his system, M_2 velocity $-u$. The

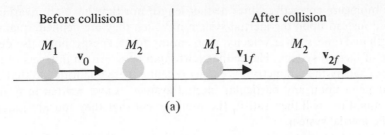

(a)

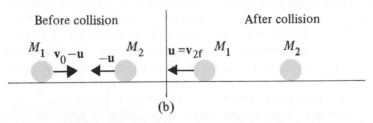

(b)

FIGURE 11.13 A one dimensional collision seen in two inertial systems according to Newtonian physics. (a) The inertial system in which M_2 is at rest prior to the collision. (b) The inertial system in which M_2 is at rest following the collision. Since the two views are related by the Galilean velocity composition equation they are not relativistically correct. However, only the classical velocity composition law is consistent with the conservation of momentum in both systems if inertial mass is assumed to be a constant independent of velocity. By making inertial mass a variable, relativity retains momentum conservation in a simple form.

respective final velocities are $v_{1f} - u$ and $v_{2f} - u$. Therefore, applying momentum conservation:

$$M_1(v_0 - u) - M_2u = M_1(v_{1f} - u) + M_2(v_{2f} - u),$$

or

$$M_1v_0 - (M_1 + M_2)u = M_1v_{1f} + M_2v_{2f} - (M_1 + M_2)u,$$

which reduces to

$$M_1v_0 = M_1v_{1f} + M_2v_{2f}.$$

Therefore, the momentum conservation principle leads to equivalent results both for an observer who regards M_2 as initially at rest, and for an observer moving with arbitrary constant velocity relative to the system.

But we know that the classical velocity composition equation is *not* strictly applicable. Instead, the second observer must apply the relativistic equation (Equation 11.7):

$$M_1\left[\frac{v_0 - u}{1 - (v_0u/c^2)}\right] - M_2u = M_1\left[\frac{v_{1f} - u}{1 - (v_{1f}u/c^2)}\right] + M_2\left[\frac{v_{2f} - u}{1 - (v_{2f}u/c^2)}\right],$$

a relation that is *not* equivalent to the expression $M_1v_0 = M_1v_{1f} + M_2v_{2f}$ for arbitrary relative velocities.

Does observer B conclude that momentum conservation is not a valid law in his system? If so he violates the symmetry principle we seek to retain. To be consistent with the results of the foregoing sections he should conclude rather that he has not written down the momenta correctly. Since neither length nor time have an invariant meaning but depend instead upon the inertial system in which they are defined, quantities based upon length and time, such as velocity, momentum, force, energy, must also depend upon the choice of inertial system. Hence the Newtonian laws written in terms of these quantities do not satisfy the symmetry. We must redefine these quantities so that their forms will not depend upon any particular inertial system. Laws written in terms of these redefined quantities will then satisfy the requirement that they too are independent of any specific inertial system.

Invariance with respect to rotations in space (Section 6.6) is tantamount to the requirement that in any particular situation the same physical conclusions must be obtained regardless of how we choose to orient the axes of our coordinate system. That requirement is satisfied if the statements of the fundamental laws of physics are based upon quantities that have an invariant meaning in all coordinate systems. Because we regarded the distance between two points as an invariant in Newtonian physics, we were justified in basing our fundamental kinematical and dynamical concepts upon length. Following that line of reasoning we concluded that a formulation in terms of three-component *vectors* would insure the invariance of physical laws with respect to rotations in three-dimensional space.

However, the distance between two points in space is *not* invariant in special relativity, but depends on the inertial system in which it is measured (Equation 11.2). Therefore, we must find an analogous quantity that does have the requisite invariance properties, and use it to redefine our basic concepts such as velocity, momentum, force, and energy.

Let Δx_a, Δy_a, and Δz_a be the components of the spatial distance between a pair of events measured in an inertial system A, and Δt_a the time interval between them measured by clocks at rest in system A. We define the *Lorentz invariant separation* (or simply the *separation*) of the events ΔS_a by generalizing the three-dimensional Pythagorean relation between the square of the distance between two points in three-dimensional space and its components (Equation 2.15):

$$\Delta S_a^2 = c^2 \, \Delta t_a^2 - (\Delta x_a^2 + \Delta y_a^2 + \Delta z_a^2), \tag{11.8a}$$

or

$$\Delta S_a^2 = c^2 \, \Delta t_a^2 \left[1 - \frac{\Delta x_a^2 + \Delta y_a^2 + \Delta z_a^2}{c^2 \, \Delta t_a^2} \right].$$

Since the quantity

$$\frac{\Delta x_a^2 + \Delta y_a^2 + \Delta z_a^2}{\Delta t_a^2}$$

has the dimensions of velocity squared (Equation 2.18a), then in the limit as Δt_a approaches zero we can substitute v_a^2 and write:

$$\Delta S_a^2 = c^2 \, \Delta t_a^2 \left(1 - \frac{v_a^2}{c^2} \right),$$

or finally,

$$\Delta S_a = c \, \Delta t_a \sqrt{1 - (v_a^2/c^2)}. \tag{11.8b}$$

If the two events separated by ΔS_a represented two successive measurements of the position and time coordinates of a moving particle in inertial system A, for example, then v_a would be its velocity in that system. Another observer B moving with the same speed as the particle would see the two events occur at the same place, and therefore to him $\Delta S_b = c\,\Delta t_b$. However, we need not define a casual connection between two events in order to define their separation. Therefore, v_a need not represent the speed of a physical particle. The ratio $\Delta S/c$ is called the *proper time interval* between two events. Since, as we are about to show, the magnitude of ΔS has an invariant magnitude in all inertial systems then so does the proper time interval. Referring to Equation 11.8b, it is clear that the proper time interval between two events is equal to the ordinary time interval measured by an observer in whose system $v_a = 0$.

Let ΔS_a and ΔS_b be the separations between the *same* two events measured in two inertial systems A and B that have speed u relative to each other. For observer B:

$$\Delta S_b^2 = c^2\,\Delta t_b^2 - (\Delta x_b^2 + \Delta y_b^2 + \Delta z_b^2)$$
$$= (c^2\,\Delta t_b^2 - \Delta x_b^2) - (\Delta y_b^2 + \Delta z_b^2).$$

The Lorentz transformations (Equations 11.7) may be used to express the coordinates measured by observer B in terms of those measured by A:

$$\Delta S_b^2 = \frac{c^2(\Delta t_a - (u/c^2)\,\Delta x_a)^2 - (\Delta x_a - (u/c)\,\Delta t_a)^2}{1 - (u^2/c^2} - (\Delta y_a^2 + \Delta z_a^2).$$

Grouping and rearranging terms,

$$\Delta S_b^2 = \frac{c^2\,\Delta t_a^2(1 - u^2/c^2) - \Delta x_a^2(1 - u_2/c^2)}{1 - u^2/c^2} - (\Delta y_a^2 + \Delta z_a^2),$$

or

$$\Delta S_b^2 = c^2\,\Delta t_a^2 - (\Delta x_a^2 + \Delta y_a^2 + \Delta z_a^2).$$

Since this is the separation in system A (Equation 11.8a) we have proved that the value of ΔS is the same in all inertial systems.

Provided the calculated value of v_a in Equation 11.8a is smaller than c we can (as already noted) always imagine an observer in another inertial system moving with just that velocity relative to system A. Therefore, v_a is the velocity of the inertial system B relative to A in which the two events occur at the same place.

It is possible for two events to occur such that:

$$\Delta x_a^2 + \Delta y_a^2 + \Delta z_a^2 > c^2\,\Delta t^2,$$

even though such events cannot be causally connected (Section 11.5). (The fact that v_a would be greater than c is of no great concern since in this case it can never represent the speed of a material particle.) If v_a is smaller than c for a pair of events then, as we have seen, an inertial system exists in which they occur at the same place. No such inertial system exists for v_a greater than c. However, it is possible to find a system in which they occur at the same *time*. Call it system B, and let it have velocity u relative to system A. For algebraic simplicity, let both events occur on the x-axis so that Δy_a and Δz_a are zero. Referring to Equation 11.5b, a time interval in system B is related to Δx_a and Δt_a by

$$\Delta t_b = \frac{\Delta t_a - (u/c^2)\,\Delta x_a}{\sqrt{1 - u^2/c^2}}.$$

If $\Delta t_b = 0$,

$$\Delta t_a = \frac{u}{c^2}\,\Delta x_a,$$

so that the relative velocity of the systems is given by:

$$\frac{u}{c} = \frac{c}{(\Delta x_a/\Delta t_a)} = \frac{c}{v_a}.$$

Since v_a is greater than c, then u is smaller than c, as it must be if it represents the velocity of a real observer. The separation in system B is given by (Equation 11.8a):

$$\Delta S_a^2 = -\Delta x_a^2.$$

Events for which $\Delta x_a^2 + \Delta y_a^2 + \Delta z_a^2$ is greater than $c^2 \Delta t^2$ are therefore said to have *spacelike* separations. Similarly, events for which the opposite is true have *timelike* separations. If $v_a = c$ then $\Delta S_a = 0$, and the separation is *lightlike*. Because ΔS has the same magnitude in all inertial systems it is obvious that the timelike, spacelike, or lightlike character of the separation between two events is also preserved in the Lorentz transformations.

▲▲ 11.8 Four-vectors. The velocity and momentum four-vectors. Dynamic mass

In Chapter 2 we defined vectors as quantities having both magnitude and direction. An alternate and in many ways more satisfactory definition can be made in terms of the transformation properties of their components with respect to rotations in three dimensions (Section 6.6). Figure 11.14 (which is based on Figure 6.4) shows the x- and y-components of a displacement Δs between two points in two Cartesian coordinate systems, A and B, whose axes are rotated through an angle θ relative to each other. (The z-axes of both systems coincide and are perpendicular to the plane of the page.) Referring to Equations 6.5, the x- and y-components in system B are related to the components in system A by

$$\Delta x_b = \Delta x_a \cos \theta + \Delta y_a \sin \theta, \tag{6.5a}$$

$$\Delta y_b = -\Delta x_a \sin \theta + \Delta y_a \cos \theta. \tag{6.5b}$$

The magnitude of the displacement squared in system B is

$$\begin{aligned}
\Delta s_b^2 &= \Delta x_b^2 + \Delta y_b^2 = (\Delta x_a \cos \theta + \Delta y_a \sin \theta)^2 \\
&\quad + (-\Delta x_a \sin \theta + \Delta y_a \cos \theta)^2, \\
&= (\Delta x_a^2 \cos^2 \theta + 2\,\Delta x_a\,\Delta y_a \cos \theta \sin \theta + \Delta y_a^2 \sin^2 \theta) \\
&\quad + (\Delta x_a^2 \sin^2 \theta - 2\,\Delta x_a\,\Delta y_a \cos \theta \sin \theta + \Delta y_a^2 \sin \theta), \\
&= \Delta x_a^2(\cos^2 \theta + \sin^2 \theta) + \Delta y_a^2(\cos^2 \theta + \sin^2 \theta), \\
&= \Delta x_a^2 + \Delta y_a^2 = \Delta s_a^2,
\end{aligned}$$

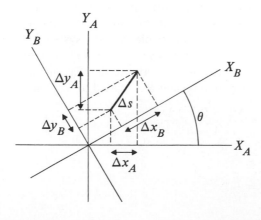

FIGURE 11.14 The components of a displacement Δs in two, two-dimensional Cartesian systems whose axes are rotated through an angle θ relative to each other (see also Figure 6.4).

the final step following from the identity $\sin^2 \theta + \cos^2 \theta = 1$. Thus the transformation equations insure the invariance of the magnitude of the displacement in the two systems.

By dividing both sides of Equations 6.5 by Δt we immediately have transformation equations for the components of velocity; multiplying by inertial mass yields transformation equations for momentum. Therefore, we may define the components of a vector in two dimensions as any set of two numbers, d_x and d_y, which obey the same transformation equations with respect to rotation as the components of displacement. That is,

$$d_{xb} = d_{xa} \cos \theta + d_{ya} \sin \theta,$$
$$d_{ya} = -d_{xa} \sin \theta + d_{ya} \cos \theta,$$

with the squared magnitude of d which has the same value in all systems, given by

$$d^2 = d_x^2 + d_y^2.$$

Invariants such as the magnitude of displacement, velocity, and d^2 in the foregoing example (as well as quantities such as mass or energy) are also called *scalars*.

It is not difficult to extend these ideas to three dimensions. If the z-axes of the systems coincide (as they do in Figure 11.14) then we also have the transformation equation,

$$\Delta z_b = \Delta z_a.$$

More generally the z-axes do not coincide, and the components of displacement are related by more complex transformation equations involving three rotation angles rather than one. However, we can still define a vector as a set of three numbers which obey the same rotational transformation equations as the components of displacement.

In special relativity we are concerned with the separation of events in *spacetime* rather than with the displacement between points in space, and, as we know, separations are given in terms of *four* numbers—three spatial components and a time interval (Equation 11.8a). The transformation equations of these four components from inertial system A to B are simply the Lorentz transformation equations (Equations 11.5). If we use the notation $\gamma = 1/\sqrt{1 - u^2/c^2}$ we can rewrite these in the form:

$$\Delta x_b = \gamma \Delta x_a - \gamma u \Delta t_a$$

$$= \gamma \Delta x_a - \frac{\gamma u}{c} (c \Delta t_a), \tag{11.9a}$$

$$\Delta y_b = \Delta y_a, \tag{11.9b}$$

$$\Delta z_b = \Delta z_a, \tag{11.9c}$$

$$\Delta t_b = -\frac{\gamma u}{c^2} \Delta x_a + \gamma \Delta t_a,$$

or

$$c \Delta t_b = -\frac{\gamma u}{c} \Delta x_a + \gamma (c \Delta t_a). \tag{11.9d}$$

These equations are in many ways analogous to Equations 6.5 with γ in Equations 11.9a and 11.9d being equivalent to $\cos \theta$, and $\gamma u/c$ to $\sin \theta$. Furthermore, we know that the squared magnitude of the separation ΔS is an invariant in all inertial systems (Section 11.7). Therefore, we shall reformulate our basic concepts by using sets of *four* related components, D_1, D_2, D_3, D_4 which obey the same transformation laws with respect to inertial systems as the components of separation Δx, Δy, Δz, and $c\,\Delta t$*, i.e., the Lorentz transformations:

$$D_{1b} = \gamma D_{1a} - \frac{\gamma u}{c} D_{4a}, \tag{11.10a}$$

$$D_{2b} = D_{2a}, \tag{11.10b}$$

$$D_{3b} = D_{3a}, \tag{11.10c}$$

$$D_{4b} = -\frac{\gamma u}{c} D_{1a} + \gamma D_{4a}. \tag{11.10d}$$

In analogy with Newtonian language we shall refer to these sets of numbers as components of *four-vectors* (because D_1 transforms like Δx, and D_4 like $c\,\Delta t$, the components D_1, D_2, D_3, and D_4 are also referred to as the x-, y-, z-, and t-components of the four-vector). We shall use subscripted capital letters to denote the components of four-vectors, in contrast with the lower-case letters used to denote the components of the ordinary three-vectors of classical dynamics. Four-vectors themselves will be denoted by placing a bar over the capital letter ($\bar{D}$) just as bold-face lower-case letters are used for three-vectors (**v**).

The magnitude of a four-vector (which we write as $|\bar{D}|$) follows from the analogy between its components and the components of separation, Δx, Δy, Δz, and $c\,\Delta t$ (Equation 11.8a):

$$|\bar{D}| = \sqrt{D_4^2 - (D_1^2 + D_2^2 + D_3^2)}. \tag{11.11}$$

Because the separation between two events is invariant with respect to transformations between coordinate systems, and because the components of any four-vectors obey the same transformation laws, it follows that the magnitude of a four-vector *also* has the same value in all inertial systems. It is this latter property which makes them useful in the formulation of the laws of physics. The magnitude of a four-vector is also called a *Lorentz-invariant scalar*.

In Chapter 2 the components of velocity were defined as the rates of change of the components of displacement with respect to time. Our first inclination might be to try generalizing the velocity components by defining them as the rates of change of the four components of separation with respect to time. But time is no longer an invariant in relativity. Therefore, if we divide Equations 11.9 by Δt_a the resulting expressions would not be equivalent to the requisite transformation laws (Equations 11.9). However, the separation ΔS is a Lorentz-invariant scalar, so we define the four components of Lorentz-invariant velocity as proportional to the rates of change of the *components* of separation with respect to the separation itself:

$$V_1 = c\left(\frac{\Delta x}{\Delta S}\right), \tag{11.12a}$$

$$V_2 = c\left(\frac{\Delta y}{\Delta S}\right), \tag{11.12b}$$

$$V_3 = c\left(\frac{\Delta z}{\Delta S}\right), \tag{11.12c}$$

$$V_4 = c\left(\frac{c\,\Delta t}{\Delta S}\right). \tag{11.12d}$$

---

* $c\,\Delta t$ rather than Δt is used so that all four components will have the same dimensions.

The magnitude of the velocity follows from Equation 11.11:

$$|\overline{V}| = \sqrt{V_4^2 - (V_1^2 + V_2^2 + V_3^2)}. \tag{11.13}$$

We can show directly that $|\overline{V}|$ is a Lorentz-invariant scalar by substituting Equations 11.12 into Equation 11.13:

$$|\overline{V}| = \sqrt{\frac{c^4 \Delta t^2 - c^2(\Delta x^2 + \Delta y^2 + \Delta z^2)}{S^2}},$$

$$= c^2 \left(\frac{\Delta t}{\Delta S}\right) \sqrt{1 - \frac{(\Delta x^2 + \Delta y^2 + \Delta z^2)}{c^2 \Delta t^2}},$$

$$= c^2 \left(\frac{\Delta t}{\Delta S}\right) \sqrt{1 - \frac{v^2}{c^2}}.$$

But according to Equation 11.8b, $\Delta S = c \Delta t \sqrt{1 - v^2/c^2} = c \Delta t / \gamma$. Therefore,

$$|\overline{V}| = c.$$

The magnitude of the Lorentz velocity is nothing other than the speed of light, which is decidedly a Lorentz-invariant scalar. Although the components of $\overline{V}$ depend upon the choice of inertial system, its magnitude does not. Thus any equation written in terms of $\overline{V}$ which is valid on one inertial system is valid in all inertial systems.

Relations between the components of $\overline{V}$ and the components of ordinary Newtonian velocity $\mathbf{v}$ follow by substituting $\Delta S = c \Delta t \sqrt{1 - v^2/c^2} = c \Delta t / \gamma$ (Equation 11.8b) into Equations 11.12. The first substitution gives

$$V_1 = c \left(\frac{\Delta x}{\Delta S}\right) = \gamma \frac{\Delta x}{\Delta t} = \gamma v_x, \tag{11.14a}$$

with analogous expressions for V_2 and V_3:

$$V_2 = \gamma v_y, \tag{11.14b}$$

$$V_3 = \gamma v_z, \tag{11.14c}$$

while substitution into Equation 11.12d yields:

$$V_4 = c^2 \left(\frac{\Delta t}{\Delta S}\right) = c\gamma. \tag{11.14d}$$

How shall we interpret these equations? For the three-dimensional velocities much smaller than c which characterize Newtonian dynamics, the factor $\gamma = 1/\sqrt{1 - v^2/c^2}$ is not appreciably different from unity, and thus to an excellent approximation the spatial components of the four-dimensional velocity are equal to the corresponding three-dimensional components, while the fourth, time-component, V_4, is constant. In dynamics we are concerned with changes in velocity (Chapter 4) and since we can assume V_4 does not differ appreciably from c even for large velocities, then we would expect changes in V_4 to be virtually undetectable at ordinary velocities. For this reason it plays no role in Newtonian dynamics. Further, since it may be regarded as a constant in these circumstances we may assume that the sum of the squares of the spatial components of the four-vector is invariant. In other words, Newtonian concepts offer a valid description of motion characterized by velocities that are much smaller than the velocity of light, as we have noted previously.

Given the four-dimensional generalization of velocity we may immediately define the components of a four-dimensional momentum vector, $\bar{P}$. If M_0 is the inertial mass of a particle *measured while at rest* then by definition:

$$P_1 = M_0 V_1, \tag{11.15a}$$

$$P_2 = M_0 V_2, \tag{11.15b}$$

$$P_3 = M_0 V_3, \tag{11.15c}$$

$$P_4 = M_0 V_4, \tag{11.15d}$$

with the magnitude of the vector given by

$$|\bar{P}| = \sqrt{P_4^2 - (P_1^2 + P_2^2 + P_3^2)}, \tag{11.16}$$

which may also be written as

$$|\bar{P}| = \sqrt{M_0 V_4^2 - (V_1^2 + V_2^2 + V_3^2)} = M_0|\bar{V}|.$$

But since $|\bar{V}| = c$ the magnitude of the invariant four-momentum is

$$|\bar{P}| = M_0 c. \tag{11.17}$$

The individual momentum components can be expressed in Newtonian terms by substituting Equations 11.14 into Equations 11.15:

$$P_1 = \gamma M_0 v_x, \tag{11.18a}$$

$$P_2 = \gamma M_0 v_y, \tag{11.18b}$$

$$P_3 = \gamma M_0 v_z, \tag{11.18c}$$

$$P_4 = \gamma M_0 c. \tag{11.18d}$$

At ordinary velocities γ is approximately one, so the spatial components are equal to their Newtonian equivalents, while P_4 is the constant product $M_0 c$. We have carefully defined the components of four-momentum in terms of the *rest mass* of a particle, its inertial mass measured while it is at rest. Standards of time and of length depend upon their relative velocities (Equations 11.1 and 11.2), and there is no justification for assuming that inertial mass will remain constant. In Chapter 4 (Section 4.1) we defined inertial mass by observing that when two bodies initially at rest interact with each other the *ratio* of their speeds following the interaction is constant (Equation 4.1):

$$\frac{v_2}{v_1} = \text{const.}$$

We then defined the inverse ratio of the inertial masses of the bodies as the inverse ratio of the speeds (Equation 4.2):

$$\frac{M_2}{M_1} = \frac{v_1}{v_2}.$$

The speeds involved in laboratory observations with macroscopic bodies are much smaller than the speed of light. Therefore, we have no assurance that Equation 4.2 is valid for very high speeds. In fact, experiments with elementary particles indicate that it is not, as an example at the end of this section will show. However, the measured speed ratio, v_1/v_2, may still be used to define the inverse inertial mass ratio of two particles *provided* we concede that inertial mass varies with velocity. That is, we define the ratio of the *dynamic* masses M_1/M_2 as:

$$\frac{M_1}{M_2} = \frac{v_2}{v_1}, \tag{11.19a}$$

and then seek an experimentally based relation between the dynamic mass, M, and the rest mass, M_0, of a particle. This turns out to be:

$$M = \frac{M_0}{\sqrt{1 - v^2/c^2}}, \tag{11.19b}$$

showing that the mass of a particle increases with its velocity.

One of the most straightforward ways to verify the consistency of Equations 11.19a and 11.19b is through a generalization of the momentum conservation law. Rearranging factors in Equation 11.19a,

$$M_1 v_1 = M_2 v_2,$$

or

$$p_1 = p_2,$$

where p_1 and p_2 are the magnitudes of the usual three momenta of the particles defined in terms of *dynamic* rather than *rest* mass. That is,

$$p = Mv = \frac{M_0 v}{\sqrt{1 - v^2/c^2}}. \tag{11.20}$$

There is no a priori reason to expect that momentum conservation should be applicable at high velocities. But experimental studies of elementary particle processes indicate that *if* the momentum of a particle is defined as in Equation 11.20 then momentum conservation has validity at arbitrarily high velocities. For example, Figure 4.6 shows the mutual annihilation of an antiproton and a proton in a liquid hydrogen bubble chamber into at least four secondary particles. In this and all elementary particle reactions, the total *three*-momentum of the system remains constant. That is, if the particles A and B interact to yield $C, D, E, \ldots$, then:

$$\mathbf{p}_A + \mathbf{p}_B = \mathbf{p}_C + \mathbf{p}_D + \mathbf{p}_E + \cdots,$$

where, to repeat, the magnitudes of the three momenta are given by Equation 11.20. Thus the experimental validity of the generalized momentum conservation law demonstrates the consistency of Equations 11.19a and 11.19b, and also shows that henceforth we must regard inertial mass as a function of velocity.

If a particle travels with velocity c then the denominator of Equation 11.19b is zero, and the dynamic mass of the particle is infinite *unless* $M_0 = 0$, in which case $M = 0/0$, which is indeterminate. It follows that if we want to assign a rest mass to a photon then $M_0 = 0$, which would have no meaning in a Newtonian context. However, the dynamic mass of a particle is always defined in terms of its interactions with another particle. Thus, for example, if both the momentum and velocity of a particle or its energy and velocity are known, then M follows at once (Sections 11.9 and 11.10). In the former case we have $M = p/v$ (Equation 11.20), and thus, for a photon, $M = p/c$. Since the momenta of photons can be defined by means of their interactions with matter (through Compton scattering, for example), they certainly have dynamic mass. In physics we are always concerned with the interactions of particles, and since photons *always* have speed

c, the fact that they must have zero rest mass should raise no conceptual difficulties. After all, they never *are* at rest!

We can now interpret the *four* momentum components given by Equations 11.18. Substituting Equation 11.20 into Equations 11.18:

$$P_1 = Mv_x = p_x, \tag{11.21a}$$

$$P_2 = p_y, \tag{11.21b}$$

$$P_3 = p_z, \tag{11.21c}$$

$$P_4 = Mc. \tag{11.21d}$$

That is, the first three components of four-momentum are the Newtonian three-momentum components defined in terms of dynamic mass M, while the fourth component is the product Mc.

The variation of the ratio of the masses of two particles with velocity can be demonstrated in any number of elementary particle interactions (Chapters 22 and 23). For example (Figure 11.15), the positive pi-meson (π^+) with rest mass about one-sixth the proton rest mass ($M_p = 1.6 \times 10^{-27}$ kg) and the positive K-meson (K^+) with rest mass slightly in excess of one-half the proton mass, each decay into a positive muon (μ^+) and a neutral particle called the neutrino (ν) about 2×10^{-8} sec after being created in a high energy proton-proton interaction (Chapter 22). That is:

$$\pi^+ \to \mu^+ + \nu,$$
$$K^+ \to \mu^+ + \nu.$$

If the particles are at rest when they decay, then for present purposes we may regard each decay as being analogous to the explosion of a shell lying on a table that propels two fragments in opposite directions. From other elementary particle experiments it is known that neutrinos always travel with speed c, which, as we have already seen, is possible if we assign them zero rest mass. Therefore, if the ratio v_μ/v_ν were constant regardless of the speeds of the interacting muon and neutrino, the muon would emerge with the same speed from both π^+- and K^+-decay reactions. Its speed can be determined in each case by stopping π^+- and K^+-mesons in a bubble chamber and observing the curvature of the muon tracks from the decays (Figure 9.29). Referring to Equation 9.18 the radius of curvature of the muon tracks should be:

$$R = \frac{Mv}{eB},$$

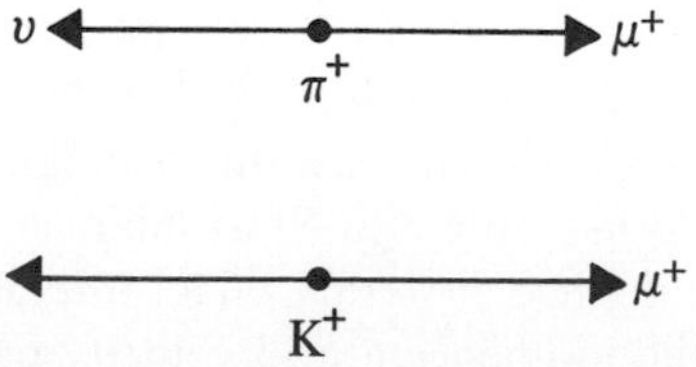

FIGURE 11.15 The decay of a π- and a K-meson at rest. The relativistically defined momenta of the μ^+ and ν are equal and opposite in both instances. However the ratios of the speeds of the decay products are different for the two decays. We conclude that inertial mass, defined as in Chapter 4, cannot be constant if momentum conservation is retained in relativity.

where e is the muon charge. Measurements indicate that the radii of curvature of muons from K^+ decay are greater than the radii of curvature of muons from π^+ decay. Therefore, the former have greater speeds. Since the ratio of the speeds of the interacting neutrinos and muons is not constant in all circumstances it follows that the ratio of their masses (Equation 4.2) can not be constant either. Thus inertial mass, defined in terms of two-body interactions, can no longer be regarded as a constant, as we have already noted.

◤◤ 11.9 The equivalence of mass and energy

How shall we interpret the component $P_4 = Mc$? We have seen that the total *three*-momentum of a system of interacting particles remains constant for arbitrary speeds. Does a similar law apply to the total *four*-momentum of a system? Figure 11.16 shows two particles of equal rest mass, M_0, approaching each other along the x-axis of a co-ordinate system. If the particles stick together following their collision then we can find some inertial system in which they are at rest after their interaction. Since their rest masses are equal, then momentum conservation requires that in this particular system their velocities before collision are equal and opposite. Applying Equations 11.19, the *dynamical* mass of each of the particles before collision is

$$M_1 = M_2 = \frac{M_0}{\sqrt{1 - v^2/c^2}},$$

and the total mass of the two particle system before collision:

$$\frac{2M_0}{\sqrt{1 - v^2/c^2}}.$$

Following their collision both particles are at rest. How, then, shall we account for the fact that the mass of the system is $2M_0/\sqrt{1 - v^2/c^2}$ rather than $2M_0$? That is, what is the origin of the excess mass?

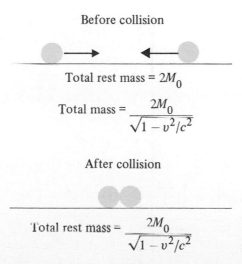

Before collision

Total rest mass = $2M_0$

Total mass = $\dfrac{2M_0}{\sqrt{1 - v^2/c^2}}$

After collision

Total rest mass = $\dfrac{2M_0}{\sqrt{1 - v^2/c^2}}$

FIGURE 11.16   A completely inelastic collision between two particles with equal rest mass approaching each other with equal and opposite velocities. The fact that the final rest mass is greater than the sum of the initial rest masses leads to Einstein's famous conclusion regarding the equivalence of mass and energy.

Using the binomial expansion (Appendix D), we may approximate the factor $= 1/\sqrt{1 - v^2/c^2} = (1 - v^2/c^2)^{-1/2}$ as

$$\frac{1}{\sqrt{1 - v^2/c^2}} = 1 + \frac{1}{2}\left(\frac{v}{c}\right)^2 + \frac{3}{8}\left(\frac{v}{c}\right)^4 + \cdots.$$

(Terms that vary as the sixth, eighth, etc. power of v/c are summarized as ....) For speeds that are small relative to c the fourth-power term is negligible compared with the term $\frac{1}{2}(v/c)^2$. Then to an excellent approximation:

$$\frac{2M_0}{\sqrt{1 - v^2/c^2}} = 2M_0\left(1 + \frac{1}{2}\frac{v^2}{c^2}\right) = 2M_0 + \frac{\frac{1}{2}(2M_0)v^2}{c^2}. \tag{11.22a}$$

That is, the mass of the two-particle system is approximately equal to its rest mass *plus* a term equal to its kinetic energy divided by the square of the velocity of light.

Any collision in which two particles stick together is called a totally inelastic collision. Such interactions do not conserve *kinetic* energy. Rather they transfer some kinetic energy into the internal energy of the colliding particles themselves (Section 7.7). If ΔU represents the internal energy of the system after the collision then the classical energy conservation equation for the collision may be written (Equation 7.14):

$$\frac{1}{2}(2M_0)v^2 = \Delta U,$$

and Equation 11.22a becomes:

$$\frac{2M_0}{\sqrt{1 - v^2/c^2}} = 2M_0 + \frac{\Delta U}{c^2}. \tag{11.22b}$$

As a result of the interaction, part of the mass of the two-particle system is transferred into internal energy of the system. In other words, Equation 11.22b implies that inertial mass and energy are basically interchangeable concepts, and that while neither the classical laws of energy and mass conservation are separately valid, we have found a *new* conservation law incorporating both energy and inertial mass. In Einstein's words, "The inertia of a body is a measure of its energy content," which is a profound insight into the nature of the concepts that is based ultimately upon the symmetry principle implied by the law of inertia and by the measured constancy of the velocity of light.

Let us define the *total energy* of a particle of mass M as:

$$E = Mc^2. \tag{11.23a}$$

Using Equation 11.19 total energy may also be written in terms of rest mass:

$$E = \frac{M_0c^2}{\sqrt{1 - v^2/c^2}},$$

which by means of the binomial expansion (Appendix D) becomes

$$E = M_0c^2\left[1 + \frac{1}{2}\left(\frac{v}{c}\right)^2 + \cdots\right] = M_0c^2 + \frac{1}{2}M_0v^2 + \cdots,$$

an approximation valid for velocities that are small compared with c. Thus the total energy of a particle is equal to a term M_0c^2 plus its kinetic energy, and we may interpret the increase in a particle's mass with velocity as an increase in that energy!

In analogy with Equation 11.23a we may call the term M_0c^2 the *rest energy* of the particle:

$$E_0 = M_0c^2. \tag{11.23b}$$

Equation 11.23b indicates that the energy equivalent to 1 kg is 9×10^{16} J. Thus one often sees statements such as: "If the entire mass of a one-kilogram object were all converted into electric energy, thirty million 100-watt bulbs could be powered for one year." We should note, however, that the "if" is fortunately very large. Matter can only be annihilated and become kinetic energy by means of some one of the fundamental interactions, and the nature of the fundamental interactions among the elementary particles apparently does not permit the conversion of more than a small fraction of any macroscopic mass into energy (Chapter 23). If this were not the case then matter would not be stable with respect to spontaneous conversion into energy.

Of course in special circumstances the rest mass of a system is changed and converted into kinetic energy. In Chapter 20 we shall deal with the best known instances of such conversion, i.e., the nuclear rearrangements upon which principles of fission and fusion bombs are based.

It is frequently convenient to express the rest masses of the elementary particles in terms of their rest energies measured in electron volts. For example, the rest mass of an electron is 9×10^{-31} kg. Hence (Equation 11.23b), it has rest energy:

$$E_0 = 9 \times 10^{-31} \times (3 \times 10^8)^2$$
$$= 8.1 \times 10^{-14} \text{ J.}$$

But (Equation 10.4) $1 \text{ eV} = 1.6 \times 10^{-19}$ J, so:

$$E_0(\text{electron}) = \frac{8.1 \times 10^{-14}}{1.6 \times 10^{-19}} = 5.1 \times 10^5 \text{ eV.}$$

Likewise, a proton with $M_0 = 1.6 \times 10^{-27}$ kg has rest energy 9.38×10^8 eV, or 938 MeV. For future use let us calculate the mass equivalent to 1 MeV (10^6 eV) energy:

$$E_0 = 1.6 \times 10^{-19} \times 10^6 = 1.6 \times 10^{-13} \text{ J,}$$

so

$$M_0 = \frac{1.6 \times 10^{-13}}{9 \times 10^{16}} = 1.78 \times 10^{-30} \text{ kg.}$$

That is,

$$1 \text{ MeV} = (1.78 \times 10^{-30} \text{ kg})c^2. \tag{11.24}$$

◣◣ 11.10 The energy-momentum four-vector. Energy-momentum conservation*

Equation 11.23a relates the total energy of a particle to its mass. Using this expression we can also write a general relation between total energy, three-momentum, and rest mass valid in any inertial system. Referring to Equation 11.21d, the fourth component of four-momentum is equal to the product Mc, and thus also:

$$P_4 = \frac{E}{c}.$$

In addition, P_1, P_2, and P_3 are equal to the x-, y-, and z-components of three-momentum defined in terms of dynamic mass (Equations 11.21a through 11.21c). Therefore, we can write the magnitude of the four-momentum squared (Equation 11.16) as

$$|\bar{P}|^2 = \frac{E^2}{c^2} - (p_x^2 + p_y^2 + p_z^2).$$

---

* This section may be omitted without serious loss of continuity.

However, $p_x^2 + p_y^2 + p_z^2 = p^2$, the magnitude of the three-momentum squared, so

$$E^2 - c^2p^2 = c^2|\bar{P}|^2. \tag{11.25a}$$

Since $|\bar{P}|$ is a Lorenz-invariant scalar Equation 11.25a is valid in *all* inertial systems. The individual values of E^2 and p^2 depend in general on the inertial system in which they are measured. However, the difference $E^2 - c^2p^2$ does not. By substituting $|\bar{P}| = M_0c$ into Equation 11.25a we can cast the relation between total energy and momentum in a more useful form:

$$E^2 - c^2p^2 = (M_0c^2)^2. \tag{11.25b}$$

This equation offers a convenient operational definition of rest energy, M_0c^2. It is the square root of the measured difference between the square of the total energy of a particle and product of the square of its momentum times c^2. From this point of view a zero rest-mass particle is simply a particle with the property that has $E = cp$ in all circumstances.

In order to illustrate the use of Equation 11.25b let us calculate the total energy in MeV and the velocity of a proton whose radius of curvature in a constant, 1.5 Wb/m² magnetic field is 2 m. The rest energy of a proton (Section 11.9) is 938 MeV, while its charge is $+1.6 \times 10^{-19}$ C.

Referring to Equation 9.18, $R = p/eB$. Then the proton's momentum is

$$p = 1.6 \times 10^{-19} \times 1.5 \times 20,$$
$$= 4.8 \times 10^{-19} \text{ kg-m/sec}^2.$$
$$cp = 3 \times 10^8 \times 4.8 \times 10^{-19} = 14.4 \times 10^{-11} \text{ J}.$$

Since cp has the dimensions of energy it can be expressed in electron volts by using the equation $1 \text{ eV} = 1.6 \times 10^{-19}$ J. Thus:

$$cp = \frac{14.4 \times 10^{-11}}{1.6 \times 10^{-19}} = 9 \times 10^8 \text{ eV}.$$

We can now substitute into Equation 11.25b to find the total energy of the proton:

$$E^2 = (9 \times 10^8)^2 + (9.38 \times 10^8)^2 = 169 \times 10^{16} \text{ eV}.$$

So,

$$E = 13 \times 10^8 \text{ eV} = 1.3 \text{ BeV (billion electron volts)}.$$

The velocity of the proton is most easily determined by comparing Equations 11.20 and 11.23a:

$$p = Mv, \qquad E = Mc^2.$$

Dividing the first by the second,

$$\frac{p}{E} = \frac{v}{c^2},$$

or

$$\frac{v}{c} = \frac{cp}{E}. \tag{11.26}$$

Then,

$$\frac{v}{c} = \frac{9 \times 10^8 \text{ eV}}{13 \times 10^8 \text{ eV}} = 0.695.$$

The proton has almost 70% the velocity of light.

What is the radius of curvature of a positive π-meson ($M_0 c^2 = 140$ MeV) with the same total energy in the same magnetic field?

The momentum of the π-meson can be calculated using Equation 11.25b:

$$cp = \sqrt{(13 \times 10^8)^2 - (1.4 \times 10^8)^2},$$
$$= 12.9 \times 10^8 \text{ eV}.$$

Referring to Equation 11.26, $v/c = 12.9 \times 10^8/13 = 0.995$, so that the π-meson's velocity is more than 99% the velocity of light. In order to find the particle's radius of curvature, its momentum must first be expressed in absolute mks units:

$$cp = 12.9 \times 10^8 \times 1.6 \times 10^{-19} = 20.6 \times 10^{-11} \text{ J},$$

$$p = \frac{20.6 \times 10^{-11}}{3 \times 10^8} = 6.9 \times 10^{-19} \text{ kg-m/sec}^2.$$

Substituting into Equation 9.18 with $q = +1.6 \times 10^{-19}$ C, we have the radius of curvature of the meson in a 1.5 Wb/m^2 magnetic field:

$$R = \frac{6.9 \times 10^{-19}}{1.6 \times 10^{-19} \times 1.5} = 2.88 \text{ m}.$$

As a further example we can find the momenta and energies of the muon and neutrino from the decay of a π-meson at rest (Figure 11.15). Since the π-meson decays at rest, the total energy of the system is equal to its 140 MeV rest energy, and the total momentum is zero. Energy and momentum conservation give

$$140 = E_\mu + E_\nu$$

$$\mathbf{p}_\mu + \mathbf{p}_\nu = 0,$$

or

$$c^2 p_\mu^2 = c^2 p_\nu^2.$$

But from Equation 11.25b, $E_\nu^2 - c^2 p_\nu^2 = 0$, since $M_{0\nu} = 0$, so $cp_\nu = E_\nu$. Also $c^2 p_\mu^2 = E_\mu^2 - M_{0\mu}^2 c^4$, and since $M_{0\mu}^2 c^4 = (106 \text{ MeV})^2$:

$$E_\mu^2 - (106)^2 = E_\nu^2,$$

or

$$E_\mu^2 = E_\nu^2 + (106)^2. \tag{a}$$

We can also write the energy conservation equation as

$$E_\mu = 140 - E_\nu,$$

so that

$$E_\mu^2 = (140)^2 - 2(140)E_\nu + E_\nu^2. \tag{b}$$

Eliminating E_μ^2 between (a) and (b),

$$(140)^2 - 2 \times 140 \times E_\nu + E_\nu^2 = E_\nu^2 + (106)^2,$$

and solving for E_ν,

$$E_\nu = \frac{(140)^2 - (106)^2}{280} = 30 \text{ MeV}.$$

The momentum of the neutrino follows from:

$$p_\nu = \frac{E_\nu}{c} = \frac{30 \text{ MeV}}{c},$$

which is also the magnitude of the muon's momentum. Finally, the total energy of the muon can be calculated using the energy conservation relation:

$$E_\mu = 140 - 30 = 110 \text{ MeV}.$$

In the foregoing example we used the energy and momentum conservation laws separately to find the energies and the momenta of decay products of a π-meson. Since energy and momentum are components of the same four-vector, the two laws can be combined into one with the statement that *the total four-momentum vector of an interacting system of particles remains constant*. In addition, the invariance of $|\bar{P}|$ insures the validity of four-momentum conservation in *all* inertial systems. If, for instance, $\bar{P}_1$ and $\bar{P}_2$ are the four-momenta of two particles before their interaction, and $\bar{P}_3$ and $\bar{P}_4$ the four-momenta of two particles that emerge from the interaction, either or both of which may be different from the initial state particles, then

$$\bar{P}_1 + \bar{P}_2 = \bar{P}_3 + \bar{P}_4. \tag{11.27a}$$

Generalization to multiparticle systems is straightforward. Like the analogous equations between three-dimensional vectors, Equation 11.27a is a shorthand notation for four separate equations relating the components of the four-vectors. In the two-dimensional collision problems of Chapter 4 we first selected a convenient coordinate system (usually choosing the x-axis as the direction of the initial momentum), and then formulated the problem in terms of conservation of the separate x- and y-components of momentum. Similarly, we may formulate these more general problems by choosing a convenient inertial system, and then expressing Equation 11.27a in terms of equations between components. The first three components of the four-vector $\bar{P}$ are related to Newtonian momentum. Therefore, in any system:

$$\mathbf{p}_1 + \mathbf{p}_2 = \mathbf{p}_3 + \mathbf{p}_4, \tag{11.27b}$$

which is simply the three-momentum conservation law. Likewise the equation between the fourth components of the four-vectors gives the energy conservation law:

$$E_1 + E_2 = E_3 + E_4. \tag{11.27c}$$

Often these equations may be applied separately, as in the π-meson decay calculation. However, in the next section we shall give an example of the use of the full four-vector law, Equation 11.27a.

Finally, it would be well to redefine kinetic energy so that it is consistent with these considerations. Since:

$$E = Mc^2 = \frac{M_0 c^2}{\sqrt{1 - v^2/c^2}},$$

we can use the binomial expansion (Appendix D to text) as in Section 11.9 to derive the approximate relation:

$$E = M_0 c^2 \left(1 + \frac{1}{2}\left(\frac{v}{c}\right)^2 + \cdots \right) = E_0 + KE,$$

which is valid for small velocities. However, at large velocities the next term in the expansion, $\frac{3}{8}(v/c)^4$, is comparable to $\frac{1}{2}(v/c)^2$. For example, if $v/c = 0.5$ then $\frac{1}{2}(v/c)^2 = 0.125$ while $\frac{3}{8}(v/c)^4 = 0.024$; the error introduced by neglecting the latter term would be $0.024/(0.125 + 0.024) = 18.4\%$. Therefore, let us redefine kinetic energy as the *difference* between total energy and rest energy:

$$KE = E - E_0 = (M - M_0)c^2. \tag{11.28}$$

At velocities small enough to justify neglecting the term $\frac{3}{8}(v/c)^4$ relative to $\frac{1}{2}(v/c)^2$ Equation 11.8 reduces to $KE = \frac{1}{2}Mv^2$.

▲▲ 11.11 Derivation of the Compton-scattering kinematic equation*

We shall now apply our general conservation principle Equation 11.27a to an interaction that cannot be formulated in Newtonian terms: derivation of the energy shift of a Compton-scattered photon (Equation 10.5). In Figure 11.17 a photon with energy $E_{\mathrm{ph}}(i)$ traveling in the x-direction scatters from an electron through an angle θ. We want to relate the scattering angle to the energy lost by the photon in the scattering process. Let $\bar{P}_{\mathrm{ph}}(i)$ and $\bar{P}_e(i)$ be the four-momenta of the photon and electron before scattering, $\bar{P}_{\mathrm{ph}}(f)$ and $\bar{P}_e(f)$ their respective four-momenta after scattering. Then the general conservation equation (Equation 11.27a) takes the form

$$\bar{P}_{\mathrm{ph}}(i) + \bar{P}_e(i) = \bar{P}_{\mathrm{ph}}(f) + \bar{P}_e(f),$$

or

$$\bar{P}_{\mathrm{ph}}(i) - \bar{P}_{\mathrm{ph}}(f) = \bar{P}_e(f) - \bar{P}_e(i).$$

The square of the four-momentum of a system is an invariant. Therefore,

$$(\bar{P}_{\mathrm{ph}}(i) - \bar{P}_{\mathrm{ph}}(f))^2 = (\bar{P}_e(f) - \bar{P}_e(i))^2,$$

or, performing the indicated multiplications,

$$|\bar{P}_{\mathrm{ph}}(i)|^2 + |\bar{P}_{\mathrm{ph}}(f)|^2 - 2\bar{P}_{\mathrm{ph}}(i) \cdot \bar{P}_{\mathrm{ph}}(f) = |\bar{P}_e(f)|^2 + |\bar{P}_e(i)|^2 - 2\bar{P}_e(i) \cdot \bar{P}_e(f),$$

which is a valid equation in all inertial systems. Now the squares of the four-momenta are equal to $(M_0c)^2$ (Equation 11.17), and the photon rest mass is a zero, so, $P_{\mathrm{ph}}^2 = 0$. Letting M_e denote the electron rest mass we have:

$$-\bar{P}_{\mathrm{ph}}(i) \cdot \bar{P}_{\mathrm{ph}}(f) = (M_ec)^2 - \bar{P}_e(i) \cdot \bar{P}_e(f).$$

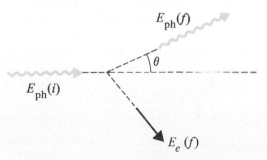

FIGURE 11.17 The Compton effect.

* This section may be omitted without loss of continuity.

Our equation involves the products of four-vectors. In order to evaluate these we introduce two rules from advanced vector algebra:

1. The product of two four-vectors, $\bar{A}$ and $\bar{B}$, is a Lorentz-invariant scalar whose magnitude expressed in terms of its components is

$$\bar{A} \cdot \bar{B} = A_4 B_4 - (A_1 B_1 + A_2 B_2 + A_3 B_3).$$

If $\bar{A}$ and $\bar{B}$ are the same vectors then the product is just the magnitude of the vector squared.

2. The product of two *three*-vectors, **a** and **b**, is a scalar relative to coordinate rotations and has magnitude

$$\mathbf{a} \cdot \mathbf{b} = a_x b_x + a_y b_y + a_z b_z.$$

Again, if $\mathbf{a} = \mathbf{b}$ the product is the square of the vector's magnitude.

3. The product of two three-vectors can also be written in terms of the magnitudes of the vectors and the angle θ between them:

$$\mathbf{a} \cdot \mathbf{b} = ab \cos \theta.$$

Using rule 1 we can write the conservation equation in terms of the components of four-vectors. For both photon and electron:

$$\bar{P}(i) \cdot \bar{P}(f) = c^2 P_4(i) P_4(f) - [P_1(i)P_1(f) + P_2(i)P_2(f) + P_3(i)P_3(f)].$$

But $P_4 = E/c$ and P_1, P_2, and P_3 are equal, respectively, to the three-momentum components p_x, p_y, and p_z, so

$$\bar{P}(i) \cdot \bar{P}(f) = \frac{E(i)E(f)}{c^2} - [p_x(i)p_x(f) + p_y(i)p_y(f) + p_z(i)p_z(f)].$$

Comparing rules 2 and 3, the sum of the products of the three-momentum components can also be written as $p(i)p(f) \cos \theta$, where θ is the angle between the initial and final momenta:

$$\bar{P}(i) \cdot \bar{P}(f) = \frac{E(i)E(f)}{c^2} - p(i)p(f) \cos \theta.$$

Our conservation equation involves a term $\bar{P}(i) \cdot \bar{P}(f)$ for both photon and electron. In the former case $M_0 = 0$ and thus (Equation 11.25b) $p = E/c$. Therefore:

$$\bar{P}_{\mathrm{ph}}(i) \cdot \bar{P}_{\mathrm{ph}}(f) = \frac{E_{\mathrm{ph}}(i)E_{\mathrm{ph}}(f)}{c^2} (1 - \cos \theta),$$

where θ is the scattering angle (Figure 11.17). The electron is initially at rest. Therefore, $E_e(i) = M_e c^2$, $p_e(i) = 0$, and

$$\bar{P}_e(i) \cdot \bar{P}_e(f) = E_e(f)M_e.$$

Substituting the two four-vector products into the conservation equation:

$$\frac{E_{\mathrm{ph}}(i)E_{\mathrm{ph}}(f)}{c^2} (1 - \cos \theta) = (M_e c)^2 - E_e(f)M_e.$$

The energy conservation equation for the system is

$$E_{\mathrm{ph}}(i) + M_e c^2 = E_{\mathrm{ph}}(f) + E_e(f),$$

so that if $\Delta E_{ph} = E_{ph}(i) - E_{ph}(f)$ is the change in the photon energy then $E_e(f) = \Delta E_{ph} + M_e c^2$, and, substituting we find:

$$\frac{E_{ph}(i)E_{ph}(f)}{c^2}(1 - \cos\theta) = (M_e c)^2 - M_e(\Delta E_{ph} + M_e c^2) = -M_e \Delta E_{ph}.$$

As we saw in Section 10.5 the energy lost by a Compton-scattered photon is usually small compared to its initial energy. If that is so then to a good approximation $E_{ph}(i)E_{ph}(f) = E_{ph}^2(i)$, and we have

$$\frac{E_{ph}^2(i)}{c^2}(1 - \cos\theta) = -M_e \Delta E_{ph},$$

or, finally, upon rearranging factors,

$$\Delta E_{ph} = -\frac{E_{ph}^2(i)}{M_e c^2}(1 - \cos\theta),$$

which is Equation 10.5 and, as we saw in Chapter 10, is consistent with experiment. Since the equation involves no more than the generalized energy-momentum relations, its experimental verification is evidence not only for the validity of the photon concept, but for special relativity as well.

The simplicity and the power of the basic energy-momentum conservation equation in solving general interaction problems should not be obscured by the rather lengthy series of algebraic manipulations required to derive Equation 10.5. Momentum, energy, and inertial mass as well as the corresponding conservation laws are unconnected in classical physics. The four-vector algebra demanded by the invariance of physical laws links the concepts and their laws, allowing us to regard them as different aspects of the same conserved quantity. By investigating the consequences of reconciling a symmetry based upon the law of inertia with the observed constancy of the velocity of light we have, with Einstein, not only arrived at a new understanding of the meaning of time and space in physics, but have achieved an unexpected insight into the relationship between three of our fundamental conservation laws. The total advance in our understanding is not inconsiderable.

▲▲ 11.12 The basic postulate of general relativity and its geometric interpretation*

Special relativity will continue to play an important role in our considerations. The unique character of the formulation we have developed becomes increasingly evident in processes that involve speeds close to the speed of light. Since many atomic, and virtually all subatomic interactions are characterized by velocities of that order, most contemporary physicists are so familiar with the special theory that they take it quite for granted. It is no exaggeration to say that many of its predictions, time dilation, the Lorentz contraction, the mass-energy equivalence, the relationship between energy, momentum, and rest mass, for instance, are unconsciously verified at high-energy accelerator laboratories several hundred times a day.

Special relativity developed from the work of several men. H. A. Lorentz sought an explanation for the measured constancy of the velocity of light by incorporating time dilation and the Lorentz contraction into a generalization of Maxwell's electromagnetic

---

*This section may be omitted without serious loss of continuity.

synthesis. H. Poincaré scrutinized some of the philosophical problems involved. A. Einstein obtained Lorentz's results from his definition of time in terms of simultaneity and the synchronization of clocks, and first derived the connection between inertial mass and energy. H. Minkowski introduced the four-dimensional formulation of the theory. Special relativity arose because of a clear experimental necessity of reconciling two fundamental sets of observations that are irreconcilable in terms of Newtonian concepts of time and space. As we have noted, its results have been completely incorporated into the central, developing stream of contemporary physics.

On the contrary, the foundation of the general theory of relativity rests almost exclusively upon the profound insight of Albert Einstein. Instead of being developed to resolve an experimentally based set of paradoxes, it arose from his insistence on following the philosophical implications of symmetry principles to their logical limits. We have mentioned the general theory on at least two previous occasions (Section 5.10, Section 6.13), and noted that it is principally concerned with the gravitational interaction. Just as the deviations from Newtonian physics predicted by special relativity became appreciable and hence readily measurable only at high velocities, so the specific deviations that follow from general relativity are evident only in the vicinity of large gravitational masses or over distances in space that are comparable to the observational capacity of the largest telescopes. Since the major activity in physics since the early years of this century has centered about atomic and subatomic processes, general relativity has been something of a sideline. However, recent interest in the fundamental character of the cosmos together with an extension of the range and precision of astronomic observations has led to a revival of interest in its implications. In any event, a brief discussion of the general theory and a few of its results is well worthwhile, if only to illustrate the majestic heights to which the human imagination and intellect may aspire when it accepts the discipline imposed by exploring the logical limits of a well-established principle.

As noted in Section 6.13, the centripetal accelerations due to the rotation of the earth on its axis and its revolution about the sun imply that a coordinate system fixed relative to the earth is not a true inertial system. In most cases the approximation that it *is* leads to only small discrepancies between theory and observation. Yet, as Einstein asked, how can we formulate the laws of physics as they *would* appear in a true inertial system without ever having experienced an inertial system? If we try to imagine what an inertial system might be we are ultimately led to a system that exists in the depths of intergalactic space far from all matter. That is, we are led to a system completely divorced from matter, hence completely removed from experience, and therefore, completely unsuited for our purposes. Thus if we follow Einstein by defining time and space in terms of observable physical processes we are led to the conclusion that a consistent formulation of physics cannot assume the existence of *any* particular preferred type of reference system. In other words, we seek a formulation which is equally valid in all possible systems, inertial systems, rotating systems, linearly accelerating systems, for instance. Given such a formulation, we may then apply it to any particular system encountered in a specific application.

As we saw in Chapter 6, the admission that the laws of physics have equal validity in all systems including noninertial systems immediately introduces the problem of the so-called fictitious forces. These forces, which originate in the noninertial character of a system, have the unique feature of producing the same acceleration on all objects independent of their masses. Of course the gravitational force exhibits precisely this feature, and thus the equivalence of gravitational and inertial mass leads to the conclusion that gravitational effects and effects due to acceleration cannot be distinguished (Section 5.10).

For instance, all objects in an elevator in free space accelerating "upward" at 9.8 m/sec² experience a downward acceleration relative to their environment which is equal to the acceleration due to gravity on earth. Conversely, all objects in a freely falling elevator on earth experience no acceleration relative to their environment. They are weightless, or, equivalently, in a gravitation-free environment.

We have seen that in special relativity space and time do not have a unique meaning in two different inertial systems. Meter sticks contract, clocks slow down. In the general theory, even meter sticks at rest relative to each other in a noninertial system warp, and clocks at rest relative to each other mark time at different rates. Thus length and time measurements in the conventional sense do not even have a unique meaning at all points in the same system.

A rather well-known example of Einstein's illustrates the point. Let us consider measurements performed by two observers. A is in an inertial system, B in a system fixed relative to a turntable that rotates rapidly from the viewpoint of observer A (Figure 11.18). When B stands at a point a distance R from the center of the turntable he experiences a fictitious outward force, Mv^2/R, where v is his speed relative to observer A. He chooses to call this a gravitational force due to distant matter, which increases in strength as he moves farther from the origin of his system at the center of the turntable.

Suppose that by using meter sticks laid end to end, observer B constructs several circles of increasing radius concentric to the center of the turntable, and observes them all from his origin where his velocity relative to observer A is zero. The purpose of the exercise is to determine the circumference of the circles. If he were to adopt the viewpoint of observer A, namely that system B is rotating, then relative to the origin of that system all the meter sticks move parallel to their lengths, and thus all contract according to Equation 11.2. Since the speed of the turntable increases toward its perimeter, the degree of contraction must also increase. Hence observer B in his noninertial system concludes that the length of a meter stick decreases with increasing gravitational force. He cannot define a unique length through his system!

If observer B wants to measure the *diameters* of his concentric circles, however, he lays the meter sticks perpendicular to the direction of "motion" and hence observes no contraction. Therefore, observer B concludes that the ratios of the circumferences to the

FIGURE 11.18 A frame of reference on a rotating turntable. Observer B measures the ratio of the circumference to the diameter of a circle centered at his origin. To observer A, in an inertial system, a meter stick along the *circumference* moves parallel to its orientation and therefore contracts whereas a meterstick along a *diameter* is perpendicular to its motion and does not. Observer B attributes the measured decrease in the ratio of the circumference to the diameter of his circles as a non-Euclidean effect. The effect becomes more pronounced with increasing r.

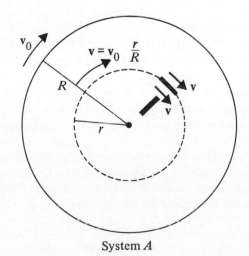

System A

diameters of the circles are *not* equal to π, *and that the theorems of Euclidean geometry are not applicable in his system.* Further, since the contraction of the circumferences increases with increasing distance from the origin of the system (i.e., with the strength of the gravitational force), he concludes that the departure from the Euclidean nature of space increases with increasing gravitational force.

As a consequence of such arguments we are led to the conclusion that the laws of physics in general relativity must be formulated in non-Euclidean geometry. In other words, we must dispense with Cartesian coordinate systems. A similar situation applies to the measurement of time. If observer *B* places a number of clocks along a radial line in his system they will slow down according to Equation 11.1, the effect increasing with increasing distance from the origin. It is not possible to define either a single time or a single length that has the same meaning everywhere *even in one reference system.*

The three spatial dimensions and time, taken together, constitute four-dimensional "space" or "spacetime." The use of conventional standards of length and time together with the assumption that these are invariant in a particular reference system is tantamount to assuming the validity of the Euclidean theorems. As we have noted, special relativity can be formulated by generalizing Euclidean geometry to four dimensions. The mathematical formulation of general relativity starts with the assumption that four-dimensional "space" becomes "warped," or non-Euclidean, in the presence of matter. However, the laws of physics are to be written in a form that is independent of *any* specific geometric assumptions (that *x*, *y*, and *z* are everywhere perpendicular, for instance). When in special relativity the laws written in terms of four-vectors are expressed in a particular inertial system, they yield expressions valid in that particular system. Their formulation in terms of four-vectors insures their validity in all such systems. Similarly, when the general relativistic laws are written in terms of a particular *geometry* determined by a particular distribution of matter, they describe effects that may be interpreted as gravitational. Thus the gravitational interaction arises as a consequence of the geometry of space itself.

▲▲ 11.13 Non-Euclidean geometry and general relativity*

Physics, and science in general, may be regarded as an open system of laws and logical consequences derived from those laws. It is open because it is based upon observations of the external universe. In contrast geometry, like all branches of pure mathematics, is *not* a science. Rather, it is a closed, logical system whose theorems and their results follow from a set of internal axioms and postulates. A result in physics is incorrect if it is in conflict with observation. A result in geometry is incorrect only if it contradicts the internal logic of the system.

In Euclidean geometry, for instance, a circle is defined not as a figure drawn on paper with a compass, but as the locus of points everywhere equidistant from a point called the center. Based upon the internal logic of Euclidean geometry we conclude that the ratio of the circumference to the diameter of a figure so defined is the number $\pi = 3.14159. \ldots$

If a figure *called* a circle is drawn on a large piece of paper with a compass, then, not by the Euclidean definition but by the *operation of drawing the circle*, we conclude that the figure is everywhere equidistant from its center. If *in addition* measurement shows the ratio of its circumference to its diameter is π we conclude that our *physical* circle is

---

* This section may be omitted without serious loss of continuity.

described by Euclidean geometry, and further that the region of space where it is drawn is Euclidean. That is, application of a particular geometry to *physical* systems first requires that measurements be performed using tangible, physical standards—meter sticks, for instance. But since meter sticks are not invariant even in special relativity it follows that a measured system need not be describable, a priori, in terms of Euclidean theorems.

Non-Euclidean geometrics were extensively studied in the nineteenth century. All are based upon a change in one or more of the Euclidean postulates. For instance, an important Euclidean postulate concerning parallel lines states that in a given plane one and only one line parallel to another line can be drawn through a given point. There are two extreme alternate postulates: (1) through a given point *any number* of lines can be drawn parallel to a given line, or (2) through a given point *no* line can be drawn parallel to a given line.

The first alteration in the postulate leads to geometry whose two-dimensional version is the geometry on the surface of a sphere. The earth is a three-dimensional body in three-dimensional space. But if measurement is restricted to its surface it is not difficult to see that the first of the alternative postulates is applicable. Choose a longitude line, for instance, and pick the North Pole as the requisite point (Figure 11.19). We may define two lines as parallel if they are mutually perpendicular to a third line. Since all longitude lines are perpendicular to the equator then by this criterion they are parallel. But all pass through the North Pole—which we have selected as our "test point"!

The shortest distance between any two points on the earth's surface in *three* dimensions is a straight-line tunnel through the earth. If we are confined to the two-dimensional surface the shortest distance between the two points is the longer, great circle distance. (For example, in three dimensions the shortest distance between the poles is the diameter, whereas the shortest distance on the surface is half the circumference.) An observer on the surface who perceived but two dimensions could *not* burrow through the earth, or even conceive of the possibility. Thus he would think of the great circle distance between two points as a straight line, for in his space it *is* the shortest distance between the points.

From this it follows that the ratio of the circumference to the diameter of a circle drawn on the surface of a sphere is *not* equal to π, and is in fact a function of diameter.

FIGURE 11.19 Any two longitude lines on the surface of a sphere are perpendicular to the equator and yet pass through both poles. In addition, the sum of the angles of the triangle formed by the two longitude lines and the equator is greater than 180°. Hence the spherical surface is decidedly non-Euclidean.

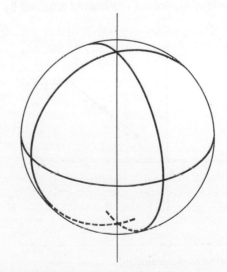

For example, the circle girdling the earth at latitude 60° N has a different circumference to diameter ratio than the equatorial circle. (The diameter of each circle is a segment of longitude passing through the North Pole.)

The second possible alteration of the Euclidean parallel-line postulate that through a given point *no* line can be drawn parallel to another line, leads to a non-Euclidean hyperbolic geometry, a geometry which in two dimensions describes the properties of a saddle-shaped surface. Other non-Euclidean geometries besides the spherical and hyperbolic types have been devised, but these two are of particular concern in general relativity. Interest in non-Euclidean geometries in the nineteenth century led ultimately to the development of powerful analytical tools that permit the properties of any geometry whatsoever to be expressed in algebraic language. Since general relativity must be free of any specific assumptions regarding the form of a geometry, Einstein incorporated these advances in pure mathematics into his theory of gravitation.

One specific example will suggest the way geometry can be used to describe gravitational effects. The shortest distance between two points in any geometry is called a *geodesic*. In three-dimensional Euclidean geometry the geodesic distance between two spatial points is a straight line; in four-dimensional Euclidean-Lorentz geometry* the geodesic "distance" between two events is a straight line in four-dimensional spacetime with length given by Equation 11.8; in two-dimensional spherical geometry the geodesic distance between two points is the great circle distance.

The force-free trajectory of a particle in an inertial system is derived from Newton's first law. Suppose such a particle is confined to the x-axis of some system. Then its velocity is constant, and its equation of motion is simply $x = vt$ plotted in Figure 11.20. From a geometric point of view the motion of the particle from the spacetime point x_1, t_1 to the spacetime point x_2, t_2 is the straight line joining the events. Therefore, we can generalize the law of inertia to state that the shortest distance between two points in spacetime is the geodesic distance.

In general relativity this law must be valid for all geometries. But near matter, spacetime is non-Euclidean, and therefore the geodesic distance between two points is not a straight line. A graph of a particle's displacement vs time is curved, meaning that its velocity increases with time, or that it accelerates. Furthermore, since its acceleration is the result of describing a non-Euclidean situation in Euclidean terms it should be the same for all particles regardless of mass, as required by the Principle of Equivalence.

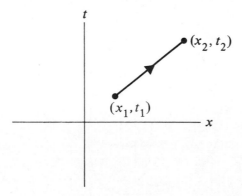

FIGURE 11.20 The space-time graph of a force-free trajectory in Euclidean space is simply the shortest distance between the spacetime events along its path—a straight line. Likewise, the force-free trajectory of a particle in another geometry is the shortest distance between the end points of its path in that geometry.

* Usually called Minkowski geometry.

◣◣ 11.14   Experimental tests of general relativity*

In virtually all instances the gravitational effects predicted by Einstein's geometric viewpoint are numerically equivalent to Newtonian predictions. Measurable non-Newtonian effects are expected only in the presence of large masses, and for that reason most experimental tests of general relativity are based upon astronomical observation. There have been but three types of tests. The first is the bending of light in a gravitational field. Einstein's formulation requires that light be propagated along a geodesic. Therefore, if light passes near a large mass it should follow the spacetime curvature induced by that mass and, from a Euclidean viewpoint, appear to curve.

The origin of the effect can also be understood in terms of the Principle of Equivalence, although the full framework of general relativity, which incorporates the warping of space, is required to yield a result in accord with experiment. In the experiment shown in Figure 11.21 observer A is in a region of space far from matter so that his geometry is Euclidean. Observer B is in a large upward accelerating elevator. A ray of light traveling along a straight horizontal line in reference frame A curves downward in frame B, since the elevator accelerates upward during the time the light traverses it. However, observer B assumes that he is not accelerating but rather is at rest in a gravitational field. Therefore, he calls the curvature of light a gravitational effect.

The magnitude of the effect is small. Seen from the earth a light ray that just grazes the sun should deviate from the path it would otherwise follow by 1.75 sec of arc. Thus a star that appears adjacent to the disk of the sun is expected to appear displaced 1.75 sec from its normal position (Figure 11.22). Clearly a star that seems to be so near the sun can only be observed when the sun is blotted out, during an eclipse for example. Measurement of so small a deviation requires very precise observations. Furthermore, interpretation of the results is difficult, requiring considerable care in defining the "normal" position. Since 1919, deviations ranging from 1.18 sec to 2.35 sec have been observed. Certainly

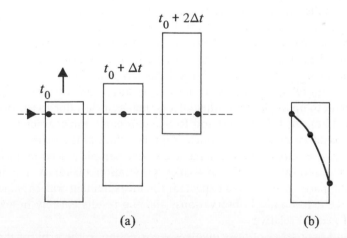

(a)   (b)

FIGURE 11.21   Passage of a horizontal light ray across an upward-accelerating elevator. (a) The elevator and leading edge of the ray (indicated by the heavy dot) as seen in inertial system A. (b) The trajectory of the ray seen by an observer at rest in the elevator.

---

* This section may be omitted without serious loss of continuity.

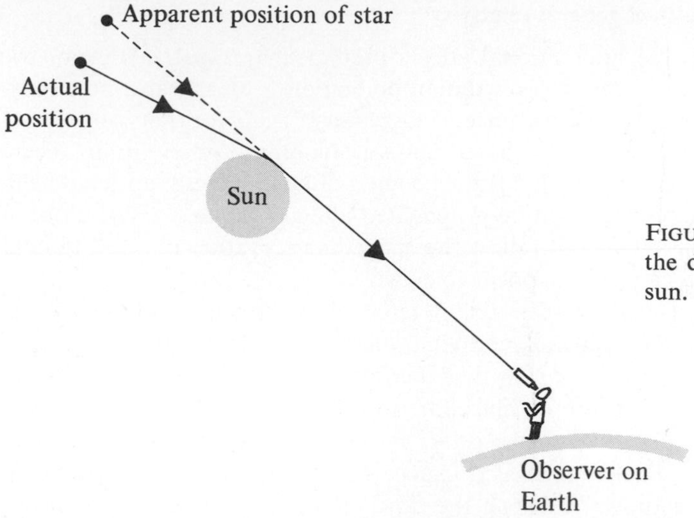

FIGURE 11.22 Observation of the deflection of starlight by the sun.

none can be explained in terms of the Newtonian gravitational interaction, but neither is it clear whether general relativity as formulated by Einstein offers a sufficient explanation.

The second series of tests involves the slowing down of clocks in a gravitational field. In Chapter 17 we shall discuss the emission of light from atoms excited by an electric discharge or raised to high temperatures. For the present it is sufficient to note that each type of atom emits light at a number of specific frequencies. A measurement of frequency is a measurement of a time interval, or a clock. It follows that since an atom on the surface of the sun is in a higher gravitational field than the same type of atom on the earth, it should emit light at a slightly lower frequency, so that its spectrum should be shifted toward lower frequencies, toward the red. The shift should be greater for light from an atom on the surface of a star that is more massive than the sun.

The magnitude of the expected shift can be correctly calculated using the Principle of Equivalence alone. Again only small effects are predicted. The frequency shift expected for an atom on the sun's surface is only two parts in a million. Such shifts have been noted, but measurement is so difficult that it is hard to state whether they are in quantitative agreement with relativity. Spectral shifts from atoms on very dense stars are larger, but more difficult to untangle from other effects such as a shift due to the optical Doppler effect (Section 13.8). In 1959 Pound and Rebka compared the characteristic frequencies of gamma-ray photons emitted from nuclei on the surface of the earth and the frequency of the gamma rays emitted from the same nuclei in a sample placed in a tower forty feet above its surface, and thus in a slightly weaker gravitational field. Although a frequency shift of only 2.5 parts in 10^{-15} was expected, the measurement was capable of far better control than the astronomical observations, and the results entirely in accord with the predictions of general relativity.

The third and final series of tests involves a correction to the orbit of the planet Mercury. Observational evidence accumulated during the nineteenth century revealed a discrepancy that could not be explained in Newtonian terms. Rather than remaining stationary relative to the stars the planet's elliptical orbit slowly rotates or *precesses* in space (Figure 11.23). The precession is slow, the perihelion moving but 43.11 ± 0.45 sec per century!

According to general relativity the four-dimensional paths of the planets are geodesics

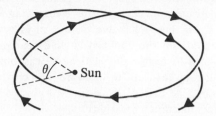

FIGURE 11.23   Precession of the perihelion of Mercury. Although the orbit of the planet is elliptical, the orbit itself does not remain fixed in the reference system of the stars but rotates slowly. The effect is very small. Although the angle θ changes by about 5000 seconds per century all but 42 seconds per century can be explained in terms of well-known perturbations due to the other planets.

in the spacetime geometry warped by the sun, a description not quite equivalent to the Newtonian inverse square representation. The relativistic formulation predicts a precession in the orbit of Mercury of 43.03 sec per century, in complete agreement with observation. Einstein's explanation of an effect that had remained an enigma for so many years was an undoubted triumph. In recent years the much smaller precessions of Venus and Earth (8.4 $\pm$ 4.8 and 5.0 $\pm$ 1.2 sec of arc per century, respectively) have been carefully measured; both are in quantitative agreement with general relativity.

We have stressed the importance of the equivalence principle in general relativity. Unless it holds exactly, a modification in the whole theory is required. In 1959, R. H. Dicke and his colleagues completed a very accurate measurement of the ratio of gravitational to inertial mass and concluded that it is equal to 1 for all substances to a precision of two parts in 10^{10}.

This result precludes a number of possible modifications of Einstein's formulation, but does not rule out all of them. Although it is no doubt true that effects due to gravitation and acceleration are equivalent, there is no unique way to write the laws of physics so that they will be independent of all frames of reference. Einstein's solution, touched upon in these pages, is appealing in its simplicity, but may not be correct. Dicke has suggested an alternate approach, and has shown that it is consistent with an astronomical measurement made by him and his colleagues.

The orbit of a planet depends, of course, upon its gravitational interaction with the sun. To an excellent approximation the magnitude of that interaction can be calculated by assuming that the sun is spherical. But Dicke's measurements, announced in 1967, suggest that it is more spheroidal (i.e., flattened at the poles) than had previously been believed. If these measurements are correct then the Newtonian-based calculations of Mercury's orbit differ from observation by about 36 sec instead of 43 sec, in disagreement with the difference calculated by Einstein.

Although all of Newtonian physics is, in principle, contained in the assumptions, axioms, definitions, and laws of the *Principia*, more than a century was required to apply that framework to all cases of interest and to understand all of its implications. This was true not because Newton carried secrets with him to the grave, but simply because the task of completing what he started required more than one lifetime. To paraphrase R. P. Feynman, Newton suggested a method for finding the rules of the game (Chapter 1). Many of the rules themselves were found by others.

A very analogous situation applies in general relativity. Einstein had stated the general consequences of his postulates in terms of his geometric ideas by 1916. He spent the remaining years of his life working out specific consequences and attempting (unsuccessfully) to extend his geometrical approach to the electromagnetic interaction. A considerable effort continues along these lines. Newtonian physics was not finished when the inverse square law was stated; on the contrary, it had scarcely begun. In a like vein, Einstein's formulation of the invariant physical laws was but the beginning. Dicke's formulation or yet another may turn out to be more in accord with experiment. Nonetheless the work of Einstein, like that of Newton, will always stand as one of the most impressive of all monuments to human creativity.

APPENDIX TO CHAPTER 11	*Derivation of the Lorentz transformation equations*

The assumptions leading to the Lorentz transformation equations (Equations 11.5) are stated in Section 11.4. Consider two inertial systems, A and B, with common x-axes. System B moves with velocity $+u$ relative to A, and at time $t_a = t_b = 0$ the origins coincide, i.e., $x_a = x_b = 0$ (Figure 11.10). Let a light pulse be emitted from the common origin at $t_a = t_b = 0$, and let it travel in the positive x_a- and x_b-direction. Then in system A the position of the pulse is given as a function of time by

$$x_a = ct_a.$$

Therefore,

$$x_a^2 = c^2 t_a^2,$$

or

$$x_a^2 - c^2 t_a^2 = 0.$$

Since the speed of light is the same in system B, then also

$$x_b^2 - c^2 t_b^2 = 0.$$

Thus we express the invariance of c by the relation

$$x_a^2 - c^2 t_a^2 = x_b^2 - c^2 t_b^2. \tag{A11.1}$$

We assume transformation equation of the form:

$$x_b = f_1 x_a + f_2 y_a + f_3 z_a + f_4 t_a,$$
$$t_b = g_1 x_a + g_2 y_a + g_3 z_a + g_4 t_a,$$

with the f's and g's functions of u and c. Because there is no contraction of length in the directions perpendicular to the relative velocity then $f_2 = f_3 = 0$. It is also reasonable to assume that $g_2 = g_3 = 0$. Hence,

$$x_b = f_1 x_a + f_4 t_a, \tag{A11.2a}$$

$$t_b = g_1 x_a + g_4 t_a. \tag{A11.2b}$$

To find the explicit form of these functions we substitute Equations A11.2 into the right side of the invariance equation, Equation A11.1, to obtain:

$$
\begin{aligned}
x_a^2 - c^2 t_a^2 &= (f_1 x_a + f_4 t_a)^2 - c^2 (g_1 x_a + g_4 t_a)^2 \\
&= f_1^2 x_a^2 + 2 f_1 f_4 x_a t_a + f_4^2 t_a^2 - c^2 (g_1^2 x_a^2 + 2 g_1 g_4 x_a t_a + g_4^2 t_a^2) \\
&= (f_1^2 - c^2 g_1^2) x_a^2 + (f_4^2 - c^2 g_4^2) t_a^2 + 2(f_1 f_4 - c^2 g_1 g_4) x_a t_a
\end{aligned}
$$

Since x_a^2 and t_a^2 are independent variables, their respective coefficients on each side of the equation are equal. Therefore,

$$f_1^2 - c^2 g_1^2 = 1, \tag{A11.3a}$$

$$f_4^2 - c^2 g_4^2 = -c^2. \tag{A11.3b}$$

Also as there is no term in $x_a t_a$ on the left,

$$2(f_1 f_4 - c^2 g_1 g_4) = 0,$$

or

$$f_1 f_4 = c^2 f_1 g_4. \tag{A11.3c}$$

Thus we have three equations relating four unknown quantities. One more can be obtained by recalling that the origin of system B travels with velocity $+u$ in system A. Therefore, when $x_b = 0$, $x_a = ut_a$. Substituting into Equation A11.2a,

$$0 = f_1 ut_a + f_4 t_a,$$

and we have

$$f_4/f_1 = -u. \tag{A11.3d}$$

The Lorentz transformation equations follow from algebraic manipulation of Equations A11.3. We first write Equations A11.3a and A11.3b as

$$c^2 g_1^2 = f_1^2 - 1,$$
$$c^2 g_4^2 = f_4^2 + c^2.$$

Multiplying the left sides and the right sides by each other:

$$c^4 g_1^2 g_4^2 = (f_1^2 - 1)(f_4^2 + c^2)$$
$$= f_1^2 f_4^2 - f_4^2 + c^2 f_1^2 - c^2.$$

Substituting Equation A11.3c on the left,

$$f_1^2 f_4^2 = f_1^2 f_4^2 - f_4^2 + c^2 f_1^2 - c^2,$$

or

$$c^2 f_1^2 - f_4^2 = c^2,$$

which can be written as

$$f_1^2 \left(1 - \frac{f_4^2}{c^2 f_1^2}\right) = 1.$$

But (Equation A11.3d) $f_4/f_1 = u$. Therefore,

$$f_1^2 \left(1 - \frac{u^2}{c^2}\right) = 1,$$

and

$$f_1 = \frac{1}{\sqrt{1 - u^2/c^2}}, \tag{A11.4a}$$

which also yields, by Equation A11.4d,

$$f_4 = -uf_1 = \frac{-u}{\sqrt{1 - u^2/c^2}}. \tag{A11.4b}$$

Substituting into Equation A11.2a we have the first Lorentz transformation equation (see Equation 11.5a):

$$x_b = \frac{1}{\sqrt{1 - u^2/c^2}}\,(x_a - ut_a).$$

To obtain g_4 we write Equation A11.3b as:

$$c^2 g_4^2 = f_4^2 + c^2 = u^2 f_1^2 + c^2,$$

or, dividing by c^2,

$$g_4^2 = \left(\frac{u}{c}\right)^2 f_1^2 + 1,$$

$$= \frac{(u/c)^2}{1 - (u/c)^2} + 1,$$

$$= \frac{1}{1 - (u/c)^2}.$$

Therefore,

$$g_4 = \frac{1}{\sqrt{1 - (u/c)^2}}. \qquad\qquad \text{(A11.4c)}$$

Finally, from Equation A11.3c,

$$g_1 = \frac{f_1 f_4}{c^2 g_4} = \frac{-u f_4^2}{c^2 g_4},$$

$$= \frac{-u \sqrt{1 - (u/c)^2}}{c^2 (1 - (u/c)^2)},$$

$$= \frac{-u/c^2}{\sqrt{1 - (u/c)^2}}. \qquad\qquad \text{(A11.4d)}$$

Substituting Equations A11.4c and A11.4d:

$$t_b = \frac{1}{\sqrt{1 - (u/c)^2}}\left(t_a - \frac{u}{c^2}\,x_a\right),$$

in agreement with Equation 11.5b.

SUGGESTIONS FOR FURTHER READING ▲▲▲

Several introductory texts contain one or more chapters on relativity; for example:

K. R. ATKINS, *Physics*, John Wiley and Sons, Inc., New York, 1965, Chapters 22–25.

ARNOLD B. ARONS, *Development of Concepts of Physics*, Addison-Wesley Publishing Co., Inc., Reading, Mass., 1965, Chapter 36.

R. P. FEYNMAN, R. B. LEIGHTON, AND M. SANDS, *The Feynman Lectures on Physics*, Vol. 1, Addison-Wesley Publishing Co., Inc., Reading, Mass., 1963, Chapters 15, 16, and 17.

The chapter on relativity from at least one advanced text is very readable, especially in its discussion of the origins of time dilation and the Lorentz contraction:

CHALMER SHERWIN, *Basic Concepts of Physics*, Holt, Rinehart, and Winston, Inc., New York, 1961, Chapter 4.

There are also several books dealing only with relativity. Some of these, in order of increasing difficulty, are:

ALBERT EINSTEIN, *Relativity*, 15th edition, Crown Publishers, Inc., New York, Chapters 1–23.

HERMANN BONDI, *Relativity and Common Sense*, Science Study Series, Doubleday and Co., Inc., Garden City, New York, 1964.

MAX BORN, *Einstein's Theory of Relativity*, revised edition, Dover Publications, Inc., New York, 1962.

EDWIN F. TAYLOR AND JOHN A. WHEELER, *Spacetime Physics*, W. H. Freeman and Co., San Francisco, 1966.

A number of the original papers on relativity are collected in:

The Principle of Relativity, Dover Publications, Inc., 1923.

A number of papers whose level is on the order of or only slightly more difficult than this chapter have been compiled by the American Association of Physics Teachers. The set was published in 1963 by The American Institute of Physics under the title *Special Relativity Theory: Selected Reprints*. Several articles dealing with the twin paradox and its resolution are included in the collection.

The relativity principle itself and its implications for the structure of space and time are beautifully treated in:

ALBERT EINSTEIN AND LEOPOLD INFELD, *The Evolution of Physics*, Simon and Schuster, New York, 1961, Chapter 3.

Several articles relating to relativity have appeared in the *Scientific American* during the past few years:

DENIS SCIAMA, "Inertia," February, 1967, p. 99.

V. L. GINZBURG, "Artificial Satellites and Relativity," May, 1959, p. 149.

GEORGE GAMOW, "Gravity," March, 1961, p. 94.

R. H. DICKE, "The Etvos Experiment," December, 1961, p. 84.

J. BRONOWSKI, "The Clock Paradox," January, 1963, p. 134.

R. S. SHANKLAND, "The Michelson-Morley Experiment," November, 1964, p. 107.

PROBLEMS AND EXERCISES ▲▲▲

NOTE: Many of these problems require that the factor $1/\sqrt{(1 - u^2)/c^2}$ be evaluated. If u^2/c^2 is sufficiently small an approximate relation based upon the binomial expansion (Appendix D) and introduced in Section 11.9 may be used. That is:

$$\frac{1}{\sqrt{(1 - u^2)/c^2}} = 1 + \frac{1}{2}\frac{u_2}{c^2} \quad \text{(approximately)}.$$

This approximation can be considered quite good if $u^2/c^2 = 0.2$ or less. For example for $u^2/c^2 = 0.19$:

$$1 + \frac{1}{2}\frac{u^2}{c^2} = 1 + \frac{0.19}{2} = 1.095,$$

whereas:

$$\frac{1}{\sqrt{1 - 0.19}} = \frac{1}{\sqrt{0.81}} = \frac{1}{0.9} = 1.111\cdots.$$

That is, the error introduced by using the approximate formula is about 1%.

The approximation becomes increasingly bad with increasing u^2/c^2, and as a rough guide should not be considered reliable for values of the squared velocity ratio greater than about 0.36 where the error introduced is about 7%.

11.1. Suppose the magnitudes of *all* velocities in the universe (including the speed of light and of all biological processes) were doubled. Do you think the change could be detected? Explain carefully.

11.2. Let the distance Δy between the upper and lower mirrors of a light clock (Section 11.2) be $\frac{1}{3}$ m, and let the clock travel with velocity $+\mathbf{u}$ in a direction perpendicular to its length relative to an observer A. According to A, what is the length of the light path from the lower to the upper mirror and back again for:

(a) $u = 0$.
(b) $u = 0.8\, c$.
(c) $u = 0.9\, c$.
(d) $u = 0.95\, c$.
(e) $u = 0.99\, c$.

What time interval does A measure with the moving clock in each instance?

11.3. The orbital velocity of the earth relative to the sun is about 3×10^4 m/sec. To an observer at rest relative to the sun:

(a) By what fraction of an inch does the 8000-mile diameter of the earth appear contracted?
(b) What is the fractional increase in the length of one earth second?

11.4. (a) A meter stick moves with velocity $0.8\, c$ in the direction of its length relative to an observer A. How long is it according to A?
(b) A clock that ticks off regular one-second intervals in its rest system also moves with velocity $0.8\, c$ relative to A. How long does he say the intervals are?

11.5. An observer notes that a clock moving with constant speed u is slow by a factor of two.

(a) What is the magnitude of u?
(b) What is the length of a meter stick moving parallel to its length with the same speed?

11.6. Viewed at rest, a triangle has one leg 1.6 m long and parallel to the x-axis, another 0.96 m long and parallel to the y-axis of a Cartesian system (see sketch).

(a) How large is the angle θ measured by an observer at rest relative to the triangle?
(b) With what speed in the x-direction must the triangle move relative to an observer A such that A measures θ as $45°$?

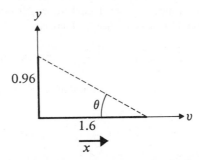

11.7. Sound waves in air (Chapter 13) travel with a constant speed of roughly 300 m/sec *relative to the air*.
(a) How would you synchronize two clocks 6000 m apart, one directly north of the other, using sound waves, if a 25 m/sec wind was blowing from the north? (You may use assistants and any reasonable apparatus you need.)
(b) How would you synchronize the two clocks if the 25 m/sec wind blew from the east?

11.8. An observer B is on a (fictitious) long railroad flat car traveling 7.5×10^7 m/sec. He has a clock, a light source, and a mirror which he places 1.5×10^8 m away from him. (The distance is determined with his calibrated meter stick.) He measures the time light requires to travel from his source to the mirror and back again. Observer A on the station platform has identical equipment and will make the same observations. The two lights flash at $t_A = t_B = 0$ just as the sources pass each other.

Answer the following questions twice: first from the viewpoint of B then from the viewpoint of A.

(a) Which mirror did the light strike first?
(b) What did the clock on the train read when the light ray on the train returned to its source?
(c) What did the clock on the platform read when the light ray on the platform returned.

Explain carefully the reasons why any apparent contradictions between your two sets of answers are really not contradictions.*

11.9. Answer, in words, the following objections to relativity.

(a) A says B's clock is slow, B says A's clock is slow. This is a logical contradiction.
(b) Relativity does not define space and time intervals uniquely. Thus anything it says about velocities, and hence about motion, is meaningless.
(c) Relativity is concerned with observation and measurement, not with what is really happening, hence it does not deal with reality.

11.10. A rocket, traveling with velocity $0.8\,c$ relative to the earth, fires a projectile with velocity $0.8\,c$ relative to the rocket. What is the velocity of the projectile seen from the earth if:

(a) It is fired straight forward from the rocket.
(b) It is fired straight backward.

11.11. A π-meson, traveling with velocity $0.9\,c$ relative to the laboratory, decays into a muon and a neutrino. The latter, massless particle travels straight forward with velocity c in the π-meson's rest system. What is the neutrino's velocity in the laboratory?

11.12. A twenty-year-old twin makes a round trip to Alpha Centuri traveling at a constant speed of $0.9\,c$ going out and returning. As seen by the earth-bound twin:

(a) How long does the trip take?
(b) How old is the traveler on his return?
(c) How old is the stay-at-home?

As seen by the traveler:

(a) What is the distance to Alpha Centuri?
(b) How long does the trip take?
(c) How old is he on return to earth?

(Alpha Centuri is four light years away from the earth, as seen from the earth.)

11.13. Calculate the square of the Lorentz-invariant separation between the following pairs of events and determine whether the separation is timelike, spacelike, or lightlike.

(a) A nucleus disintegrates at time $t = 0$ (first event); 5×10^{-7} sec later a particle is detected 30 m away (second event).
(b) A particle is detected at the counter 30 m from the disintegrating nucleus 5×10^{-8} sec after the disintegration.

---

* Problems 11.7 and 11.8 were supplied by Professor Robert Adair of Yale University.

(c) A particle is detected at the counter 10^{-7} sec after the nuclear disintegration. Which of these sets of events *could* be causally connected?

11.14. Find the velocities of inertial systems in which:

(a) The timelike events of Problem 11.13 are simultaneous.
(b) The spacelike events occur at the same place.

11.15. The rest mass of an electron is 9×10^{-31} kg. What is its mass if its speed is:

(a) $0.8\,c$.
(b) $0.9\,c$.
(c) $0.95\,c$.
(d) $0.99\,c$.

11.16. What are the rest energies in joules and in electron volts of:

(a) An electron ($M_0 = 9 \times 10^{-31}$ kg).
(b) A π-meson ($M_0 = 4.2 \times 10^{-28}$ kg).
(c) A proton ($M_0 = 1.6 \times 10^{-27}$ kg).

11.17. Find the total energy, the kinetic energy, and the momentum of an electron with speed:

(a) $0.8\,c$.
(b) $0.9\,c$.
(c) $0.95\,c$.
(d) $0.99\,c$.

N.B.: Momentum may be conveniently expressed in units of eV/c. (Why?) 1 eV/c = 5.35×10^{-28} kg-m/sec.

11.18. What is the mass of a 2 MeV photon?

11.19. What is the minimum energy a photon must have to produce an electron-positron pair, if the photon itself completely disappears in the process? The positron has the same mass as the electron and equal but opposite charge. (See Section 20.8.)

11.20. In the fusion of four protons to form a helium nucleus in the center of the sun (Chapter 20) about 5×10^{-29} kg disappear.

(a) How much energy is liberated in the process?
(b) One kilogram of hydrogen contains about 6×10^{26} protons. How much energy would be liberated by fusion if all the protons in a kilogram of hydrogen reacted?
(c) How many 100-watt bulbs could be powered for a year with the energy released in part b?

11.21. What mass is equivalent to the energy supplied to a 100-watt light bulb in one year?

N.B.: 1 year = 3.14×10^7 sec.

11.22. The *solar constant* is defined as the amount of solar energy that would fall on a one square meter surface of the earth each minute in the absence of the earth's rotation and atmospheric absorption. Its value is 8.4×10^4 J. The mean distance between the sun and earth is 1.5×10^{11} m.

Use these data to calculate the mass loss from the sun per second.

[HINT: First calculate the fraction of the sun's energy that falls perpendicularly on a one square meter surface at the orbit of the earth.]

11.23. The two-mile-long Stanford linear accelerator (Chapter 21) produces an electron beam with 20 BeV total energy.

(a) What is the ratio of the total energy of the electrons to their rest energy? Of their mass to their rest mass?

(b) How long would the accelerator appear to such an electron? (1 BeV $= 10^9$ eV.)

11.24. Determine for one of the 20 BeV-electrons of Problem 11.23:

(a) The energy in joules.
(b) The momentum in kg-m/sec.
(c) The radius of curvature in a 2.0 Wb/m² magnetic field.

11.25. Determine, for a 10 MeV electron and a 10 MeV proton (rest masses 9×10^{-31} kg and 1.6×10^{-27} kg, respectively):

(a) The ratios of total energy to rest energy.
(b) The momenta of the particles.
(c) The particles' radii of curvature in a 1.0 Wb/m² magnetic field.

11.26. (a) A thirty-meter-wide elevator in intergalactic space accelerates upward at a constant rate of 1000 m/sec². By what vertical distance does a light ray traveling across it appear to be deflected to an observer at rest in the elevator?

(b) What is the vertical deflection of a light ray that just grazes the surface of the sun?

The sun's diameter is about 1.4×10^9 m, and the gravitational acceleration on its surface is about 208 m/sec².

N.B.: The result of a correct general relativistic calculation that takes account of the non-Euclidean nature of the space around the sun is twice as great as the answer to part b.

11.27. A point on the rim of a ten-meter-radius turntable moves with speed 0.9 c. Estimate:

(a) The ratio of the circumference to the diameter of a five-meter-radius circle on the table seen by an observer at its center.
(b) The "gravitational" force he measures on a one-kilogram particle at five meters from the center.
(c) The length of one second measured by a clock at five meters from the center.

Repeat these calculations for a point on the rim of the table.

11.28. Will a clock in an earth satellite one hundred miles above the earth run slow or fast? Explain.

11.29. With the aid of the accompanying sketch, find an expression for the circumference of a circle on the surface of a sphere as a function of the polar angle θ, and the radius R of the sphere. Interpret your result for $\theta = 90°$ and $\theta = 180°$.

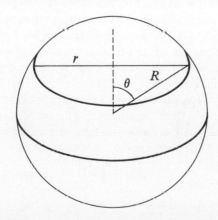

The electromagnetic field

▲▲ 12.1 The electric and magnetic fields in special relativity

Let us return now to the "paradox" first encountered in Section 9.6 (see Figure 9.39). An observer B measures an electrostatic force F_B between two charges at rest relative to his inertial system:

$$F_B = \frac{1}{4\pi\epsilon_0} \frac{q_1 q_2}{y^2}.$$

However, an observer A moving with constant velocity $-u$ relative to the charges and in a direction perpendicular to the line joining them measures a magnetic force in addition to the electrostatic force, and, provided the equations of Chapters 8 and 9 are valid, would find that the total force between the charges is (Equation 9.29):

$$F_A = \frac{1}{4\pi\epsilon_0} \frac{q_1 q_2}{y^2} \left(1 - \frac{v^2}{c^2}\right) = F_B\left(1 - \frac{v^2}{c^2}\right),$$

in violation of the invariance of physical laws with respect to inertial systems.

As might be expected, the origin of the paradox is rooted in the Newtonian concepts of time and space. Let us examine another situation in which one observer measures only an electrostatic force while the second sees, in addition, a magnetic force, this time taking advantage of our knowledge of special relativity. A parallel plate capacitor (Section 8.3, Figure 8.11) consists of two equally and oppositely charged plane conductors with parallel faces. The electric field in the gap between them is constant and directed from the positively to the negatively charged plane. It is reasonable to assume that the magnitude of the field is proportional to the charge per unit area on each plate. For instance, if the area of the plates were increased but the total charge held constant we would expect a redistribution of the charge over the larger area and a consequent decrease in the magnitude of the field at any point in the gap. In other words, the field strength is proportional to the density of the lines of force in the gap. Therefore, a decrease in the density of lines of force due to a redistribution of the charge over a larger area implies a decrease in field strength. A more detailed analysis shows that the magnitude of the electric field of a capacitor with parallel plates of area A is

$$E = \frac{1}{\epsilon_0}\left(\frac{Q}{A}\right), \tag{12.1}$$

where Q is the total charge on either of the plates.

An observer B at rest relative to a capacitor whose plates have dimensions Δx_b and Δz_b (Figure 12.1a) sees an electric field in the y-direction and, according to Equation 12.1 finds that its strength is

$$E_y(B) = \frac{1}{\epsilon_0}\left(\frac{Q}{\Delta z_b\,\Delta x_b}\right).$$

But to Observer A who sees the capacitor moving in the x-direction with velocity $-\mathbf{u}$ (Figure 12.1b), the x-dimension of the plates appears contracted (Equation 11.2), while the z-dimension is unaltered. Therefore, he measures the *larger* field:

$$E_y(A) = \frac{1}{\epsilon_0}\left(\frac{Q}{\Delta z_a\,\Delta x_a}\right) = \frac{Q}{\epsilon_0(\Delta z_b\,\Delta x_b\sqrt{1 - u^2/c^2})}.$$

This result is independent of the fact that the field is due to a parallel plate capacitor. It is also true for the electric field produced by a point charge, for example. Whenever the motion of a single charge or set of charges results in a squeezing or compression of lines

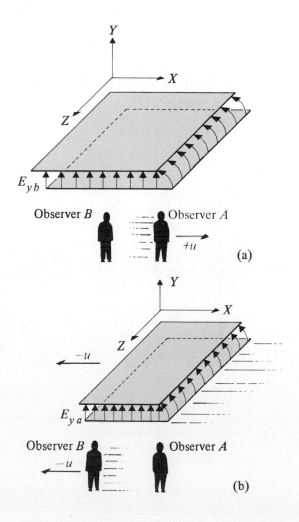

FIGURE 12.1   Observer A moving with constant velocity $+\mathbf{u}$ perpendicular to the gap of a capacitor (a) sees the capacitor moving with velocity $-\mathbf{u}$. Therefore, from his point of view the dimensions of the plates contract in the direction of relative motion (b). Since both observers measure the same total charge on the plates, the density of the lines of force in the gap appears greater to A than to B. Therefore, the "moving" observer measures a greater electric field strength.

of force (Figure 12.2), then the resultant electric field is a function of the relative velocity of the source charge. If E_0 is the field strength measured when the charge is at rest, then

$$E_\perp = \frac{E_{0\perp}}{\sqrt{1 - u^2/c^2}},$$ (12.2)

where $E_\perp$ is the field strength perpendicular to the direction of relative motion.

Equation 12.2 is not applicable unless the direction of relative motion results in a crowding of the lines of force. If a parallel plate capacitor moves in a direction *parallel* to the field (the y-direction in Figure 12.1a) the gap contracts, but the area of the plates remains unchanged and the field has the same value in all inertial systems.

Returning to the case of the moving capacitor (Figure 12.3), since Observer A sees a *moving* charge he also measures a *magnetic* field in the gap. If a time interval $\Delta t_a = \Delta x_z/-u$ is required for the capacitor to travel across a plane perpendicular to the x-direction in inertial system A, then the moving charge constitutes a current of magnitude

$$I = \frac{Q}{\Delta t_a} = \frac{Q}{(\Delta x_a/-u)} = -\frac{Qu}{\Delta x_b \sqrt{1 - u^2/c^2}}.$$

The field produced by the current must be perpendicular to the direction of motion, i.e., in the y- or z-directions. From geometric symmetry arguments it is reasonable to assume that it is uniform within the gap and parallel to the plates in the z-direction. Its magnitude, based on a more detailed analysis, turns out to be

$$B_z(A) = \mu_0\left(\frac{I}{\Delta z}\right),$$

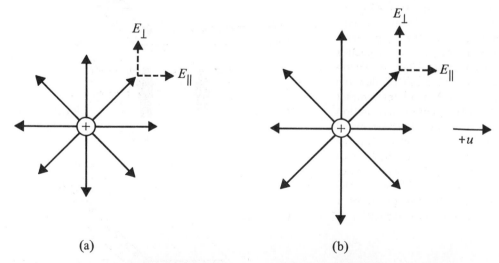

(a)   (b)

FIGURE 12.2   Electric field of a moving point charge. When the charge is at rest relative to an observer (a) the magnitude of its electric field is the same at all equidistant points. If the charge moves with constant velocity (b) the field components perpendicular to its direction of motion are greater than when it is at rest, while its parallel field components are unchanged. Therefore, the field is stretched in the perpendicular directions and assumes spheroidal rather than spherical symmetry.

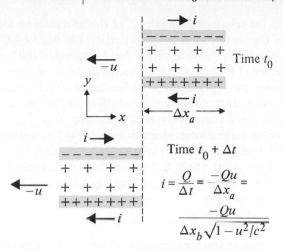

FIGURE 12.3 An observer who sees a parallel plate capacitor traveling with constant velocity $-\mathbf{u}$ sees a current that flows in the negative x-direction in the positively charged plate, and in the positive direction in the negatively charged plate. Applying the right-hand screw convention to both currents, the magnetic field in the gap is in the negative z-direction, or into the page as shown.

or, substituting the expression for the current measured by A,

$$B_z(A) = \frac{-\mu_0 Q u}{\Delta z_b \, \Delta x_b \sqrt{1 - u^2/c^2}}.$$

But the electric field in the rest system (B) is $(1/\epsilon_0)(Q/\Delta x_b \, \Delta z_b)$. Thus we may express the *magnetic* field measured by Observer A in terms of the *electric* field measured by Observer B:

$$B_z(A) = \mu_0 \epsilon_0 \frac{u E_y}{\sqrt{1 - u^2/c^2}},$$

or, since $c^2 = 1/\mu_0 \epsilon_0$ (Equation 9.27),

$$B_z(A) = -\frac{u E_{y0}}{c^2 \sqrt{1 - u^2/c^2}}. \tag{12.3}$$

That is, electric and magnetic field strengths *depend upon the inertial system in which they are measured*.

The total energy and the momentum of a particle have somewhat analogous properties, their separate magnitudes depending upon the inertial system in which they are defined. However, the magnitude of the combined energy-momentum four-vector (Section 11.10) is a Lorentz invariant scalar. Hence in special relativity it is convenient to regard total energy and momentum as different aspects of the same basic quantity.

Although the analysis is a little more involved, a similar conclusion follows for the electric and magnetic fields, namely, that they are but two different aspects of the more fundamental *electromagnetic field*. The effects of the electromagnetic field are the same in all inertial systems, but the manner in which the field separates into electric and magnetic parts depends upon the inertial system in which it is described.

Ultimately both aspects of the electromagnetic field are defined in terms of the forces they exert upon charges, and force itself defined by the time rate of change of momentum.

Thus a critical test of the relativistic "mixing" of the fields can be made by determining if the descriptions of the motion of a charged particle obtained by observers in two different inertial systems can be related to each other by means of the four-vector apparatus we developed in Chapter 11 to deal with the general problem of motion at high velocities. If two such descriptions are connected by the fundamental relations of relativistic kinematics then we shall conclude that the dynamical effects of the electromagnetic field really *are* independent of any specific inertial system, as asserted.

In order to simplify the mathematics as much as possible we consider motion transverse to the direction of relative motion of the two observers so that each measures the same momentum. The uniform electric field E_y in the parallel plate capacitor shown in Figures 12.1 and 12.3 exerts a force upon a charge q in the gap which an observer B at rest relative to the capacitor measures as

$$F_B = qE_b.$$

This force causes a change in the y-component of the particle's momentum measured as

$$\frac{\Delta p_{yb}}{\Delta t_b} = qE_b.$$

Observer A sees both an electric and a magnetic force. Since the charge moves with the capacitor in the negative x-direction in system A and the magnetic field is in the negative z-direction, the magnetic force is also in the negative y-direction and of magnitude quB_a (Equation 9.15). Therefore, the total force seen in system A is:

$$F_a = qE_a + quB_a.$$

Substituting Equations 12.2 and 12.3, we can express the force measured by Observer A in terms of the electric field measured in the rest frame B:

$$F_a = \frac{qE_b}{\sqrt{1 - u^2/c^2}} \left(1 - \frac{u^2}{c^2}\right) = qE_b\sqrt{1 - u^2/c^2}.$$

Therefore, the change in y-component of the momentum measured in system A is given by

$$\frac{\Delta p_{ya}}{\Delta t_a} = qE_b\sqrt{1 - u^2/c^2}.$$

Since the momentum change is perpendicular to the direction of motion it has the same value in both systems, i.e., $\Delta p_{yb} = \Delta p_{ya}$ (Equations 11.10 and 11.21). However, from Observer B's point of view clocks in system A run more slowly than in his system:

$$\Delta t_a = \frac{\Delta t_b}{\sqrt{1 - u^2/c^2}}.$$

Substituting into the above equation for the momentum change in system A:

$$\frac{\Delta p_{yb}}{\Delta t_b} \sqrt{1 - u^2/c^2} = qE_b\sqrt{1 - u_2/c^2},$$

or

$$\frac{\Delta p_{yb}}{\Delta t_b} = qE_b,$$

identical to the momentum change in the same time interval Δt_b that is measured directly in the rest frame. Thus, when Observer A transforms the results of his measurements into

the description preferred by Observer B he finds that he has reached the same fundamental conclusion, and that his alternative description of the fields is in accord with the
fundamental symmetry principle upon which special relativity is based.

▶▶ 12.2 Faraday's law of induction

It is not surprising that the electric and magnetic fields are two related aspects of one
electromagnetic field. On the contrary, since even nonrelativistically the separate fields
are ultimately defined in terms of the interactions between charges it would be surprising
if there were *not* a fundamental relation between them.

In Chapter 9 (Section 9.5) we explored another relationship between the fields. The
magnetic flux Φ_B through a surface of area A is defined by Equation 9.24 as:

$$\Phi_B = AB \cos \theta,$$

where θ is the angle between the field direction and the perpendicular to the surface (see
Figure 9.35). Faraday's law (Equation 9.25) states that a change in the magnetic flux
through an area induces an EMF in any closed loop surrounding the area:

$$\mathcal{E} = -\frac{\Delta \Phi_B}{\Delta t}.$$

An EMF in an electric circuit (such as a closed loop) performs work $q\mathcal{E}$ in transporting a
charge q around the circuit (Figure 12.4). If Δl is the distance between two points on the

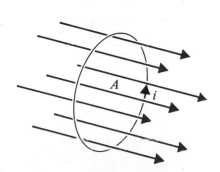

Direction of increasing **B**

$$\Phi_B = BA$$

$$\mathcal{E} = -\frac{\Delta \Phi_B}{\Delta t}$$

(a)

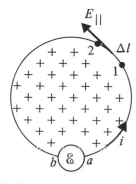

$W_{ab} = q\mathcal{E}$

$W_{12} = qE_\parallel \Delta l$

W_{ab} = Sum of all such contributions
around the loop.

$$\therefore q\mathcal{E} = q \int_a^b E_\parallel \, \Delta l = -q \frac{\Delta \Phi_B}{\Delta t}$$

(b)

FIGURE 12.4   (a) A changing magnetic field perpendicular to a wire loop causes a
current to flow in the loop and therefore induces an EMF around it. The work
performed in transporting charge around the loop is equal to the work that would
be performed if the ends of a loop of the same dimensions and resistance were
attached across the terminals of any other source which delivered the same EMF
and which had zero internal resistance. (b) From these considerations it follows
that the induced EMF is equal to the integral of the parallel component of the
electric field around the loop.

loop measured along the loop then also the work performed in transporting a charge Δq between the two points is $qE_\parallel \Delta l$, where $E_\parallel$ is the component of the electric field parallel to Δl. Therefore, the EMF around a closed loop of length l is equal to the sum of all elements of $E_\parallel \Delta l$, or the integral of the parallel component of the field around the loop.*

$$\mathscr{E} = \int E_\parallel \, dl, \tag{12.4}$$

and we can write Faraday's law in the form:

$$\int E_\parallel \, dl = -\frac{\Delta \Phi_B}{\Delta t}. \tag{12.5a}$$

Equation 12.5a states that *a changing magnetic flux induces an electric field about any closed loop which surrounds the flux change.*

In all the problems we shall consider in detail the area of the surface through which the flux changes will be constant and its plane perpendicular to the changing field. Hence we shall be able to write:

$$\frac{\Delta \Phi_B}{\Delta t} = A \frac{\Delta B}{\Delta t}.$$

If, in addition, geometric symmetry arguments can be involved to select a closed path of length l over which the induced field is both constant and parallel to the path at all points, then

$$\int E_\parallel \, dl = El,$$

and Faraday's law assumes the simpler form:

$$El = -A \frac{\Delta B}{\Delta t}. \tag{12.5b}$$

Let us note carefully that A and l *need* not be related. A refers to the total cross-sectional area through which the magnetic field changes, whereas l is the length, or circumference, of the closed path over which the electric field is induced. The changing magnetic field may be confined to a limited area. However, Equations 12.5 imply that its change induces an electric field around *any* closed loop enclosing all or part of that magnetic field—even a loop whose cross section is much larger than the field it encloses. Therefore, the electric field induced by a changing magnetic field need *not* be confined to the region in space in which the magnetic field changes.

Figure 12.5a shows a circular loop of radius r which encloses and is concentric with a very long tightly wound solenoid of radius R. The total magnetic flux through a cross section of the solenoid is $\pi R^2 B$, since the field is confined inside the cylindrical volume with cross section $A = \pi R^2$. When this field changes it induces an EMF around the

---

* Since a change in the magnetic flux through an area partially or fully enclosed by such a loop induces a nonzero EMF, it follows that the induced field $\mathscr{E}$, unlike the electrostatic field force of a static charge, is not a conservative field (see Section 7.2).

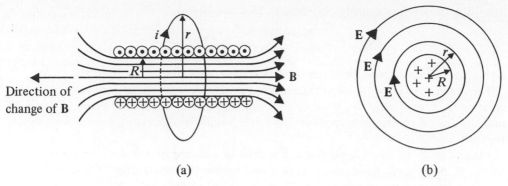

(a)   (b)

FIGURE 12.5 (a) A long solenoid of radius R surrounded by a loop of radius r concentric with it. The current in the solenoid is into the page in the upper coils, and the magnetic field is in the direction indicated. When the field *decreases*, current is induced in the loop as shown. (b) End-on view of the solenoid during the time its magnetic field is decreasing. The induced electric field lines are circles concentric with the solenoid.

circular loop r whose length is $2\pi r$. All parts of the loop are equidistant from the solenoid; therefore, the electric field induced around it should be uniform and we may write

$$2\pi r E = -\pi R^2 \frac{\Delta B}{\Delta t},$$

or

$$E = -\frac{R^2}{2r}\frac{\Delta B}{\Delta t}. \tag{12.6}$$

Now we have taken the point of view that the existence of an electric field in a particular region of space does not depend upon whether or not there happens to be any charge present for that field to accelerate. The circular loop in Figure 12.5a may be regarded as a convenient means for detecting the induced electric field, but not necessary to its existence. In other words, we expect the changing magnetic field in the solenoid to induce an electric field *regardless* of whether or not loops of wire are present to detect its presence. According to Equation 12.6 the strength of the induced electric field outside the solenoid is inversely proportional to the distance from its center. Its lines of force (Figure 12.5b) lie in planes perpendicular to the direction of the changing magnetic field and, from the symmetry of the situation, must be concentric circles.

Suppose a uniform magnetic field confined to a cylindrical volume with circular radius 5×10^{-2} m rises from 0.2 to 0.7 Wb/m^2 in 0.01 sec. What is the magnitude of the induced electric field in a circle with the same radius concentric to the cylinder?

The rate of change of the magnetic flux through a surface parallel to the plane of the circle is

$$\frac{\Delta \Phi_B}{\Delta t} = (\pi R^2)\frac{\Delta B}{\Delta t},$$

$$= 3.14 \times (5 \times 10^{-2})^2 \left(\frac{0.7 - 0.2}{10^{-2}}\right),$$

$$= 39.4 \times 10^{-2} \text{ Wb/sec.}$$

Substituting into Equation 12.5b with $l = 2\pi R = 0.314$ m,

$$E = \frac{39.4 \times 10^{-2}}{3.14 \times 10^{-1}} = 1.25 \text{ N/C,}$$

a result which could have been obtained directly from Equation 12.6.

The magnitude of the induced field in this case is rather small, as may be seen by calculating the charge which if placed on the cylinder axis would produce a field of the same magnitude. Of course the *direction* of this field would be different from the direction of the induced field.

Electric fields of appreciable magnitude may be induced by rapidly varying magnetic fields. If in the previous example the field had increased from 0.2 to 0.7 Wb/m² in 10^{-6} sec, then

$$\frac{\Delta\Phi_B}{\Delta t} = 39.4 \times 10^4 \text{ Wb/sec,}$$

and on a circle of radius 5×10^{-2} m,

$$E = 1.25 \times 10^4 \text{ N/C.}$$

Since the induced field varies inversely with distance a field of magnitude equal to the 1.25 N/m field of our previous example is induced at a distance $10^4 \times 5 \times 10^{-2} = 500$ m from the cylinder axis.

If the *change* in a magnetic field is not constant in time then the magnitude of its induced electric field will also vary. Figure 12.6 plots a magnetic field whose value is given as a function of time by

$$B = B_0 \sin (2\pi ft),$$

where f is the frequency of its oscillation, and B_0 is a constant. (Such a field could be produced by a current in a solenoid varying with the same frequency.) It may be shown that as Δt approaches zero (see Section 9.6 and Problem 2.33):

$$\lim_{\Delta t \to 0} \frac{\Delta[\sin (2\pi ft)]}{\Delta t} = \frac{d[\sin (2\pi ft)]}{dt} = 2\pi f \cos (2\pi ft).$$

Substituting into Equation 12.5b we obtain an expression for the induced field as a function of time:

$$El = -2\pi f AB \cos (2\pi ft).$$

At $t = 0$, $\sin (2\pi ft) = 0$, and the magnetic field is zero. However, $\cos (2\pi ft) = 1$ so the magnitude of the induced field is a maximum. In contrast, when the magnetic field attains its maximum value the induced electric field is zero. When $t = 1/2f$, $\sin (2\pi ft) = \sin (\pi) = 0$. The magnetic field is again zero, and the magnitude of the electric field again a maximum, although its direction is the opposite of its direction at the beginning of the cycle.

Let us calculate the maximum value of the electric field induced at a 5×10^{-2} m circle in the solenoid of our previous example if the magnetic field varies sinusoidally with a frequency of 10^5 cycles per sec and has a maximum value of 0.75 Wb/m². The maximum magnitude of the induced field is attained when $\cos (2\pi ft) = 1$:

$$E = \frac{2\pi f AB_0}{l}.$$

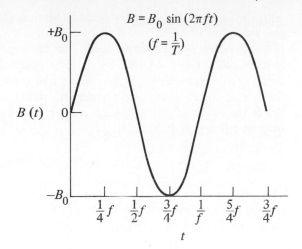

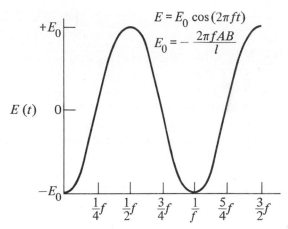

FIGURE 12.6 A magnetic field varying with time as $\sin(2\pi ft)$ where $f = 1/T$ is its frequency of oscillation, induces an electric field which varies as $\cos(2\pi ft)$.

As before, $A = \pi R^2$, $l = 2\pi R$, so

$$E = \pi R f B_0$$
$$= 3.14 \times 5 \times 10^{-2} \times 10^5 \times 7.5 \times 10^{-1}$$
$$= 1.18 \times 10^4 \text{ N/C}.$$

Since the induced field varies inversely with distance its maximum magnitude 500 m from the coil axis is 1.18 N/C.

▲▲ 12.3 Maxwell's equations. The propagation of electromagnetic radiation

We have now discussed two distinct, experimentally verified sources of electric fields: point charges (and charge distributions) that produce fields in accord with Coulomb's law (Equations 8.1) and changing magnetic fields, which induce fields given by Faraday's law (Equations 12.5). However, we have related magnetic fields only to moving charges (and equivalently to permanent poles). Reflecting on the general conclusions of Section 12.1 we might have reason to suspect this asymmetry. For whereas it is often convenient to consider electric and magnetic fields separately, in special relativity they are aspects of a single electromagnetic field. Although one observer might perform the experiments with the solenoid and loop discussed in Section 12.2 and conclude that he measures only the induction of an electric field by a changing magnetic field, an observer in another inertial system would measure fields that are expressible as combinations of the electric and magnetic fields obtained by the first observer. When carried out in mathematical detail these arguments imply the existence of a law which is symmetric to Faraday's law: *a changing electric field induces a magnetic field throughout all space.*

Let the *electric flux* Φ_E through any area A (Figure 12.7) be defined in analogy with magnetic flux (Equation 9.24):

$$\Phi_E = AE \cos \theta. \tag{12.7}$$

Then the symmetric law may be stated as follows: a change in the *electric* flux through the surface induces a *magnetic* field, B, whose magnitude integrated about any closed loop about the flux is determined by

$$\int B_\| \, dl = \frac{1}{c^2} \frac{\Delta \Phi_E}{\Delta t}, \tag{12.8a}$$

where $B_\|$ is the component of the field parallel to the loop. (This equation is strictly valid only if no currents are enclosed in the loop; in the latter event another term must be added.) Except for the constant $1/c^2$ and the difference in sign, the expression is completely analogous to Equation 12.5a. The differences are consequences of the detailed relativistic invariance requirement. When the area A is constant and its plane perpendicular to the changing field and, further, when the induced magnetic field is constant over the integration path, dl, then we have the analogue of Equation 12.5b:

$$Bl = \frac{A}{c^2} \frac{\Delta E}{\Delta t}. \tag{12.8b}$$

Figure 12.8 shows a capacitor with circular, parallel plates of radius R connected via a conducting wire to a source of EMF which maintains an equal and opposite charge on the plates and therefore a constant electric field in the gap. Suppose that the EMF of the source increases steadily. Then additional current flows in the conductor, removing negative charge from the positive capacitor plate, depositing an equal negative charge per unit time upon the negative plate. Since the field in the gap is proportional to the charge upon the plate (Equation 12.1a) it must steadily increase with time. In that case the

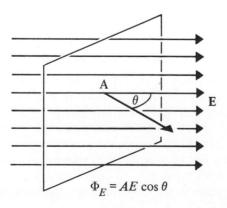

FIGURE 12.7 The electric flux Φ_E through a surface is defined in terms of the field through the surface, the area of the surface, and the angle between its perpendicular and the field direction.

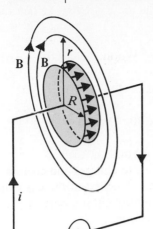

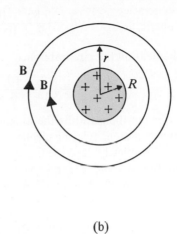

(a)   (b)

FIGURE 12.8   (a) The electric field increasing across the gap of a circular, parallel plate capacitor induces a magnetic field whose lines of force are circles concentric with the plates.   (b) End-on view of the capacitor and induced field.

strength of the magnetic field everywhere on a circle of radius r enclosing the changing field is given by

$$2\pi r B = \frac{\pi R^2}{c^2}\frac{\Delta E}{\Delta t},$$

or

$$B = \frac{R^2}{rc^2}\frac{\Delta E}{\Delta t}, \tag{12.9}$$

an expression analogous to Equation 12.6. The lines of force of the induced field have a circular symmetry and lie in planes perpendicular to the direction of the changing electric field (Figure 12.8b).

One may ask why Equations 12.8, unlike Faraday's law, had to be based upon deduction rather than on measurement. The answer is twofold: first, it is easier to produce a large rapidly changing magnetic field in the laboratory than a changing electric field of comparable magnitude. Second, it is easier to measure the induced electric field, for the force of the electric field upon charge in a wire, resulting in an EMF, is far greater than the magnetic force upon the slowly moving charge that constitutes a laboratory current. However, sufficiently delicate experiments can, in fact, detect an induced magnetic field such as the one shown in Figure 12.8.

Let the radii of the circular plates of a capacitor be 5×10^{-2} m, and let the electric field across the gap change from 0 to 10^5 N/C in 10^{-6} sec. (Such a field would be produced by a 10^3 V potential difference across a 10^{-2} m gap—see Equation 8.11a.) Then the rate of change of the flux in the capacitor is

$$\frac{\Delta \Phi_E}{\Delta t} = 3.14 \times (5 \times 10^{-2})^2 \frac{10^5}{10^{-6}},$$

$$= 7.85 \times 10^8 \text{ N/C-sec.}$$

Substituting into Equation 12.8b:

$$Bl = \frac{7.85 \times 10^8}{9 \times 10^{16}} = 8.7 \times 10^{-9} \text{ Wb/m.}$$

Hence the field on the circumference of the capacitor is

$$B = \frac{8.7 \times 10^{-9}}{2 \times 3.14 \times 5 \times 10^{-2}} = 2.8 \times 10^{-8} \text{ Wb/m}^2,$$

roughly one ten-thousandths the magnetic field of the earth.

The four equations relating electric and magnetic fields to charges and currents and to each other completely describe the electromagnetic field. The first of these is Coulomb's law (Equation 8.4 and Figure 8.5), which specified the electrostatic part of the electric field at a point with radius vector $\mathbf{R}$ relative to a point charge q:

$$\mathbf{E} = \frac{1}{4\pi\epsilon_0} \frac{q}{R^2} \frac{\mathbf{R}}{R},$$

The second of the four relations is Equation 9.15, which gives the magnitude of the magnetic field a distance R from a charge q traveling with speed v:

$$B = \frac{\mu_0}{4\pi} \frac{qv}{R^2} \sin \theta,$$

where θ is defined in Figure 9.26a. (The direction of $\mathbf{B}$ is perpendicular to the plane of $\mathbf{v}$ and $\mathbf{R}$; see Figure 9.26b.) The remaining two relations are provided by the induction laws, i.e., Faraday's law (Equation 12.5a):

$$\int E_\parallel \, dl = -\frac{\Delta \Phi_B}{\Delta t},$$

and its symmetric counterpart (Equation 12.8a):

$$\int B_\parallel \, dl = \frac{1}{c^2} \frac{\Delta \Phi_E}{\Delta t}.$$

Taken together with the equations for the forces upon moving charges in the field these four equations constitute a complete summary of the classical electromagnetic interaction, even as Newton's laws of motion and the law of gravitation summarize the classical gravitational interaction. When written in a somewhat more general mathematical form the four field equations are referred to as Maxwell's equations, in honor of James Clerk Maxwell (Figure 12.9), the nineteenth-century British physicist who first deduced Equation 12.8 using symmetry arguments and then used the equations to demonstrate that the electromagnetic interaction is propagated with the velocity of light. We justified the need for Equation 12.8 by appealing to special relativity. However, Maxwell did not have the benefit of our hindsight. In fact, by showing that light is a fundamental manifestation of the interaction between charges he also showed that its velocity must be constant in all inertial systems. Thus we owe our hindsight to Maxwell, for of course the invariance of the speed of light is the cornerstone of special relativity.

When the current (and therefore the magnetic field) in a very long solenoid changes, the solenoid is surrounded by an induced electric field of magnitude $E = (R/2r)(\Delta B/\Delta t)$, whose configuration is shown in Figure 12.5. However, from the symmetric analogue of Faraday's law (Equation 12.8) it follows that Figure 12.5 is not a complete representation

FIGURE 12.9 James Clerk Maxwell (1831–1879). (Courtesy of the American Institute of Physics, Center for the History and Philosophy of Physics.)

of the electromagnetic field associated with the changing current in the solenoid. When the induced electric field appears at a particular point in space it induces a *magnetic* field. Thus a changing electric field must always be associated with a changing magnetic field, or, from the viewpoint of special relativity, the two aspects of a changing electromagnetic field cannot be dissociated from each other. The orientations of the two induced fields relative to each other and to the solenoid is shown in Figure 12.10.

We now ask a crucial question: how rapidly are the induced fields established? What time interval elapses between the instant the current begins to change and the time the induced fields appear at some particular distance from the center of the coil? If the elapsed time is greater than zero so that the fields are not established instantaneously at distant points, we would also expect the time lag to increase in direct proportion to r. At any particular time, t_1, the fields will not have appeared at all points in space and thus will be nonzero only within a cylindrical volume of radius r_1. After a time interval Δt the radius of the cylinder enclosing the fields will have increased by Δr (Figure 12.11). The advance of the cylindrical front implies that the induced electromagnetic field is propagated away from the solenoid with velocity $v = \Delta r/\Delta t$. Following Maxwell, we can use Equations 12.5 and 12.8 to relate the strengths of the electric and magnetic parts of the field to each other, and show that its velocity of propagation is 3×10^8 m/sec.

It is advantageous to analyze the propagation of a field whose configuration lends itself

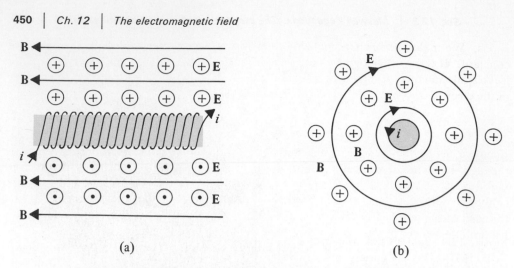

(a)　　　　　　　　　　　　　　　　(b)

FIGURE 12.10   (a) Directions of the induced electric and magnetic fields surrounding a solenoid in which the current is increasing. The coil is wound with a left-handed pitch from the left end to the right end. (b) A view into the right-hand end of the coil.

to rather simple mathematical treatment.* At great distances from a solenoid the curvature of the electric lines of force is so small over small arc length that they may be approximated as straight, parallel lines. (Alternately, we could consider the rigorously plane field configurations propagated from a changing sheet of current.) Let us choose a coordinate system in which the electric field vectors are in the x-direction, the magnetic field vectors in the y-direction. Then the propagation direction must be parallel to the

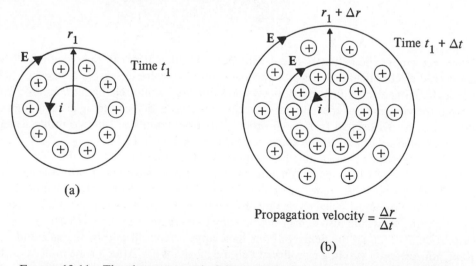

$$\text{Propagation velocity} = \frac{\Delta r}{\Delta t}$$

(b)

FIGURE 12.11   The electromagnetic field configuration induced by the increasing current in the solenoid of Figure 12.10 at (a) a time t_1 after the current starts to increase, and (b) a time Δt later. The propagation velocity of the field is defined as the rate at which the cylindrical front advances.

* The author is grateful to Professor Robert Adair for suggesting this treatment.

z-axis. We make the further idealizing assumption that, once established, the fields are constant. If we construct a small rectangle in the yz-plane with dimensions Δy, Δz, then if the front advances from one of its boundaries to the other during the time Δt the change in the electric flux through the area is (Figure 12.12a):

$$\frac{E \, \Delta z \, \Delta y}{\Delta t} = Ev \, \Delta y,$$

since we define the velocity of propagation as $v = \Delta z/\Delta t$. The changing electric flux through the rectangle induces a magnetic field around the perimeter related to the changing flux by Equation 12.8a. Since the area is rectangular the integral $\int B_\parallel \, dl$, the sum of the products $B_\parallel \, \Delta l$ over all segments of the perimeter, reduces to four terms: one for each of the four sides of the boundary. But the induced field is in the y-direction and has no component in the z direction. Further, the induced field at the far y-side of the rectangle is still zero at the end of the time interval we are considering, since the advancing front has not yet crossed that boundary, and we have idealized by assuming the fields once established are constant.* Therefore, the integral reduces to but one term, $B \, \Delta y$, and substituting $\Delta\Phi_E/\Delta t = Ev \, \Delta y$ into Equation 12.8a we have:

$$B \, \Delta y = \frac{1}{c^2} \, Ev \, \Delta y,$$

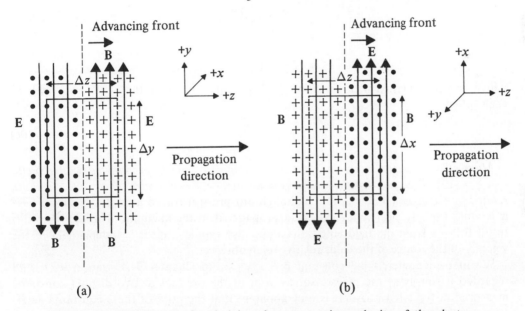

FIGURE 12.12 Diagrams for deriving the propagation velocity of the electromagnetic field in a vacuum. The field propagates in the positive z-direction; its velocity is such that the front at which the fields reverse their directions advances a distance Δz in a time Δt. (a) Shows the configuration of the fields in the yz-plane when the front has advanced halfway across the small rectangle with dimension $\Delta y \, \Delta z$. The electric field direction is out of the page to the left of the front, into the page to the right. (b) is a view of the field configuration in the xz-plane at the same time. The magnetic field is into the page to the left of the advancing front, out of the page to the right.

---

* The infinitely sharp discontinuity between the region of field and no field is an idealization not encountered in practice. However, the end results we seek do not depend upon our specific model.

or

$$B = \frac{v}{c^2} E. \tag{12.10a}$$

The magnitude of the induced *electric* field may be found by following an analogous procedure (Figure 12.12b). A rectangle with dimensions Δx, Δz is constructed along the front in the xz-plane; the change in *magnetic* flux through that area in a time Δt is

$$B \frac{\Delta z \, \Delta x}{\Delta t} = Bv \, \Delta x,$$

Again, the integral of the induced electric field around the perimeter reduces to $E \, \Delta x$. Applying Faraday's law (Equation 12.5b),

$$E \, \Delta x = Bv \, \Delta x,$$

or

$$E = vB. \tag{12.10b}$$

We now have two equations relating the induced fields to each other. Substituting the second into the first,

$$B = \left(\frac{v^2}{c^2}\right) B,$$

or, finally,

$$v = c,$$

which, when combined with Equation 12.10a, relates the strengths of the two fields to each other:

$$B = \frac{E}{c}. \tag{12.10c}$$

Maxwell's equations imply that the electromagnetic field is propagated with velocity $c = 3 \times 10^8$ *m/sec and that the strengths of the magnetic and electric parts of the field are related by the equation* $B = E/c$.* Although our proof involved a relatively simple case it is valid for any electromagnetic field propagated in the vacuum. The fact that this result follows from the field equations alone also implies that it is independent of the velocity of the source of the fields relative to an observer.

We first encountered the constant $c = 1/\sqrt{\mu_0 \epsilon_0}$ in Chapter 9 (Equation 9.27) and regarded it simply as the inverse square root of the product of two distinct constants measured in the laboratory. It is now apparent that the ratio of these constants determines the velocity with which the combined fields are propagated. Since c is based upon these two constants, a change in c implies a change in the constant—or a variation in the ratio of the electrostatic to the magnetic force between two charges moving with constant velocity (Equation 9.29). But c is also the measured velocity of light in vacuum. Therefore, we conclude not only that visible light is a special case of electromagnetic propagation, but also that the velocity of light cannot depend upon our choice of inertial system. We have come full circle to special relativity.

---

* The relation between B and E depends on the system of units used, and will therefore be different in a text using cgs rather than mks units. But the relation $v = c$ is independent of units. This is a fundamental distinction between the two conclusions of the above treatment.

What happens to the fields propagated from the solenoid when its current *stops* changing? The magnetic field surrounding a long wire carrying a *constant* current (Figure 9.9) collapses when the current ceases to flow. In a sense the field belongs to the wire and the energy stored in the field returns to the wire when the current ceases.

The situation is different for the induced fields of a changing current. While the current is still changing the source is surrounded by the spreading, induced fields; after the current stops changing the fields are no longer induced. However, the fields that *were* induced while the current *was* changing continue to induce each other, continue to propagate outward from the source. The induced fields do *not* belong to the source that produces them. Unlike the energy stored in the magnetic field of a constant current, the electromagnetic energy carried by the induced electromagnetic field does not return to its source. Therefore, we may say that a changing current, or more basically an accelerated charge, *radiates* electromagnetic energy, and regard field propagation as a mechanism of energy transfer between charges.

◣◣ 12.4 The connection between the electromagnetic field and charge. Photon exchange model of the field. The photon-wave paradox

The property of matter called charge is completely intertwined with electromagnetic interaction and thus with the electromagnetic field. In the absence of charge there would be no interaction. Conversely Coulomb's law, the simplest manifestation of the interaction, serves as the basic definition of the property itself. In the foregoing chapters we have taken the viewpoint that a charge is more fundamental than the electromagnetic field it produces or that acts upon it. The assumption conforms to our intuitive ideas regarding matter and its interactions. However, it is not the only one possible.

Figure 12.13, which represents the field of a point charge by means of its lines of force, can also be used to define the charge in terms of the field. Since the electric field of a point charge varies inversely as the square of the distance from the charge it must be infinite at $R = 0$, i.e., at the charge itself.* Hence we might define a point charge as a point at which the electric field has infinite magnitude, a so-called *field singularity*, or

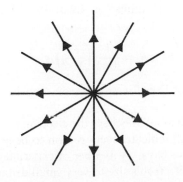

FIGURE 12.13 Conventional representation of the electric field of a positive point charge at rest by means of its lines of force. Since the presence of the charge can only be detected through the medium of the field, then it is also possible to regard the field as primary and the charge as a region where it becomes highly condensed.

---

* Provided Coulomb's law remains unaltered at very small distances. See Chapter 23.

more pictorially a point at which the lines of force are highly condensed. Motion of the charge in the field can be interpreted as motion of the singularity, or, equivalently, as a spatial and temporal variation in the field itself. Hence from this point of view the charge and field are regarded as one merged entity rather than as an inseparable pair.

Since the electromagnetic field has the ability to perform work upon a charge, it contains energy so that the concentration of the field in a very small volume implies a high concentration of energy within that region. But in special relativity, inertial mass and energy are equivalent concepts. Therefore, it is tempting to attribute the inertial mass of an electron, whose interactions are overwhelmingly electromagnetic,* to the interaction *itself.* It may be shown that the energy stored in an electric field E per unit volume is

$$\frac{\text{Energy}}{\text{Volume}} = \frac{\epsilon_0 E^2}{2}.$$

Then the total electrical energy contained in a spherical volume of radius R due to a point charge q located the center of the sphere is

$$\text{Energy} = \frac{\epsilon_0}{2}\left(\frac{q}{R^2}\right)^2\left(\frac{4}{3}\pi R^3\right) = \frac{2\pi\epsilon_0}{3}\left(\frac{q^2}{R}\right).$$

Using the mass-energy relation:

$$Mc^2 = \frac{2\pi\epsilon_0}{3}\left(\frac{q^2}{R}\right).$$

Rearranging factors, the radius of a spherical electromagnetic entity is

$$R = \frac{2\pi\epsilon_0}{3}\left(\frac{q^2}{Mc^2}\right).$$

For an entity with the fundamental charge, such as the electron,

$$R = \frac{2\pi\epsilon_0}{3}\left(\frac{e^2}{Mc^2}\right).$$

Now $1/4\pi\epsilon_0 = 9 \times 10^9$ mks units, $e = 1.6 \times 10^{-19}$ C, $M = 9 \times 10^{-31}$ kg. Therefore on this model the "electron radius" is 4.2×10^{-16} m. A more careful analysis yields the result

$$R = \frac{1}{4\pi\epsilon_0}\left(\frac{e^2}{Mc^2}\right), \tag{12.11}$$

which has the value 2.5×10^{-15} m for an electron, and is called the *classical electron radius.*

Of course we have no reason at all to believe the electron is a uniformly charged sphere, and as succeeding chapters will indicate, every reason to believe that we *cannot* push the classical formalism as far as we have. A number of experiments at high-energy electron accelerators have probed the electron's size to very small distances (Chapter 22). All are consistent with the conclusion that the electron is smaller than 10^{-17} m. In other words, no experiment has yet shown that the electron is anything but a point. But according to

---

* As shown in Section 8.2, the gravitational interaction between two electrons is completely negligible compared with their electromagnetic interactions. The electron also participates in the weak interactions (Chapters 20–23). However, the effects of these are also very much smaller than the electromagnetic effects.

the foregoing analysis the energy and thus the inertial mass of a point is infinite, and not 9×10^{-31} kg. Even very sophisticated calculations based on quantum field theory (Chapter 22) but analogous to our procedure lead to an infinite electron mass. So whereas the idea that charge is a singularity in the electric field is very attractive, all of its quantitative details have not yet been satisfactorily worked out. Nonetheless, the model does provide a number of insights that are at least in qualitative accord with experiment.

The effects of a repulsive force between two particles may be represented directly as an exchange of momentum between them. This is not surprising since, after all, we defined force in Chapter 4 as the time rate of change of momentum. In Figure 12.14, two men on a frictionless surface (ice skaters, for instance) exchange momentum by throwing a ball back and forth between them. When the first skater throws the ball he recoils slightly. The second skater likewise recoils when he *catches* the ball, and recoils again when he throws it back to the first skater.

Now if we did not *observe* the exchange of the ball between the skaters we might conclude that they exerted a direct, repulsive force upon each other. Upon closer examination we might see the ball and, with the skaters' cooperation, perform several experiments. We would then ascertain that the "repulsive force" is directly proportional to the number of balls exchanged per second and to the momentum imparted to each. As long as each skater caught and returned all of the balls thrown to him the magnitude of the observed, repulsive force would not depend upon the separation of the interacting men, although the time required for the *transmission* of the force between them would increase in direct proportion to that separation. For instance, if one skater were to double the velocity of each of the balls he throws, the resulting increase in the repulsive force would not be apparent until the second skater received the first of these new, higher velocity balls. Likewise, if the first skater quit throwing balls altogether the second would not know about it until after he had received the last one thrown.

The skater model represents a classical analogue of a repulsive, particle-exchange interaction in a one-dimensional universe, a universe in which all of the exchanged particles are constrained to move along a straight line. It is somewhat harder to rationalize

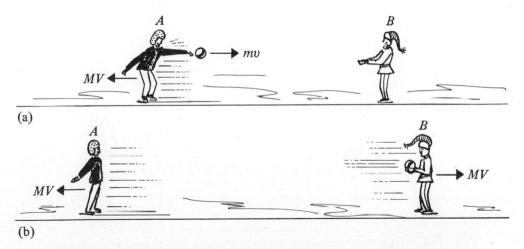

FIGURE 12.14 Classical particle exchange model of a one-dimensional repulsive force between two ice skaters playing catch. (a) Skater *A* has just thrown the ball, giving it a momentum *mv* and therefore recoiling with an equal and opposite momentum. (b) Skater *B* recoils with the same momentum after catching the ball.

an *attractive* particle exchange force, although the substitution of a boomerang for the ball has been suggested (Figure 12.15).

Generalization to a three-dimensional Euclidean universe is straightforward. Let us assume that two particles transfer momentum to each other by exchanging some sort of intermediate particle, and that the force between them originates in this exchange mechanism. We also assume that each of the interacting particles emits the intermediate particles uniformly in all directions in a given time interval.

Let R be the distance between the interacting particles, and imagine that a sphere of that radius is constructed with its center at particle 1 (Figure 12.16). Then the ratio of the exchanged particles emitted by 1 to the number received by particle 2 is proportional to the fraction of the surface area of the sphere which is subtended by 2. Letting A be the surface area of the latter we can express the magnitude of the resulting exchange force as:

$$F = \frac{kA}{4\pi R^2},$$

since $4\pi R^2$ is the surface area of the entire sphere. Here k is a proportionality constant related, presumably, to the number of exchange entities emitted per unit time and the momentum carried by each, and characterizes the intrinsic strength of the interaction. Thus we find that in a three-dimensional, Euclidean universe, the particle exchange model implies a force inversely proportional to the square of the distance between the interacting particles, as observed for both the electrostatic and the classical gravitational forces.

Does this model have any correspondence to the real world? As we have emphasized repeatedly the entire electromagnetic field concept is based upon the observed interaction of charges. Hence there is no a priori reason to believe that all its properties cannot be interpreted in terms of some sort of exchange mechanism, though admittedly the exchanged particles cannot have all the properties we commonly associate with classical particles. In terms of an exchange model the sources of the field, the charges, or the field singularities, become sources and absorbers of the exchanged entities. The fundamental

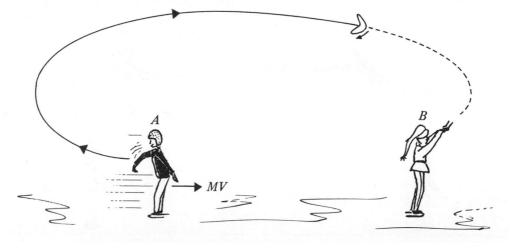

FIGURE 12.15 Classical particle exchange model of a one-dimensional *attractive* force between two skaters exchanging a boomerang. Skater A has thrown the boomerang away from B and therefore recoils in the direction of B. The boomerang follows the curved path indicated so that B will recoil in the direction of A after catching it.

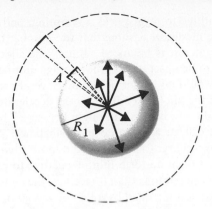

FIGURE 12.16   Classical particle exchange model of a repulsive force in three-dimensional space.   A small object a distance R_1 from another object with surface area A emits particles uniformly in three dimensions.   Therefore, in any given time interval the same number pass through equal areas on an imaginary sphere of radius R_1 centered upon the emitter.   It follows that the number of exchange particles intercepted by the second object per unit time is proportional to the ratio of its surface area to the surface area of the sphere, $4\pi R_1^2$.   The area of the appropriate imaginary sphere increases as the square of the separation, between the interacting bodies.   Therefore, the magnitude of the force between them decreases inversely as the square of their separation.

charge $e = 1.6 \times 10^{-19}$ C is related in detail to the ability of a charge to emit and absorb the fundamental, exchanged entities that we describe classically in terms of the fields. We have noted that the particle exchange model representing the force between two charges at rest should vary in all directions as the inverse square of the interacting particles. When a pair of interacting charges moves relative to an observer he sees the distance between them contracted in the direction of their relative motion, and hence believes that each emits particles uniformly through a spheroidal rather than through a spherical surface (Figure 12.2). Therefore, he no longer measures a simple $1/R^2$ dependence, and may well try to formulate the interaction in terms of two fields, one that does not vary with velocity and one that does, i.e., the electric and magnetic fields.

Can we identify the photons of Chapter 10 with the hypothesized carriers of the electromagnetic interaction? The model presents difficulties. We know that photons cannot be regarded as classical particles; but neither can we attribute all classical particle properties to the presumed carriers of an exchange interaction. Energy conservation is a more serious problem. When an electron emits a photon, the electron loses energy. On the particle exchange model either its rest mass or its kinetic energy would therefore decrease. But two charges at rest relative to each other and to an observer can emit photons only at the expense of their rest masses, for their kinetic energies are zero. If each were to receive a photon from the other at precisely the same time it emitted another, the rest masses would be constant. But this assumption almost implies preplanning on the part of each electron and is hard to justify. As we shall learn in Chapter 21 and 22, quantum mechanics permits short term fluctuations in mass and energy, and hence resolves the problem easily: an electron at rest need not receive and emit photons simultaneously provided the *average* number it receives during a short time interval is equal to the average number it emits.

We have by no means proved the photon-exchange model of the electromagnetic interaction, and must continue to regard it as a tempting, perhaps even a fruitful representation. In terms of the model we assume that the number of photons exchanged per unit time by two charges at rest is balanced. But if one should start to accelerate we would expect the balance to be upset so that the average number of photons emitted and received by each particle would no longer be equal. Several predictions follow from this conjecture. First, some of the photons emitted by the accelerating charge and previously absorbed by the other would now be free and might be "seen" by some sort of laboratory apparatus, a photoelectric cell, or a human eye, for instance. Second, the nature of the interaction between the two charges would become more involved than the interaction between two charges at rest or in uniform motion relative to each other. Finally, if the accelerated charge emits more photons than it receives, the emission of photons (the production of light?) should be accompanied by a loss of energy by the emitting charge.

All three of these related expectations are borne out by observation. For instance, x-ray photons are produced when electrons are brought to rest in matter (Section 10.4). Faraday's law of induction implies that the electromagnetic field of an accelerated charge, which produces a time-varying magnetic field, *is* more complicated than the field of a uniformly moving charge. Finally, a rigorous analysis on the same lines as Section 12.3 shows that electromagnetic radiation, or light in the general sense of Chapter 10, is produced by accelerating charge, which thereby loses energy, and detected when the propagated fields accelerate other charge, in the retina of the eye or in photographic film, for instance.

Thus we have two mechanisms for the production, transmission, and detection of light. We have the photon model, which is in accord with a great deal of experimental evidence (Chapter 10), and offers an attractive particle exchange model for the electromagnetic interaction. On the other hand, Maxwell's equations, which involve only the classical fields, certainly lead to the observed velocity of light, also show that an accelerating charge is the source of light, and are consistent with several other experimental tests to be discussed in Chapter 13.

Do the field and photon mechanisms contradict each other? Not necessarily. The electromagnetic field is detected only when it transfers energy to a system of charge. If, as in Chapter 10, we regard photons as discrete, irreducible packets of electromagnetic energy which do not necessarily have all the attributes of classical particles, then we might interpret Maxwell's field equations as equations governing the emission and propagation of photons, and the photons themselves as carriers of the electromagnetic field.

As long as the photon model does not contradict either of the results of direct measurements or the validated conclusions drawn from Maxwell's equations, we may continue to regard it as acceptable. But we must recognize at once that there are fundamental distinctions between the propagation of the electromagnetic field (Section 12.3) and the classical description of particle motion. The latter is based upon the assumption that an entity, the particle, is localized in space and time. However, the strengths of the field at a particular point and at a particular time (in Figure 12.10, for instance) are related both to the field strengths at all *other* points at that same time, and also to the field strengths at *that* point at all *other* times. In other words, the fields cannot be localized either in space or in time. This conclusion was implied by the language we used in Section 12.3, describing the propagation of the field in terms of a *front* whose position *changes* in time. We can measure, and discuss the *strength* of the field at a point in time or space, but cannot refer to the field itself in those terms.

The language used in reference to field propagation has a great deal more in common with the description of water waves, for instance, than with classical particle motion. For that reason light is often said to be propagated as an *electromagnetic wave*. But even as a model of light based upon photons assumed to have all the attributes of classical particles cannot be reconciled with the double slit interference experiment (Section 10.6), a *classical* wave model cannot be reconciled with the photoelectric effect, for that effect requires that the energy transferred to an electron must be localized in time and space. We are brought full circle to the first of two paradoxes presented in Section 10.6, the apparently irreconcilable interpretations of the photoelectric effect and the double-slit interference experiment.

SUGGESTIONS FOR FURTHER READING ▲▲▲

Most introductory texts deal semiquantitatively with Maxwell's laws and the electromagnetic field. Among these are:

K. R. ATKINS, *Physics*, John Wiley and Sons, Inc., New York, 1965, Chapters 18 and 19.

JAY OREAR, *Fundamental Physics*, John Wiley and Sons, Inc., New York, 1961, Chapter 8.

ARNOLD B. ARONS, *Development of Concepts of Physics*, Addison-Wesley Publishing Co., Inc., Reading, Mass., 1965, Chapter 27.

PROBLEMS AND EXERCISES ▲▲▲

12.1. A parallel plate capacitor with a 2×10^{-2} m gap and square plates with dimension 0.1×0.1 m produces a constant electric field of magnitude 10^5 V/m in the positive x-direction (across the gap). Sketch the capacitor and the lines of force of the electric field seen by:

(a) An observer at rest relative to the capacitor.
(b) An observer moving with velocity $0.8\,c$ relative to the capacitor in the x-direction.
(c) An observer moving with velocity $0.8\,c$ in the y-direction (i.e., parallel to the gap).

12.2. (a) What is the magnitude of the total charge on the capacitor plates in Problem 12.1?
(b) What current is measured by an observer who travels with velocity $0.8\,c$ in the y-direction relative to the plates?
(c) Sketch the magnetic lines of force seen by the moving observer.

12.3. What is the direction of the total electromagnetic force on a positive charge at rest in the gap of the capacitor of Problem 12.1 as seen by:

(a) An observer at rest relative to the capacitor.
(b) An observer moving with constant velocity $0.8\,c$ relative to the capacitor and in the y-direction.

12.4. What electric and magnetic fields are seen by an observer who moves with constant velocity $0.8\,c$ relative to the capacitor of Problem 12.1 in:

(a) The x-direction.
(b) The z-direction.

12.5. What is the *ratio* of the magnetic to the electric field magnitude seen by an observer who travels in the y-direction relative to the capacitor in Problem 12.1 with constant velocity:

(a) $0.1\,c$.
(b) $0.8\,c$.

(c) 0.9 *c*.
(d) 0.95 *c*.
(e) 0.99 *c*.

12.6. A long solenoid of radius 0.06 m wound with 6000 turns of wire per meter carries a 5 A current. Another similarly wound solenoid of radius 0.04 m is placed coaxially within the first one.

(a) What is the magnetic field (magnitude and direction) inside the large solenoid?
(b) If the current in the first solenoid drops from 5 to 0 A in 10^{-5} sec what current is induced in the smaller coil? Let the resistance of the smaller coil be 3 ohms.

12.7. Suppose the small solenoid in Problem 12.6 were removed from the larger one. If the current then dropped from 5 to 0 A in 10^{-5} sec:

(a) What electric field (magnitude and direction) would be induced on a 0.04 m radius circle centered upon and coaxial with the solenoid axis?
(b) What force would the induced field exert on a $+10^{-6}$ C charge?

12.8. The two circular, 0.04 m radius, parallel plates of a capacitor are each given a total charge of 4×10^{-8} C (one plate positive, one negative).

(a) What is the electric field strength in the gap?
(b) If the capacitor is discharged in such a way that the charge on the plates drops to 2×10^{-6} C in 10^{-5} sec, what is the magnitude and direction of the magnetic field induced at the outer diameter of the gap? (Assume the charge decreases at a constant rate, and that the magnetic field is symmetric relative to the axis passing through the centers of the two plates.)

12.9. What steady current in a long wire along the axis of the capacitor plates in Problem 12.8 would produce a magnetic field at the outer diameter of the gap of the same strength as the changing electric field?

12.10. The current in a long solenoid varies with time in the manner shown in the accompanying sketch.

(a) Sketch the time variation of the magnetic field produced in the vicinity of the solenoid. (Choose units of B/B_{max} for the vertical scale.)
(b) Sketch the time variation of the electric field induced by the changing magnetic field of part a in units of E/E_{max}.

N.B.: At large distances from the solenoid the induced magnetic field depends both on the current and on the induced electric field.

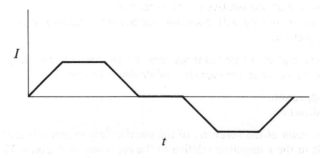

12.11. The magnitude of the charge on one of the parallel plates of a circular capacitor varies with time as shown in the sketch.

(a) Sketch the time variation of the electric field in the gap (choose units of E/E_{max}).

(b) Sketch the time variation of the magnetic field induced by the changing electric field of part a in units of B/B_{max}.

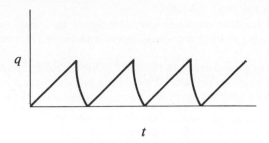

12.12. The current in a long solenoid of radius 0.05 m varies with time as:

$$I = I_0 \sin (2\pi ft),$$

with

$$I_0 = 1 \text{ A}, \qquad f = \frac{10^6}{2\pi} /\text{sec}.$$

(a) What is the maximum magnetic field produced?

(b) What is the magnitude of the maximum induced electric field on a 0.04 m radius circle centered upon and perpendicular to the solenoid axis?

12.13. Plot the current, the magnetic field, and the electric field of Problem 12.12 as functions of time.

12.14. A straight wire 100 m long coincident with the y-axis of a Cartesian coordinate system with its midpoint at the origin carries 10 A current which flows in the positive direction.

(a) What magnetic field (magnitude and direction) is produced on the x-axis at $x = +3$ m?

(b) If the current drops steadily to zero in 10^{-6} sec, what electric fields (magnitude and direction) will be induced on the sides of a 0.1×0.1 m square area centered at $x = +3$ m and parallel to the xy-plane?

(Assume the magnetic field at any one time is uniform across the square area.)

12.15. (a) Plot the induced electric field of Problem 12.14b as a function of time starting 10^{-6} sec before the magnetic field (at the square) begins changing, to 10^{-6} sec after it stops changing.

(b) Sketch the time variation of the magnetic field induced by the changing induced electric field of part a in the region of the square. What is its direction?

(c) How soon after the current in the wire starts to decrease do the fields of parts a and b make their appearance at the center of the square?

12.16. A 60-kg man standing on a platform which can move on frictionless wheels along a straight, level track is initially at rest relative to his twin located 40 m down the track on an identical platform. The first man throws a 0.3 kg ball to the other with velocity 20 m/sec. The second man catches it and throws it back with the same speed. (Assume he does so instantaneously.)

(a) What is the recoil velocity of the first man on throwing the ball? On catching it again?

(b) With what approximate average force do the two brothers repel each other during the first 4 sec of the exchange?

12.17. A small, spherical object emits in each second 10,000 particles of mass 10^{-4} kg uniformly in all directions and traveling outward at 10^6 m/sec.

    (a) How many particles per second pass through a 2-m radius spherical surface centered on the small sphere?

    (b) How many particles per second are intercepted by a body with surface area 10^{-2} sq m located 2 m from the small sphere and perpendicular to the radius vector from it?

    (c) With what average force does the small sphere repel the body in part b?

    (d) How many particles per second would the body of part b intercept if it were 4 m from the small sphere? With what average force would it be repelled in this case?

Classical wave motion

13

▶▶ 13.1 General properties of waves

In Chapter 2 we defined a particle as an entity whose motion is uniquely specified by a single time-varying displacement vector. Since a rigid, extended body is defined by the condition that all points within its volume maintain fixed spatial distances with respect to each other, the particle description can be extended to the analysis of the interaction of such bodies. Thus we were able to develop a system of dynamics based upon the interaction of particles that served us well.

The essentials of the particle idea are localizability and the assumption that physical phenomena may be treated in terms of the interactions of these independent, localizable entities. But on the other hand, the classical electromagnetic field propagated from an accelerating charge is *not* localizable, as we have already noted, and therefore not describable in terms of a classical particle model. The double slit interference experiment (Section 10.6) shows the nonlocalizability of the propagated fields quite clearly, for in order to observe an interference pattern a beam of light must be directed at two separated slits. If either is closed the pattern changes. Thus we cannot localize the electromagnetic field at one or the other slit.

Many purely mechanical processes exhibit certain nonlocal properties. For example, the motion of a vibrating guitar string can be described in terms of the motion of each of its particles. However, it is more fruitful to speak of the motion of the string as a whole, that is, of the *collective* motion of the particles. Likewise, ripples on a lake can be described in terms of the motion of the individual water molecules. But it is more fruitful to refer to the way in which the entire set of ripples behaves. Both these mechanical examples are best described in terms of wave propagation, and as we shall see, both have a great deal in common with the propagation of the electromagnetic field. Therefore, at this point it is desirable to develop the mathematical description of mechanical waves so that we can understand what the term *electromagnetic wave* really implies.

Let us define a wave as any *disturbance* which is propagated through space. For instance, a stone thrown onto a lake sets up a train of ripples, and this *disturbance* is propagated out from the original point of impact. It is important to note three implications of the definition from the outset: first, wave propagation does *not* involve a transfer of *matter*, but rather the propagation of a *disturbance*. Water molecules oscillate up and down perpendicular to the surface of the lake, but do not move any appreciable distance

463

from their original positions. It is the oscillation *itself* which is propagated and thus non-local. The motion of each individual molecule is still in accord with the particle description.

Second, whereas the motion of a particle is described in terms of a succession of its point, spatial positions, to conceive of a wave at a point is a contradiction. Rather, wave motion is a collective phenomenon involving both a finite region of space and a finite duration in time.

Third, wave propagation always involves the transmission of energy. Since water molecules oscillate in a direction perpendicular to the surface, for instance, they clearly have both kinetic and potential energy, and it is this energy which is transmitted between the water molecules.

We shall first consider one-dimensional wave kinematics using as a prototype the waves propagated along a taut string. Then we shall extend the description to waves in two and three dimensions, and finally examine the possibility of describing the continuous transfer of energy by the electromagnetic field (which is certainly a disturbance) in terms of the mathematical apparatus developed to describe wave propagation in material media.

▲▲ 13.2 Wave kinematics in one dimension. The linear superposition principle

If we fasten a long string at one end and give the free end a sharp snap, a pulse travels down its length. For simplicity, we make the initial assumption that the shape of the pulse does not change as it propagates, an assumption whose reasonableness is justified by experiment. Figure 13.1 shows the deformed string at three different times: t_1, t_2, and t_3. Let us choose the *x*-axis as its undeformed, equilibrium position. If the pulse travels a distance Δx in a time Δt then *by definition* its velocity is

$$v = \frac{\Delta x}{\Delta t}. \tag{13.1}$$

Formally, Equation 13.1 is identical with the definition of *particle* velocity. But *physically* there is an important distinction between the two types of velocities: one involves the motion of a material point; the other involves the motion of a finite spatial disturbance. Therefore, we should not expect all of our intuitive ideas about particle velocities to be applicable when we refer to waves.

To describe a wave on a string we must describe its deformation, or the variation in its departure from equilibrium as a function of time. At a particular time, t_1, the shape of the string may be described by giving the displacement from equilibrium, y, of every segment along its length, x:

$$y = f_1(x) \qquad \text{at time } t_1.$$

At a later time, t_2, its shape is given by *another* function of x:

$$y = f_2(x) \qquad \text{at time } t_2.$$

At still later times the shape is described by still different functions. Thus we require a different function of x for every instant of time, or, equivalently, an expression that is a function of *both* x and t. Since we have assumed that the *shape* of the pulse does not change as it is propagated, the functions $f_1(x)$, $f_2(x)$, etc., can be simply related to each other in terms of a symmetry argument. Suppose that two observers stationed at the points 1 and 2 in Figure 13.1 each selected his observation station as the origin of his coordinate system. Then at time t_2 observer 2 would describe the pulse *in his system* by

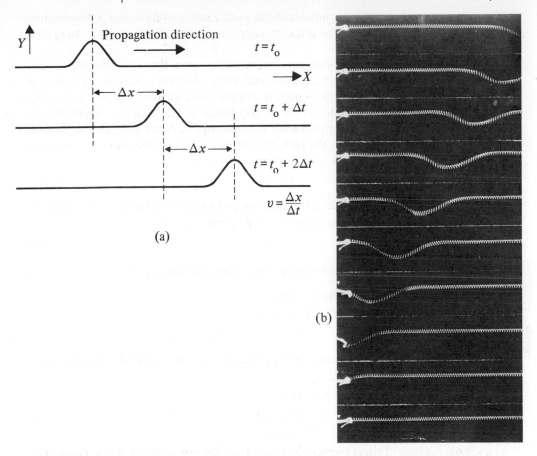

FIGURE 13.1 (a) A taut string propagating a pulse to the right with velocity v shown at three equally spaced times. Since we assume that the shape of the pulse does not change as it is propagated, the deformation of the string is described completely by an equation giving the displacement, y, of each small segment as a function of x, the distance of the segment from the end of the string. (b) Photograph of a pulse propagated along a spring. (Photograph from *PSSC Physics*, D. C. Heath and Co., Boston, © 1965.)

precisely the same function that observer 1 uses at time t_1 in *his* system. A third observer, traveling along with the wave at velocity v, would say that the shape of the pulse did not change at all.

Let A be a coordinate system fixed in the laboratory, and B a system moving with velocity v along with the wave. (We assume that v is much smaller than the velocity of light.) When the observers are adjacent to each other they set their clocks at $t = 0$. At a later time, t, the moving observer, and the pulse will both have traveled a distance vt from the stationary observer. Therefore, the two coordinate systems are related by the Galilean transformation (Equations 6.13):

$$x_b = x_a - vt.$$

That is, if x_a is a point on the string measured in the stationary system, an observer in the moving system will assign that same point the coordinate $(x_a - vt)$ in *his* system. Now if the moving observer, B, describes the pulse with the function $f(x_b)$, it follows that the fixed observer, A, will describe the pulse with the same *functional form*, but will substitute the expression $(x_a - vt)$ for x_b. For instance, suppose the function is $y = x_b^2$. In system A it must be $y = (x_a - vt)^2$.

However, the two observers synchronize their watches when they are adjacent to each other. Therefore, at $t = 0$, $x_a = x_b$. If the stationary observer describes the pulse as $y = f(x_a)$ at $t = 0$ it follows that at subsequent times he must use the form $y = f(x - vt)$. Since we shall normally be interested in the description of waves from the viewpoint of a stationary observer we shall henceforth omit the subscript a, concluding that in general one-dimensional waves moving to the *right* are described by *any* function of x and t in which these variables occur in the combination:

$$x - vt. \tag{13.2a}$$

By an analogous argument, a pulse of the same shape traveling to the *left* is described by the same functional form with the variables in the combination:

$$x + vt. \tag{13.2b}$$

No other combination of x and t describes a wave. Thus the functions

$$y = A(x + vt)^2,$$
$$y = A \sin k(x - vt),$$
$$y = A^z \qquad \text{where} \qquad A = x + vt,$$

all describe waves, although the shapes of the pulses in the three cases differ considerably. On the other hand the functions

$$y = xvt,$$
$$y = x^2 - v^2 t^2,$$

do *not* describe waves.

As a simple example of these remarks let us consider the propagation of the rectangular pulse shown in Figure 13.2. At time $t = 0$ the shape of the string is described by the three equations:

$$y = 0 \qquad \text{for} \qquad x \text{ smaller than } x_{10},$$
$$y = y_1 \qquad \text{for} \qquad x \text{ greater than } x_{10}, \text{ but smaller than } x_{20},$$
$$y = 0 \qquad \text{for} \qquad x \text{ greater than } x_{20}.$$

If the pulse travels to the right the positions of its boundaries, x_1 and x_2, are given at all subsequent times by:

$$x_1 = x(0) + vt \qquad \text{or} \qquad x_1 - vt = x(0),$$
$$x_2 = x(0) + vt \qquad \text{or} \qquad x_2 - vt = x(0).$$

Therefore, the traveling pulse is described by the equations:

$$y = 0 \qquad \text{for} \qquad x \text{ smaller than } [x(0) + vt],$$
$$y = y_1 \qquad \text{for} \qquad x \text{ between } [x(0) + vt] \text{ and } [x(0) + vt],$$
$$y = 0 \qquad \text{for} \qquad x \text{ greater than } [x(0) + vt].$$

Since the particles on a string that is propagating a wave are being accelerated in the y-direction, it follows that a time-varying force acts upon each of them. When two or more forces act upon a single particle the resultant force is the vector sum of the two, and the acceleration of the particle is proportional to the resultant force. By extending this

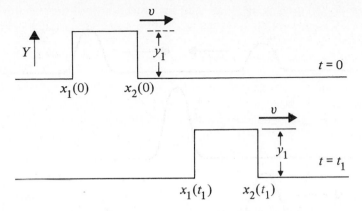

FIGURE 13.2   Two successive views of a rectangular pulse propagated to the right with velocity v. Since the pulse shape remains constant in time, $x_2(t) - x_1(t) = x_2(0) - x_1(0)$ for all times so that the time-dependence of the wave may be specified in terms of the time variation of the boundaries, $x_1(t)$ and $x_2(t)$.

principle to the continuous distribution of particles along a string we would expect that the total effect of two or more waves propagated simultaneously on the same string could be obtained by a vector addition of the effects of the individual waves at all points. This extension of the vector addition rule of particle dynamics is borne out by experiment, and is known as the *linear superposition principle*.

Figure 13.3a shows three successive views of two pulses on a string. The first is traveling to the right and described by some function $y = f_1(x - vt)$; the second, traveling to the left, is described by some other function $y = f_2(x + vt)$. Each wave displaces each segment of the string; the net displacement caused by the two waves is simply the sum of the two separate displacements, both before, during, and after the time the pulses cross each other.

Figure 13.3b illustrates the superposition principle applied to pulses of equal and opposite amplitudes traveling in opposite directions. Since the displacement of each point on the string at a given time is the vector sum of the displacements of the individual pulses, these pulses cancel exactly when they cross, giving the string a net displacement of zero over its entire length.

If the length of a taut string is finite, its ends must be tied to some sort of rigid supports. Figure 13.4a shows the behavior of a pulse at such a termination. Since the pulse would continue to be propagated beyond the boundary if that boundary did not exist, then the string must exert a vertical, time-varying force upon the termination whose magnitude is a function of the displacement it *would* have had in the absence of the termination. Newton's third law implies that the termination exerts an equal and opposite downward force upon the string. As a consequence a pulse is sent back along the string. A detailed analysis shows that this reflected pulse has an amplitude which is equal and opposite to the original pulse that was incident upon the rigid termination.

If the termination is not completely rigid the force exerted by the string may result in a slight, time-varying displacement of the termination so that the amplitude of the reflected pulse has a diminished amplitude. The same conclusion follows from energy conservation, if we measure the energy carried by the pulse in terms of its amplitude. When a string is terminated by tying it to a heavier string which is itself free to oscillate, then the force exerted by the lighter string at the boundary results in the propagation of a pulse

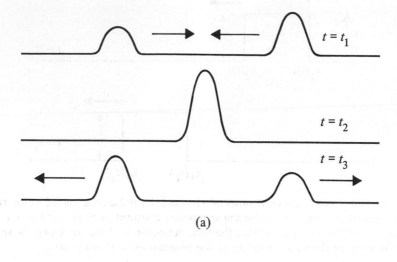

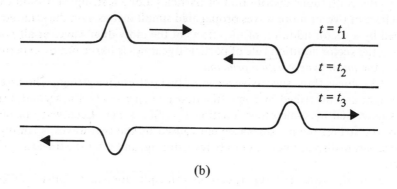

(a)

(b)

FIGURE 13.3   (a,b) According to the linear superposition principle the total deformation of a medium caused by the simultaneous propagation of two or more waves
through it is the vector sum of the deformations caused by the separate waves.
(c,d) (opposite) Photographs of two crossing pulses. (Photographs from *PSSC
Physics*, D. C. Heath and Co., Boston, © 1965.)

down the heavier string in the original direction, as well as the propagation of a reflected
pulse back along the light string (Figure 13.4b).

▶▶ 13.3 Sinusoidal waves

The simultaneous propagation of two or more simple pulses can lead, through their
superposition, to wave forms of considerable complexity. Conversely, we might expect
that a complicated wave could be analyzed into several simple, simultaneously propagated
forms.

This expectation is borne out in fact. Using advanced mathematical techniques it may

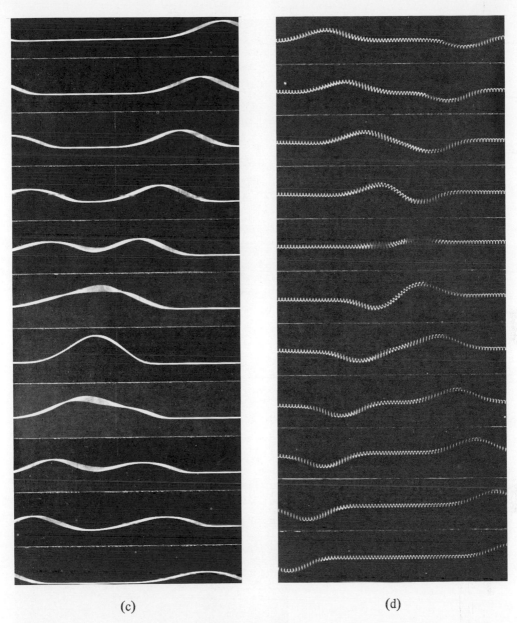

(c)   (d)

be shown that a great many standard sets of wave forms exist such that any arbitrary wave can be expressed as a linear superposition of the members of a set. The simplest of these consists of the sinusoidal waves described by equations of the form

$$y = A \sin k(x \pm vt), \tag{13.3a}$$

$$y = A \cos k(x \pm vt), \tag{13.3b}$$

where A, the amplitude, and k are constants, and the positive and negative signs represent left- and right-traveling waves, respectively.

Equations 13.3 are reminiscent of the equations of motion of an harmonic oscillator

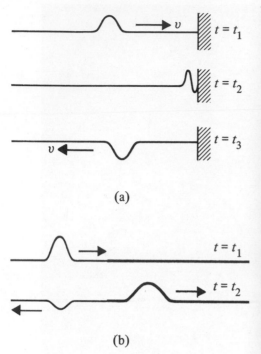

(a)

(b)

FIGURE 13.4 (a) Reflection of a pulse at a completely rigid boundary. (b) Reflection of a pulse on a light string at its boundary with a heavier string and the resultant propagation of a pulse along the latter. (c) Photograph of a pulse reflected from a rigid boundary. (Photograph from *PSSC Physics*, D. C. Heath and Co., Boston, © 1965.)

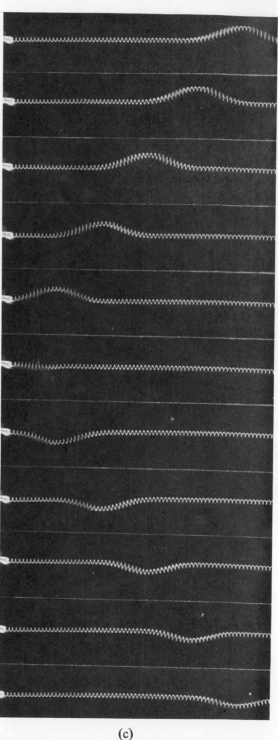

(c)

(Section 4.10), save for the fact that they involve the variable x as well as the variable t. We may regard a sinusoidal wave on a string as a natural extension of simple harmonic motion, by demonstrating that the motion of each segment is simple harmonic motion in the y-direction.

Figure 13.5 shows a section of a sinusoidal wave at three successive times, separated by one-eighth of a period of oscillation. Let us concentrate upon a short segment near the origin, $x = 0$. According to Equation 13.3a the vertical displacement of that segment is given as a function of time by

$$y = A \sin (\pm kvt),$$

an equation (Equation 4.25) which describes simple harmonic motion with period $T = 2\pi/kv$, and amplitude y_0. Then since $k = 2\pi/Tv$ we have, for a right-traveling wave (Equation 13.3a):

$$y = y_0 \sin \left[\frac{2\pi}{T} \left(\frac{x}{v} - t \right) \right]. \tag{13.4}$$

Now Equation 13.4 gives the vertical displacement of any point on the string as a function of time. Therefore, all *pairs* of variables, x and t, for which the expression $(2\pi/T)(x/v - t)$ has the same value, represent equivalent displacements. At a particular time t_1 the value of the term at the origin is $-2\pi t_1/T$; at another time t_2 *another* point on

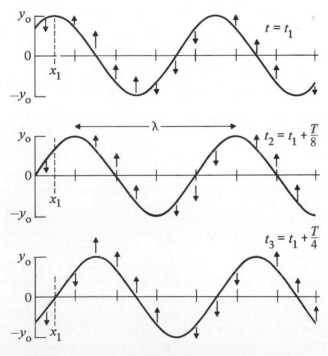

FIGURE 13.5   Three successive snapshots of a sinusoidal wave on a long string. Each point moves with simple harmonic motion in the y-direction. (Instantaneous directions are indicated by the arrows.) Each point lags behind $x = 0$ in direct proportion to its distance from it. (For example, the point x_1 is always one-eighth of a period behind $x = 0$.) Therefore, the wave is propagated to the right. The wavelength λ is the distance between any two successive maxima.

the rope, x_2, will have the same displacement as the point $x = 0$ has at $t = t_1$ *provided* that

$$\frac{-2\pi t_1}{T} = 2\pi\left(\frac{x_2}{vT} - \frac{t_2}{T}\right),$$

or

$$t_2 = t_1 + \frac{x_2}{v}.$$

Since x_2 is greater than zero, t_2 must be later than t_1. A similar relationship can be derived for other times and other points. Therefore, *every* segment of the string oscillates with the same period as every other segment, but lags behind any point to its left in direct proportion to its distance from that point. *In other words, the simple harmonic oscillation is propagated to the right with velocity v.*

Since the period of the sine function is 2π radians, any point x_1 whose displacement at time t_1 is

$$y = y_0 \sin 2\pi\left(\frac{x_1}{vT} - \frac{t_1}{T}\right),$$

has the same displacement *at the same time* as all other points, x_n, for which

$$\sin 2\pi\left(\frac{x_n}{vt} - \frac{t_1}{T}\right) = \sin 2\pi\left[\left(\frac{x_1}{vt} - \frac{t_1}{T}\right) + n\right],$$

where n is any integral number, 1, 2, 3, ..., etc. That is, all x_n which satisfy the criterion

$$\left(\frac{x_n}{vT} - \frac{t_1}{T}\right) = \left(\frac{x_1}{vT} - \frac{t_1}{T}\right) + n,$$

or

$$x_n = x_1 + nvT, \qquad n = 1, 2, 3, \ldots,$$

have the same displacement at the same time as the point x_1. The product vT has the dimension of a length, and is called the *wavelength*, λ (Greek "lambda"), of the wave. That is:

$$\lambda = vT,$$

and

$$x_n - x_1 = n\lambda. \tag{13.5}$$

All points separated by an integral number of wavelengths always have the same displacements at the same time.

It is not difficult to understand the meaning of this result. We know that the displacement of any segment lags behind the segment at the origin in direct proportion to its distance from that point. Thus for one particular distance between two segments, the lag between the times at which they have the same displacement will be one period. In that case the lagging segment has the same displacement as the leader, but is an entire period behind it. Since the wave propagates to the right with velocity v, then in time T it will reproduce itself exactly, having moved one wavelength to the right. Since $v = \Delta x/\Delta t$, and we know that if $\Delta t = T$ then $\Delta x = \lambda$, we have $v = \lambda/T$, in accord with Equation 13.5. Using this equation we may rewrite Equation 12.4:

$$y = y_0 \sin 2\pi\left(\frac{x}{\lambda} - \frac{t}{T}\right).$$

For a wave traveling to the left the minus sign is replaced with a plus, so that in general the expression

$$y = y_0 \sin 2\pi\left(\frac{x}{\lambda} \pm \frac{t}{T}\right) \tag{13.6a}$$

describes the propagation of a sinusoidal wave in one dimension.

A more general description of a sinusoidal wave assumes the form

$$y = y_0 \sin 2\pi\left[\left(\frac{x}{\lambda} \pm \frac{t}{T}\right) + \phi\right], \tag{13.6b}$$

where ϕ (Greek "phi"), the *phase angle*, is a constant whose value depends upon the initial conditions chosen for the description of the wave. When $x = 0$ and $t = 0$, Equation 13.6b reduces to $y = y_0 \sin \phi$. If, as in the preceding paragraphs, we choose $y = 0$ when x and $t = 0$ it follows that $\phi = 0$. But we might also have decided to start measurements when the displacement of the string at the origin was, say $y_0/2$. Then we would require that $\sin \phi = \frac{1}{2}$, or $\phi = \pi/6$. In particular, it is very often convenient to choose initial conditions for maximum displacement at the origin, or $y = y_0$. Then $\sin \phi = 1$, and $\phi = \pi/2$. But of course the cosine function leads the sine function by exactly $\pi/2$ radians. Therefore, we could also describe the same wave with the same initial conditions by

$$y = y_0 \cos 2\pi\left(\frac{x}{\lambda} \pm \frac{t}{T}\right), \tag{13.6c}$$

which for $x = 0$, $t = 0$ reduces to $y = y_0$, as required. Finally, we could also incorporate a constant phase angle into Equation 13.6b:

$$y = y_0 \cos 2\pi\left[\left(\frac{x}{\lambda} \pm \frac{t}{T}\right) + \phi\right], \tag{13.6d}$$

if, in some instance, we found it convenient to describe a wave with a cosine function and nonzero phase angle.

It is often useful to describe the time variation of a sinusoidal wave in terms of its *frequency*, f, rather than its period. The two quantities are simply the reciprocals of each other, or

$$f = \frac{1}{T}. \tag{13.7}$$

Substituting into Equation 13.7 we obtain a fundamental relation between wavelength, frequency, and velocity of propagation:

$$v = f\lambda, \tag{13.8}$$

and may also write Equations 13.6 in the alternate, but completely equivalent forms

$$y = y_0 \sin 2\pi\left[\left(\frac{x}{\lambda} \pm ft\right) + \phi\right], \tag{13.9a}$$

$$y = y_0 \cos 2\pi\left[\left(\frac{x}{\lambda} \pm ft\right) + \phi\right]. \tag{13.9b}$$

◢◣ 13.4 A note on wave dynamics

We have not yet asked how or why a particular wave form is excited by a particular external force. The propagation velocity of a wave on a string is related to both the tension of the string and its mass per unit length. Figure 13.6a shows a pulse propagating along a string with velocity v. Let us consider the pulse from the viewpoint of an observer who is also moving to the right with velocity v. He is at rest relative to the crest of the wave, but sees the string itself moving to the left with velocity v. Let T_1 and T_2 be the respective tensions on the left and right ends of a small segment l of the string. If the segment is sufficiently small it may be approximated very well as the arc of a circle of radius R.* In that case the magnitudes of the tensions are equal, and the net force upon the segment is given by their vector sum, $\mathbf{F}$ (Figure 13.6b). If ρ is the mass of the string per unit length, then the acceleration of the segment of length l follows from Newton's second law:

$$F = \rho l a.$$

However, the acceleration is centripetal:

$$F = \rho l \frac{v^2}{R}.$$

Since the segment of arc is very small the triangle formed by l and the two radii in Figure 13.6a is similar to the force triangle in Figure 13.6b, and $F = (l/R)T$, where T is the magnitude of the tension. Therefore,

$$\frac{l}{R} T = \rho l \; \frac{v^2}{R},$$

and, finally,

$$v = \sqrt{T/\rho}. \tag{13.10}$$

Equation 13.10 relates the propagation velocity of the wave to the linear mass-density and tension of the string. It is analogous to the relationship between the period of an harmonic oscillator, its spring constant, and its mass (Equation 4.24). We may further exploit the analogy to calculate the energy carried by a wave.

For a pure sinusoidal wave each segment of mass M oscillates with simple harmonic motion. Therefore, its maximum potential energy (and by energy conservation its total

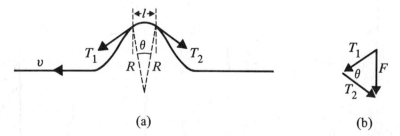

(a)   (b)

FIGURE 13.6   (a) The crest of a wave as seen by an observer traveling with the propagation velocity of the wave. To this observer the string itself moves to the left with velocity v, while the crest is stationary. The vector difference between the tensions $\mathbf{T}_1$ and $\mathbf{T}_2$ at the ends of a small segment of length l and mass ρl produces a centripetal acceleration toward the center of curvature of the segment. (b) Force triangle for calculating the vector $\mathbf{T}_1 - \mathbf{T}_2$. This triangle and the geometric triangle with sides R, R, and l (part a) are similar.

---

* The end result we seek does not depend on the circular crest assumption since R ultimately cancels out.

energy) is $\frac{1}{2}ky_0^2$, where y_0 is its maximum amplitude and k its equivalent "spring constant" (Equation 7.8). But the period of a spring is related to k and M by $T = 2\pi\sqrt{k/M}$, so that $k = (2\pi f)^2 M$, where f, the frequency is equal to $1/T$. Therefore, if ρ is the mass of the string per unit length, the total energy carried by the wave per unit length must be

$$\text{Energy/unit length} = \frac{1}{2}ky_0^2 = (2\pi f y_0)^2 \frac{\rho}{2}. \tag{13.11}$$

As the string oscillates, this energy is transferred along its length so that it is propagated in the direction of the wave. In Section 13.1 we gave a general definition of a wave as a disturbance. Any such disturbance invariably involves energy transfer; in a sense the energy transfer *is* the disturbance. Thus in very broad terms, a wave may be thought of as a means for transferring energy through space, a characteristic shared by vibrating strings and electromagnetic fields.

◤◤ 13.5 Standing waves in one dimension

An infinitely long string may propagate waves with any frequency whatsoever, and propagate them all simultaneously. The frequencies that may be propagated by a terminated string are limited, as we shall see presently. However, the propagation of a wave with a single frequency is quite an uncommon occurrence. We have noted that any wave form whatsoever may be represented in terms of a linear superposition of several sinusoidal waves. Figure 13.7 suggests how several sinusoidal waves of different amplitudes

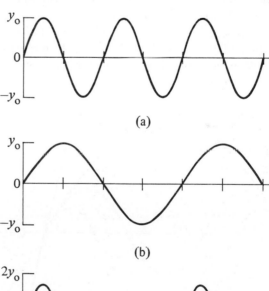

FIGURE 13.7 Linear superposition of two sinusoidal waves (parts a and b) to yield part c.

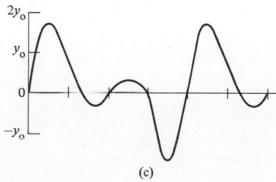

and frequencies may be combined to yield a complex wave form. The *amplitudes* of the contributing waves depend upon the external force that excites the wave, just as the amplitude of an oscillating spring depends upon its initial displacement. The contributing frequencies themselves depend upon the termination conditions, and not all need be present, whereas the propagation velocity depends, as we have seen, upon the tension of the rope and its density. As might be anticipated, the total energy carried by a more complicated wave is the sum of the energies carried by each of its sinusoidal components.

Figure 13.8 shows segments of three right-traveling sine waves on a string with different amplitudes as well as different frequencies. Their sum bears an approximate resemblance to the alternating rectangular pulse shown by the dashed line. A sufficient number of additional sine waves with the proper amplitudes and frequencies superimposed upon these three would reproduce the rectangular pulse to any desired precision.

Figure 13.8 shows short segments of three wave trains which presumably continue on both to the left and the right of the diagram, and thus approximate a whole series of alternating positive and negative rectangular pulses. But by superimposing an infinite number of sine waves with the proper amplitudes and with wavelengths varying continuously between the limits λ_A and λ_B, it is possible to cancel all but one of these pulses so that a single rectangular pulse (Figure 13.2) is propagated by the string. The narrower the rectangle, the broader the wavelength spectrum contributing to it. If the pulse is really an infinitesimally narrow spike, *all* wavelengths from 0 to ∞ are required.

The latter possibility raises an interesting point that bears on the question of localizing a wave. Since a wave is a means of propagating energy, then the location of the energy in space at a given time is more or less indefinite, depending on how much the wave is spread out. For an infinite superposition, however, the wave becomes a spike, and the location of the energy is definite at all times. But this is precisely the definition of a *particle*, which also carries energy and has a well-defined position as a function of time.

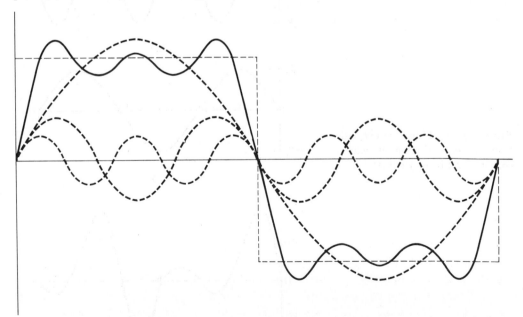

FIGURE 13.8 Segments of three sine waves with different amplitudes and frequencies (heavy dashed lines) whose sum approximates the alternating series of rectangular pulses shown by the light dashed line.

Therefore, at least on this formal, mathematical level, a particle can be represented in terms of waves!

If plucked near its center, a string a length l whose ends are tied to rigid supports will vibrate with a set of natural frequencies determined by its length, its mass, and its tension. We can analyze the characteristic vibrations of the string in terms of a superposition of the waves it propagates.

When first plucked, waves are propagated along the string toward the two terminations. These initial wave forms can be quite complicated, depending both upon the detailed nature of the external force that excites them and the properties of the string itself. However, this transient behavior will not last indefinitely. The initial waves may be regarded as linear superpositions of many sinusoidal components. At the terminations each component will be reflected with opposite amplitude.

Consider the superposition of two components with identical amplitude y_{0i} and identical frequency f_i, one traveling to the left and one to the right. For mathematical convenience we shall describe the components in terms of cosines rather than sines (Equation 13.6c). The displacement of the string resulting from the superposition of these components is

$$y_i = y_{0i} \cos 2\pi\left(\frac{x}{\lambda_0} - f_i t\right) + \cos 2\pi\left(\frac{x}{\lambda_i} + f_i t\right).$$

To simplify the expression, we use the trigonometric identity (Appendix B to text):

$$\cos A + \cos B = 2 \cos \tfrac{1}{2}(A + B) \cos \tfrac{1}{2}(A - B),$$

with

$$A = 2\pi\left(\frac{x}{\lambda_i} + f_i t\right), \qquad B = 2\pi\left(\frac{x}{\lambda_i} - f_i t\right).$$

Then,

$$y_i = 2y_{0i}\left(\cos 2\pi \frac{x}{\lambda_i}\right) \cos 2\pi f_i t, \tag{13.12a}$$

or letting

$$Y_i(x) = 2y_{0i} \cos 2\pi \frac{x}{\lambda_i}, \tag{13.12b}$$

$$y_i = Y_i(x) \cos 2\pi f_i t.$$

Since $T_i = 1/f_i$,

$$y_i = Y_i(x) \cos 2\pi \frac{t}{T_i}, \tag{13.12c}$$

which is precisely the form of the oscillating spring equation *except* that the amplitude $Y_i(x)$ is not constant, but depends upon x and varies continuously from $2y_{0i}$ to 0. Therefore, there are points along the string that oscillate with period T_i and amplitude *twice* that of either of the component, traveling waves. There are also points, separated from these by $x = \lambda_i/4$, which do not oscillate at all (amplitude = 0), and there are all possible intermediate cases. In other words, the two opposite traveling waves combine to give a wave that is not propagated at all. It stands in one place, and is called a *standing wave* (Figure 13.9).

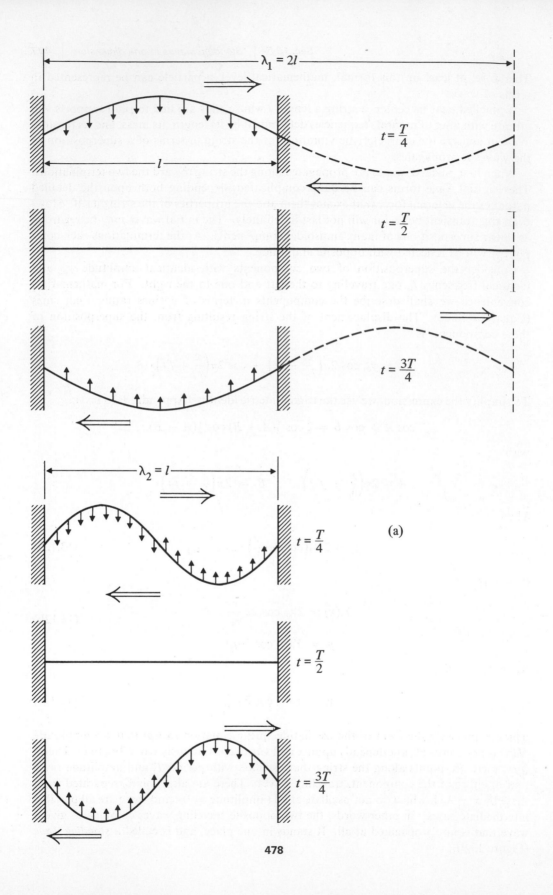

(a)

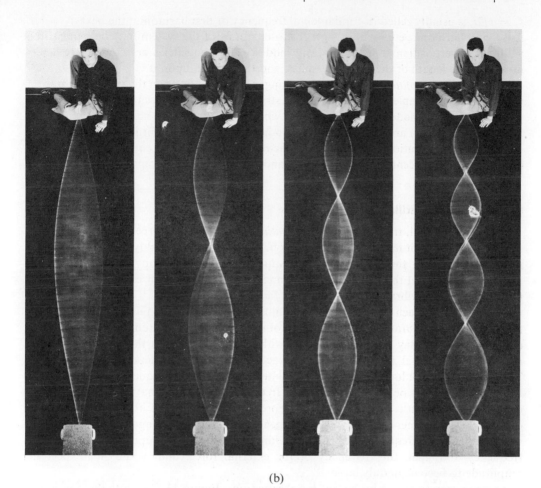

(b)

FIGURE 13.9 (a) The two longest standing wave modes on a string of length *l* at the ends of three successive quarter periods. Short arrows indicate the direction of motion of each segment. These patterns may be analyzed as superpositions of equal wavelength, equal amplitude sinusoidal waves traveling in opposite directions. (Long double arrows show the propagation directions of the contributing traveling waves.) (b) Photographs of standing waves on a vibrating string. (Photographs from *PSSC Physics*, D. C. Heath and Co., Boston, © 1965.)

Because the string is rigidly fastened at its two ends, it cannot move at those two points. Therefore, these must *always* be points of zero amplitude, or *nodes*. Since $\cos 2\pi(x/\lambda_i) = 0$ for $\pi/2$, $3\pi/2$, $5\pi/2$, etc., it follows that the two ends may *only* be separated by $\frac{1}{2}$, 1, $1\frac{1}{2}$, 2, ..., or, in general, $n/2$ wavelengths:

$$\lambda_n = \frac{2l}{n}, \qquad n = 1, 2, 3, \ldots. \tag{13.13a}$$

Frequencies corresponding to these wavelengths follow from Equation 13.8:

$$f_n = \frac{v}{\lambda_n} = v\left(\frac{n}{2l}\right), \tag{13.13b}$$

where the velocity of propagation, v, is given by Equation 13.10. Thus the string has a set of natural vibrational frequencies called its *normal modes*. The lowest of these,

$f_1 = v/2l$, is usually called its fundamental frequency or first harmonic; the next, $f_2 = v/l$, its second harmonic, etc. All possible free oscillations of the system may be represented as linear superpositions of these normal modes. The frequencies are completely determined by the length of the string, its mass, and the tension upon it.

However, the *amplitude* of each contributing mode depends upon the way the vibration is excited. For example, in Figure 13.10a, a string is plucked at its center. Therefore, that point cannot be a node in the subsequent vibration pattern, and consequently all even modes ($n = 2, 4, 6,$) are suppressed, or in other words have amplitude zero. If, on the other hand, the vibration is excited by displacing the quarter points equally and oppositely (Figure 13.10b) the center is always a node and all odd modes are suppressed.

▶▶ 13.6 Forced oscillations and resonance

When an external, time-varying force *continues* to act upon a freely vibrating, elastic medium even after it has set it into vibration, motion is considerably more complicated initially. However, the frictional forces which are present in any real medium will eventually damp out the free oscillations, and a vibration pattern characteristic of the force results. This vibration is then called a *forced oscillation*.

For example, if each time a certain pendulum swings through equilibrium it is subject to a force of short duration in the direction of its motion, its amplitude will increase after each "kick" and may become very large within a few cycles. In this example the frequency of the external, time-varying force exactly matches the frequency of the pendulum. Therefore, the pendulum continues to oscillate with its natural frequency. However, the situation would not be so favorable if the frequency of the external force and the pendulum differed greatly. In such cases the force would be applied at a different part of each cycle, sometimes working with the pendulum, sometimes against it. Hence we would expect the frequency of the pendulum to depend both upon its own natural frequency and upon the frequency of the external force, and would not expect its amplitude to become unduly large.

These expectations are borne out by observation. Figure 13.11a plots the amplitude

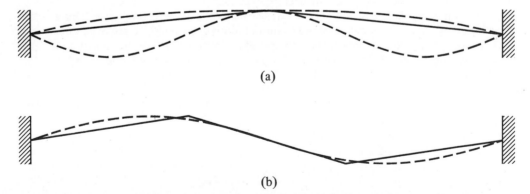

(a)

(b)

FIGURE 13.10   (a) When a string is set into vibration by plucking it at its center the center remains a point of maximum amplitude. Hence only modes satisfying this criterion (i.e., those with odd n) are excited. The modes corresponding to $n = 1$ and 3 are shown by the dashed lines. (b) In contrast, if the string is set into vibration asymmetrically, its midpoint remains at rest so that only modes with even n are excited. The mode corresponding to $n = 2$ is shown by the dashed line.

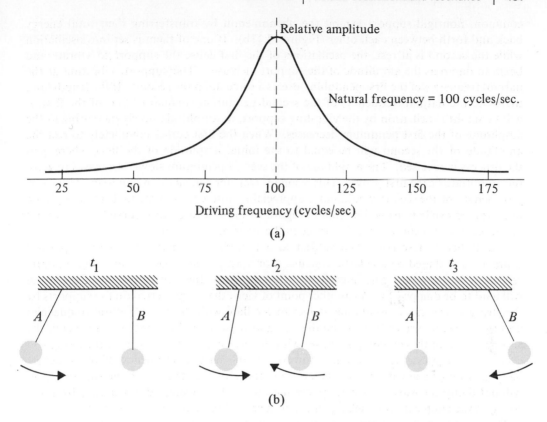

FIGURE 13.11   (a) Amplitude of a pendulum with natural $f_0 = 100$ cycles/sec driven by a sinusoidally varying force as a function of the driving frequency. The amplitude of the system is appreciable only in the vicinity of the resonance frequency, $f = f_0$. (b) Motion of two equal length, equal mass pendula coupled by a non-rigid support.   Initially (time t_1) A is set into motion with B at rest. A gradually transfers energy to B so that at time t_2 the pendula oscillates with equal amplitudes.   Ultimately (time t_3) A is at rest and B is oscillating with the original amplitude of A.   Thereafter the energy transfer proceeds from B back to A.

of a pendulum against the difference between its natural frequency, f_0, and the frequency of an external driving force.   The amplitude of the pendulum reaches its maximum for $f = f_0$, and decreases for larger and smaller frequencies.   When the frequency of an external force is equal to the natural frequency of the system that it is forcing into oscillation, the force and the system are in *resonance*.   The amplitude of a system in resonance with an outside force may become so large that the system literally shakes itself to pieces.   However, the internal frictional forces associated with most systems damp the amplitude and usually prevent the system from destroying itself.   Figure 13.11a is the resonance curve for a pendulum.   The width of the peak at the point where the amplitude decreases to one-half its maximum value (the full width at half-maximum) is related to these damping forces.   The broader a curve, the greater the damping, and consequently, the less likely a catastrophe.

Resonance is observed for all types of oscillating systems.   Two pendula hung from a common, nonrigid support exhibit the phenomenon by transferring their total energy back and forth between each other (Figure 13.11b). If one of them is set into oscillation while the second is at rest, the oscillations of the first cause the support to vibrate and begin to damp as the amplitude of the support increases. The support, vibrating at the natural frequency of the first pendulum, exerts a force upon the second. If the length (and therefore the natural frequency) of the second pendulum is equal to that of the first, it will be set into oscillation by the vibrating support, its amplitude slowly increasing as the amplitude of the first pendulum decreases. When the first comes completely to rest the amplitude of the second will be equal to the initial amplitude of the first, whereupon the process is reversed. The amplitude of the second pendulum slowly decreases to zero, the amplitude of the first grows. This resonant transfer can go on indefinitely. However, if the length of the second pendulum is appreciably different than the first, the amplitude of its forced oscillations will be small. Figure 13.11c is a resonance curve for the second pendulum as a function of the difference in the lengths of the pair.

The ability to resonate when subject to a periodic, external force is an important characteristic shared by all elastic systems. For example, nonrigid, terminating supports reflect the waves on a string imperfectly. Consequently, the free vibrations of the string will tend to be damped. From another point of view, the force exerted on the supports by the string causes the supports themselves to oscillate with their own natural frequencies and to propagate waves back along the string at these same frequencies. In general, the superposition of these secondary waves with the original normal modes of the string will eventually suppress the vibration. However, if the natural frequency of the supports happens to coincide with one of the normal modes of the string then the superposition will not damp the wave. Rather, the oscillation will be transferred indefinitely from the string to the supports and back again to the string. The system is in resonance.

These considerations suggest a method by which a wave may be used to transfer energy from one oscillating system to another. Let a taut string be attached at both ends to equal masses suspended from identical springs which are constrained to oscillate vertically (Figure 13.12). If the natural frequency of these oscillators coincides with one of the normal modes of the string, the two springs and the mediating string constitute a resonant system. When one member of the pair of springs is set into oscillation it transfers energy to the second via the string, and as the two springs are identical the second is driven into oscillation. Energy is transferred back and forth between the springs just as it is transferred back and forth between two coupled pendula. The amplitude of the entire resonating system will continue to increase indefinitely if the amplitude of the first spring is sustained in some way (by driving it with a small motor for example).

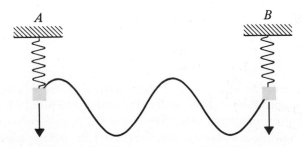

FIGURE 13.12 Resonance transfer of energy between two identical harmonic oscillators by means of a wave on a string.

▲▲ 13.7 Waves in two and three dimensions

The propagation of waves on a taut string typifies one-dimensional wave motion. Generalization to wave propagation in two- and three-dimensional media is straightforward. For example, a rock thrown onto the surface of a lake momentarily distorts the water at the impact point. The deformation propagates outward from that point, and is describable in terms of the vertical displacements of all points on the surface of the lake as functions of time. If we can regard all directions from the source point as being equivalent, then the vertical displacements of all points that are equidistant from the source will be equal at the same time. Therefore, the deformation propagates from the impact point in a series of concentric circles.

If y is the direction perpendicular to the surface and R the distance from the source to a particular point on the surface, then at any given time the displacement, y, is a function of R alone. As in the one-dimensional case the precise form of the functional relation varies with the details of the excitation and with the boundary conditions of the lake. However, any circular wave whatsoever may be represented as a linear superposition of several circular, harmonic components, each with its own amplitude y_0, and frequency, $f = 1/T$, which may be approximated by

$$y = y_0 \sin 2\pi\left(\frac{R}{\lambda} - \frac{t}{T}\right).$$ (13.14)

A pure sinusoidal circular wave consists of a series of equally spaced concentric crests alternating with concentric circular troughs, the whole train spreading outward from the common center. One wavelength is defined as the distance between successive crests, or, alternately, between successive troughs (Figure 13.13). Water molecules at a particular distance from the center of the spreading pattern oscillate vertically about their equilibrium positions with period T so that in one-half a period the positions of the crests would all become positions of the troughs, and vice versa. The propagation velocity of the wave is a function of the properties of the water only, and, as in the one-dimensional case, is equal to the product of the wavelength of sinusoidal component by the frequency of that component.

The amplitude y_0 for circular waves is not constant over the entire lake, but decreases with R, the distance from the source. We can easily prove this by using energy conservation arguments. An analysis similar to that which led to Equation 13.11 shows that the energy carried by a circular wave per unit arc length along a circular crest is proportional to the square of its amplitude. Therefore, the *total* amplitude energy transported across a circle of radius R per cycle is proportional to the product of the square of the amplitude times the circumference of the circle:

Energy at circle $\propto y_0^2(2\pi R)$.

That is, as the crest of the wave spreads, its energy is distributed over circles of increasing circumference. Since in the absence of damping, the total energy carried by a wave crest is constant, it follows that y_0 is inversely proportional to the square root of R.

If we are interested in the wave at points so far from the source that the curvature of the wave fronts is negligible, they may be approximated as straight lines. In that event displacement of the water at all points on any line perpendicular to the direction of propagation (x) will be approximately the same at the same time, and the wave may be

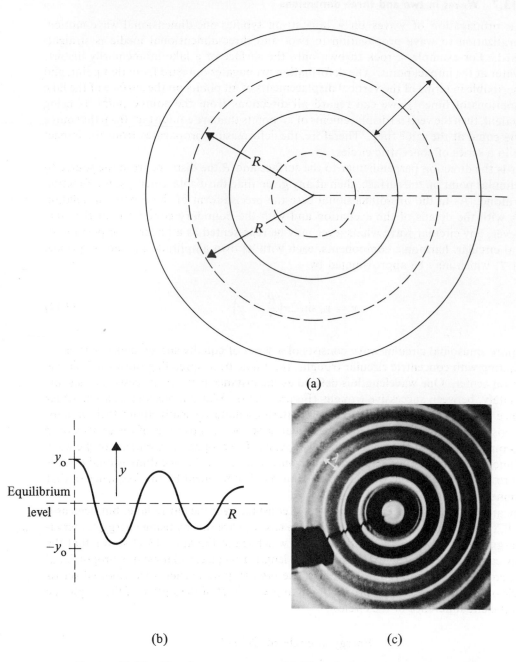

FIGURE 13.13 Circular water waves. (a) View downward on to the surface at a particular instant showing the instantaneous positions of crests (solid circles) and troughs (broken circles). (b) Profile view of the water level as a function of R along the dashed line in part a at the same time. (c) Photograph of circular waves in a ripple tank. (Photograph from *PSSC Physics*, D. C. Heath and Co., Boston, © 1965.)

described as a function of x and t, rather than R and t (Figure 13.14). Such waves may always be represented as linear superpositions of the sinusoidal components:

$$y = y_0 \sin 2\pi\left(\frac{x}{\lambda} - \frac{t}{T}\right), \tag{13.15}$$

with y_0 approximately constant. Because this equation is precisely equivalent to the equation for one-dimensional waves on a taut string (Equation 13.6), we would expect two-dimensional waves to exhibit many of the general characteristics of one-dimensional waves, in particular, reflection with reversed amplitude at the boundary of the propagating medium. We would also expect a two-dimensional elastic medium to be able to sustain standing waves. In fact, standing waves in two dimensions arise for precisely the same reasons as they do in one dimension: in order to satisfy the requirement that the waves vanish at all points outside the medium. Consider water waves in a rectangular tank with sides L_1 and L_2, for instance (Figure 13.15a). These waves must vanish at the perpendicular boundaries with the result that only the frequencies satisfying a condition analogous to Equation 13.13b are maintained:

$$f_{mn}^2 = v^2\left[\left(\frac{m}{2L_1}\right)^2 + \left(\frac{n}{2L_2}\right)^2\right], \tag{13.16}$$

$$m = 0, 1, 2, 3, \ldots,$$

$$n = 0, 1, 2, 3, \ldots,$$

where v is the propagation velocity of the waves, and each choice of m and n defines a particular normal mode of the vibrating system. If $n = 0$ then the standing patterns are parallel to the side L_1, and Equation 13.16 reduces to

$$f_{m0} = v\left(\frac{m}{2L_1}\right),$$

in agreement with Equation 13.13b. Standing surface waves terminated by nonrectangular boundaries have normal modes whose frequencies are determined by more complicated conditions than Equation 13.16, but are nonetheless specified by two indices, m and n, that can assume all integral values (Figure 13.15b).

Very little need be added in order to extend the formalism to three dimensions. For instance, when a shell explodes it compresses the layers of air in its immediate vicinity, and the deformation of the air, the condition of abnormally high pressure, propagates outward as a pressure wave. In several special but important cases the air pressure at any given time is the same at all points equidistant from the source. Therefore, the disturbance propagates as a series of concentric spherical shells centered upon the source, and at any given time should be a function of R alone. Again, any such three-dimensional pressure wave may be described by a linear superposition of sinusoidal waves, concentric spherical shells containing air at a pressure momentarily greater than normal, alternating with spherical shells containing air at pressures momentarily less than normal. The wavelength must then be the distance between succeeding pressure maxima. As time progresses the air at a given distance from the source is alternately compressed and rarified so that after one-half a period the high pressure regions become low pressure regions, and vice versa. Therefore, the wave is described by giving the departure in the pressure from its equilibrium level at all points in space and at all time:

$$p = p_0 \sin 2\pi\left(\frac{R}{\lambda} - \frac{t}{T}\right), \tag{13.17a}$$

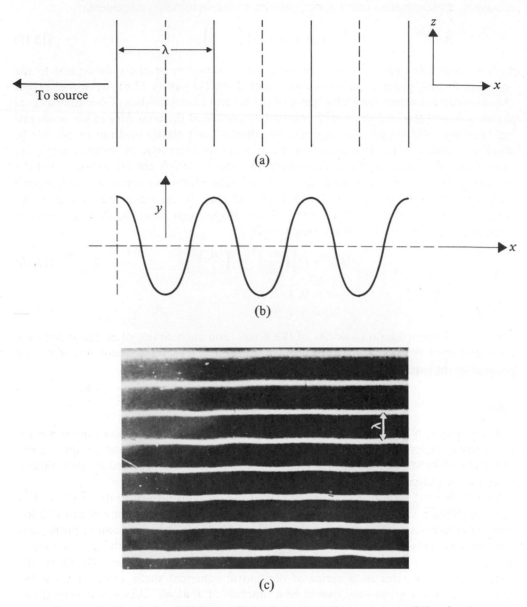

(a)

(b)

(c)

FIGURE 13.14   At large distances from the source, the curvature of the circular waves becomes small over distances comparable to several wavelengths, so that the instantaneous surface deformation for a given value of x is, to a good approximation, independent of z, and the amplitude of each crest is equal. (a) Surface view of plane waves propagated in the positive x-direction at a particular time. (b) Profile view of the water level at a particular z plotted as a function of x. At any given time the profile view is the same for any value of z. (c) Photograph of plane waves in a ripple tank. (Photograph from *PSSC Physics*, D. C. Heath and Co., Boston, © 1965.)

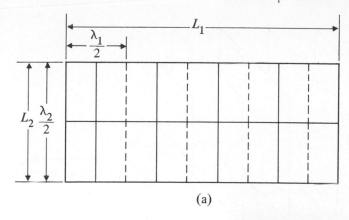

(a)

FIGURE 13.15 (a) A standing wave pattern in a rectangular pan of water. Dashed lines indicate positions of the nodes (lines of zero displacement), solid lines the antinodes (lines of maximum displacement). (b) Standing wave pattern in a circular tank. (Photograph from *PSSC Physics*, D. C. Heath and Co., Boston, © 1965.)

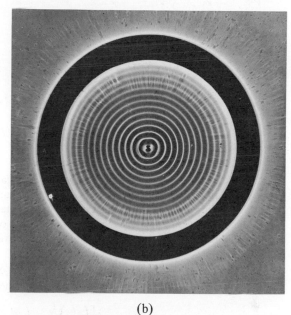

(b)

where p_0 is the maximum excess pressure. Since the energy carried by an expanding wave front is proportional to p_0^2, then the product p_0^2 times $4\pi R^2$, the area of the expanding, spherical, front, must be constant to conserve energy. Therefore, p_0 is inversely proportional to R.

At distances far from the source the curvature of the equal-pressure regions becomes negligible, and the wavefronts may be approximated as a series of plane parallel sheets (Figure 13.16). If x is the propagation direction of these plane waves then a single sinusoidal component is described by

$$p = p_0 \sin 2\pi\left(\frac{x}{\lambda} - \frac{t}{T}\right), \tag{13.17b}$$

which, again, is exactly the form of Equations 13.6 for a sinusoidal wave on a string.

The free vibrations of elastic solids may be represented in terms of the normal, standing wave modes of the solid with frequencies determined by the dimensions of the solid and

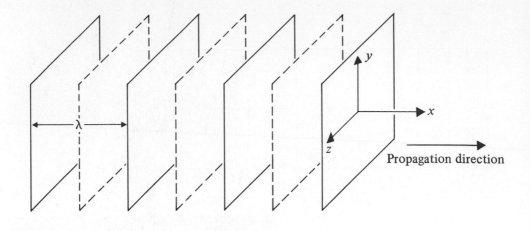

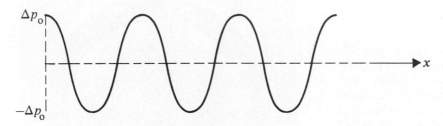

FIGURE 13.16 A plane pressure wave propagated in the x-direction shown at a particular instant. The excess pressure is a maximum at all points on the planes with solid edges, a minimum at planes with dotted edges. (The instantaneous value of excess pressure is plotted below as a function of x.) As time progresses the excess pressure at each plane varies sinusoidally between $\pm \Delta p_0$ with frequency f.

expressible in terms of three running indices. For example, a rectangular solid of dimensions L_1, L_2, and L_3 has normal modes with frequencies:

$$f_{lmn}^2 = v^2\left[\left(\frac{l}{2L_1}\right)^2 + \left(\frac{m}{2L_2}\right)^2 + \left(\frac{n}{2L_3}\right)^2\right],$$ (13.18)

$$l = 0, 1, 2, \ldots,$$
$$m = 0, 1, 2, \ldots,$$
$$n = 0, 1, 2, \ldots.$$

Here v is the velocity of the waves and, generalizing Equation 13.10, is inversely proportional to the square root of the density of the solid and directly proportional to the square root of its compressibility (analogous to the Hooke's law constant for a spring). If $m = n = 0$, the planes of equal vibration are all parallel to face of area L_2L_3, and Equation 13.8 reduces to Equation 13.13b.

▶▶ 13.8 Sound waves. The Doppler effect

We have seen that elastic bodies vibrate at one or more natural frequencies determined in part by their dimensions, in part by the way they are bounded, and in part by their composition. We would expect bodies to respond to small periodic changes in the pressure of their environments provided the frequency of the pressure change coincided with one of their natural frequencies. In other words, pressure waves can drive properly tuned detectors into oscillation; indeed the detection of such waves as *sound* is based on just this sort of resonance behavior. Tuning forks, for example, are constructed to oscillate at single frequencies, and, consequently, to excite and respond to single-frequency pressure waves. It follows that an array of tuning forks, each with a different natural frequency, could be used to determine the frequency components of any pressure wave. If the response of each fork also produced an electric current proportional to the response amplitude, and the various electric current signals were fed to a computer, the continuous response of the complete array could be tabulated almost instantaneously and the original wave analyzed.

In its ability to differentiate acoustical frequencies from a few hundred to about fifteen thousand cycles per second the human ear is analogous to a large array of tuning forks. The electric circuits in the model may be likened to the nerve circuits, and, of course, the large computer to a part of the brain. As it reconstructs incoming acoustical waves from the messages sent by the ear, this section of the brain communicates with another containing the memory and, from the information stored there, is able to determine whether the wave was produced by an automobile engine, a jet aircraft, or a violin.

The frequencies and relative amplitudes of the components of a complex acoustical wave determine the quality of the sound interpreted by the brain. A wave containing only strong components of the first, third, and fifth harmonic of a wave, for instance, differs in quality from a wave containing equal components of the second and fourth as well, and differs also from a wave containing the same harmonics but with different relative amplitudes. Differences in the sound produced by different musical instruments is based upon exploitation of this principle.

Sound from a violin, for instance, is produced by causing its strings to vibrate in standing wave patterns, control of the basic first harmonic frequency being attained by varying the lengths of the strings. The particular *quality* of a violin, however, is vested in its frame which resonates with the strings, suppressing certain harmonics and emphasizing others. Similarly an organ is basically a large series of resonators. Each pipe, being of a specific length, resonates with a particular standing wave pattern produced by forcing air into it. The quality of an organ rests on the ability of its pipes to suppress and to reinforce particular harmonics. The normal modes of a stretched membrane are analogous to surface waves on water. Thus the tone of a drum, such as the tympanum or the Indian tabla, can be changed by varying the tension of the membrane, thereby altering the propagation velocity and frequency of its standing waves (Equation 13.16).

Since any object that oscillates with a sufficiently large amplitude can destroy itself, acoustical resonance can also be a destructive phenomenon. Enrico Caruso is said to have shattered crystal goblets merely by singing at their natural frequencies; the shattering of windows by supersonic jet aircraft is becoming an all too familiar occurrence. And if ancient Hebrew historians are to be credited, it appears that the trumpeters of Joshua discovered, somehow, the natural frequency of the walls of Jericho.

It is interesting to compare the acoustical frequencies measured by two observers with constant velocity relative to each other. An observer at rest with respect to the medium through which a wave is propagated relates its velocity and wavelength by the equation $f = v/\lambda$.

However, another observer moving with velocity $-u_0$ through the medium parallel to the direction of propagation measures the wave velocity not as v but as $v + u_0$ (Equation 6.15). As his measurement of wavelength will be the same as that of the first observer, he concludes that the frequency of the wave is $(v + u)/\lambda$ or, in terms of the measurement of observer 1,

$$f' = \frac{v + u_0}{\lambda} = \frac{v}{\lambda}\left(1 + \frac{u_0}{v}\right) = f\left(1 + \frac{u_0}{v}\right). \qquad (13.19a)$$

If the observer is in relative motion toward the source of the waves he sees more maximum displacements per unit time than the stationary observer, and hence measures a higher frequency. If the observer is in relative motion away from the source (the sign of u_0 negative in Equation 13.19a) he sees fewer maxima per second and thus measures a lower frequency (Figure 13.17a).

A different expression is obtained if the *source* rather than the observer moves with velocity u_s relative to the medium through which the waves are propagated (Figure 13.17b). If v and f are the propagation velocity and the frequency of the waves when the source is at rest, and if the source is moving through the medium with velocity u toward an observer at rest, the distance between successive wavefronts is compressed so that

$$\lambda' = \frac{v}{f} - \frac{u_s}{f}.$$

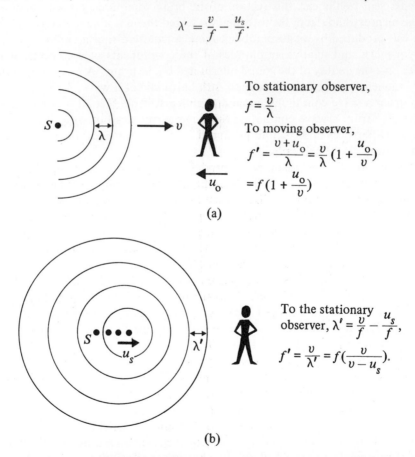

To stationary observer,
$$f = \frac{v}{\lambda}$$
To moving observer,
$$f' = \frac{v + u_0}{\lambda} = \frac{v}{\lambda}\left(1 + \frac{u_0}{v}\right)$$
$$= f\left(1 + \frac{u_0}{v}\right)$$

(a)

To the stationary observer, $\lambda' = \frac{v}{f} - \frac{u_s}{f}$,
$$f' = \frac{v}{\lambda'} = f\left(\frac{v}{v - u_s}\right).$$

(b)

FIGURE 13.17 The Doppler effect. (a) An observer moving with velocity $-u_0$ opposite to the propagation direction of waves traveling with veolcity v measures their velocity as $v + u_0$, and their frequency as $f' = (v + u_0)/\lambda$. (b) When the source moves through the medium, it partially catches up with the waves it has emitted so that the wavelength measured by a stationary observer is $\lambda' = (v - u_s)/f$, and the frequency $f' = v/\lambda = f(v/v - u_s)$.

Likewise, if the source is receding,

$$\lambda' = \frac{v}{f} + \frac{u_s}{f},$$

so that if the source is moving, a stationary observer detects the frequency

$$f' = \frac{v}{\lambda'} = \frac{v}{(v \pm u_s)/f} = f\left(\frac{v}{v \pm u_s}\right). \tag{13.19b}$$

The change in frequency due to motion of the source or detector of waves is called the *Doppler effect*. It is typified, for acoustical waves, by the increase in the pitch of a train whistle approaching an observer and its decrease in pitch when receding. Equations 13.19 implies the ability to outrun a wave. If the velocity of the detector is greater than the wave velocity, then f is smaller than zero, and this is meaningless. When a source moves through a medium more rapidly than the velocity of the wave it propagates—in other words when it attempts to outrun its own waves—the medium reacts violently and propagates a shock wave. In the acoustical case the onset of this shock wave, and the violence with which it reacts upon the source, leads to the phenomena associated with the well-known sound barrier. At supersonic velocities both the shock wave and the ordinary acoustical waves propagated by a jet engine are left behind.

Since light is propagated as a wave we would expect a frequency shift if a source and detector moved relative to each other. However, for propagation in a vacuum, relativity implies that there can be no difference between the cases in which the source moves and the observer moves. The simplest derivation of the optical Doppler shift is based upon the photon model of light. From Equation 10.8 we know that the energy of a photon is inversely proportional to the characteristic wavelength of a beam of light in which it travels, and therefore, directly proportional to frequency, v.* Anticipating Section 17.3 we can write

$$E = hv,$$

where $h = 6 \times 10^{-34}$ J-sec is known as *Planck's constant*. Since the photon has zero rest mass, then, using Equation 11.25b, its momentum is $p = E/c = hv/c$.

As we know, total energy depends on the inertial system in which it is measured. Let E be the energy of a photon in a frame of reference in which its source is at rest, and E' its energy as measured by a detector moving away from the source with velocity $+u$. Further, let the photon be emitted in the direction parallel to the relative motion of source and observer so that its momentum is entirely in that direction. Now (Equations 11.18 and 11.23a) p and E/c are the first and fourth component of the four-momentum vector $\bar{P}$ which transform according to Equations 11.10. Therefore, the photon energy measured by the detector is given by

$$\frac{E'}{c} = \frac{(-u/c)p + E/c}{\sqrt{1 - (u/c^2)}}.$$

Substituting $E = hv$, $E = hv'$, $p = hv/c$,

$$\frac{hv'}{c} = \frac{(hv/c)(1 - u/c)}{\sqrt{1 - (u/c)^2}},$$

---

* The Greek letter v (nu) is conventionally used for electromagnetic frequencies.

From Quantum Mechanics

$E = h\upsilon$　　$E' = h\upsilon'$

u

Source

Observer

From Special Relativity

$$\frac{h\upsilon}{c} = \frac{\frac{h\upsilon}{c}\left(1 - \frac{u}{c}\right)}{\sqrt{1 - u^2/c^2}}$$

$$\therefore \upsilon' = \sqrt{\frac{c-u}{c+u}}\,\upsilon$$

(a)

RELATION BETWEEN RED-SHIFT AND DISTANCE FOR EXTRAGALACTIC NEBULAE

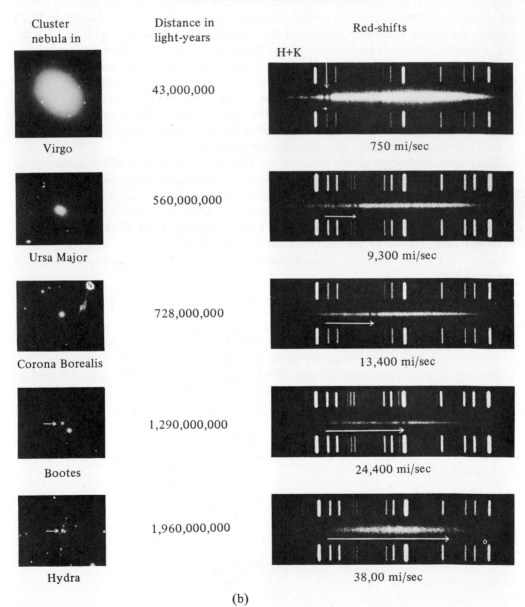

Cluster nebula in	Distance in light-years	Red-shifts
Virgo	43,000,000	750 mi/sec
Ursa Major	560,000,000	9,300 mi/sec
Corona Borealis	728,000,000	13,400 mi/sec
Bootes	1,290,000,000	24,400 mi/sec
Hydra	1,960,000,000	38,00 mi/sec

H+K

(b)

or, canceling h/c on both sides of the equation and noting that $\sqrt{1 - (u/c)^2} = \sqrt{(1 - u/c)(1 + u/c)}$,

$$\nu' = \sqrt{\frac{1 - u/c}{1 + u/c}}\,\nu$$

$$= \sqrt{\frac{c - u}{c + u}}\,\nu, \qquad (13.20a)$$

which is the apparent frequency measured by the detector. If the source and detector move toward each other, then u is replaced by $-u$, and

$$\nu' = \sqrt{\frac{c + u}{c - u}}\,\nu. \qquad (13.20b)$$

As we have previously noted, an atom emits light at a series of discrete frequencies which appear as a series of lines on a photograph taken of the light with a prism spectrometer. The compositions of the stars and galaxies can be deduced from such line spectra. In the early 1920's the astronomer Edwin Hubble first noted that the spectra of very distant galaxies are displaced toward lower frequencies (i.e., toward the red end of the visible spectrum) relative to the spectra measured for emission from the same atoms on earth. From these observations he concluded that the source of the light, the galaxies, is *receding* from the earth (Equation 13.20a). He further noted that the shift, and therefore, the recessional velocity, increases with the distance of the galaxies, and thus concluded that the universe is expanding. Galactic velocities of more than 40% the speed of light relative to the earth have been measured by refining Hubble's observational methods.

◤◤ 13.9 Electromagnetic waves: general properties

The discussion of the foregoing sections has involved many of the same terms we used in Chapter 12 to describe the propagation of electromagnetic fields in vacuo. Although all the examples of waves we have given require a medium of propagation, be it a string, water, or air, that requirement is imposed in each case by the specific nature of the propagated disturbance itself, and not by the general, formal description of waves as disturbances propagated through space.

FIGURE 13.18   (opposite page) (a) Origin of the optical Doppler effect. A photon with frequency ν has energy $E = h\nu$ (Chapter 17). Since the energy of a particle depends on the inertial system in which it is observed, then the frequency of light emitted by a source in motion relative to an observer will be detected as a lower or higher frequency depending upon whether the source moves away from or toward the observer. (b) Red shifts (i.e., Doppler shifts in which wavelengths are displaced toward the red end of the spectrum) for four distant stellar objects. The four insets to the left show the objects as seen by the 200-in. Hale telescope at Mount Palomar. Dispersed light from these four sources appear as bright tapered streaks in the four insets to the right, and show two dark, discrete lines displaced increasingly to the right in the four cases. These have been identified as the same two lines of the element calcium, part of whose spectrum (emitted by a source on earth) appears above and below each stellar spectrum. Arrows indicate the shift of these lines for each source. (Photograph from the Mount Wilson and Palomar Observatories.)

For example, since a water wave specifically involves the oscillation of water molecules, there certainly can be no water waves without water; similarly, sound cannot be propagated in a vacuum since a pressure wave presupposes the existence of matter to compress. However, if the specific nature of some particular disturbance does *not* require that it be carried by matter, then it may satisfy the basic criteria and qualify as a wave, even though propagated in vacuo.

An electromagnetic field whose strength varies both as a function of time and space qualifies as a disturbance, since it will exert a time-varying force upon any charge that happens to be in the region through which it is propagated. As we know, Maxwell's field equations imply that an electromagnetic field is propagated with velocity $c = 3 \times 10^8$ m/sec from an accelerating charge, or, equivalently, from a time-varying current. Since the idea of an electromagnetic *disturbance* is implicit in the description of the field propagation, we are justified in speaking of the propagation of that disturbance as an *electromagnetic wave*.

However, an all important distinction must be made between waves propagated with and without material media. In the former case the medium itself may act as a detector of the waves; in the latter case a separate detector is *always* required. For example, although it may often be easier to use a bobbing cork for the detection of water waves, nonetheless it is possible to see the ripples in the water directly. However, an electromagnetic wave can *only* be detected when it transfers energy to a charge or to a group of charges, the nerve endings in the retina of the eye, for instance. Thus it is never possible to "see" a complete electromagnetic wave or even to measure all of its properties simultaneously in the same way that one might see a complete water wave.

In order to understand the meaning of the wave description as applied to the propagation of an electromagnetic field, let us consider an idealized experiment that might be used in the direct detection of an "electric" wave, ignoring for the moment the accompanying magnetic part of the field, and even suspending, where necessary, some of the restrictions on the measurements of time and space imposed by the special theory of relativity.

Suppose that a number of small, identical, positive test charges were placed equidistantly along a straight line and were initially at rest (Figure 13.19).

If at a particular time t_1 we observe that the test charge located at the point is accelerated in the positive y-direction for a very short period of time, we conclude that the charge was subject to an electric field in the positive y-direction during the short time interval Δt beginning at t_1, and that the magnitude of the field as a function of time must have been proportional to the acceleration of the charge itself. Similarly, if at the later times, t_2, t_3, t_4, t_5, ..., each of the successive charges along the line is given the same acceleration we conclude that each was subject in turn to an identical electric field. If in addition the time delay between the accelerations of any two charges is proportional to the distance between them we might conclude that an electric field of short duration had been propagated in the x-direction, implying that the magnitude of the field as a function of time measured by an observer at x_1 was the same function measured at a *later* time by an observer at x_2. As this description is analogous to that given for the pulse on a string in Section 13.2, we can define the propagation velocity of the field as the ratio between the separation of any two charges to the measured interval between the times when the field is identical at the charges:

$$c = \frac{x_2 - x_1}{t_2 - t_1} = \frac{x_3 - x_2}{t_3 - t_2} = \frac{x_4 - x_3}{t_4 - t_3}, \ldots$$

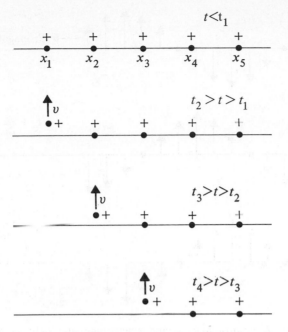

FIGURE 13.19 Idealized method for the direct detection of an electromagnetic pulse of short duration traveling to the right. Small particles with equal mass and equal positive charge are placed along the x-axis. Their successive, equal accelerations in the y-direction indicate that each has been subject to an electric force of the same magnitude and in the same direction, suggesting that an electric field in the y-direction is traveling along the axis.

Therefore, as in Section 13.2, the measured disturbance, the electric field, depends upon x and t in the combination $(x - ct)$; that is,

$$E(x, t) = f(x - ct),$$

and the field is propagated as a right-traveling wave.

Let us extend the mathematical analogy by considering the properties of the time-varying electric field described by the equation

$$E = E_0 \sin 2\pi\left(\frac{x}{\lambda} - \frac{t}{T}\right), \tag{13.21}$$

an equation of the same form as Equation 13.17b describing a pressure wave in three dimensions. Because Equation 13.21 does not depend upon y and z, the magnitude and direction of the electric field at a particular time depends only upon x, and therefore, must have the same value for all points on a plane specified by the same value of x, i.e., on any plane perpendicular to the x-axis. In one period, T, the strength of field at all points on such a plane intersecting the x-axis at the point x_1, say, varies in time from a maximum $+E_0$ to a minimum $-E_0$ and back again to $+E_0$ (Figure 13.20). The values of the field vectors at all points on parallel planes to the right of x_1 lag behind their values at x_1 in direct proportion to their distance from x_1. By definition, the wavelength λ is the

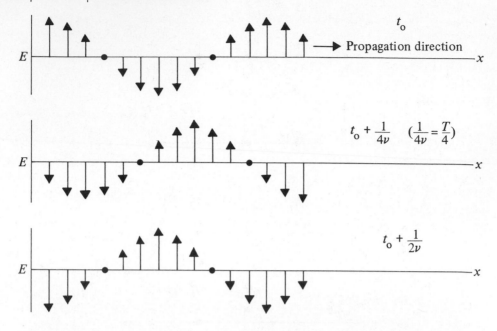

FIGURE 13.20 A sinusoidally-varying electromagnetic field at several points along the x-axis and at three times one-quarter cycle apart. The arrows indicate the instantaneous direction and relative magnitude of the electric field as a function of x. The magnetic field varies sinusoidally with the same frequency but is zero when the electric field is a maximum or minimum and a maximum or minimum when the electric field is zero. It is always perpendicular both to the electric field and to the direction of propagation.

distance between any two planes at which the field strengths are always equal. As with any wave, the propagation velocity, c, is related to the period and wavelength by

$$c = \frac{\lambda}{T}.$$ (13.22a)

Again, the frequency of the wave is defined as the reciprocal of the period, although the symbol ν is conventionally used for electromagnetic frequencies, so

$$c = \lambda \nu.$$ (13.22b)

How might such a wave be detected? The most direct method would be an extension of the scheme illustrated in Figure 13.19. We could conceive of a three-dimensional lattice array of identical, positive test charges attached to identical springs with natural frequencies equal to the natural frequency of the electric wave. The changing electric field at each charge would exert a force upon that charge and cause the spring system to oscillate at its resonance frequency.

Maxwell's equations provide the dynamical basis for the propagation of electromagnetic waves, and imply that a magnetic "wave" of strength $B = E/c$ (Equation 13.10c) must always accompany the electric waves whose propagation we have been discussing. Therefore, each charge in an array will also be subject to a time-varying magnetic force if it is in motion. Of course, it is really misleading to speak of the propagation of electric and magnetic waves; rather we should speak of the propagation of an electromagnetic wave, as required by special relativity. Nonetheless, the arrays of charges we have been using in our examples do constitute possible detectors of electromagnetic waves. In fact, the electrons in the ubiquitous television dipole antennas qualify as this sort of charge array. Their oscillations in resonance with an incident wave constitute a time-varying current used to activate the television receiver. However, electromagnetic waves are often detected by less direct methods.

▲▲ 13.10 The electromagnetic spectrum

According to Maxwell, the source of an electromagnetic wave must be a changing current, or, equivalently, an accelerating charge. Therefore, we would expect the time variation of the waves radiated from the current to mirror the time variation of the current itself. If the current in a solenoid were reversed several times a second, the direction of the radiated field would also reverse, though of course the reversal of the field at a point a distance R from the coil would occur a time $t = R/c$ after the reversal of the current. Similarly, if the current in the coil varied sinusoidally with frequency ν (i.e., $i = i_0 \sin 2\pi\nu t$), the electromagnetic field radiated from the coil would also be represented as a pure sine wave of frequency ν.

The spatial configurations of the radiated fields depend upon the specific geometry of the source. Since Faraday's electric law and the symmetric, magnetic induction law (Equations 12.5a and 12.8a) must be used to determine the fields of an accelerating charge, the configurations of the radiation fields are usually different from the steady fields produced by a source with the same geometry.

Radiation field configurations for a number of simple cases such as an oscillating point charge or an oscillating current in a straight wire or a solenoid may be determined by using Maxwell's equations. Figure 13.21 shows the electric field configuration of an oscillating electric dipole antenna at the four quarter points of its cycle ($t = 0$, $1/4\nu$, $1/2\nu$, and $3/4\nu$). Magnetic field lines are perpendicular to the plane of the page. The dipole may be regarded as a short, vertical segment of wire in which the current oscillates up and down. Thus during one-half of the cycle the upper half is positively charged, the lower half negatively charged, with the reverse being true during the second half-cycle.

From the foregoing discussion we expect any periodically varying current to radiate an electromagnetic wave with frequency equal to its own frequency, and conclude that the only limitation on the possible frequencies of these waves is imposed by limitations in the frequencies attainable at the sources. Of course the detection of an electromagnetic wave also involves the acceleration of charge or the induction of a current, and although the arrays of charges discussed in the last section might be used in some cases, a more common detection scheme involves resonance. Thus, for instance, the current induced in a solenoid of identical construction to a source solenoid and oriented parallel to it would constitute a detector of the intervening radiated waves. The frequency of the waves would then be mirrored by the frequency of the induced current. Similarly, the current induced in an identical dipole antenna would detect the waves of Figure 13.21. Therefore, since both the production and the detection of electromagnetic waves depends upon the ability of a system to oscillate, the production and detection of waves in a particular frequency range may well require apparatus that is quite different from the production and detection in a different frequency range. It follows that the origin and the effect of waves, and therefore their qualitative character, changes as a function of their frequency.

The first direct tests of these ideas were carried out by Heinrich Hertz who produced

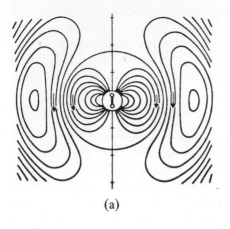

(a)

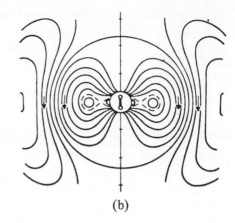

(b)

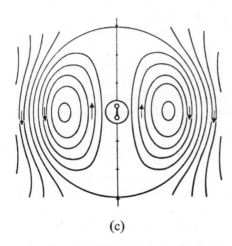

(c)

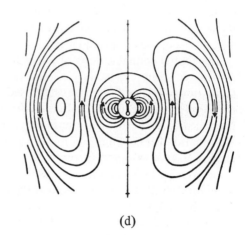

(d)

FIGURE 13.21 Electric field propagated outward from an oscillating dipole at the four quarter points in its cycle ($t = 0$, $T/4$, $T/2$, and $3T/4$). The dipole may be regarded as a short, vertical segment of wire in which the current oscillates sinusoidally. During one-half the cycle the charge in the upper half segment is positive, the charge in the lower half negative; during the other half cycle these directions are reversed. (From Jerry B. Marion, *Classical Electromagnetic Radiation*, Academic Press, New York, 1966.)

and detected wavelengths on the order of ten meters in length. His experiments, performed in the last decade of the nineteenth century, marked the first artificial production of electromagnetic waves.

Hertz's method is illustrated in Figure 13.22. The source of his waves was an electrical discharge between two polished metal spheres. Normally air is an excellent insulator, but if a sufficiently high charge builds up on a body the surrounding air becomes a temporary conductor, and permits a discharge to another nearby body.

Lightning, a discharge between a charged cloud and the earth, is an example of temporary conduction by air. The phenomenon can also be demonstrated in the laboratory. For instance, a discharge is observed between two polished metal spheres separated by a short air gap if a high charge is built upon one of them. The breakdown across the gap is caused by disassociation of the air atoms into positive and negative ions. During and

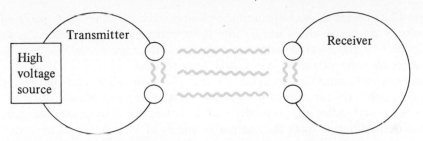

FIGURE 13.22 Hertz's apparatus for producing and detecting electromagnetic waves. A high voltage builds up across the gap between two polished metal spheres connected to the source by a wire loop and causes a periodic discharge between them. The oscillating ions in the gap produce electromagnetic waves of short duration which induce an EMF in the receiver loop sufficient to cause a discharge across the gap between its spheres.

immediately following the discharge the ions oscillate across the gap and eventually recombine into neutral atoms. According to Maxwell their oscillations should result in the emission of electromagnetic waves. Hertz detected these waves with a receiver consisting of a loop of wire whose ends terminated in two polished spheres separated by a short gap. Charge in the wire, oscillating in resonance with the waves, built up a charge difference on the spheres and caused a breakdown of the air gap. By measuring the wavelength and frequency of the waves, Hertz showed their velocity of propagation was 3×10^8 m/sec, in accord with Maxwell. These "Hertzian waves," which serve as carrier waves for radio transmission, are now called radio waves. Receiving antennas are basically nothing more than refinements of Hertz's detector.

In the more than sixty years that have intervened since Hertz's experiments the advance of technology has permitted the production and detection of electromagnetic waves over a broad spectrum ranging down to wavelengths on the order of tenths of millimeters (Figure 13.23). As expected, the characteristics of the electronic circuits required to produce and detect wavelengths in different regions of the spectrum vary considerably, as do the qualitative properties of the waves themselves. References dealing with the development of electronics technology as well as with the many applications of electromagnetic waves are given at the end of the chapter.

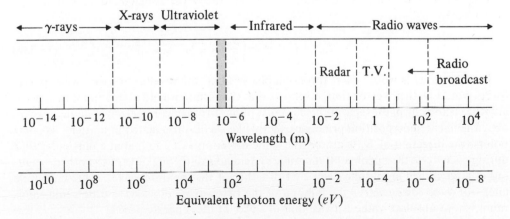

FIGURE 13.23 The electromagnetic spectrum. (The visible portion is shown as a dark, narrow band.)

Figure 13.23 brings us once again to the photon-wave paradox. The spectrum of the electronically produced waves merges into the spectrum of the infrared. As we know from Chapter 10, the infrared sprectrum merges into the region of visible light, which in turn merges into the ultraviolet, x-ray, and γ-ray regions.

Is there any justification for speaking of infrared or visible light and Hertzian waves in the same breath? Do the radiations have any relationship in common other than their velocity in vacuo? After all, properties such as color, normally associated with visible light, are quite different from the qualitative effects of Hertz's ten-meter waves which cause an electrical breakdown across a gap. Infrared radiation is detected when the energy it transfers to atoms in matter manifests itself as heat. Visible light transfers energy to the rods and cones in the retina of the eye. No one has ever observed or measured directly the high frequency oscillations of the tungsten atoms in an incandescent filament, nor watched the vibrations of atoms in the nerve endings of the retina as they respond to incident light. Therefore, we must inquire into the meanings of the terms wavelength and frequency when used in connection with visible light.

▶▶ 13.11   Interference and diffraction

The double-slit interference experiment, first performed by Thomas Young in the early eighteenth century, demonstrated the wave nature of light long before Maxwell showed its electromagnetic character. In Chapter 10 we presented interference from a purely experimental point of view. Now we shall show that it is consistent with the wave model.

Figure 13.24 shows two slits separated by a distance d and illuminated by monochromatic light of wavelength λ. We may regard each as a source of electromagnetic waves of equal wavelength and amplitude. If the slits are equidistant from the primary source, the waves at the slits are in phase. That is, the time variation of the electric vector at one of them neither lags behind nor leads the other. The waves propagated from the slits A and B are described by the time variation of the electric vectors at all points in space. If S_A is the distance from slit A to a particular point then (Equation 13.21):

$$E_A = E_0 \cos 2\pi\left(\frac{S_A}{\lambda} - \frac{t}{T}\right), \qquad (13.23a)$$

where E_0 is the maximum value of the field; for mathematical convenience we use the cosine rather than the sine function. Likewise, the wave propagated from slit B is described by

$$E_B = E_0 \cos 2\pi\left(\frac{S_B}{\lambda} - \frac{t}{T}\right). \qquad (13.23b)$$

Since both fields would exert forces on charges and the resultant of the two separate forces would be their vector sum, it follows that the resultant field at any point in space is also the vector sum of the separate fields at that point. In other words, electromagnetic waves obey the linear superposition principle exactly like waves propagated in matter. At some points, the direction of E_A is always the same direction as E_B so that at a particular time during each cycle the maxima of one wave system add to the maxima of the other, resulting in a combined amplitude twice that of either of the separate waves. One-half cycle later—*at these same points*—the minima of the two waves coincide, resulting in a minimum whose absolute value is twice that of either of the separate waves.

At *other* points, at a particular time, *maxima* of one wave coincide with equal and opposite *minima* of the other, resulting in a combined amplitude equal to zero. One-half period later the maxima of the first wave have become minima, and vice versa, so that the zero amplitude points *remain* zero amplitude points at all times.

At a particular point a distance S_A from slit A and a distance S_B from slit B the magnitude of the electric field is given by the sum of the waves from the individual slits:

$$E = E_0\left[\cos 2\pi\left(\frac{S_A}{\lambda} - \frac{t}{T}\right) + \cos 2\pi\left(\frac{S_B}{\lambda} - \frac{t}{T}\right)\right]. \tag{13.24a}$$

But $\cos A + \cos B = 2\cos\frac{1}{2}(A - B)\cos\frac{1}{2}(A + B)$ (Appendix B to text). Letting $A = 2\pi(S_A/\lambda - t/T)$ and $B = 2\pi(S_B/\lambda - t/T)$, we have

$$E = 2E_0\cos\frac{\pi}{\lambda}(S_A - S_B)\cos 2\pi\left(\frac{S_A}{2\lambda} + \frac{S_B}{2\lambda} - \frac{t}{T}\right). \tag{13.24b}$$

If we let

$$E_R = 2F_0\cos\frac{\pi}{\lambda}(S_A - S_B), \tag{13.25a}$$

$$\Phi_R = \frac{1}{2}\left(\frac{S_A}{\lambda} + \frac{S_B}{\lambda}\right), \tag{13.25b}$$

and substitute in Equation 13.24b, we have for the time variation of the resultant electric vector at the point in question,

$$E(t) = E_R\cos 2\pi\left(\frac{t}{T} + \Phi_R\right). \tag{13.25c}$$

Equation 13.25c shows that the time variation of the field at any point is identical with the time variation of the separate fields, but that its maximum value, E_R, is a variable depending upon the difference in the distances from the point to the slits. According to Equation 13.25a, $E_R = \pm 2E_0$ when $\cos(\pi/\lambda)(S_A - S_B) = \pm 1$, or $(\pi/\lambda)(S_A - S_B) = 0, \pi, 2\pi, 3\pi, \ldots$. That is,

$$\Delta_n = S_A - S_B = n\lambda. \tag{13.26a}$$

For these points Equations 13.35a and 13.25c imply that $E(t) = 2E_0\cos 2\pi(t/T + \Phi_R)$; the resultant field oscillates with an amplitude which is the sum of the individual maxima from the separate slits.

On the other hand for $(\pi/\lambda)(S_A - S_B) = \pi/2, 3\pi/2, 5\pi/2, \ldots$; that is,

$$\Delta_n = S_A - S_B = \frac{(2n + 1)}{2}\lambda, \qquad n = 0, 1, 2, 3, \ldots, \tag{13.26b}$$

$E_R = 0$, and the two fields cancel each other at all times.

The energy delivered to a region in space per unit time is proportional to the *square* of the electric vector at that point (see the analogous one-dimensional expression, Equation 13.11). Therefore, at points where the condition specified by Equation 13.26a is satisfied, the energy is proportional to $4E_0^2$; at points specified by Equation 13.26b the energy is zero.

As in Chapter 10 (Section 10.6) we can relate the path differences $\Delta = S_A - S_B$ to the distances between the slits and the position of the bright (or dark) fringes on a screen a perpendicular distance S_0 from the slits. Referring to Figure 13.24:

$$\Delta_n = d\theta_n,$$

so

$$x_n = S_0\theta_n = S_0\left(\frac{\Delta_n}{d}\right),$$

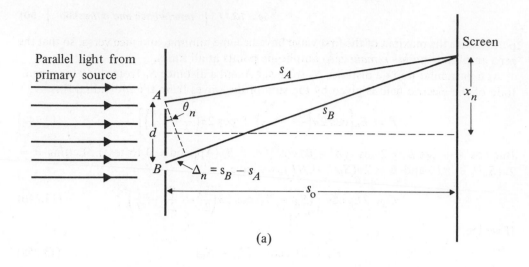

(a)

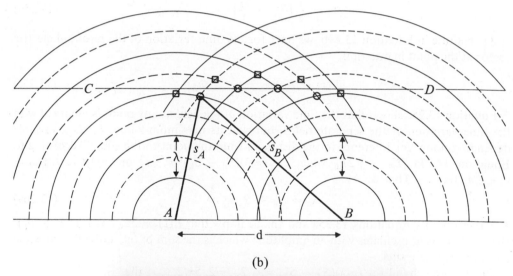

(b)

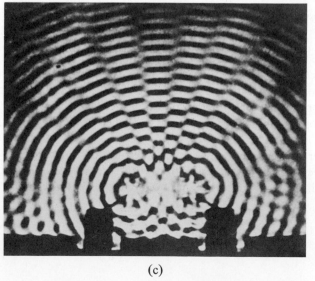

(c)

502

if θ_n is small (i.e., S_0 much greater than d). The positions of the bright fringes are obtained by substituting Equation 13.26a:

$$\text{(maxima)} \qquad x_n = S_0\left(\frac{n\lambda}{d}\right), \qquad n = 0, 1, 2, \ldots, \qquad (13.27a)$$

so that the spacing between two adjacent maxima is

$$\Delta_x = x_{n+1} - x_n = S_0\left(\frac{\lambda}{d}\right). \qquad (13.27b)$$

Likewise, the positions of the minima are obtained by substituting Δ_n from Equation 13.26b:

$$\text{(minima)} \qquad x_n = S_0\left(\frac{2n+1}{2}\right)\frac{\lambda}{d}, \qquad n = 0, 1, 2, \ldots. \qquad (13.27c)$$

In Chapter 10 we obtained these same relations starting from an observed slit pattern rather than from the assumption of a wave model of light. There we interpreted λ as simply a convenient, characteristic number for relating the geometry of the slit apparatus to the observed fringe pattern. The agreement between the expressions in this section and in Chapter 10 suggests that we are justified in identifying the characteristic measured length λ from our earlier analysis as a wavelength in the sense that we defined the term in the foregoing sections of this chapter.

The diffraction of light from a single slit may be understood in the same terms. In Figure 13.25 a plane wave of light is incident upon a slit of width a. If we regard each small strip across the slit as a secondary source of cylindrical waves, then from the foregoing discussion we expect reinforcements and cancelations between these waves in the region beyond the slit.

Let us concentrate upon the secondary waves originating from the center and the extreme left edge. Referring to Equation 13.26b, cancellation occurs at points for which the path difference from these secondary sources is $\Delta_n = [(2n+1)/2]\lambda$. From Figure 13.26, $\Delta_n = (a/2)\theta_n$; $x_n = S_0\theta_n$. Hence on a distant screen the minimum points for the resultant of these wavelets are specified by:

$$\text{(minima)} \qquad x_n = (2n+1)S_0\frac{\lambda}{a}, \qquad n = 0, 1, 2, \ldots; \; -1, -2, \ldots. \qquad (13.28a)$$

Continuing this analysis we note that for every segment on the left half of the slit there is a segment on the right half a distance $a/2$ removed such that the wavelets from the two

FIGURE 13.24 (opposite page) (a) Geometry of the double-slit interference apparatus. (b) Explanation of interference in terms of the wave model. Circular waves radiating outward from each slit are shown at one particular instant. Solid lines represent maxima, broken lines minima. The composite amplitude at any point in space depends upon the difference $S_A - S_B$. Points where maxima from the two sources coincide have amplitudes twice that of the two contributing waves. One-half cycle later minima from the two sources coincide at these same points, and vice versa. However, points at which a maximum from one source coincides with a minimum from the other at one time have zero resultant displacement at all times. (b) Interference maxima and minima near the plane CD perpendicular to the page (the position of the screen in part a) are boxed, zeros are circled. (At greater distances from the two sources these maxima, minima, and zeros would all be closer to the plane than suggested here.) (c) Double-source interference of water waves in a ripple tank.

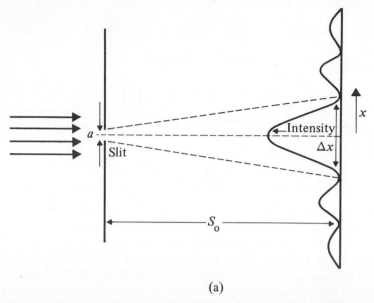

(a)

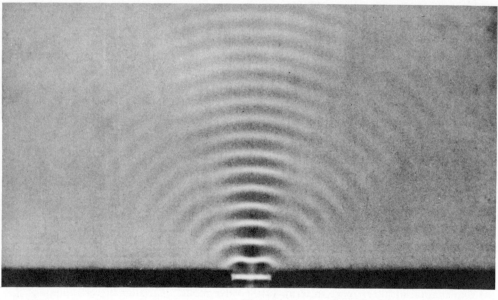

(b)

FIGURE 13.25 (a) Diffraction pattern from a single rectangular slit of width *a*. The intensity of the light on a distant screen is plotted as a function of *x*, the distance along the screen measured from its center. Since the relative intensities of the secondary maxima decrease rapidly with increasing *n*, the width of the central maximum (Δx) is usually taken as a measure of the spread in the incident beam due to its diffraction by the slit. (b) Diffraction of water waves passing through a narrow slit. (Photograph from *PSSC Physics*, D. C. Heath and Co., Boston, © 1965.)

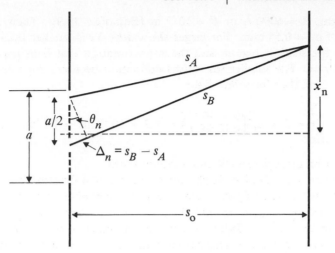

FIGURE 13.26 Diagram used for deriving the condition for the occurence of diffraction minima. The slit is regarded as being subdivided into many smaller slits, each of them the source of a circular wave train. Each subsource in the upper half of the slit is paired with another in the lower half separated from it by one-half the slit width. The condition for a minimum on the screen due to waves from these two subsources is the minimum condition for two slits separated by a distance $a/2$. Since the same condition for the occurrence of a minimum applies to all such pairs of subsources, it also applies to the entire slit.

segments cancel each other at all points satisfying Equation 13.28a. Hence this equation specifies the positions of the diffraction minima for the entire slit. The positions and relative intensities of diffraction maxima are obtained in a similar way, that is, by adding the contributions from each subsegment of the slit. The analysis is more complicated than in the double slit interference case, for in effect a great many slits rather than only two are involved. A detailed analysis shows that the pattern is symmetric about $x = 0$ (the center of the screen), and that the intensity decreases rapidly beyond the first two symmetric minima. Therefore, most of the light is confined in the region between these two minima, and the width of this central maximum may be regarded as a measure of the amount the light is diffracted by the slit.

We can now understand why light passing through a narrow slit spreads outside the shadow region. From Equation 13.28a, the first minima to the left and right of the central maximum corresponds to $n = 0$ and $n = -1$, that is, $x_0 = S_0(\lambda/a)$, $x_{-1} = -S_0(\lambda/a)$. Therefore, the width of the bright region between the two symmetric minima is (Figure 13.25a):

$$\Delta x = 2S_0 \frac{\lambda}{a}. \tag{13.28b}$$

Since Δx varies inversely as the slit width it follows that the width of the central region increases as the slit is narrowed. A Δx greater than a implies the central bright region is broader than the geometric shadow region, while a Δx equal to a implies that the regions coincide exactly. Hence we can determine the minimum slit width such that there is no apparent spreading by setting $\Delta x = a$ in Equation 13.28b to yield

$$a = \sqrt{2S_0\lambda}.$$

For yellow light, $\lambda = 6000$ Å or 6×10^{-7} m (Equation 10.9). Then if $S_0 = 0.5$ m, $a = 5.5 \times 10^{-4}$ m $= 0.55$ mm. For larger slit widths Δx is smaller than a, there is no spreading into the shadow region, and the approximation that light travels in straight lines is a good one. For smaller slit widths diffraction becomes apparent. If $a = 0.05$ mm $= 5 \times 10^{-5}$ m, then for yellow light,

$$x = 2 \times 0.5 \left(\frac{6 \times 10^{-7}}{5 \times 10^{-5}}\right) = 1.2 \times 10^{-2} \text{ m}, = 1.2 \text{ cm}.$$

The width of the bright region is 600 times the slit width.

In our discussion of the double-slit pattern, we neglected diffraction from the individual slits. In view of the above analysis we would expect the double-slit pattern to be a super-position of two single-slit patterns and the double-slit pattern discussed earlier. Comparing Equations 13.27 and 13.28a, however, we conclude that if the slit widths are small relative to their separation the spacing between the single-slit minima will be large relative to the spacing between the bright double-slit fringes. The net effect is a diminution in the intensity of the latter with increasing distance from the central bright fringe, and an eventual shading off of the entire pattern.

◢◤ 13.12 Summary: The wave and particle aspects of light

We have shown that both the characteristic double-slit and single-slit patterns observed on a distant screen are *consistent* with the wave model of light. But in what sense do they prove that the wave model is unique and sufficient? The wavelength of visible light as measured with a double-slit interference apparatus ranges from about 4000 Å for blue light to roughly 7600 Å at the red end of the spectrum. Since the velocity of light is 3×10^8 m/sec, these wavelengths correspond to frequencies on the order of 10^{14} cycles/sec. As there is no way to observe directly an electric vector whose magnitude varies from maximum to minimum and again to maximum in less than 10^{-14} sec we measure instead the *energy* transported to a region on a screen averaged over many cycles, an energy which in the wave model is proportional to the square of the amplitude of the wave. Nor do we actually observe the cylindrical wave patterns emanating from the slits. We merely infer their existence from the measured interference pattern and from our model.

We can state with assurance that the interference phenomenon is *not inconsistent* with the wave model, for the predictions of the model lead to the pattern we observe. We can go further and repeat the arguments of Chapter 10 to show that the double-slit pattern is *inconsistent* with a classical particle model. The intensity (or energy) at the bright fringes is four times the intensity from each of the separate slits, while according to a particle model the intensity could be at most twice the individual intensities. On the wave model the minimum intensity at the screen is zero, as observed. But there is no way that the simultaneous arrival of two particles at the same point on the screen could result in the disappearance of both without a trace.

If a monochromatic beam of uniform intensity is incident upon a surface, then according to the wave model the energy delivered to the surface per unit time is proportional to E_0^2. Therefore, a beam of red light can deliver the same total energy to a metallic surface as a beam of ultraviolet light, provided the amplitudes of the electric vectors are the same in both cases. Yet even a weak beam of ultraviolet light results in the emission of electrons from a copper surface, whereas even a very intense beam of red light cannot induce photoemission no matter how long it shines on the copper. Observations such as these led us to the photon model in Chapter 10.

One set of experiments suggests a particle model for light and rules out a wave model; another set leads to precisely opposite conclusions. But in fact we have pushed our models too far. The properties of light suggested by the photoelectric effect are *consistent* with a particle model, but do not prove that photons have all the properties we associate with classical particles. Likewise, the interference experiment is *consistent* with a wave model, but need not imply that light has all the attributes of classical waves.

Therefore, we must find a new description of light which is consistent with both sets of experiments. To do so we shall have to abandon the implicit classical assumption that it is possible, in principle, to have complete knowledge of a physical system, and be led instead to the conclusion that the fundamental laws of nature are laws of probability and not of certainty. We shall gain a great deal in return for this concession, for the new description, quantum mechanics, turns out to be valid not only for light but also for electrons, protons, and all the fundamental entities composing the physical universe.

The new description is based upon probability. We have already seen that although we are able to determine whether an electron in copper *can* absorb sufficient energy from a beam of light to free itself from the metal, we cannot say whether or not a *particular* electron *will* absorb a photon. We can only state the probability of such an occurrence, and thus predict the number of electrons that will be emitted from a block of copper in a given length of time if a great many photons are incident upon its surface.

From this same point of view, if a single photon is incident upon a pair of slits we can have no certain knowledge of which slit it will traverse or at what point its path will finally terminate. However, we might hope to find a law giving the probability of finding it at a particular point on the screen. Then if many photons were incident upon the slit we could predict the *number* reaching the screen in each band. In fact, we already know these numbers, for they are correctly predicted by the classical wave model.

However, before we can understand this quantum mechanical description of light we should understand something about the mathematical meaning of probability and its application to some purely classical problems. In addition it will be advantageous to have some idea of the classical view of atomic process that prevailed before the advent of the quantum theory in the early years of the present century.

SUGGESTIONS FOR FURTHER READING ▲▲▲

Most introductory texts in physics treat wave motion. Among them are:

ARNOLD B. ARONS, *Development of Concepts of Physics*, Addison-Wesley Publishing Co., Inc., Reading, Mass., 1965, Chapter 22.

K. R. ATKINS, *Physics*, John Wiley and Sons, Inc., New York, 1965, Chapters 19, 20, and 21.

JAY OREAR, *Fundamental Physics*, John Wiley and Sons, Inc., New York, 1961, Chapter 10.

Physical Science Study Committee, *College Physics*, Raytheon Education Co., Boston, 1968, Chapters 6, 7, 8, and 9.

The many available paperback books on waves, the physics of music, and the uses of electromagnetic waves include:

WINSTON E. KOCH, *Sound Waves and Light Waves*, Science Study Series, Doubleday and Co., Garden City, N.Y.

R. A. WALDRON, *Waves and Oscillations*, Momentum Series, D. Van Nostrand and Co., Princeton, N.J., 1964.

WILLARD BASCOM, *Waves and Beaches: The Dynamics of the Ocean Surface*, Science Study Series, Doubleday and Co., Garden City, N.Y., 1964.

ARTHUR H. BENADE, *Horns, Strings, and Harmony*, Science Study Series, Doubleday and Co., Garden City, N.Y.

WILLEM A. VAN BERGEIGK, JOHN R. PIERCE, AND EDWARD E. DAVID, JR., *Waves and the Ear*, Science Study Series, Doubleday and Co., Garden City, N.Y.

JESS J. JOSEPH, *The Physics of Musical Sound*, Momentum Series, D. Van Nostrand and Co., Princeton, N.J.

DONALD G. FINK AND DAVID M. LUTYENS, *The Physics of Television*, Science Study Series Doubleday and Co., Garden City, N.Y.

ROBERT M. PAGE, *The Origin of Radar*, Science Study Series, Doubleday and Co., Garden City, N.Y.

JOHN R. PIERCE, *Electrons and Waves: An Introduction to the Science of Electronics and Communications*, Science Study Series, Doubleday and Co., Garden City, N.Y.

JOHN R. PIERCE, *Quantum Electronics: The Fundamentals of Transistors and Lasers*, Science Study Series, Doubleday and Co., Garden City, N.Y.

Articles related to particular types of waves occasionally appear in the *Scientific American*:

J. D. KRAUS, "Radio Telescopes," March, 1955, p. 36.

E. F. MCCLAIN, "The 600-Foot Radio Telescope," January, 1960, p. 45.

A. L. SCHAWLOW, "Optical Masers," June, 1961, p. 52.

A. L. SCHAWLOW, "Advances in Optical Masers," July, 1963, p. 34.

E. D. BLACKHAM, "The Physics of the Piano," December, 1965, p. 88.

PROBLEMS AND EXERCISES ▲▲▲

13.1. A pulse on a taut string travels to the right with velocity 5 m/sec. Its shape at time $t = 0$ is given by the equations:

$y = 0$ if x is smaller than 0 or greater than 0.1 m.

$y = 0.2x$ if x is greater than 0 but smaller than 0.05 m.

$y = 0.02 - 0.2x$ if x is greater than 0.05 m but smaller than 0.1 m.

(a) Sketch the waveform at $t = 0$.
(b) Write a set of equations describing the waveform as a function of time.
(c) Plot the wave at $t = 0.02$ sec and at $t = 0.1$ sec.

13.2. (a) The string in Problem 13.1 is 2.5 m long and terminates at a rigid binding post. Plot the form of the reflected wave at $t = 0.7$ sec.
(b) Suppose the reflected wave of part a crosses a right-traveling pulse of the form in Problem 13.1a and b. Plot the deformation of the string for partial overlapping and for complete overlapping.

13.3. A sinusoidal wave on a long string is described by the equation $y = 0.3 \sin 2\pi(20x - 200t)$.

(a) What is its wavelength? Its frequency? Its velocity?
(b) What is the tension of the string if it has a mass per unit length of 1 kg/m?
(c) Plot the waveform over two wavelengths at some particular time, and at a time one-quarter cycle later.

13.4. (a) How does the waveform in Problem 13.3 differ from the wave described by $y = 0.3 \cos 2\pi(20x - 200t)$? (If not immediately evident plot the two waves at some time.)

(b) How does the wave differ from the wave

$$y = 0.3 \sin 2\pi(20x - 200t + \phi)$$

for $\phi = \frac{1}{8}$? For $\phi = \frac{1}{4}$?

13.5. (a) Let the equation $y = A(R) \sin 2\pi(20x - 200t)$ similar to that of Problems 13.3 and 13.4 describe a plane wave on the surface of a lake. Plot the positions of the crests and troughs of the wave (as a function of x and z) at a particular time and again one-quarter cycle later.

(b) Plot the positions of the crests and troughs of the circular surface wave $y = A(R) \sin 2\pi(20R - 200t)$ as a function of R at a particular time and one-quarter period later.

(c) Why is $A(R)$ a function of R rather than a constant as in 13.3 and 13.4?

13.6. A string simultaneously propagates the three waves

$$\text{i. } y = 0.3 \sin 2\pi(20x - 200t),$$

$$\text{ii. } y = 0.2 \sin 2\pi(40x - 400t),$$

$$\text{iii. } y = 0.1 \sin 2\pi(60x - 600t).$$

(a) Plot the three separate waves over 0.1 m at some particular time, t_1.

(b) Use the graphs of part a to plot the superposition of (i) and (ii) over 0.1 m at time t_1.

(c) Repeat part b to find the superposition of all three waves.

(d) What would you expect the composite waveform to look like $\frac{1}{400}$ sec later, that is, after the wave (i) has gone through another half-cycle?

13.7. (a) A violin string is 0.5 m long. What is the wavelength of its fundamental normal mode? Of its second, third, and fourth harmonics?

(b) If the string is tuned to a fundamental frequency of 440 cycles/sec (A above middle C), what are the frequencies of the harmonics?

(c) What are the velocities of the waves on the string?

13.8. (a) Sketch the configurations of the four standing wave modes of Problem 13.7.

(b) How would the sound from the string change if the tension of the string were decreased by 4%?

(c) Suppose a bow clamps the vibrating string precisely at its center. Based upon part a, which of the harmonics would you expect to be suppressed?

13.9. A 0.2 m long violin string of mass per unit length 1.2×10^{-4} kg/m vibrates with fundamental frequency 250 cycles/sec.

(a) What is the tension of the string?

(b) What is the tension of a string of the same length and mass that vibrates at twice the frequency?

(c) What is the length of a string with the same mass per meter under the same tension which vibrates at twice the fundamental frequency?

13.10. The velocity of sound in a gas is equal to $\sqrt{E/d}$, where E is the elastic modulus of the medium (analogous to the Hooke's law constant for a spring), and d is its volume density (mass per unit volume). The velocity of sound in air at room temperature and atmospheric pressure is about 300 m/sec.

(a) The frequency of middle C is 256 cycles/sec. What is the corresponding wavelength in air?

(b) The elastic modulus of helium at atmospheric pressure is roughly the same as that of air, but its volume density is only about 25% as great. What is the velocity of sound in helium?

(c) What is the frequency of a wavelength corresponding to middle C in helium?

13.11. A rectangular membrane with dimensions $L_1 = 0.1$ and $L_2 = 0.2$ m held under uniform tension vibrates in such a way that $m = 1$, $n = 2$ in Equation 13.6. If $v = 1000$ m/sec:

   (a) What is the frequency of the vibration?
   (b) Sketch the standing wave pattern. That is, draw the membrane and identify the lines for which the displacement is always zero.

13.12. (a) Repeat Problem 13.12 for the mode $m = 2$, $n = 0$.
   (b) Repeat Problem 13.12 for the mode $m = 2$, $n = 2$.

13.13. What are the three lowest frequency acoustical oscillations that can be maintained in a hollow, rectangular cavity with dimensions $0.1 \times 0.12 \times 0.15$ m? The velocity of sound in dry air is about 300 m/sec.

   N.B.: For Problems 13.14, 13.15, and 13.16: The velocity of sound in dry air is about 300 m/sec.

13.14. As a fast train approaches a small station at 50 m/sec the engineer blows the whistle, which has a 600 cycle/sec frequency.

   (a) What frequency does an observer on the station platform hear?
   (b) What frequency does the observer on the station platform hear as the train recedes from him?

13.15. The train in Problem 13.14 is now at rest in the yards, but still blowing its whistle. Another train approaches it at 50 m/sec.

   (a) What frequency does a passenger on the second train hear?
   (b) What frequency does he hear as he recedes from the stationary train?

13.16. After a fast train has passed an observer on a station platform the observer notes that the frequency he hears from the whistle of the receding train is exactly half the frequency he heard when the train was approaching. What is the velocity of the train?

13.17. An observer at rest on a still day hears a factory whistle blow at a frequency of 1000 cycles/sec. Suddenly a 20 m/sec wind arises blowing in the direction from factory to observer. What frequency does the observer hear now?

13.18. (a) With what relative velocity must a star recede from the solar system if blue light (4000 Å) from the star appears as yellow light (6000 Å) on Earth?
   (b) With what relative velocity must the star recede if a 2.0 eV photon emitted from the star is identified as a 1.0 eV energy photon on earth?

13.19. Relative stellar recessional velocities of $0.4\,c$ have been measured using observed optical Doppler shift data. If radiation were emitted from such a star with wavelength 3×10^{-7} m (in the ultraviolet), what wavelength would be observed on earth? In what region of the spectrum would it lie?

13.20. A motorist, hailed into traffic court for going through a red light, explains that due to the fact that he was approaching the light the radiation he saw was actually green. The judge reflects on this, then fines the motorist for speeding.

   If the motorist was being truthful, how fast was he going? (Take the wavelengths of red and green lights as 7500 and 5000 Å, respectively.)

13.21. An harmonic oscillator rests upon a smooth, horizontal table top. An 8.1 N force is required to displace the 0.1 kg mass by 1 m.

   (a) What is the natural frequency of the system?
   (b) If the mass were charged, with what frequency electromagnetic radiation would the system resonate?
   (c) What is the wavelength of the resonance radiation in part b?

13.22. The system of Problem 13.21 is a rough model of an oscillating molecule. For instance, a water molecule oscillates in resonance with infrared radiation. This molecule consists of a heavy oxygen nucleus, two bound protons, and accompanying electrons. The positively charged protons and the oxygen nucleus are bound together electrostatically by the intervention of the electrons; this binding force may be approximated by Hooke's law.

(a) If the mass of a proton is 1.6×10^{-27} kg and the protons oscillate about the oxygen nucleus in resonance with 10^{-6} m radiation, what is the "spring constant" of the system?

(b) The charge on a proton is $+1.6 \times 10^{-19}$ C. What is the amplitude of the electric field (i.e., the maximum value of the electric vector) for electromagnetic radiation that displaces the protons 5×10^{-11} m from their equilibrium positions?

[HINT: When a proton is at its maximum distance from the oxygen nucleus the force exerted on it by the "spring" must be equal and opposite to the force exerted upon it by the electric field.]

(c) What is the energy of the oscillating molecule?
(d) What is the energy of one photon of the radiation of part a?
(e) How many of these photons must the water molecule absorb to attain the energy calculated in part c?

13.23. Sources 1 and 2 in the accompanying diagram each emit radiation with wavelength 0.03 m, and amplitude $E_0 = 1$ unit. Find the positions of the first three interference maxima and the first two minima along the line connecting 1 and the point x_1. (This line is perpendicular to the line connecting the sources.) Let $d = 0.12$ m.

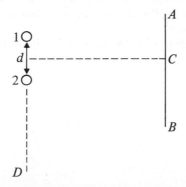

13.24. (a) With the conditions described in Problem 13.23 let the line AB, parallel to the line of the sources, be 0.3 m from the pair. The midpoint C is certainly an interference maximum (why?). Find the position of the first minimum along this line in the direction of B and the next maximum. Plot the intensity E_R^2 (see text) as a function of the distance from C to this second maximum.

(b) Now let the sources be conventional radio antenna broadcasting with amplitude $E_0 = 1$ unit, frequency 10^6 cycles/sec (1 megacycle) and separated by $d = 150$ m. Let the points C and D each be 1500 m from the midpoint between the sources. At which of these points is radio reception better at 1 megacycle?

13.25. The resolving power of an optical instrument is defined in terms of its ability to produce separated images of two nearby objects. If the assumption that light is propagated in rays were rigorously valid then a system could be designed to produce a point image of a point source. However, diffraction at the circular aperture of an optical instrument inevitably spreads the point image into a small circle.

Although the diffraction pattern produced by a circular aperture differs in detail from the rectangular pattern discussed in the text, the spread of the pattern is still proportional to λ/a.

(a) Given this fact determine the radius of the radio telescope operating on a 0.21 m wavelength that has the same percentage resolving power for two (apparently) nearby astronomical point sources as the human eye does for yellow light from the same sources.

(b) What diameter radio telescope has the same resolving power as the 200-in. diameter Hale telescope at Mount Palomar?

13.26. When Galileo first turned his telescope to the heavens he noted with surprise that while the images of the planets appeared larger than with the naked eye, the images of the stars were smaller. Why?

N.B.: Galileo's explanation of the effect was incorrect.

13.27. Suppose you wanted to test the familiar planetary model of the hydrogen atom by taking a picture of such an atom with a specially designed x-ray microscope. It is known that the radius of the hydrogen atom is on the order of 10^{-10} m and that the total energy with which the electron is bound to the proton is -13.6 eV.

(a) About what wavelength x-rays would you use in order to obtain a well-defined picture of the orbit? Why?

(b) A beam of light, of course, can also be regarded for some purposes as a beam of photons. Suppose one of the photons used to make the picture (wavelength determined in part a) Compton scattered from the electron at 90° to its original direction. How much energy would it lose?

(c) Using energy conservation and your answer to part b, what is the ratio of the energy transferred to the electron by the photon to the binding energy of an electron in hydrogen?

(d) With the results obtained above as a guide, comment on the possibility of photographing atoms.

The classical atom: an introduction

14

Greek ideas on the nature of matter. Atomic theory and the unity of the sciences

The search for an understanding of the fundamental nature of matter was a central theme in ancient natural philosophy, and remains the focal point of contemporary physics. R. P. Feynman has asserted that if it were necessary to compress the maximum amount of scientific information into a single sentence, he believes that sentence would be something like this:

> . . . all things are made of atoms . . . little particles that move around in perpetual motion, attracting each other when they are a little distance apart, but repelling upon being squeezed into one another.*

The words used by Feynman—particles, motion, attracting, repelling, distance—all suggest the possibility of applying the familiar concepts and methods of Newtonian dynamics to the study of the internal properties of matter. But the context in which the words appear should warn us to proceed with caution. Newtonian particle dynamics is based upon the interactions of directly observable, macroscopic bodies—colliding billiard balls, falling stones, satellites, for instance—while our knowledge of atomic processes is based upon much less direct evidence.

That atoms cannot be seen is a misleading truism, valid only if the act of "seeing" is defined in its most literal sense. However, since typical atomic masses range from 10^{-27} to 10^{-25} kg, we should not necessarily expect atoms to behave in every respect as if they were miniature billiard balls. Surprisingly enough, the assumption that they *can* be so regarded is quite fruitful and, as we shall see, permits considerable insight into several of the gross, macroscopic properties of matter. But just as we have been led by experimental evidence to conclude that photons are not classical particles, so we shall ultimately be led to a similar conclusion as we consider experimental evidence relating to the nature of atoms and their interactions. The paradox we face regarding light, that its properties can be interpreted neither in terms of a classical particle nor a classical wave model, will ultimately be generalized to encompass *all* microscopic physical processes.

There is little doubt that the body of facts and ideas referred to as the atomic hypothesis must stand as one of the most significant and impressive intellectual edifices of all

---

* R. P. Feynman, R. B. Leighton, and M. Sands, *The Feynman Lectures on Physics*, Vol. I, Chapter 1, Addison Wesley Publishing Co., Reading, Mass., 1963, p. 2.

time. In this and the next two chapters we shall trace the evolution of the classical concept of the atom obtained by applying the Newtonian methods we have developed in the foregoing chapters, and conclude that the existence of atoms is as well verified as the existence of stars, for instance. Even though it is well to note the inadequacy of classical atomic theory at the outset, "inadequate" and "completely incorrect" are not synonymous. A number of microscopic processes *can* be analyzed in considerable detail by using classical physics, and for that reason classical atomic theory is well worth studying for its own sake. But when the Newtonian assumptions are probed too far then they do yield incorrect conclusions. Thus by studying the classical theory we shall also be in a better position to understand its limitations.

Since contemporary atomic theory is the most recent attempt to reduce the various forms of matter to a few fundamental constituents, a brief review of its historical antecedents is in order. These theories predate Newton by more than two millenia, and whereas they are not "scientific" in the modern accepted sense of the word, several of their general assumptions are reflected in our modern approach to the problem of finding "the nature of things."

Sometime during the sixth century B.C., the Ionian philosopher Thales sought a unified theory of the physical universe by taking water as the primordial basis of all things. In so doing he also assumed implicitly that all the forms and phenomena of the universe result not from chance or caprice, but rather that they may be represented in terms of some rational order. His idea that all things ultimately reduce to water seems primitive in retrospect. But his choice of water as the fundamental basis is not nearly so significant as is the fact that he made *some* rational assumption, for it has been argued that the assumption of rationality characterized the momentous transition from an advanced, involved, sophisticated mythology to the first rudimentary natural philosophy.

Succeeding philosophers chose other substances as their primordial bases: Anaximenes an airlike substance, and Heraclitus, fire, or heat. It remained for Empedocles to assume four basic states of matter or *elements*—earth, water, air, and fire—and to base his philosophy upon the interaction of the four.* The earliest complete commentary on these and other systems appear in Aristotle's *Metaphysics*. Reviewing the work of the Ionians, he complained that their theories of matter and its changing forms fail to provide sufficient and consistent mechanisms for the interaction and evolution of the basic elements into observable, changing forms. In the words of the *Metaphysics*, "wood does not of itself become a bed nor bronze a statue," implying that earth, water, air, and fire cannot of themselves unite and evolve to form even rocks, let alone trees or men. Conversely, neither rocks nor trees nor men can be reduced merely to four inert elements. Although the Ionians had spoken of the elements changing, interacting, coming together, and separating to yield all observed gradations of matter, they had not provided the external causes or the rationale that Aristotle held to be requisite to such endless change.

Aristotle accepted the four basic Ionian elements, and added the idea that each individual form evolves according to some preordained purpose toward a final natural state. In his philosophy this external, superimposed rationale was sufficient to mold the elements into the observable forms. We discussed the consequences of this view when applied to the problem of motion in Chapter 3. More generally, it implied that detailed investigation of the nature of things in terms of their basic physical components was

---

* The elements of the ancients were not assumed to be the earth, water, air, and fire observed of terrestrial experience, but rather idealizations of these terrestrial forms. To avoid confusion modern translators sometime render the Greek elements with words such as dry dust, moisture, air, and heat rather than in the conventional manner.

fruitless, and that natural philosophy could best prosper by cataloguing the variety of material forms and studying their growth toward their predetermined ends.

Aristotle also discussed and rejected the ideal world theory of Plato and the atomic theory of Democritus. Plato's ideal world was populated with so-called predicates, each representing an ideal attribute. Forms in the observable, changing world were held to be reflections of one or more of these ideals.

Democritus hypothesized the noncontinuity of matter and spoke instead of a physical universe composed of atoms and the void, of myriad tiny indivisible particles whose constant motion and interaction create all forms of macroscopic matter.

Echos of these ideas are evident in contemporary scientific thought. The four inter-acting elements of the Ionians were replaced by more than one hundred chemical elements in the eighteenth, nineteenth, and twentieth centuries, and these in turn by one hundred or so elementary particles. If matter is defined as the sum of its interactions then the Ionian idea that matter interacts of itself is correct, but so is Aristotle's conviction that a man, for instance, is more than the sum total of this chemical elements, and the element carbon something more than the sum of its constituent elementary particles. Each of two elementary forms of matter, A and B, is defined in terms of its interactions. If A and B unite the result need not merely be $A + B$, but a new, distinct form: $A + B$ plus the interaction of A and B, a form which is new and distinct because its interactions with other forms of matter must also be new and distinct. The idea of defining a basic set of interactions is reminiscent of the Platonic ideal. We now define fundamental forms of matter in terms of properties such as charge and inertial mass, and these are reminis-cent of the Platonic predicates. Finally, credit must go to Democritus for the first re-corded suggestion that matter cannot be infinitely subdivided, but rather has as its basis discrete sets of particles called *atoms*.

Although the ideas of the Greek philosophers have their modern counterparts, their systems of natural philosophy are not scientific theories. Without diminishing their importance it can be fairly stated that all are speculative systems. None is based upon a consistent series of quantitative measurements nor developed in quantitative detail. The system of Plato suggests a fruitful approach toward the construction of a quantitative system. But it makes no attempt at a consistent enumeration of the predicates, nor does it seek to understand all their properties. Indeed the Platonic separation of the ideal and visible world denies the possibility of such a program.

Similarly, the speculation of Democritus offers, in a modern context, a tempting means of description, but does not discuss the specifics of the various types of atoms and their interactions. The Greek natural philosophers differed from Newtonian and contemporary scientists both in general outlook and in motivation. Hence Greek natural philosophy is quite different from modern science.

A detailed theory of matter could only evolve when the quantitative approach sym-bolized and summarized in Newton's *Principia* was applied to the problem. Since this approach is based on quantitative experimental data, a detailed theory of matter must be based on quantitative measurements of its properties.

Almost all such detailed studies are concerned with one or more of the varied processes through which the structure of matter changes. In fact, as we noted in Chapter 1 it is possible to differentiate between the various branches of science in terms of the types of processes with which each is most intimately concerned. Thus, for instance, biology studies the structure and changes in living forms of matter, and among other things, tries to understand in detail the differences that make these highly complex structures alive rather than inert. Astronomy is concerned with the material structure and changes in structure of the stars and planets, geology with the detailed forms and processes which characterize the earth.

Physics and chemistry deal with the simplest material forms and processes and therefore are fundamental to all of the other specializations. Most of the distinctions made between these two disciplines are really artificial. They are justified chiefly on historical grounds, and have become increasingly blurred in recent decades. A detailed study of the historical evolution of the two fields and the eventual merging of the concepts of one with those of the other is both fascinating and revealing. Contemporary merging of the bases of the sciences continues on an accelerated scale so that in fact as well as in principle the basic concepts of physics are common currency of all scientific disciplines. The elementary particles of physics, through their basic interactions, form the large-scale structures of the stars, or, in different circumstances, of atoms. The processes through which these atoms combine to form molecules, and through which these molecules change their forms as they interact with each other, is the subject matter of chemistry, and the properties of and changes in large collections of these atoms and molecules the province of physics, chemistry, or geology depending on circumstance. Perhaps the most fascinating question in all contemporary science is being studied in the border zones between physics, chemistry and biology and asks, quite simply, why some special, highly complex molecules, seemingly little different quantitatively from others, are so qualitatively different that they form the basis of all living things.

There are numerous reasons why the branches of science continue to exist separately and why, for instance, it is virtually impossible for one person to be simultaneously an expert in physics, geology, and biology. These are partly historic, partly practical: there was detailed curiosity about the structure of the earth's crust and the growth of plants long before the formulation of a detailed atomic theory, and further, there are more appropriate methods for studying the earth's crust or plant anatomy than the one that starts with the atomic representation of physics. Although all natural processes must ultimately be reducible to the basic interactions of physics, nature is so lavish and often so subtle in its use that it is virtually impossible for one individual to master more than a fraction of one field of science, let alone be equally conversant in all.

There is a further and more basic reason for the distinctions, related to Aristotle's reluctance to think of qualitative difference solely in terms of quantitative difference. As we have indicated, a carbon atom is more than just the sum of its elementary constituent particles. It is the sum of these plus their interactions and thus qualitatively different from a simple collection. Similarly, a large group of interacting carbon atoms has different properties than would be expected from studying one isolated carbon atom. A man is more than the dollar's worth of chemicals he contains, and a society of man more than a collection of individuals. Such a view, quite distinct from the mechanical view of the universe, implies that an understanding of the observable universe requires study not only of the basic constituents of matter, but places a premium upon their interactions and upon the qualitatively differences resulting from the interactions. In short, it requires detailed study not only in each of the traditional disciplines but also in the border zones between them.

Thus although for practical reasons the number of specialized branches of science has multiplied in recent decades, the atomic theory bridges conceptual gaps that previously existed and provides an underlying unity among them all.

▲▲ 14.2 Elements and compounds. Dalton's atomic theory

The first quantitative atomic hypothesis evolved from the study of chemical processes. From a macroscopic viewpoint, chemical change involves a complete loss in the identity of the participating substances, whereas, in contrast, physical change involves only a change in form. Often the distinction is clearcut, just as often it is not. If a lump of coal is crushed, for instance, it remains coal; if burned, its carbon combines with oxygen to form carbon dioxide. The former change is clearly physical, the latter clearly chemical. But it is not immediately clear why we should designate the freezing of water to form ice as a change in form rather than identity, and thus as physical rather than chemical. Therefore, the above distinction between chemical and physical change leaves much to be desired. However, it will serve until we establish a few basic facts on atomic structure.

In his review of the philosophical systems of his predecessors, Aristotle remarks, almost casually, that "obviously" all had assumed that the total amount of matter in the universe is constant. From a quantitative viewpoint there is no reason why the assumption should be obvious a priori. In fact, its casual acceptance by Aristotle provides some measure of the differences in approach between Greek natural philosophy and quantitative physical science. The proposition was proved experimentally only as a result of the quantitative investigations of Antoine Lavoisier in the late eighteenth century. In a series of experiments he demonstrated that burning is a chemical reaction in which the substance involved combines with oxygen. By carefully collecting all the gaseous products evolved in such a reaction he showed that the total mass of the reacting substances remains constant regardless of changes in identity. Thus he established the principle known as the conservation of matter, a principle, that as special relativity shows, is equivalent to the conservation of energy.

Lavoisier's work also placed chemistry on a quantitative foundation. Thenceforth the masses of the participating substances were considered information pertinent to the investigation of chemical reactions. The next major step was made in the early nineteenth century when John Dalton showed that the *ratio* of the masses of the substances in any particular reaction is always the same.

Carbon monoxide or carbon dioxide, produced when carbon burns and thus combines with oxygen, have properties that are quite obviously different from a mixture obtained by merely placing pulverized coal in a flask of oxygen. The components of the mixture must react, in these cases burn, in order to produce forms of matter retaining neither the properties of carbon nor of oxygen. Hence carbon monoxide and carbon dioxide are chemical combinations or *compounds*, whereas pulverized coal and oxygen is a physical combination, or a *mixture*. Similarly, hydrogen and oxygen combined in a flask retain their separate properties, and thus constitute a mixture. But when elevated to a high temperature the separate gases combine with explosive violence to form a chemical compound, water, merging their identities into a new substance.

Investigations along these lines lead to the hypothesis that almost all forms of matter are compounds (or a mixture of compounds) of a reasonably small number of basic substances called *elements*. Of course the idea is a very old one as we have noted, and the definition in terms of ultimate substances purely empirical. In order to find the elements that constitute a compound, the compound must be broken down by chemical means into its components, the components themselves broken down, and the process continued ad infinitum until no means suffice for further analysis. The resulting set of substances are then, by definition, elements. In principle, all the elements could be found by analyzing all possible substances in this way. Fortunately there are easier procedures based upon the known internal structure of atoms (Chapter 19). But the first listing of the elements in the nineteenth century was based upon the empirical method, and established the fact that such well-known substances as hydrogen, carbon, nitrogen, oxygen, aluminum, copper, silver, lead, and gold are all elements. The total contemporary list has over one hundred entries, considerably more than the ancient four, but nonetheless small compared to the great number of compounds observed in nature.

Yet from another point of view the number of observed chemical combinations is surprisingly small. Carbon and oxygen do not form an infinite number of compounds but, in fact, only two, carbon monoxide and carbon dioxide. Similarly, hydrogen and oxygen form only water and hydrogen peroxide, and nitrogen and hydrogen only ammonia. A number of elements, helium and argon among them, form *no* compounds with other elements.* With the exception of carbon and hydrogen, most pairs of elements combine with each to form three or four compounds at most. The existence of compounds consisting of three or more elements increases the number of chemical combinations, but again a rule of simplicity is discernible. Any three or four elements combine into no more than two, three, or four compounds, if they combine at all. Once more the carbon-based compounds are exceptions, but the exceptions that make life possible (Chapter 19).

As a result of his research on the formation of compounds Dalton was able to state two empirical laws. The first is called the law of definite proportions:

• The mass ratios of the elements in a given compound is constant.

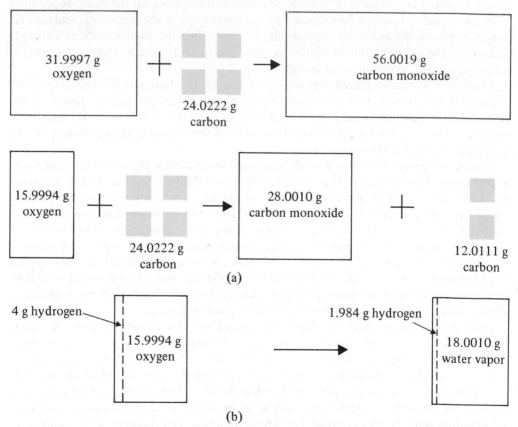

FIGURE 14.1 The law of definite proportions in the chemical reaction of (a) carbon and oxygen to form carbon monoxide, and (b) hydrogen and oxygen to form water vapor.

---

* This is only partially correct since at least one of the so-called inert gases, xenon, has been made to form compounds with other elements. However, the general tenor of these remarks is not altered thereby.

For instance, when a sample of carbon monoxide is decomposed and its constituents weighed, the ratio of the mass of the carbon to the mass of the oxygen is invariably 12.0111:15.9994. That is, 28.0105 g (or 28.0105 × 10^{-3} kg) of carbon monoxide contains 12.0111 g of carbon and 15.9994 g of oxygen. (Because matter is conserved the sum of the masses of the constitutents is equal to the mass of the compound.) Likewise, 56.0210 g of carbon monoxide contains 24.0222 g of carbon and 31.9997 g of oxygen. It follows that 24.0222 g of carbon can burn completely to form carbon monoxide only if at least 31.9997 g of oxygen is available. If, say, only 15.9994 g were available then only 12.0111 g of carbon could react. The excess would remain carbon (Figure 14.1a).

Similarly, by inducing a decomposition reaction it can be shown that 18.0154 g of water contains hydrogen and oxygen in the mass ratio 2.016:15.9994. Hence if 4 g of hydrogen and 15.9994 g of oxygen were placed in a flask and ignited, all the oxygen but only 2.016 g of the hydrogen would be consumed (Figure 14.1b).

Dalton's second empirical law is called the law of multiple proportions:

- Whenever two elements can combine to form more than one compound the ratio of the proportions in which the element appears in each compound is always the ratio of two integers.

Thus, for example, the hydrogen to oxygen mass ratio in water is invariably 2.016:15.9994, and the same ratio in hydrogen peroxide is 1.008:15.9994. Therefore, the ratio of the proportion of hydrogen in water to its proportion in hydrogen peroxide is 2:1, while the ratio of the proportions for oxygen is 1:1. Likewise, the carbon to oxygen ratio in carbon monoxide is 12.0111:15.9994 and 12.0111:31.9988 in carbon dioxide. Comparing the two compounds, carbon has a 1:1 ratio, oxygen a 1:2 ratio.

▲▲ 14.3 Atomic and molecular weights. Some basic types of chemical reactions

Both of Dalton's laws can be interpreted by means of a rudimentary model based on the hypothesis that a macroscopic sample of any element cannot be indefinitely subdivided, but consists rather of a great number of identical, microscopic, basic units called *atoms*. In Dalton's theory these atoms are themselves indivisible, but such an assumption is not required. It is only necessary to assume that the atoms maintain their integrity in all chemical processes. The atoms of each element are assumed to be identical. Those of different elements differ at least in their mass. Hence the number of types of atoms is equal to the number of elements.

The basic unit of each compound is assumed to be a *molecule* consisting of several atoms in combination. On this basis a chemical reaction is a process in which molecular structures are rearranged. The conservation of matter is assured by the assumption that such reactions only involve rearrangements. In contrast, classical *physical* processes involve no change in molecular structure.

Suppose the molecules of a compound consist of one atom each of element A and B of mass m_a and m_b, respectively. On the above assumptions the mass of each molecule is $m_a + m_b$, and the mass ratio of the atoms $m_a:m_b$. A total mass M_A of element A will consist of $n = M_A/m_A$ atoms; if n molecules $A + B$ are to be formed then n atoms of element B must also be available, and therefore, a mass $M = nM_B$ is required (Figure 14.2a). It follows that the ratio of the bulk masses is precisely the ratio of the atomic masses, i.e.

$$\frac{M_A}{M_B} = \frac{nM_A}{nM_B} = \frac{m_A}{m_B},$$

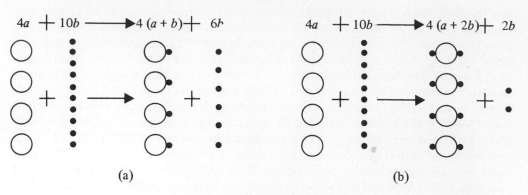

FIGURE 14.2 Explanation of the laws of (a) definite and (b) multiple proportions in terms of the Daltonian atomic hypothesis.

so that a definite *proportion* of the two elements is required regardless of the mass of the final compound.

Now suppose another compound exists whose molecules consist of one atom of A and two of B. If n atoms of A are available, clearly twice the number of atoms of B are required for complete reaction (Figure 14.2b). Therefore, the ratio of the mass of B is twice as great as in the former compound, in accord with the law of multiple proportions.

The two laws can, in fact, be used to establish the ratios of the masses of various atoms *provided* the molecular composition of the compounds they form can also be established. For instance, the carbon to oxygen ratio in carbon monoxide is 12.0111:15.9994. *If* a molecule of the compound consists of one atom of each type, then 12.0111 g of carbon contains exactly the same number of atoms as 15.9994 g of oxygen. Therefore, the ratio of the masses of the individual atoms must also be 12.0111:15.9994. Since the carbon to oxygen ratio in carbon *di*oxide is 12.0111:31.9988, a molecule of this compound contains twice the number of oxygen atoms as a molecule of carbon monoxide.

The *atomic weight* of an element, which we shall designate by the letter A, is a dimensionless number proportional to the mass of the corresponding atoms. As we shall discuss in detail later (Chapter 20), macroscopic samples of most elements contain atoms with two or more different masses, called isotopes. Since macroscopic quantities are always involved in chemical reaction studies, the chemical, definite proportion ratio obtained for two elements is actually the ratio of the averages of the two sets of isotopic masses. The unified atomic weight scale, established in 1961 by the International Union of Pure and Applied Physics, assigns the atomic weight A = 12.000 to the most abundant of the two stable isotopes of carbon.* The absolute mass of the corresponding atom can be measured by a method discussed in Chapter 20, and the average mass of both carbon isotopes in a macroscopic sample turns out to be 12.0111 times heavier. Therefore, the *chemically* defined atomic weight of carbon is 12.0111.

The law of definite proportions can now be used to assign chemical atomic weights to the other elements *provided* the number of atoms of each type in a given molecule can also be deduced. *If* carbon monoxide really contains one carbon and one oxygen atom per molecule, then since the elements enter the compound in the mass ratio

---

* Previously, atomic weights were specified by defining $A = 16.000$ as the *chemically* determined atomic weight of oxygen. The atomic weights on the oxygen scale can be found by multiplying atomic weights on the unified carbon scale by 1.00032.

12.0111 : 15.9994, oxygen has atomic weight A = 15.9994. In fact, detailed studies show that this assumed molecular structure for carbon monoxide is correct. The *molecular* weight of a compound is defined analogously to atomic weight as a number proportional to the mass of one of its molecules, and is likewise based upon the assignment of 12.000 as the atomic weight of the most abundant carbon isotope. Molecular weights are calculated simply by adding up the atomic weights of the elements in the compound. Thus carbon monoxide has molecular weight 12.0111 + 15.9994 = 28.0105, carbon dioxide 12.0111 + 2 × 15.9994 = 44.0099. Similarly, since chemical analysis shows that hydrogen has atomic weight A = 1.0080 and a more detailed analysis confirms the assumption that water molecules each contain one oxygen and two hydrogen atoms, the molecular weight of the compound is 2 × 1.0080 + 15.994 = 18.0154. Hydrogen peroxide, whose molecules consist of two hydrogen and two oxygen atoms, has molecular weight 2 × 1.0080 + 2 × 15.9994 − 34.0148.

The letters C, H, and O are used to denote the elements carbon, hydrogen, and oxygen, respectively. Compounds are designated by combining the symbols for the elements according to the assumed structure of their molecules. For instance the symbol for carbon monoxide, CO, implies that each molecule has one carbon and one oxygen atom; the corresponding symbols for carbon dioxide and water are CO_2 and H_2O, respectively.

TABLE 14.1   *Chemical Atomic Weights of Some Common Elements*

Element	Symbol	Atomic Weight*
Hydrogen	H	1.0080
Helium	He	4.0026
Lithium	Li	6.939
Carbon	C	12.0111
Nitrogen	N	14.0067
Oxygen	O	15.99994
Sodium	Na	22.9898
Aluminum	Al	26.9815
Chlorine	Cl	35.453
Iron	Fe	55.847
Copper	Cu	63.54
Silver	Ag	107.870
Tin	Sn	118.69
Gold	Au	196.967
Lead	Pb	207.19
Uranium	U	238.03

* Based on the uniform carbon standard. From *American Institute of Physics Handbook*, 2nd edition, Section 7, McGraw-Hill Book Co., Inc., New York, 1963, p. 9.

Table 14.1 contains a list of atomic weights of some common elements. All of the hundred-odd elements are given in Table 19.2. The mode of listing used, called the Periodic Table, is discussed in Chapter 19. Many of these atomic weights were first deduced from chemical reaction studies together with an assumed rule of simplicity. Other methods which literally involve counting individual atoms (see Section 20.2, for example) corroborate the chemical assignments, and are used to determine atomic weights of those elements that form no compounds. Hydrogen, with atomic weight 1.008, or roughly 1, is the lightest of all atoms, followed by helium with atomic weight roughly 4, then lithium with atomic weight roughly 7, etc.

The periodic listing raises a number of intriguing questions, not the least of which is why the elements have the particular atomic weights they have, why, for instance, hydrogen is 1.008 rather than simply 1, and why the weights approximately equal to 2 and 3 are missing completely. Granting the fact that nature has no reason to comply with aesthetics, the "irrationalities" are nonetheless somewhat unsettling and a spur to a deeper investigation.

The notation employed in the explicit description of chemical reactions is suggestive of the atomic hypothesis. A reaction in which the element X combines with the element Y to form the compound XY is written

$$X + Y \rightarrow XY, \tag{14.1a}$$

while the breakdown of the compound XY is

$$XY \rightarrow X + Y. \tag{14.1b}$$

A slightly more complicated reaction, the replacement of the element Y in a compound XY by the element Z with the subsequent liberation of Y becomes

$$Z + XY \rightarrow XZ + Y, \tag{14.1c}$$

and so on.

Since chemical reactions reflect molecular composition, a sufficient number of atoms of each type must be provided in any reaction equation. Thus, for instance, the equation

$$X + Y \rightarrow X_2 Y$$

violates the conservation of matter, since the formation of the molecule $X_2 Y$ requires twice as many atoms of type X as of type Y; rather the equation must be

$$2X + Y \rightarrow X_2 Y, \tag{14.2a}$$

implying that two atoms of X combine with one atom of Y to form one molecule of the compound $X_2 Y$. Similarly, the reaction leading to the formation of $X_2 Y_3$ is written

$$2X + 3Y \rightarrow X_2 Y_3. \tag{14.2b}$$

Such reaction equations are said to be *balanced*.

Free atoms of oxygen and hydrogen do not exist at room temperature; rather the basic unit of each gas is a diatomic molecule composed of two atoms in combination and symbolized as O_2 and H_2, respectively. Using chemical reaction notation the burning of carbon may then be written

$$C + O_2 \rightarrow CO_2 \tag{14.3a}$$

if carbon dioxide is the end product, or

$$2C + O_2 \rightarrow 2CO \tag{14.3b}$$

if carbon monoxide results, the latter equation implying that two carbon atoms must combine with one diatomic oxygen molecule to yield two carbon monoxide molecules. Similarly, the formation of water is symbolized as

$$2H_2 + O_2 \rightarrow 2H_2O, \tag{14.4a}$$

while its dissociation is

$$2H_2O \rightarrow 2H_2 + O_2. \qquad (14.4b)$$

Finally, a typical displacement reaction occurs with explosive violence when the element sodium (Na, from the Latin *natrium*) frees one of the hydrogen atoms in water and forms sodium hydroxide

$$2Na + 2H_2O \rightarrow 2NaOH + H_2. \qquad (14.5)$$

The use of these chemical equations simplifies the calculation of the quantities of matter involved in specific chemical reactions. Sodium, for instance, has atomic weight about 23. How much water is required to react with 23 g of the element according to Equation 14.5, and how much sodium hydroxide and hydrogen result from the reaction?

According to the equation two atoms of sodium react with two molecules of water to form two molecules of sodium hydroxide and one hydrogen molecule (molecular weight 2). Since water has a molecular weight roughly equal to 18, it follows that 18 g are required to react completely with the sodium. Similarly, sodium hydroxide has molecular weight $23 + 16 + 1 = 40$; therefore, 40 g of sodium hydroxide are produced, and as only one hydrogen molecule is produced for each two sodium hydroxide molecules, the final mass of hydrogen is 1 g.

The assumption that 23 g of sodium, 12 g of carbon, 16 g of oxygen, and 1 g of hydrogen all contain equal numbers of atoms is basic to the representation of chemical reactions even on Dalton's rudimentary atomic theory. Use of a unit of mass called the *mole* is convenient in chemistry. By definition, a mole of any substance contains the same number of atoms or molecules as a mole of any other. The mass of one *gram-mole* is obtained simply by writing the word *grams* after the weight of the substance, and the mass of one *kilogram-mole* by using the word *kilogram* rather than *gram*. Hence one kilogram-mole of hydrogen has mass 1.008 kg, one kilogram-mole of carbon 12.011 kg, etc. Similarly the mass of one kilogram-mole of water is about 18 kg, that of sodium hydroxide 40 kg. The number of atoms or molecules in a mole—known as *Avogadro's number*, N_0—turns out to be enormous!

$$N_0 = 6.025 \times 10^{26} \text{ atoms/kg-mole}. \qquad (14.6)$$

Since the mass of one mole of hydrogen is 1.008 kg it follows that the mass of a single hydrogen atom is very small, explicitly,

$$M_H = \frac{1.008}{N_0} = 1.66 \times 10^{-27} \text{ kg},$$

but nonetheless 1837 times the mass of an electron ($M_e = 9 \times 10^{-31}$ kg, Section 9.7).

◤◤ 14.4 The electrolysis of water. Charge structure of atoms and molecules

Although the assumptions of Dalton's atomic theory permit an interpretation of his empirical laws of chemical interactions, the insight they provide into the fundamental properties of atoms is at best rudimentary and leaves many questions unanswered. Why, for instance, do elements differ so much in their bulk properties? The two elements of smallest atomic weight, helium and hydrogen, are both gases, but while the latter readily reacts with other elements to form compounds, the former does not react at all. The next elements in order of atomic weight, lithium, beryllium, boron, and carbon, are solids, followed in order by nitrogen, oxygen, and fluorine, which are gases. Hydrogen and oxygen, both gases, combine to form a liquid, while solid carbon and gaseous oxygen combine to form gaseous carbon monoxide or carbon dioxide. A fully developed atomic theory should be able to interpret all these macroscopic differences in terms of the inter-actions of constituent atoms and molecules, and more basically, should be able to explain why the atoms interact at all.

Classical physics permits two possible types of interaction: gravitational and electro-magnetic. Because of their small masses, the former interaction between atoms is far too weak to explain chemical binding. On the other hand the latter alternative requires that atoms have a charge structure.

The modern concept of charge as a basic property of matter was noted briefly in Section 9.7. Perhaps the most direct evidence for the electromagnetic nature of atomic and molecular interactions comes from the electrolysis experiments, i.e., the electrolytic de-composition of liquid compounds. If, for instance, metallic electrodes are immersed in water and attached to the terminals of a storage battery, hydrogen is released at the negative electrode (cathode), oxygen at the positive (the anode).*

In terms of chemical notation, the reaction is just Equation 14.4b:

$$2H_2O \rightarrow 2H_2 + O_2.$$

S. Arrhenius explained electrolysis by assuming that Equation 14.4b summarizes a several-step process. Specifically he assumed that water molecules do not break up directly into neutral hydrogen and oxygen *atoms*, but rather into charged entities called *ions*, or atoms that have picked up or lost the one or more units of fundamental charge, *e*. Since hydrogen is released at the cathode then presumably, its ions are attracted toward that electrode and are positive (Figure 14.3). If each hydrogen ion has a single excess positive charge then, to conserve charge, each oxygen ion must have *two* excess negative charges. A singly ionized positive atom, *X*, is written X^+, a single ionized

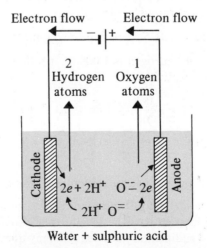

FIGURE 14.3   The electrolysis of water.

---

* A small amount of sulphuric acid must also be added to the water to initiate the reaction; its function does not change the basic point of the argument.

negative ion X^-. Therefore, the first step in the electrolysis reaction, Equation 14.4b, the initial breakdown of the neutral water molecules, is written

$$2H_2O \rightarrow 4H^+ + 2O^{--}, \tag{14.7a}$$

balancing both charge and mass. Since electrons (e^-) carry the current from storage battery to electrodes and back again, the hydrogen ions are neutralized by the addition of electrons at the cathode and become neutral atoms:

$$4H^+ + 4e^- \rightarrow 4H, \tag{14.7b}$$

which then combine to form hydrogen molecules:

$$4H \rightarrow 2H_2. \tag{14.7c}$$

Presumably, then, a hydrogen ion is a hydrogen atom from which an electron has been subtracted. It follows that an *oxygen* ion is an oxygen atom with two excess electrons which it gives up at the anode:

$$2O^{--} \rightarrow 2O + 4e^-. \tag{14.7d}$$

The four electrons supplied by the battery to neutralize the hydrogen ions are returned in the neutralization of the oxygen. Therefore, the net charge flowing out of the battery per unit time is balanced by the net charge flowing into it. Finally, the oxygen atoms combine to form a molecule:

$$2O \rightarrow O_2, \tag{14.7e}$$

and Equation 14.4b is complete.

Clearly this ionic dissociation reaction complicates the Daltonian model. Atoms can no longer be regarded as microscopic hard spheres, but rather as complexes of charged particles. Atoms of both hydrogen and oxygen, and presumably all other atoms as well, seem to consist of relatively heavy* positive cores to which one or more electrons are bound electrostatically. Apparently these atoms are also able to lose one or more of their electrons, or to gain one or more in addition, and thus become ions.

There is no reason why the charge structure of atoms should be pertinent only in electrolysis. Indeed, it provides a promising avenue of approach to the problem of molecular structure and therefore to the whole field of chemical reactions. Modern representations of hydrogen and oxygen atoms are shown in Figure 14.4. The hydrogen atom consists of a singly charged, positive core, or nucleus, about 10^{-15} m in diameter and one electron with an orbital diameter about 10^{-10} m centered at the nucleus. The oxygen atom has a nucleus with eight positive charges and sixteen times the mass of the hydrogen nucleus; the nucleus is a few times 10^{-15} m in diameter and is surrounded by eight electrons at diameters ranging from 10^{-10} to 10^{-11} m. Therefore, the diameters of these atoms are essentially the diameters of their outer orbits. This representation should not be taken too literally (see Chapters 17 and 19), but will serve for present purposes.

At distances that are large compared with their diameters, atoms appear to be neutral entities since at, say, 10^{-9} m the electric field due to an equal positive and negative charge 10^{-10} m apart should practically cancel. But if two or more atoms are very close together their charge structures should be important, and they should interact electromagnetically. The nucleus of one might be expected to attract the electrons of another, and vice versa, while the respective nuclei and electrons of each repelled each other. If,

---

* The mass of a hydrogen atom is 1837 times the mass of an electron.

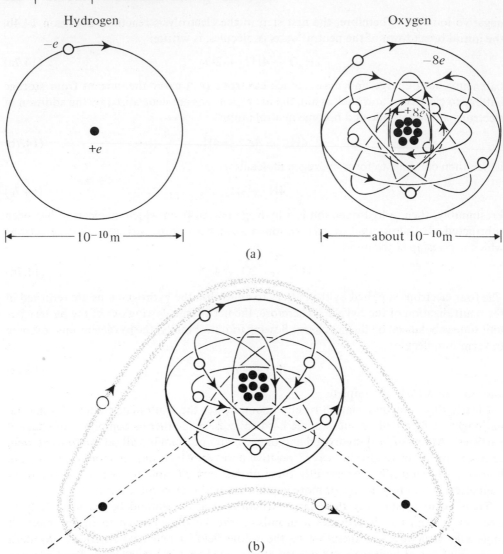

FIGURE 14.4 (a) Planetary model of a hydrogen and an oxygen atom. (b) When two hydrogen and one oxygen atom come close together they may share their outer electrons and form a water molecule. The bond angle of water (the angle between the dashed lines intersecting at the oxygen nucleus) is 105° (Chapter 19).

for instance, two hydrogen and one oxygen atom could be forced close enough together, the various attractions between their components might be greater than the various repulsions, binding the three into a water molecule. Since the net charge of all atoms is zero, it is clear that such a system can only be bound if spatially arranged so that its mutually attractive components are closer together than mutually repulsive components.

No system of classical charged particles can remain stable if only electrical forces are present. Therefore, the mechanism of chemical binding cannot be understood in detail in classical terms. Nevertheless, the basic idea implicit in this model is correct. On this model two or more atoms can form a stable molecule if and only if they can attain a favorable spatial orientation with respect to each other. It follows that a detailed investigation of the spatial structure of electron orbits should be pertinent to the study of chemical reactions.

The electromagnetic model of chemical reactions is appealing for a number of reasons, not the least one being the possibility of applying our knowledge of macroscopic electromagnetic phenomena on the atomic scale. In these terms, for instance, a combination reaction is interpreted as the forcing together of atoms until they can bind themselves together electrostatically, while a dissociation reaction must be understood in terms of some mechanism that ruptures the electrostatic bonds.

The electromagnetic model should apply to interactions between similar as well as dissimilar atoms and molecules. If a flask of oxygen is basically a collection of identical oxygen molecules then the macroscopic properties of the gas should follow from the interactions of these molecules.

Most elements and simple compounds can exist in the solid, the liquid, or the gaseous *states*. Because an element or a compound has the same basic chemical properties regardless of its state, changes in state are regarded as *physical* changes. On a microscopic basis they do not involve changes in molecular structure, but rather changes in the nature and strength of the interaction between their atoms or molecules. Therefore, the collective behavior of large systems of molecules may be studied by investigating the general properties of the states. The gaseous state is particularly simple in this regard as it may be represented by a microscopic model that does not involve detailed knowedge of internal molecular structure and can therefore concentrate upon the description of the total molecular system in terms of a minimal number of assumed molecular properties.

▲▲ 14.5 Pressure exerted by a gas. Boyle's law

The most general property of any gas is its ability to fill a volume. Since a gas in a container is only prevented from expanding further by the container, it follows that the gas exerts a force upon the confining walls. *Pressure* is defined as the *magnitude* of the force exerted upon a unit area of surface:

$$p = \frac{F}{A}. \tag{14.8}$$

According to Newton's third law the confining wall of a container exerts an equal and opposite pressure upon the gas. In the mks system pressure is measured in newtons per square meter, although other, more convenient units are also frequently used (see below).

A gas at rest relative to its container exerts pressure at all points within the container. This is clear from the following argument. Suppose a small, flat disk of area A were suspended in a container of gas. Since the gas is in equilibrium relative to the container the disk also remains at rest. Therefore, the force and therefore also the pressure on both its sides must be equal. In particular, the pressure on each of the container walls is the same. Hence the magnitude of the *force* on a particular wall is proportional to its surface area.

Boyle's law is an empirical relation between the pressure exerted by (and therefore upon) a gas and the volume to which it is confined. It states that the pressure exerted by a gas is inversely proportional to the volume it occupies *provided* both its total mass, M, and temperature, T, remain constant:

$$pV = C \quad \text{if } T = \text{const}, \quad M = \text{const}, \tag{14.9a}$$

where C is a constant whose value depends on the molecular weight, total mass, and temperature of the gas. The temperature involved in Boyle's law may be defined, temporarily, simply as a quantity measured with a thermometer. Volume is measured in cubic meters, though the liter, 10^{-3} cu m, is a smaller, more convenient unit. It is worth noting that one liter is approximately equal to one quart.

If p_0 and V_0 are, respectively, an arbitrary standard pressure and standard volume, and p and V another possible pressure, volume combination, Equation 14.9a may be rewritten as

$$pV = p_0 V_0 \qquad \text{if } T = \text{const}, \qquad M = \text{const.} \tag{14.9b}$$

Therefore, a sample of gas, if confined to a one-liter volume, exerts twice the pressure it would exert if confined to a two-liter volume at the same temperature. Conversely, twice the pressure is required to confine it in the smaller volume. In Figure 14.5a, a piston is used to reduce the volume of a container to half its volume. Therefore, the pressure on the piston has doubled, and, as its surface area is constant, it must exert twice as much force upon the gas.

The force applied to the gas in Figure 14.5b is due to the weight of the piston alone. Therefore, the pressure and volume of the gas are constant and completely specified by Boyle's law. The equilibrium between piston and gas serves as a simple representation of atmospheric pressure. An atmospheric pressure roughly equal to 14.7 lb/sq in. (1.0324×10^5 N/sq m) at sea level is caused by the compression of the oxygen and nitrogen at the earth's surface by the weight of these gases at higher altitudes. These layers act analogously to the piston in Figure 14.5b, compressing the gas at the surface until its pressure is sufficient to balance their weight. Counter pressure exerted by the confined gas equally on all surfaces prevents the complete collapse of the atmosphere.

Since the weight of the atmospheric "piston" decreases with increasing altitudes the compression of a given mass, and therefore, the atmospheric pressure, also decreases with

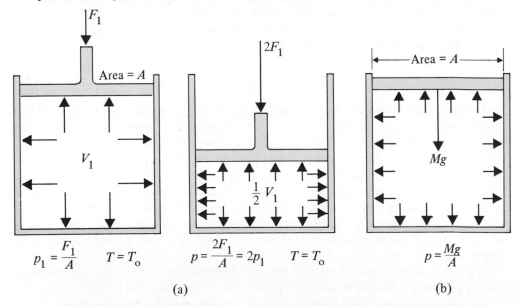

FIGURE 14.5 (a) Boyle's law applied to a constant-temperature gas compressed by an external force applied to a piston. (b) A gas in equilibrium with a piston that exerts a force Mg due to its weight only.

altitude. Changing conditions in the upper atmosphere, analogous to a change in the weight of the "piston," cause fluctuations in terrestrial pressures. Therefore, measurements of these changes provide an indication in the behavior of the upper atmosphere.

Pressures are very often measured in terms of *atmospheres*, one atmosphere being equal to 1.0325×10^5 N/sq m, or normal sea level pressure.

▲▲ 14.6 Molecular interpretation of Boyle's law

A simple microscopic interpretation of Boyle's law assumes that the molecules of a gas are in constant, random motion, and that the average distance between any two of them is much greater than their diameters. If this is so then two molecules "see" each other as electrically neutral entities and can be regarded as hard, noninteracting spheres.

In the absence of interactions each molecule must proceed along a straight line path with constant velocity. If there is no correlation between the velocity vectors of the molecules, the system will tend to disperse, or expand indefinitely. However, molecules will "bounce" from, and thus exert a force upon, an intervening wall. Since there are more than 10^{22} molecules in a liter of gas at atmospheric pressure each small area of wall surface will be peppered many times a second by these microscopic forces and a continuous, macroscopic force will be observed. If compressed, the number of molecules per unit volume increases. Therefore, the collision frequency at the walls, and as a result the macroscopic pressure, must also increase.

We can work out a few quantitative details of the model with little difficulty. For mathematical simplicity, let the gas be confined to a rectangular volume with sides of length X, Y, Z, parallel, respectively, to the x-, y-, and z-axes of some coordinate system (Figure 14.6a). Let each molecule have mass m, and assume that the container walls are completely rigid. Then if a molecule collides with a wall its direction will be reversed, but, by the conservation of energy, the magnitude of its velocity will remain unaltered.

Consider the collision of a molecule with a wall perpendicular to the x-axis of the coordinate system (Figure 14.6b). If its velocity components before collision are v_x, v_y, and v_z, then after collision (as only its direction is reversed) its velocity components will be $- v_x$, v_y, and v_z. Therefore, its momentum change is in the x-direction and of magnitude

$$\Delta p = m[v_x - (-v_x)] = 2mv_x. \tag{14.10a}$$

After "bouncing" off the wall the molecule travels with velocity components $- v_x$, v_y, v_z until it encounters the opposite wall, again reverses the x-component of its velocity and travels back again to the first wall with the same components it had prior to its previous encounter. Since the length of the box in the x-direction is X, the time taken for a round trip from one wall is

$$\Delta t = \frac{2X}{v_x}. \tag{14.10b}$$

Applying Newton's second law, the magnitude of the *average* force exerted on the wall by the molecule in time Δt is

$$F_x = \frac{\Delta p}{\Delta t} = \frac{2mv_x}{\Delta t}.$$

Using Equation 14.10b,

$$F_x = \frac{mv_x^2}{X}, \tag{14.10c}$$

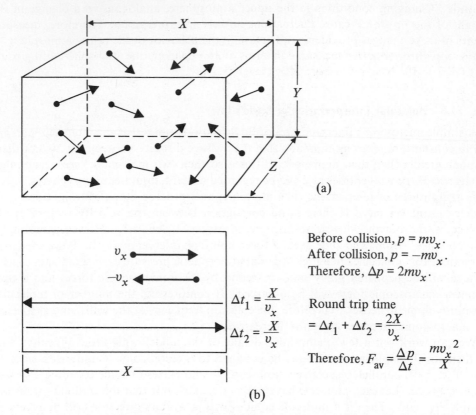

FIGURE 14.6 (a) Hard sphere molecular model of a gas. (b) Derivation of the average force exerted by one molecule on a wall perpendicular to X.

which shows that the average force exerted by each molecule is constant *provided* the velocity of each remains constant.

The total macroscopic force on the wall is equal to the sum of the forces exerted by each molecule. If there are N molecules in the box each one should have an x-component of velocity even though it may be zero in some cases. Therefore, if the x-component of molecule 1 is v_{1x}, of molecule 2 is v_{2x}, etc., the total force on the wall is

$$F_{Tx} = \frac{m}{X}(v_{1x}^2 + v_{2x}^2 + v_{3x}^2 + \cdots + v_{nx}^2).$$ (14.11a)

By definition the mean square x-component of velocity, $\bar{v}_x^2$ is

$$\bar{v}_x^2 = \frac{v_{1x}^2 + v_{2x}^2 + v_{3x}^2 + \cdots + v_{nx}^2}{N}.$$ (14.11b)

Substituting into Equation 14.11a,

$$F_{Tx} = \frac{Nm\bar{v}_x^2}{X}.$$ (14.11c)

By definition (Equation 14.8) the pressure on the wall is the force, F_T, divided by the area of the wall, YZ. Therefore,

$$p = \frac{F_T}{YZ} = \frac{Nm\bar{v}_x^2}{XYZ},$$ (14.12a)

or since the volume of the box $V = XYZ$,

$$pV = Nm\bar{v}_x^2. \tag{14.12b}$$

The product of the macroscopic pressure exerted by the gas on its confining volume is constant *if* the average x-component of molecular velocity is constant. Therefore, in terms of the molecular model the quantity $Nm\bar{v}_x^2$ is to be identified with the constant C in Equation 14.9a. Since the type of gas confined in our box is characterized by the masses of its molecules, m, and since the total mass of the confined gas is equal to the product Nm, then the pressure exerted by a gas confined to a specific volume depends both upon the type and the mass of the gas considered, in accord with Boyle's law. But the law also requires that the yet to be defined quantity called temperature must remain constant. Examining Equation 14.12b we conclude that temperature must be connected with mean molecular velocities.

Before seeking a quantitative definition of temperature it is useful to write Equation 14.12b in terms of total velocity rather than one particular component. As before, let molecule 1 have components v_{1x}, v_{1y}, v_{1z}, molecule 2 components v_{2x}, v_{2y}, v_{2z}, etc. According to the usual vector addition rule these components are related to the total velocities, v_1, v_2, etc., by

$$v_1^2 = v_{1x}^2 + v_{1y}^2 + v_{1z}^2,$$
$$v_2^2 = v_{2x}^2 + v_{2y}^2 + v_{2z}^2,$$
$$\vdots \qquad\qquad \vdots \quad . \tag{14.13a}$$

Adding these equations for all the molecules:

$$\text{Sum } (v^2) = \text{Sum } (v_x^2) + \text{Sum } (v_y^2) + \text{Sum } (_z^2),$$

and defining mean square velocities $\bar{v}_x^2$, $\bar{v}_y^2$, $\bar{v}_z^2$ in analogy with Equation 14.11b:

$$N\bar{v}^2 = N(\bar{v}_x^2 + \bar{v}_y^2 + \bar{v}_z^2),$$

or

$$\bar{v}^2 = \bar{v}_x^2 + \bar{v}_y^2 + \bar{v}_z^2, \tag{14.13b}$$

the sum of the mean squares of the three components of the molecular system is equal to the mean square total velocity. If there are many molecules, each moving at random, there is no reason to believe the average component in one direction is different than in any other. Therefore, we assume

$$\bar{v}_x^2 = \bar{v}_y^2 = \bar{v}_z^2, \tag{14.14a}$$

and Equation 14.13b yields

$$\bar{v}_x^2 = \tfrac{1}{3}\bar{v}^2. \tag{14.14b}$$

Substituting in Equation 14.12b we have

$$pV = \tfrac{1}{3}Nm\bar{v}^2, \tag{14.15a}$$

an equation that relates the macroscopic pressure and volume of a gas to their number, mass, and mean velocity. Since the mean kinetic energy of the gas molecules is $\tfrac{1}{2}m\bar{v}^2$, Equation 14.15a may also be written as

$$pV = \tfrac{2}{3}N\overline{KE}, \tag{14.15b}$$

a form which is highly suggestive since it implies that the energy conservation principle might be applicable to the study of the internal properties of gases.

▲▲ 14.7 Microscopic and macroscopic meaning of temperature

It is convenient to define a quantity T that will serve as a macroscopic measure of the mean square molecular velocity, $\bar{v}^2$:

$$kT = \tfrac{1}{3}m\bar{v}^2, \tag{14.16a}$$

with k a constant called the Boltzmann constant,* whose value depends upon the units (as yet unassigned) of T. Written in terms of mean kinetic energy the quantity is

$$kT = \tfrac{2}{3}\overline{KE}. \tag{14.16b}$$

The above defined quantity should be regarded in the first instance as no more than a convenient macroscopic measure of the mean molecular kinetic energy of the gas molecules. However, we can show that it may also be interpreted as its temperature. As a first step let us combine the defining Equation 14.16b, with our derived equation, Equation 14.15b:

$$pV = NkT. \tag{14.17a}$$

The number of molecules, N, in this equation is equal to nN_0, where n is the number of kilogram-moles of gas confined to the volume, and N_0 is Avogadro's number (Equation 14.6). Making this substitution in Equation 14.17a,

$$pV = n(kN_0)T.$$

Defining a new constant R, the universal gas constant,

$$R = kN_0, \tag{14.17b}$$

we can also write

$$pV = nRT. \tag{14.17c}$$

Equations 14.17 imply that the only difference between gases is a difference in their molecular weights. This is clearly a gross oversimplification, but follows inevitably from the fact that mass is the only property we have specifically attributed to the molecules. In consequence, a kilogram-mole of any gas (containing, by definition, 6×10^{26} molecules) at a given temperature and pressure must always occupy the same volume. More generally, if three of the four variables of Equations 14.17 are known (i.e., pressure, volume, mass in kilogram-moles, and temperature) the fourth is immediately determined.

These statements rest however upon the validity of the microscopic model. Therefore, if a macroscopic means of measuring the gas temperature T can be devised, observational tests of Equations 14.17 provide a means to investigate the validity of the model.

The usual method of defining temperature is completely operational. It is a quantity measured with a thermometer. To find a suitable thermometer, let us *assume* that:

1. The freezing of pure water at a pressure of one atmosphere (or the melting of pure ice) in equilibrium with water-saturated air always occurs at a constant temperature;

---

* Named for the nineteenth-century German physicist Ludwig Boltzmann.

2. The boiling of pure water in equilibrium with water-saturated air at one atmosphere pressure always occurs at a constant temperature.

Suppose a one-liter container of oxygen, a one-liter container of hydrogen, and a one-liter container of helium are each placed on a large block of melting ice and the gas in each slowly bled off until the pressures exerted by the gas in each container are equal (Figure 14.7a). By definition, each gas is then at the same ice-defined temperature. Measurement shows that their respective masses have the same ratio as their molecular weights. Therefore, each one of the equal volumes contains the same fraction of a kilogram-mole, and the gas temperature T, defined by Equation 14.16b, is equivalent to the ice temperature.

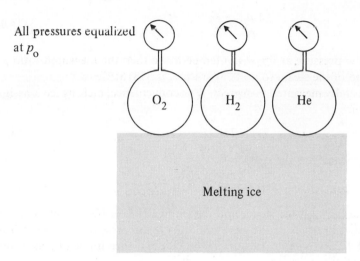

All pressures equalized at p_o

O$_2$ H$_2$ He

Melting ice

$T_o = 273.16\,°K$
by definition

(a)

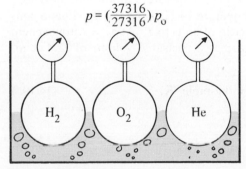

$p = \left(\dfrac{37316}{27316}\right) p_o$

H$_2$ O$_2$ He

Pure boiling water

$$T = T_o\left(\dfrac{p}{p_o}\right) = 373.16\,°K$$

(b)

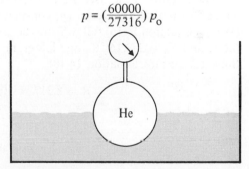

$p = \left(\dfrac{60000}{27316}\right) p_o$

He

Hot liquid

Therefore, $T = 600.00\,°K$

(c)

FIGURE 14.7 (a and b) Calibration of an oxygen, a hydrogen, and a helium gas thermometer in terms of ice temperature (defined as 273.16 °K) and boiling-water temperature. (c) Use of one of the calibrated thermometers (say helium) to measure a temperature of 600 °K.

When the three flasks are immersed in boiling water each exerts a pressure 37316/27316 times the pressure it exerts at the ice temperature (Figure 14.7b). Therefore, gas temperature and steam temperature are also equivalent, and Equation 14.17c is a valid description of the three gases at both temperatures.

Let T_0 be the temperature of melting ice at sea level and p_0 the pressure exerted by the gas in a sealed container with some standard volume. According to Equation 14.17c,

$$p_0 V = nRT_0.$$

If the gas exerts some other pressure p, then its temperature is defined by Equations 14.17. Since mass, n, and volume, V, remain constant, the ratio of the two temperatures is equal to the ratio of the two measured pressures:

$$\frac{p}{p_0} = \frac{T}{T_0}. \tag{14.18a}$$

In particular, if p is the pressure at the *steam* temperature then the measured ratio p/p_0, and therefore, the ratio of the steam to ice temperature, is 37316:27316.

Temperatures are usually measured in *degrees*. For convenience, melting ice is assigned the arbitary temperature

$$T_0 = 273.16°. \tag{14.18b}$$

It follows that boiling water has the temperature

$$T = 373.16°, \tag{14.18c}$$

and that the difference between the steam and ice temperature is 100°. Any other temperature may be defined in terms of the gas standard. If the pressure of the gas in our thermometer is 60000/27316 times its pressure at the ice point then it must be recording a temperature equal to 600° (Figure 14.7c).

Temperatures based on Equations 14.18 are called *absolute* or Kelvin* temperatures, and the notation $T°K$ used as an abbreviation for "temperature in absolute degrees." Values for both the universal gas constant R (Equation 14.17b) and the Boltzmann constant k (Equation 14.16) follow from the assignment of units to T. At $p_0 = 1$ atmosphere (atm) and $T_0 = 273.16°K$, one kilogram of gas has a measured volume of 22.4 cu m. Substituting into Equation 14.18c,

$$R = 8.317 \times 10^3 \text{ N-m/kg-mole }°K, \tag{14.19a}$$

whereas

$$k = \frac{R}{N_0} = 1.381 \times 10^{-23} \text{ J/}°K. \tag{14.19b}$$

It is useful to note (Equation 14.17c) that 22.4 liters of gas at a pressure $p_0 = 1$ atm and a temperature $T_0 = 273.16°K$, the so-called standard temperature and pressure, has a mass of 10^{-3} moles and contains 6×10^{23} molecules. One liter at these conditions has mass 4.46×10^{-5} kg-moles, and contains roughly 3×10^{22} molecules.

In many applications the direct use of Equation 14.17c is cumbersome and unnecessary. A more suitable form for such purposes can be easily obtained. If p_1, V_1, n_1, and T_1 are

---

*Named for the nineteenth-century British physicist, Lord Kelvin.

the pressure, volume, mass (in kg-moles), and absolute temperature of a gas, and p_2, V_2, n_2, T_2 the same quantities under different conditions, then

$$p_1 V_1 = n_1 R T_1,$$

and

$$p_2 V_2 = n_1 R T_1,$$

Therefore,

$$\frac{p_1 V_1}{p_2 V_2} = \frac{n_1 T_1}{n_2 T_2}, \tag{14.20}$$

If seven of the eight variables in Equation 14.20 are known, the unknown variable follows immediately. Since the proportion does not involve an absolute constant it may be used with "inconsistent" units such as atmospheres or liters, whereas use of Equation 14.17c with the value of R noted above (Equation 14.18a) requires conversion of all quantities to consistent mks units. Naturally Equation 14.20 requires that p_1 and p_2 and V_1 and V_2 be expressed in the same units.

The *centigrade* temperature scale defines the temperature of ice as 0 °C, the temperature of boiling water as 100 °C, and derives its name from the fact that there are 100 degrees between these two points. Conversion between the absolute and Centigrade scale is simple (see Equations 14.18a and 14.18b):

$$t \,°\text{C} = T \,°\text{K} - 273.16. \tag{14.21}$$

It is often more convenient to express temperature in Centigrade than in absolute degrees, but Centigrade temperatures do not have the fundamental interpretation implied by Equation 14.16 nor can they be used directly in Equations 14.17. Therefore, the capital T is usually reserved for the absolute scale.

It is also possible to use gas thermometers to define other types of thermometers. For example, the height of a mercury column in a capillary tube increases with increasing gas temperature, and therefore can itself be used to measure temperatures. Similarly the electric current that flows in a length of platinum wire connected to a standard storage battery increases with the gas temperature of the wire, suggesting that a platinum wire thermometer can be devised. These and other thermometers are simpler to use than gas thermometers, but must be regarded as secondary standards. Of course they are only useful over a limited temperature range. A mercury thermometer will not function at temperatures above the boiling point of mercury nor below its freezing point. A platinum thermometer will not remain intact above the melting point of platinum.

We may calculate the mean kinetic energy of a gas molecule at any given temperature from Equation 14.16b and the numerical value of the Boltzmann constant, k (Equation 14.19b). At 300 °K, or 27 °C, a value usually taken as room temperature since it is about 80 °Fahrenheit, we have

$$kT = 1.381 \times 10^{-23} \times 3 \times 10^2 = 4.14 \times 10^{-21} \text{ J}.$$

Therefore, the molecule has mean kinetic energy $\frac{3}{2}kT = 6.21 \times 10^{-21}$ J (Equation 14.16b), and according to our model the total internal kinetic energy of one kilogram-mole of any gas at 300° is

$$6 \times 10^{26} \times 6.21 \times 10^{-21} = 3.7 \times 10^5 \text{ J}.$$

Because the mean kinetic energy of a molecule is so small when expressed in joules it is often more convenient to use the electron volt. According to Equation 10.4,

$$1 \text{ eV} = 1.6 \times 10^{-19} \text{ J}.$$

Therefore, at 300 °K,

$$kT = \frac{4.14 \times 10^{-21}}{1.6 \times 10^{-19}} = 0.026 \text{ eV},$$

so that the mean molecular kinetic energy at room temperature, $\frac{3}{2}kT$, is roughly $\frac{1}{25}$ eV.

▲▲ 14.8 Defects in the simple molecular gas model. A statistical gas model

We have seen that the temperature defined in terms of the microscopic gas model can be identified with the commonly defined macroscopic concept, and have also noted that Equations 14.17 are valid over the temperature range from melting ice to boiling water. Equation 14.17c is called the *ideal gas law*, and any gas described by the law is an *ideal gas*. In Chapter 15 we shall discuss deviations from Equations 14.17 and show that these occur, as expected, under conditions where the assumptions about a simple molecular model are no longer valid.

However, a more immediate and fundamental defect is the failure of the model to provide a mechanism for temperature change even under conditions for which the macroscopic ideal gas law is completely valid. If a liter of oxygen at 0 °C and one atmosphere pressure is combined with an equivalent volume at 100 °C, the mixture eventually attains an intermediate temperature. According to Equation 14.16b the mean kinetic energy of the molecules that comprised the first volume must have increased on mixing, and the molecules of the second must have decreased. This implies an interaction between the two sets and we conclude that even the molecules of a single isolated gas interact with each other.

In fact, this is entirely reasonable, for if the molecules of a gas are in random motion there must inevitably be collisions between them. However, it is contrary to one of the basic assumptions of Section 14.6. At any instant molecules are moving in all possible directions with all conceivable velocities. If two of them collide, both the magnitudes and directions of their respective velocities will change so that at a later time the directions and velocities of all the molecules will be completely different from what they were at the earlier time.

At first sight it appears very unlikely that this chaotic system should lead to the simple observed macroscopic behavior described by Equations 14.17, but in fact this is precisely the observed outcome. If all velocity vectors were specified at a given instant, and if the interactions between the molecules were completely known, then, *in principle*, Newtonian methods could be used to calculate the entire future course of the system. But as there are more than 10^{22} molecules in a liter of gas at standard temperature and pressure, it is obvious that such a program could never be carried out.

The seeming hopelessness of the situation, however, stimulates a new method of attack. Since there *are* so many molecules in even a small volume, then if at time t_1 a certain molecule has a particular velocity vector, we expect that at any later time t_2 *another* molecule should have the same vector—simply because there are so many molecules (Figure 14.8)! If the molecules are regarded as indistinguishable there should be no difference between a "snapshot" taken at t_1 and one taken at t_2. A *moving* picture of the system would show a tremendous chaos of molecules moving in all directions, colliding

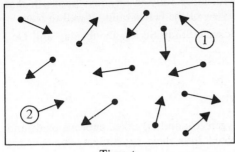
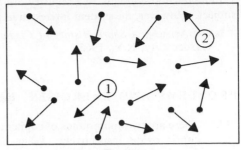

Time t_1 Time t_2

FIGURE 14.8   Justification of the statistical gas model. Even though the path of each individual molecule must be regarded as unpredictable, a snapshot of the entire array of molecules at time t_1 would look very much the same as another taken at a later time. Although there is no way to predict where molecule 1 will be at time t_2, since there are so many molecules it is reasonable to assume that at t_2 some other molecule (2 in the sketch) will have the same spatial coordinates and the same velocity vector that molecule 1 had at time t_1.

and changing their vectors. Little sense could be made of the motion of any *one* of them. But concentration of the *system* rather than the *individuals* leads to the conclusion that very little really happens. For each molecule knocked out of a particular path another will almost certainly be knocked in.

Therefore, the revised ideal gas model assumes that (1) the molecules in random motion make random collisions, that (2) their mean separation is sufficient to permit a mean free travel length between collisions equal to several times their mean diameters, and (3) that they interact only when they collide. Finally, we assume that momentum and energy are conserved in each collision so that the total momentum and energy of the system and the average momentum and energy per molecule remains constant as long as the system is isolated.

Since the motion of each molecule is completely random it is quite impossible to say what any particular one is doing at any time. The only possible course is to make an informed guess about *how many* molecules have a particular velocity at a particular time. Because there are so many molecules these informed guesses turn out to be very good indeed. Therefore, our new method of attack will involve the mathematics of probability.

SUGGESTIONS FOR FURTHER READING ▲▲▲

Probably the best treatments of the evolution of classical atomic theory in any basic physics text are:

> ARNOLD B. ARONS, *Development of Concepts of Physics*, Addison-Wesley Publishing Co., Inc., Reading, Mass., 1965, Chapters 28 and 29.

> GERALD HOLTON AND DUANE H. D. ROLLER, *Foundations of Modern Physical Science*, Addison-Wesley Publishing Co., Inc., Reading, Mass., 1958, Chapters 21–25.

Most basic physics texts (including the two cited above) treat the subject of ideal gases. For example:

> K. R. ATKINS, *Physics*, John Wiley and Sons, Inc., New York, 1965, Chapter 11.

> JAY OREAR, *Fundamental Physics*, John Wiley and Sons, Inc., New York, 1961, Chapter 6.

Fundamental concepts of chemistry are dealt with more fully in any text books in that subject. However, the student interested in an overview of the field would do well to read:

ISAAC ASIMOV, *A Short History of Chemistry*, Science Study Series, Doubleday and Co., Garden City, N.Y., 1965.

PROBLEMS AND EXERCISES ▲▲▲

14.1. There are two compounds of copper and oxygen (Cu and O) called cuprous oxide and cupric oxide, respectively. When decomposed into their constituent elements the former compound is found to yield twice the amount of copper for the same mass of oxygen as the latter.

(a) If the basic molecule of each compound contains one oxygen atom what is the smallest number of copper atoms each can contain?
(b) Assuming the simple assignments of part a are valid what are the standard chemical formulas for the two compounds?
(c) Again assuming the validity of your answer to part a write the two decomposition reaction equations using standard chemical notation.

14.2. The decomposition of 0.318 kg of cupric oxide yields 0.064 kg of oxygen. Assuming the validity of your answers to Problem 14.1 determine the approximate atomic weight of copper. (Take the atomic weight of oxygen as 16.)

14.3. When samples of ferrous oxide and ferric oxide containing the same masses of oxygen are decomposed, the former compound yields 1.5 times as much iron (Fe) as the latter. If it is known that a molecule of ferrous oxide contains one oxygen atom:

(a) What is the minimum possible number of iron atoms in the molecules of each compound?
(b) Assuming the designations from part a are correct write the standard chemical formulas for the two compounds.
(c) Again assuming the validity of part a write the two decomposition reaction equations using standard chemical notation.

14.4. The decomposition of 0.320 kg of ferric oxide yields 0.096 kg of oxygen. Assuming your answers to Problem 14.3 are correct determine the approximate atomic weight of iron. (Take the atomic weight of oxygen as 16.)

14.5. The decomposition of 1.823 kg of hydrochloric acid (HCl) yields 0.0504 of diatomic hydrogen and x kg of diatomic chlorine gas.

(a) Determine x.
(b) Determine the approximate atomic weight of chlorine (take the atomic weight of hydrogen as 1.008).
(c) Write a correctly balanced equation for the decomposition reaction using standard chemical notation.

14.6. Zinc (Zn) reacts with hydrochloric acid (HCl) in a replacement reaction to yield zinc chloride ($ZnCl_2$) and hydrogen gas.

(a) Write a correctly balanced equation describing the reaction.
(b) If 0.131 kg of zinc is consumed in a reaction that yields 0.0040 kg of hydrogen, what is the atomic weight of zinc? (Take the atomic weight of hydrogen as 1.01.)

14.7. Methane (CH_4), an organic gas, burned at a high temperature yields water vapor and carbon dioxide.

(a) Write a correctly balanced equation for the reaction.

(b) Approximately how much water vapor and how much cabon dioxide are produced when 0.2 kg of methane burns completely?

(c) How much oxygen is consumed in the reaction?

14.8. Assuming the ionic dissociation mechanism for electrolysis given in the text:

(a) How many electrons are supplied by the source of EMF for each hydrogen ion (H^+) neutralized at the cathode? How many are returned for each oxygen ion (O^{--}) neutralized at the anode?

(b) What charge flows around the circuit each time an oxygen and two hydrogen molecules are produced according to the series of steps summarized by

$$2H_2O \rightarrow 2H_2 + O_2?$$

(c) What mass of water is decomposed per second if the current from the source of EMF is 10^{-3} A?

14.9. A cylindrical tank 2 m high with a circular, 0.5 m radius cross section contains hydrogen at a pressure of 5 atm.

(a) What total force (in newtons) does the gas exert on the lid of the tank?

(b) If all of the hydrogen in the tank were transferred to another cylindrical tank with the same cross section but 1.5 m high what would its pressure be, assuming its temperature remained constant?

14.10. A cyclindrical tank contains 2 cu m of helium at a pressure of 2 atm and a temperature equal to 300 °K. How does the pressure change if each of the following changes are made one at a time with all other conditions remaining as stated above:

(a) The volume is reduced to 0.5 cu m.

(b) The temperature is increased to 500 °K.

(c) The helium is replaced by an equal mass of nitrogen (normal state N_2).

(d) The helium atoms are replaced by the same *number* of diatomic nitrogen molecules.

14.11. The volume of a tank containing helium is reduced by a factor of 2.5. What accompanying temperature change will:

(a) Restore the original pressure in the tank?

(b) Produce twice the original pressure?

14.12. The accompanying sketch illustrates the measurement of atmospheric pressure with a manometer. A long glass tube with a uniform cross section of area A and closed at one end, is filled with mercury (or some other liquid) then erected vertically in a pan containing the same liquid with the open end of the tube beneath the surface. The level in the tube drops until the force exerted on the layer of liquid at the bottom of the tube by the column above it is equal to the force exerted by the atmosphere on the liquid in the pan.

(a) Write an expression giving the magnitude of the force exerted by the liquid column upon an area A at the surface of the open pan in terms of the density of the liquid, ρ, the height of the liquid in the tube, h, the area, A, and the acceleration due to gravity, g.

(b) Write an expression for the force exerted by the atmosphere on an area A at the liquid surface, letting p be the pressure of the atmosphere.

(c) Obtain an expression giving p, the atmospheric pressure at the liquid surface, as a function of ρ, g, and h by combining your answers to parts a and b.

(d) Atmospheric pressure at sea level is about 1.03×10^5 N/m², the density of mercury is 1.36×10^4 kg/m³. Show that the height of the mercury in a manometer column under these conditions is about 0.76 m.

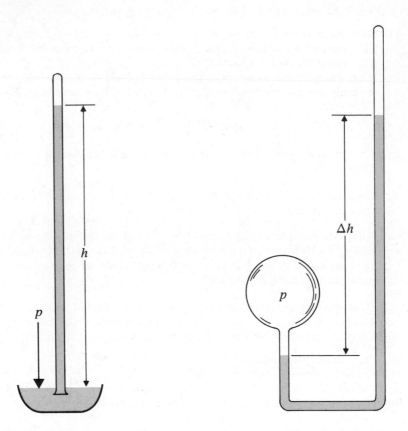

14.13. The manometer principle (Problem 14.12) can be easily adapted to the measurement of a pressure whose origin is not atmospheric. In the accompanying sketch a vessel containing gas at an unknown pressure p communicates with the open end of a long, bent tube of uniform cross section which contains mercury. The space above the mercury at the closed end of the tube is evacuated.

(a) Derive an expression for the pressure p in terms of the density of mercury, ρ (1.36×10^4 kg/m³), the height of the liquid column, Δh, and the acceleration due to gravity, g.

(b) If $\Delta h = 0.2$ m, what is the pressure in the closed vessel in N/m³?

14.14. How many air molecules are there in a one-cubic-meter volume at 27 °C:

(a) At atmospheric pressure.

(b) If the pressure is equivalent to 10^{-12} m of mercury, i.e., equal to the residual pressure of the best attainable vacuums. (Atmospheric pressure is equivalent to 0.76 m of mercury. See Problem 14.12.)

14.15. An ideal gas is confined to a rectangular container. How does its pressure and temperature vary if:

(a) The mean velocity of its molecules is doubled?

(b) The number of molecules is doubled but their mean velocity held constant?

(c) The length of the tank is doubled but the other two dimensions and the mean velocity of the molecules held constant?

14.16. A one-cubic-meter vessel contains 0.028 kg of nitrogen at a temperature equal to 27 °K. What is its pressure?

14.17. A one-cubic-meter vessel contains 50 atm of methane (CH_4) at 27 °C. What is the mass of the gas?

14.18. Calculate the mean kinetic energy in electron volts, of a helium atom at:

(a) The liquefaction temperature of oxygen (80 °K). (The liquefaction temperature of hydrogen is 20 °K, of helium 4 °K.)

(b) The boiling point of water.

(c) The surface of the sun (6000 °K).

(d) The center of the sun (2×10^7 °K).

14.19. What are the mean velocities of (a) a helium atom, and (b) an argon atom (atomic weight 40) at the last three temperatures of Problem 14.18?

Classical probability and statistics

15

▲▲ 15.1 Determinism in classical physics

Both Newtonian dynamics and Maxwell's electrodynamics, as well as the relativistic modifications introduced by Einstein, rest upon the principle of complete determinism, the assumption that it is possible to give a description of a physical system at one particular time that is sufficient to permit a complete prediction of the system's behavior at all later times, as well as to unravel its history at all earlier times. Thus, for example, in the absence of any other bodies in the solar system, the orbit of a planet about the sun can be completely determined from a knowledge of the relative positions of the sun and planet at some given time, the respective velocity vectors at that time, the mass of the sun and planet, and the gravitational constant, G (Sections 5.6 and 5.7). The interactions of the planet with the other bodies in the system, the other planets, as well as satellites and comets, perturbs its simple, Keplerian orbit (Section 5.8). Nonetheless, a knowledge of the position and momentum vectors of all these bodies at a given time permits one to write down the equations of motion of each body in terms of these initial conditions and Newton's second law of motion, and, given a computer, to calculate the orbit of each to any desired precision.

Many other examples of classical determinism appear in the preceding chapters. The motion of an harmonic oscillator follows from its mass, its spring constant, and its initial displacement; the amplitude, velocity, and frequency components of a pulse on a taut string are determined by the tension of the string, its mass, its length, and the manner in which it is set into vibration. Also, presumably, the electromagnetic field of a solenoid is completely determined at all points in space and at all times by Maxwell's equations once the geometry of the solenoid and the time variation of its current are given. However, our discussion of the photon-wave paradox should cast some doubt upon the possibility of extrapolating this particular example to arbitrarily high frequencies.

If a system consists of a great many individual components it may be impossible to obtain the knowledge required for a complete calculation of its behavior as a function of time, or to perform the requisite calculations even if that knowledge were obtainable. The fastest electronic computers perform calculations in times on the order of 10^{-6} seconds, for instance. Given a system of 10^{21} molecules, 10^{15} sec, or about thirty million years, would be required to make one calculation per molecule, even granted the possibility of knowing the positions and velocity vector of each molecule at a specific time. Clearly we cannot hope to treat the interactions of the molecules composing a gas in the same way that we treat the interactions of the planets. But in Chapter 14 we discussed a simple model based upon the average energy of the molecules in a gas rather than upon the specific energy of each, and found that the model led to a correct though limited description of the gas's macroscopic behavior. Given only partial knowledge we applied the methods of classical physics and extracted a number of partial, though exceedingly useful conclusions regarding the macroscopic behavior of the molecular aggregate.

Statistical mechanics applies the methods of mathematical probability to such large aggregates. In the foregoing chapter we were concerned only with the mean energy of the molecules in a gas. By applying concepts of probability, we shall extend the ideal gas model and derive a number of further conclusions. For instance, we shall be able to determine not only the mean energy of the aggregate, but also the expected fraction of molecules with any other specific value of kinetic energy.

Although we shall abandon the *practical* application of classical determinism, it does not necessarily follow that we must abandon the principle itself. Rather, we might argue that but for the limitations imposed by time, technique, and the storage capacity of computers, we could treat the interactions of molecules just as completely as we treat the interactions of the planets. We give up complete determinism for practical rather than for fundamental reasons, substituting statistical determinism in its place. When we use the terms classical statistics (or classical probability) we imply that the methods of probability are being used for *practical* rather than for *fundamental* reasons.

▲▲ 15.2 The quantitative meaning of probability

There are two possible outcomes of a flipped coin: "heads" and "tails." Given the mass of the coin, the distribution of mass over its volume, the specific details of the force applied when it is flipped, and the air resistance it encounters, then, presumably, the outcome of any particular toss could be completely determined. But lacking such detailed knowledge we must abandon the hope of predicting the outcome of any particular toss and assume that the two alternatives have equal a priori probabilities of occurring. In other words, we assume that on each particluar toss of the coin, "heads" is just as likely to come up as "tails." Likewise we assume that on a particular throw of a single die, any one of the six faces is just as likely to come up, or that if a card is drawn from a freshly shuffled deck, it is just as likely to be any one of the fifty-two, or that each of the 10^{22} molecules in a liter of gas is just as likely to be on the left side of the container as on the right at any particular time. Such assumptions institutionalize our ignorance of the systems. Statistical methods accept such statements of ignorance and attempt to make the most of them.

By definition, an assignment of probability one to a particular outcome of an event implies 100% probability, or absolute certainty, that the event will occur with that outcome. Probability zero implies complete certainty that the event will *not* occur in that way. If there are several different possible outcomes of a particular event, two possible ways in which a tossed coin may come up, fifty-two possible cards that may be drawn from a deck, for instance, then we must assign each possible outcome a probability between zero and one. Now it is completely certain that *one* of the possible outcomes will occur on each trial, and thus it follows that the *sum* of the individual probabilities must be unity. Given N possible outcomes with equal a priori likelihood that any one will occur, the probability of each outcome's occurring in a single trial must be $1/N$. The probability that *either* heads or tails results in any single toss of a coin is 1; since there are two possible, equally probable outcomes, the probability of each must be $\frac{1}{2}$. Likewise, the probability of drawing *any* card from a freshly shuffled deck, the ace of spades, the king of hearts, the two of diamonds, for example, must be $\frac{1}{52}$.

These a priori probability assignments represent the best possible informed guesses about the outcome of the events. If a coin is tossed ten times, the *most probable* outcome is five heads and five tails. The most probable outcome of 10,000 tosses is 5000 heads and 5000 tails. However, these results are only *probable*, they are by no means certain. It is *possible* that ten tails will result in ten throws of a coin, even that 10,000 will come up in 10,000 throws, though the latter outcome is highly improbable. Therefore, in dealing with the probable behavior of large systems, we are interested not only in the most probable outcome, but also in the probability that any specific departure, or *fluctuation*, from that most probable outcome will occur.

The *percentage fluctuation, F,* between an actual observed outcome of many trials, which we write as $P(A)$, and the calculated, most probable outcome of that series, P_0, is defined as the ratio of the difference between the two numbers and P_0, multiplied by 100:

$$F = 100 \left[\frac{P_0 - P(A)}{P_0} \right]. \tag{15.1}$$

Thus if seven tails are thrown in ten tosses of a coin, or if seven thousand are thrown in ten thousand trials, the percentage fluctuation from the most probable value in each case is $100 \times (7 - 5)/5 = 40\%$. The probability that a particular percentage fluctuation from the most probable outcome will occur decreases in direct proportion to the *square root* of the number of trials that contribute to the observation. Since $(10,000/10)^{1/2} = (1000)^{1/2} = 31.6$, it follows that a 40% fluctuation from the most probable outcome is more than thirty times as likely to occur if ten coins are tossed than if ten thousand are tossed. As we would have expected intuitively, the reliability of the predictions based upon our informed guess increases with the number of trials.

▶▶ 15.3 Compound probabilities. Sequences and combinations

We shall usually be interested in the probability that particular sequences or combinations of simple events will occur. When a coin is flipped twice (or equivalently, when two coins are flipped), we assume that the outcome of the first trial cannot influence in any way the outcome of the second. A contrary assumption would attribute a memory of a sort to the coin, or, in the case of two coins, an interaction between them. We may call such independent events *mutually exclusive* or *uncorrelated*. There are two basic questions we may ask about the outcome of a series of such mutually exclusive events: (1) the probability a particular *sequence* of events will occur in *N* trials, and (2) the probability that one of the particular *set* of events will occur in *N* trials. A rule for combining simple probabilities is applicable to each question; we may refer to them as the AND rule and the OR rule, respectively:

AND rule:

- The probability that a particular sequence of mutually exclusive outcomes will occur in *N* trials is the *product* of the individual probabilities for each trial.

Thus, for instance, the probability of throwing a 4 on the first throw of a die *and*, a 2 on the second is $1/6 \times 1/6 = 1/36$.

OR rule:

- The probability that any *one* of a set of mutually exclusive outcomes will occur is the *sum* of the individual probability of each one.

That is, the probability of throwing *either* a 4 *or* a 2 in one throw of a die is $\frac{1}{6} + \frac{1}{6} = \frac{1}{3}$.

Since the probability of throwing a head in one toss of a coin is $\frac{1}{2}$, the probability of throwing a head in two trials must be $\frac{1}{2} \times \frac{1}{2}$, or $\frac{1}{4}$. Likewise, the probability of the sequences HT, TH, or TT must also be $\frac{1}{4}$. As we would have expected, the probabilities of each of the four possible outcomes of two tosses are equal, and their sum unity. Similarly, the probability of any particular sequence of three tosses, say HTH, TTH, or HHH, must each be $\frac{1}{2} \times \frac{1}{2} \times \frac{1}{2} = \frac{1}{8}$. There are eight possibilities, and each has equal a priori probability. Generalizing, the probability of each possible sequence occurring in N tosses must be $(\frac{1}{2})^N$. Therefore, the probability of the sequence HTHT in four tosses is equal to the probability of the sequence HHHH, namely $\frac{1}{16}$.

We must now make an important and fundamental distinction between the probability of observing a particular *sequence* of results in N trials, and the probability of observing a particular *number*, or *combination* of specific results in N trials. The probability of observing the sequence HHHT in four trials is $\frac{1}{16}$, equal to the probability of observing HHHH. But the probability of observing three heads and one tail in four trials is *greater* than the probability of observing four heads simply because there is only one way in which the latter result may materialize. On the contrary, there are *four* ways to throw three heads and one tail in four trials: HHHT, HHTH, HTHH, and THHH. Applying the OR rule, the probability of the combination is the sum of the probabilities of the four equivalent sequences, or $4 \times \frac{1}{16} = \frac{1}{4}$. Therefore the combination three heads, one tail in four trials is four times as probable as four heads. Similarly, since there are six ways to toss two heads, two tails:

$$\text{HHTT, TTHH, HTHT, THTH, THHT, HTTH,}$$

the probability that the result two heads, two tails will materialize in four trials is $6 \times \frac{1}{16} = \frac{3}{8}$, an outcome that is more probable than any other combination, as expected. It is the most probable outcome *not* because the coin "remembers" that it has come ud tails twice in two tosses and must therefore compensate. Rather, it is most probable because it may occur in more different ways than any other.

The difference between the concepts of a *sequence* (or permutation) of mutually exclusive outcomes, and a *number* (or combination) of events is the pivotal point that must be grasped in order to apply mathematical probability to large aggregates of molecules. Suppose a box contains four molecules, and we ask for the probability that all four will be found in the left half of the box at a given time (Figure 15.1). If the molecules do not interact and are in random motion, the probability that any one of them will be on the left side at any time is $\frac{1}{2}$, and therefore, the probability that all four will be on the left is $(\frac{1}{2})^4 = \frac{1}{16}$. We might also want to find the probability that molecule A is in the right half of the box, while B, C, and D are on the left. The probability that the three will be on the left is $(\frac{1}{2})^3 = \frac{1}{8}$; the probability that A is on the right is $\frac{1}{2}$. Therefore, the probability of the desired sequence, A on the right, B, C, D on the left is $\frac{1}{8} \times \frac{1}{2} = \frac{1}{16}$, exactly the same probability that all are on the left. Likewise, the probability that B alone or C alone or D alone is on the right must be $\frac{1}{16}$.

However, the probability that a *specific* molecule is in the left half of the box and the others all on the right is not terribly interesting, since we cannot follow the motion of individual molecules. Rather, we must regard all of them as being identical, and calculate the probability that a specific *number* will be found in the right half of the box with the remainder on the left. Since there are four ways that one molecule can be on the right, and the others on the left, the probability of the combination three left, one right must be $4 \times \frac{1}{16}$, or $\frac{1}{4}$. Therefore, this particular arrangement is four times as probable as the arrangement with all molecules on the left. Likewise, a three-three division has probability $6 \times \frac{1}{16} = \frac{3}{8}$, and is more probable than any other division.

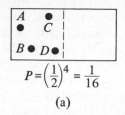

$$P = \left(\frac{1}{2}\right)^4 = \frac{1}{16}$$

(a)

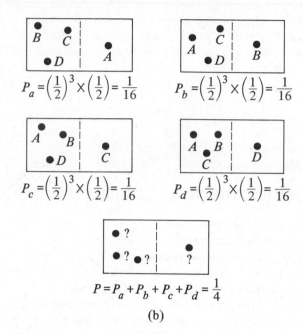

$$P = P_a + P_b + P_c + P_d = \frac{1}{4}$$

(b)

FIGURE 15.1   (a) The probability of finding all of four molecules in the left half of a box is $(\frac{1}{2})^4 = \frac{1}{16}$. (b) The probability of finding three *specific* molecules in the left half of a box and the remaining molecule on the right is also $\frac{1}{16}$. However, the probability of finding *any* three on the left and the other on the right is the sum of the probabilities of the way this outcome can occur, or $\frac{1}{4}$.

From the foregoing argument we can readily understand why gases expand to fill any confining volume. The molecules are distributed more or less uniformly over the entire volume *not* because of a repulsive force between them, not because they "know" what the others are doing, but quite simply because there are many more ways that they can be distributed over the entire volume than crowded into one corner. If we were to follow the random motion of one molecule for some time we might indeed find it on the left side of the box for a much longer time than on the other. However, since there are many molecules in the box, the course of any one of them is immaterial; we are interested only in the fact that at any specific time the number on the left and on the right will be equal, even though at a later time the individuals that compose the group on the left will certainly be different from the individuals that composed the group at an earlier time. Of course, we do *not* expect that there will *always* be an equal number of molecules on the two sides of the box, for an even division is not a certain division. It is simply the most probable. With four molecules, we would expect an even division about $\frac{3}{8}$ of the time, three on the left $\frac{1}{4}$ of the time, all on the left $\frac{1}{16}$ of the time. With 10^{22} molecules we would expect the probability of a *large* percentage fluctuation from the most probable division to be infinitesimal, and would also expect that smaller, more probable fluctuations would average out over periods of time that are long compared to the characteristic time required for a molecule to traverse the box. Nonetheless, since the molecular model explains the expansion of a gas in terms of a statistical argument, we must regard the law of expansion as highly probable rather than completely certain.

▲▲ 15.4 Probability distributions. The Gaussian function

In the foregoing section we calculated the probability of obtaining three heads and one tail in four tosses of a coin by simply listing and counting the possible sequences contributing to that combination. In principle, we could calculate the probability of each possible combination of heads and tails for any number of tosses—eight, ten, one thousand—by following the same procedure. But since the number of equivalent sequences contributing to each possible combination increases rapidly as the number of trials increases, the counting procedure rapidly become tedious.

A more systematic method of counting equivalent sequences of mutually exclusive events, each of which has two possible outcomes, is based upon the general binomial expansion (see Appendix D to text):

$$(a + b)^n = a^n + na^{n-1}b + \frac{n(n - 1)}{2} a^{n-2}b^2 + \frac{n(n - 1)(n - 2)}{2 \times 3} a^{n-3}b^3 + \cdots + b^n.$$

$$(15.2)$$

For example, for $n = 4$,

$$(a + b)^4 = a^4 + 4a^3b + 6a^2b^2 + 4ab^3 + b^4,$$

whereas if $n = 8$,

$$(a + b)^8 = a^8 + 8a^7b + 28a^6b^2 + 56a^5b^3 + 70a^4b^4 + 56a^3b^5 + 28a^2b^6 + 8ab^7 + b^8.$$

If a and b are the respective probabilities of obtaining one outcome or the other in a single trial, then the number of sequences contributing to the result that M outcomes of type b and $N - M$ outcomes of type a will be observed in N trials is the coefficient of the term $a^{N-M}b^M$ in the expansion $(a + b)^N$, and the probability of obtaining that particular number in N trials is equal to the term itself.

For instance, in the coin tossing problem, a is the probability of obtaining a head in a single trial, b the probability of obtaining a tail. Therefore, $a = b = \frac{1}{2}$. The number of sequences contributing to the combination three heads, one tail in four trials is the coefficient of the term a^3b in the expansion $(a + b)^4$, or 4, while the probability of obtaining three heads, one tail is $4(\frac{1}{2})^3\frac{1}{2} = \frac{4}{16}$, in agreement with the results obtained by enumerating and counting the sequences (Section 15.3). Similarly, fifty-six sequences contribute to the combination of three heads, five tails in eight trials, whereas the probability of obtaining that particular combination is $56(\frac{1}{2})^3(\frac{1}{2})^5 = \frac{56}{256}$.

The calculated probabilities for all possible combinations of heads and tails for four trials and eight trials, respectively, are shown in the graphs of Figures 15.2a and 15.2b. These graphs are called the *distribution functions* of the probabilities in the four-trial and eight-trial cases. Both are peaked at the value $N_h = N_t$, both show that the probability of obtaining a particular combination decreases as the symmetry of the combination decreases. However, the probability of obtaining an even division of heads and tails is greater in the four-trial than in the eight-trial case, simply because in the latter instance there are a greater number of other available alternatives.

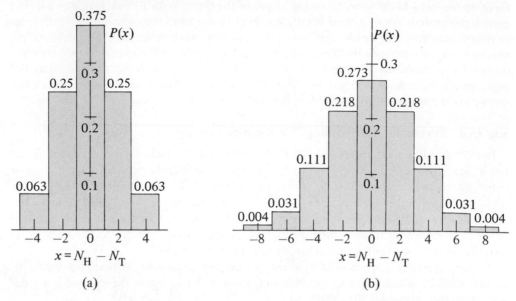

FIGURE 15.2   The calculated probabilities for all possible combinations of heads and tails for (a) four trials, and (b) eight trials.

Because the distribution functions are derived on the basis of the equal a priori probability assumption, they are of no particular value in predicting the outcome of a *single* sequence, of four, or of eight, tosses of a coin. However, if we were to tabulate the actual observed combinations in four tosses and repeat the experiment, say, fifty times (or, equivalently, to toss four coins fifty times each) we would expect to obtain four heads in about one-sixteenth of the cases, three heads, one tail in one-fourth of the cases, two heads, two tails in three-eighths of the cases. Applying the distribution function to the problem of four molecules in a container, we expect to find all molecules in the left half of the container about one-sixteenth of the time, three on the left one-fourth of the time, two on the left three-eighths of the time, one on the left one-fourth of the time, and none on the left one-sixteenth of the time. We would expect the same results if we exchanged the left and right sides, so that a particular fluctuation in favor of the left side would occur about as often as the same fluctuation in favor of the right side. Therefore, the average number of molecules on the left side over a long period of time should equal the average number found on the right side.

The probability that a particular percentage fluctuation from the most probable outcome will be observed can be obtained directly from these distribution functions. If four coins are thrown a great many times, we expect the most probable combination, two heads, two tails, to occur in three-eighths of the trials. The combination three heads, one tail represents a fluctuation of $(3 - 2)/2 = 50\%$ from the most probable outcome. Since the probability of this particular fluctuation is $\frac{1}{4}$, whereas the probability of obtaining a symmetric two head, two tail combination is $\frac{3}{8}$, the relative probability of observing the fluctuation is $\frac{1}{4}/\frac{3}{8} = 66.66...\%$. If eight coins are tossed, a 50% fluctuation from the most probable combination is obtained whenever the combination six heads, two tails is observed, since $(6 - 4)/4 = 0.50$. But since the probabilities of obtaining the four-four and the six-two combinations are $\frac{70}{256}$ and $\frac{28}{256}$, respectively, the relative probability of the fluctuation is $\frac{28}{70} = 40\%$, considerably smaller than the probability of obtaining the same *percentage* fluctuation when only four coins are thrown.

Likewise, if eight molecules were confined to a box we would expect to find an even four-four division less frequently than we expect to find the even two-two division in the four-molecule case. But in addition, we expect any particular *percentage* fluctuation to occur less frequently. By extending these arguments, when 10^{22} molecules are confined to a box, we expect the probability of any particular division between the left and right, even the most probable, symmetric division, to be small. But we also expect the probability of obtaining a large fluctuation from symmetry to be *very* small so that the number of molecules found on the left and the right should be very nearly the same at all times. In other words, we may regard the spatial distribution of molecules in the box as uniform.

Figures 15.2a and 15.2b plot the probabilities of various head-tail combinations for four and eight trials against $N_H - N_T$, the difference in the number of heads and tails. When the number of trials becomes very large, the step form of the functions may be approximated by a continuous curve with a well-known functional form that is called the *Gaussian* or *normal* distribution. Two such curves, for $N = 100$ and $N = 1000$, respectively, appear in Figure 15.3a. As expected, the probability of a completely

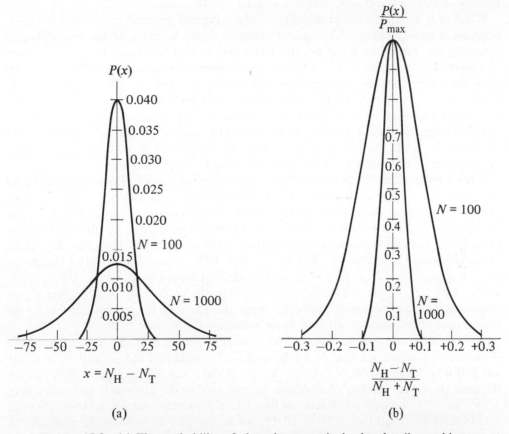

(a)	(b)

FIGURE 15.3   (a) The probability of observing a particular heads-tails combination plotted as a function of $N_H - N_T$ for $N = N_H + N_T = 100$ and 1000. These curves are called *Gaussian* distributions. The vertical scale is set so that the area under each curve, which is the probability of observing *some* outcome in N trials, is unity. (b) The Gaussian curves of part a replotted with scale changes. The horizontal scale is the asymmetry of the combinations, $(N_H - N_T)/N$, while the vertical scale is the ratio of the probability for a given combination to that of the maximum or most probable combination.

symmetric division decreases with increasing N, but so does the relative probability of obtaining a particular percentage fluctuation from the most probable, or mean value. Even though the probability of obtaining, say, $x = N_H - N_T = \pm 26$ is about twice as great for 1000 as for 100 trials, that value of x represents 513 heads or a 2.6% fluctuation from the mean in the former case, but 63 heads, or a 26% fluctuation in the latter.

Figure 15.3a is plotted in such a way that the total probability of observing some combination in N trials (i.e., the area under the curve) is unity. Figure 15.3b replots the data of Figure 15.3a to facilitate comparison between the relative probability of obtaining a given fluctuation from the mean in each of the two cases. The horizontal scale is the asymmetry of a head-tail division, or $(N_H - N_T)/N$, rather than the absolute difference, $N_H - N_T$, while the vertical scale is the ratio of the probability for that asymmetry to the probability for the most probable (the symmetric) combination. Thus the horizontal scale is compressed ten times as much for $N = 1000$ as for $N = 100$, while the vertical scale of the former is stretched about three times as much as the vertical scale of the latter. (Actually, the heights of the curves in Figure 15.3a are proportional to $1/\sqrt{N}$ so that the stretching factor is $\sqrt{1000/100} = \sqrt{10} = 3.16\ldots$.)

When N is very large the probability of observing any one particular head-tail combination is small (Figure 15.3a), and it becomes useful to speak of the probability of observing any one of the set of possible combinations that fall within a particular range of values. For example, if $N = 1000$ the most probable combination is 500 heads, 500 tails. All combinations ranging from 450 heads, 550 tails to 550 heads, 450 tails $(N_H - N_T = \pm 100)$ are within $\pm 10\%$ of the most probable combination. Applying the OR rule (Section 15.3), the probability of obtaining a combination that falls within $\pm 10\%$ of the mean must be the sum of the probabilities of all the combinations within that 10% range. Referring to Figure 15.3a we see that for $N = 1000$ the probability of observing a combination *outside* the $\pm 10\%$ range is negligible.

If the combinations for N trials follow a Gaussian distribution (Figure 15.3b), it may be shown that the probability of observing an outcome that lies within $\pm \sqrt{N}$ of the most probable outcome is about 70%, the probability of observing an outcome within $\pm 2\sqrt{N}$ of the most probable outcome about 90%. In other words, 70% of all outcomes are expected to have fluctuations no greater than $\pm 100\sqrt{N}/N\%$. If $N = 100$, 70% of all outcomes should be within $(\sqrt{100}/100) \times 100 = 10\%$ of the most probable symmetric combination, while if $N = 1000$, 70% of the outcomes should lie within $(\sqrt{1000}/1000) \times 100 = 3.16\ldots\%$ of the symmetric division. Thus the probability of observing a particular percentage fluctuation from the mean decreases in inverse proportion to the square root of the number of trials, as we anticipated in Section 15.2.

The Gaussian distribution function can also represent the probability that among the N molecules confined in a box, N_r will be found in the right half at a given time, N_l in the left half if in Figure 15.3b, $x = (N_l - N_r)/N$. If there are 10^{22} molecules then 70% of the time the *excess* number of molecules on one side or the other will be smaller than $\sqrt{10^{22}}$, or 10^{11}. Because the fractional fluctuation from the most probable distribution is infinitesimally small $(10^{11}/10^{22} = 10^{-11})$, we are justified in treating the molecules in the container as if they were uniformly distributed throughout the volume.

▶▶ 15.5 Applications of the Gaussian distribution function

Since the Gaussian distribution functions of Figure 15.3 are derived on the assumption of N mutually exclusive, or uncorrelated outcomes, we expect such distributions to have a range of application beyond the coin problem. For example, there should be no correlation between the heights of any two men selected at random from a large group. In such a large group we would expect the heights of several men to be in the range between 5'7" and 5'8", the heights of several more in the range from 5'8" to 5'9", etc. If we made a plot of the number of men with heights in each of the observed one-inch ranges, then by inspection we could determine the most probable height represented by the group (about 5'9½" in Figure 15.4a). The average value of a distribution need not coincide with the most probable value as it does in the coin problem or in any other set of observations whose distribution function is Gaussian. But if a large group of men were selected for measurement, we would expect to find about as many of them shorter than 5', as taller than 5'9½". Furthermore, we would expect to find more men with heights close to the average (small fluctuations from the most probable value) than with heights much greater or much less than average (large fluctuations). Finally we would expect about as many tall men as short men.

All of these characteristics qualitatively describe the Gaussian distribution: (1) a most probable value equal to the average value, (2) small fluctuations from the average more probable than large fluctuations, and (3) fluctuations in one direction equally as probable as fluctuations in the other direction. Therefore, if we had to guess how the heights of

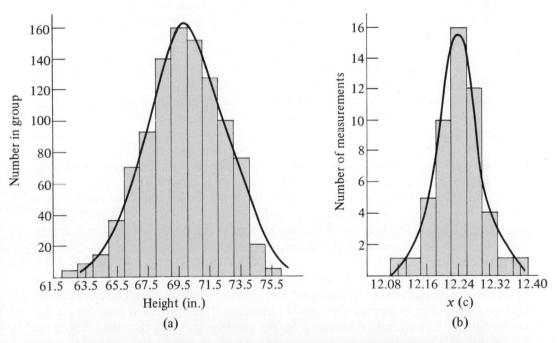

FIGURE 15.4 (a) The measured height distribution of 1000 men. The length of each vertical bar is proportional to the number of men in the group whose heights fell within that particular 1-in. interval. The smooth curve is the best Gaussian fit to the measured data and gives the expected number in each interval. (b) Distribution of fifty measurements of a length made with a meter stick graduated to 0.2 cm. Each vertical bar is proportional to the number of measurements that fell within that particular 0.04-cm interval. The smooth curve is the best Gaussian fit to the measurements.

1000 men chosen at random would be distributed, we would select a Gaussian function. However, if we actually *did* select such a group of men for an experiment we would almost certainly find that their heights did *not* conform exactly to the Gaussian expectation, for that distribution does *not* represent a certainty.

A series of length measurements made with the same meter stick are also expected to have a Gaussian distribution about the mean, most probable value of the length. Using a meter stick graduated every 0.2 cm, it is possible to state with certainty that a particular length falls between 12.2 and 12.4 cm, for instance, and by estimation, to quote a value of about 12.24 cm. Remeasuring the same length with a different part of the meter stick might yield the estimate 12.36 cm, still another estimate could be 12.28 cm, and again 12.26 cm. By making a great many measurements and plotting the number of measurements falling within each 0.2 cm range, we arrive at the most probable value of the length (Figure 15.4b). Because we expect the individual measurements to be uncorrelated, there should be about as many that are larger than the most probable value as there are those that are smaller. Further, most fluctuations should be small. Therefore, the various measurements should follow a Gaussian distribution.

Now if we plotted the results of some presumably uncorrelated series of observations, the number of heads and tails in one hundred tosses of ten coins, the heights of 500 men, the results of fifty measurements of the same length, and found a *decided* deviation from the expected distribution, we might conclude that one of our assumptions about the basic observations was in error. If in one hundred trials we observed seventy heads, thirty tails more often than any other combination, and almost never observed seventy tails, thirty heads, we would suspect that the coins we used were "loaded," and therefore, the assumption of heads and tails being equally probable in a single toss incorrect. We would have to incorporate the "loading" into the assignment of the fundamental probabilities if we wanted to calculate a realistic distribution function.

Similarly, if we found that the most probable height of a group of 500 men was 5'10" to 5'11" but that 290 men in the group were taller than that, while only 210 were shorter, we might, upon investigation, discover that our group included three visiting basketball teams, and therefore, that the heights of several members *were* correlated. Likewise, a series of length measurements that deviated appreciably from a Gaussian distribution would suggest either an inaccurately graduated meter stick or a biased observer.

The Gaussian distribution is based upon the assumptions that the fundamental elements have equal a priori probability, and are completely uncorrelated. Different types of distribution function follow if either or both of these assumptions is not applicable. In succeeding sections of this chapter we shall discuss two such non-Gaussian distributions.

We have indicated in brief the use of a distribution function in testing the lack of correlation of the elements of an aggregate, and in determining the nature of a correlation that may exist. Our three examples should also suggest the limitations imposed on this important use of distribution functions by the fundamental fact that they reflect the probability of a particular series of results. We cannot be certain that a coin is loaded until we observe a *decided* deviation from the expected Gaussian distribution, nor that a group of men have atypical heights unless the group is very large. A detailed mathematical analysis leads to specific criteria for determining whether or not a deviation is "decided," whether a group is atypical. For our purposes it is sufficient to remember that the percentage fluctuation from the most probable value is expected to decrease as the number of trials (or elements) increases. (This is true for any distribution, not just the Gaussian.) Therefore, if this anticipated trend is *not* observed, we have reason to suspect the assumed distribution itself. We would not be surprised if seven out of ten tosses of a coin came up heads, but we would begin to suspect difficulties if, continuing, we tossed sixty-five out of one hundred heads, then 706 out of one thousand. It would then appear that the most probable number of heads in ten tosses was about seven, rather than five, and that we were observing small fluctuations around that most probable value, rather than a constant, large percentage fluctuation about the expected a priori mean value of five.

▲▲ 15.6 The Rutherford scattering distribution and the nuclear atom

Let us consider, briefly, a distribution function that is decidedly *not* Gaussian. In a series of experiments culminating around 1912, Ernest Rutherford and his collaborators discovered the existence of the atomic nucleus by observing the scattering of alpha particles by very thin metallic foils and finding that the distributions in their scattering angles was inconsistent with the then current model of atomic structure.

For the present it is sufficient to state that a number of very heavy elements, uranium, thorium, polonium, radium, for example, undergo spontaneous radioactive decay,

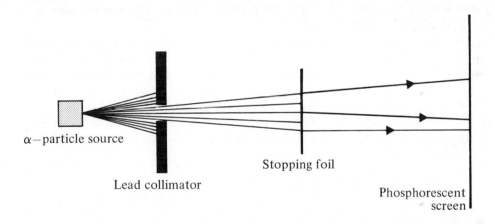

(a)

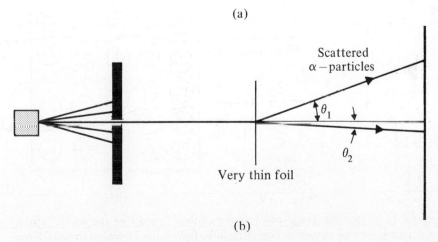

(b)

FIGURE 15.5   (a) Apparatus to measure the range of α-particles in a thin metallic foil. (b) Use of the apparatus with a very thin foil to measure the probability of α-particle scattering as a function of scattering angle θ.

emitting particles with several million electron volt energies (MeV), each having two fundamental units of positive charge, and mass equal to that of a helium atom. These energetic particles, alpha particles, are one of the three possible products in radioactive decay. The other two, beta particles and gamma rays, are energetic electrons and photons, respectively (Chapter 20). Of the three radioactive components, alpha particles have the smallest ability to penetrate matter, being brought to rest usually by a metallic foil a few millimeters thick. Rutherford and his colleagues first observed evidence for the nuclear hypothesis while performing measurements to determine the range of alpha particles as a function of energy in various materials. Their apparatus is shown schematically in Figure 15.5a.

The alpha particles emitted from a radioactive source (say thorium, which emits 4.18 MeV alpha particles) are collimated into a well-defined beam by a hole in a thick lead plate, and allowed to impinge upon a phosphorescent screen which acts as a detector. The number of particles reaching the detector per unit time is measured as metallic foils of increasing thickness are introduced into the beam until eventually all are stopped by the intervening material. In one such experiment the collaborators measured instead the number of alpha particles scattered into each angular range (with respect to the incident beam) by a foil that was too thin to stop them (Figure 15.5b). Their results were unexpected, and led to the nuclear hypothesis.

During the last decade of the nineteenth century, J. J. Thomson measured the charge to mass ratio of cathode ray particles and argued, convincingly, that these particles, electrons, were a fundamental constituent of all matter (Section 9.7). Thomson then proposed a model of the atom in which the negatively charged electrons were assumed to be embedded in a positively charged matrix constituting the bulk of the atomic mass (Figure 15.6a). On the basis of this model, the positive matrices of the atoms composing a solid, a gold foil, for instance, would be almost in contact with each other (Figure 15.6a).

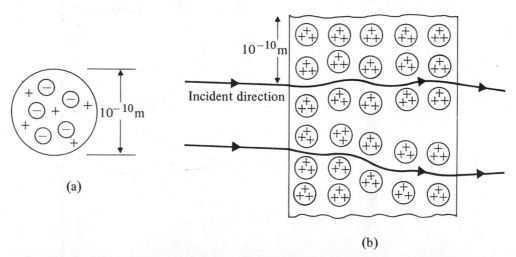

(a)

(b)

FIGURE 15.6 (a) The Thomson "plum pudding" model of the atom. (b) A microscopic view of a cross section of metallic foil on the Thomson model. Since each α-particle interacts many times with the positive matrices, and since the vector sum of these interactions is approximately zero, the particle suffers only a small deflection from its incident direction.

Likewise, an alpha particle would consist of a doubly positive matrix with its neutralizing electrons missing. When one of these alpha particles entered a thin gold foil consisting of relatively few atomic layers, its positive charge would interact electrostatically with the surrounding atoms. However, because of the close proximity of positive and negative charge on all sides, the particle would be subject only to a series of rather small net deflections in the direction perpendicular to its path. Hence it would pursue a zig-zag course through the foil and emerge with its directions only slightly altered (Figure 15.6b).

Since many small deflections would be expected for each incident particle with the probability of a deflection in either direction equally probable, the distribution of scattering angles around 0° on the Thomson model is Gaussian, and Rutherford and his colleagues should have observed that distribution. Instead they found far too many alpha particles scattered through large angles relative to the incident beam direction. Indeed a very few scattered backward (Figure 15.7). Their results implied that many of the particles suffered large net deflections in one direction, which suggests that they were subject to one rather large interaction rather than a series of small, almost equal and opposite interactions.

The conclusion that a single relatively large interaction is more probable than many small, equal and opposite interactions led Rutherford to propose that the bulk of a gold atom's mass is concentrated in a very small, positively charged core called the *nucleus* (which we now know has a diameter on the order of 10^{-14} m), surrounded by planetary electrons equal in number to the nuclear charge and with orbital radii on the order of

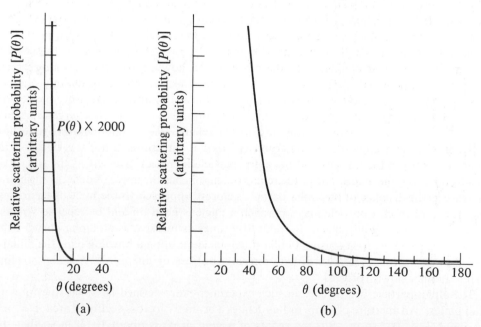

FIGURE 15.7 The measured probability of α-particle scattering from a thin foil plotted as a function of scattering angle θ relative to the incident α-direction. The vertical scale of the graph for angles smaller than 20° (a) is 2000 times the scale for scattering angles greater than 40° (b) indicating that the angular deviation for most of the α-particles is small. However, the observation that a few *do* scatter through large angles cannot be explained on the basis of the Thomson model of the atom.

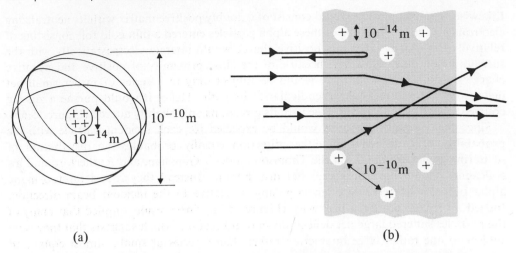

FIGURE 15.8 (a) The Rutherford or planetary model of the atom. (b) Microscopic view of a cross section of metallic foil on the Rutherford model. Since the nuclei are far apart it is very unlikely that an α-particle will suffer more than a single interaction of appreciable magnitude. Therefore, most will not be deflected at all, but a few will be deflected at large angles.

10^{-10} m (Figure 15.8a). Thus the centers of positive charge in a gold foil are separated by about 10^{-10} m instead of being almost adjacent as in the Thomson model (Figure 15.8b). When an alpha particle traverses the foil it can scarcely fail to make several close collisions with electrons. But since its mass is more than 7000 times greater, these interactions are somewhat analogous to the passage of a bowling ball through an obstacle course of ping pong balls. That is, the ping pong balls are deflected considerably whereas the bowling ball proceeds on its way virtually without hindrance. However, when an alpha particle comes within reasonable proximity of a heavy positively charged nucleus, it is, of necessity, very far away from any other nucleus. It will suffer a strong repulsion and hence a large angle deflection from its original direction. Since the electrostatic repulsion between the nucleus and the alpha particle increases inversely as the square of their separation, the magnitude of the repulsion, and hence the angle of deflection, should increase as the distance of the alpha particle's closest approach to the nucleus decreases. In a few rare cases a particle may approach a nucleus head on and be repelled straight backward. Since a gold nucleus is about fifty times as massive as an alpha particle, the situation is roughly analogous to a billiard ball incident upon a bowling ball: the billiard ball may be scattered backward, with virtually no loss of energy, leaving the bowling ball to lumber slowly forward.

The alpha-particle beams used in such experiments are defined by small apertures in lead plates. An aperture of 1 mm radius defines a beam with cross-sectional area $A = \pi r^2$, or about 3×10^{-6} sq m. But the radius of a gold atom is about 10^{-10} m so that the alpha particle beam impinging on a thin foil must encompass about 10^{14} atoms. Since the position of each alpha particle is so crudely defined relative to the nuclei of the foil, how is it possible to speak in terms of interaction distances on the order of 10^{12} or 10^{13} m not to mention head-on collisions?

Many alpha particles impinge upon the foil each second. Hence we may assume that the particles are uniformly distributed over the cross-sectional area of the beam, and therefore that during each one-second interval an equal number will traverse each small cross section of the foil. Since we assume the foil is so thin that each particle scatters once at most, and since we also assume the interaction between a nucleus and an alpha particle is purely electromagnetic, then the number of alpha particles that scatter through a particular angle is directly related to a particular distance of closest approach to *any* nucleus. The specific nucleus does not matter. The closer the nuclei are to each other, the greater the probability that any particular alpha particle will undergo a large scattering, simply because it will be presented with a greater number of changes to interact.

On the basis of these assumptions an expression can be derived for the probability that an alpha particle will be scattered through a particular angle, an expression known as an *angular distribution* (Figure 15.7). Its general form depends only upon the assumption that each particle undergoes at most one Coulomb interaction, just as the general form of a Gaussian distribution assumes completely uncorrelated events. But the specific details of the angular distribution, its rate of change with angle, for instance, depends upon the distance between the nuclei in the foil and the magnitude of their positive charge. Hence Rutherford's angular distribution measurements, his determination of the fraction of particles scattered into each range of angles, served not only to test the general nuclear hypothesis, but also measured the charge on the gold nuclei and the intranuclear distance.

Because probability is invoked to derive the Rutherford angular distribution, verification of the form of the distribution requires that a large number of particles be scattered into each angular range. For example, Figure 15.7 predicts that the ratio of the number of particles scattered at 5° to the number scattered at 10° should be 8:1. As fluctuations from these predictions are expected, a measurement of sixteen particles at 5° and three at 10° would be insufficient grounds for discarding the distribution. Percentage fluctuations are expected to decrease as the number of particles increases so that we would expect the ratio to converge toward the expected 8:1 ratio: 160:24, 1600:197, 16,000:2064, for example. However, if continued measurement yielded ratios such as 160:33, 1600:287, 16,000:3176, we would begin to be suspicious of the fundamental assumptions underlying the derived distribution function.

Rutherford and his coworkers carried out a systematic study of alpha particles scattering as a function of incident energy and scattering material. In a very few of the experiments with light nuclei they did indeed observe significant deviations from the expected Coulomb distributions, discrepancies that implied a then unexplained breakdown in their basic assumptions. In fact, these deviations originated when an occasional alpha particle came within a sufficiently small distance of a nucleus to interact not only with its charge but also with the strong, internal short-range forces responsible for the binding of its constituent neutrons and protons to one another (Chapter 20). These unwelcomed deviations demonstrated directly the existence of this new type of force, and signaled the exploration of the internal structure of the nucleus itself.

◣◣ 15.7   The distribution of molecular energies in an ideal gas

The expected Gaussian distribution of heads and tails for a great many tosses of a coin is based on the assumption that a single toss has equal a priori probability of coming up heads or tails and that no result is correlated with any other. The Rutherford distribution follows from the specific physical restriction that the probability of a particle's scattering through a particular angle is related to its probability of coming within a particular minimum distance of a nucleus. Similarly, the fraction of the gas molecules in one part of a container at a given instant is Gaussian, since we can assume that the position of any one molecule is not correlated with the positions of the others. However, in order to calculate the distribution of the momenta and energies of the molecules in the container, we must impose physical restrictions. First we assume that the total energy and momentum of the system remains constant provided the system remains isolated, and that in each collision the total momentum and energy cannot change. Since there are a great many molecules in a container of gas we also assume that in any time interval long compared with the mean time between molecular interaction, all possible transfers of energy and momentum between two particles will occur. Thus if we calculate the number of molecules in a particular energy range at one instant we can expect to find the same *number* in that range at any later time.

There are a great many ways in which the total kinetic energy of a system of interacting molecules may be divided among the individual molecules. For example:

1. Molecule A has all the energy, all others have none;
2. Molecule B has all the energy, all others have none;
3. Molecules A and B share the total energy equally, all others have zero energy;
4. Molecules A and C share the total energy equally, all others have zero energy;
5. Molecule A has three times the energy of Molecule B which in turn has twice the energy of C; all other molecules have zero energy;
6. Molecules A, B, and C have zero energy: all other molecules share the total equally.

If we assume that the motion of the molecules (and hence their collisions) are completely random, each of these six possible divisions of energy has equal a priori probability of occurring as a result of a particular sequence of collisions. But the 10^{22} molecules in a liter of gas are not labeled A, B, C, etc. Rather, they are indistinguishable, and therefore, there is no way to differentiate between "sequences" 1 and 2 or between "sequences" 3 and 4. It follows that the distribution function for the energy must be based upon *combinations* such as:

1. One molecule has all the available energy, the others have none;
2. Two molecules share all available energy equally;
3. Two molecules share all available energy, but one has twice the energy of the other;
4. Three molecules share the energy equally;
5. All molecules have equal energies.

Since the number of ways each of these combinations can be attained differs, so does the probability of each. If there are N particles in the container, there are N possible ways to obtain combination 1: the first with A taking all energy, the second with B taking all, etc. Similarly, combination 2 follows if either A and B, or A and C, or B and C share. Since each molecule may pair with every other in this way there are $N(N - 1)/2$ possibilities,* and combination 2 is $(N - 1)/2$ times more probable than combination 1. By the same token, combination 3 is more probable than 2, and 4 more probable than 3. It may be surprising to note that combination 5, with all molecules sharing the energy equally, is highly improbable since there is but *one* way such a division may occur.

Specific distribution functions giving the fraction of molecules expected in each small range of energy are called *Maxwell-Boltzmann* distributions. If there are N_0 molecules

---

* The number of pairs that can be formed from a set of N objects would be N^2 if we regarded the pairs AB and BA as different and also allowed each object to pair with itself so that A^2, B^2, etc., would also be counted. But $AB = BA$ for the molecules, and since a molecule does not pair with itself there are $N(N - 1)/2$ combinations instead.

in a container, the number $N(KE)$ with kinetic energies in the small range KE to $KE + \Delta(KE)$ is

$$N(KE)\, \Delta KE = N_0 C_e \sqrt{KE}\, e^{KE/kT}\, \Delta KE, \qquad (15.3)$$

where $e = 2.178\ldots$ is the base of the natural system of logarithms (see Appendix C to text), k is the Boltzmann constant (Equation 14.19b), T the absolute temperature of the gas, and N_0 the total number of molecules. (The constant C_e has the value $2/(\pi^3 kT)^{3/2}$.) Because the mean kinetic energy of a molecule is equal to $\frac{3}{2}kT$ (Equation 14.16b), the total kinetic energy of a system of N molecules is $\frac{3}{2}NkT$. Therefore, the total energy of a gas, and hence the total number of ways that energy may be divided among the molecules, should increase with temperature. Maxwell-Boltzmann distribution functions for two different temperatures are shown in Figure 15.9. The widths of the functions increase

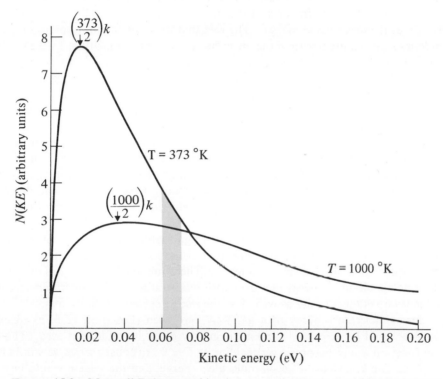

FIGURE 15.9 Maxwell-Boltzmann kinetic energy distributions at 373 °K (100 °C) and 1000 °K. The number of molecules in an ideal gas with kinetic energies in a given interval is proportional to the area under the appropriate curve between the limits of the interval (Equation 15.3). (For example, the shaded area on the graph is proportional to the fraction of the molecules in an ideal gas at 373 °K with kinetic energies between 0.06 and 0.07 eV.) The vertical scale is arbitrary but is selected such that the total areas under the two curves, and therefore the total numbers of particles involved, are equal. In both cases the most probable energy is $\frac{1}{2}\, kT$, and there are more molecules with energies greater than $\frac{1}{2}\, kT$ than with energies smaller than $\frac{1}{2}\, kT$. Since the molecules have a considerably greater range of energies at 1000° than at 373°, the fraction found within a particular energy interval is smaller at the higher temperature. In addition, the higher temperature curve is much broader than the lower temperature curve.

with increasing temperature, consistent with the assumption that an increase in total energy implies an increase in the number of ways in which the energy may be divided among the molecules.

These distribution functions may also be used to calculate the mean (or average) kinetic energy per molecule, with the result that $\overline{KE} = \frac{3}{2}kT$ in accord with the simple model of Chapter 14. However, the *most probable* energy of the aggregate is only $\frac{1}{2}kT$, or one-third the mean energy. This conclusion follows directly from the restrictions imposed on the system by energy conservation. A mean energy equal to the most probable energy would imply that an equal division of energy among the molecules is the most probable division. But we have seen that this distribution is, in fact, *not* very probable, since there is but one way it can occur. The difference between the mean and most probable energies is tantamount to stating that combinations in which a few molecules have energies much greater than the mean while many more have much smaller energies are highly probable. This is consistent with the form of the distribution function since we note that an appreciable fraction of the molecules have greater than two, three, or even five times the mean value of $\frac{3}{2}kT$. The fact that many of the molecules in a gas *do* have energies so much greater than the mean has important implications in the study of chemical reaction mechanisms.

Because of the very large number of molecules in a liter of gas at atmospheric pressure, we would expect the Maxwell-Boltzmann distribution functions to reflect the actual energy division among the molecules of an ideal gas, provided the motion of the molecules is random and uncorrelated. Figure 15.9 (and Equation 15.3) shows that both the mean energy of the molecules in an ideal gas and the distribution of their energies are uniquely determined by the absolute temperature of the gas. Thus temperature is a purely statistical concept and has a well-defined meaning only for systems that are large enough to permit the application of statistical methods with some degree of confidence. It is quite meaningless to speak of the temperature of a single molecule or of a small aggregate.

Since the molecules in an ideal gas are indistinguishable, the broadening in the distribution function with increasing temperature also implies an increase in the range of possible energies available to a single molecule. Therefore, the *uncertainty* in our knowledge of a single molecule's energy increases with temperature, and temperature becomes a partial measure of the *disorder* as well as of the *energy content* of the system.

If the mean molecular energy of a gas were zero then (Equation 15.3) its absolute temperature would be zero, and the kinetic energy of *all* its molecules zero. The distribution function would become a vertical line at $T = 0$. In consequence we would have completely certain knowledge of each molecule's energy, and the system would be completely determined. In reality the ideal gas model fails at low temperatures since the molecules attract each other to form liquids and ultimately solids. Hence no physical gas exists at absolute zero. Nonetheless, the basic idea of absolute zero as the temperature at which we could have complete knowledge of the microscopic energy of a system is applicable to real solids, although the distribution functions for their atoms or molecules is more complicated than Equation 15.3.

Absolute zero is often referred to as the temperature at which all atomic and molecular motion ceases. But such an interpretation is too simple. The atoms or molecules of any macroscopic sample of matter may also have internal modes of motion which need not be affected by random interactions between the molecules and hence do not contribute to the kinetic energy, and the temperature, of the sample. But internal motion is ordered and thus not subject to temperature change. Therefore, although all motion in a system need not cease at $T = 0$, absolute zero nevertheless remains the lowest definable temperature and characterizes a state of complete order.

We shall return to the question of disorder in Sections 16.4 and 16.5.

▲▲ 15.8 Applications of the molecular distribution function

Suppose a sample containing N_1 molecules of a particular gas, say oxygen, at a temperature T_1 is mixed with another sample of the same gas consisting of N_2 molecules at a temperature T_2. Before mixing, the two samples have respective total kinetic energies $N_1 k T_1$ and $N_2 k T_2$. Since the total energy of the mixture will be $N_1 k T_1 + N_2 k T_2$, the final equilibrium temperature $\overline{T}$ of the mixture will be intermediate between the two original temperatures:

$$k\overline{T} = \frac{N_1 k T_1 + N_2 k T_2}{N_1 + N_2},$$

so

$$\overline{T} = \frac{N_1 T_1 + N_2 T_2}{N_1 + N_2}. \tag{15.4}$$

Because the temperature of a gas determines not only the mean energy of its constituent molecules but also their energy distribution (Figure 15.9), Equation 15.4 implies that collisions between the molecules of the two mixed samples ultimately results in a redistribution in the energies of the aggregate. The temperature of the mixture will only be uniform, however, when the redistribution is complete and the assumption of an equal *a priori* probability of energy division among the available possibilities is valid.

Of the two samples, the warmer originally contains the greater proportion of molecules with energies much higher than the final mean. Clearly the redistribution of energies can only occur if a good many of these "fast" molecules share some of their energy with the slower molecules. But because of the time reversal symmetry discussed in Chapter 6 (Section 6.8) we cannot assume that every collision between a fast and slow molecule results invariably in an energy transfer to the slow molecule. Each individual collision process is restricted only by energy and momentum conservation.

It is just as probable that an energetic molecule will emerge from a collision with even more energy as with less energy, and we cannot assume that fast molecules somehow seek out and collide with the slow molecules in preference to other fast molecules. However, if *several* molecules with energies much greater than the mean energy collide with several whose energies are smaller than the mean, the probability that many members if the two sets will emerge with their energies closer to the mean should certainly be greater than the probability that all of the fast molecules will gain energy at the expense of the slower ones. There are simply many more ways in which the former result may occur. Just as in coin-tossing, there are more ways to approach a symmetric than an asymmetric division. Thus the intermediate energy distribution function for a mixture of two gases at different temperatures follows from the random nature of the collisions, a randomness that makes the maintenance of the original separate energy distribution functions a highly improbable occurrence.

The Maxwell-Boltzmann distribution functions shown in Figure 15.9 are plotted against molecular kinetic energies. But since kinetic energy $= \frac{1}{2}mv^2$, a distribution function for molecular velocities may also be derived (Figure 15.10). Two different gases at the same temperature will both have the same *energy* distribution function. However,

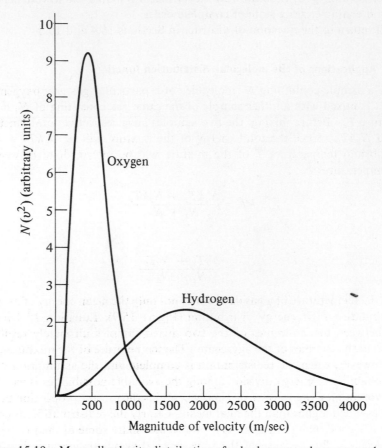

FIGURE 15.10 Maxwell velocity distributions for hydrogen and oxygen molecules at 373 °K. The vertical scale is arbitrary but chosen such that the areas under the curves, and therefore the total numbers of molecules, are equal in the two cases.

their velocity distribution functions, and hence their mean velocities, will differ. If M_1 and $\bar{v}_1^2$ are the mass and the mean square velocity (Equations 14.11b and 14.13b) of the molecules of one gas and M_2 and $\bar{v}_2^2$ the corresponding quantities of a second, different gas that is completely mixed with the first, then since $kT_1 = kT_2$, and therefore $\overline{KE}_1 = \overline{KE}_2$, we have

$$M_1\bar{v}_1^2 = M_2\bar{v}_2^2,$$

or

$$\frac{\bar{v}_1}{\bar{v}_2} = \sqrt{\frac{M_2}{M_1}}. \tag{15.5}$$

That is, the ratio of the magnitudes of the mean molecular velocities of two gases at the same temperature is equal to the inverse ratio of their masses. Oxygen (O_2) with molecular weight about sixteen times greater than hydrogen (H_2) (Table 14.1) has one-fourth its mean velocity at the same temperature.

The mass of an oxygen molecule is about thirty-two times the mass of a hydrogen atom, or $32 \times 1.6 \times 10^{-27} = 5.1 \times 10^{-26}$ kg. Referring to Section 14.7 the mean kinetic energy of a gas at room temperature (300 °K) is 6.21×10^{-21} J. Therefore the mean velocity of an oxygen molecule at this temperature is

$$\bar{v} = \frac{2 \times 6.21 \times 10^{-21}}{5.1 \times 10^{-26}}$$

$$= 4.8 \times 10^2 \text{ m/sec.}$$

Nitrogen molecules (N_2) with mass $\frac{28}{32}$ times the mass of an oxygen molecule have only a slightly larger mean velocity at room temperature, whereas the mean velocity of a hydrogen molecule is about four times larger. Since temperature determines the velocity distribution as well as the mean velocity in a gas, a given volume of hydrogen at a given temperature contains a much greater number of fast molecules than an equal volume of oxygen or nitrogen at the same temperature.

In Chapter 7 (Section 7.6) we calculated the escape velocity from the earth as about 10^4 m/sec by determining the kinetic energy required at the surface to overcome completely its gravitational force. At 300 °K the *mean* velocity of a hydrogen molecule is smaller than escape velocity by a factor of five, the mean velocity for oxygen and nitrogen smaller by a factor of twenty. Thus even though no molecule with velocity precisely equal to the *mean* velocity at room temperature has sufficient velocity to escape completely from the earth's gravitational influence, the probability of finding a hydrogen molecule with velocity approximating or exceeding escape velocity is considerably larger than the comparable probability for oxygen or nitrogen. Therefore, we would expect a greater abundance of the heavier gases near the surface, as in fact we observe. Refining the argument a bit, the distance that a molecule with velocity less than escape velocity can rise above the surface increases with the square of its velocity at the surface. A Maxwell distribution giving the number of molecules as a function of velocity rather than kinetic energy may be derived in much the same way Equation 15.4 was derived, with the result:

$$\frac{N(v^2)}{N_0} = Av^2 e^{-mv^2/2kT},$$

with

$$A = \left(\frac{4}{\sqrt{\pi}}\right)\left(\frac{M}{2kT}\right)^{3/2}.$$

Hence the density of molecules of a particular mass decreases with altitude as the negative exponential function, consistent with the decrease in atmospheric pressure as a function of altitude. However, the distribution in v^2 at the surface, and therefore, the rate at which pressure decreases with altitude also depends on molecular mass. Figure 15.10 shows velocity distribution curves for both oxygen and hydrogen at room temperature. Since the latter is far broader and peaks at a higher value of velocity we would expect an increase in the concentration ratio of hydrogen to oxygen with increasing altitude, as observed. By these same arguments we would expect a planet or satellite with a considerably smaller mass than the earth's to have little or no oxygen and nitrogen in its atmosphere, and conversely that a planet with a considerably larger mass might well have an atmosphere of hydrogen. These expectations are also borne out. The atmosphere of Venus is mainly carbon dioxide, and the moon has no atmosphere at all, whereas the dominant gas in the atmosphere of the planet Jupiter is hydrogen.

Equation 15.5 may be applied to the phenomena called Brownian motion to determine the value of the Boltzmann constant, k, and therefore, Avogadro's number, N_0. The granular nature of smoke may easily be observed with a rather low-power microscope. Even a rather superficial examination shows that smoke particles are in constant, random motion, buffeted about, it would seem, by collisions with invisible particles. (This phenomenon was first reported in the early nineteenth century by the biologist Robert Brown, for whom it was named.) Of course the invisible buffeting particles are simply the oxygen and nitrogen molecules of the atmosphere. If we think of the smoke particles as constituting a "gas" at the same temperature as the nitrogen and oxygen, then detailed measurements of their motion over a long and extended time permits a determination of their velocity distribution function, and from it their mean velocity. The mean kinetic energy of the "gas," and hence the product $kT = \frac{1}{2}M\bar{v}^2$ follows immediately from the average mass of the particles. Since we assume that the temperature of the smoke is equal to the temperature of the atmosphere, we then have an experimentally determined value of the Boltzmann constant, k, and given the value of the universal gas constant, R, which can be found by measuring the pressure of a known mass of gas in a known volume at a known temperature (Equation 14.17c) we can calculate Avogradro's number, $N_0 = R/k$ (Equation 14.17b). Finally, because we know the mass of one mole of any gas, we may use N_0 to calculate the mass of a molecule of that gas.

The value of Avogadro's number determined by studying Brownian motion agrees with the value obtained by other methods, electrolysis measurements, for example, and this fact gives us some assurance that the statistical model is a valid microscopic representation of an ideal gas.

►► 15.9 Limitations of the ideal gas model. The liquid and solid states

The ideal gas model we have discussed in this and the preceding chapter assumes that molecules may be treated as structureless point masses which interact only when they collide, and then only as if they bounce off each other like billiard balls. This assumption might well be called the minimal interaction assumption, and leads inevitably to what must be regarded as the fundamental limitation of the model: the fact that but for their masses all gases are completely identical if they have the same number of molecules.

The results we have obtained attest to the remarkable success of this simple model. Yet a closer examination of molecular structure suggests that it cannot be valid under all conditions. Evidence from electrolysis and from Rutherford scattering requires that atoms and molecules have an internal charge structure and that therefore their interactions should be electromagnetic. Rutherford's simple, planetary model represents atoms as entities with heavy, positive nuclei surrounded by negative electron shells with diameter approximately 10^4 times larger. If two such atoms are separated by one hundred or even ten times their diameters, they "see" each other as neutral particles and therefore, do not interact. However, their charge structures become apparent when their separation is only a few times their internal dimensions, since then their electron shells are much closer together than their nuclei. In such cases the increasing electrostatic repulsion between them results in a continuous decrease in their relative kinetic energies and eventually becomes sufficient to change their relative directions of motion. For the moment we may think of molecules and molecular interaction in the same terms.

As long as the interaction between two atoms is limited to these near encounters be-tween their outer, negative shells that interaction may be approximated by assuming that the atoms are actually hard spheres that "bounce" upon contact, and otherwise ignore each other. Since their charge structure is not pertinent, the minimal interaction model is excellent. On some occasions the outer shells of two atoms or molecules may overlap so that one can "see" the positive nucleus of the other. In such cases there is some tendency for the pair to form a bound structure, but if the relative kinetic energy of the interacting atoms is sufficiently high, such an intermolecular bond will have small probability of remaining intact.

Two related effects result in deviations from this rather simple behavior. (1) At sufficiently high pressures the average distance between atoms or molecules becomes comparable to their sizes. The molecules can no longer travel appreciable distances between interactions, but in fact are in almost constant interaction with their neighbors. (2) If simultaneously the gas temperature is sufficiently low there is a high probability that two or more molecules may form stable bonds with each other. Both effects imply a correlation between the motion of the separate molecules and thus a breakdown of the random motion assumption. If the degree of correlation is sufficiently high, very few molecules will be able to move at random. Hence the assembly loses its ability to expand, and liquefaction occurs.

These remarks suggest that the behavior of a gas should exhibit increasingly marked deviations from the ideal gas law, $pV = nRT$ (Equation 14.7c) with increasing pressures and decreasing temperatures, that these deviations should become serious near the liquefaction temperature, that the liquefaction temperature should increase with increas-ing pressure, and that it should depend critically upon the structure of the gas molecules.

Oxygen at atmospheric pressure liquefies at 90 °K and shows marked deviations from the ideal gas law as its temperature is reduced to around 100 °K. Nitrogen, with $\frac{28}{32}$ the molecular mass of oxygen, liquefies at 78 °K. The liquefaction temperatures of both gases increase with pressure, as expected. Above a characteristic critical temperature that is different for each gas, *no* pressure suffices for liquefaction, though the high pressure deviations from ideal behavior become quite serious.

Hydrogen molecules are considerably lighter, and therefore presumably smaller, than oxygen molecules. As expected, the liquefaction temperature of oxygen is correspond-ingly lower, 20 °K. In contrast to hydrogen and oxygen, helium exists in an *atomic* rather than a molecular state. Since a helium *atom* is smaller and more symmetric than a hydrogen *molecule*, the element has the very lowest of all liquefaction temperatures, 4 °K at atmospheric pressure, and continues to behave as an ideal gas down to about 20 °K. Therefore, a helium gas thermometer (Chapter 14) has a greater range of validity than any other thermometer.

Differences in molecular masses do not always suffice to determine differences in liquefaction temperatures, however. Oxygen, with molecular weight 32, liquefies at 90 °K, while water, with molecular weight 18, liquefies at 373 °K. According to our qualitative discussion, liquefaction should occur when the probability of correlation between molecules becomes sufficiently high. Since such correlations result from electro-magnetic interactions, the charge distribution within a molecule is pertinent information. Figures 15.11a and 15.11b show the charge structure of oxygen and water molecules (see Chapter 19), and suggest why the asymmetric distribution of the water molecules implies a relatively high liquefaction temperature.

As the interactions between molecules become increasingly important the semifree nature of the liquid state gives way to the highly correlated solid state with the molecules

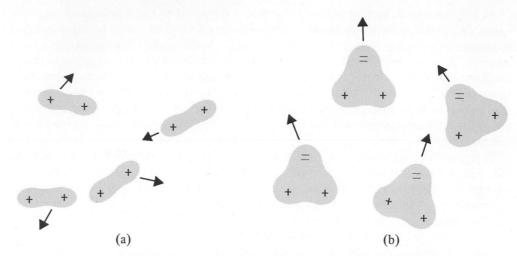

FIGURE 15.11   (a) Oxygen molecules are formed from two identical atoms and have symmetric charge structures so that the electric fields due to their positive and negative charges cancel each other at large distances. It follows that two such molecules interact only when their separations are comparable to their dimensions. (b) However, water molecules are formed from two hydrogen and one oxygen atom. Since the latter bind the electrons more tightly, one side of each molecule is more negative than the other. Hence the net electric field of each molecule at large distances is not zero, and water molecules interact over much larger distances than oxygen molecules.

exerting sufficient forces on each other to bind themselves into a rigid structure. Of course the macroscopic temperature concept applies to both liquids and solids. Although the detailed microscopic interpretation is more involved than in the gaseous state, temperature is nonetheless related to the general idea of disorder discussed in Section 15.7. The molecules of nonmetallic solids are bound together into well-defined arrays but oscillate about their equilibrium positions with randomly distributed energies that are related to the temperature of the solid. The bonds between metallic atoms are more complicated, however, and leave many of the planetary electrons free to migrate at random throughout the body of the metal (Section 8.6). For many purposes these semi-free electron aggregates may be treated as a gas confined only by the boundaries of the metal. For instance, the model leads to a qualitative understanding of the ejection of electrons from a hot metal (Section 9.7). Since it correlates the energy distribution of the electrons with the temperature of the metal, it thus implies that at high temperatures a reasonable fraction have energies greater than their binding energies. The electron gas model of metals also leads to a correct quantitative description of the conduction of both electricity and heat. It should be noted, however, that the distribution function for the electron gas is quite different from the Maxwell distribution (Equation 15.3).

Liquids may be regarded as a transitional state between the virtually free gaseous systems and the highly correlated solid systems. Molecules should still be able to move away from each other, but not too far. The probability of cluster formation should be high, yet some molecules should retain sufficient velocity to escape correlation with others. The evaporation of liquids, interpreted as the escape of the faster molecules, attests to the random nature of such a system. Disorder is still apparent, and the temperature concept applicable.

It is quite easy to understand why the macroscopic properties of different gases are much more similar to each other than are the macroscopic properties of solids. Microscopically, gases are minimally interacting systems, and therefore, the detailed structure of their molecules is not manifest. On the other hand, the detailed nature of the bonds between atoms and molecules, and therefore, the detailed properties of the atoms and molecules themselves, are very pertinent to the macroscopic properties of the solid state. In fact, there should be as many different types of solids as there are differences between molecules. Therefore, experimental studies of the solid state offer a rich source of information on intermolecular forces, and for this reason, among others, the study of the solid state is a lively field of contemporary research in physics.

SUGGESTIONS FOR FURTHER READING ▲▲▲

Most basic physics texts do not discuss mathematical probability and statistics in any detail. Two that do so but on a more advanced level are:

R. P. FEYNMAN, R. B. LEIGHTON, AND M. SANDS, *The Feynman Lectures on Physics*, Vol. 1, Addison-Wesley Publishing Co., Inc., Reading, Mass., 1963, Chapters 6, 39–43.

CHALMER SHERWIN, *Basic Concepts of Physics*, Holt, Rinehart, and Winston, Inc., New York, 1961, Chapter 7 and Appendix V.

Three monograms, again on a somewhat more advanced level, are:

WAYNE A. BOWERS, *Distributions*, © The University of Washington, Seattle, 1966.

J. G. DASH, *Heat Motion in Matter*, © The University of Washington, Seattle, 1966.

HAROLD A. DAW, *An Experimental Introduction to Kinetic Theory*, © The University of Washington, Seattle, 1967.

A more general treatment of the applications of probability theory in many fields including science is:

WARREN WEAVER, *Lady Luck: The Theory of Probability*, Science Study Series, Doubleday and Co., Garden City, N.Y., 1963.

For a survey introduction to the mathematics of probability see:

M. KOC, "Probability," *Scientific American*, Sept., 1964, p. 92.

A. J. AYER, "Chance," *Scientific American*, October, 1965, p. 44.

PROBLEMS AND EXERCISES ▲▲▲

15.1. (a) What is the probability that when a die is thrown twice it will come up 6 the first time and 2 the second time?

  (b) What is the probability of obtaining a 6 and a 2 in a single throw of a pair of dice?

15.2. (a) A pair of dice is thrown, one of which comes up 6. What is the probability that the other comes up 2?

  (b) A die is thrown three times, coming up 6 each time. What is the probability of obtaining a six on the next throw?

15.3. (a) What is the probability that a 6 will *not* come up in a single throw of a die?

  (b) A pair of dice is thrown, one of them coming up 6. What is the probability that the other does *not* come up 6?

15.4. (a) What is the probability of obtaining the ace of spades in one draw from a freshly shuffled deck?

  (b) What is the probability of obtaining any one of the four aces in one draw?

  (c) What is the probability of obtaining a 2 in one draw?

15.5. (a) What is the probability that in three successive throws of a single die a 6 will come up the first time, anything but a 6 will come up the second time, and a 6 will again come up the third time?

(b) What is the probability that in three throws of a single die a 6 will come up only twice?

15.6. (a) What is the probability of drawing the ace of spades, the ace of hearts, and the ace of diamonds in succession from a freshly shuffled deck of cards?

(b) What is the probability of drawing the three aces in any order in three tries?

Assume that each card is replaced in the deck before the next is drawn.

15.7. (a) What is the probability of obtaining two *specific* aces in three draws from a freshly shuffled deck of cards? In four draws?

(b) What is the probability of obtaining *any* two aces in three draws from a freshly shuffled deck of cards? In four draws?

Assume for both parts of the problem that each card is replaced in the deck before the next is drawn.

15.8. Use the binomial expansion (Equation 15.2) to determine the probability of obtaining three heads in:

(a) Five tosses of a coin.
(b) Seven tosses of a coin.

15.9. The binomial expansion method (Equation 15.2) may be applied to the die-throwing problem by letting a be the probability that a specific face (say 4) will come up on a single throw, and b the probability that it will *not* come up on a single throw. (a) What is the probability that three and only three 5's will come up in five throws of a single die? (b) In seven throws?

15.10. (a) In 100 tosses of a coin, heads come up 58 times. What is the percentage fluctuation of this outcome from the most probable outcome?

(b) Referring to Figure 15.3a what is the probability of obtaining 58 heads in 100 tosses relative to the most probable outcome?

(c) In 1000 tosses of a coin heads comes up 508 times. What is the percentage fluctuation of this outcome from the mean value?

(d) Referring to Figure 15.3a, what is the probability of obtaining 508 heads in 1000 tosses relative to the most probable outcome?

(e) Discuss the relationship between your answers to parts a–b and c–d.

15.11. (a) Using Figure 15.3a, estimate the probability of obtaining an outcome $x = N_H - N_T$ between 10 and 15 relative to that of obtaining an outcome within ± 2.5 of the most probable outcome in 100 tosses of a coin.

(b) Repeat part a for 1000 tosses of a coin.

(c) Discuss the relationship between your answers to parts a and b.

15.12. It is suspected that a certain coin is loaded because upon tossing it N times a 5% fluctuation from the most probable outcome is obtained. How large must N be before the judgment made on this statistical basis can be said to have at least a 70% chance of being correct?

15.13. Toss a coin 100 times keeping a record of the number of times heads and tails come up. Referring to Figure 15.3a what was the a priori probability of obtaining the result you did obtain?

15.14. A measured distribution function for the coin-tossing problem can be obtained if a large enough group of people (say twenty-five or more—all the students in your class, for instance) each toss a coin 100 times, record their results, then plot the number of times each outcome $x = N_H - N_T$ comes up as a function of x. (Alternately, each member of a smaller group can perform two or three 100-toss experiments and record the results of each one.)

Carry out this cooperative experiment and compare your results with the most probable prediction given by the appropriate Gaussian curve of Figure 15.3a. Are the discrepancies between the predicted and the actual distributions reasonable? Explain.

15.15. The diffusion of gas from a container can be discussed in terms of the two Gaussian curves plotted in Figure 15.3a.

Concentrate upon a molecule 2×10^{-2} m from the top of a container from which the lid has just been removed. Suppose that the pressures inside and outside the container are equal and so small that on the average a molecule travels 10^{-3} m before colliding with another molecule. Assume for simplicity that after each collision a molecule either travels straight up ($+ x$) or straight down ($- x$) for a distance $x = 10^3$ m. Then let the horizontal axis in Figure 15.3a be the distance in millimeters (10^{-3} m) of the molecule from its starting point ($x = 0$) after N collisions, and let N be counted starting from the time the lid is removed from the container.

(a) Estimate the probability of finding the molecule outside the container after 100 collisions. After 1000 collisions. (Recall that the area under both curves is equal to 1 and that both are symmetric about $x = 0$.)

(b) Repeat part a for a molecule initially 4×10^{-2} m from the top of the container.

(c) Discuss the relevance of these calculations to the problem of diffusion from a container.

15.16. In a class of 120 students the distribution of grades on an examination were:

Grade Range	Number of Grades in Range
96–100	0
91–95	1
86–90	2
81–85	5
76–80	8
71–75	10
66–70	29
61–65	26
56–60	25
51–55	8
46–50	12
41–45	2

(a) What was the average grade on the test? The most probable grade (the one occurring most frequently)? The median grade (the grade such that there are an equal number of higher grades as there are lower grades)?

(b) Students are frequently interested in whether their grades are to be "curved." The term implies that if the distribution is Gaussian (follows a Gaussian curve) then all grades are to be shifted upward or downward so that the most frequently occurring grade is set at a predetermined value, say 75. What does the assumption of a Gaussian grade distribution imply about the examination and the students taking it?

(c) Plot the grade distribution given above as a function of x, the deviation of a particular grade range from the most frequently occurring grade. Is the distribution a reasonable approximation to a Gaussian? Do you think the grades should be "curved"? If so how would you go about doing it?

15.17. In a repetition of the Rutherford experiment (Figure 15.5b) a small counter, placed one meter from a thin gold foil and positioned such that $\theta = 40°$, detects 1500 scattered α-particles per minute. About how many scattered particles per minute would be expected at 90°? At 120°?

15.18. In a Rutherford scattering experiment, performed with a very weak source of α-particles, 150 scattered particles are detected at 40°, 8 in an equal length of time at 120°, and 1 at 140°.

   (a) Assuming the 40° rate is the "true" Rutherford rate calculate the percentage deviations from the expected outcomes at the two large angles (refer to Figure 15.7).
   (b) Are these deviations significant? Explain.

15.19. The mean kinetic energy of a molecule in an ideal gas at temperature T is $\frac{3}{2}kT$, the most probable value $\frac{1}{2}kT$.

   (a) Distinguish between these two energies with reference to Figure 15.9.
   (b) Discuss a possible reason for the fact that the mean and most probable values differ for a Maxwell-Boltzmann distribution whereas they are identical for a Gaussian distribution.

15.20. (a) At 373 °K, what is the ratio of the number of molecules in an ideal gas with energies one-half the mean kinetic energy ($\frac{3}{2}kT$) to the number with the mean energy? What is the ratio of the number with twice the mean kinetic energy to the number with the mean kinetic energy?
   (b) Repeat part a for an ideal gas at 1000 °K.
   (c) Compare your answers to parts a and b and discuss the significance of the comparison.

15.21. (a) What is the ratio of the number of oxygen molecules at 373 °K with speeds one-half the most probable speed to the number with the most probable speed? What is the ratio of the number with twice the most probable speed to the number with the most probable speed?
   (b) Repeat part a for hydrogen at 373 °K.
   (c) Compare the results of parts a and b and discuss the significance of the comparison.

15.22. A vessel contains 0.02 kg of hydrogen and 0.32 kg of oxygen at 373 °K.

   (a) What are the most probable kinetic energies of the oxygen and the hydrogen molecules?
   (b) What is the ratio of the number of *hydrogen* molecules with the most probable velocity of the *oxygen* molecules relative to the number of *oxygen* molecules with the most probable velocity?
   (c) Estimate the fraction of oxygen molecules with speeds greater than the most probable speed.
   (d) Estimate the fraction of *hydrogen* molecules with speeds greater than the most probable speed for *oxygen*.

   [HINT: The areas under the curves in Figure 15.10 are equal. In order to answer parts c and d set them equal to N, the number of hydrogen or oxygen molecules.]

$$\textit{Heat and energy} \quad \Big| \quad \mathbf{16}$$

◣◣ 16.1 An ideal gas engine. The first law of thermodynamics

The absolute temperature of a substance is related to the mean kinetic energy of its constituent atoms or molecules, $\overline{KE}$. In particular, for an ideal gas (Equation 14.16b),

$$\overline{KE} = \tfrac{3}{2}kT,$$

where k is the Boltzmann constant (Equation 14.19b). Because the total molecular energy in an ideal gas with N hard sphere molecules is completely kinetic, its total internal energy is simply

$$U = N\overline{KE} = \tfrac{3}{2}NkT. \tag{16.1a}$$

If n is the mass of the gas in kilogram moles, then $N = nN_0$ (where N_0 is Avogadro's number) and since $N_0 k = R$, the universal gas constant (Equation 14.17b), we may also write

$$U = \tfrac{3}{2}nN_0 kT = \tfrac{3}{2}nRT. \tag{16.1b}$$

Because all gases expand when heated, they have the ability to perform work. In Figure 16.1, a cylinder containing an ideal gas at temperature T_1 is placed in contact with a heat source maintained at a higher, constant temperature T_2. Some time later the cylinder and its contents, having absorbed heat from the external source, are also at temperature T_2. The weight of the piston keeps the gas at a constant pressure. Therefore, the temperature change, $\Delta T = T_2 - T_1$ leads to a volume change $\Delta V = V_2 - V_1$ (Equation 14.17c) and the piston rises a distance $l = \Delta V/A$, where A is its cross-sectional area. The work performed by the expanding gas is (Equations 7.1 and 14.8):

$$W = Fl = pAl = p\,\Delta V.$$

Since $pV = nRT$ then $p\,\Delta V = nR\,\Delta T$, and we have

$$W = nR\,\Delta T, \tag{16.2a}$$

or, equivalently, in terms of the number of molecules and the Boltzmann constant k:

$$W = Nk\,\Delta T. \tag{16.2b}$$

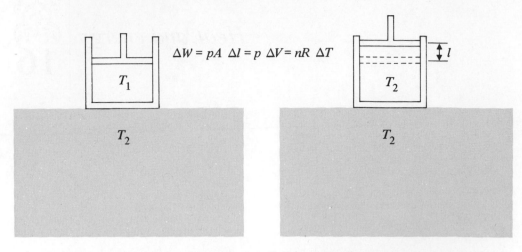

$$\Delta W = pA \; \Delta l = p \; \Delta V = nR \; \Delta T$$

FIGURE 16.1 An ideal gas engine. A cylinder of gas initially at a temperature T_1 absorbs heat from a large reservoir at a higher temperature T_2 and ultimately establishes temperature equilibrium with it. As it does so it expands at a constant pressure against the weight of the piston performing work $\Delta W = pA \, \Delta l = nR \, \Delta T$.

However, since the temperature has increased, so has the internal energy of the gas (Equation 16.1):

$$\Delta U = \tfrac{3}{2} nR \, \Delta T = \tfrac{3}{2} Nk \, \Delta T.$$

Therefore, the *total* energy expended as the gas performs its work in raising the constant-pressure piston is

$$E = W + \Delta U = nR \, \Delta T + \tfrac{3}{2} nR \, \Delta T = \tfrac{5}{2} nR \, \Delta T = \tfrac{5}{2} Nk \, \Delta T. \tag{16.3}$$

Since we assume the cylinder and heat source together constitute an isolated system this energy must have been absorbed from that source. Therefore, we may regard heat sources as special types of energy sources. For the same reason, the total internal energy of a substance, U, is sometimes referred to as its heat content.

Suppose the temperature of a steam engine containing 1.8×10^{-2} kg of water vapor increases from 500 to 1300 °K. How much does the mean energy per molecule increase? How much work is performed? What is the total energy absorbed from the heat source? Assume that water vapor can be treated as an ideal gas and that the engine is constructed as shown in Figure 16.1.

Referring to Table 14.1, the molecular weight of water (H_2O) is approximately 18 so that the engine's cylinder contains 10^{-3} kg-moles or (Equation 14.5) 6×10^{23} molecules. The temperature change $\Delta T = 1300 - 500 = 800$ °K. Therefore using Equation 16.1a with $N = 1$ and $k = 1.38(10)^{-23}$ J/ °K (Equation 14.9b) the mean energy per molecule increases by

$$\Delta KE = \tfrac{3}{2} \times 1.38 \times 10^{-23} \times 8 \times 10^2$$

$$= 1.65 \times 10^{-20} \text{ J}.$$

It is useful to express this result in electron volts (Equation 10.4):

$$\Delta KE = \frac{1.65 \times 10^{-20}}{1.6 \times 10^{-19}} = 0.106 \text{ eV}.$$

The work performed by the engine is obtained by substituting into Equation 16.2a:

$$W = 6 \times 10^{23} \times 1.38 \times 10^{-23} \times 8 \times 10^2 = 6.6 \times 10^3 \text{ J};$$

while the total energy absorbed from the heat source is (Equation 16.3):

$$\tfrac{5}{2}\Delta U = 16.5 \times 10^3 \text{ J.}$$

Any physical system with the capacity to convert energy from an external and/or an internal source into mechanical work may be called an engine whether it is an ideal gas engine like the steam engine in the foregoing example, an internal combustion engine, a hydrogen bomb, a growing plant, or a purely mechanical device whose operation does not involve changes in temperature. It is important to note that the work performed by an engine is usually accompanied by a change in the internal energy of the working substance itself, as was the case for our ideal steam engine.

Thermodynamics is concerned with the energy conversion processes that characterize the performance of mechanical work by all types of engines. The first law of thermodynamics is a restatement of the generalized energy conservation law of Chapter 7 (Section 7.8). If in performing work W an engine absorbs heat Q from an external source while changing its own internal energy by ΔU and its macroscopic kinetic energy by ΔKE, then

$$Q + \Delta KE = \Delta U + W. \tag{16.4}$$

The distinction between KE and U is worth noting explicitly. The former is kinetic energy associated with any moving parts of the engine such as its gears or pistons whereas U is the energy associated with its atoms and molecules. In the steam engine example we assumed implicitly that the piston was at rest at the beginning of the expansion cycle and moved slowly during the cycle so that ΔKE could be neglected relative to W.

The analysis of a few rather simple mechanical processes in which $Q = 0$ will clarify the meaning of the terms in Equation 16.4. A *ballistic pendulum* is a simple device for measuring the velocity of a bullet (Figure 16.2a). When a bullet of mass m and (unknown) velocity v is shot into the pendulum bob M, the combined system recoils with a velocity V determined by momentum conservation:

$$mv = (m + M)V.$$

Following the impact, the system behaves like any other pendulum, converting its kinetic energy $\tfrac{1}{2}(m + M)V^2$ into gravitational potential energy, and therefore rising to a height y relative to V^2 by:

$$(m + M)gy = \tfrac{1}{2}(m + M)V^2.$$

Measurement of y leads to V and hence to the unknown impact velocity v.

We may regard the pendulum as an engine that absorbs external kinetic energy $\Delta KE = \tfrac{1}{2}mv^2$ from the bullet, and in raising itself to a height y performs work $(m + M)gy$. Applying the first law of thermodynamics (Equation 16.4) with $Q = 0$ the internal energy change involved must be

$$\Delta U = Q - W = \tfrac{1}{2}mv^2 - (m + M)gy.$$

Since ΔU is not converted into mechanical work it must be identified with the deformation and heating of the block caused by the impact of the bullet.

When a block of mass M approaches an inclined plane with velocity v, the plane itself becomes an engine capable of transforming the kinetic energy of the block, $\tfrac{1}{2}Mv^2$, into

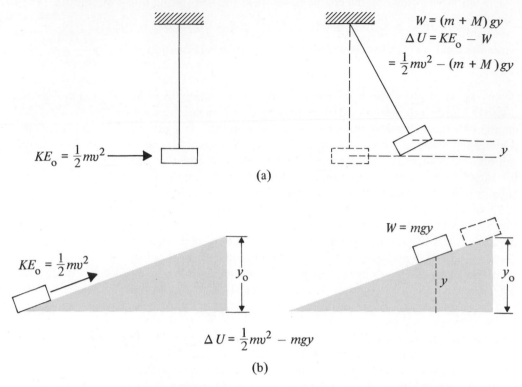

$$KE_0 = \frac{1}{2}mv^2$$

$$W = (m + M)gy$$

$$\Delta U = KE_0 - W$$

$$= \frac{1}{2}mv^2 - (m + M)gy$$

(a)

$$KE_0 = \frac{1}{2}mv^2$$

$$W = mgy$$

$$\Delta U = \frac{1}{2}mv^2 - mgy$$

(b)

FIGURE 16.2 (a) A ballistic pendulum analyzed as an engine. The initial kinetic energy of the bullet is transformed partially into external work, $(m + M)gy$, and partially into internal energy, ΔU. (b) Likewise, the initial kinetic energy of a body sliding up a rough inclined plane is converted partly into work, Mgy, and partly into internal energy of the body and surface. If the body would have risen to a height y_0 on a smooth plane of the same inclination, then $\Delta U = Mg(y_0 - y)$.

the useful work of raising the block to a height y (Figure 16.2b). If the plane is frictionless the internal energy does not change, and $\frac{1}{2}Mv^2 = Mgy$. But the mass must also perform work in order to overcome any frictional retardation it may encounter. Therefore, in general ΔU will not be zero and the surface temperature of the plane will increase. Since according to Equation 16.4,

$$\Delta U = \tfrac{1}{2}Mv^2 - Mgy.$$

The temperature increase is accomplished at the expense of the work performed by the plane, and the mass will not rise as far as it would have in the absence of friction.

A carefully controlled experiment of this sort would permit a precise measurement of the frictional heating, and prove experimentally that the loss in mechanical energy is equal to the increase in the internal energy.

The nineteenth-century British physicist, James Prescott Joule performed measurements in this vein. Figure 16.3 shows a sketch of one of his definitive experiments. A mass M is attached by means of a rope and pulley system to a set of paddle wheels enclosed in a small tank filled with water. When the mass falls it converts part of its potential energy into its own free-fall kinetic energy $\Delta KE = \frac{1}{2}Mv^2$, and also does work to drive the paddle wheels of total mass m against the resistance of the water. The loss in mechanical energy of the falling mass is therefore equal to the sum of the change in the internal energy of the water, ΔU, and the kinetic energy of the paddle wheels, $\frac{1}{2}mv^2$:

$$\Delta U = mgy - \frac{1}{2}(mv^2 + \frac{1}{2}MV^2).$$

Thus the water temperature increases, as Joule discovered. His studies provided conclusive proof that temperature is a measure of internal energy.

The first law of thermodynamics is most useful when applied to the analysis of processes involving the absorption of nonmechanical energy Q from external sources. We have calculated both the work performed and the internal energy change involved in the expansion of an ideal gas against a constant pressure (Equations 16.2 and 16.3). Therefore, as we have already concluded, the heat supplied by the constant temperature source (Figure 16.1) must be

$$Q = W + \Delta U = \tfrac{5}{2}nR\,\Delta T.$$

The efficiency of an engine is defined as the ratio of the work it performs to the total energy it absorbs. Therefore, an ideal gas engine has efficiency $(nR\,\Delta T)/(\tfrac{5}{2}nR\,\Delta T) = 40\%$. The remaining 60% of the input energy is dissipated as internal energy which causes a temperature rise.

Suppose that the external pressure applied to a piston confining an ideal gas to a cylinder is reduced. Since the gas pressure will be greater than the pressure exerted by the piston, the gas will expand until equality is reestablished. Now if the cylinder is isolated from all external energy sources, then $Q = 0$ during the expansion, and from Equation 16.4 it follows that $W = -\Delta U$. The work of expansion against the piston can only result from a reduction of the internal energy of the gas, and the temperature drops.

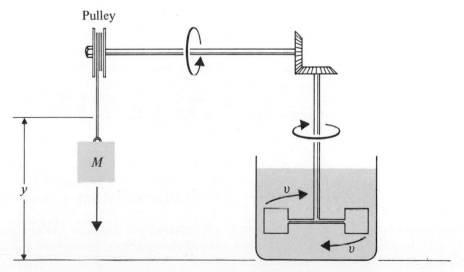

Figure 16.3 An apparatus used by Joule to demonstrate the equivalence of mechanical and thermal energy. The potential energy of the falling mass M is converted partly into kinetic energy of the body and the paddle wheels, and partly into internal energy of the water that resists the motion of the paddles.

Conversely, when the external pressure on the piston is increased, then work is performed *on the gas*. If isolated, $-W = \Delta U$, and its temperature rises.

Similar conclusions follow from the microscopic gas model. When a molecule collides with a completely rigid wall, energy conservation requires that it rebound with no change in the magnitude of its velocity. (The derivation of Equations 14.17 were based in part on this assumption.) But if one wall of a container is a nonrigid piston, such a collision results in a transfer of energy to or from the piston. Therefore the energy and hence the velocity of the rebounding molecule must change. The expansion of the gas against the piston results in a reduction of its total energy, and a consequent reduction in its temperature.

▶▶ 16.2 Internal molecular and atomic energy

We have shown that the total internal energy of n moles of an ideal gas at an absolute temperature T is $\frac{3}{2}nRT$ (Equation 16.1). This energy is due entirely to the random kinetic energy of the molecules that constitute the gas, and since it is directly proportional to temperature, is called *thermal energy*. If atoms and molecules were really hard, structureless spheres, the total internal energy of matter would be entirely thermal. But in fact the constituent atoms and molecules of a substance do have internal structure, and by virtue of their structure, possess internal potential energies that are considerably greater than their random, thermal kinetic energies. It follows that the total internal energy of any macroscopic substance is also considerably greater than its total internal *kinetic* energy. Therefore we would expect that if an engine were to use part of the internal *potential* energy of its working substance it could perform a good deal more work than if ΔU were associated with a change in thermal energy alone.

A hydrogen atom consists of a singly charged, negative electron bound electrostatically to a positive proton. On the classical planetary model the system is analogous to the sun and one of its planets. Referring to Equation 7.11b the work that would have to be performed in the latter case in order to increase the separation of the two bodies from R to infinity is $+GM_1M_2/R$. Therefore, the system has negative potential energy $-GM_1M_2/R$. By analogy, since the force between an electron and proton in hydrogen is electrostatic (Equation 8.1) the potential energy of the system is $-(1/4\pi\epsilon_0)(e^2/R)$, where $1/4\pi\epsilon_0$ is the Coulomb's law constant and e the fundamental charge. Therefore, the total internal energy of the hydrogen atom is

$$E = KE + PE = \frac{1}{2}Mv^2 - \frac{1}{4\pi\epsilon_0}\frac{e^2}{R},$$

where M is the electron mass and v its speed relative to the proton. Provided E is negative, then external work must be performed to disrupt the system. The absolute value of E for a bound system is called its *binding energy* since it provides a measure of its stability against disruption. As we shall learn in Chapter 17 the binding energy of an electron in hydrogen is 13.1 eV.

The potential energy graphs introduced in Chapter 7 are useful in the analysis of atomic and molecular processes. Figure 16.4 shows such a graph for the hydrogen atom with the three horizontal lines representing three different values of total energy, or binding energy. (As we shall learn in Chapter 17 only a certain discrete set of total energies is permitted.)

The concept of binding energy is easily extended to more complex systems. For instance we spoke of the binding energy of the semifree electrons in metals in connection with the

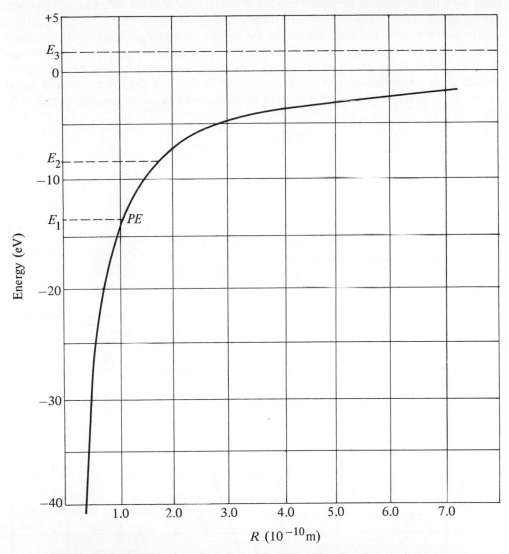

FIGURE 16.4 Energy diagram for a hydrogen atom showing the electrostatic potential energy of the electron relative to the proton as a function of their separation. Two of the three total energy lines represent the energy of bound states of the atom, while the third is positive, indicating that at that energy the electron has sufficient kinetic energy to escape completely from the proton. As will be shown in Chapter 17, only a particular set of bound state energies is permitted. However, there is no restriction on total energy in free states.

photoelectric effect (Section 10.3, Figure 10.6). Hydrogen and oxygen in their normal states consist of the diatomic molecules H_2 and O_2, respectively (Sections 14.3 and 14.4), which for simplicity we may regard as combinations of two identical atoms bound to each other and therefore with total energy smaller than zero. A specific value of total energy is represented as a horizontal line on the appropriate energy graph for the molecule (Figure 16.5). Because the internal kinetic energy of a molecule is never smaller than zero the separation between the atomic centers for a given value of total energy ranges between the minimum and maximum values given by the intersection of the total energy and the potential well. Hence the atoms in a molecule oscillate relative to each other with a maximum amplitude that decreases with their total energy (compare Figure 7.10). If the total energy is greater than zero the maximum separation is infinite and the system is no longer bound. As we shall discover in the next chapter the total internal energy of a hydrogen molecule may only assume a certain set of discrete values. The

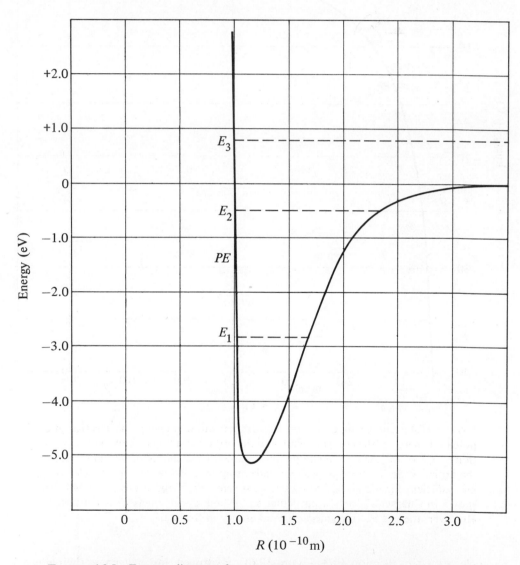

FIGURE 16.5 Energy diagram for an oxygen molecule showing its internal potential energy as a function of the distance between its two nuclei, and three different values of total energy. Two of these represent bound states of the molecule, the third its complete dissociation into two neutral atoms. (The internal, bound state energies of molecules, like the bound state energies of atoms, are quantized. See Chapter 17.)

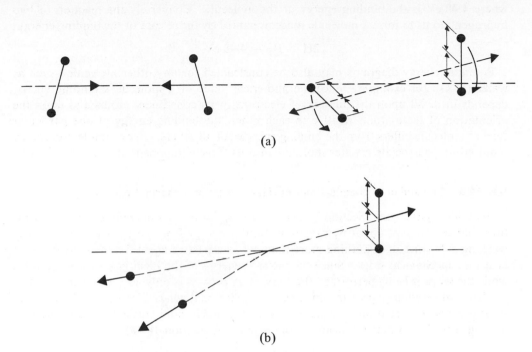

(a)

(b)

FIGURE 16.6 (a) In a collision between two diatomic molecules part of the initial translational energy may be transferred into internal energy of vibration along the molecular axis and/or of rotation. If sufficient energy is available (b), one or both of the molecules may even dissociate into two atoms.

minimum internal energy in a hydrogen molecule is -4.48 eV, in oxygen -5.08 eV. The normal binding energies of the molecules are the absolute values of those energies, or 4.48 eV and 5.08 eV, respectively.

A collision between two hard, structureless molecules results in an exchange of external or *translational* kinetic energy. When two diatomic molecules collide, not all of the energy transferred need be manifested as translational, thermal energy, however. Some of it may also be transferred into the internal vibrational energy of the systems (Figure 16.6). In a macroscopic sample of such a gas we would expect the mean translational and vibrational energies to be comparable, if we assume that in any collision the probability of energy transfer into the two alternate modes is equal. At room temperature (300 °K) the mean translational kinetic energy of a molecule, kT, is about $\frac{1}{40}$ eV. Therefore, very few oxygen or hydrogen molecules in a macroscopic sample have internal energies greater than the 5.08 or 4.48 eV required for dissociation into their free atomic states, and atomic hydrogen exists in reasonable abundance only at very high temperatures (Figures 15.9 and 15.10). For instance, even at 3000 °K less than 10% of the hydrogen in a given sample is in the atomic form. The energy required for dissociation is more easily obtained by passing an electric discharge through the sample, as we shall see presently. Whatever the source of the requisite energy, we may summarize the dissociation of hydrogen as

$$H_2 + 4.48 \text{ eV} \rightarrow 2H,$$

where 4.48 eV is the binding energy of the molecule. Conversely the reaction of two hydrogen atoms to form a molecule is accompanied by the release of the binding energy:

$$2H \rightarrow H_2 + 4.48 \text{ eV}.$$

Potential energy diagrams may also be constructed for any other molecule—such as water (H_2O), for example. Since the numerical value of a molecule's binding energy depends in detail upon the number of electrons in its constituent atoms and upon the orientation of these atoms relative to each other, the binding energy of one particular type of molecule differs from the binding energies of all others. For example, the energy required to disassociate a water molecule into its three component atoms is 13.22 eV.

▲▲ 16.3 Conversion of chemical and nuclear energy into thermal energy

In an ideal gas engine (Section 16.1) the work performed results *in toto* from temperature changes brought about by the absorption of energy from an external source. The working substance does nothing more than act as a passive agent for the conversion of heat into mechanical work. Since the internal energy of the ideal gas always increases while the work is being performed the conversion process is only 40% efficient.

Chemical reaction engines in which part of the internal *potential* energy of the working substances is converted into mechanical work are much more efficient. The burning of hydrogen to form water by means of the reaction (Equation 14.4a),

$$2H_2 + O_2 \rightarrow 2H_2O,$$

is a two-step process requiring the dissociation of two hydrogen and one oxygen molecules followed by the recombination of the resulting six atoms to form two water molecules. That is,

$$2H_2 + O_2 \rightarrow 4H + 2O \rightarrow 2H_2O.$$

Referring to the foregoing section, the binding energy of H_2 is 4.48 eV, the binding energy of O_2, 5.08 eV. Therefore, $2 \times 4.48 + 5.08 = 14.03$ eV must be supplied to two hydrogen and one oxygen molecules in order to cause their dissociation (Figure 16.7). How-

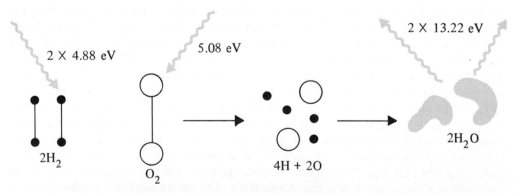

FIGURE 16.7 Pictorial representation of the formation of two water molecules from two hydrogen molecules and one oxygen molecule. A total energy of 14.03 eV is required to dissociate the three original molecules; when the six free atoms recombine into two water molecules an energy of 26.44 eV is released. Hence the net gain in energy is 12.41 eV.

ever, the internal energy of a water molecule relative to the state of complete separation of its three atoms is -13.22 eV, so that the net decrease in the internal energy resulting from the above reaction is $2 \times 13.22 - 14.03 = 12.41$ eV. The energy liberated by the reaction manifests itself as an increase in the translational thermal energies of the molecules.

Of course the above binding energies are much greater than the $\frac{1}{40}$ eV mean molecular energy at room temperature, and for that reason almost no molecules in a hydrogen-oxygen mixture react to form water. However, the reaction may be triggered by introducing a relatively small but concentrated amount of external energy into the mixture. For example, an electric discharge causes the ionic dissociation of most of the molecules along its path. Many of these will recombine to form water, subsequently transferring some of the kinetic energy they gain to surrounding atoms. Some of these will receive sufficient energy in this way to disassociate, and upon recombining transfer more thermal energy to the mixture. Given the proper circumstances the external discharge can trigger a chain reaction which converts virtually all of the hydrogen and oxygen into water vapor within a fraction of a second.

Let 6×10^{22} molecules of H_2 (10^{-4} kg-moles or 2×10^{-4} kg) react completely with 3×10^{22} molecules of O_2 to form 6×10^{22} water molecules. What is the total change in the molecular potential energy?

Since there are as many reactions as there are oxygen molecules and each reaction decreases the molecular potential energy by $12.4 \times 1.6 \times 10^{-19} = 2 \times 10^{-18}$ J, then

$$\Delta PE = -3 \times 10^{22} \times 2 \times 10^{-18} = -6 \times 10^4 \text{ J.}$$

We can apply the first law of thermodynamics to the reaction, writing ΔU as the sum of the changes in the internal potential and thermal energies (Equation 16.1).

$$Q = \tfrac{3}{2}nR\,\Delta T + \Delta PE + W + \Delta KE.$$

Here Q is the energy supplied by the triggering spark, W the work performed as a result of the reaction, and ΔKE any macroscopic kinetic energy change associated with the reaction. Consider for the moment the case in which the reaction occurs in a completely rigid container so that both W and ΔKE are zero. Then

$$\Delta T = \frac{2}{3}\left(\frac{Q - \Delta PE}{nR}\right).$$

Usually the external energy Q is relatively small. Its function is to induce the conversion of potential to thermal energy rather than to supply all the energy for conversion into work as in Section 16.1. If we set it equal to zero we can calculate the *minimum* temperature change resulting from the formation of 10^{-4} kg-miles (6×10^{22} molecules) of water vapor:

$$\Delta T = \frac{2 \times 6 \times 10^4}{10^{-4} \times 8.3 \times 10^3} = 1.45 \times 10^5 \text{ °K.}$$

It should be emphasized that this result assumes the reaction takes place in a completely rigid container. Clearly the increase in the pressure of the water vapor resulting from such a large, sudden temperature change would rupture most containers, permitting the gas to expand and cool itself. Similarly if the reaction occurred in a properly designed cylinder sealed with a moving piston (Figure 16.1), the expanding vapor could perform useful work. Such an arrangement constitutes an internal combustion engine. Since in this case neither W nor ΔKE is zero in the first law equation, the temperature would not rise as far as it would if no expansion took place. If work is performed the total internal energy of the gas decreases. But unless the vapor expands freely so that the final temperature change is zero the *thermal* energy is greater than it was before the reaction occurred.

Any chemical reaction that results in the liberation of thermal energy is called an *exothermic* reaction—in contrast with *endothermic* reactions which are sustained only by a net expenditure of external energy. Since the burning of hydrogen is exothermic, the inverse reaction, dissociation of water into molecular hydrogen and oxygen, must be endothermic. We have discussed a particular case of this reaction, electrolysis, in Section 14.4. There the sustaining external energy is supplied by a source of EMF, such as a battery.

Typical chemical reactions liberate energies on the order of a few to a few tens of electron volts per reacting atom. Typical nuclear reactions liberate energies a million times larger. Let us consider, briefly, the fusion of two nuclei of heavy hydrogen (or deuterium)* to form a helium nucleus (Figure 16.8a). Each of the deuterium nuclei consists of a proton and a neutron of approximately the same mass bound into a system by the strongly attractive intranuclear force (see Chapter 21). Likewise, the helium nucleus contains two protons and two neutrons. Because it is a bound system, work must be performed to separate a helium nucleus into two deuterium nuclei. Hence the internal potential energy of the nucleus is negative relative to a state of two free deuterium nuclei. Consequently the reaction

$$2D \rightarrow He$$

represents a transition to a lower potential energy state and is accompanied by the evolution of kinetic energy.

For present purposes it is sufficient to note that two protons, two neutrons, or a proton and a neutron attract each other with a strong force of completely nuclear origin and with a strength much greater than the electromagnetic force, but that the force is effective only if the separation between the interacting particles is smaller than about 1.4×10^{-15} m. Two protons repel each other electromagnetically, whereas the electromagnetic interaction between two neutrons or a neutron and a proton arising from the interaction between the intrinsic magnetic dipole moments of the particles (Sections 9.1 and 9.3) is small and may be disregarded here.

Figure 16.8b plots the potential energy of two deuterium nuclei relative to their free state as a function of their separation, R. As the nuclei approach each other, the mutual repulsion of their protons increases. Therefore, the potential energy of the system becomes increasingly positive until the protons and neutrons are within 1.4×10^{-15} m (the range of the nuclear force). Thereafter the interaction is strongly attractive. At these small distances the two deuterium nuclei are in a potential well with a depth of about 25 MeV and constitute a bound deuterium nucleus. Even as the two hydrogen and one oxygen molecules and their recombination into water liberates an energy of 12.4 eV, so the fusion of two deuterium nuclei into helium liberates about 25 MeV. But there the electrostatic repulsive barrier presents a formidable obstacle.

Using the electrostatic analogue to Equation 7.11b the potential energy of two particles with charge e separated by a distance R is

$$PE = \frac{1}{4\pi\epsilon_0} \frac{e^2}{R}.$$

---

* Deuterium is an isotope of hydrogen with atomic weight 2.015 (Section 20.2).

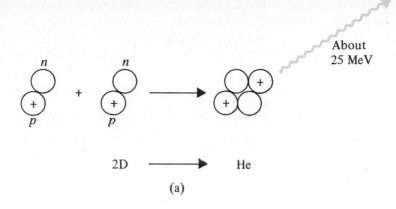

(a)

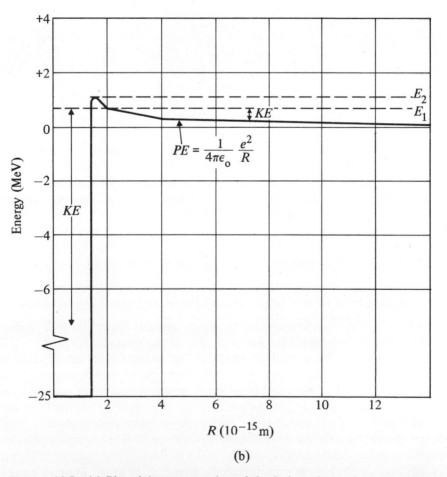

(b)

FIGURE 16.8 (a) Pictorial representation of the fusion of two deuterons (deuterium nuclei) into an α-particle (helium nucleus) with the release of about 25 MeV. (b) Energy diagram for the two-deuteron system. At separations greater than 1.4×10^{-15} m the force between the deuterons is repulsive and therefore, their potential energy positive. At smaller distances the primary interaction between them is the very strongly attractive nuclear force.

Substituting $R = 1.4 \times 10^{-15}$ m, the range of the nuclear force, we obtain an estimate of the maximum height of the barrier:

$$PE = \frac{9 \times 10^9 \times (1.6 \times 10^{-19})^2}{1.4 \times 10^{-15}} = 1.6 \times 10^{-13} \text{ J},$$

or

$$PE = \frac{1.6 \times 10^{-13}}{1.6 \times 10^{-19}} = 10^6 \text{ eV}.$$

The temperature of a macroscopic sample of deuterium gas with the same mean kinetic energy follows from the relation $\overline{KE} = \frac{3}{2}kT$:

$$T = \frac{2 \times 1.6 \times 10^{-13}}{3 \times 1.38 \times 10^{-23}}$$

$$= 7.7 \times 10^8 \text{ °K},$$

or almost one billion degrees!

Temperatures on this order exist only in the interiors of very massive stars (the temperature of the sun's core is estimated to be about 20 million degrees). However, if the *mean* temperature of a deuterium sample is on the order of a million degrees or so a small fraction of the nuclei* have sufficient energies to react. The liberation of the reaction energy provides more nuclei with the requisite energy so that virtually the entire sample can fuse into helium. A considerable research effort has been centered on the problem of raising gases to several million degrees rather slowly, so that fusion, or thermonuclear reactions, such as the one we have been describing, may be initiated in a controlled manner. None has succeeded thus far. However, the million degree temperature may be generated suddenly by exploding a uranium or plutonium fission bomb (Chapter 20) which serves the same purpose as the electric discharge that triggers hydrogen burning. In this case the fusion device becomes a hydrogen bomb. Of course the energy liberated is enormous. A 10^{-4} kg-mole sample of deuterium contains 6×10^{22} molecules (D_2) at room temperature. At a million degrees 12×10^{22} nuclei will be available for fusion so that 6×10^{22} reactions may occur. Since each reaction liberates about 25 million electron volts, then

$$\Delta PE = (6 \times 10^{22}) \times (25 \times 10^6) \times (1.6 \times 10^{-19}) = 2.2 \times 10^{11} \text{ J}.$$

Even if only 1% of the deuterium fuses, the figure remains impressive and suggests the reason for the well-documented destructive power of thermonuclear bombs.

In these sections we have outlined briefly a few technological applications of the energy conservation principle disguised as the first law of thermodynamics. But of course the applicability of the principle is much broader than these examples suggest. We have defined an engine as any system capable of converting energy from external and/or internal sources into useful work. Biological systems clearly satisfy the definition. Plants use electromagnetic energy radiated from the sun to form complex organic compounds from carbon dioxide, water, and chemicals of the soil, and use part of the internal energy liberated through these processes to do work, i.e., to grow. Human beings, too, are thermodynamic "engines," able to derive internal energy by initiating complex chemical reactions, and able to convert part of that energy into work.

---

* At these temperatures collisions have stripped virtually all the atoms of their electrons since the electron binding energy in hydrogen (or deuterium) is only 13.6 eV.

◤◤ 16.4 The second law of thermodynamics. Entropy

The laws of classical physics, momentum and energy conservation, the laws of motion, of gravitation, and of electromagnetism, for instance, are characterized by invariance with respect to time reversal (Section 6.8). None implies a preferred direction in time. A motion picture of a projectile moving along its trajectory, of an oscillating spring or pendulum, of two colliding billiard balls, or of the moon in its orbit would appear the same if run backward or forward. Hence all of these phenomena, and the laws governing their behavior are reversible.

Yet there are also a very great many processes whose reversals, even though consistent with energy and momentum conservation, are not observed. A mixture of ice and hot water ultimately becomes tepid water. But tepid water does not spontaneously separate into ice and steam, although energy conservation would not prohibit half of the molecules from transferring a disproportionate share of their energy to the other half. Likewise, a body moving along a rough, level surface does not extract heat from the surface and use the additional energy to accelerate itself.

The ideal gas engine of Section 16.1 converts heat energy from an external source partially into work, partially into internal energy. Energy conservation does not forbid the transfer of heat from the gas back to source, resulting in a decrease in the temperature and internal energy in the gas. But the process is never observed. Heat does not "flow" spontaneously from a cool to a warm body, but in the opposite direction.

Work is performed against the piston by the expansion of the hot gases formed by chemical reactions in an internal combustion engine. Energy could also be conserved if the piston reversed its direction, raised the temperature of the water vapor sufficiently to induce its dissociation and recombination into hydrogen and oxygen molecules, and caused emission of an electrical discharge. But, again, no such inverse chemical engines have ever been operated.

Among the laws of classical physics, the second law of thermodynamics is unique in specifying a direction in time for natural phenomena. In its simplest form the law is based on the nonobservation of a large class of processes and states that:

- Heat cannot be transferred *spontaneously* from a source at a lower temperature to a source at a higher temperature.

Of course refrigerators and air conditioners transfer heat from cold to warm sources. But they expend energy in the process so that the transfers are not spontaneous.

We have already touched upon the seeming inconsistency between the reversibility of the basic physical laws and the directional nature of so many observed macroscopic processes (Section 15.8). If we examine such processes from the microscopic statistical point of view they turn out to be highly improbable rather than strictly forbidden as the above empirically based statement of the second law implies. Consider a box containing ten black and ten white marbles. If it were shaken up we would expect the two colors to be distributed more or less evenly throughout its volume. Certainly the probability of finding all black marbles in the left half of the box and all white marbles in the right half would be very small.

Suppose we started with the colors separated. After shaking the box once we might find six white and four black on the left, four white and six black on the right. The probability of finding the *same* six white and four black marbles on the left after shaking the box several more times is very small and equal to the probability of attaining complete separation once again. But since there are many ways to obtain a six-four, four-six division but only one way to obtain complete separation we expect the former outcome to occur quite often while the latter should almost never be observed.

A glass of tepid water remains tepid for the same reason. When two molecules collide the faster has an equal probability of gaining or losing energy. *If and only if* in every encounter between two molecules a large energy transfer in favor of the faster one were more probable, and in addition, *if and only if* every fast molecule migrated upward while every slow molecule migrated downward, then tepid water *would* spontaneously separate into hot and cold layers. But since we are loathe to attribute such a degree of willfullness to the molecules, we conclude that a random energy distribution is maintained by the molecular collisions.

Suppose that in every collision the energetic water molecules *did* gain energy at the expense of the less energetic ones. Eventually a few would have sufficient energies to dissociate. If all the dissociated hydrogen atoms formed hydrogen molecules, and all the oxygen atoms oxygen molecules, and if thenceforth all the gas molecules *lost* energy in their collisions with water molecules, then ultimately all of the water would have spontaneously dissociated and recombined into cold hydrogen and oxygen! The sequence of events leading to that outcome is so improbable that it sounds fanciful. But it cannot be dismissed as strictly forbidden.

We may equate the order in a statistical system with the idea of uniqueness or definability. In these terms we regard a state with ten black marbles in the left half of a box and ten white marbles in the right half as more ordered than a homogeneous mixture of colors throughout the box, for the former state may be attained in only one unique way. In collection of molecules, the separation of water into hot and cold layers constitutes a higher degree of molecular order than a homogeneous tepid mixture. Similarly, the internal potential energies of a set of molecules are well defined and therefore, ordered, while their kinetic energies are random and therefore disordered. Finally, the disorder of a gas increases with its temperature since the number of ways its thermal energy may be distributed among its constituent molecules also increases (Section 15.8).

Any process forbidden by the second law of thermodynamics would, if it occurred, be characterized by a spontaneous increase in the order of a system. From the microscopic point of view any such occurrence is highly improbable. To be sure the order in *part* of a system may be increased but always at the expense of the order in another part. For example, a liter of tepid water may be separated into two half-liters at different temperatures. Part, but not all, of the thermal energy extracted from the cooler half might even be used to heat the other half. But additional external energy must be supplied to initiate and to complete the separation, necessitating an increase in disorder at the energy-producing source. Similarly, the electrolytic separation of water into hydrogen and oxygen results in an increase in the ordered, internal potential energies of the molecules, but it is accomplished at the expense of disordering chemical reactions within the battery supplying the EMF for the system.

The statistically-oriented restatement of the second law of thermodynamics is based upon the observed tendency of all systems toward disorder:

• Any isolated physical system will, if left to itself, proceed toward a state of maximum disorder. If already in a state of maximum disorder a system will remain in that state.

The *entropy* of a system is a quantitative measure of its disorder. Using this concept the second law states that:

• The entropy of an isolated system tends toward a maximum.

▲▲ 16.5 The second law and available energy. Heat death of the universe

Taken together, the first and second laws of thermodynamics imply that the internal disorder of an isolated physical system always increases as a result of performing work. Let us consider a two-step cycle in which the ideal gas engine of Section 16.1 performs work and then is returned to almost its original state ready to perform more (Figure 16.9).

STEP 1. The cylinder containing an ideal gas at a temperature T_1 is placed in contact with a heat reservoir at the higher temperature T_2 and allowed to come into temperature equilibrium with it. As a result the gas expands, does work against the constant pressure piston, and increases its own internal energy (Section 16.1). *However, the heat it absorbs reduces the reservoir temperature.*

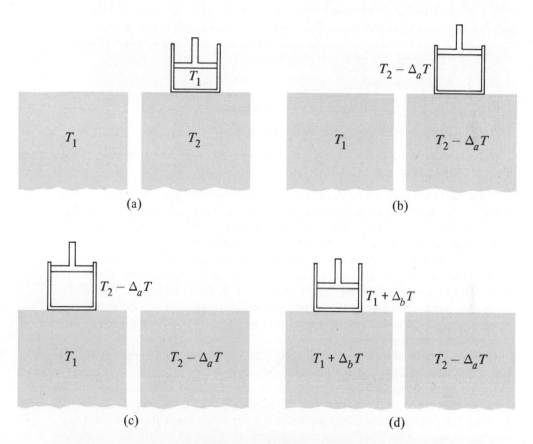

(a)

(b)

(c)

(d)

FIGURE 16.9 Cyclic operation of an ideal gas engine between two finite heat reservoirs. In (a) the engine has just been taken from the left reservoir at a temperature T_1 and placed on the right reservoir at the higher temperature T_2. After establishing temperature equilibrium and performing its work, (b) the engine is placed back upon the lower temperature reservoir (c) and comes into equilibrium once again at a lower temperature. Since the heat reservoirs are *not* infinite, the operation of the engine lowers the temperature of the hotter and raises the temperature of the cooler reservoir. Therefore, a smaller amount of work will be performed during the next cycle. Ultimately when the temperatures of the reservoirs are equal, no work at all will be performed.

STEP 2. The cylinder is placed upon a heat reservoir at its original temperature T_1 and permitted to come into temperature equilibrium with it. As the gas cools the constant weight of the piston compresses it. But since heat is transferred to the reservoir its temperature rises so that at equilibrium both the cylinder and reservoir are at a temperature slightly higher than T_1.

If we regard the two reservoirs and the ideal-gas-containing cylinder as an isolated system it follows from Equation 16.2 that the work performed in each expansion cycle is proportional to the temperature differences between the reservoirs. But the two-step process reduces the temperature difference so that on the next cycle a smaller amount of work will be performed whereas the temperature difference is decreased even further. Since each cycle reduces the distinction between the reservoirs then even though the order in the high temperature reservoir increases, the homogeneity of the system (reservoirs plus engine) and hence the total disorder of the system, increases. After a sufficient number of cycles there will be no difference at all between the reservoirs, the system will be unable to perform any more work, and will be in a state of maximum disorder.

A four-cycle internal combustion engine cycle provides another example.

STEP 1. A hydrogen-oxygen mixture in a cylinder is ignited by a spark.

STEP 2. The resulting hot water vapor expands and cools.

STEP 3. The piston reverses, expelling the vapor.

STEP 4. More hydrogen and oxygen flow into the cylinder from nearby tanks and prepare to react.

If the gas tanks and engine constitute an isolated system it is clear that the process will cease as soon as the hydrogen and oxygen supply is expended. Furthermore, since in the work cycle the two distinct gases are replaced by a single substance the end result is an increase in the homogeneity, and therefore, in the disorder of the system.

These examples suggest that only a fraction of a system's internal energy is available to perform work. The ideal gas engine could operate forever only if the two reservoirs were infinite so that their temperatures could remain constant. If the reservoirs are finite the system ultimately settles at an equilibrium temperature midway between T_1 and T_2 and does no further work even though (Equation 16.1) the total amount of internal energy is in general not zero.

It is also reasonable to assume a connection between the degree of disorder in an isolated system and its remaining available energy. More generally, it becomes clear on reflection that all macroscopic processes in any system occur because of differences between parts of the system, and that the processes themselves reduce those differences. A stone falls to the ground because there is a net force upon it. Current flows along a conductor because an EMF maintains a potential difference across the conductor. A gas absorbs heat from a reservoir because it is at a lower temperature and expands in order to reduce the difference between its pressure and the pressure of its environment. Hydrogen and oxygen molecules react because there is a difference between their internal potential energies and the internal potential energy of water.

The first law of thermodynamics would permit several of these processes to proceed spontaneously in the opposite direction thereby increasing the differences between parts of the systems and reconstituting the fraction of the energy available to perform work. But the second law states that these reversals are highly improbable processes. Therefore, we conclude that any physical system when left to itself will eventually attain its maximum possible degree of homogeneity or disorder, and that when this occurs all its internal macroscopic processes will have ceased.

This conclusion is not limited to the simple processes or to the classes of engines we have considered in detail. For instance, in the germination, growth, death, and decay of a plant the total energy supplied by the sun, and the earth, and its environment is ultimately returned in a different form. The formation of a highly organized form such as a plant constitutes a local increase in order. But the second law of thermodynamics implies that the ability of the earth (and sun) to create more plants decreases very slightly when that plant is produced. Likewise when a relatively well organized star is formed from diffuse galactic matter the ability of the galaxy to produce new stars is inevitably reduced.

If the universe as a whole is regarded as an isolated system the second law of thermodynamics predicts a gloomy end. The expenditure of its total available energy necessitates a gradual decrease in the rate at which natural processes occur. Consequently, the organization of matter into highly differentiated forms such as stars, planets, rocks, plants, animals, and men, must inevitably give way to increasing disorganization and homogeneity. Eventually, when no process can occur anywhere, the universe will have run down completely. In that distant epoch nothing will remain save a vast, dead sea of disorganized matter at a temperature a few degrees above absolute zero. Time will have come to an end; the so-called *heat death* will have occurred.*

Heat-death has worried philosophers from the time the idea was conceived. Those who attach ultimate meaning to the physical universe itself can hardly be comforted by assurances that the end of the solar system as we know it is a much more immediate eventuality. Various mechanisms have been proposed in attempting to spare the universe its seemingly inevitable fate. For example, certain biological processes might result in an increase in its total order rather than in the total disorder. It has also been suggested that if we regard the universe as infinite then it must contain infinite energy and hence an infinite capacity for useful work. Again, the running down of the universe has been connected with its expansion. Conceivably its total disorder might begin to decrease if and when a contraction cycle commences.

None of these escape mechanisms may be categorically ruled out. On the other hand there is no observational basis for granting any of them more than speculative status. Perhaps it is sufficient to realize that in its vastness the universe has many largely unexplored regions, and that there are still many unexplained and no doubt even undiscovered processes occurring within it. If from a purely statistical point of view the evolution of matter into forms as highly organized as stars must be regarded as very unlikely, then the undisputed existence of sentient human beings has a probability that is unthinkably small. In fact, on the cosmological time scale the emergence of man has been very rapid indeed.

SUGGESTIONS FOR FURTHER READING ▲▲▲

Among the many introductory physics texts that consider heat and work are:

ARNOLD B. ARONS, *Development of Concepts of Physics*, Addison-Wesley Publishing Co., Inc., Reading, Mass., 1965, Chapter 19.

K. R. ATKINS, *Physics*, John Wiley and Sons, Inc., New York, 1965, Chapter 12.

R. P. FEYNMAN, R. B. LEIGHTON, AND M. SANDS, *The Feynman Lectures on Physics*, Vol. 1, Addison-Wesley Publishing Co., Inc., Reading, Mass., 1963, Chapters 44, 45, and 46.

---

* In this sense "heat-death" is a misnomer; "cold-death" would seem a more appropriate term.

GERALD HOLTON AND DUANE H. D. ROLLER, *Foundations of Modern Physical Science*, Addison-Wesley, Inc., Reading, Mass., 1958, Chapters 19 and 20.

Two paperbacks of interest are:

D. K. C. MACDONALD, *Near Zero: The Physics of Low Temperatures*, Science Study Series, Doubleday and Co., Garden City, N.Y.

MARK W. ZEMANSKY, *Temperatures Very High and Very Low*, Momentum Series, D. Van Nostrand and Co., Princeton, N.J., 1964.

PROBLEMS AND EXERCISES ▲▲▲

16.1. A cylinder of volume V contains n moles of helium at an absolute temperature T. A second cylinder of equal volume contains $2n$ moles of helium at the same temperature.

(a) How do the mean energies of the helium atoms compare in the two cases?
(b) What is the ratio of the total internal thermal energies of the gases in the two cylinders?

16.2. Two cylinders of equal volume each contain n moles of helium. However, the temperature of the gas in the second cylinder is twice that of the gas in the first.

(a) How do the mean energies of the helium atoms compare in the two cases?
(b) What is the ratio of the total internal thermal energies of the gases in the two cylinders?

16.3. An ideal gas engine containing 0.14 kg of helium at 300 °K is placed in contact with a very large heat source at 1000 °K and comes into thermal equilibrium with it while expanding at constant pressure. How much work is performed? How much energy is extracted from the source?

16.4. Suppose that the heat source in Problem 16.3 is not infinite, but so constructed that its temperature decreases by 1° for each 5 J extracted from it.

(a) What is the temperature of the source after the ideal gas engine performs its work?
(b) If another identical engine at 300 °K is now placed on the source how much work will it perform in expanding at constant pressure?
(c) What is the temperature of the source after the second engine has performed its work?

16.5. A constant-pressure ideal gas engine is to be constructed using argon (atomic weight 40) as the working substance. The engine is to be capable of lifting a 500-kg load 10 m, and is to work between 2000 and 300 °K.

(a) What mass of argon is required?
(b) If the pressure is maintained at 10 atm throughout the expansion, what are the initial and final volumes occupied by the gas?

16.6. The *kilocalorie* (kcal) is a unit defined as the amount of heat required to raise the temperature of 1 kg of water 1 °C. Joule's experiments (described in the text) established its value at 4.2×10^3 J.

(a) How many kilocalories does the ideal gas engine of Problem 16.3 extract from the source?
(b) By how many kilocalories does its internal energy increase in the process of doing work?

16.7. A 5×10^{-3} kg bullet traveling at 200 m/sec lodges in the 0.5 kg bob of a ballistic pendulum.

(a) How far does the pendulum rise?
(b) What is the increase in its internal energy?

16.8. (a) The mean kinetic energy of the molecules in a sample of hydrogen is equal to their dissociation energy (4.88 eV). What is the temperature of the gas?

   (b) What would the temperature be if the mean kinetic energy of the hydrogen *atoms* in a gas sample were equal to the ionization energy (i.e., the binding energy, 13.6 eV) of hydrogen?

16.9. A *photoinduced* reaction may occur if a molecule absorbs a photon that supplies it with sufficient energy for dissociation.

   (a) What is the wavelength of the minimum energy photon that can induce the dissociation of a hydrogen molecule?

   (b) In what region of the electromagnetic spectrum do these photons lie?

16.10. About 10^4 kcal of heat energy (4.2×10^7 J—see Problem 16.6) are required to convert 1 kg-mole of boiling water at 100 °C into 1 kg-mole of steam at the same temperature.

   Estimate the potential energy of a water molecule in the 100° liquid relative to its immediate neighbors. (Assume the potential energy of a water molecule in the gaseous state is negligible.)

16.11. Sodium (Na—atomic weight 23) reacts spontaneously with water at room temperature to yield sodium hydroxide and hydrogen through the reaction (Equation 14.5):

$$2Na + 2H_2O \rightarrow 2NaOH + H_2.$$

For each sodium atom that reacts, 11.4 eV are released.

   (a) What total energy is evolved when 0.2 kg of sodium reacts completely with water?

   (b) The hydrogen gas evolved in the reaction frequently burns with explosive violence Is this reasonable? Explain.

[HINT: Under what conditions does hydrogen burn?]

16.12. When the organic gas methane (CH_4) burns, water vapor and carbon dioxide are produced, and an energy equal to 23.8 eV per reacting methane molecule is released.

   (a) Write a correctly balanced equation describing the reaction.

   (b) If 0.08 kg of methane in a rigid container which is initially at 300 °K burns completely, what is its final temperature? (Assume no heat is transferred to the container.)

   (c) If the high-temperature water vapor and carbon dioxide from the reaction in part b expand very slowly against a constant-pressure piston, how much work is performed?

16.13. (a) What net energy must be supplied by a battery to dissociate 0.001 kg of water by electrolysis?

   (b) If the dissociation of the water requires thirty min, what current flows from the battery?

   (c) Calculate the power supplied by the battery and, using your answer to part b, the effective resistance between the electrodes. (Assume the resistance of the leads between the battery terminals and the electrodes is negligible.)

16.14. According to the special theory of relativity, kinetic energy and inertial mass are equivalent. How much does the mass of 0.02 kg of oxygen change when it is heated from 300 to 3000 °K?

16.15. The binding energy of a hydrogen molecule is 4.88 eV. According to special relativity, what is the mass difference between two free hydrogen atoms and one hydrogen molecule? What is the fractional mass difference, $\Delta M/M$?

16.16. The atomic weight of a deuteron (heavy hydrogen nucleus) is 2.0141; the atomic weight of a helium nucleus is 4.0026.

(a) What change in mass occurs when two deuterons fuse into a helium nucleus? (The atomic weight of a proton is 1.008, its mass in absolute units 1.6×10^{-27} kg.)

(b) According to the mass-energy equivalence relation of special relativity, how much energy in electron volts is evolved in each fusion reaction?

16.17. (a) The first pair of accompanying sketches represents photographs of two billiard balls—one taken before, one taken after their collision. Can you determine which photograph was taken first? Explain.

(b) The second pair of sketches shows a set of thermometers embedded in a copper rod which is being heated at one end. Can you determine which photograph was taken first?

(c) Compare your answers to parts a and b and discuss the significance of the comparison.

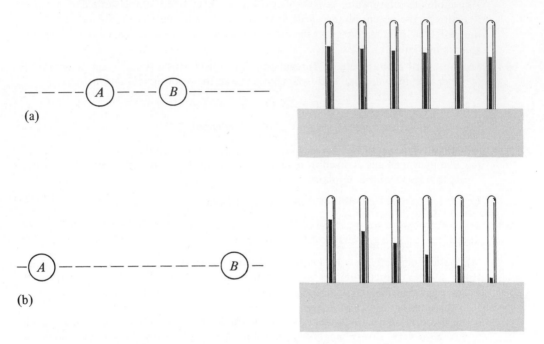

(a)

(b)

16.18. You as a patent attorney are asked to file a claim for a new type of engine to power a ship. The inventor claims that the engine will take in sea water at about 280 °K, extract heat from it to power the ship, and return ice to the ocean.

Discuss the economic feasibility of the device.

16.19. An inventor claims to have designed a perpetual motion machine that works as follows:

i. A source of EMF supplies energy for the electrolysis of water;

ii. the hydrogen and oxygen liberated enter a cylinder where they react.

iii. The energy evolved in the reaction drives the generator which is the source of EMF for the electrolysis, while the water vapor is returned for electrolysis.

Analyze each step of the cycle as completely as you can to determine the feasibility of the machine. (You may assume that all moving parts are frictionless.)

16.20. An inventor claims to have perfected a perpetual motion machine that works as follows:

i. An alternating current flows in a long solenoid. As the current increases its magnetic field draws a magnetized iron rod into the coil. When the direction of the current changes the magnetized rod is expelled from the coil.

ii. The iron rod is attached, via a system of frictionless bearings, to a fly wheel that drives a generator which supplies the alternating current for the coil.

Analyze each step of the cycle as completely as possible to determine whether or not the machine will work as the inventor claims.

Introduction to the quantum theory

17

▲▲ 17.1 The mechanical outlook and the microworld

The two centuries following publication of Newton's *Principia* witnessed a tremendous evolution both in the techniques of making physical measurements and in the methods and concepts used to interpret the resulting data. By the end of the nineteenth century the basic Newtonian framework had been modified and generalized to encompass a vast range of natural phenomena. We now refer to this entire body of concepts and applications as classical physics. Its most fundamental tenet was complete determinism, the belief that it is possible, in principle, to learn enough about any physical system at a particular time to unravel its past history and to determine its entire future behavior.

The idea that all physical systems may be comprehended in terms of human-scale mechanical models is a very appealing, albeit a rather naïve extension of the deterministic assumption. We have already seen that practical necessity requires that complete determinism be abandoned as a working procedure when the Newtonian methods are applied to the internal properties of matter. Nevertheless, classical statistics retains both the *principle* of determinism as well as the idea that gas molecules may be represented in terms of some sort of scale model (Chapters 15 and 16). Both the special and the general theories of relativity also assume that the laws of physics are completely deterministic, and in that sense must be regarded as modifying rather than breaking with the classical tradition. However the scale idea is explicitly rejected. The propagation of light cannot be comprehended in terms of a straightforward extension of classical particle propagation, and it is not particularly easy to *visualize* clocks that slow down or lengths that contract as their velocities increase.

It is quite astounding, in retrospect, that the simple Newtonian core of ideas bears up so well when applied to phenomena as diverse as the propagation of light or the internal properties of gases. Newton's laws of particle dynamics were based upon the observed behavior of falling bodies and planets in the solar system. That they could be extended to incorporate the rather abstract representation of nonmaterial electromagnetic fields on the one hand, and the statistical gas model on the other, is more surprising than the fact that they ultimately proved inadequate. However, it was the refinement of classical concepts and methods in precisely these two fields that finally revealed the approximate nature of Newtonian physics. When applied to problems as far removed from ordinary

594

experience as the propagation of light or the internal structure of atoms the classical methods led to results at best paradoxical, at worst patently absurd.

A spring, oscillating with a 5 cycle/sec frequency, may excite a wave on a string with the same frequency. Light, as we know, may be interpreted as an electromagnetic wave whose frequency is on the order of 10^{14}/sec. Therefore, in the most literal interpretation its source must be a charge oscillating with the same frequency. We are immediately tempted to think in terms of a scale model: a tiny charge on a spring oscillating at 10^{14} cycles/sec. But 10^{14}/sec is far beyond the directly observable range of frequencies; it is quite impossible to construct a laboratory spring-mass system to oscillate with even a remotely equivalent frequency. Therefore, it is not at all clear that an oscillating charge should behave in every way like a macroscopic spring system.

Likewise, although energy and momentum conservation are apparently applicable to the interactions of the molecules in a gas it is not at all clear that these molecules should behave in all respects as if they were colliding billiard balls. Indeed, we know that the internal potential energy of a molecule is ten to one hundred times larger than its mean kinetic energy at room temperature, and that internal structure plays the indispensable role in chemical reactions.

By the beginning of the present century there were already a few indications of the fact that microscopic processes cannot be completely comprehended in terms of macroscopic scale models. Hence it was clear that the classical concepts would require some sort of modification. In 1900 Max Planck derived a correct expression for the distribution of electromagnetic frequencies emitted by an incandescent solid by assuming that electromagnetic energy can only be emitted and absorbed in discrete packets, or *quanta*. During the next few years the idea that microscopic systems only assume discrete or *quantized* sets of internal energies, rather than any arbitrary energies whatsoever, was successfully extended to a number of other problems—most notably to the photoelectric effect by Albert Einstein (1905), then to the structure of the hydrogen atom by Niels Bohr (1913). These modifications of the Newtonian system became known, collectively, as the *quantum theory*.

However, the quantum theory that evolved from the work of Planck, Einstein, Bohr, and others retained many of the fundamental features of classical physics. In particular neither the assumption of complete determinism nor the idea that understanding could follow from some sort of scale model was explicitly abandoned, although the types of models required became increasingly exotic. As the century progressed it became increasingly evident that the classical framework could not be saved merely by grafting the quantized energy postulate onto it. The photon-wave paradox, already discussed extensively in Chapters 10 and 13, admits to no such simple solution. In addition, the Bohr model for internal atomic structure proves to be quantitatively valid only for hydrogen. More important, there are general questions relating to the sizes of atoms, the internal binding of molecules, and the internal structure of nuclei that classical physics is not even able to formulate.

By 1926, Werner Heisenberg and Erwin Schrödinger had succeeded in formulating new and consistent approaches to the problem of describing atomic processes. Both of them explicitly abandoned both the scale model idea and, most important, the assumption of complete determinism. Hence their work represented the most decisive break with Newtonian physics since the days of its founder. During the ensuing years the formulations of Heisenberg and Schrödinger became the foundation for a completely new system of physics, called *quantum mechanics*. Its concepts and methods have provided the fundamental tools required to understand the internal structure of atoms and nuclei and the interactions of the elementary particles. In addition, they have given us a far more profound insight into the structure of the physical universe than classical physics was ever able to offer.

In this chapter we shall discuss the "old" quantum theory as it evolved through the work of Planck, Bohr, and Einstein, and in the next present a few of the fundamental concepts of quantum mechanics itself.

▲▲ 17.2 Specific heats of diatomic gases

The statistical model outlined in Chapter 15 incorporates, as a fundamental tenet, the assignment of an equal a priori probability to each of the possible distributions of total internal energy among the molecules of an ideal gas. By 1859 it was already clear that this most basic assumption of the model might be dubious, since it led to predictions for diatomic gases (such as hydrogen and oxygen) at variance with observation.

The number of *degrees of freedom* of an atom or molecule is defined as the number of different, independent ways the total energy of the molecule can manifest itself. Since the velocity vector of a classical particle may be resolved into three mutually perpendicular components, each atom or molecule in an ideal gas has at least three degrees of freedom, namely, kinetic energy of translation in each of three mutually perpendicular directions. To the extent that the *internal* energies of the atoms or molecules remain constant in collision processes we may conclude that only these degrees of freedom are available. The binding energy of a helium atom is about twenty electron volts, for instance. Since the mean thermal energy at room temperature is only one-fortieth of an electron volt the probability of ionization by collision is negligible. Therefore, the energy transferred between two colliding helium atoms is all external kinetic energy (or kinetic energy of translation) and we are justfied in neglecting the internal structures of the atoms and assigning three degrees of freedom to each of them. Since the mean kinetic energy of a molecule in a gas at a temperature T is $\frac{3}{2}kT$ (Equation 14.16b), then to the extent that internal energies can be ignored we may attribute a mean energy of $\frac{1}{2}kT$ to each of the three degrees of freedom of the atom or molecule.

The assumption that molecules may be treated as structureless particles is, however, quite unjustified for diatomic molecules such as hydrogen, nitrogen, or oxygen. Since the constituent atoms of these molecules need not remain fixed relative to each other, part of the energy transferred between colliding molecules may be manifested as a change in their internal, vibrational kinetic energies (Section 16.2). A diatomic molecule may also rotate about any axis perpendicular to its interatomic bond. Since there are two mutually perpendicular axes which are in turn perpendicular to the bond direction the molecule has two independent modes of rotational kinetic energy (Figure 17.1) in addition to its vibrational energy, and therefore, two additional ways in which its energy might change in a collision with another molecule. In other words, diatomic molecules have *internal* as well as *external* degrees of freedom: two vibrational modes (one kinetic energy mode, one potential energy mode) and two rotational modes. Taken together with the three translational modes common to all atoms and molecules, these molecules each have a total of seven degrees of freedom. If we assume that energy transfer to each of these modes is equally probable, then the total mean energy of a molecule in an ideal diatomic gas at temperature T must be $\frac{7}{2}kT$, in contrast to the $\frac{3}{2}kT$ applicable to monatomic gases such as helium and argon. Of this energy $\frac{3}{2}kT$ is external (translational or thermal) energy and $\frac{4}{2}kT$ internal.

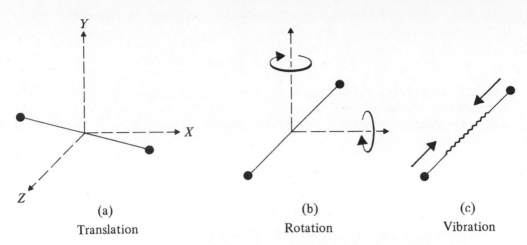

(a) Translation

(b) Rotation

(c) Vibration

FIGURE 17.1 The seven degrees of freedom (independent modes of motion) of a diatomic molecule. (a) Its center of mass may have independent velocity components in three mutually perpendicular directions. (b) It may rotate independently about two perpendicular axes which are themselves perpendicular to its bond axis. (c) Its constituent atoms may oscillate relative to each other. (There are two vibrational degrees of freedom: one of kinetic energy, the other of potential energy.)

According to the statistical model any external energy absorbed by a gas is distributed equally among the several degrees of freedom of its molecules. Temperature, however, is a manifestation only of the three translational kinetic energy modes. Therefore, if a mole of helium and a mole of hydrogen both absorb the same amount of external energy under the same conditions we would expect a *smaller* temperature increase for the hydrogen since more than half the additional energy should be distributed among its internal degrees of freedom. Even though this expectation is in *qualitative* accord with observation at normal temperatures, the increase in temperature expected for hydrogen is greater than the prediction based upon the assumption of an equipartition of energy among the seven degrees of freedom, and leads to the nonclassical conclusion that restrictions must be placed upon the possible internal energy states of the molecules.

The *molar specific heat* of a gas is defined as the amount of heat that must be added to one mole of the gas in order to increase its temperature by one degree Kelvin (absolute), or more simply, as the ratio of the heat added to the resultant temperature change. According to the first law of thermodynamics, external energy absorbed by a gas may be manifested both as mechanical work performed by the gas in its thermal expansion and as an increase in its internal energy. Clearly, then, the molar specific heat of any gas is not uniquely defined, but depends rather upon the amount of work the gas performs as a result of absorbing the external energy. It is customary to define two different specific heats corresponding to absorption of energy under two distinct types of restriction: (1) that the volume occupied by the gas does not change, so that no work is performed, and (2) that the work is performed in such a way that the pressure exerted by the gas remains constant.

The total internal energy U of one mole of gas with N_0 constituent molecules each with d degrees of freedom is $(d/2)N_0kT = (d/2)RT$, where $R = N_0k$ is the ideal gas constant

(Equation 14.7b). Substituting this expression into Equation 16.4 (the first law of thermodynamics) with $\Delta KE = 0$ we obtain

$$\Delta Q = \Delta U + W = \frac{d}{2} R \Delta T + W,$$

where ΔQ is the external energy absorbed by the gas and W is the work it performs. The molar specific heat at constant volume, C_V, is defined as the ratio $\Delta Q/\Delta T$ when the volume occupied by the gas does not change. Since a gas performs work only when it expands, the constant volume condition implies that $W = 0$ and we have

$$C_V = \frac{\Delta Q}{\Delta T} = \frac{d}{2} R,$$

$$V = \text{const.}$$

(17.1a)

On the other hand the work performed by a volume expansion ΔV against a constant pressure P is $P \Delta V$ (Section 16.1), which is equal to $R \Delta T$ for one mole of an ideal gas irrespective of the degrees of freedom of its molecules (Equation 16.2). Thus in the constant pressure case we have

$$\Delta Q = \frac{d}{2} R \Delta T + R \Delta T = \frac{(d + 2)}{2} R \Delta T,$$

so that the specific heat at constant pressure, C_P, is

$$C_P = \frac{\Delta Q}{\Delta T} = \frac{(d + 2)}{2} R.$$

$$P = \text{const.}$$

(17.1b)

As anticipated from our earlier qualitative discussion the molar specific heat of a gas increases with the number of degrees of freedom of its molecules.

There are several reasons why these simple results are not expected to be in precise quantitative accord with observation. The statistical gas model of Chapters 14 and 15 assumes that the mean distance between the molecules of a gas is very large relative to the dimensions of the molecules themselves and that the molecular interactions are uncorrelated and restricted to contact collisions. Departures from these conditions modify the simple ideal gas law conclusions, and in particular the expressions for the specific heats. Nonetheless, we expect these modifications to affect both the specific heats at constant volume and at constant pressure in very much the same way. Therefore their ratio,

$$\frac{C_P}{C_V} = \frac{d + 2}{d},$$

(17.2a)

should be far less sensitive to details of the molecular interactions and should, in fact, depend only upon the assumption of an equipartition of energy between the degrees of freedom. For a monatomic gas, $d = 3$, so

$$\frac{C_P}{C_V} = \frac{5}{3} = 1.667\ldots,$$

(17.2b)

whereas for a diatomic gas with $d = 7$,

$$\frac{C_P}{C_V} = \frac{9}{7} = 1.286\ldots.$$

(17.2c)

TABLE 17.1   *The Measured Ratio* $\gamma = C_P/C_V$ *for Selected Gases*

Gas	Chemical Symbol	Temperature (°K)	$\gamma = C_P/C_V$
Argon	A	288	1.668
Helium	He	93	1.660
Neon	Ne	292	1.64
Hydrogen	H_2	288	1.410
Nitrogen	N_2	288	1.404
Oxygen	O_2	373	1.399
Methane	CH_4	288	1.31
Ethane	C_2H_6	288	1.22

We note that both ratios are pure numbers which depend only on the number of degrees of freedom of the molecules and not upon temperature, pressure, volume, or any other macroscopic or external variable.

Measured specific heat ratios for several gases at normal temperatures are listed in Table 17.1. The ratio for hydrogen is also given as a function of temperature in Figure 17.2. For the three monatomic gases, helium, neon, and argon, the measurements are in approximate accord with the prediction based on the assumption that the atoms have three degrees of freedom (Equation 17.2b). The measured ratios for the diatomic gases hydrogen, oxygen, chlorine, and nitrogen, are larger than predicted at normal temperatures. More seriously, Figure 17.2 shows that at least for hydrogen the ratio also depends upon the temperature at which it is measured, in clear disagreement with Equation 17.2c. At temperatures less than about 80 °K the specific heat ratio for hydrogen is approximately 1.6, a value characteristic of a gas whose molecules have but three

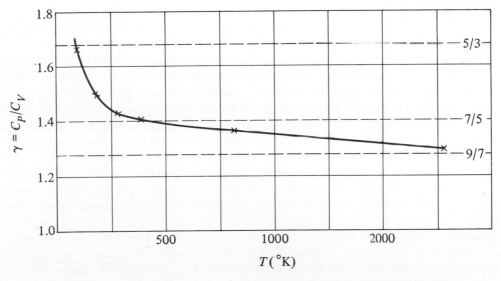

FIGURE 17.2   The measured ratio $\gamma = C_P/C_V$ for hydrogen as a function of temperature. Values of the ratio corresponding to the classical predictions for 3, 5, and 7 degrees of freedom, respectively, are indicated by the horizontal dashed lines.

degrees of freedom (Equation 17.3b). The ratio decreases with increasing temperature, and at room temperature (300 °K) has a value equal to 1.4, or about $\frac{7}{5}$, suggesting that its molecules have five degrees of freedom! The full seven degrees of freedom only manifest themselves at temperatures exceeding 2000 °K. This same general type of behavior, namely a specific heat ratio that decreases with temperature and approaches the expected classical value only at high temperatures, is exhibited not only for other diatomic gases such as oxygen and nitrogen, but also for more complex atoms that are expected to have more than seven degrees of freedom. (See the entries for the organic gases, ethane and methane in Table 17.1, for instance.)

A study of Table 17.1 leads inevitably to the conclusion that the internal and external degrees of freedom of a diatomic molecule cannot be treated as equally probable energy modes except at rather high temperatures. At very low temperatures the hydrogen molecules exhibit only their three modes of external, translational energy, and do not seem free to rotate or vibrate. The rotational, but not the vibrational degrees of freedom, are manifested at normal temperatures, whereas rather high temperatures are required before the vibrational modes are operative. This temperature trend is often summarized by stating that the rotational vibrational degrees of freedom "freeze out" at low temperatures.

Maxwell recognized the problem of the specific heats as early as 1859, but was unable to offer a solution. Classical physics provides no mechanism to justify the successive freezing out of the vibrational and rotational energy modes with decreasing temperature. In fact, the temperature dependence of the specific heat ratios may be rationalized only by restricting the allowable rotational and vibrational energies to definite sets of quantized values. A potential energy diagram for a diatomic molecule such as oxygen or hydrogen is shown in Figure 17.3. In analogy with the macroscopic harmonic oscillator potential (Chapter 7) we have heretofore assumed that any value of the total vibrational energy is permitted, represented graphically by any horizontal line whatsoever. If all values of total energy are permitted, it also follows that the vibrational energy of the molecule may *change* by any arbitrary amount as the result of a collision. This assumption leads immediately to the a priori equivalence of energy transfer to the vibrational and translational degrees of freedom.

However, let us now restrict the possible total internal energies to a set of levels labeled $E_0, E_1, E_2, \ldots, E_n$ (which from detailed quantum mechanical considerations are evenly spaced). Then a particular molecule with internal energy E_0 can change its internal state only by absorbing enough energy to make a transition to the state E_1. The molecule cannot absorb an energy smaller than $\Delta E = E_1 - E_0$ simply because it cannot exist in a state whose energy is greater than E_0 yet smaller than E_1. If the temperature of a gas is so low that the mean translational kinetic energy of its molecules is considerably smaller than the spacing between the level E_0 and E_1, the probability that a molecule will absorb sufficient energy by collision to make the transition to E_1 is negligible. Hence energy transfer by collision will be manifested almost entirely as external kinetic energy. The vibrational modes are effectively frozen out. At higher temperatures sufficient energy is available to populate the higher levels, and energy transfer between the vibrational and thermal energy modes becomes possible. Because the vibrational modes of the hydrogen molecule are manifested only for temperatures in excess of 1000 °K (Table 17.1) we conclude that the spacing between its vibrational energy levels (Figure 17.3) must be on the order of a few tenths of an electron volt, comparable to the mean external kinetic energy in that temperature range.

The freezing and unfreezing of the rotational degrees of freedom of hydrogen may be

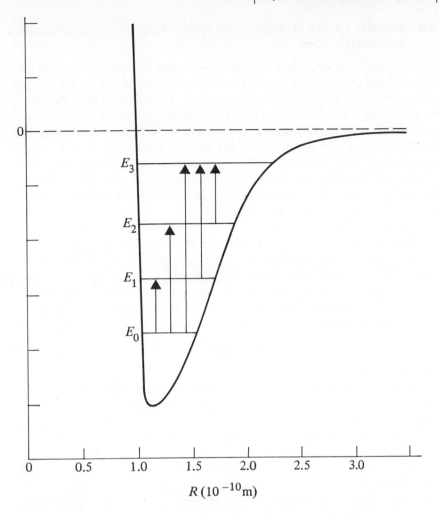

FIGURE 17.3 Internal energy diagram for a diatomic molecule. Classically the total energy of the bound system (represented by a horizontal line in the well) can assume any value whatsoever. But the specific heat data indicate instead that the total internal energy is restricted to a definite set of values. Therefore, the internal energy of the system can change only if it absorbs sufficient energy to make a transition (represented by the arrows) to a higher allowed state. (The total energies shown in the figure are illustrative only. They do not correspond quantitatively to the energies in any particular molecule.)

rationalized by making a similar assumption: namely that the molecule has only a specified, quantized set of rotational energies. A molecule with a particular, allowed value of rotational energy may make a transition to a higher state by absorbing sufficient energy. Hence if the probability of absorbing sufficient energy is small the molecule remains in its lowest possible rotational state. Because the rotational degrees of freedom unfreeze at lower temperatures than the vibrational degrees, we conclude that the spacing between the rotational levels is considerably smaller than the vibrational level spacing.

▲▲ 17.3 Radiation spectra of incandescent solids. Planck's quantum hypothesis. The photoelectric effect

There is a direct and important connection between the quantization of the internal molecular energies and the photon model of light, introduced in Chapter 10. In order to derive the most basic results of the statistical gas model (including the results of the foregoing section) it is not necessary to understand the details of the intermolecular energy transfer processes. Rather, it is sufficient to know that the molecular interactions conserve both energy and momentum. But of course the basic interaction is electromagnetic (Section 14.4). Therefore, the quantization of the internal molecular energies implies that the molecules can only emit and absorb well-defined discrete packets of electromagnetic energy. In the language of Chapter 10, the interaction of two molecules in a gas is mediated by an exchange of photons.

Use of the word "photon" in connection with internal molecular structure immediately suggests that the specific heat problem is symptomatic of difficulties in the classical framework that cannot be patched over merely by the ad hoc assumption of energy quantization. We have yet to face up to the problem that no classical model explains all the experimental properties of light. A classical particle model, the photon model, is consistent with the demands of the photoelectric effect; a classical wave model is required to rationalize the observed interference of light. Hence it is not unreasonable to expect that a theory resolving the apparent duality in the nature of light might also fundamentally modify our ideas about microscopic systems whose interactions can be discussed in terms of the photon exchange language.

Although the specific heat problem had been recognized by 1860, the quantum hypothesis did not come until 1900, when it was introduced in another context by Max Planck. Einstein's theory of the photoelectric effect (whose essential ingredients were discussed in Chapter 10) was introduced in 1905, though not completely verified experimentally until 1916.

Significantly (or ironically) the problem that led Planck to the quantum hypothesis had appeared admirably suited to an interpretation based upon well-known classical methods. When heated, solid bodies radiate electromagnetically. At relatively low temperatures their radiation is confined principally to the infrared regions of the spectrum; at higher temperatures appreciable energy is also emitted at visible wavelengths. That is, heated solids become incandescent: "red hot" if their radiation is confined to the infrared and long wavelength visible region; "white hot" when they emit appreciably in the yellow, blue, or ultraviolet.

Newton first demonstrated the continuous nature of the radiation spectra from incandescent solids (or liquids, or dense gases such as the sun) by dispersing the emitted light with a prism (Section 10.1). However, although incandescent bodies radiate over a broad range of electromagnetic frequencies, they do not emit the same amount of energy (i.e., intensity) at all frequencies. Rather, the observed radiated intensity is a rather involved function of both temperature and frequency. Curves showing measured frequency distributions of emitted radiation are given in Figure 17.4 for two different temperatures. As the temperature of the radiating body is increased, the frequency ν_0 at which maximum emission is observed shifts to a higher value so that the relative intensity at shorter wavelengths increases. The *total* energy emitted, measured by the area under the curves, also increases.

Statistical method appears admirably suited to the problem of deducing the observed radiation spectra in terms of the microscopic structure of matter. We may think of the

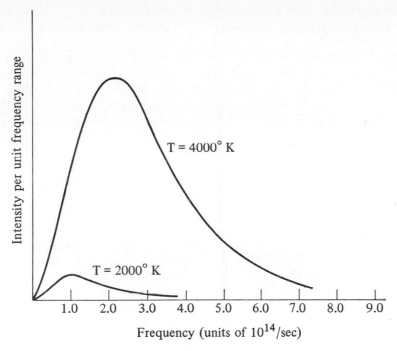

FIGURE 17.4   The intensity spectrum of an ideal, perfectly emitting incandescent solid plotted as a function of frequency at 2000 and 4000 °K.

incandescent body as an "engine" that converts energy from an external heat source into electromagnetic radiation. Because radiation is produced by accelerating charge, the energy conversion mechanism must involve the oscillation of the microscopic charge systems within the body. Comparing Figure 17.4 with the Maxwell-Boltzmann molecular energy distribution for an ideal gas (Figure 15.9), it is reasonable to conclude that the radiation spectra reflect a statistical distribution of energy among microscopic oscillations of various frequencies. There is no need to attribute any particular detailed structure to the oscillators. Rather, it is sufficient to assume that they interact via the transfer of electromagnetic radiation.

The statistical gas model assumes that the total internal energy of the gas is distributed at random among its molecules by some general sort of intermolecular collision mechanism. By enumerating the number of possible ways the total energy can be so divided, we arrive at a distribution function specifying the number of molecules in each particular range of kinetic energies. Likewise, to calculate the radiation spectrum of an incandescent body, we assume that its constituent oscillators transfer energy between each other by means of the radiation. If these oscillators can have all possible frequencies, we may then enumerate the possible ways the energy may be distributed among them and arrive at a distribution function giving the probability that radiation of a particular frequency exists in equilibrium with the oscillators.

Unfortunately, the result is in violent disagreement with observation, for it predicts that the probability of emission, and hence the radiated intensity, is a continuously increasing function of frequency. In other words, the model requires that most of the radiation should be in the ultraviolet region of the spectrum and beyond. But of course neither the sun nor charcoal in a fireplace radiates overwhelmingly in the ultraviolet. In fact, the measured curves of Figure 17.4 show intensity maxima in the infrared or the visible regions of the spectrum with only a small proportion in the ultraviolet even at a very high temperature.

Max Planck deduced the correct form of the radiation spectra by superimposing his quantum hypothesis upon the classical statistical model. He assumed that an oscillator is *not* free to emit and absorb arbitrarily small amounts of energy, but rather that the energy is transferred in well-defined packets of minimum size proportional to frequency. That is, the *quantum* of energy that can be emitted or absorbed by an oscillator of frequency v is

$$E = hv. \tag{17.3}$$

These quanta of energy are photons, although the latter designation was not current until about 1905. Planck's quantum hypothesis leads to the required reduction in the probability that a high frequency photon is emitted relative to the probability that a lower frequency photon is emitted, simply because the latter type of process implies a smaller change in energy than the former. Exactly the same mechanism inhibits energy transfer by collision to the vibrational modes of hydrogen molecules. These modes cannot absorb energy at all unless the requisite minimum is available, and at normal temperatures the probability of its being available is very small.

The precise shapes of the high-frequency portions of the observed incandescent radiation spectra (Figure 17.4) permits a numerical determination of Planck's constant. Its best value, based on contemporary measurements, is

$$h = 6.6251 \times 10^{-34} \text{ J-sec}, \tag{17.4a}$$

though $h = 6.6 \times 10^{-34}$ J-sec is sufficiently accurate for our purposes. Since Planck's constant is intimately associated with atomic and nuclear processes it is frequently useful to express its value in electron volt-seconds by applying the conversion factor given by Equation 10.4:

$$h = \frac{6.6 \times 10^{-34}}{1.6 \times 10^{-19}} = 4.1 \times 10^{-15} \text{ eV-sec.} \tag{17.4b}$$

Planck's constant plays a central role in contemporary physics. The velocity of light in vacuo is the only other number of comparable importance.

Historically, the next application of Planck's quantum hypothesis was made by Einstein in his theory of the photoelectric effect (1905). Of course we used the photoelectric effect to introduce the photon model of light (Section 10.4). According to Einstein's theory an electron in a metal is only able to absorb minimum, discrete amounts of energy from a beam of light. Hence, we assume the light consists of many of these discrete quanta, and that the maximum kinetic energy of the emergent electrons is equal to the difference between the energy of the irradiating photons and the binding energy of the electrons in the metal (Equation 10.3):

$$KE = E_{\text{ph}} - E_{\text{b}}.$$

To be consistent with Planck's hypothesis the photon energy must be related to the frequency of the radiation by $E = hv$ (Equation 17.3). Therefore, we have

$$KE = hv - E_{\text{b}}, \tag{17.5}$$

which implies that the maximum kinetic energy of the emergent electrons increases with irradiating frequency, as observed. R. A. Millikan's experiments (performed in 1916 and discussed in Chapter 10) verified Einstein's theory. Graphs of the measured maximum kinetic energy of the emergent electrons as functions of irradiating frequency are straight lines, as required by Equation 17.5 (Figure 17.5; see also Figure 10.6). These experiments also measured the value of Planck's constant, since the slopes of the curves, $\Delta(KE)/\Delta v$, are equal to h for all metals. The value of the constant obtained by Millikan was in complete accord with the estimate made by Planck from the shapes of the black body spectra. Hence, Einstein's theory of the photoelectric effect is completely consistent with Planck's quantum hypothesis.

▲▲ 17.4 The Correspondence Principle

We have considered in some detail the experimental observations that led to the energy quantization assumption. None of them explicitly denies the possibility of thinking in terms of scale models. However, the implied models have features that are decidedly nonclassical.

Suppose we choose to visualize vibrating diatomic molecules and the Planck charged

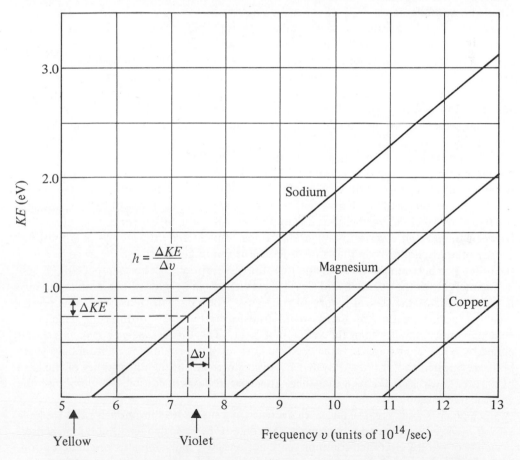

FIGURE 17.5 The measured maximum kinetic energy of the electrons ejected from sodium, magnesium, and copper plotted as a function of the electromagnetic radiation falling on the metals. According to Einstein's theory of the photoelectric effect, the common slope of the straight lines is equal to Planck's constant.

oscillators as minute harmonic oscillator systems. According to Equation 7.6, the maximum potential energy of a spring given in terms of its stiffness constant, k, and its amplitude, x_0, is $\frac{1}{2} k x_0^2$. Since k is constant for a particular spring, an oscillator can gain or lose energy only by changing its amplitude. But Planck's proposal implies that the model oscillators can only change their amplitudes in finite steps, each corresponding to a decrease in energy by $h\nu$. They are not permitted to linger at intermediate amplitudes. In other words, the radiation oscillators are only permitted a series of discrete, quantized amplitudes.

What time interval is required to make a transition between two amplitude states? The question is irrelevant. Valid physical questions can be asked only about measurable physical states. Planck's hypothesis implies that a charged oscillator can emit only specified amounts of energy. Any question about the time required to emit a photon is a question relating to the existence of the oscillator at an energy state less than one quantum away from a permitted level. To answer such a question requires measurement of the oscillator's energy in that state. But Planck has expressly denied that possibility. Therefore, intermediate amplitudes are physically undefined, and it becomes necessary to think of the oscillators as making discontinuous quantum jumps between their various allowed amplitude states.

We immediately extrapolate to a familiar, macroscopic spring, and recoil at the suggestion that this spring, oscillating for instance with an amplitude of 0.1 m should suddenly and discontinuously jump to an amplitude of 0.05 m. But although such extreme jumps are not observed with macroscopic springs, it is not inconsistent to regard such systems as having only certain permitted amplitudes. Suppose a 0.1 kg mass is oscillating at the end of a spring with stiffness constant 0.4 N/m. The frequency of the system is 2 cycles/sec. According to Planck's rule the minimum energy it can lose is $h\nu = 13.2 \times 10^{-34}$ J.

If its amplitude is 0.1 m then its energy must be 0.002 J, or about 10^{30} times the minimum amount it can lose (Equation 7.6). Therefore, an energy loss $h\nu$ is equivalent to an amplitude change of about 8×10^{-17} m, a distance less than one-tenth the radius of a hydrogen nucleus. In other words, the permitted amplitude levels of the macroscopic oscillator are so close together that it is impossible to distinguish a continuous transition between them from a series of quantum jumps. But in *microscopic* systems the total energy of an oscillator is on the same order as the minimum energy that can be lost, and the difference between the classical and quantum assumptions becomes important.

The merging of the quantum and classical predictions in a region of common experience is reminiscent of the special theory of relativity. The Galilean transformations are an excellent approximation to the Lorentz transformations at "ordinary" velocities— velocities much smaller than the velocity of light. The *Correspondence Principle* enunciated by Niels Bohr states that the classical laws must approximate quantum laws when both are applied to "ordinary" systems. It is a statement of the universality of the laws of nature, and rejects the idea that there are separate laws operating in the microscopic and the macroscopic realms.

Since macroscopic springs *appear* to decrease in amplitude continuously, and we have always believed that they do, continuity has come to be regarded as a "common sense" principle of nature. But such common sense notions have had a long history of deception. There is no a priori reason why continuity should be a more natural state of affairs than discontinuity. Planck's hypothesis has shown that quantum jumps are required for the solution of the incandescent body problem. The fact that they cannot be visualized suggests the depth of the prejudice laid down by years of "common sense" reasoning.

Planck's hypothesis can be visualized no better than Einstein's hypothesis concerning the constancy of the velocity of light in all inertial systems. Yet both are requisite to an understanding of natural phenomena. It is naïve to believe that nature must somehow conform to the terms of ordinary human experience, even in regions far removed from such experience. On the other hand, we do have a right to be dissatisfied with Planck's hypothesis unless we regard it as a step in the direction of a reformulation of Newtonian mechanics, for there is something unsettling about a theory that leaves all but one small portion of the classical framework intact.

▶▶ 17.5 Atomic spectra. The Balmer series in hydrogen

Derivation of a correct description of the continuous spectra radiated by incandescent bodies assumes a rapid interchange of the electromagnetic radiation between the oscillators. The assumption is valid for a solid, a liquid, or a dense gas in which the molecular or atomic oscillators interact almost continuously with each other, and hence constantly gain and lose energy. We have seen, for instance, that at normal temperatures, hydrogen molecules all have the minimum possible internal vibrational energy; that is, they are in the vibrational *ground state*. But at sufficiently high temperatures a good many will be able to absorb sufficient energy to make transitions to a higher, excited state. However, at normal pressures no excited molecule will remain in an excited state for too long a time, since it will rapidly transfer energy to another molecule by collision.

An entirely different situation applies in dilute gases whose pressures are about one-thousandth atmospheric pressure (i.e., on the order of one millimeter of mercury, Section 14.5). Under these conditions an atom or molecule will travel a considerable distance (on the average) before colliding with another. Hence a hydrogen molecule may be able to lose its excess energy and return to its ground state (or some other lower energy state) by spontaneously emitting a photon rather than by colliding with another molecule. If E_i is the initial internal energy of the molecule and E_f its final internal energy the emitted photon has energy $\Delta E = E_i - E_f$. Applying Planck's equation, $E = h\nu$ (Equation 17.3) the electromagnetic frequency corresponding to the transition is

$$\nu = \frac{1}{h}(E_i - E_f). \tag{17.6}$$

Thus we would not expect the spectrum of a hot, dilute gas to be continuous. Rather, it should consist of a series of lines at discrete frequencies, each corresponding to a transition between two internal energy levels.

The detailed character of the emission spectrum of a gaseous element or compound depends in detail upon the structure of its atoms or molecules. However, the general character of molecular and atomic spectra are quite different. The emission lines of molecules correspond to transitions between vibrational and rotational energy levels (Section 17.2) and are normally confined to the red and infrared regions of the spectrum. In contrast, many of the lines of atomic spectra, corresponding to internal excitations of the atoms themselves, are in the visible and ultraviolet region.

In addition to the evidence they offer for energy quantization, atomic spectra provide one of the best methods for determining the numerical values of the internal atomic energy states. For this reason they have been studied extensively since the late nineteenth century. Figure 17.6 shows the visible part of the discrete emission spectrum obtained when an electrical discharge is passed through a dilute sample of hydrogen. Since the

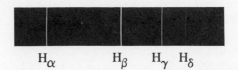

$$\text{H}_\alpha \qquad\qquad \text{H}_\beta \quad \text{H}_\gamma \ \text{H}_\delta$$

FIGURE 17.6 Several lines of the Balmer series of atomic hydrogen. The lines labeled H_α, H_β, H_γ, and H_δ have wavelengths 6.562×10^{-7}, 4.860×10^{-7}, 4.340×10^{-7}, and 4.101×10^{-7} m, respectively, and correspond to $n = 3, 4, 5,$ and 6 in Equation 17.7a.

arc carries sufficient energy to dissociate the hydrogen molecules (Section 16.2), the spectrum is characteristic of atomic rather than molecular hydrogen.

The first quantitatively correct deduction of an atomic spectrum from an atomic model was made by Niels Bohr in 1913. However, in 1884 J. J. Balmer found a rather simple empirical relation that correctly reproduced the observed visible wavelengths of the atomic hydrogen spectrum (Figure 17.7):

$$\frac{1}{\lambda} = R_\text{H}\left(\frac{1}{2^2} - \frac{1}{n_i^2}\right), \tag{17.7a}$$

where R_H (the Rydberg constant) $= 1.097 \times 10^7$/m, and n_i may assume any integral value greater than 2. If, for instance, $n_i = 3$, substitution into Equation 17.7a yields $\lambda = 6.562 \times 10^{-7}$ m, the wavelength of the red line in the spectrum. Likewise, $n_i = 4$ implies $\lambda = 4.861 \times 10^{-7}$ m, $n_i = 5$, $\lambda = 4.340 \times 10^{-7}$ m, etc., in agreement with Figure 17.6.

The series of spectral lines described by Equation 17.7a and shown in Figure 17.6 is now called the Balmer series, in honor of the discoverer of the equation. A very suggestive relation follows if the "2" in that equation is replaced by a number n_f which, like n_i, can also assume all integral values:

$$\frac{1}{\lambda} = R_\text{H}\left(\frac{1}{n_f^2} - \frac{1}{n_i^2}\right). \tag{17.7b}$$

If $n_f = 2$, Equation 17.7b reduces to Equation 17.7a for the Balmer series. But if $n_f = 1$ and n_i assumes the successive values $2, 3, 4, \ldots$, a series of lines in the ultraviolet is specified. Likewise if $n_f = 5$, $n_i = 6, 7, 8, \ldots$, series successively farther in the infrared are expected. All of these series have been observed, and are well described by Equation 17.7b. Thus the complete spectrum of atomic hydrogen is represented simply by changing successively the values of two integers in the equation.

It is convenient to rewrite the generalized Balmer equation 17.7b in terms of frequency instead of wavelength:

$$\nu = \frac{c}{\lambda} = cR_\text{H}\left(\frac{1}{n_f^2} - \frac{1}{n_i^2}\right).$$

The Planck relation (Equation 17.6) determines the energy of the photons corresponding to these frequencies:

$$\Delta E = h\nu = hcR_\text{H}\left(\frac{1}{n_f^2} - \frac{1}{n_i^2}\right), \tag{17.8a}$$

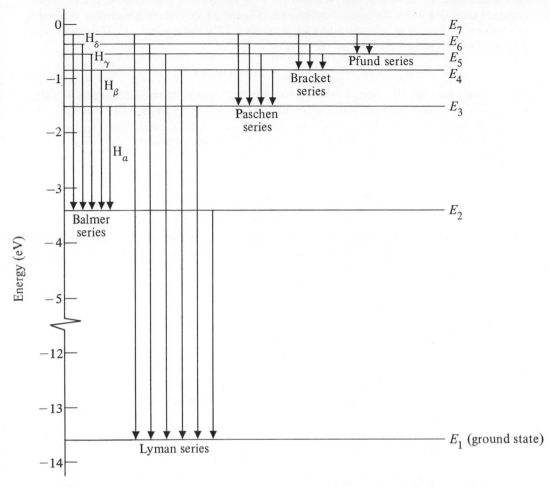

FIGURE 17.7 Schematic representation of the seven lowest energy levels in hydrogen derived from measured spectra. Transitions to the level E_2 (shown by labeled arrows) correspond to lines in the Balmer series, while the sets of transitions to E_1, E_3, E_4, and E_5 correspond to lines in the series discovered respectively by Lyman, Paschen, Brackett, and Pfund.

or, inserting the known numerical values of h, c, and R_H,

$$\Delta E = 21.76 \times 10^{-19}\left(\frac{1}{n_f^2} - \frac{1}{n_i^2}\right) \text{ J} \tag{17.8b}$$

$$= 13.6\left(\frac{1}{n_f^2} - \frac{1}{n_i^2}\right) \text{ eV}. \tag{17.8c}$$

If (as Bohr assumed) the observed lines in the hydrogen spectrum represent transitions between quantized, internal energy states of the atom, then Equations 17.8 must specify the energy differences between states labeled with the integers n_i and n_f. That is, when an atom in state E_i emits a photon and makes a transition to a state E_f the energy of the emitted photon must be $E_i - E_f$. It follows from Equation 17.8c that the energies of the two states must be $E_i = -13.6/n_i^2$ eV and $E_f = -13.6/n_f^2$ eV, respectively, the negative energies implying that the states are bound (Figure 17.7). More generally, since *all* transitions in hydrogen are described by Equation 17.8 the energy of *all* the internal atomic states must be specified by the relation

$$E_n = -hcR_H/n^2 = -13.6/n^2 \text{ eV}, \tag{17.9}$$

where *n* may assume all integral values. We note as a special case that when $n = 1$ the atom is in its lowest possible state, or *ground state* with energy equal to -13.6 eV. If the atom absorbs 13.6 eV the electron has sufficient energy to free itself from the proton. Hence the binding energy (or ionization energy) of the atom is 13.6 eV, in agreement with measurements based on chemical reaction studies (Section 16.2).

▲▲ 17.6 Bohr's theory of the hydrogen atom

According to the classical planetary (or Rutherford) model, the single electron in a hydrogen atom orbits about the central, heavy proton much as the planets of the solar system revolve about the sun, except that the binding force is electrostatic rather than gravitational in origin (Section 14.4, Section 15.6).

If for simplicity we restrict our attention to circular electron orbits, then the electrostatic force between proton and electron (Equation 8.1) is centripetal:

$$\frac{Mv^2}{R} = \frac{1}{4\pi\epsilon_0}\left(\frac{e^2}{R^2}\right), \tag{17.10a}$$

where *v* is the orbital speed of the electron, *R* the orbital radius, and $e = 1.6 \times 10^{-19}$ C, the fundamental charge. Using this relation we can immediately write down an expression for the electron's kinetic energy in terms of *e*, *R*, and the electrostatic force constant ϵ_0:

$$KE = \frac{1}{2}Mv^2 = \frac{1}{4\pi\epsilon_0}\left(\frac{e^2}{2R}\right).$$

The potential energy of the electron follows from Equation 8.13

$$PE = -\frac{1}{4\pi\epsilon_0}\left(\frac{e^2}{R}\right).$$

Therefore the total energy of the electron in a circular orbit of radius *R* is

$$E = KE + PE = -\frac{1}{4\pi\epsilon_0}\left(\frac{e^2}{2R}\right), \tag{17.10b}$$

or one-half the potential energy.

Classically there is no reason to restrict the value of *R* in Equations 17.10. A hydrogen atom should be able to absorb and emit any arbitrary energy simply by adjusting its radius accordingly. But this would imply a continuous rather than a discrete spectrum for atomic hydrogen. Thus the classical planetary model is inconsistent with observation.

There is another, more fundamental difficulty with the planetary model. The apparent symmetry of the solar system and the hydrogen atom is immensely appealing. But the symmetry is more apparent than real. *The electrostatic* force is analogous in form to the gravitational force. But the proton and electron interact *electromagnetically*, not just electrostatically. As a result no classical charged planetary system can be stable. An electron in a circular (or ellipitcal) orbit accelerates centripetally, and hence radiates electromagnetic energy (Section 12.4), and as the electron loses energy its orbit must shrink (Equation 17.10b). In other words, the acceleration implies a continuously decreasing orbital radius, and the complete collapse of the structure within a fraction of a second. Hence the Rutherford planetary hydrogen atom would have a short lifetime, in contrast with the observed stability of hydrogen.

Bohr's theory of the hydrogen atom assumes a set of stationary internal states corresponding to a set of permissible orbital radii, and thus, through Equation 17.10b, to a set of quantized internal energies. These states are specified by requiring that the corresponding orbital angular momentum of the electron, L (Equation 6.12), must be an integral multiple of Planck's constant divided by 2π:

$$L - n\frac{h}{2\pi}, \tag{17.11a}$$

where $n = 1, 2, 3, \ldots$. If we restrict our attention to circular orbits then $L = MvR$, with M and v the mass and velocity of the electron, and

$$MvR_n = n\frac{h}{2\pi}. \tag{17.11b}$$

By eliminating v between Equations 17.10a and 17.11b we obtain an expression for the hypothesized radii of the stationary orbits in terms of known constants and the running index n:

$$R_n = \left(\frac{\epsilon_0 h^2}{\pi M e^2}\right)n^2. \tag{17.12a}$$

Evaluating the constants, we have

$$R_n = (0.53 \times 10^{-10})n^2 \text{ m}. \tag{17.12b}$$

That is, the quantization of angular momentum according to Bohr's prescription (Equation 17.11) implies that the permitted, circular electron orbits have radii proportional to the square of a running integer. Setting $n = 1$ we obtain the radius of the first Bohr orbit in hydrogen: $R_1 = 0.53 \times 10^{-10}$ m, a number in good agreement with detailed evidence from the statistical gas model. The second Bohr orbit ($n = 2$) has four times the radius of the first, the third Bohr orbit nine times its radius, etc. (Figure 17.8).

The energies of the allowed states of the hydrogen atom follow directly by substituting the value of R from Equation 17.12a into Equation 17.10b:

$$E_n = -\left(\frac{Me^4}{8h^2\epsilon_0^2}\right)\frac{1}{n^2}. \tag{17.13a}$$

This expression, which like Equation 17.12a contains no unknown factors, may be evaluated numerically to give

$$E_n = -\frac{13.6}{n^2} \text{ eV}, \tag{17.13b}$$

in complete quantitative agreement with the empirical equation (Equation 17.9) deduced experimentally from the hydrogen spectrum.

Bohr's theory of the hydrogen atom as we have presented it here, rests on three postulates:

1. The Rutherford model is basically valid and, with two exceptions, may be described in classical terms.

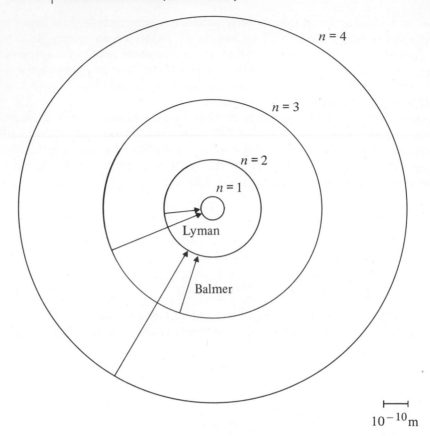

FIGURE 17.8   Circular electron orbits in hydrogen calculated on the Bohr model.
Each orbit corresponds to a different energy state. Two Balmer transitions and
two Lyman transitions are indicated by the arrows (compare with Figure 17.7).

2. EXCEPTION 1: An electron is in a stationary state, and does not radiate classically
   if its orbital angular momentum is an integral multiple of $h/2\pi$ (Equation 17.11).
   This condition, in addition to the classical electrostatic force law, suffices to specify
   both the radii and energies of the stationary (or quantized) states.
3. EXCEPTION 2: In making a transition between two stationary states the atom emits
   (or absorbs) a photon whose energy is specified by the Planck hypothesis, $E = h\nu$,
   and the requirements of energy conservation.

Of the three postulates the first is Rutherford's, the third an extension of the Planck law.
Bohr's second postulate was his own, unique contribution and, as we have seen, led to
the first successful determination of the internal energies of an atomic (or molecular)
system.

   In terms of the Bohr model the electron revolves about the central proton only in one
of a number of stationary orbits whose radii are specified by Equations 17.12 (Figure
17.8) and may change its energy only by making a transition to another stationary orbit.
Consequently the atom can emit or absorb only those photons whose energies permit
these transitions. Since there is no way to observe an electron in an orbit which is not
specified by Equations 17.12, the model provides no information about the electron
unless it is in an allowed orbit. Therefore, if we choose to regard the atom as a scaled-

FIGURE 17.9 Lord Rutherford (left) and Niels Bohr with Lady Rutherford and Mrs. Bohr. (Courtesy of the American Institute of Physics, Center for the History and Philosophy of Physics.)

down classical system we are required to talk in terms of instantaneous "quantum jumps" between the levels.

It is interesting to examine Bohr's second postulate in the light of his Correspondence Principle (Section 17.4) which requires the predictions of classical laws to approximate those of quantum laws when both are applied in the region of ordinary experience. Let us examine a transition between two adjacent orbits specified by very large values of n (Equation 17.12) so that we can assume the approximate validity of classical physics. If ΔR is the radial distance between them then (Equation 17.10a) the work performed by the electrostatic force F_e when an electron makes a transition from the higher to the lower orbit is

$$W = F_e \, \Delta R = \left(\frac{Mv^2}{R} \right) \Delta R.$$

However, energy conservation requires that the change in orbit be accompanied by the emission of a photon with energy $h\nu$ so that

$$h\nu = \frac{Mv^2 \, \Delta R}{R},$$

or

$$\Delta R = \frac{h\nu R}{Mv^2}.$$

We now assume that R is so large that classical electromagnetism is also valid. In that case the frequency of the emitted photon is equal to the orbital frequency of the electron in its orbit:

$$\nu = \frac{1}{T} = \frac{v}{2\pi R},$$

or

$$v = 2\pi R\nu.$$

Thus we may write

$$v^2 = 2\pi v R\nu,$$

so that

$$\Delta R = \frac{h}{2\pi Mv},$$

or

$$Mv\,\Delta R = \frac{h}{2\pi}.$$

But the expression on the left-hand side of the equation is just the change in the orbital angular momentum of the electron in making the transition between the two orbits. Therefore, although the derivation of this result is based on classical relations that we know are only approximately valid even for large radii, it is interesting to note that the result itself is equivalent to Bohr's second postulate (Equation 17.11), namely that the orbital angular momentum change in a transition between two adjacent stationary states is $h/2\pi$.

In addition to predicting the correct energy levels in hydrogen, the Bohr model also fixes the radius of the atom at 0.53×10^{-10} m (Equation 17.12) since the minimum energy state of the system corresponds to that orbital radius. Thus the theory has a fundamental built-in scale of distance. In contrast, although the mean radius of the earth's orbit is determined (via Newton's laws) by its orbital speed, classical laws do not fix that speed at its measured value, nor does classical physics forbid the scaling of hydrogen atoms down to any arbitrary size. In other words, classical physics is totally incapable of accounting for the fixed size of the hydrogen atom, or indeed of any atom.

As we have seen (Section 6.9), Galileo had already obtained evidence for some sort of fundamental scale in nature when he noted that the strength of macroscopic matter does *not* remain invariant with respect to changes in scale. If a particular type of atom did not have a fixed size then it would be possible to scale a dog up to the size of an elephant merely by expanding all its atoms. But, as we noted in Chapter 6, that is impossible, for all atoms of a given type are completely identical, even though classical physics cannot rationalize the identity. Because the radius of the hydrogen atom is fixed by Planck's constant (Equation 17.12a) the numerical value of that constant determines the fundamental, limiting role which is in many ways analogous to, but more subtle than, the role of the velocity of light in special relativity. It is possible to think of the profound results of special relativity as consequences of the fact that material velocities cannot be scaled upward indefinitely. We may expect similar insights to emerge from a consistent theory incorporating the scale limitations imposed by Planck's constant.

▲▲ 17.7 Difficulties with Bohr's theory

Since the spectra of all atoms exhibit a discrete line structure similar to (though generally more complicated than) the hydrogen spectrum (Figure 17.10) it follows that the internal energy states of all atoms are quantized and that their spectra should be interpretable in terms of transitions between these quantized states. However, the complete, quantitative Bohr model as presented in Section 17.6 is applicable to hydrogen alone. The helium atom, though second only to hydrogen in terms of structural simplicity, exhibits a considerably greater conceptual complexity. According to the classical Rutherford planetary model, helium consists of two electrons in planetary orbits about a central, doubly charged nucleus. The internal energy of the *hydrogen* atom is a function only of the radius of the electron orbit (Equation 17.10b). But each electron in the helium atom interacts not only with the nucleus but also with its neighbor. Since the latter interaction depends upon the separation of the two electrons a classical determination of the atom's internal energy would require knowledge not only of the orbital radii, but also of the relative positions of the electrons *in* their orbits.

There is absolutely no experimental justification for taking the planetary model so literally. On the contrary, there is considerable fundamental evidence *against* such an interpretation. Consequently, neither the Bohr postulates alone nor any additional ad hoc assumptions are sufficient for a quantitative determination of the helium spectrum.

In general the situation remains at least as hopeless for atoms of even greater complexity. However, the alkali metals—lithium, sodium, potassium, and cesium (with three, eleven, nineteen, and fifty-five electrons, respectively)—have structures that make them partially analyzable in terms of a modified Bohr model. The orbit of one of the electrons in each of these atoms has a radius considerably greater than the radii of the remaining electrons. Hence the outer electron "sees" a core with a single positive charge, the nuclear charge Z, partially neutralized by the $Z - 1$ inner electrons (Chapter 19). In the first approximation the classical energy of the outer electron is given by an

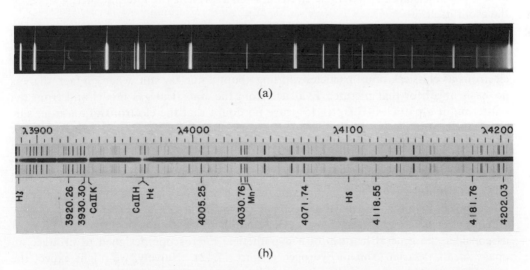

FIGURE 17.10 Parts of the spectra of (a) mercury and (b) iron. Wavelengths indicated on the latter are in angstrom units (1 Å = 10^{-10} m). (The iron spectrum is a photograph from the Mt. Wilson and Palomar Observatories.)

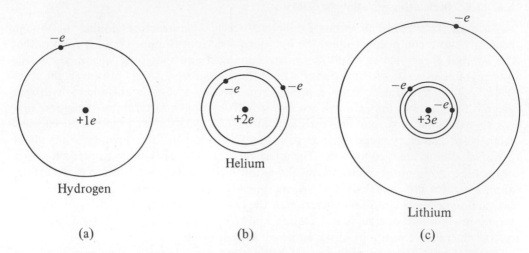

FIGURE 17.11 Literal (and incorrect) planetary models for (a) hydrogen, (b) helium, and (c) lithium in which the radius of each electron orbit and the position of the electron *in* that orbit is assumed to be knowable. The latter information is not required in the Bohr model, but would be in an analogous model for helium or lithium. Since one of the three electrons in lithium has a much larger radius than the other two, the Bohr model can be applied with some limited success, as explained in the text. However, it fails completely for helium.

expression analogous to Equation 17.10b, and application of the Bohr quantization rule for angular momentum yields the stationary levels for that electron. Actually the core electrons do not shield the nucleus completely. Therefore, the electrostatic force on the outer electron is not really represented adequately as the force between two point charges. However, as long as the core electrons absorb no energy and remain in their lowest possible states, these single electron levels represent the internal energy states of the atom itself.

These additional, partial qualitative successes of the Bohr theory, indeed, even its apparent triumph in quantitatively describing the hydrogen spectrum, should not obscure its fundamental, conceptual inadequacy. The literal planetary model implies a picture of electrons as classical, point particles whirling about a nuclear sun, when, in fact, there is no basis at all for that picture. Evidence from the statistical gas model and from the scattering of α-particles (Chapter 15) leave no doubt that the electrons of an atom surround the central nucleus at distances on the order of 10^{-11} to 10^{-10} m. Furthermore, the successful interpretation of atomic spectra not only requires the quantization of internal atomic energies but also provides a tool for measuring these energies. Therefore, the planetary analogue serves as a useful, working hypothesis. But if it is expected to yield information based upon the positions of two "planetary" electrons in their orbits, the model not only fails completely but becomes almost absurd.

No conceivable set of measurements can possibly localize an electron in its orbit. Let us consider the general features of a hypothetical microscope designed to produce an image of an electron orbit in hydrogen (Figure 17.12). Naïvely, we might expect the atom to cast its shadow if illuminated with a beam of parallel light, and could try designing a lens system to magnify that shadow. An object casts a sharp shadow, however, only when illuminated with light propagated in straight lines, or rays; that is, only

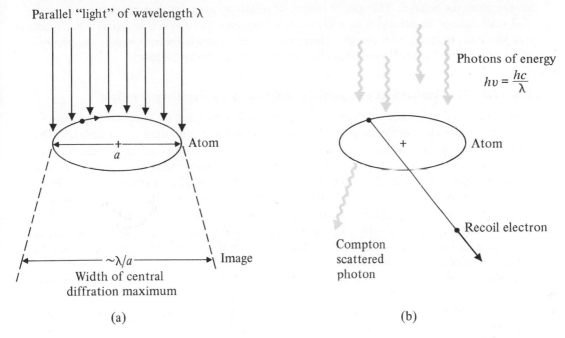

Parallel "light" of wavelength λ

Atom

a

~λ/a | Image

Width of central
diffration maximum

(a)

Photons of energy

$$h\upsilon = \frac{hc}{\lambda}$$

Atom

Recoil electron

Compton
scattered
photon

(b)

FIGURE 17.12   An attempt to photograph a hydrogen atom by illuminating it
with "light" of wavelength λ showing the interaction process on the basis of (a)
the classical wave model, and (b) the photon model of light.

if diffraction effects are small. But according to Equation 13.28, a single slit of width a
diffracts a beam of parallel, monochromatic light of wavelength λ such that θ, the angular
width of the central maximum, is on the order of λ/a. For a slit ten times greater than the
wavelength (i.e., $\lambda/a = 0.1$), $\theta \simeq 0.1$ radian $\simeq 6°$, while for $\lambda/a = 0.01$, $\theta \simeq 0.6°$. If our
atom is to cast a sharp shadow it should be illuminated with "light" whose wavelength
is no greater than, say, one one-hundredth its diameter. Since the radius of the first Bohr
orbit is about 10^{-10} m, we require light with a wavelength on the order of 10^{-12} m.

But can an image of a hydrogen atom really be formed with such a beam of light? Its
frequency is $\nu = c/\lambda = 3 \times 10^{20}$ sec. Therefore, the Planck law (Equation 17.3) implies
that each of its photons carries about one million electron volts energy so that our beam
of "light" is, in reality, a beam of very energetic x-ray photons with energies about 10^5
times the 13.6 eV binding energy of the electron in the atom! Hence the interaction of
the "light" with the orbital electron must inevitably eject that electron from the atom
via Compton scattering (Chapter 10). Our apparatus destroys the system we hoped to
observe! If in order to avoid this problem we used a low energy photon beam the associated wavelength would be greater than the size of the atom. For instance, yellow light
with 1 eV photons would not perturb the atoms unduly. But its wavelength is on the
order of 6×10^{-7} m, more than one thousand times the diameter of the first Bohr orbit.

In classical physics we assume implicitly that the process of measurement need not
perturb the system being measured. We may reflect light from a billiard ball without
worrying about the momentum transferred by the incident photons, for instance. But it
is clear that the implicit assumption cannot be scaled down indefinitely to the microscopic

level. Hence neither can we expect to scale down all of our ideas based on the way macroscopic particles behave. The special theory of relativity assumes that properties of space and time cannot be defined separately from measurements of space and time. We must likewise incorporate the fundamental limitation on our knowledge imposed by the process of measurement into any consistent theory of microscopic interactions.

◣◣ 17.8 The classical idea of a particle. Heisenberg's uncertainty principle

Our repeated reference to electrons as particles has avoided all questions relating to whether or not the implications of that designation have unlimited applicability. The complete kinematic description of a classical particle's motion requires specification of its momentum vector at all points along its trajectory. As we have seen, these classical demands cannot be satisfied completely for an electron bound in a hydrogen atom. How well can they be met for the much simpler case of a free electron moving in a straight line with a constant velocity vector? If we could measure the time and space coordinates of a free electron at two well-defined points along its linear trajectory we would succeed in specifying its kinematics completely. After all, we applied exactly the same procedure to the kinematics of an automobile in Chapter 2.

It should be clear from our earlier discussion that we must inevitably fail in this endeavor. Suppose we Compton scatter a narrow, parallel beam of photons from the moving electron (Section 10.5, Section 11.11) and record the position at which a scattered photon strikes a phosphorescent screen. The point in space at which the photon was scattered by the electron would then be determined (Figure 17.13), but only in the

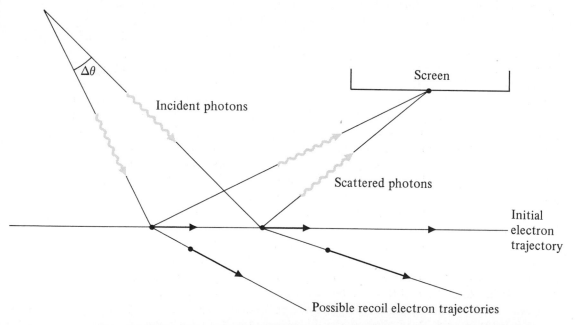

FIGURE 17.13 An attempt to measure simultaneously the position and momentum of a free electron to arbitrary precision. Because of diffraction the incident photon direction is uncertain. Therefore, the point at which it scattered from the electron is also uncertain. The position measurement is improved by reducing the wavelength of the incident light. However, the probability that the electron will suffer an appreciable deflection from its path is also increased.

approximation that the photons are propagated rectilinearly from their source. The diffraction of light implies that we really measure a scattering region instead of a point, and that the definition of that region improves as the wavelength of the incident light decreases. But according to Equation 10.5 the energy transferred to an electron in the Compton scattering of a photon is proportional to the square of the incident photon energy. Therefore, since a decreasing wavelength implies an increasing photon energy, the probability that the scattering deflects the electron substantially from its presumably linear trajectory increases along with the certainty in the measurement of its position. But unless we can measure the electron's position at two points along its path we cannot determine its momentum. Of course we can reduce the uncertainty in its trajectory by illuminating the electron with low energy photons. However, in that case, the assumption of rectilinear propagation for the photons becomes increasingly bad, and our knowledge of the electron's position when it scattered the photon increasingly uncertain.

We conclude, then, that the kinematics of a free electron cannot be specified with arbitrary precision, for the means we employ to sharpen our knowledge of its position inevitably blur our *simultaneous* knowledge of its momentum. Our right to call an electron a classical particle is therefore limited. A simultaneous measurement of position *and* momentum to arbitrary precision requires a method involving no momentum transfer to the electron. But that requirement is completely unrealistic. All physical processes, without exception, *are* interaction processes, and interactions imply momentum transfer (Sections 4.1 and 4.2). A stone falls because it interacts with the earth, gas molecules transfer energy to each other because they interact electromagnetically, a student sees a printed page because the photons reflected from that page interact with the receptor rods and cones of his eye.

It should also be clear that no nonoptical method of measuring the electron's trajectory can lead to a substantial improvement in the position and momentum measurements. Suppose we tried to measure the position of an electron by scattering another electron from it. To attain precision we would first have to define the trajectory of that second electron. Otherwise the measurement itself would be correspondingly uncertain. But if we found a way to measure the trajectory of that *second* electron to arbitrary precision we could then turn about and use the well-defined electron trajectory to measure the trajectory of a *photon* to arbitrary precision. Consequently, we could regard photons as completely localized, classical particles. But this conclusion would imply the rectilinear propagation of light in all circumstances, in fundamental disagreement with observation.

We have already noted the "dual" character of light which manifests an apparent particlelike structure in the photoelectric and Compton effects (Chapter 10) but an apparent wavelike structure in diffraction and interference experiments (Chapter 13), taking the viewpoint that diffraction effects limit the classical particlelike character of photons. But our ability to localize an electron, and thus to call it a classical particle, also seems to be limited. Hence the observed "duality" of light is *not* an exclusive property of the electromagnetic interaction, but reflects instead a fundamental limitation on our ability to understand microscopic processes in terms of classical models.

A quantitative expression for this fundamental limit is suggested by the diffraction of light. The diffraction by a slit of width Δx is characterized quantitatively by the angle θ which measures its maximum spread from the geometric shadow region (Figure 17.14a), where $\theta \cong \lambda/\Delta x$ (Section 13.11). Suppose that a parallel, monochromatic beam of light of wavelength λ is incident upon the slit. Initially the momentum of each photon in the beam is parallel to the y-axis of the system. The slit defines the *position* of a single photon in the beam to a precision Δx. How well can we predict the momentum of a single photon

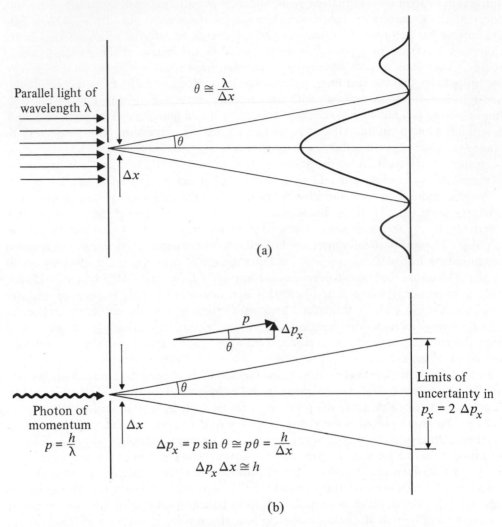

FIGURE 17.14 Derivation of the relation between the uncertainty in the position and momentum of a photon from the single-slit diffraction experiment.

whose position is so limited? We know what its angular deflection will be to within $\pm\,\theta$; therefore (Figure 17.14b), Δp_x, the uncertainty in the x-component of its momentum, after passing through the slit is (for small θ):

$$\Delta p_x = p_0\theta = \frac{p_0\lambda}{\Delta x}$$

or

$$\Delta p_x\,\Delta x = p_0\lambda.$$

As the certainty in the photon's position increases, the certainty in its momentum component in the *direction of the position measurement* simultaneously *decreases*. We have assumed that we can measure both the width of the slit and the angle θ to arbitrary precision. As this assumption will rarely be valid, a more realistic statement is

$$\Delta p_x \, \Delta x \gtrsim p_0 \lambda.$$

Planck's law relates the frequency of light to the energy carried by its photons, or, since $\nu = c/\lambda$,

$$E = h\nu = \frac{hc}{\lambda}.$$

Likewise, the energy and momentum of a photon are connected by a fundamental equation of relativity (Equation 11.25b with $M_0 = 0$):

$$p = \frac{E}{c}. \tag{17.14}$$

By eliminating E between these equations, we have

$$p = \frac{h}{\lambda}, \tag{17.15}$$

which, when substituted into the uncertainty relation, yields the result:

$$\Delta p_x \, \Delta x \gtrsim h. \tag{17.16}$$

In 1926, after a careful analysis of many processes, Werner Heisenberg (Figure 17.15) concluded that Equation 17.16 expresses a general and fundamental limitation upon our

FIGURE 17.15 Werner Heisenberg. (Courtesy of the American Institute of Physics, Meggers Gallery of Nobel Laureates.)

ability to measure *simultaneously*, and thus to know, the position and momentum of *any* entity, be it a photon, an electron, an atom, or even a billiard ball. Hence the relationship is called the Heisenberg uncertainty principle:

• The product of the *simultaneous* uncertainty in the position and momentum of an entity is *at best* equal to Planck's constant.

Suppose we want to know the y-component of a free particle's position to a precision of 0.5×10^{-10} m, the radius of the first Bohr orbit in hydrogen. How well can we specify the y-component of its velocity under these circumstances? Assuming nonrelativistic velocities, $\Delta p = M \Delta v$ and, from the uncertainty principle (Equation 17.16),

$$\Delta v = \frac{h}{M \Delta x}.$$

If we are concerned with a body whose mass is on the order of a kilogram,

$$\Delta v = \frac{6 \times 10^{-34}}{1 \times 0.5 \times 10^{-10}} = 3 \times 10^{-24} \text{ m/sec.}$$

Clearly we could never even approach a velocity measurement to that precision. Hence the Heisenberg principle imposes no restraint upon classical systems. But if we are dealing with an electron, then $M_e = 10^{-30}$ kg and

$$\Delta v = 1.2 \times 10^7 \text{ m/sec.}$$

The *uncertainty* in the electron's velocity is 4% the velocity of light! It is inconsistent to think of its velocity as less than 4% c. Otherwise the *uncertainty* in its velocity would be less than is required by the Heisenberg principle.

Our treatment is approximate since it neglects the relativistic increase in the electron's mass with velocity. Nevertheless, it is clear that an electron cannot be confined in a hydrogen atom if the atom's dimensions are very much smaller than 0.5×10^{-10} m. For as Δx decreases, then Δp increases and therefore the electron's kinetic energy must inevitably increase as well. But if the kinetic energy increases too much then the sum of the (negative) potential and kinetic energies of the electron will become positive, and hence the system will no longer be bound. Thus the Heisenberg principle implies the existence of a fundamental atomic scale of distance.

Let us try improving our estimate on the size of the hydrogen atom. If we concede that we know nothing about the position of the electron in an orbit, its position uncertainty is equal to the orbital circumference, or $2\pi R$. From the Heisenberg principle the minimum momentum in an orbit of radius R must be consistent with

$$Rp = \frac{h}{2\pi},$$

or, since $p = Mv$,

$$MvR = \frac{h}{2\pi},$$

which is precisely the second Bohr postulate for the case $n = 1$ (Equation 17.11). The uncertainty principle, applied to the problem of determining the size of the hydrogen atom, yields precisely the same result as the ad hoc theory of Bohr. But although the second Bohr postulate is mathematically consistent with the Heisenberg principle, the implicit Bohr-Rutherford planetary picture is not. We cannot treat electrons as classical point particles in well-defined orbits simply because their momenta are uncertain to at least $h/2\pi R$.

◣◣ 17.9 The limits of measurement. De Broglie's wave postulate. Diffraction of x-rays and electrons by crystals

Position and momentum, as defined in Chapters 2 and 4, are intrinsically classical concepts applicable to systems whose properties can be determined, in principle, to arbitrary precision. But the Heisenberg principle states that these concepts *cannot* be used to yield a complete description of a microscopic system in the sense that knowledge of the position and momentum vector of a planet at a given time suffices to determine the entire future course of its motion. No measurements we can perform determine in advance the momentum of a particular photon after it passes through a diffraction slit, although we can place limits upon that momentum; similarly, we cannot determine in advance the angle through which an electron will scatter a photon (see Compton scattering, Section 10.5), although we can relate the scattering angle to the initial and final photon energies (Equation 10.5, Section 11.11).

The source of the apparent photon-wave duality for light may be traced directly to the limited applicability of the classical position and momentum concepts. Our present goal is the description of microscopic systems. But it is obvious that we can only observe the *macroscopic* manifestations of these systems. The wavelength of visible light is inferred when diffracted by a slit a few tenths of a millimeter wide. Photon energies are deduced from the maximum energy of the photoelectrons they ejected from a metallic surface, while the apparatus used to measure the electron energies themselves involves electrodes, a voltage source, and a current-measuring meter (Figure 10.5). The energy levels of atoms may be determined from their spectra which are recorded on film with systems of prisms and lenses. Because we must infer the behavior of these microscopic systems through their interactions with macroscopic systems, and because macroscopic systems are described in terms of *classical* concepts such as momentum and position, we *must* describe the microscopic systems in terms that can eventually yield the best possible values of momenta and positions even though we are aware in advance of the ultimate limitations we shall encounter.

Of course we might try to work out a theory of microscopic processes in terms of concepts having no classical analogues and no connection with classical concepts. But there would be no way to determine whether or not such a theory had any correspondence with the real world. At the other extreme we could bypass intermediate classical constructs such as momentum and try to evolve a theory leading to predictions in terms of directly observable quantities such as the reading on a galvanometer or the separation, in meters, of the spectral lines on a photographic plate. But it would be exceedingly difficult to form a coherent picture of microscopic systems from a theory of this sort. The propensity of the human mind to think in terms of pictures, no matter how abstract, and to reason and extrapolate from these pictures cannot be denied. But the Heisenberg principle forbids the assumption that the behavior of microscopic systems can be inferred completely from these semiclassical pictures. It provides a criterion for judging the limits of their applicability.

The paradox of the "dual" nature of light, then, reduces to nothing more than the limited applicability of any single classical model of light. But what determines in a given instance which partial analogue we are permitted? Simply the particular aspects of light we choose to emphasize in that instance, or, yet more simply, the classical apparatus we are using. The associated wavelength λ of a photon with momentum p is h/p (Equation 17.15). If a beam of photons passes through a slit whose width is on the order of one hundred times this wavelength, or less, then (Equation 13.28) we expect a considerable departure from the classical particle model, and the classical wave analogue becomes more suitable for describing the resultant diffraction pattern. In these terms *the classical wavelength, λ, becomes a measure of the departure in a given instance from the classical particle analogue.* The Heisenberg principle permits that approximate analogue only when the position defined by an apparatus is much greater than λ.

On the other hand, in the photoelectric effect the light irradiating a metallic surface transfers its energy to electrons in discrete quanta. Hence a measurement of the process implies a considerable departure from the classical wave model. The measurement determines the energy and therefore the momentum of the photons, and suggests a particle model of light.

We have emphasized the general applicability of the Heisenberg principle. It follows that the above considerations are valid for electrons as well as for photons, and that, in particular, considerable departures from the classical particle analogue should become evident in any measurement that defines the position of an electron. Since none of the semiclassical measurements of the electron's properties impose sufficiently stringent position limitations we have heretofore been justified in calling it a classical particle. For example, the Millikan oil drop experiment (Section 9.7) measures the velocity, and therefore, the momentum of a charged oil drop, thus specifying the position of the electron only to within the diameter of the drop. However, the Heisenberg principle suggests that measurements with photons and electrons under "comparable" conditions should yield comparable results. Our problem is to specify the meaning of the term "comparable" conditions.

In 1923 Louis de Broglie suggested that Equation 17.15 be generalized by associating a wavelength λ with *any* entity of momentum p by the equation

$$\lambda = \frac{h}{p}, \tag{17.17}$$

thus providing the required comparability criterion. We can interpret the wavelength of an electron in the same way we interpret the wavelength of a photon: as a measure of the extent to which we can use the classical particle model. Whenever an apparatus limits the position of an electron to within a few hundred times its associated wavelength, we should be able to observe significant departures from the classical particle model. Thus, for instance, a beam of electrons should exhibit diffraction effects quite analogous to the diffraction of light.

However, the diffraction of visible light is observable only with a slit no wider than several hundred times its wavelength. Otherwise the effects are so small that the rectilinear propagation assumption appears valid (Equation 13.28). The wavelength of yellow light is about 6×10^{-7} m; the momentum of an electron of comparable wavelength (Equation 17.17) is 6×10^{-23} kg-m/sec corresponding to a kinetic energy, $p^2/2m$, of about 10^{-24} J or 3×10^{-6} eV. Therefore, in order to observe electron diffraction effects comparable to those of visible light we require a monochromatic beam of free electrons with exceedingly low energies. A free electron beam of any reasonable energy may be obtained by "boiling" the electrons off a hot filament and then accelerating them with a high voltage between the filament and a second electrode (Figure 17.14; see also Figure 9.39). If the magnitude of the accelerating potential is V volts, the energy of the electrons reaching the anode is eV joules, or V electron volts, by definition (Equation 10.4). Since

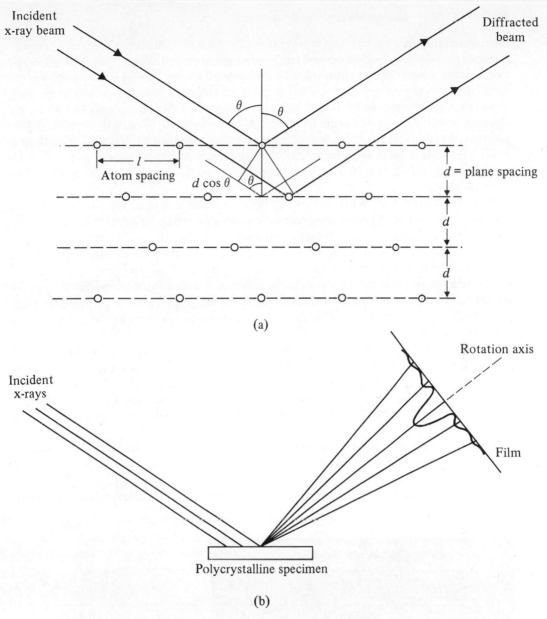

(a)

(b)

FIGURE 17.16 (a) Schematic diagram of Bragg x-ray diffraction from a crystal. The regularly spaced atomic planes which reflect the x-rays act like a series of slits. Reinforcement occurs when the path difference between the x-rays reflected from adjacent planes is an integral number of wavelengths. Cancellation occurs when the path differences are each a half-odd integral number of wavelengths. From the diagram the pertinent path difference, expressed in terms of the incident and reflected angle and the plane spacing, is $2d \cos \theta$. Therefore, maxima occur for θ such that $\cos \theta = n\lambda/2d$, where $n = 1, 2, 3, \ldots$. (From Derek L. Livesey, *Atomic and Nuclear Physics*, Blaisdell Publishing Co., Waltham, Mass., 1966.) (b) X-ray diffraction from a specimen containing many crystals. The spacing of the atomic planes in each crystal is the same, however, their orientation relative to each other is random. The effect is to rotate the diffraction pattern about an axis through its center, producing a series of concentric bright and dark rings.

the temperature of a hot filament is several hundred degrees, the mean thermal energy of the emergent electrons will be several tenths of an electron volt even before their acceleration. Hence a beam of free electrons with well-defined energy cannot be obtained by this method unless the energy they acquire in their acceleration is much greater than their initial thermal energy. But a 10,000 volt accelerating potential, for example, implies an electron wavelength on the order of 10^{-11} m, comparable to x-ray rather than visible wavelengths. In fact, the diffraction of x-ray photons even by a slit less than a tenth of a millimeter wide cannot be detected for the same reason that we would not expect to detect the diffraction of a 10,000 eV electron beam: the wavelengths are far too small in both cases.*

However, about 1913, W. H. and W. L. Bragg realized that since the spacing between the planes formed by the atoms in a regular crystal is on the order of 10^{-9} m or less they might serve as natural "slits" for x-ray diffraction studies (Figure 17.16). The planes define the positions of incident x-rays to about one hundred times their wavelength. Therefore there must be an uncertainty in the momentum of the outgoing x-ray photons, or a spreading of the beam. Because many different planes contribute to the diffraction effects and the crystal is three dimensional, the resultant pattern is more complicated than the simple slit pattern but is nonetheless completely comprehensible in terms of the classical wave analogue (Figure 17.17).

In 1927, C. P. Davisson and L. H. Germer in the United States and G. P. Thomson in England performed crystal diffraction experiments using an electron rather than an x-ray beam. The undoubted similarity between their results (Figure 17.18) and the Bragg x-ray diffraction patterns left no doubt that electrons and photons exhibit comparable behavior under comparable conditions according to the De Broglie prescription (Equation 17.17).

Then is an electron a wave? No more than a photon is a wave. By the same reasoning an electron is not a classical particle, although we shall often call it a particle for want of a better term. Rather, an electron is an entity that can sometimes be partially described in classical particle terms. Likewise, it is often possible (and profitable) to describe a beam

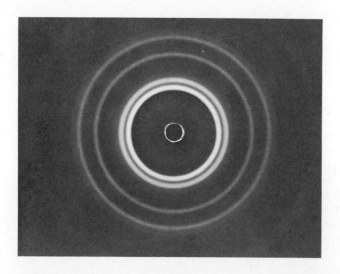

FIGURE 17.17 A diffraction pattern produced by an x-ray beam on polycrystalline aluminum. (Film Studio, Education Development Center.)

---

* However, the diffraction of electrons by an extremely fine slit has been observed.

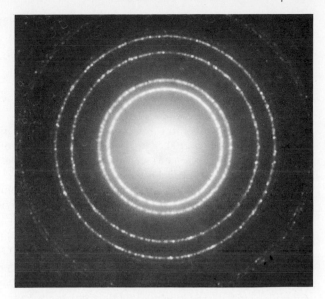

FIGURE 17.18 A diffraction pattern produced by an electron beam on polycrystalline aluminum. (Film Studio, Education Development Center.)

of electrons in terms of a classical wave model. That is the meaning of the De Broglie hypothesis.

Because neither the photon nor the electron can be adequately described in terms of one single classical model we cannot be forever satisfied with partial classical analogues. Rather, we must develop a new and fundamental theory that is able to rationalize the diverse behavior of these particles. Although that theory will contain many new and seemingly strange features we expect that it will at least describe both photon and electron, since both exhibit "comparable behavior under comparable conditions."

SUGGESTIONS FOR FURTHER READING ▲▲▲

Introductory physics texts, almost without exception, have one or more chapters on the old quantum theory, and at the very least, touch upon topics such as the Heisenberg Uncertainty Principle and the De Broglie relation. See, for instance:

ARNOLD B. ARONS, *Development of Concepts of Physics*, Addison-Wesley Publishing Co., Inc., Reading, Mass., 1965, Chapters 34 and 35.

K. R. ATKINS, *Physics*, John Wiley and Sons, Inc., New York, 1965, Chapters 26–28.

GERALD HOLTON AND DUANE H. D. ROLLER, *Foundations of Modern Physical Science*, Addison-Wesley Publishing Co., Inc., Reading, Mass., 1958, Chapters 30–35.

There are several nontechnical books written by the founders of quantum theory which are well worth reading:

NIELS BOHR, *Atomic Physics and Human Knowledge*, John Wiley and Sons, Inc., New York, 1958.

ALBERT EINSTEIN AND LEOPOLD INFELD, *The Evolution of Physics*, Simon and Schuster, New York, 1961, Chapter 4.

WERNER HEISENBERG, *Physics and Philosophy*, The Harper Brothers, New York, 1962.

ERWIN SCHRÖDINGER, *Science, Theory, and Man*, Dover Publications, New York, 1947.

The historical evolution of quantum theory is treated in:

GEORGE GAMOW, *Thirty Years That Shook Physics*, Science Study Series, Doubleday and Co., Garden City, N.Y.

Several of the more significant experiments in the evolution of quantum physics are discussed in detail in the monogram:

GEORGE L. TRIGG, *Crucial Experiments in Quantum Physics*, © University of Washington, Seattle, 1966.

PROBLEMS AND EXERCISES ▲▲▲

17.1. (a) What is the total *translational* molecular kinetic energy in one kilogram mole of hydrogen at 500 °K? In one kilogram mole of helium at the same temperature?

   (b) What is the *total* kinetic energy of the molecules in one kilogram mole of hydrogen at 500 °K? (See Figure 17.2.)

   (c) Suppose enough energy is added to the helium, maintained at constant pressure, to raise its temperature by 10 °K. If the same energy is added to one kilogram mole of hydrogen at 500 °K by how much will its temperature increase?

17.2. (a) How much work is performed by a hydrogen ideal gas engine working at constant pressure as the gas is heated from 500 to 2000 °K?

   (b) How much energy does the gas absorb in the process?

   (c) How does the efficiency of the engine compare with the efficiency of a helium engine? (Assume that on the average six degrees of freedom are operative between the two temperatures. See Figure 17.2.)

17.3. According to the results you obtained (hopefully) in Problem 17.1, hydrogen at any reasonable temperature contains more internal energy than an equal number of moles of helium at the same temperature.

   Comment on the feasibility of an engine that would increase the temperature of hydrogen in a container, and thus make it do work, by transferring energy from the vibrational and rotational to the translational modes of the molecules.

17.4. According to Figure 17.2, five degrees of freedom are operative in hydrogen at about 400 °K while all seven are operative at about 2000 °K.

   Using these data, estimate the order of magnitude spacing between (a) the rotational, and (b) the vibrational energy levels in hydrogen.

17.5. The *Wien displacement law* is a classically derived relation giving the wavelength at which an ideal radiator emits at the maximum intensity (the peaks of the curves in Figure 17.4) in terms of the temperature of the body:

$$\lambda_{\text{peak}} = \frac{A}{T},$$

where the constant $A = 2.9 \times 10^{-3}$ m °K. (The peak value for any given temperature is somewhat higher if the radiator is not ideal.)

   What is the temperature of an ideal piece of charcoal if its peak radiation intensity is at the extreme red end of the visible spectrum ($\lambda = 7.8 \times 10^{-7}$ m)? Are most outdoor barbecues really this hot? If not why is charcoal "red hot"? (Charcoal is fairly close to being an ideal radiator.)

17.6. Rocket-borne instruments show that the peak of the sun's radiation spectrum is at a wavelength of 4.65×10^{-7} m. Use the Wien displacement law to estimate its surface temperature.

17.7. Referring to Figure 17.4, what is the photon energy corresponding to the maximum intensity emitted from an ideal radiator at 4000 °K? What is the radiation intensity (relative to the maximum) for photons that are emitted with twice the peak energy? What is the radiation intensity for photons emitted with one-half the peak energy?

17.8. (a) What is the maximum wavelength radiation that can induce photoelectric emission from sodium? From copper? (The minimum electron binding energies are 2.4 eV and 4.3 eV, respectively.) In what regions of the spectrum do these wavelengths fall?

(b) Ultraviolet radiation with $\lambda = 2 \times 10^{-7}$ m falls on a sodium and a copper surface. What are the maximum kinetic energies of the electrons emitted in each case?

17.9. (a) What are the wavelengths corresponding to the three lowest energy lines of the Balmer series?

(b) To what photon energies do they correspond?

17.10. (a) What are the wavelengths corresponding to the two longest wavelength lines in the Lyman series in hydrogen ($n_f = 1$ in Equation 17.7b)?

(b) In what region of the spectrum do these wavelengths lie?

(c) What photon energies correspond to these wavelengths?

17.11. Suppose that an extragalactic object appeared to be receding from our galaxy at a rate such that the longest wavelength line in the Lyman series of their emission spectrum ($n_f = 2$ in Equation 17.7b) was Doppler-shifted into the blue portion of the spectrum (i.e., the wavelength would appear at about 4.0×10^{-7} m when seen on the earth).

(a) What would be the corresponding speed of recession?

(b) What would be the apparent wavelength of the second Lyman line from such a source ($n_f = 3$)?

17.12. During the nineteenth century Fraunhofer observed a series of discrete dark lines in the otherwise continuous emission spectrum from the sun. It is now known that these lines are due to the absorption and therefore the removal of some of the light from the sun by the cooler gases in its atmosphere. Since atoms emit radiation at discrete frequencies they should absorb it at the same frequencies. Hence the intensity of the observed radiation spectrum from the sun should be reduced at a number of discrete frequencies, as Fraunhofer observed.

However, not all the wavelengths of the gases in the sun's atmosphere appear in the Fraunhofer set of lines (though all the lines that *do* appear *do* have frequencies corresponding to emission lines). For example many of the Lyman lines in hydrogen are present but the Balmer lines are missing. If this reasonable? Why?

[HINT: Consider the probable temperature of the solar atmosphere.]

17.13. The helium *ion* He$^+$, which consists of one electron and a doubly charged nucleus, has a spectrum that is very well described by the Bohr model. Calculate:

(a) The ground-state energy of the ion.

(b) Its ground-state radius.

(c) The wavelength corresponding to the longest wavelength lines in its "Balmer" and its "Lyman" series. ($n_f = 2$ and 1, respectively, in Equation 17.7b.)

17.14. (a) What is the orbital angular momentum of the earth in its orbit about the sun? (Assume a circular orbit. Pertinent data appear in Appendix E.)

(b) According to the Bohr theory what is the value of the quantum number n corresponding to that orbital angular momentum?

(c) How much would the radius of the earth change if it made a quantum jump to the next smallest angular momentum value?

17.15. According to Equation 9.21b, an electron in an orbit with angular momentum L has an orbital magnetic dipole moment:

$$\mu_l = \frac{e}{2M} L.$$

(a) What is the magnitude of the orbital dipole moment in the ground state of the hydrogen atom according to the Bohr model? In the first excited state?

In Section 19.2 it is shown that an electron has an *intrinsic* magnetic dipole moment (related to its intrinsic spin) which has magnitude:

$$\mu_s = \frac{e}{M_l}\frac{h}{4\pi},$$

where h is Planck's constant. Since on the Bohr model the orbital electron "sees" itself at the center of a circular *proton* orbit (think of the Ptolemaic system) it also "sees" a field due to the circulating proton current.

(b) Derive an expression for the field seen by the orbiting electron in the ground state of hydrogen in terms of the orbital dipole moment of the ground state (part a) and the Bohr radius, R_1. (See Equation 9.10.)

(c) The electron has magnetic orientation energy due to the alignment of its intrinsic dipole moment in the field calculated in (b). Express the energy difference between its parallel and antiparallel (0 and 180°) alignments in terms of μ_l, μ_s, and R_1.

(d) Express the difference in orientation energy (part c) in terms of e, h, M, and R_1, and determine its value in electron volts.

(e) What effect would you expect the difference in spin orientation energies to have on the energy levels in hydrogen?

17.16. How wide (or narrow!) would a rectangular slit have to be in order to produce a central diffraction maximum twice as wide with:

(a) Yellow light ($\lambda = 6 \times 10^{-7}$ m).
(b) X-rays ($\lambda = 10^{-10}$ m).
(c) 2000 eV electrons.

17.17. Compare the wavelengths of

(a) A photon and an electron with energies of 1000 eV.
(b) A neutron and an electron with energies of 1000 eV.
(c) A neutron and an electron with velocities 0.1 c.

(The mass of the neutron is 1.6×10^{-27} kg.)

17.18. *Thermal* neutrons are obtained when neutrons passing through a thick absorber interact with a sufficient number of its nuclei to attain a Maxwell energy distribution at the absorber temperature. They then are effectively a neutron gas.

(a) What is the neutron wavelength corresponding to the most probable thermal neutron energy in a thermal distribution at room temperature?

(b) Thermal neutrons produce diffraction patterns when they scatter from crystals. Estimate the magnitude of the effect by calculating the width of the diffraction maximum that would be produced if a neutron beam with the wavelength calculated in part a were diffracted by a 10^{-10} m slit.

17.19. During the 1920's it was believed by some that there were electrons as well as protons in nuclei. Given the fact that nuclear diameters are on the order of 10^{-14} m or less and typical nuclear energies a few MeV, explain why the model is untenable.

17.20. Why is it possible to ignore the undoubted fact that a proton has an associated wavelength when calculating its orbit and energy in a cyclotron?

17.21. (a) What wavelength x-rays would have to be used to obtain a sharp photograph of an electron orbit in hydrogen?

(b) What energy photons correspond to these x-rays?

(c) How much energy would one of these photons transfer to the orbital electron in Compton scattering through 90°?

(d) How does the energy calculated in part c compare with the ground state energy of the atom?

17.22. The Heisenberg principle is usually associated with atomic and subatomic processes. Yet of course macroscopic processes must also be consistent with it. In order to see that they are, consider the following problem:

(a) A very smooth metal cube of mass 0.1 kg rests on a horizontal surface. Estimate the precision to which the position of one of its vertical sides (Δx) could be determined. Explain your answer.

(b) Using the Heisenberg principle and your answer to part a, determine the *maximum* precision to which the velocity of the cube could be known.

(c) Of course classically, velocity is related to distance by $\Delta v = \Delta x / \Delta t$. Although the cube is presumably at rest it might be moving so slowly that its motion could only be detected if observed over a long enough time. Suppose the velocity of the cube is equal to the uncertainty in velocity determined in part b. For how many years would you have to watch it in order to see it move the distance Δx estimated in part a? (1 yr = 3.14×10^7 sec.)

The principles of quantum mechanics

18

▲▲ 18.1 The double-slit interference experiment. Probability amplitudes and their superposition

We now seek a description of the properties and interactions of microscopic systems consistent with the limitations based on observation which we found in the foregoing chapter. Like the classical Newtonian description, this quantum mechanical formalism may be regarded as a set of concepts, postulates, and experimentally-derived rules for correlating a broad range of experimental data. Hence the formalism need not necessarily comply with any "intuitive" or "common sense" ideas. From long familiarity many elements of the Newtonian system appear to be almost intuitive, but a review of Chapters 3 and 4 will indicate that the sole criterion for their validity rests upon their consistency with quantitative observational data. There is nothing at all self-evident about the law of inertia. Galileo's long travail to establish the essence of that law in the face of Aristotelian preconceptions should indicate as much. Nor are momentum and force intuitive concepts. Rather, the concepts were devised precisely because they are useful in the formulation of a rather simple description of interacting particle systems. Given the law of inertia as a postulate, given concepts such as momentum and force, it is possible to deduce a set of fundamental rules—Newton's laws—which adequately describe and predict the behavior of macroscopic particle interactions at moderate velocities.

We shall now develop a set of concepts and rules that permit a consistent description of microscopic interactions. Following Feynman we begin with an analysis of the double-slit interference experiment (Section 10.6, Sections 13.11 and 13.12) in terms of a non-classical particle model.* In a sense the experiment will be analogous to the general two-particle interaction experiments on which we based the concepts of inertial mass and momentum and formulated the fundamental laws of momentum conservation in Chapter 4.

Figure 18.1 shows the now familiar apparatus. A pair of narrow, closely spaced slits, illuminated with a parallel beam of monochromatic light, produces a series of bright and dark fringes (which we call intensity maxima and zeros) on a distant screen. The interpretation of the phenomenon in terms of the classical wave model is straightforward.

---

* R. P. Feynman, R. B. Leighton, and M. Sands, *The Feynman Lectures on Physics*, Vol. I, Addison-Wesley Publishing Co., Inc., Reading, Mass., 1963, Chapter 37.

Intensity maxima represent regions on the screen where the electric field vectors from the two slits reinforce each other; intensity zeros are regions where the field vectors from the two slits cancel. When either one of the two slits is closed the interference pattern gives way to a single-slit diffraction pattern. In particular, a region on the screen corresponding to an intensity zero of the interference pattern will, in general, no longer be a zero when one of the two slits is closed. Hence interference is a coherent phenomenon requiring the cooperative effects of light from both slits.

But double-slit interference cannot be rationalized in terms of a classical particle model. The energy associated with the light impinging on the viewing screen is carried in quantized packets, or photons. A small photoelectric cell placed at the position of an intensity maximum would produce a photocurrent. Suppose the photocurrent is amplified and used to drive a loudspeaker. When the intensity incident upon the slits is relatively large there will be a steady hum, indicating a constant current from the photocell. But as the incident intensity is reduced the steady hum gives way to a series of randomly timed blips or clicks. Individual electrons from the photocell, and therefore, indirectly, the individual photons impinging on the photocell are now being counted. The random timing of the loudspeaker clicks implies that the arrival time of a photon at the screen is also random. But we expect that in any relatively long period of time the number of photons arriving at the intensity maximum will be almost constant. When the intensity of the incident light increases, the number of photons arriving at a position of intensity maxima is essentially constant over even a very short interval of time, and the current from the photocell steady.

These remarks suggest that we should formulate a photon theory of interference in statistical terms, interpreting the observed intensity pattern as the probability distribution for a single photon from the source to arrive at a particular point x on the screen. This approach is certainly consistent with the fact that formation of the observed pattern requires a great many incident photons. However, we immediately encounter difficulties. Let $P_{AB}(x_0)$ be the probability that a photon arrives at a point x_0 when both slits are open. Because the full intensity pattern is to be interpreted as a probability distribution, then $P_{AB}(x_0)$ is proportional to the measured intensity at x_0. If we choose x_0 as an intensity zero then clearly $P_{AB}(x_0) = 0$.

Now suppose one of the slits is closed. In general, the intensity observed at the point x_0 will *not* remain zero. According to the OR rule for combining probabilities (Section 15.3) the probability that *either* of two events will occur is the sum of the probabilities for the individual events. Then if $P_A(x_0)$ and $P_B(x_0)$ are the respective probabilities for a photon to arrive at point x_0 with only slit A or only slit B open, we would expect that $P_A(x_0) + P_B(x_0) = P_{AB}(x_0)$. But we can find several values of x_0 for which neither $P_A(x_0)$ nor $P_B(x_0)$ is zero but $P_{AB}(x)$ *is* zero. Since probabilities are never smaller than zero we conclude that the classical OR theorem—and therefore classical statistics itself— is not applicable. More generally, if the individual single slit diffraction patterns can be interpreted as distribution functions giving the probability of a photon's arrival at a point x on the screen, then classical statistics leads to the conclusion that the interference pattern should be the sum of the diffraction patterns. But this is clearly not true.

How can we resolve the difficulty? We must conclude that when both slits are open *no* photons arrive at the intensity zeros. Clearly, then, the probability of a photon's arrival at any point x depends upon the number of slits that are open. Does each photon split in two with one-half going through each slit? If so, the energy of each is also halved, and, from the Planck law ($E = h\nu$) so is the frequency and therefore the color of the light. But the bright interference fringes formed by yellow light are yellow, not infrared. In

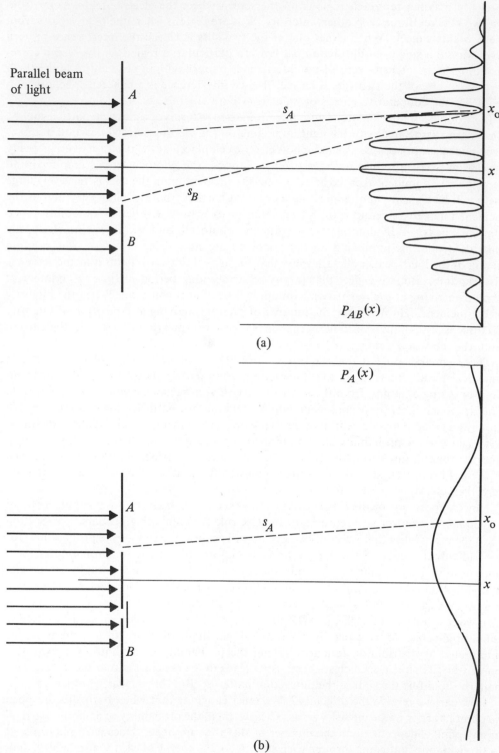

Parallel beam
of light

$P_{AB}(x)$

(a)

$P_A(x)$

(b)

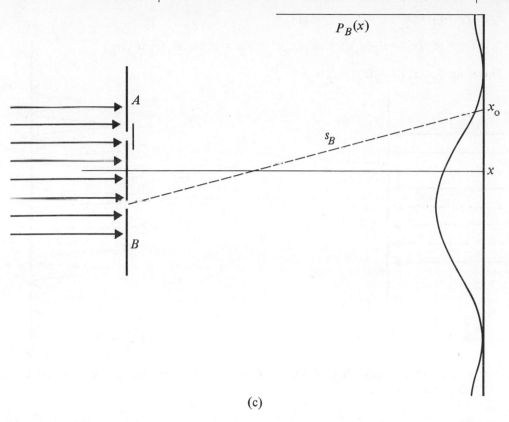

(c)

FIGURE 18.1   Failure of the classical wave model of light. (a) Let $P_{AB}(x_0)$ be the probability that a photon will arrive at the screen with both slits open, (b) $P_A(x_0)$ the probability it will arrive at x_0 with A alone open, and (c) $P_B(x_0)$ the corresponding probability for B alone open. From the sketches it is obvious that $P_{AB}(x_0) \neq P_A(x_0) + P_B(x_0)$.

addition, the assumption that a photon splits in two attributes to them a sort of pre-knowledge concerning the state of the slit system. We might try other ad hoc assumptions as well—complicated types of motion of the photons back and forth through both slits before arrival at the screen, for instance. But these too would imply that the photons have a preknowledge of the system.

Since the classical wave model *does* lead to a consistent description of the double-slit interference experiment, we may use it as a guide to a description of the experiment in terms of photon probabilities. As in Chapter 13, Section 13.11, we let $E_A(x)$ designate the electric field that arrives at x from slit A, and let $E_B(x)$ designate the corresponding value of the field at x from slit B (Figure 18.2). If S_A and S_B are the respective distances from the slits to x (Figures 13.2 and 13.24b) we have (Equations 13.23):

$$E_A(x) = E_0 \cos 2\pi\left(\frac{S_A}{\lambda} - \frac{t}{T}\right), \tag{13.23a}$$

$$E_B(x) = E_0 \cos 2\pi\left(\frac{S_B}{\lambda} - \frac{t}{T}\right), \tag{13.23b}$$

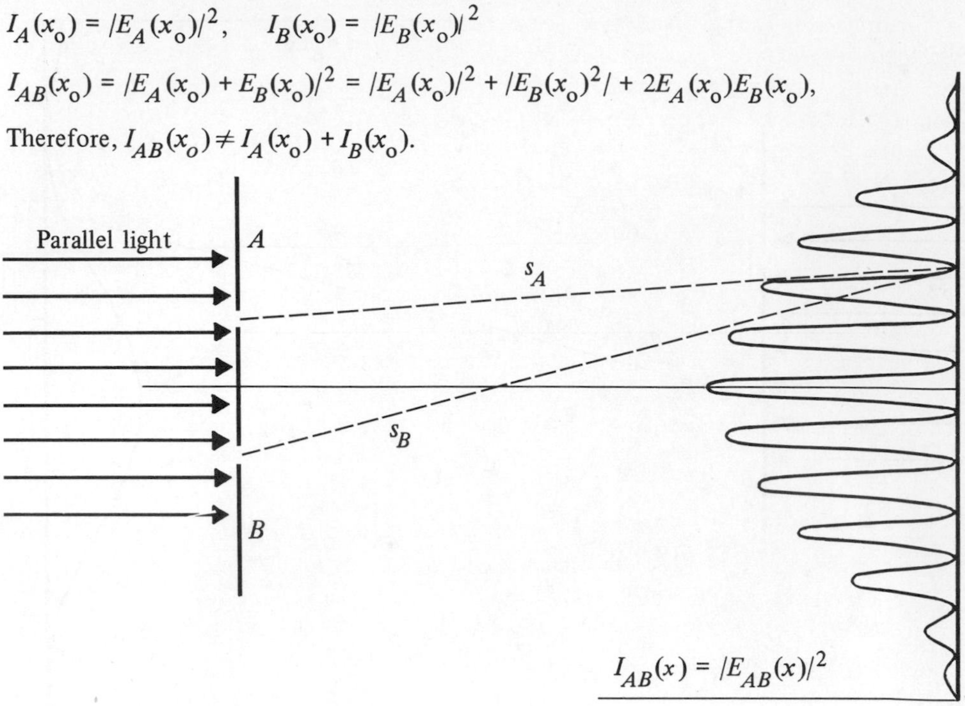

$I_A(x_o) = |E_A(x_o)|^2, \quad I_B(x_o) = |E_B(x_o)|^2$
$I_{AB}(x_o) = |E_A(x_o) + E_B(x_o)|^2 = |E_A(x_o)|^2 + |E_B(x_o)^2| + 2E_A(x_o)E_B(x_o),$
Therefore, $I_{AB}(x_o) \neq I_A(x_o) + I_B(x_o)$.
Parallel light
A
s_A
x_o
x
s_B
B
$I_{AB}(x) = |E_{AB}(x)|^2$

FIGURE 18.2 Explanation of the double-slit pattern according to the classical wave model of light.

where E_0 is the maximum value of the two individual fields. When both slits are open, the resultant field at x is simply the sum of the contributions from the two slits:

$$E_{AB}(x) = E_A(x) + E_B(x), \tag{18.1}$$

which, upon substitution of Equations 13.23a and 13.23b, leads immediately to Equation 13.24.

However in the interference experiment we do not measure the resultant electric field directly. Rather, we measure the *intensity* of the light averaged over many cycles of oscillation. Intensity is proportional to the energy arriving at the screen per unit time, which is in turn proportional to the *square* of the resultant field vector (Equation 13.11); therefore, the quantity we measure is proportional to

$$|E_{AB}|^2 = |E_A(x) + E_B(x)|^2 = |E_A(x)|^2 + |E_B(x)|^2 + 2E_A(x)E_B(x). \tag{18.2}$$

The first term in Equation 18.2, $|E_A(x)|^2$, is proportional to the intensity at x when only slit A is open, the second proportional to the intensity when only slit B is open. Since both are square terms they are always greater than or equal to zero. However, the *interference* term, $2E_A(x)E_B(x)$, can be negative, depending on the relative values of S_A and S_B corresponding to a particular choice of x. In fact, for all points x which satisfy the condition (Equation 13.26b):

$$S_A - S_B = \pm\frac{(2n+1)}{2}\lambda, \qquad n = 0, 1, 2, 3, \ldots,$$

the interference term is equal to the negative sum of the direct terms, $|E_A(x)|^2 + |E_B(x)|^2$, and the total intensity is zero.

To summarize, in the classical wave description we first write down the resultant electric field in terms of the individual fields, then square the resultant field to find the observable energy, attributing the observed interference pattern to the presence of the cross product between the fields. If we let $I_{AB}(x)$ be the intensity at x with both slits open, and $I_A(x)$ and $I_B(x)$ be the intensity at x with only A or only B open, then on the basis of Equation 18.2,

$$I_{AB}(x) \neq I_A(x) + I_B(x).$$

The resultant intensity at x is *not* equal to the sum of the intensities from the individual slits, but involves an interference term as well.

In attempting to describe the interference experiment in terms of classical particles we assumed that the probabilities for the arrival of a photon from x with both or one slit open were proportional to the observed intensities, and found that the classical OR law was not valid. That is,

$$P_{AB}(x) \neq P_A(x) + P_B(x).$$

We can now trace the difficulty to the absence of a cross term in the combination equation. But there is no precedent for such a cross term from classical particle physics. Therefore, we must *invent* a way to obtain such a term if we are going to describe the double slit interference experiment in terms of photons.

Without further ado we introduce an entirely new quantity to describe a process or an event called a *probability amplitude* (or simply *amplitude*) designated by the letter ϕ (Greek "phi"). We define the amplitude for a particular event in such a way that its *square* is equal to the probability that the event will occur.

$$P = |\phi|^2. \tag{18.3}$$

For example, if $\phi_A(x)$ is the amplitude for a photon from the source (in Figures 18.1 and 18.2) to arrive at a point x on the screen when slit A above is open, then the probability for that event is

$$P_A(x) = |\phi_A(x)|^2. \tag{18.4a}$$

Similarly, if $\phi_{AB}(x)$ is the amplitude for a photon from the source to arrive at x with both slits open,

$$P_{AB}(x) = |\phi_{AB}(x)|^2. \tag{18.4b}$$

Since we introduce the amplitude concept for the specific purpose of describing the interference results in terms of photons, we now assume that the amplitude for a photon to arrive at x with slit A open is proportional to the classical value of the electric field at x from slit A, and make similar assumptions for the amplitudes $\phi_B(x)$ and $\phi_{AB}(x)$. That is,

$$\phi_A(x) \sim E_A(x, t), \tag{18.5a}$$

$$\phi_B(x) \sim E_B(x, t), \tag{18.5b}$$

$$\phi_{AB}(x) \sim E_{AB}(x, t). \tag{18.5c}$$

Given this set of assumptions, Equation 18.1 implies that

$$\phi_{AB}(x) = \phi_A(x) + \phi_B(x), \tag{18.6}$$

an equation reminiscent of the OR theorem of classical probability except that it involves *amplitudes* instead of *probabilities*. In fact, we may refer to Equation 17.6 as the quantum mechanical OR rule:

* The amplitude for any process or event that can occur in a number of alternate *and experimentally indistinguishable* ways is the sum of the amplitudes for the individual ways.

The amplitude for a particular process, like the electric field from a single slit, is *not* a directly observable quantity. It is related to observable quantities through its connection with the probability for that process. Applying Equation 18.3 to the interference amplitude sum (Equation 18.6) we have

$$P_{AB}(x) = |\phi_A(x) + \phi_B(x)|^2 = |\phi_A(x)|^2 + |\phi_B(x)|^2 + 2\phi_A(x)\phi_B(x),$$

which, from Equation 18.4, may also be written:

$$P_{AB}(x) = P_A(x) + P_B(x) + 2\phi_A(x)\phi_B(x).$$

The probability that a photon from the source will arrive at a point x with *both* slits open is the sum of the probabilities for its arrival with each of the two slits alone open *plus* an additional term representing the interference between two *amplitudes*. Unlike the probabilities, the amplitudes may assume negative as well as positive values. In particular, for a given set of x's the interference term may assume a sufficiently large negative value to cancel the effect of the direct sum $P_A(x) + P_B(x)$. Hence the description of photon behavior in terms of amplitudes solves the interference problem, a not unexpected result in view of our identification of amplitudes with classical field vectors.

▲▲ 18.2 Superposition of amplitudes continued. Determinism in quantum mechanics. Notes on the helium atom and the hydrogen molecule

Have we really introduced anything new or have we merely rewritten the classical wave description of double-slit interference in terms of a different set of symbols? Whereas we conceive of the classical field vector E as describing the spatial and temporal variation of a continuous electric field, the amplitude ϕ determines the probability of detecting a single photon. Hence the amplitude and field descriptions are conceptually quite distinct. Classical physics describes the motion of a particle—its kinematics—in terms of time-varying positions and momentum vectors, and then seeks a set of rules, or dynamical laws, relating the interactions of particles to changes in their positions and momentum vectors. In quantum mechanics we describe the motion of an entity—or "particle"—by means of the spatial and temporal variation of its amplitude, a quantity which is in general a function of a number of variables including momentum and energy. Hence a particle's amplitude specifies its kinematics, though only in terms of probabilities, while the dynamical problem reduces to determining the behavior of the amplitude for any given interaction.

The nonclassical OR rule, generally called the *linear superposition principle*, lies at the heart of the quantum mechanical formalism. It leads directly to the possibility of nonclassical interference effects *provided* a particular event can occur in more than one alternate and indistinguishable way. In order to emphasize the meaning of this basic requirement we consider a variant of the double-slit experiment (Figure 18.3). Here instead of a single source, separate point sources are placed behind each slit, each of them

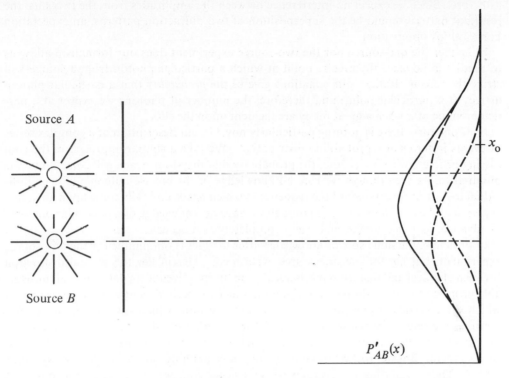

FIGURE 18.3 An experiment with two uncorrelated sources. The resultant intensity pattern is the sum of the two single-source patterns. That is, $P_{AB}(x) = P_A(x) + P_B(x)$.

radiating photons at the same frequency but in a manner that is completely uncorrelated with the other. What pattern do we expect on the screen?

In the single-source, double-slit experiment we sought the amplitude for an event that could occur in one of two alternate and indistinguishable ways. That is, a photon from the source could arrive at a point x on the screen via one of two alternate routes. Significantly, we could not predict which of the slits the photon would traverse, nor could we infer that information after the photon reached the screen. But the new version of the experiment (Figure 18.3) presents a different problem. A photon from source A can reach x by traversing slit A, or a photon from source B can reach x by traversing slit B. We do not have two alternate and indistinguishable ways in which the *same* event may occur. Rather, we have two alternate and distinguishable *events* that may occur simultaneously and independently. Hence the probability that a photon will arrive at the point x is determined by the *classical* OR theorem. That is,

$$P'_{AB}(x) = P_A(x) + P_B(x), \tag{18.7}$$

with

$$P_A(x) = |\phi_A(x)|^2,$$

$$P_B(x) = |\phi_B(x)|^2,$$

as before. Since we expect no interference between the amplitudes from the two slits, the resultant pattern should be the superposition of two diffraction patterns, an expectation borne out by observation.

In neither the one-source nor the two-source experiment does our formalism allow us to predict in advance the precise point at which a particular photon from a source will strike the screen. Rather, our equations give us the *probability* that a particular photon arrives at a particular point, and therefore, the number of photons we expect at a particular value of *x* when a great many are incident upon the slits.

Now of course there is nothing particularly novel in our description of a complex series of events in terms of a probability distribution. We take a similar approach in the coin tossing problem when we predict the probability that fifty-four heads will come up in one hundred tosses even though we lack all knowledge of the precise outcome of each individual toss. But we can record the sequence in which heads and tails come up in an actual experimental test. Therefore, even though we have no knowledge of a particular outcome in advance, we can examine each event completely as it occurs.

In principle, the same sort of knowledge after the fact is obtainable for the two-source experiment, but *not* for the one-source experiment. Herein lies the pivotal distinction between classical and quantum mechanical probability. Even if we determine all measurable properties of the light incident upon the slits from a single source we cannot predict which slit a particular photon will traverse nor determine which slit it *did* traverse *after* it strikes the screen. Suppose we turned the source intensity down so that, say, only ten photons per minute reached the screen. In that way we could record the arrival time for each of them. But we would not know which slit each photon traversed on its way to the screen. Thus, according to the rules of the last section, we would expect a long time exposure to reveal the familiar single-source, double-slit pattern.

Now suppose each one of the slits were alternately blocked for one minute so that we knew that a particular photon arriving during a particular one-minute time interval must have gone through the unblocked slit. We would have complete after-the-fact knowledge of each photon's path from source to screen. As we would know exactly how each event occurred there would no longer be any indistinguishable alternatives involved in the way it *could* have occurred. Formally, the problem is then identical to the two-source problem, and hence a long time exposure would show *not* a single-source interference pattern from two slits, but the superposition of two single-slit diffraction patterns. In order to reconstruct the path of a photon from source to screen we eliminate all but one of the alternate ways it can get to the screen. But when we limit the alternatives we change the experiment and destroy the interference pattern.

We conclude that complete knowledge of a photon's behavior is incompatible with the single-source double-slit interference pattern. Classical physics rests on the assumption that complete knowledge of a system at a given time permits both the prediction of its future and the reconstruction of its past. But in order to describe the double-slit interference experiment in terms of photons, we must abandon complete determinism. No measurements we can make, either before the light is incident upon the slits, or after it strikes the screen, suffice to determine exactly what will happen to a particular photon or what *did* happen to it.

Is it possible that it is our ignorance which forces us to abandon complete determinism? Have we failed to make a crucial measurement that would allow us to predict uniquely the path of each photon? The question has been debated endlessly. No lesser physicists than Albert Einstein and Max Planck took the viewpoint that there must be "hidden" variables describing the photon beam that would permit the restoration of determinism if we could identify them. But neither Einstein nor Planck nor any other proponents of the idea was ever able to suggest even idealized experiments that could reveal the nature of these hidden variables. Niels Bohr and John von Neuman, among others, have offered a series of rather subtle arguments which presumably demonstrate the incompatibility of the hidden variable assumption with the basic formalism of quantum mechanics. Although there have been recent suggestions that these arguments may not be final, the fact remains that no successful theory of microscopic processes that does *not* abandon determinism has ever been devised. On the other hand, quantum mechanics has been very successful in describing such processes.

The essence of quantum mechanics is contained in the description of physical systems in terms of nonobservable probability amplitudes, and in the rules for combining those amplitudes when our knowledge of a process will not distinguish between the alternate ways in which it can occur. Let us summarize our rules for these amplitudes:

1. An event is to be described by an amplitude which is related to the probability for the event to occur by $P = |\phi|^2$ (Equation 18.3).
2. If an event can occur in more than one way, and if there is no way to determine which alternative is actually followed, the *amplitude* for the event is the sum of the *amplitudes* for the individual alternatives (Equation 18.6).

   We refer to this rule as the linear superposition principle, or the quantum mechanical OR theorem.

But

3. If an event can occur in more than one experimentally distinguishable way, then its *probability* is the sum of the *probabilities* for the two alternatives (Equation 18.7). This is just the *classical* OR theorem.

We have illustrated these rules, and in an informal sense even "derived" them, from the double-slit interference experiments. But they have a far wider applicability. In fact, there is no present evidence for their inadequacy. For example, suppose we want to calculate the probability of finding a helium atom in a state which, on the planetary model, would be described by assigning one electron to an orbit labeled as 1, the other to an orbit labeled 2. Because there are two alternate, indistinguishable ways in which that state can be constructed—(1) electron A in orbit 1, B in orbit 2, or (2) A in 2 and B in 1— the amplitude for the state is the sum of the amplitudes for the alternatives (Figure 18.4) and the probability of finding the atom in that state involves an interference term (or

FIGURE 18.4 The probability of finding a helium atom in a state with one electron in state 1, the other in state 2 is the square of the sum of the amplitudes corresponding to the two indistinguishable ways the atomic state may be constituted.

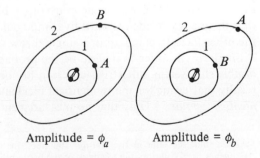

Amplitude = ϕ_a Amplitude = ϕ_b

Probability of the state = $|\phi_a + \phi_b|^2$

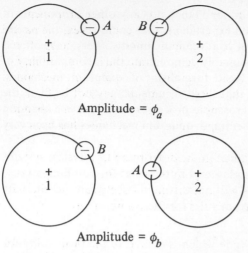

Amplitude = ϕ_a

Amplitude = ϕ_b

Probability of the state = $|\phi_a + \phi_b|^2$

FIGURE 18.5   The probability for a state in molecular hydrogen in which one electron is at a given distance from one proton, the other a given distance from the other is the square of the sum of the amplitudes corresponding to the two indistinguishable ways that molecular state may be constituted.

cross-product term) between the amplitudes.* Again, a hydrogen molecule is a system of four interacting particles: two protons and two electrons. Neither electron can be said to belong to a particular proton. Rather, they are shared. However, we can express the sharing as the sum of the amplitudes for two indistinguishable states: (1) electron A with proton 1 and B with proton 2, and (2) electron B with proton 1 and A with proton 2 (Figure 18.5). Hence the probability for finding the molecule in its bound state contains a cross term between these two amplitudes. Neither the helium atom nor the hydrogen molecule is describable in classical terms—regardless of the ad hoc additions assumed— because no ad hoc assumption can reproduce the effect of the interference between amplitudes.

▲▲ 18.3   Quantum states

Suppose we want to determine experimentally the most probable outcome of a single throw of a rather subtly loaded die. The result of one throw would be insufficient for the purpose, for it would yield absolutely no information about the probable outcome of the next one. In order to determine the probable outcome of a single event it is necessary to examine the outcomes of many *identical* events. Thus if we observed that in one hundred throws the number five came up much more than one-sixth of the time we would conclude that the die was loaded toward five, and could also calculate the probability for each of the other faces to come up in a single throw.

Similarly, in order to determine the probability that a single photon incident upon a double-slit system will strike a screen at some particular point, we must observe the results that ensue for many identical incident photons. What do we mean by the term *identical photons*? Only that no measurements performed on the incident beam of light

---

* As we shall see later in the chapter the electrons in an atom are not really in well-defined orbits. However, it is still possible to speak of the probability of finding an electron at a given mean distance from a nucleus.

reveal any differences between the beam's constituent photons. Of course it is an idealization to assume that the incident light in any real double-slit experiment is completely monochromatic, and the photons therefore completely monoenergetic. There will always be a spread of frequencies around the central, nominal value. Nonetheless, it should be possible to determine the fraction of the total number of incident photons in each energy interval.

If no measurement can be performed, even in principle, that will distinguish among the members of a group of microscopic entities, then these entities are in the same *state*. Hence the concept of state is closely related to the idea of identity or indistinguishability as well as to the act of measuring the properties of a large group of entities. The states themselves are labeled by the dynamical variables that are measured, by energy, position, or momentum, for instance. In a very real sense, the state of a system is defined by the macroscopic and therefore classical apparatus that is used to measure its properties. Thus, for instance, the photons in a completely monochromatic beam of light are all in the state labeled by the energy $E = h\nu$.

If the entities of a particular system are all in a single state and if the measurement of a particular dynamical variable made on the system can yield only one result then the state is defined as a *pure* state of that variable. In contrast, if more than one result can occur then we have a *mixed* state of the variable.

It is important to understand the distinction between a *mixture* of states and a *mixed* state. For example, many different energies are represented in a beam of light with a spread of frequencies. But since the photons in each small energy interval can be distinguished experimentally from those in another then we are dealing with a mixture of many different pure energy states. On the other hand no measurement can predict which of two slits a particular photon will traverse. Therefore, the photons incident upon a double-slit system are in the same energy state. But since we know any given photon may go through either of the slits, then their position state is *mixed*.

When a single measurement is made on a system, obviously only a single result can be obtained, though successive measurements on identical systems may each yield different results. Then performing a measurement on a system in a *mixed* state automatically puts the system into a *pure* state of the variable being measured. Succeeding measurements on an identical system can yield other results and thus place the systems in other pure states of the same variable. *Therefore, a mixed state of a particular variable can always be represented as the superposition of a number of pure states.* That is, if $\phi_a, \phi_b, \ldots, \phi_n$ are the amplitudes for each of several pure states, then the amplitude for a particular mixed state is given by

$$\phi_{ab,\ldots,n} = \alpha_a\phi_a + \alpha_b\phi_b + \cdots + \alpha_n\phi_n, \tag{18.8}$$

where $\alpha_a, \alpha_b, \ldots, \alpha_n$ are constant. Evidently, many different mixed states may be formed from the same set of pure states by changing the values of the constants.

If a system is in a mixed state then there is no way to predict the results of a measurement in advance. Thus the superposition rule (Equation 18.8) is a formal statement of quantum mechanical indeterminacy.

As an example of these remarks, let us reconsider the single-source double-slit experiment, this time concentrating on those photons that terminate at a particular x_0 on the screen. A position measurement at the slit plane can be made by blocking one slit or the other. Then with slit B blocked, all photons arriving at x_0 are in the pure position state described by the amplitude $\phi_A(x_0)$; likewise by blocking slit A we define the amplitude for the pure state $\phi_B(x_0)$. According to Equation 18.8 the amplitude for the mixed state when both slits are open is a superposition of ϕ_A and ϕ_B. If the slits are identical and the light source equidistant from them, then it is reasonable to take $\alpha_A = \alpha_B \equiv \alpha$ so that we have

$$\phi_{AB}(x_0) = \alpha(\phi_A(x_0) + \phi_B(x_0)),$$

which reduces to Equation 18.6 if $\alpha = 1$.

It is important to realize that a system which is in a pure state of one variable need not be in a pure state of every other variable. Thus, in the double-slit experiment with monochromatic light, the photons are in a pure state of energy but a mixed state of position. More important, the fact that a system *is* in a pure state of some variable may imply that it *cannot* be in a pure state of another. Suppose we perform a series of measurements to determine the momentum state of the electrons in a beam and obtain the same result repeatedly. Then by definition, the electrons are in a pure momentum state. But in that case we have no knowledge at all about their positions (Equation 17.6), so that a position measurement could yield *any* result. It follows that a pure momentum state is a *mixed* position state and may be expressed as a superposition of such states from $x = -\infty$ to $+\infty$. Conversely, a pure position state may be represented as an infinite superposition of pure momentum states. We shall return to this point in a later section.

◢◣ 18.4 Elements of complex algebra

Explicit functional expressions for amplitudes corresponding to any given state, a free particle state, or the state of an electron bound in a hydrogen atom, for instance, follow from a general method given by Werner Heisenberg in 1925, or alternately (and equivalently) from the solution of a differential equation deduced a year later by Erwin Schrödinger. We shall discuss the later formulation briefly in Section 18.9, and in addition consider the somewhat more general properties of microscopic systems that follow from the amplitude rules developed in the foregoing sections. In general an amplitude cannot be expressed as a function of a real number. Instead, their arguments are *complex*. Hence before we can discuss even the simplest sorts of problems we must understand the main outlines of complex algebra.

For our purposes we may regard a complex number as a mathematical entity consisting of two related ordinary, or "real," numbers. In this sense they are very much like vectors which are fundamentally sets of three—or four—numbers related to each other in a special way. We shall designate complex numbers by placing a bar above an algebraic symbol ($\overline{A}$). Any complex number may be written as the sum of two parts: its *real* part, and its *imaginary* part (although the connotations of the latter term are unfortunate):

$$\overline{A} = a_1 + ia_2. \tag{18.9}$$

Here a_1 is a real number (the real part of A), and ia_2 an imaginary number. The latter is written as the product of a real number, a_2, and the unit imaginary symbol i, defined by the relation $i^2 = -1$.

There is nothing more mysterious about imaginary numbers, than, say, irrational numbers. The primitive idea of a number as something related to the process of counting is applicable only to the positive integers. More generally, we may define a number as any mathematical entity satisfying defined sets of algebraic rules suggested by the relations among the real integers, a definition that greatly increases the power of the number concept. Thus, for instance, we know that whereas the square root of the integer 4 is another integer, the integer 2 has no integral square root. However, we do not say that it is impossible to find $\sqrt{2}$, for it has a well-defined physical meaning. According to the Pythagorean theorem, $\sqrt{2}$ is the hypoteneuse of the right isosceles triangle whose equal legs are each one unit long. Rather than give up when we encounter $\sqrt{2}$, we define a new class of numbers—the irrational numbers.

Similarly, the expression $\sqrt{-4}$ cannot be expressed in terms of our usual numbers—integral, fractional, or irrational—since the square of any of these numbers is always positive. Therefore, we invent a new set of numbers, the imaginary numbers, by the simple expedient of defining the symbol $i = \sqrt{-1}$. Then if we want to evaluate $\sqrt{-4}$ we write $\sqrt{-4} = \sqrt{-1} \times \sqrt{4} = 2i$. Granted, we cannot use these numbers for counting, but neither do the irrational numbers serve that purpose. It makes no more sense to speak of $\sqrt{2}$ oranges than of $2i$ oranges.

It may be shown that the complex numbers are the most general possible set of numbers, since any one of the set of defining arithmetic operation performed on a complex number will lead to another complex number. Hence we need not invent or define any other classes. (Both the real and the imaginary numbers are special cases of the complex numbers. If $a_2 = 0$ in Equation 18.9 then A is real, whereas A is imaginary if $a_1 = 0$.) We shall use these complex numbers as a convenient means of expressing and working with the two related real numbers, a_1 and a_2.

Complex numbers obey all the manipulative rules of ordinary, real numbers with the sole proviso that in any sequence of operations their real and imaginary parts are handled separately. In addition, there are a few algebraic operations pertinent to complex numbers alone.

For example:

1. To find the sum of two (or more) complex numbers, add their real and imaginary parts separately. If

$$\bar{A} = a_1 + ia_2, \quad \text{and} \quad \bar{B} = b_1 + ib_2,$$

then

$$\bar{C} = \bar{A} + \bar{B} = (a_1 + b_1) + i(A_2 + b_2). \tag{18.10}$$

2. The product of two complex numbers is the sum of the four terms obtained by multiplying both parts of the first number by both parts of the second:

$$\bar{C} = \bar{A}\bar{B} = (a_1 + ia_2)(b_1 + ib_2),$$
$$= a_1b_1 + ia_2b_1 + ia_1b_2 + i^2a_2,$$

or, since $i^2 = -1$,

$$\bar{C} = \bar{A}\bar{B} = (a_1b_1 - a_2b_2) + i(a_2b_1 + a_1b_2). \tag{18.11}$$

The *conjugate* of a complex number, $\bar{A}$ (designated by the symbol $\bar{A}^*$), is the complex number in which the i in $\bar{A}$ is replaced by $-i$ (or $-i$ by i). That is, if

$$\bar{A} = a_1 + ia_2,$$

then

$$\bar{A}^* = a_1 - ia_2.$$

Because real numbers are complex numbers whose imaginary parts are zero, a real number and its conjugate are equal. Similarly, the conjugate of an imaginary number is equal to its own negative.

The *absolute square* of a number $|\overline{A}|^2$ is defined as the product of that number by its conjugate:

$$|\overline{A}|^2 = \overline{A}\overline{A}^* = (a_1 + ia_2)(a_1 - ia_2),$$
$$= a_1^2 + i(a_1a_2 - a_2a_1) - i^2a_2^2, \tag{18.12a}$$
$$= a_1^2 + a_2^2,$$

a number that is always real and positive. Finally, we define the *absolute value* of a complex number $|\overline{A}|$ as the square root of its absolute square or, alternately (Equation 17.11a), as the positive square root of the sum of the squares of its two real constituents. That is,

$$|\overline{A}| = \sqrt{|\overline{A}|^2} = \sqrt{a_1^2 + a_2^2}. \tag{18.12b}$$

Clearly, the absolute value of a real number is equal to the number itself, while the absolute value of an imaginary number, ia_2, is simply a_2.

A very useful geometric convention relates complex numbers to two-dimensional vectors. Referring to Figure 18.6, let us call the horizontal x-axis of a Cartesian coordinate system the real axis of the complex plane, and call the vertical y-axis the imaginary axis. In order to represent the number $\overline{A} = a_1 + ia_2$ in this coordinate plane we lay out lengths on the real and imaginary axes proportional to a_1 and a_2, respectively. Then by definition (Equation 18.12b) the absolute value of the number, $\overline{A}$, is proportional to the hypotenuse of the right triangle with legs a_1 and a_2. The angle between the hypotenuse and the real axis, θ, is called the *phase angle* of the number where, from Figure 18.6,

$$\tan \theta = \frac{a_2}{a_1}. \tag{18.12c}$$

Hence the real and imaginary parts of $|\overline{A}|$ may be regarded as its components since (Figure 18.6):

$$a_1 = |\overline{A}| \cos \theta, \tag{18.13a}$$
$$a_2 = |\overline{A}| \sin \theta, \tag{18.13b}$$

so that A may also be written in the form

$$\overline{A} = |\overline{A}|(\cos \theta + i \sin \theta). \tag{18.13c}$$

Therefore, a complex number may be expressed in two alternate ways: *either* as the sum of its real and imaginary parts (Equation 18.9), *or* in terms of its absolute value $|\overline{A}|$ and phase angle θ. Equations 18.12 relate these two alternatives.

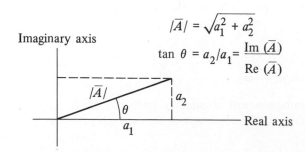

$$|\overline{A}| = \sqrt{a_1^2 + a_2^2}$$
$$\tan \theta = a_2/a_1 = \frac{\text{Im }(\overline{A})}{\text{Re }(\overline{A})}$$

FIGURE 18.6 Geometric interpretation of the complex number $\overline{A} = a_1 + ia_2$.

A third and final mode of expressing complex numbers—the exponential mode—turns out to be most convenient for our purposes. If B and b are both real numbers, the expression $A = B^{ib}$ (B raised to an imaginary power) is in general a complex number. Its absolute square follows from Equation 18.12a:

$$|\overline{A}|^2 = \overline{A}\overline{A}{}^* = (B^{ib})(B^{-ib}).$$

An appendix to the text reviews the algebraic rules for manipulating exponents. In particular, if A, a, and b are numbers of any kind—real, imaginary, or complex—we have

$$A^a \times A^b = A^{a+b}, \tag{18.14a}$$

$$(A^a)^b = A^{ab}. \tag{18.14b}$$

Therefore, the absolute square of B^{ib} is

$$|\overline{A}|^2 = (B^{ib})(B^{-ib}) = B^{i(b-b)} = B^0 = 1.$$

The absolute square of *any* real number raised to *any* imaginary power is unity and thus its absolute value must be ± 1.

Using Equation 18.13c we may write

$$B^{ib} = \cos\theta + i\sin\theta,$$

where the phase angle, θ, is some function of the real numbers B and b. We now state, without proof, a rather remarkable theorem, known as the Euler theorem. If the number B is the base of the natural system of logarithms, $e = 2.178\ldots$, then it follows that

$$e^{\pm ia} = \cos a \pm i\sin a, \tag{18.15a}$$

for *any* value of a whatsoever. Because the absolute value of e^{ia} is ± 1, any complex number which, by using Equation 18.13c, may be expressed in terms of its amplitude and phase angle as

$$|\overline{A}|(\cos a \pm i\sin a),$$

may also be written as $|\overline{A}|e^{\pm ia}$, since, from Equation 18.15a,

$$|\overline{A}|e^{\pm ia} = |\overline{A}|(\cos a \pm i\sin a). \tag{18.15b}$$

The usefulness of the exponential notation derives from the ease with which exponents may be manipulated (Equations 18.14). In the next section we shall discuss an application from classical physics, and then return to the formal development of quantum mechanics. However, let us close our brief survey of complex algebra with a purely mathematical example: the extraction of the nth root of the imaginary number ia. Since ia is a complex number with absolute value a and real part zero we may write it in the form

$$ia = ae^{ib}.$$

Referring to Figure 18.6, $b = \pi/2$ radians (or 90°), since the real part of ia is zero. Thus,

$$ia = ae^{i(\pi/2)}.$$

Now to extract the nth root we write

$$\sqrt[n]{(ia)} = (ia)^{1/n} = (ae^{i(\pi/2)})^{1/n},$$

or, from Equation 18.14b,

$$\sqrt[n]{ia} = \sqrt[n]{a}\, e^{i(\pi/2n)}.$$

Finally, using Equation 18.14b,

$$\sqrt[n]{ia} = \sqrt[n]{a} \left[\cos\left(\frac{\pi}{2n}\right) + i\sin\left(\frac{\pi}{2n}\right) \right].$$

If in particular we want to determine the square root of i then $a = 1$, $n = 2$, and

$$\sqrt{i} = \cos\left(\frac{\pi}{4}\right) + i\sin\left(\frac{\pi}{4}\right),$$

or, since $\pi/4$ radians $= 45°$,

$$\sqrt{i} = \frac{\sqrt{2}}{2}(1 + i).$$

To check this result we square it:

$$\frac{\sqrt{2}}{2}(1 + i) \times \frac{\sqrt{2}}{2}(1 + i) = \frac{1}{2}(1 + 2i + i^2) = i,$$

as anticipated.

▲▲ 18.5 Description of electromagnetic waves using complex algebra

The use of complex algebra often facilitates the algebraic manipulations that are frequently encountered in dealing with classical waves. Any electromagnetic plane wave may be represented mathematically as the superposition of a number of sinusoidal components, each with a definite wavelength, λ, and amplitude, E_0 (Section 13.9):

$$= E_0 \sin 2\pi\left(\frac{x}{\lambda} - \frac{t}{T}\right),$$

or, since $\nu = 1/T$,

$$E = E_0 \sin 2\pi\left(\frac{x}{\lambda} - \nu t\right).$$

The expression

$$E = E_0 \cos 2\pi\left(\frac{x}{\lambda} - \nu t\right)$$

also describes a monochromatic sinusoidal plane wave, provided a different convention for $x = 0$, $t = 0$ is adopted (compare Equations 13.6a and 13.6c). Now from Equation 17.14b, the *real* part of the complex function

$$\bar{E} = E_0 e^{2\pi i[(x/\lambda) - \nu t]} \tag{18.16a}$$

is simply

$$\mathrm{Re}(\bar{E}) = E_0 \cos 2\pi\left(\frac{x}{\lambda} - \nu t\right),$$

suggesting that plane waves may also be described by using the exponential form given by Equation 18.16a. In order to make it simpler to write exponential functions, we shall henceforth use the notation

$$\exp (x) = e^x.$$

Thus Equation 18.6a becomes

$$\bar{E} = E_0 \exp \left[2\pi i \left(\frac{x}{\lambda} - vt \right) \right]. \qquad (18.16b)$$

The advantage in using the exponential notation derives from the comparative ease with which exponentials may be manipulated relative to the trigonometric functions. For example, Equations 13.24 and 13.26, which relate to the single-source double-slit interference pattern, are much more simply derived using exponential than trigonometric notation.

As in Section 13.11 (and Section 18.1) we label the two slits A and B. Let the electric field from slit A at a point a distance S_A from that slit be given by the real part of

$$\bar{E}_A = E_0 \exp \left[2\pi i \left(\frac{S_A}{\lambda} - vt \right) \right], \qquad (18.17a)$$

and the field from slit B at a distance S_B by the real part of

$$\bar{E}_B = E_0 \exp \left[2\pi i \left(\frac{S_B}{\lambda} - vt \right) \right]. \qquad (18.17b)$$

The intensity due to either wave is just E_0^2 which is equal to $|\bar{E}_A|^2$ (or $|\bar{E}_B|^2$) since

$$|\bar{E}_A|^2 = E_0 \exp \left[2\pi i \left(\frac{S_A}{\lambda} \right) - vt \right] \times E_0 \exp \left[-2\pi i \left(\frac{S_A}{\lambda} - vt \right) \right] = E_0^2.$$

The *resultant* field at the screen (Figure 13.23) is the real part of the complex sum

$$\bar{E}_{AB} = \bar{E}_A + \bar{E}_B.$$

However, we measure the energy on the screen, and not the resultant field. Therefore, we are interested in the absolute square of $\bar{E}_{AB}$:

$$\begin{aligned} |\bar{E}_{AB}|^2 &= (\bar{E}_A + \bar{E}_B)(\bar{E}_A^* + \bar{E}_B^*), \\ &= |\bar{E}_A|^2 + |\bar{E}_B|^2 + (\bar{E}_A \bar{E}_B^* + \bar{E}_B \bar{E}_A^*). \end{aligned} \qquad (18.18)$$

Let us now evaluate the three terms in this expression. Since

$$\bar{E}_A^* = E_0 \exp \left[-2\pi i \left(\frac{S_A}{\lambda} - vt \right) \right],$$

we can use the relation $e^a e^{-a} = e^{a-a} = e^0 = 1$ to give

$$|\bar{E}_A|^2 = \bar{E}_A \bar{E}_A^* = E_0^2,$$

which is a real number. We also use the relation $e^{a-b} = e^a e^{-b}$ to write

$$|\bar{E}_A| = E_0 \exp \left(2\pi i \frac{S_A}{\lambda} \right) \exp (-2\pi i vt),$$

$$|\bar{E}_B| = E_0 \exp \left(2\pi i \frac{S_B}{\lambda} \right) \exp (-2\pi i vt),$$

so that

$$\bar{E}_A \bar{E}_B^* = E_0^2 \exp\left(2\pi i \frac{S_A}{\lambda}\right) \exp\left(-2\pi i \frac{S_B}{\lambda}\right) \exp\left(-2\pi i \nu t\right) \exp\left(2\pi i \nu t\right),$$

$$= E_0^2 \exp\left(2\pi i \frac{S_A}{\lambda}\right) \exp\left(-2\pi i \frac{S_B}{\lambda}\right),$$

$$= E_0^2 \exp\left[\frac{2\pi i}{\lambda}(S_A - S_B)\right].$$

Thus we have for the full interference term in Equation 18.18:

$$\bar{E}_A \bar{E}_B^* + \bar{E}_A^* \bar{E}_B = E_0^2 \left[\exp\left[\frac{2\pi i}{\lambda}(S_A - S_B)\right] + \exp\left[-\frac{2\pi i}{\lambda}(S_A - S_B)\right]\right],$$

which is of the form $e^{ia} + e^{-ia}$ or, using Euler's theorem,

$$e^{ia} + e^{-ia} = \cos a + i \sin a + \cos a - i \sin a = 2 \cos a.$$

Therefore,

$$\bar{E}_A \bar{E}_B^* + \bar{E}_A^* \bar{E}_B = 2E_0^2 \cos 2\pi\left(\frac{S_A - S_B}{\lambda}\right),$$

which when substituted into Equation 18.18 along with $|\bar{E}_A|^2 = |\bar{E}_B|^2 = E_0^2$ gives

$$|\bar{E}_{AB}|^2 = 2E_0^2 \cos 2\pi\left(\frac{S_A - S_B}{\lambda}\right),$$

an expression describing the interference pattern as a function of the difference in the two path lengths from the two slits to a point on a screen (Figure 13.23). When $S_A - S_B = [(2n + 1)/2]\lambda$, $\cos 2\pi(S_A - S_B)/\lambda = -1$, and $E_{AB}^2 = 0$. Hence this condition describes the intensity zeros of the pattern, in agreement with Equation 13.36b. On the other hand, when $S_A - S_B = n\lambda$, $\cos 2\pi(S_A - S_B)/\lambda = 1$, and $E_{AB}^2 = 4E_0^2$, an intensity maximum (Equation 13.26a).

▲▲ 18.6 Free-particle amplitudes and their superposition. The Heisenberg uncertainty principle

The description of double-slit interference in terms of photons involves amplitudes rather than classical fields. However, the general mathematical formalism does not differ from the classical wave description, as a comparison of Sections 18.1 and 18.5 indicates. Hence, as in Section 18.1, we assume that the amplitudes $\phi_A(x)$ and $\phi_B(x)$, which are related to the probabilities for a photon incident upon the double-slit system to reach the point x via slits A and B, respectively, are propotional to the corresponding electric field intensities.

More generally, the real part of the expression,

$$\bar{E}_n = E_{0n} \exp\left[2\pi i\left(\frac{x}{\lambda_n} - \nu_n t\right)\right],$$

describes a sinusoidal wave with definite wavelength λ_n and frequency ν_n $(\nu_n \lambda_n = c)$. Referring to Equation 17.3, a definite classical electromagnetic frequency corresponds to a definite photon energy:

$$E_n = h\nu_n,$$

while from Equation 17.15, the photon momentum corresponding to λ_n is

$$p_n = \frac{h}{\lambda_n}.$$

A classical plane wave is characterized by a series of plane, parallel fronts propagated in the x-direction (Figure 13.16). Hence the photons in a beam of light represented classically by a plane wave are all propagated in the x-direction, and thus we may let the amplitude for a photon state with definite energy E_n and definite momentum p_n be given by the complex function:

$$\phi_n(x, t) = \bar{a}_n \exp\left[\frac{2\pi i}{h}(p_n x - E_n t)\right],$$

where $\bar{a}_n$ is a constant.* This expression may be written in a more compact form by using the notation $\hbar = h/2\pi$. Then,

$$\phi_n(x, t) = \bar{a}_n \exp\left[\frac{i}{\hbar}(p_n x - E_n t)\right]. \tag{18.19}$$

We shall now assume that the complex function, Equation 18.19, is the amplitude not only for a free photon but also for *any* free, noninteracting particle with definite momentum p_n and definite energy E_n. Although as shown in the next section this result is a direct consequence of the Schrödinger equation, we may also take it as a basic postulate of quantum mechanics, even as we take the law of inertia as a basic postulate of Newtonian mechanics. The ultimate justification for both postulates rests with their consistency with observable evidence.

Of course probability amplitudes are not directly observable. In Section 18.1 (Equation 18.3) we defined an amplitude as the square root of a measurable probability. In view of the complex character of Equation 18.19 we generalize that definition so that the numerical value of the probability for finding the particle at a particular value of x (say x_0) is equal to the *absolute* square of the amplitude function evaluated at x_0:

$$P(x_0) = |\phi(x_0)|^2. \tag{18.20}$$

The probability at a given value of x is always a real number whereas the corresponding amplitude is usually complex. Since *two* real numbers are required to specify a complex number it follows that an amplitude usually cannot be completely determined by taking the square root of a measured probability.

Up to this point we have been using the term "probability for a particle to arrive at a point" a bit loosely, and we shall have to formulate our ideas with more precision. Obviously the probability that a particle arrives at a single mathematical point is zero, since the number of points is unbounded. However, we may define the probability that a particle is found in a small region in the neighborhood of a particular point. In fact, this is actually the sense in which we have been using $P(x_0)$. Thus we introduce a function $P(x)$ called the *probability density* or *probability distribution function* such that the probability of finding the particle between x and $x + \Delta x$ is $P(x)\,\Delta x$.

---

* Actually this form is appropriate for a free particle traveling to the right. The form

$$\bar{a}_n \exp\left[\frac{2\pi i}{h}(p_n x + E_n t)\right]$$

describes a left-traveling particle. (See Sections 13.2 and 13.7.)

By taking the absolute square of Equation 18.19 we obtain a function proportional to the probability distribution function for a free particle with definite momentum:

$$P(x) \sim |\bar{\phi}|^2 = \bar{a}_n \exp\left[\frac{i}{\hbar}(p_n x - E_n t)\right]\bar{a}_n^* \exp\left[-\frac{i}{\hbar}(p_n x - E_n t)\right]$$

$$= |\bar{a}_n|^2.$$

That is, the probability distribution for a free particle with well-defined momentum is constant. There is an equal probability of finding it anywhere, or, in other words, its position is completely undetermined. This result is consistent with the Heisenberg principle (Equation 17.16). However, since it follows from the postulates of quantum mechanics, it should be regarded as more fundamental.

In order to evaluate the constant $\bar{a}_n$ we note that the probability of finding the particle *somewhere* must be unity. Suppose we know that it is confined within a volume with linear dimensions X, Y, and Z. If X is sufficiently large the uncertainty in momentum required by the Heisenberg principle will be so small that we can still regard the momentum as definite. Then since the probability distribution is constant we have

$$P(x)X = |\bar{a}_n|^2 X = 1,$$

or

$$|\bar{a}_n|^2 = \frac{1}{X}.$$

Thus the probability for **finding** the particle in a small interval Δx is simply

$$P(x)\,\Delta x = \frac{\Delta x}{X}.$$

That is, it is directly proportional to the size of the interval throughout the entire volume.

Let us now consider a problem in which a free particle may have either of the definite momenta p_n or p_m. In the language of quantum mechanics, the particle may be in either of the two definite momentum states. Hence according to the rules of Section 18.3 its amplitude is the superposition of the free-particle amplitudes for the two states (Equation 18.19):

$$\bar{\phi}_{mn} = \bar{\phi}_m + \bar{\phi}_n = \bar{a}_n \exp\left(\frac{i}{\hbar}p_n x\right) + \bar{a}_m \exp\left(\frac{i}{\hbar}p_m x\right).$$

The constants $\bar{a}_n$ and $\bar{a}_m$ are determined by requiring that the probability for finding the particle somewhere is unity. However, their values will differ from the value of $\bar{a}_n$ in the previously considered case. Because we are interested in the spatial dependence of the mixed state, the time-dependent parts have been separated from the amplitudes and will be ignored.

In order to determine the variation in the probability distribution function with x we calculate the absolute square of $\bar{\phi}_{mn}$:

$$|\bar{\phi}_{mn}|^2 = |\bar{\phi}_m|^2 + |\bar{\phi}_n|^2 + (\bar{\phi}_n\bar{\phi}_m^* + \bar{\phi}_n^*\bar{\phi}_m)$$

$$= |\bar{a}_n|^2 + |\bar{a}_m|^2 + \bar{a}_n\bar{a}_m^* \exp\left[\frac{i}{\hbar}(p_n - p_m)x\right]$$

$$+ \bar{a}_n^*\bar{a}_m \exp\left[-\frac{i}{\hbar}(p_n - p_m)x\right].$$

If for simplicity we assume that measurements of momentum yield the results $p = p_n$ and $p = p_m$ with equal probability then we have $\bar{a}_n = \bar{a}_m = \bar{a}$ so that the expression becomes:

$$|\bar{\phi}_{mn}|^2 = 2|\bar{a}|^2 + |\bar{a}|^2\left(\exp\left[\frac{i}{\hbar}(p_n - p_m)x\right] + \exp\left[-\frac{i}{\hbar}(p_n - p_m)x\right]\right).$$

The interference term has the form $e^{ib} + e^{-ib}$ which, using Equation 18.15a is

$$e^{ib} + e^{-ib} = \cos b + i \sin b + \cos b - i \sin b = 2 \cos b.$$

Therefore the probability distribution function is

$$P_{mn}(x) = 2|\bar{a}|^2\left[1 + \cos\left[\frac{x}{\hbar}(p_n - p_m)\right]\right]. \tag{18.21}$$

Because of the interference between the amplitudes for the two momentum states, the probability of finding the particle at a particular position is not a constant as it is when the momentum is well defined. Rather, it oscillates, going through a series of maxima and zeros as a function of x (Figure 18.7). In order to find $|\bar{a}|^2$ we recall that if $P(x)$ does not vary appreciably over an inverval Δx then the probability for finding the particle in Δx is $P(x)\,\Delta x$. Since $P_{mn}(x)$ in Equation 18.21 is not constant, the total probability for finding the particle in a volume of length X is the sum of the terms $P_{mn}(x)\,\Delta x$ over the entire length. Thus $|\bar{a}|^2$ may be determined by calculating the area under the curve in Figure 18.7 and then adjusting $|\bar{a}|^2$ until that area is equal to 1, or, equivalently, by evaluating the integral

$$\int_0^X P_{mn}(x)\,dx.$$

Generalizing the above results, the amplitude for a free-particle state which is the superposition of n pure states with the respective momenta $p_1, p_2, \ldots, p_n$ is

$$\bar{\phi}_{12\cdots n} = \bar{\phi}_1 + \bar{\phi}_2 + \cdots + \bar{\phi}_n$$

$$= \bar{a}_1 \exp\left(\frac{i}{\hbar}p_1 x\right) + \bar{a}_2 \exp\left(\frac{i}{\hbar}p_2 x\right) + \cdots + \bar{a}_n \exp\left(\frac{i}{\hbar}p_n x\right),$$

so that the probability distribution function for the mixed state is

$$P(x) = |\bar{\phi}_1|^2 + |\bar{\phi}_2|^2 + \cdots + |\bar{\phi}_n|^2 + \bar{\phi}_1\bar{\phi}_2 + \bar{\phi}_1^*\bar{\phi}_2 + \cdots$$
$$+ \bar{\phi}_1\bar{\phi}_n^* + \bar{\phi}_1^*\bar{\phi}_n + \cdots + \bar{\phi}_2\bar{\phi}_n^* + \cdots.$$

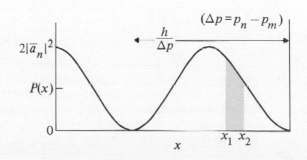

FIGURE 18.7 Probability distribution function for the superposition of two free-particle states with momenta p_n and p_m. The probability of finding the particle in a region bounded by x_1 and x_2 is proportional to the area under the distribution curve between those values of x.

Referring to Equation 18.21, the interference products reduce to terms such as

$$\phi_1\bar{\phi}_2^* + \phi_1^*\bar{\phi}_2 = 2\bar{a}_1\bar{a}_2^* \cos \frac{x}{\hbar}(p_1 - p_2),$$

$$\phi_1\bar{\phi}_n^* + \phi_1^*\bar{\phi}_n = 2\bar{a}_1\bar{a}_n^* \cos \frac{x}{\hbar}(p_1 - p_n),$$

$$\vdots \qquad\qquad\qquad\qquad \vdots$$

Now the absolute squares of complex constants $\bar{a}_1, \bar{a}_2, \ldots, \bar{a}_n$ determine the probability of finding the particle in each of the several momentum states. It is reasonable to suppose that any arbitrary probability distribution function could be constructed given a sufficient number of momentum states and a proper choice of the constants. In particular, it is possible to find combinations that yield a series of strong, narrow, well-separated maxima, implying that the location of the particle becomes increasingly certain as the uncertainty in its momentum increases (Figure 18.8).

When we say that the momentum of a free particle is uncertain we usually mean that its value may range anywhere between the limits p_0 and p_n rather than (as implied in our discussion) that it may have any one of a number of discrete, well-defined values. However, formally there is nothing new in this more usual situation. The amplitude is an *infinite* superposition of any free-particle states, the momentum of the states varying continuously between the two limits. Because an infinite number of states is involved, the sum over the states must be replaced by its limiting value, an integral over the continuously varying momentum. Again, the interference between the contributing amplitudes yields a probability distribution that is not constant in x. In fact, free-particle probability distribution functions for continuous momentum states are characterized by a single maximum, implying that the probability for finding the particle is high only for a small range of x. Furthermore, as the range of the possible momentum states (and

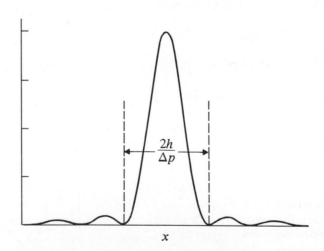

FIGURE 18.8 Probability distribution function for the superposition of a continuum of free-particle states between the limits p_n and p_m. The probability for finding the particle is appreciable only in a region $2h/\Delta p$ in extent ($\Delta p = p_n - p_m$). As Δp increases the size of that region decreases, in agreement with the Heisenberg uncertainty principle.

therefore the uncertainty in momentum) increases, so the width of the maximum decreases, consistent with the Heisenberg principle.

The mathematics of superposition, or at any rate the verbal description and the figures, ought to seem very familiar. In Section 13.5 we discussed the superposition of pure sinusoidal waves to yield any desired wave form or single, narrow pulse. Now we find that a superposition of many free-particle momentum states leads to a probability distribution that is localized in space.

Of course the parallel is no accident. We used the fact that the classical wave description is often valid for light to deduce the amplitude for a free photon with definite energy and momentum. Hence we were assured at once that our formalism would be consistent with the classical wave model for any case in which that model has approximate validity. But we then extended our conceptual framework by asuming that the same function (Equation 18.19) gave the amplitude for *any* free particle with definite energy and momentum, be it a photon, electron, proton, or baseball. The justification for that assumption is simply that (Section 17.9) under comparable conditions photons and electrons (and presumably protons and baseballs) behave analogously. If we apply the De Broglie equation $\lambda = h/p$ (Equation 17.17), and let the Planck relation $E = h\nu$ be applicable to any particle then the free-particle amplitude becomes

$$\exp\left[2\pi i\left(\frac{x}{\lambda} - \nu t\right)\right],$$

a function whose real part, $\cos 2\pi(x/\lambda - \nu y)$, describes a classical wave.

Are we to conclude that electrons have wavelike properties? Certainly the mathematical parallels are tempting. But the cosine function, when applied to a wave on a string, measures the displacement of the string from equilibrium. When applied to an *electron*, on the other hand, the absolute square of the same function leads to the probability distribution function for the electron. Hence although the mathematical formalism suggests a parallel, the physical situations are very different. Light, as we know, has some properties that are describable in terms of a classical particle model, others that require a classical wave model. We often say, for convenience, that light has wavelike properties. But we would make the statement about a *photon* only if we meant that the amplitude for a photon has the same mathematical form as the equivalent classical electric field vector.

Of course there is no classical analogue to the electron amplitude. Therefore, to say that an electron has wavelike properties is to make a statement that is even more formal than the equivalent statement made about a photon. It is possible to speak about electrons being described by waves in probability space. However, the abstraction is not only difficult, but often misleading—especially since the complex amplitudes describing the state of an electron requires that the space must also be complex! Conceptually, it is simpler to concede that an electron, like a photon, is neither a classical particle nor a classical wave. Instead, it is an entity whose behavior can be described in terms of the quantum mechanical amplitude formalism developed in this chapter.

▲▲ 18.7 The Schrödinger equation. Solution for a free-particle state*

In quantum mechanics, as in Newtonian mechanics, the behavior of interacting systems of particles is considerably more interesting than free-particle motion. We have

---

* This section may be omitted without serious loss of continuity.

FIGURE 18.9 Erwin Schrödinger. (Courtesy of the American Institute of Physics, Center for the History and Philosophy of Physics.)

assumed that the functional form of the free-particle amplitude for a state with well-defined momentum and energy is given by Equation 18.19. That assumption is in many ways analogous to the law of inertia in classical physics. To determine the way in which a particle behaves when subject to any specific interaction, it is necessary to deduce its amplitude as a function of time and space in that situation.

There are two general types of questions we may ask about a quantum mechanical system. First, what are its states and their corresponding amplitudes? Second, given that a system is in a particular state at a particular time what is the probability that it will later be found in another state? For example, we are interested in knowing the energies and amplitudes of the hydrogen atom's internal states, as well as the probability that if the atom *is* in one of these states now it will be in another one later. In this section and the next we shall present a general method first given by Erwin Schrödinger (Figure 18.9) in 1926 for dealing with the problem of finding the states of a system, and in a later section touch upon the problem of determining transition probabilities between states.

Schrödinger's method requires that a differential equation, now known as the Schrödinger equation, be solved. It is applicable to any system in which the interaction is expressible in terms of potential energy, and in which special relativistic effects may be neglected. Generalized, relativistically correct versions of the equation are required to determine the states of systems whose speeds are comparable to the speed of light.

In the Appendix to Chapter 2 we define the *first derivative* of a function $f(x)$ with respect to x as the rate of change of that function with x. That is, if $f(x + \Delta x)$ and $f(x)$ are the values of the function at the beginning and end points of an interval, then its first derivative is

$$\frac{df}{dx} = \lim_{\Delta x \to 0} \frac{f(x + \Delta x) - f(x)}{\Delta x}. \tag{18.22a}$$

Expressions for the derivatives of several types of functions were calculated using this definition and listed in Table 2.1 in the Appendix to Chapter 2. For example, if $f(x) = ax^n$, where a and n are constants, then, referring to the table,

$$\frac{df}{dx} = nax^{n-1}.$$

Since the first derivative of a function of x is itself a function of x then it too has a'first derivative which is known as the *second derivative* of the function and is written as d^2f/dx^2. That is,

$$\frac{d^2f}{dx^2} = \frac{d}{dx}\left(\frac{df}{dx}\right). \tag{18.22b}$$

For example, the x-component of the instantaneous velocity of a particle is the ratio of the change in the x-component of its displacement to the time interval over which it changes as the length of the interval approaches zero:

$$v_x = \underset{\Delta x \to 0}{\text{limit}} \frac{\Delta x}{\Delta t} = \frac{dx}{dt}.$$

Likewise, the x-component of instantaneous acceleration is defined as the rate of change of v_x with time:

$$a_x = \underset{\Delta x \to 0}{\text{limit}} \frac{\Delta v_x}{\Delta t} = \frac{dv_x}{dt}.$$

Therefore, a_x is the *second* derivative of x with respect to time:

$$a_x = \frac{dv_x}{dt} = \frac{d}{dt}\left(\frac{dx}{dt}\right) = \frac{d^2x}{dt^2}.$$

In the nonrelativistic approximation, Newton's second law for a force $F(x)$ with a component in the x-direction alone acting on a particle of mass M may be written:

$$Ma_x = M\frac{d^2x}{dt^2} = F(x),$$

with an obvious generalization for forces with y- and z-components as well. This is a *differential equation* (Appendix to Chapter 4) relating the derivative of a function (x) to an algebraic expression which also involves that function. We encountered one particular example in Chapter 4 and another in Chapter 5. If the force upon the mass M is a linear restoring force or Hooke's law force (Sections 4.10 and 4.11), $F = -kx$, then the differential equation assumes the form

$$M\frac{d^2x}{dt^2} = -kx,$$

whereas for an inverse square gravitational force between the sun with mass M_s and a planet, we derived a pair of coupled differential equations in x and y (Section 5.6):

$$\frac{d^2x}{dt^2} = -GM_s\left(\frac{x}{R^3}\right),$$

$$\frac{d^2y}{dt^2} = -GM_s\left(\frac{y}{R^3}\right),$$

with $R^2 = x^2 + y^2$. Both differential equations may be regarded as prescriptions for finding the displacement of the particle in question as a function of time. In the case of the linear restoring force we found that the displacement x could be expressed as a function of t in terms of the trigonometric functions (Appendix to Chapter 4):

$$x = A \cos \omega t + B \sin \omega t,$$

with $\omega^2 = k/M$, and A and B arbitrary constants. But frequently the solution to a differential equation cannot be expressed in closed form and must be expressed as a table of numbers. Thus we obtained a numerical solution to the coupled differential equations for inverse-square central-force motion, although in that particular case advanced analytical methods do in fact yield a solution in algebraic form.

The time-independent Schrödinger equation* in one dimension is a differential equation relating the amplitude $\bar{\phi}(x)$ for the state of a particle of mass M to the total energy E_n of the state and the potential energy $V(x)$ as a function of x:

$$\frac{d^2\bar{\phi}}{dx^2} = \frac{2M}{\hbar^2} [V(x) - E_n]\bar{\phi}. \tag{18.23}$$

Like any other differential equation it is a prescription for determining the value of the dependent variable (in this case $\bar{\phi}$) as a function of the independent variable (in this case x) whenever the function on the right side [$V(x)$] is given explicitly. Equation 18.23 has solutions in simple forms for only a few cases. Nevertheless it can always be solved numerically by means of methods analogous to those used with the inverse-square central-force problem in Section 5.6. Such solutions may be presented in tabular or, more conveniently, in graphical form.

Some relatively simple but representative solutions of the Schrödinger equation are presented in this section and the next. As our first example we consider the free-particle solution. In that case $V(x) = 0$ and we have

$$\frac{d^2\bar{\phi}}{dx^2} = -\frac{2M}{\hbar^2} E_n\bar{\phi}.$$

Since $V(x) = 0$ the energy is completely kinetic and in the nonrelativistic approximation,

$$E_n = (KE)_n = \frac{p_n^2}{2M},$$

where p_n is the momentum of the free-particle state. Then

$$\frac{d^2\bar{\phi}}{dx^2} = -\left(\frac{p_n}{\hbar}\right)^2 \bar{\phi} \tag{18.24}$$

is the Schrödinger equation for a free particle with momentum p_n. If this equation is to be consistent with the development in Section 18.5, its solution must be equal to the spatial part of Equation 18.19. In order to show that it is we must first determine the derivative of the exponential function e^{bx}, or exp (bx), where b is a constant.

Applying the definition of the first derivative (Equation 18.22a), we have

$$\frac{d}{dx} [\exp (bx)] = \lim_{\Delta x \to 0} \frac{\exp [b(x + \Delta x)] - \exp (bx)}{\Delta x}.$$

To evaluate the numerator of the expression we note from Appendix A to the text that the exponential function e^a may be expressed as an infinite series whose first terms are

$$e^a = 1 + a + \frac{a^2}{2} + \frac{a^3}{3 \times 2} + \frac{a^4}{4 \times 3 \times 2} + \cdots.$$

---

* The more general one-dimensional Schrödinger equation is a differential equation involving the time coordinate as well as the spatial coordinate. However, in cases where the potential energy is not a function of time, the time dependence of the corresponding amplitude goes as exp $[(i/\hbar)E_n t]$. Since this is so in all the problems we shall consider in quantitative detail, the time variation of ϕ will be ignored.

Therefore,

$$\exp[b(x + \Delta x)] = 1 + b(x + \Delta x) + \frac{b^2(x + \Delta x)^2}{2} + \cdots,$$

$$= 1 + bx + b\,\Delta x + \frac{b^2x^2 + 2b^2x\,\Delta x + b^2\,\Delta x^2}{2},$$

$$\exp(bx) = 1 + bx + \frac{bx^2}{2} + \cdots,$$

and

$$\frac{\exp[b(x + \Delta x)] - \exp(bx)}{\Delta x} = \frac{b\,\Delta x + b^2x\,\Delta x + (b^2/2)\,\Delta x^2}{\Delta x} + \cdots,$$

$$= b\left(1 + bx + \frac{b}{2}\Delta x + \cdots\right),$$

which, when $\Delta x \to 0$, becomes

$$b(1 + bx + \cdots).$$

But the terms in parentheses are the first two terms in the series expansion of $\exp(bx)$. Therefore we suspect that the first derivative of the function with respect to x is simply

$$\frac{d}{dx}[\exp(bx)] = b\exp(bx),$$

an expectation borne out by a more rigorous analysis.

Referring to the table of derivatives in the Appendix to Chapter 2 we note that the first derivative of the product of a constant by a function is the product of the constant by the first derivative of the function:

$$\frac{d}{dx}[af(x)] = a\frac{df}{dx}.$$

Thus,

$$\frac{d}{dx}[a\exp(bx)] = ab\exp(bx). \tag{18.25a}$$

The second derivative may be written down by inspection:

$$\frac{d^2}{dx^2}[a\exp(bx)] = ab^2\exp(bx). \tag{18.25b}$$

Returning now to the Schrödinger equation for a free particle let us assume a solution of the form

$$\phi = \bar{a}_n \exp(ibx),$$

where i is the unit imaginary index, and then try to justify the assumption. (This assumption is really an educated guess based on our experience with the postulated free-particle amplitude in the previous section.) Using Equation 18.25b,

$$\frac{d^2\phi}{dx^2} = i^2b^2\bar{a}_n\exp(ibx) = -b^2\bar{a}_n\exp(ibx),$$

which when substituted into the free-particle Schrödinger equation (Equation 18.24) gives

$$-b^2\bar{a}_n\exp(ibx) = -\left(\frac{p_n}{\hbar}\right)^2\bar{a}_n\exp(ibx).$$

Canceling common terms,

$$b = \pm \left(\frac{p_n}{\hbar}\right),$$

so that our assumed form is a solution for either $b = +(p_n/\hbar)$ or $b = -(p_n/\hbar)$. That is, we have the *two* solutions:

$$\phi(x) = \bar{a}_{n+} \exp\left(\frac{ip_n x}{\hbar}\right), \tag{18.26a}$$

$$\phi(x) = \bar{a}_{n-} \exp\left(-\frac{ip_n x}{\hbar}\right). \tag{18.26b}$$

The sum of these solutions is also a solution, for if its second derivative is substituted into Equation 18.24, that equation is satisfied. Note that the differential equation does *not* give a unique value for the constants $\bar{a}_{n+}$ and $\bar{a}_{n-}$. Rather, these are determined by separate physical conditions. For instance, the first calculation in Section 18.5 corresponded to the choice $\bar{a}_{n-} = 0$, for in that case the spatial part of Equation 18.19 agrees with the solution obtained here. The constant $\bar{a}_n$ was then evaluated by requiring that the probability of finding the particle somewhere in a box of length X be unity.

▲▲ 18.8 Energy states in a deep rectangular potential well*

The free-particle solution of the Schrödinger equation serves as a useful guide in solving a more interesting problem—determining the states of a particle whose potential energy is negative and constant over a finite region of space. A graph of such a potential, called a rectangular well, is shown as a function of X in Figure 18.10. Several values of constant total energy are also indicated. When the particle is located between the limits $-X/2$

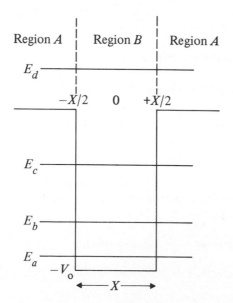

FIGURE 18.10 A rectangular potential well showing the three regions (A, B, A) in which the kinetic energy of a particle remains constant. The total energies E_a, E_b, and E_c correspond classically to bound states, the total energy E_d to a free state. The three bound-state energy lines are extended beyond the well to indicate that quantum mechanically a bound particle has a nonzero probability of being found in one of these classically forbidden regions.

*This section may be omitted without serious loss of continuity.

to $+X/2$ its potential energy is $-V_0$; otherwise its potential energy is zero. The kinetic energy of the particle is, of course, the difference between its total and its potential energy. Therefore classically a particle with total energy smaller than zero is confined within the well. But as we shall see presently this feature is *not* preserved in quantum mechanics.

In the nonrelativistic approximation, momentum and kinetic energy are related by

$$p^2 = 2M(KE).$$

Therefore an alternate form of the free-particle Schrödinger equation (Equation 18.24) is

$$\frac{d^2\phi}{dx^2} = -\frac{2M(KE)}{\hbar^2}\,\phi, \tag{18.27a}$$

and the free-particle amplitudes (Equation 18.26) may be written:

$$\phi = \bar{a}_{n\pm} \exp\left[\pm\frac{i}{\hbar}2M(KE)_n x\right].$$

Now the bracket $[V(x) - E]$ on the right side of the *full* one-dimensional Schrödinger equation (Equation 18.23) is equal to the negative of the kinetic energy so that again we may write:

$$\frac{d^2\phi}{dx^2} = -\frac{2M[KE(x)]}{\hbar^2}\,\phi. \tag{18.27b}$$

In most cases the potential energy and thus also the kinetic energy of a particle varies with x, and this important distinction between the free-particle and general forms of the Schrödinger equation (Equations 18.27a and 18.27b, respectively) should be borne in mind.

However, for the square well potential there are three separate regions in which the kinetic energy of the particle is constant so long as the particle remains within that region. These are labeled A and B in Figure 18.10. In the former two regions, defined by $x < -X/2$ and $x > X/2$, the particle has potential energy zero, while in the latter region from $-X/2$ to $X/2$ its potential energy is $-V_0$. Thus free-particlelike solutions are separately applicable in regions A and B. That is,

$$\phi_A(x) = \bar{a}_{n\pm} \exp\left[\pm\frac{i}{\hbar}\sqrt{2M(KE)_{nA}}x\right], \tag{18.28a}$$

$$\phi_B(x) = \bar{b}_{n\pm} \exp\left[\pm\frac{i}{\hbar}\sqrt{2M(KE)_{nB}}x\right]. \tag{18.28b}$$

If the total energy of a particle is positive, then its kinetic energy is positive in all three regions and as in the classical case it may pass freely from one region to another. However, its kinetic energy $[E - (-V_0) = E + V_0]$ is greater in region B than in regions A so that the real part of its amplitude, $\cos[\sqrt{2M(KE)}(x/\hbar)]$, oscillates more rapidly in the region of the well. (All values of positive total energy are permitted. However, for kinetic energies such that $h/\sqrt{2M(KE)}$, the wavelength of an oscillation in the well is an integral fraction of X, the width of the well, the constant $\bar{b}_n$ may be considerably larger than $\bar{a}_n$, indicating that the particle has a higher probability of being found in that region than elsewhere.* This situation is shown in Figure 18.11.)

---

* The reasons for this behavior are related to the requirement that the amplitude and its slope must be continuous across the boundaries between regions. These general requirements are outlined later in this section and worked out in detail for the negative energy solutions in the Appendix.

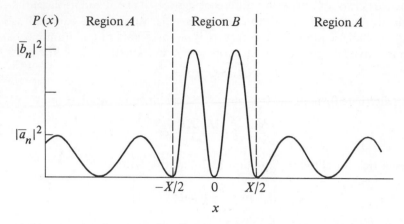

FIGURE 18.11 Probability distribution function for a particle with positive total energy in the vicinity of the negative potential energy rectangular well shown in Figure 18.10. The distribution function is oscillatory both in the region of the well and outside it, and all values of total energy are permitted. However, if the amplitude (and therefore the probability distribution) goes through an integral number of oscillations between $-X/2$ and $X/2$ then, for reasons outlined in the discussion of the negative energy states in the well, the maxima of the probability distribution are much greater inside the well region than outside. This situation is depicted here for a case in which the total energy of the particle is one and one-half times the magnitude of its potential energy between $-X/2$ and $X/2$.

If the total energy of a particle is negative but greater than V_0 then in region B its kinetic energy is also positive and the real part of the amplitude again has the form $\bar{b}_n \cos [\sqrt{2M(KE)_n}(x/\hbar)]$. However, in regions A its kinetic energy is negative and thus $\sqrt{-2M(KE)_n}$ imaginary. In that case the exponent $(i/\hbar)\sqrt{-2M(KE)_n}\,x$ is the product of two imaginary numbers and is therefore *real*. In order to see this more clearly we substitute $\sqrt{-2M(KE)_n} = \sqrt{-p_n^2} = ip_n$ into Equation 18.28b to obtain

$$\phi_A(x) = \bar{b}_{n\pm} \exp \left[\pm \frac{p_n x}{\hbar} \right], \tag{18.28c}$$

which is a *real* function provided the constant $\bar{b}_n$ is real. From Equation 18.28c a particle with momentum p_n has nonzero amplitude beyond the limits of the well and thus some probability of being found there. Although this conclusion is inconsistent with classical physics it may perhaps be understood better by realizing that if a particle stops at the boundary of the well, as it does classically, its position is well defined. But we also assume a definite value for the momentum, in disagreement with the Heisenberg principle. Therefore, the particle cannot be confined completely within the boundaries.

Some physical insight must be brought to bear on the negative energy square well problem in order to complete its solution. Figure 18.12 plots the functions $\exp(\alpha x)$ and $\exp(-\alpha x)$ for several values of the constant α. These functions increase from one to infinity as the argument αx increases from zero to infinity but decrease from one to zero for arguments smaller than zero. Since probability distributions cannot be infinite the

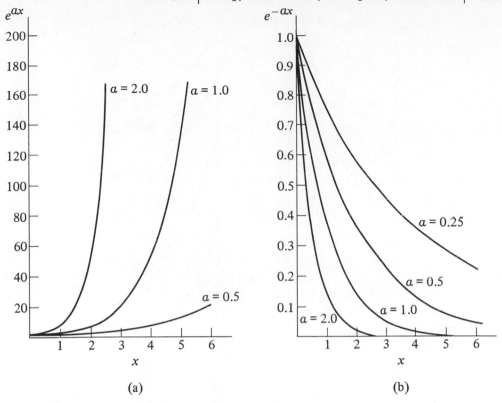

FIGURE 18.12 (a) The positive exponential function $e^{\alpha x}$ vs x for $\alpha = 0.5$, 1.0, and 2.0. (b) The negative exponential function $e^{-\alpha x}$ vs x for $\alpha = 0.25$, 0.5, 1.0, and 2.0. (See also Figure C.1, Appendix C to text.)

real, positive exponential solutions have no physical meaning so that for the regions A we are left with (see Equation 18.28c):

$$\phi_A(x) = \bar{a}_{n+} \exp\left(+\frac{p_n x}{\hbar}\right), \qquad x < -\frac{X}{2},$$

and

$$\phi_A(x) = \bar{a}_{n-} \exp\left(-\frac{p_n x}{\hbar}\right), \qquad x > \frac{X}{2}.$$

These are shown in Figure 18.13 for several different values of $p_n/\hbar$. Clearly, the rate at which the amplitude (and therefore the probability) decreases beyond the well boundaries increases with momentum, or [since $p = 2M(KE) = 2M(E + V_0)$] with the potential energy. For an infinitely deep well the probability of penetration beyond the boundary is zero.

The most general form of the amplitude within region B is the sum of the positive and negative imaginary exponential solutions of Equation 18.28b:

$$\phi_B(x) = \bar{b}_{n+} \exp\left[\frac{ip_n x}{\hbar}\right] + \bar{b}_{n-} \exp\left[-\frac{ip_n x}{\hbar}\right]$$

$$= \bar{b}_{n+}\left[\cos\left(\frac{p_n x}{\hbar}\right) + i \sin\left(\frac{p_n x}{\hbar}\right)\right] + \bar{b}_{n-}\left[\cos\left(\frac{p_n x}{\hbar}\right) - i \sin\left(\frac{p_n x}{\hbar}\right)\right].$$

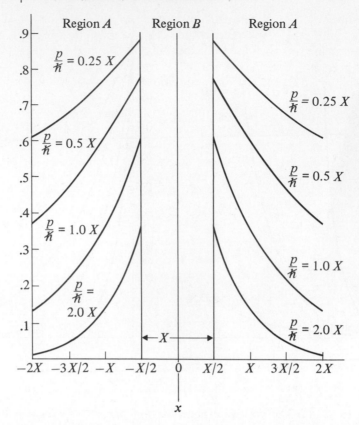

FIGURE 18.13 Amplitudes for negative total energy states plotted as functions of x in the classically forbidden regions outside the potential well boundaries for different values of $p/\hbar$. (The coefficients a_n of all amplitudes are assumed to be equal.)

If we let the constants $\bar{b}_{n\pm}$ be real and set both equal to c_n this becomes

$$\phi_B(x) = 2c_n \cos\left(\frac{p_n x}{\hbar}\right). \tag{18.28d}$$

However, we might also choose $\bar{b}_{n+} = -id_n$, $\bar{b}_{n-} = id_n$ in which case we have

$$\phi_B(x) = 2d_n \sin\left(\frac{p_n x}{\hbar}\right). \tag{18.28e}$$

Thus we are led to two classes of oscillatory amplitudes within the well, both of which, as we shall see, are physically meaningful.

It is reasonable to assume that both the magnitudes and slopes of the amplitude functions are continuous at the boundaries between the regions.* The first of these conditions establishes the relative magnitudes of the constants a and c or a and d. The

---

* These conditions were used to match the positive energy amplitudes (Figure 18.11) at the boundaries between the regions.

absolute magnitudes of the constants follows from the requirement that the total probability of finding the particle somewhere must be unity, as in Section 18.5. Figure 18.14a is an example of a situation in which the magnitude of $\phi(x)$ is discontinuous and is rejected as physically meaningless.

The somewhat more subtle continuity condition on the slope of the amplitude is illustrated by Figures 18.14b to 18.14d. In the first two examples the slopes are discontinuous. Thus only the functions shown in Figure 18.14d, in which both the magnitudes are continuous, have physical meaning. But we have seen that the slope of the exponential solutions at the boundary depend on momentum (Figure 18.13). Therefore the slope continuity condition restricts the physically meaningful amplitudes to a discrete set specified by a discrete set of momenta. *In other words, the allowed values of momentum, and therefore of energy within the well, are quantized.* This important conclusion is not restricted to the square well but is true for *any* bound quantum mechanical system whatsoever. Thus energy quantization, which was an ad hoc assumption in the old quantum theory of Planck, Einstein, and Bohr, *follows as a natural and necessary consequence of the quantum mechanical postulates.*

A complete solution to the rectangular well problem, then, requires that the momenta for which the slope continuity condition is satisfied be found. As the general problem requires considerable algebra, we defer it to the chapter Appendix. Here we shall apply the condition to the special case of an infinitely deep well, for which (Figure 18.13) the

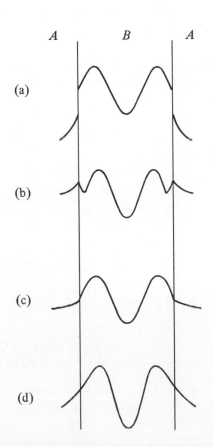

FIGURE 18.14 Continuity conditions at the boundaries of the rectangular well. In (a) the magnitudes of the amplitudes are discontinuous, in (b) and (c) the slopes fail to meet the continuity requirement. However, (d) qualifies as a physically meaningful solution to the problem of finding the negative energy amplitudes since it satisfies both continuity conditions.

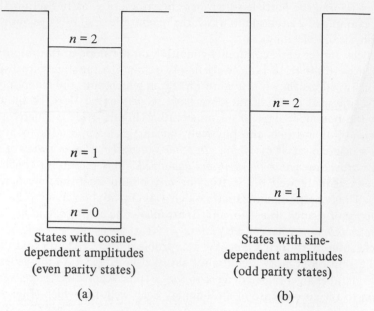

States with cosine-
dependent amplitudes
(even parity states)

(a)

States with sine-
dependent amplitudes
(odd parity states)

(b)

FIGURE 18.15 (a) The three lowest energy states with cosine-dependent amplitudes in an infinitely deep rectangular well. (b) The two lowest energy states with
sine-dependent amplitudes in an infinitely deep rectangular well.

amplitude becomes zero at the boundaries. That is, the real exponential part of the
amplitude is zero everywhere and we require for the cosine solution inside the well
(Equation 18.28d):

$$\phi_B\left(\pm\frac{X}{2}\right) = 2c_n \cos\left(\pm\frac{p_n}{\hbar}\frac{X}{2}\right) = 0.$$

This condition is satisfied for p_n such that

$$\pm\frac{p_n}{\hbar}\frac{X}{2} = \frac{(2n+1)}{2}\pi, \qquad n = 0, 1, 2, 3, \ldots,$$

or

$$p_n = \pm\frac{(2n+1)\hbar\pi}{X} = \frac{(2n+1)h}{2X}, \qquad n = 0, 1, 2, \ldots, \qquad (18.29a)$$

since $\hbar = h/2\pi$. Thus the permitted values of kinetic energy in the well corresponding to
the *cosine* solution are

$$(KE)_n = \frac{p_n^2}{2M} = \frac{(2n+1)^2 h^2}{8MX^2}, \qquad n = 0, 1, 2, \ldots, \qquad (18.29b)$$

and the total energy can assume the values $E_n = (KE)_n - V_0$.

The amplitudes with the sine rather than the cosine dependence in the well must also
vanish at the boundaries:

$$\phi_B\left(\pm\frac{X}{2}\right) = 2d_n \sin\left(\pm\frac{p_n}{h}\frac{X}{2}\right) = 0,$$

which requires that

$$\frac{p_n}{h}\frac{X}{2} = n\pi, \qquad n = 1, 2, 3, \ldots,$$

or

$$p_n = \frac{2n\pi h}{X} = \frac{nh}{X}, \qquad n = 1, 2, 3, \ldots, \tag{18.29c}$$

so that the permitted values of kinetic energy corresponding to the *sine* dependent amplitudes are

$$KE_n = \frac{p_n^2}{2M} = \frac{n^2 h^2}{2Mx^2}, \qquad n = 0, 1, 2, 3, \ldots. \tag{18.29d}$$

Thus there are *two* energy levels for each value of the integer n except 0* corresponding to the cosine-dependent amplitudes, one to the sine-dependent amplitudes. Substituting 0, 1, and 2 into Equations 18.29b and 18.29d we arrive at more explicit expressions for these energies:

$$KE_0^{(c)} = \frac{h^2}{8MX^2},$$

$$KE_1^{(s)} = \frac{h^2}{2MX^2},$$

$$KE_1^{(c)} = \frac{9h^2}{8MX^2},$$

$$KE_2^{(s)} = \frac{2h^2}{MX^2},$$

$$KE_2^{(c)} = \frac{25}{8}\frac{h^2}{MX^2},$$

where the superscripts (c) and (s) designate kinetic energies corresponding to the cosine- and sine-dependent amplitudes, respectively. The two sets of states clearly alternate when arranged in order of increasing kinetic energy (Figure 18.15).

The energy difference between the two lowest levels in an infinitely deep rectangular well follows at once from the above tabulation:

$$(\Delta KE)_0 = \frac{3}{8}\frac{h^2}{MX^2} = \frac{16.5 \times 10^{-68}}{MX^2}\text{ J,}$$

where we have substituted $h = 6.6 \times 10^{-34}$ J-sec.

---

* $n = 0$ is eliminated from the sine solutions since it implies $p_n = 0$ and (Equation 18.28e) zero amplitude in the well.

For an electron ($M = 9 \times 10^{-31}$ kg),

$$(\Delta KE)_0 = \frac{1.8 \times 10^{-37}}{X^2} \text{ J.}$$

Then if $X = 10^{-6}$ m,

$$(\Delta KE)_0 = 1.8 \times 10^{-25} \text{ J} = 1.1 \times 10^{-6} \text{ eV.*}$$

The energy separation is so small that for most purposes we are justified in regarding the states as continuous. But for $X = 10^{-10}$ m, the radius of the hydrogen atom,

$$(\Delta KE)_0 = 1.8 \times 10^{-17} \text{ J} = 110 \text{ eV.,}$$

which is a considerable difference. (Actually, the measured separation between the first two levels in hydrogen is only 10.2 eV. Since the electron in a hydrogen atom is bound in an electrostatic well rather than a rectangular well the discrepancy is not surprising.)

Finally, for a proton with $M_p = 1.6 \times 10^{-27}$ kg bound in a well with $X = 6 \times 10^{-15}$ m (the approximate diameter of the nucleus $_6C^{12}$),

$$(\Delta KE)_0 = \frac{16.5 \times 10^{-68}}{1.6 \times 10^{-27} \times (6 \times 10^{-15})^2},$$

$$= 2.9 \times 10^{-12} \text{ J} = 1.8 \times 10^7 \text{ eV} = 18 \text{ MeV,}$$

Amplitudes

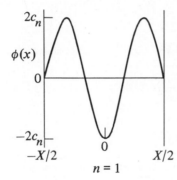 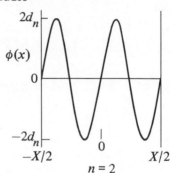

Probability densities

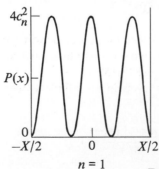 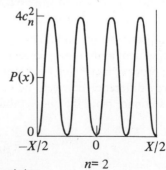

Even parity states

(a)

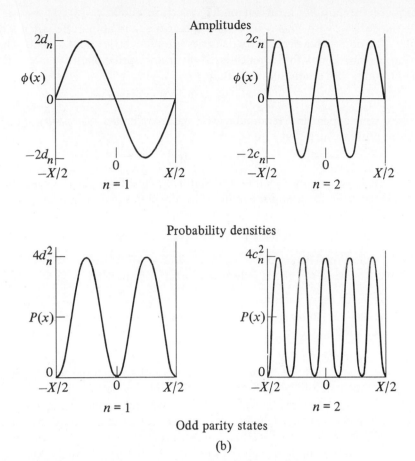

FIGURE 18.16 (a) Amplitudes and probability densities for the even parity (cosine-dependent) states with $n = 1$ and $n = 2$ in an infinitely deep rectangular well. (b) Amplitudes and probability densities for the odd parity (sine-dependent) states with $n = 1$ and $n = 2$ in an infinitely deep rectangular well.

which is larger than the observed 4.4 MeV separation between the first two states in $_6C^{12}$ by a factor of four. This is surprisingly good agreement in view of the fact that once again an infinitely deep rectangular well is a rather poor representation of the nuclear potential energy.

The cosine-dependent and sine-dependent amplitudes for $n = 1$ and $n = 2$ are shown in Figure 18.16, together with their corresponding probability densities (i.e., their squares). Note that whereas both sets of probability densities are symmetric about the center of the well ($x = 0$), only the cosine dependent *amplitude* is symmetric about the center. The sine dependent amplitude is *antisymmetric*. This also follows from the fact that whereas

$$\cos(-y) = \cos(y),$$
$$\sin(-y) = -\sin(y).$$

In Chapter 6 we discussed reflectional invariance (or parity conservation) in classical physics, a principle stating that the designations "left" and "right" are arbitrary. At first sight it appears that the antisymmetric sine-dependent amplitudes violate the principles since they are *not* invariant under reflection about $x = 0$. However, reflectional invariance deals with *directly observable* quantities, and amplitudes are not directly observable. The observable probability densities *are* symmetric about $x = 0$. Therefore our solution is consistent with the reflectional invariance principle.

In general, states with amplitudes such that

$$\phi(-x) = \phi(x)$$

(such as the cosine dependent rectangular well state) are called *even parity states*, while those with amplitudes such that

$$\phi(-x) = -\phi(x)$$

(such as the sine dependent rectangular well state) are called *odd parity states*. Since the probability distribution function for a state is the absolute square of the amplitude then, in both cases,

$$P(-x) = P(x),$$

as required by reflectional invariance.

We shall have more to say about reflectional invariance in Section 23.5.

▲▲ 18.9 Notes on the states in a Coulomb potential. Barrier penetration. Transition amplitudes*

Although we have shown that energy quantization follows of necessity for a particle bound in a rectangular well, the numerical results given by Equations 18.29b and 18.29c are not in quantitative accord with observation. The spacing between the first two energy levels in hydrogen is 10.2 eV rather than the 110 eV we have calculated (Equation 17.9), and the separation between the higher levels decreases rather than increases with increasing n (compare Figures 17.7 and 18.15). Furthermore, the spacing between levels in a nucleus usually ranges from a few tenths to a few MeV so that the 18 MeV we have calculated is somewhat high.

These discrepancies are not surprising in view of the approximate nature of our treatment. In the first place no potential well is infinitely deep. For a rectangular well of finite depth V_0, the permitted values of momentum are obtained, as already noted, by matching the slopes of the amplitudes at the boundaries of the region (see chapter Appendix). Since the amplitude inside the well need not drop to zero at the boundaries, the permitted values of associated wavelength $\lambda_n = \hbar/p_n$ increase as the well becomes shallower. Therefore the values of the quantized energies shift downward.

In the second place the rectangular well does not correspond to any real physical situation. For instance, the electron in a hydrogen atom is not bound in such a potential well but rather, in a well determined primarily by the form of the electrostatic potential $V(r) = -(1/4\pi\epsilon_0)(e^2/R)$ (Figure 18.17). This is the potential that must be used in the three-dimensional Schrödinger equation (which is a natural generalization of the one-dimensional form given by Equation 18.23) in order to determine the amplitudes and energies of the bound states in hydrogen. Since the potential energy is not constant the relatively simple exponential forms encountered in the last two sections are no longer solutions to the Schrödinger equation. In fact the requisite solutions (which are of course the amplitudes for the energy states of the atom) are quite complicated and cannot be

---

* This section may be omitted without serious loss of continuity.

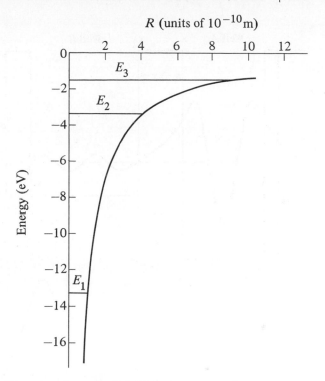

FIGURE 18.17 Potential energy well for the hydrogen atom showing the three lowest energy levels (compare with Figure 17.7).

expressed in any familiar form. However the energies of the corresponding states reproduce those predicted by the ad hoc Bohr model of Chapter 17. In addition, there is frequently a close correspondence between the maxima of the probability distributions for the states and the values of the Bohr radii (Equation 7.12). But whereas the simple Bohr model assumes circular orbit the Schrödinger equation yields, in addition, probability distributions of more complicated shapes. Using semiclassical language, the radius R alone is insufficient to specify the orbits of an atom.

We shall return to the question of atomic states in Chapter 19 and present a few pertinent results, based on the solutions to the Schrödinger equation, which show that quantum mechanics permits a complete, quantitative understanding of atomic structure.

As noted in the foregoing section a particle bound in an attractive potential well has a nonzero probability of being found outside the well (Equation 18.28e and Figure 18.13). An important, measurable consequence is illustrated in Figure 18.18a which shows two rectangular wells of depth $-V_A$ and $-V_B$ separated by a barrier of width $\Delta x = X_1 - X_2$. Classically a bound, negative-energy particle in one well would be confined there forever. But quantum mechanically there is some probability that a particle initially in well A will penetrate the barrier and appear in well B, and vice versa.

The former situation is illustrated in Figure 18.18. Within well A the amplitude assumes the familiar $\cos [(p_n/\hbar)x]$ form of Section 18.8 with p_n one of the discrete set of values determined by the width of the well. At X_1, the right-hand boundary, this solution joins smoothly onto a solution of the form $\exp [-(p_n/\hbar)x]$ (Equation 18.28c) so that although the probability of finding the particle beyond the boundaries (the square of the amplitude) decreases with the distance from the boundary it may still be appreciable at $x - X_2$, the left-hand boundary of well B, provided $X_1 - X_2$ is not too large. At X_2 the kinetic energy of the particle is again positive and the exponential solution joins smoothly with a cosine solution.

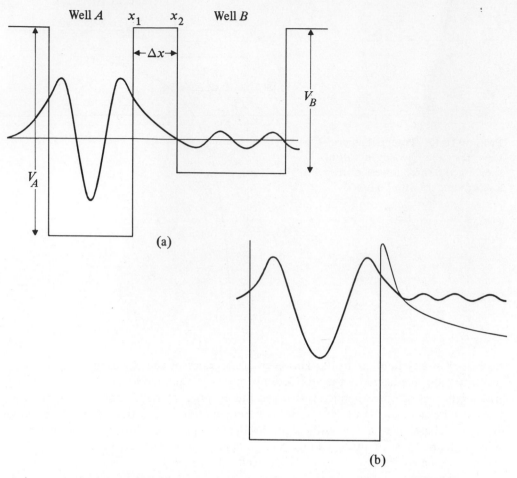

FIGURE 18.18 (a) Barrier penetration between rectangular wells. A particle in a negative total energy state in A has a nonzero amplitude outside A, and therefore a nonzero amplitude in B. Since the amplitude in the classically forbidden region between the wells decreases exponentially with their separation, so does the maximum amplitude in B relative to the maximum amplitude in A. (b) Penetration through a nonrectangular barrier.

Referring to Equation 18.28c the exponentially decaying amplitude has the form

$$\phi(x) = a \exp\left(-\frac{p_n x}{\hbar}\right), \qquad X_1 < x < X_2,$$

so that the probability distribution within the barrier is

$$P(x) = \phi^2(x) = a^2 \exp\left(-\frac{2p_n x}{\hbar}\right), \qquad X_1 < x < X_2.$$

Thus the probability of finding the particle at the right-hand boundary of well B relative to the probability of finding it at the right-hand boundary of well A is

$$\frac{P(X_1)}{P(X_2)} = \frac{a^2 \exp\left(-\frac{2p_n X_1}{\hbar}\right)}{a^2 \exp\left(-\frac{2p_n X_2}{\hbar}\right)} = \exp\left(-\frac{2p_n}{\hbar}\Delta x\right). \qquad (18.30)$$

That is, the probability of barrier penetration decreases exponentially with the thickness of the well.

Suppose an electron ($M_e = 9 \times 10^{-31}$ kg) with 10 eV kinetic energy is momentarily at the right-hand boundary of well A. What is the probability that it will penetrate a barrier with $\Delta x = 10^{-9}$ m and appear in well B instead of remaining in well A?

$$KE = 10 \text{ eV} = 1.6 \times 10^{-18} \text{ J,}$$

so that

$$p = 2M(KE) = 2 \times 0.9 \times 1.6 \times 10^{-24} = 1.7 \times 10^{-24} \text{ kg-m/sec,}$$

and

$$\frac{2p\,\Delta x}{\hbar} = \frac{2 \times 1.7 \times 10^{-33}}{6.6 \times 10^{-34}/6.28} = 8.1.$$

Thus,

$$\frac{P(X_1)}{P(X_2)} = \exp\left(\frac{-2p\,\Delta X}{\hbar}\right) = e^{-8.1} = \frac{1}{3000},$$

where we obtain the final result from Appendix A to the text. If, for instance, the electron makes repeated transits back and forth across well A, then on the average it should appear in well B after three thousand round trips.

According to Equation 18.30 the barrier penetration probability decreases with the width of the barrier, which is reasonable. However, the momentum dependence of the expression is deceptive in comparison with more realistic potential functions.

In Figure 18.18b the barrier width itself decreases with increasing total energy and thus with momentum, in contrast with the constant barrier width of Figure 18.18a. Thus the penetration probability should also decrease as a particle's total energy approaches the top of the barrier. In fact, Figure 18.18b corresponds more closely to the potentials encountered in real situations than the rectangular barrier of Figure 18.18a.

The fact that a particle may penetrate a potential barrier even though classically it has insufficient energy to surmount it has a number of important consequences. For example, in Section 16.3 we stated that hydrogen and oxygen molecules can react to form water only if they first dissociate into free atoms or ions. But it now appears that the reaction may proceed even if the external energy supplied is less than the total binding energy of the molecules. Similar remarks apply to the initiation of the thermonuclear reactions discussed in the same section. Barrier penetration also permits one type of radioactive decay of nuclei (α-decay, see Chapter 20).

In these last few sections we have determined states and amplitudes for a number of simple situations by solving the Schrödinger equation. The second type of problem mentioned at the beginning of Section 18.7, i.e., finding the probability that a particle known to be in a given state at one time will later be found in another state, is generally more involved mathematically. Therefore, only a cursory outline of the approach to it is given here.

The type of probability that must be determined in dealing with this type of problem is called a *transition* probability from one state to another, and, like any other quantum mechanical probability, is the absolute square of an amplitude, in this case a *transition* amplitude. These may be determined (in the nonrelativistic approximation) by solving a second differential equation of Schrödinger's, though there are alternate methods as well.

Let us consider in brief the formal quantum mechanical description of the Rutherford scattering (Section 15.6). A parallel, monoenergetic beam of α-particles is incident upon a thin metallic foil (say gold) whose nuclei scatter the particles through various angles (Figure 18.19a). The probability distribution for scattering an α-particle is measured as a function of θ (Figure 18.19b), and it is necessary to deduce the nature of the interaction that causes the scattering from these data. Using quantum mechanical language, the

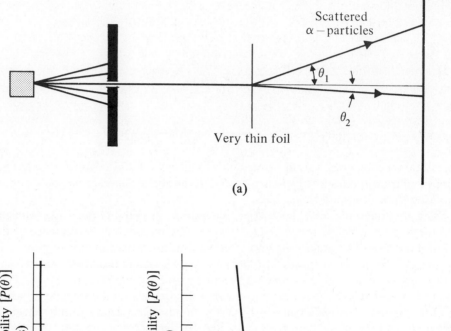

(a)

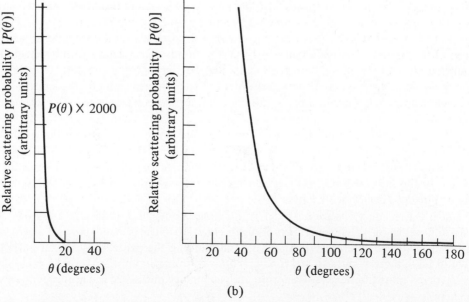

(b)

FIGURE 18.19 (a) Rutherford scattering apparatus. (b) Measured distribution function for scattering as a function of scattering angle.

interaction of an α-particle with a gold nucleus causes it to make a transition from one state to another. In order to solve the scattering problem, the various states involved must be identified and then the transition amplitudes between them calculated.

Each of the incident α-particles is initially in the same pure energy state, since we assume a monoenergetic incident beam.* If we confine our attention to an elastic scattering process in which neither the α-particles nor the gold nuclei absorb internal energy then the final, post-scattering states are specified by the same energy as the initial, pre-scattering states and are distinguished from one another by the scattering angle θ. Thus a continuum of final states labeled by θ are available to an α-particle. The scattering problem is solved by determining the transition amplitude from the initial, pure energy state into each of these final states, or, in other words, by determining the transition amplitude as a function of scattering angle.

The functional form of the initial, monoenergetic free particle amplitude $\bar\phi_i$ is given by Equation 18.19 and has been used extensively in the foregoing sections. Since it is the interaction of α-particles and gold nuclei that causes transitions between this state and the final states $\bar\phi_f(\theta)$ we may think of the interaction as the connecting link between the states. In order to formulate this idea we note that the basic superposition theorem of quantum mechanics (Section 18.3, Equation 18.8) permits us to think of the *initial*-state amplitude as a sum, or (since they form a continuum) as an integral over all possible final-state amplitudes. Then each interaction picks out, or projects, one of the final states, $\bar\phi_f(\theta)$, from that sum. We seek a function which, when it multiplies the initial-state amplitude $\bar\phi_i$, picks out a final-state amplitude $\bar\phi_f(\theta)$ whose absolute square gives the observed probability distribution for α-particle scattering. That function will then represent the interaction itself. Algebraically all of this is summarized by

$$\bar\phi_f(\theta) = V\bar\phi_i, \tag{18.31}$$

where in the present instance V describes the interaction between an α-particle gold nucleus. Classically the Rutherford scattering interaction is electrostatic, a fact which serves as a guide in deducing its quantum mechanical equivalent. However, most interesting interactions in nuclear and elementary particle physics lack classical equivalents so that the task of deducing the form of the interaction function usually becomes quite involved.

▲▲ 18.10 Identical particles. Bose and Fermi particles. The Pauli exclusion principle

All of the problems we have presented thus far are soluble in terms of single-particle amplitudes. Many photons are required to produce a measurable double-slit interference pattern, but we describe the pattern in terms of an amplitude for a single photon incident upon the double-slit system, assuming that the same amplitude describes all the photons in the beam of light incident upon the double-slit system. Similarly, although many atoms contribute to a measurable spectrum, we can describe the internal states of a hydrogen atom in terms of the bound probability amplitude of a single electron.

However, many processes involve either the simultaneous or the sequential occurrence of two or more related events. For instance, to specify a particular state of a helium

---

* Strictly speaking, we should speak in terms of states of an α-gold-nucleus system. However, for simplicity we assume the latter nuclei are so heavy that their recoil energy after scattering is negligible.

atom we must know the state of each of its electrons (Figure 18.4). Likewise, the probability that an excited hydrogen atom returns to its ground state in two steps, emitting one photon after another, depends jointly upon the transition amplitude for each step.

Suppose we have two distinguishable particles, 1 and 2, and know both the probability $P(A1)$ of finding 1 in some state A, and the probability $P(B2)$ of finding 2 in some other state B. If the classical AND rule (Section 15.3) is valid, the joint probability of finding 1 in A and 2 in B is simply the product of the separate probabilities:

$$P(A1, B2) = P(A1)P(B2).$$

The "particles" might be coins, for instance with state $A =$ heads, state $B =$ tails. Then (as in Chapter 15) application of the AND rule gives the probability that the first coin will come up heads, the second tails. Of course quantum mechanically, events are associated with amplitudes. Hence the AND rule becomes

$$|\phi(A1, B2)|^2 = P(A1, B2) = P(A1)P(B2) = |\phi(A1)|^2|\phi(B2)|^2 = |\phi(A1)\phi(B2)|^2,$$

or

$$\phi(A1, B2) = \pm\phi(A1)\phi(B2). \tag{18.32}$$

That is, the amplitude for two simultaneous or sequential events is either the positive or the negative product of the amplitudes for the separate two events *provided* the events are *distinguishable*. We shall presently spell out the distinguishability proviso in more detail.

Given the same two particles and the same two states, we can also ask for the probability of finding 1 in B while 2 is in A. Applying the AND rule to the separate probabilities,

$$P(B1, A2) = P(B1)P(A2),$$

or, in terms of the amplitudes for the two distinguishable events,

$$\phi(B1, A2) = \pm\phi(B1)\phi(A2).$$

Now suppose we want to calculate the probability of finding one particle in state A and the other in B without regard to which of the particles is associated with each of the states. Assuming the particles are experimentally *distinguishable* we can apply the classical OR theorem. To express this probability in terms of the previously calculated joint probabilities, we write

$$P(A, B) = P(A1, B2) + P(B1, A2).$$

In terms of amplitudes,

$$P(A, B) = |\phi(A1)\phi(B2)|^2 + |\phi(B1)\phi(A2)|^2. \tag{18.33a}$$

The probability of finding both particles in the *same* state, say C, follows immediately, for in that case the two terms in the sum are equal:

$$P_{\text{both}}(C) = |\phi(C1)\phi(C2)|^2 + |\phi(C2)\phi(C1)|^2,$$
$$= 2|\phi(C1)\phi(C2)|^2. \tag{18.33b}$$

Unless there is some measurement that can in principle distinguish between two entities, the labels "photon 1" and "photon 2," or "electron 1" and "electron 2," for instance, cannot imply any intrinsic physical difference between the two entities. The designations are used for book-keeping purposes only and Equations 18.33 are *not applicable*. Given two identical particles, two photons, two electrons, or two hydrogen atoms, for instance, there is no way to determine the probability of finding 1 in state A, 2 in state B. At best we can deduce the probability that *one* of the two, regardless of label, will be in each of the states. Because there are two experimentally indistinguishable ways in which two particles may occupy two states—i.e., particle 1 in A and 2 in B, or vice versa—the amplitudes for the two alternatives must interfere.

As before we let $\phi(A1)$ and $\phi(B2)$ be the amplitudes for particle 1 to be in state A and for particle 2 to be in state B, respectively. The amplitude for the two particles to be in their respective states together must then be $\phi(A1)\phi(B2)$. Likewise, the amplitude for finding 1 in B and 2 in A is $\phi(B1)\phi(A2)$. (Because this amplitude is obtained from the first by exchanging the roles of the two particles, it is often called the *exchange* amplitude, while the amplitude $\phi(A1)\phi(B2)$ is the *direct amplitude*. Obviously the designations are interchangeable.)

We would expect the amplitude for finding one particle in A, the other in B regardless of label to be

$$\phi(A, B) = \phi(A1)\phi(B2) + \phi(B1)\phi(A2),$$

with the probability one particle in each state given as usual by $|\phi(A, B)|^2$. However, that expectation is borne out only for one class of particles, collectively called Bose particles or *bosons* since their statistics were first investigated by the Indian physicist Satyandranath Bose. For another class of particles, called Fermi particles or *fermions* after Enrico Fermi, the amplitude $\phi(A, B)$ turns out to be the *difference* between the direct and exchange amplitudes rather than their sum. That is,

$$\phi(A, B) = \phi(A1)\phi(B2) - \phi(B1)\phi(A2).$$

The probabilities for the two classes of particles follow immediately:

For bosons: $\quad P(A, B) = |\phi(A1)\phi(B2) + \phi(B1)\phi(A2)|^2,$ $\qquad$ (18.34a)

For fermions: $\quad P(A, B) = |\phi(A1)\phi(B2) - \phi(B1)\phi(A2)|^2.$ $\qquad$ (18.34b)

All of the fundamental particles and in addition all composite systems such as atoms and nuclei appear to fall into one of two classes. Photons belong to the boson class, as do a large group of particles called mesons with masses between the electron and proton mass. On the other hand, electrons, protons, and neutrons as well as muons, neutrinos, and hyperons (Chapters 22 and 23) are fermions, so that all atoms and nuclei are composed of fermions. An atom with an *odd* number of electrons is also a fermion, an atom with an *even* number of electrons a boson. Likewise, if the number of protons plus neutrons in a nucleus is odd the nucleus is a fermion, if even the nucleus is a boson. A normal hydrogen atom is thus a fermion, as is its nucleus, but a helium atom and its nucleus (with two protons and two neutrons) is a boson.

That the difference between the two classes is far from trivial can best be seen by deducing from Equations 18.34, the probability of finding two identical particles in the *same* state, C. If the particles are identical *bosons*, Equation 18.34a yields:

For bosons: $\quad P_{\text{both}}(C) = |\phi(C1)\phi(C2) + \phi(C1)\phi(C2)|^2$
$$= |2\phi(C1)\phi(C2)|^2 = 4|\phi(C1)\phi(C2)|^2. \qquad (18.35a)$$

Comparing this result with Equation 18.33a we see that the probability of finding two identical bosons in the same state is *twice* the probability expected for classical or for distinguishable particles. If the same sort of calculation were carried out for three, four, or any number of identical bosons, we would find that the ratio of the probability for identical bosons to the corresponding classical probability *increases* with the number of particles in the state. In other words, Bose particles "like" to be in the same state. In fact if a certain state already contains n identical bosons the a priori probability that another will enter the same state is n times the classical probability, so that as the number of identical bosons in a particular state increases, the probability that more will enter the state also increases. This is to be contrasted with the classical case in which the probability of finding a particle in a given state is independent of the number already present.

Fermi particles behave in a totally different manner. Applying Equation 18.34b, the probability of finding two identical *fermions* in the same state is zero! That is,

$$\text{For fermions:} \quad P_{\text{both}}(C) = |\bar{\phi}(C1)\bar{\phi}(C2) - \bar{\phi}(C1)\bar{\phi}(C2)|^2 = 0. \quad (18.35b)$$

This conclusion, that the presence of one fermion in a state excludes all other *identical* fermions, is called the *Pauli Exclusion Principle*, after the Swiss physicist Wolfgang Pauli who suggested its necessity on the basis of empirical arguments. Because only one fermion can be found in any given quantum mechanical state the electrons in a complex atom must all occupy *different* states so that the structure of atoms is quite different than it would be if all electrons could occupy the same state. In fact, chemical distinctions between atoms, based upon the familiar shell model, follow chiefly from the restriction imposed by the Pauli principle (Chapter 19).

The general considerations of this section have much in common with the symmetry viewpoint of Chapter 6. For example, the statement that physical laws are symmetric with respect to rotations in space implies that the designations "north," "south," "up," and "down" have no intrinsic physical meaning. Rather, they are labels assigned arbitrarily to coordinate systems in order to describe physical events in a convenient way. The conclusion that these labels have no absolute meaning leads to the requirement that the laws of physics must be written in terms of vectors, quantities that do not vary when a coordinate system is rotated.

Likewise, the statement that two electrons are in all ways identical implies that the designations "electron 1" and "electron 2" are artificial. We continue to use the labels because they are convenient. However, if physical laws are really invariant with respect to the interchange of the labels 1 and 2, then the square of the amplitude $\bar{\phi}(A1)\bar{\phi}(B2)$ cannot correspond to a physically measurable probability. Rather, we must deal in terms of a properly *symmetrized* amplitude which includes the exchange as well as the direct amplitude (Equations 18.33). There are two alternate ways to symmetrize a two-particle amplitude—one of them involving a positive, one a negative sign—and there is no a priori reason to prefer one rather than the other. Both alternatives, it seems, are found in nature, with consequences that will become increasingly apparent in the remaining chapters of the text.

APPENDIX TO CHAPTER 18 | *Solutions to Schrödinger's Equation for a Finite Rectangular Well*

The amplitudes appropriate to the three regions A, B, and A in Figure 18.10 are given by Equations 18.28c, 18.28d, and 18.28e:

$$\phi_A(x) = a_{n-} \exp\left(\frac{p_{An}}{\hbar} x\right), \qquad x < -\frac{X}{2},$$

$$\phi_B(x) = 2c_n \cos\left(\frac{p_{Bn}}{\hbar} x\right),$$

or

$$-\frac{X}{2} \leqq x \leqq \frac{X}{2},$$

$$\phi_B(x) = 2d_n \sin\left(\frac{p_{Bn}}{\hbar} x\right),$$

$$\phi_A(x) = a_{n+} \exp\left(-\frac{p_{An}}{\hbar} x\right), \qquad x > \frac{X}{2}.$$

Since the total energy is constant the momenta in regions A and B are *not* equal, and we have used the notation p_{An} and p_{Bn} to note this important fact explicitly. In fact, the desired states are pure states of energy and not momentum. Nonrelativistically the connection between the variables is

$$p_{nA} = \sqrt{2M(KE)_{nA}} = \sqrt{2ME_n},$$

and

$$p_{nB} = \sqrt{2M(KE)_{nB}} = \sqrt{2M(-E_n + V_0)},$$

where E_n is the *magnitude* of the negative total energy and V_0 the magnitude of the negative potential energy. (The magnitude of E_n must be smaller than V_0, otherwise the kinetic energy inside the well would also be negative.) Since it is more appropriate to express the amplitudes in terms of total energy rather than momentum we make the appropriate substitutions to obtain

$$\phi_A(x) = a_{n-} \exp\left[\sqrt{2ME_n}\,\frac{x}{\hbar}\right], \qquad x < -\frac{X}{2}.$$

$$\phi_B(x) = 2c_n \cos\left[\frac{\sqrt{2M(-E_n + V_0)}}{\hbar} x\right],$$

or

$$-\frac{X}{2} \leqq x \leqq \frac{X}{2},$$

$$\phi_B(x) = 2d_n \sin\left[\frac{\sqrt{2M(-E_n + V_0)}}{\hbar} x\right],$$

$$\phi_A(x) = a_{n+} \exp\left[-\sqrt{2ME_n}\,\frac{x}{\hbar}\right], \qquad x > \frac{X}{2}$$

where, from our experience with the infinite well calculation (Section 18.8) we take the constants a_{n-}, a_{n+}, c_n, and d_n as real.

We shall carry out the detailed calculation of the energy states for the even parity, cosine amplitudes only, since the calculation for the odd parity states is completely analogous. In order to relate the constants a_{n-}, c_n, and a_{n+} we require that the amplitudes be equal at the boundaries. At the right boundary ($x = X/2$) this condition is

$$a_{n+} \exp\left[-\sqrt{2ME_n}\,\frac{X}{2\hbar}\right] = 2c_n \cos\left[\frac{\sqrt{2M(-E_n + V_0)}}{2\hbar} X\right],$$

so that

$$c_n = a_{n+} \frac{\exp\left[-\sqrt{2ME_n}(X/2\hbar)\right]}{2 \cos\left[\sqrt{2M(-E_n + V_0)}(X/2\hbar)\right]}. \tag{A18.1}$$

Since the cosine amplitudes are symmetric about $x = 0$ then $a_+ = a_-$ so that the subscripts $\pm$ will no longer be required. (On the other hand, the antisymmetry of the sine solutions requires $a_{n+} = -a_{n-}$.)

The *slopes* of the amplitudes, defined as their first derivatives with respect to x, must also be equal at the boundaries. For the exponential amplitude we have (Equation 18.25b):

$$\frac{d\phi(x)}{dx} = -a_n\left(\frac{\sqrt{2ME_n}}{\hbar}\right)\exp\left(-\frac{\sqrt{2ME_n}}{\hbar}x\right),$$

while for the cosine solution (see Problems 2.33),

$$\frac{d\phi(x)}{dx} = -2c_n\left[\frac{\sqrt{2M(-E_n + V_0)}}{\hbar}\right]\sin\left[\frac{\sqrt{2M(-E_n + V_0)}}{\hbar}x\right].$$

Thus at $x = X/2$:

$$a_n\left(\frac{\sqrt{2ME_n}}{\hbar}\right)\exp\left(-\frac{\sqrt{2ME_n}}{\hbar}\frac{X}{2}\right) = 2c_n\left[\frac{\sqrt{2M(-E_n + V_0)}}{\hbar}\right]\sin\left[\frac{\sqrt{2M(-E_n + V_0)}}{\hbar}\frac{X}{2}\right].$$

Substituting the value of c_n from Equation A18.1,

$$a_n\left(\frac{\sqrt{2ME_n}}{\hbar}\right)\exp\left(-\frac{\sqrt{2ME_n}}{\hbar}\frac{X}{2}\right)$$

$$= 2a_n\exp\left(-\frac{\sqrt{2ME_n}}{\hbar}\frac{X}{2}\right)\left[\frac{\sqrt{2M(-E_n + V_0)}}{\hbar}\right] \times \frac{\sin\left[\frac{\sqrt{2M(-E_n + V_0)}}{\hbar}\frac{X}{2}\right]}{2\cos\left[\frac{\sqrt{2M(-E_n + V_0)}}{\hbar}\frac{X}{2}\right]}.$$

But the factor $a_n\exp\left[(-\sqrt{2ME_n}/\hbar)(X/2)\right]$ appears on both sides of this last equation and may be canceled. In addition, since $\sin y/\cos y = \tan y$, we have

$$\frac{\sqrt{2ME_n}}{\hbar} = \frac{\sqrt{2M(-E_n + V_0)}}{\hbar}\tan\left[\frac{\sqrt{2M(-E_n + V_0)}}{\hbar}\frac{X}{2}\right].$$

E_n is the only remaining unknown. Therefore, the solution to this equation gives the values of the energy levels in the finite well. However, since E_n appears both inside and outside the tangent function the equation is a transcendental function that cannot be solved algebraically; rather, a graphical or numerical method is normally required.

However, we can obtain an approximate solution for the low-lying states in a very deep well. Since E_n is the *magnitude* of the total energy, it will also be very large in this case. If it were infinite (as it would be for the low-lying states in an *infinite* well) then the term $\sqrt{2ME_n}/\hbar$ would also be infinite. But $-E_n + V_0$ is finite. Therefore, we require that if E_n is one of the permitted states, then

$$\tan\left[\frac{\sqrt{2M(-E_n + V_0)}}{\hbar}\frac{X}{2}\right] = \infty.$$

Since $\tan y = \sin y/\cos y$, this is tantamount to requiring that

$$\cos\left[\frac{\sqrt{2M(-E_n + V_0)}}{\hbar}\frac{X}{2}\right] = 0,$$

or since $p_n = \sqrt{2M(-E_n + V_0)}$,

$$\cos\left(\frac{p_n}{\hbar}\frac{X}{2}\right) = 0,$$

which is satisfied for

$$p_n = \frac{(2n + 1)\pi\hbar}{X} = \frac{(2n + 1)h}{2X}, \qquad n = 0, 1, 2, \ldots.$$

This is precisely the condition we found for the even parity states in Section 18.8. Energies for the odd parity states can be found by carrying out the above procedure for the sine-dependent amplitudes.

SUGGESTIONS FOR FURTHER READING ◣◣◣

The approach to the basic rules of quantum mechanics in this chapter follows the excellent treatment given in:

R. P. FEYNMAN, R. B. LEIGHTON, AND M. SANDS, *The Feynman Lectures on Physics*, Vol. 1, Addison-Wesley Publishing Co., Inc., Reading, Mass., 1963, Chapters 37 and 38.

Chapter 22 of this reference is a very good introduction to number systems. In addition, the first few chapters of Feynman's third volume, while more advanced, are still very readable. Another good introduction to quantum mechanics appears in the monogram:

LEONARD EISENBUD, *The Conceptual Foundations of Quantum Mechanics*, © University of Washington, Seattle, 1966.

Two nonmathematical articles from the *Scientific American* deserve special mention:

GEORGE GAMOW, "The Principle of Uncertainty," January, 1958, p. 51.

GEORGE GAMOW, "The Exclusion Principle," July, 1959, p. 74.

PROBLEMS AND EXERCISES ◣◣◣

18.1. A parallel beam of yellow light ($\lambda = 6 \times 10^{-7}$ m) is incident upon a pair of equal rectangular slits separated by 10^{-5} m. What is the distance between successive maxima on a screen 1 m away?

18.2. In order to estimate the number of photons required to produce an observable interference pattern, note that the human eye can just detect yellow light incident upon the retina with a power of 1.7×10^{-18} watts (1 W = 1 J/sec). Suppose the interference pattern produced with the system in Problem 18.1 is confined to ten maxima of equal intensity which are barely visible, and that all the light is reflected from the screen and detected by an observer.

(a) On the average how many photons per second fall into each maximum band?

(b) On the average how many photons per second pass through the slit system?

18.3. A beam of yellow light about ten times too weak to be detected by the human eye is incident upon a double-slit system. A distant screen is photographed four times using high speed film capable of detecting individual photons. The exposure times used are equal respectively to 60 sec, 1 sec, $\frac{1}{10}$ sec, and $\frac{1}{100}$ sec. Sketch the probable appearance of each photograph.

18.4. The persistence time of the human eye is about $\frac{1}{30}$ sec. That is, two images falling on the retina within a shorter time interval do not appear as distinct. (This fact makes it possible for both motion pictures and television to simulate motion by presenting a rapid sequence of still pictures.)

A very intense source of yellow light is incident upon a double-slit system. Each slit is equipped with a shutter that periodically opens and closes for $\frac{1}{100}$ of a second. What pattern is observed on a distant screen if the apparatus is arranged so that:

(a) Both shutters open and close together.

(b) When one shutter is open, the other is closed.

(c) When one shutter is about to open, the other has its slit half closed.

18.5. (a) A parallel beam of white light is incident upon a double-slit system. A red filter is placed in front of one slit, a green filter in front of the other. What pattern is observed on a distant screen?

    (b) The red and green filters are replaced with a pair of filters that pass slightly different wavelengths, both of which appear as the same shade of yellow to a certain observer, however. What pattern does he observe on a distant screen?

[HINT: What pattern would a more discerning observer see?]

18.6. A parallel beam of 1000 eV electrons is incident upon a pair of very fine slits 10^{-5} m apart. What image is produced on a film 1 m away?

18.7. A parallel, monochromatic beam of light is incident upon three slits.

    (a) Write a formal expression (i.e., an expression similar to Equation 18.6) for the amplitude corresponding to the passage of a photon from the light source to the screen via the triple slit system.

    (b) Write a formal expression for the probability that a photon from the source arrives at a position x on the screen.

18.8. Two of the three slits in Problem 18.7 are illuminated with a parallel beam of monochromatic light; the third is illuminated by a separate source of the same wavelength. Write a formal expression for the probability that a photon arrives at a position x on the screen.

18.9. (a) Find the sum, difference, and product of the complex numbers $6 + 3i$ and $10 + 5i$.

    (b) What are the conjugates of the two numbers?

    (c) What are their absolute squares and absolute magnitudes?

18.10. (a) Plot the two numbers from Problem 18.9 in the two-dimensional complex plane (Figure 18.6).

    (b) Determine the phase angles of the numbers either from the graph or a table, and express the numbers in exponential notation.

18.11. Determine the phase angles of:

    (a) A positive real number.

    (b) A negative real number.

    (c) A negative imaginary number.

    (d) A complex number with equal, positive real and imaginary parts.

    (e) A complex number whose real part is one-half its absolute magnitude.

    (f) A complex number whose imaginary part is one-half its absolute magnitude.

[HINT: Plot the numbers in the complex plane.]

18.12. Extract the three cube roots of 8 and prove directly that they are cube roots.

18.13. According to the basic rules of quantum mechanics the amplitudes for the two (or more) experimentally indistinguishable ways in which an event may occur interfere with one another. Even though the *probability* for one of the routes may be much smaller than the other, noticeable interference effects may nevertheless occur.

Parallel, monochromatic light from a single source is incident upon a pair of slits whose centers are separated by ten times its wavelength. However, one of the slits is narrower than the other and passes only one-hundredth the intensity.

    (a) What is the ratio of the *amplitudes* corresponding to the two slits?

    (b) Write an equation for the resultant intensity at a distant screen as a function of the difference between the distance from the slits to a point x on the screen (i.e., $S_A - S_B$) and λ.

    (c) Sketch the intensity pattern and determine the ratio of the intensity at the maxima to the intensity at the minima.

18.14. An alternate form of the Heisenberg principle relates the uncertainty in the characteristic energy of a process to the time interval during which it occurs:

$$\Delta E \,\Delta t \geq h.$$

Use the form of the free-particle amplitude and arguments from special relativity to show that this relation is consistent with the form of the Heisenberg principle encountered in Chapter 17.

18.15. Suppose the kinetic energy of a free particle is known to complete precision (i.e., the particle is in a pure state of energy). From Problem 18.14, what can be said about the time at which it will be found in a certain region?

18.16. Plot the probability density as a function of x for a free particle that has equal probabilities of being found in either the momentum states p_n or p_m if:

(a) $\Delta p/\hbar = 10^{+10}$/m ($\Delta p = p_n - p_m$).

(b) $\Delta p/\hbar = 2 \times 10^{+10}$/m.

(c) Discuss the difference in the two results from the point of view of the Heisenberg principle.

18.17. (a) Derive an expression for the probability density for a free particle which may be found in either of two momentum states but has four times the probability of being found in one than the other.

(b) Sketch the probability density as a function of x for $\Delta p/\hbar = 10^{+10}$/m ($\Delta p = p_n - p_m$).

18.18. (a) Derive an expression for the probability density for a free particle that has equal probabilities of being found in one of three equally spaced momentum states, $p_1, p_2,$ or p_3.

(b) Sketch the probability density as a function of x for $\Delta p/\hbar = 10^{+10}$/m ($\Delta p = p_1 - p_2 = p_2 - p_3$).

18.19. (a) Write the differential equation for the motion of a (classical) particle in free fall by equating the product of its mass and its acceleration, written as the second derivative of its displacement with respect to time, to the force acting upon it.

(b) Show that the usual free-fall equation ($y = y_0 + v_0 t + \frac{1}{2}gt^2$) is in fact a solution to the differential equation by substituting the second derivative of this expression directly into your answer to part a.

18.20. In Chapter 4 we found that the motion of an harmonic oscillator with mass M and spring constant k is described by

$$x = x_0 \cos\left(2\pi \frac{t}{T}\right),$$

with the period T given by $T = 2\pi\sqrt{M/k}$.

(a) Express the above equation of motion in complex exponential notation (i.e., the equation of motion should be the real part of your expression).

(b) Take the second time derivative of your complex equation and show by direct substitution into the differential equation for the system (Section 18.6) that it is a solution (For simplicity, consider the case where $M/k = 1$ so that $T/2\pi = 1$.)

18.21. How would the spacing between the energy levels in a very deep rectangular well change if the width of the well were very slowly decreased to one-tenth its original value?

18.22. Determine the energies and plot the amplitudes and probability densities for both the even and odd parity states with $n = 3$ in an infinitely deep rectangular well.

18.23. According to Figure 18.16 (and Problem 18.22) the probability density at several locations in a rectangular well is zero for all values of n greater than zero. Does this imply that if a particle is in one region of the well it can never be found in another region separated from it by a zero? Explain.

18.24. Consider a potential well in the shape of a very long, inverted trapezoid (see sketch). Assuming the amplitudes in the well have roughly a cosine or sine dependence, would you expect the energy level spacing in the well to be smaller than, about the same as, or greater than the spacing in a rectangular well of the same depth and width equal to the small base of the trapezoid? Explain.

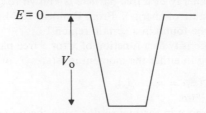

18.25. It is shown in the text that the probability densities for both even parity states $[\phi(-x) = \phi(x)]$ and odd parity states $[\phi(-x) = -\phi(x)]$ are invariant under reflection. Show, however, that the probability density for a *superposition* of an even and an odd parity state would *not* be invariant under reflection, and that therefore parity conservation requires that the parity of any state must be definite. That is, it may either be even or odd, but not both.

18.26. A family lives at the base of a cliff 10 m high and 20 m wide. A road on the same level as their house comes to a dead end at the other side of the cliff. Estimate the probability that a 1000-kg automobile traveling at 25 m/sec will penetrate the gravitational potential barrier and appear in the family's living room.

N.B.: To a good approximation $e^a = 10^{0.43a}$.

18.27. A measurement is to be made of the probability that two particles which approach each other with equal and opposite momenta scatter at 90° to their incident directions. The accompanying sketch shows the two ways in which one particle or the other could be scattered at 90° into the detector. Show that the probability for either particle to scatter into the detector is twice as great for identical Bose particles (α-particles for instance) as for nonidentical particles(an α-particle and a gold nucleus, for instance), and that the 90° scattering probability is zero for identical Fermi particles (protons or electrons).

[HINT: Assign amplitudes ϕ_A and ϕ_B to the two possibilities shown in the sketch.]

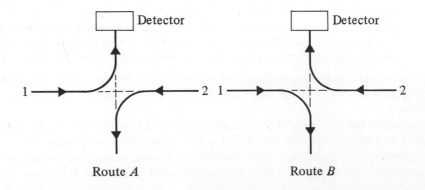

Route *A*   Route *B*

18.28. Two identical particles fall randomly into two different states. Show that the probability of one of the states being empty is one-half for distinguishable particles, two-thirds for identical bosons, and zero for identical fermions.

N.B.: You need not write down or even consider amplitude in answering this question. Simply consider the number of distinguishable compound states available to the two-particle system in each case.

Atomic states and the structure of matter

19

▲▲ 19.1 States of the hydrogen atom. Quantum numbers

The quantum mechanical theory of the hydrogen atom assumes that the electrostatic interaction between proton and electron can be described in terms of the classical potential energy (Equation 8.13b) of two particles with charges of magnitude e:

$$PE = -\frac{1}{4\pi\epsilon_0}\left(\frac{e^2}{R}\right),$$

where R is the distance between the particles. In the foregoing chapter (Section 18.8) we found that the probability amplitudes, and therefore the internal energy states of a particle bound in a one-dimensional rectangular potential well, are quantized. The same general conclusion is applicable to any bound system, in particular, to the bound electron-proton system whose potential energy, plotted as a function of R, is shown in Figure 18.17. However, both the amplitude functions and the numerical values of their associated energies depend upon the detailed form of the interaction potential.

A systematic determination of the amplitudes and energies for the bound electron in hydrogen requires the solution of Schrödinger's equation in three dimensions, which is a natural generalization of its one-dimensional form (Equation 18.23). However, several of the general characteristics of the solutions can be predicted from the one-dimensional rectangular potential solutions of Chapter 18 and the conservation of energy and angular momentum.

The amplitudes and magnitudes of the discrete energy states in a one-dimensional rectangular potential are specified by the value of a single running index or *quantum number*, n, which assumes only integral values. A quantitative expression for the energies of the bound states follows from the algebraic form of the amplitudes (Equations 18.28) and the continuity conditions imposed on the amplitudes and their slopes at the boundaries of the potential (Section 18.8 and Appendix to Chapter 18). Solutions to the three-dimensional Schrödinger equation for a particle confined in a three-dimensional enclosure depend, quite naturally, upon x, y, and z. It is not unreasonable to suppose that imposition of the continuity requirements at each of the three sets of boundaries will lead to amplitudes for discrete states specified by *three* quantum numbers, l, m, and n, instead of one. In fact, this supposition is borne out by the detailed solutions.

If a number of identical systems are all in the same pure state of a dynamical variable such as momentum or energy, then by definition, measurements performed on each of the systems always yield the same numerical result (Section 18.3). In other words, the value of the dynamical variable does not depend on time, which is tantamount to saying that it is a conserved quantity. Although it is by no means obvious, one-dimensional solutions to the Schrödinger equation can always be expressed in terms of the pure states of one conserved quantity. Energy (or equivalently linear momentum) was chosen as that quantity in the one-dimensional rectangular well solution. Likewise, three-dimensional solutions may be expressed in terms of states which are simultaneously pure states of *three* conserved quantities. In the case of the hydrogen atom it is natural to select total energy as one of the three quantities. Also since the force between the electron and proton is central the angular momentum of the system remains constant (Section 6.11). Because angular momentum is a vector its constancy implies the conservation of *two* scalar quantities that may be chosen as its magnitude and one of its components, say *z*, in the same coordinate system.

In summary, the solutions to the Schrödinger equation for the hydrogen atom are conveniently expressed as states of total energy, *E*, the magnitude of orbital angular momentum **L**, and the *z*-component of angular momentum, L_z. By imposing the three-dimensional boundary conditions on the corresponding amplitudes, expressions analogous to Equations 18.29 are obtained giving the permitted values of each quantity in terms of its own integral quantum number.

The total internal energy of a hydrogen atom is restricted to the discrete set

$$E_n = -\frac{Me^4}{8h^2\epsilon_0^2}\frac{1}{n^2} = -\frac{Me^4}{32\pi^2\hbar^2\epsilon_0^2},$$ (19.1)

where *M* and *e* are the mass and charge of the electron respectively, $\hbar = h/2\pi$, and *n*, the *principal quantum number*, can assume all integral values greater than zero (but not zero itself). Equation 19.1 is identical to Equation 17.13a, obtained from the Bohr model. Since the latter model yields quantitatively correct results for the hydrogen energy spectrum, the agreement between Equations 17.13a and 19.1 is not surprising. The states corresponding to $n = 1$, $n = 2$, and $n = 3$ are shown on the energy diagram of Figure 18.17.

The magnitude of the orbital angular momentum of the electron about the proton in hydrogen can assume the values

$$L = \sqrt{l(l+1)}\frac{h}{2\pi} = \sqrt{l(l+1)}\,\hbar,$$ (19.2)

where the *orbital quantum number l* for a particular state is restricted to zero and to positive integers *less* than the principal quantum number *n* of the state. That is, *l* may range in integral steps 0 to $n - 1$. For example, if $n = 1$ the only possible value of *l* is given by Equation 19.2 with $l = 0$. But if $n = 2$ there are two sets of states, one identified with $l = 1$, the other with $l = 0$. Equation 19.2 replaces the ad hoc Bohr quantization rule for angular momentum (Equations 17.11).

The third quantum number, *m* (often called the magnetic quantum number for reasons given in the next section), is identified with the permitted values of the *z*-component of angular momentum, L_z, which are given by

$$L_z = m\frac{h}{2\pi} = m\hbar.$$ (19.3)

For a particular value of orbital quantum number, l, the magnetic quantum number can assume any of the $(2l + 1)$ integral values ranging from $-l$ to $+l$. For instance, if $l = 2$ then $m = -2, -1, 0, +1$, or $+2$. The five possible orientations of angular momentum corresponding to these five numbers may be represented by a vector diagram of the type shown in Figure 19.1. The z-component of angular momentum, L_z, is given in terms of the magnitude of the total angular momentum, L, and the orientation angle θ by

$$L_z = L \cos \theta.$$

Referring to Equations 19.2 and 19.3,

$$\cos \theta = \frac{L_z}{L} = \frac{m}{\sqrt{l(l + 1)}}.$$

For $l = 2$, $l(l + 1) = 6$ and

$$\cos \theta = \frac{-2}{\sqrt{6}}, \frac{-1}{\sqrt{6}}, 0, \frac{1}{\sqrt{6}}, \frac{2}{\sqrt{6}}.$$

Significantly, $\cos \theta$ is never ± 1 so that the angular momentum vector always has components in the x- and y-directions. However, neither the Schrödinger solution nor any other quantum mechanical model specifies these other two components so that there is a remaining uncertainty in the orbital angular momentum of the hydrogen atom which is, in fact, completely consistent with the Heisenberg principle.

As we shall see in the next section, one additional quantum number, called the *intrinsic spin quantum number* of the electron, must be given before the state of an electron in

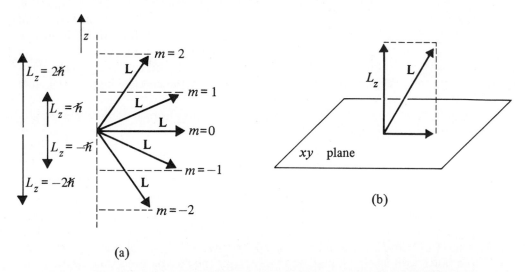

(a)

FIGURE 19.1 (a) The five possible z-components of angular momentum for $l = 2$. The lengths of the arrows are proportional to the magnitude of the total angular momentum, their directions are such that their components in the z-direction are proportional to $-2\hbar, \hbar, 0, +\hbar$, and $2\hbar$. (b) Even after the magnitude and z-component of angular momentum are fixed, the direction of the vector remains uncertain since its component perpendicular to z may lie anywhere in the xy plane.

hydrogen can be uniquely specified. However to an excellent approximation, numerical values of the integers n, l, and m together with Equations 19.1, 19.2, and 19.3, suffice to determine the total energy and the magnitude of the angular momentum for each electron state.

If the hydrogen atom were a classical system, then in addition each possible set of quantum numbers would also specify a different electron orbit. Instead, each set labels a distinct amplitude whose mathematical form follows from the Schrödinger equation and whose absolute square yields a distinct three-dimensional probability distribution for the electron. Because these distributions are functions of the three spatial co-ordinates their shapes can be quite complicated. Thus the probability of finding the electron at a particular point in space generally varies with θ, the angle between the x-axis and the radius vector from the proton to that point, as well as with r, its distance from the proton as shown in Figure 19.2. However, in general the probability of finding the electron at a particular distance from the proton is appreciable only within a rather limited range of r, as shown by the graphs of Figure 19.3, which plot the probability distribution $P(r)$ as a function of r for $l = 0$ and $n = 1, 2,$ and 3. (The value $l = 0$ always corresponds to a spherically symmetric distribution, i.e., a distribution which depends on r alone and not on θ as do the $l = 2$ distributions of Figure 19.2.) As we

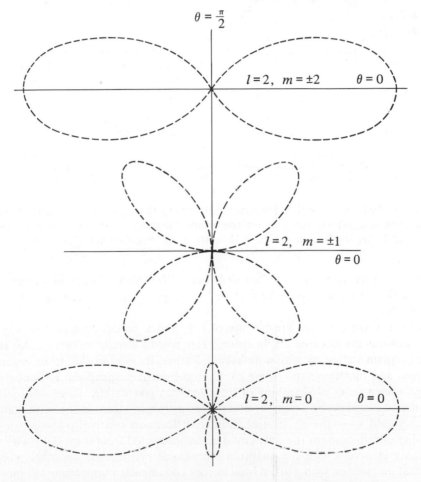

FIGURE 19.2   Shapes of the probability distributions for $l = 2$.

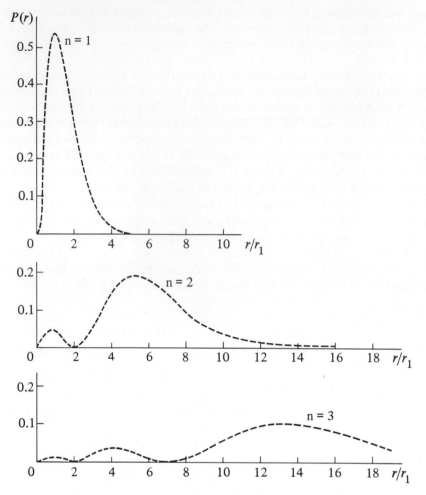

FIGURE 19.3 Distribution functions $P(r)$ giving the probability of finding the electron at a given distance r from the proton for states in hydrogen with $n = 1$, 2, and 3. (r_1 is the Bohr radius, 0.53×10^{-10} m. See Chapter 17.)

might have anticipated, none of the distribution functions shown in Figure 19.3 is sharply peaked, for that would be tantamount to granting the electron a set of well-defined orbits.

Occasionally these results are misinterpreted, and a model proposed in which the atomic electrons are smeared out in space. This notion is quite incorrect. An electron does not remain stationary within an atom. Rather, its motion should be regarded as continuous and indeterminate. If we could momentarily suspend the Heisenberg principle and take a series of snapshots of the atom in a given state, or, equivalently, take simultaneous snapshots of a number of different hydrogen atoms in the same state, each snapshot would show the electron at a different location relative to the proton. The probability distribution for the state could be reconstructed from these data, with results presumably in accord with the quantum mechanical predictions. In other words, we expect that an electron with a given total energy and angular momentum will move over the entire region in which it has a high probability distribution within a very short time interval. Hence the average negative charge distribution for each state in hydrogen coincides with the quantum mechanical probability distributions. Since the electron in hydrogen manifests itself externally through its electromagnetic interactions, the ground state probability distribution also defines the size and shape of the hydrogen atom.

According to the Bohr correspondence principle (Section 17.4) the probability distributions for the electron in a hydrogen atom would approach the orbits expected from Newtonian physics if the atom could be scaled up to macroscopic dimensions. Since the resulting planetary model of the atom is so familiar it is worth discussing it briefly, though by now it should be clear that the quantitative features of the model should not be taken too seriously.

Three variables are required to specify the elliptical orbit of a planet in a three-dimensional coordinate system fixed with respect to the sun. If the total energy of the planet is known, then the major axis of the orbit (i.e., twice the distance from tip to tip, Figure 19.4 and Figure 3.12) can be determined by drawing a horizontal line representing that energy on a gravitational potential energy graph (Figure 7.12). Therefore, the total energy of a planet fixes one of the three variables and also provides a relation between the orbital velocity of the planet and its distance from the sun, or radius vector. In general, the average distance from the sun increases with total energy, even as with the maxima of the probability distribution of Figure 19.3.

However, an infinite number of elliptical orbits each with a different eccentricity, or more precisely a different minor axis, can correspond to every choice of a major axis. Kepler's second law offers another equation between the radius vector and velocity. Together with energy conservation, this law permits a complete determination of the orbit in two dimensions (and thus, of its minor axis) provided the orbital velocity at one point in the orbit is given. Since Kepler's second law is equivalent to angular momentum conservation (Section 6.11), it follows that a planet's energy and the magnitude of its angular momentum uniquely specify its orbit in a plane.

A complete description of a planetary orbit in *three* dimensions requires that the orientation of its plane be specified relative to some reference plane. (The plane containing

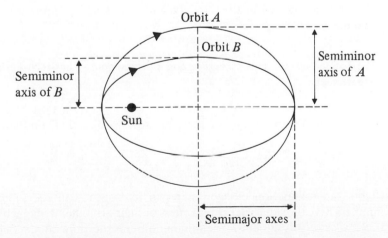

FIGURE 19.4 The total energy of a planet in an elliptical orbit about the sun depends on its semimajor axis but *not* its semiminor axis, while the angular momentum of the planet depends on the lengths of *both* axes. Thus two orbits with the same major axes but different minor axes have the same energy but different orbital angular momenta.

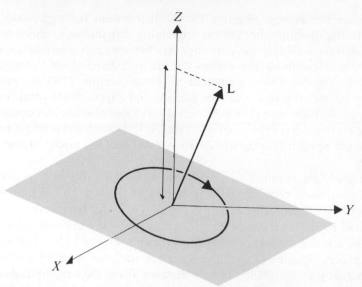

FIGURE 19.5   The direction of the angular momentum of a planet is perpendicular to the plane of its orbit. Therefore, if the *z*-component of **L** in a coordinate system defined by the stars is constant, the planet's orbital plane maintains its orientation in that system.

the orbit of the earth, called the *ecliptic*, is frequently used for that purpose.) Now the direction of a particle's angular momentum vector is always perpendicular to the plane containing its radius and its velocity vectors. Since the direction of a planet's angular momentum is constant* the direction of that perpendicular and thus the orientation of its orbital plane remains fixed relative to a coordinate system defined by the fixed stars (Figure 19.5), even as in the quantum mechanical model of the hydrogen atom. Because it is constant and implies the invariance of a planet's orbital plane, it is convenient to choose L_z as the last of the three dynamical quantities required to specify its orbit in three dimensions.

▲▲ 19.2 The Zeeman effect. Fine structure and electron spin. The Stern-Gerlach experiment

The frequency of a photon emitted by an atom in making a transition from an excited state with energy E_2 to a state with lower energy E_1 follows directly from Planck's law of energy conservation:

$$h\nu = E_2 - E_1. \tag{17.6}$$

To a very good approximation electron states in hydrogen with the same principal quantum numbers have the same energy regardless of their orbital and magnetic quantum numbers.† Because of this circumstance (among others) the Bohr model, which labels

---

* Because of the small noncentral forces exerted by the other planets the angular momentum of a planet actually varies slightly. However, the angular momentum of the entire system is conserved.
† As we shall see below, the energy of an electron state does have a very small dependence on the intrinsic spin quantum number of the electron.

the energy of each electron "orbit" with a single quantum number, reproduces the observed emission spectrum of hydrogen.

In more complex atoms the energy of the electron states is a function of l as well as n.* These two quantum numbers are primarily responsible for determining the size and shape of the electron probability distributions (Figures 19.2 and 19.3), while the magnetic quantum number m specifies its orientation relative to a particular coordinate system. Perhaps this is best understood by referring to the semiclassical planetary model in which the plane of the orbit remains fixed in space. In that case the direction of the orbital angular momentum (which is perpendicular to the orbital plane), and therefore the component L_z in a fixed reference direction, are also constant (Figure 19.4). If the reference direction can be chosen at will then the very arbitrariness of the selection implies that the internal energy states cannot depend upon that direction. Thus the orbital planes of the electrons in each atom in a sample of hydrogen gas will be randomly oriented relative to the arbitrary reference direction. Using quantum mechanical language, each atom in a state specified by a given orbital number l will be in a mixed state of L_z describable as a superposition of the $2l + 1$ pure states of L_z.

In order to obtain experimentally measurable distinctions between states with the same **L** but different L_z, the measuring apparatus itself must define a *non*arbitrary reference direction. Then according to the definition of pure states (Section 18.3) the result of each

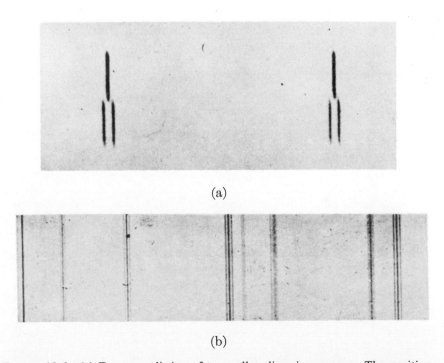

(a)

(b)

FIGURE 19.6   (a) Zeeman splitting of two yellow lines in mercury. The position of the spectral lines in the absence of a magnetic field is shown by the lower line for each triplet. (b) Zeeman splitting of seven lines of the iron spectrum. (From Zeeman's *Researches in Magneto-optics*. Yerkes Observatory Photograph.)

See footnote †, p. 692.

measurement of L_z must be one of the $2l + 1$ values $L_z = m\hbar$ given by Equation 19.3. A nonarbitrary external reference direction can be established by placing the sample in a magnetic field. Since the force on an electron will no longer be the central coulomb force alone, a shift in the electron's energy levels is expected. In fact, for sufficiently intense fields the energies of all states with $m \neq 0$ change in proportion to m and to the magnetic field strength. If the spectrum of the atom is measured under these circumstances each spectral line which in the absence of the field represents a transition between groups of states labeled with distinct values of l and n but several values of m, splits into a multiplet of lines representing transitions between states with distinct values of all three quantum numbers (Figure 19.6).

The splitting of spectral lines in a magnetic field is called the Zeeman effect after Pieter Zeeman, who discovered it in 1896. If (speaking semiclassically) the orbiting, charged electron is regarded as a current loop then, of course, it is easy to see why a magnetic field exerts a force upon it. The effect of a magnetic field on a classical current loop is conveniently specified in terms of the equivalent magnetic dipole moment of the loop, μ_l (see Equation 9.14, and the discussion leading to it in Section 9.3). If the perpendicular to the plane of the loop (the direction of the dipole moment and also of the angular momentum) is oriented at an angle θ relative to a magnetic field of strength B (Figure 19.7) its potential energy of orientation relative to $\theta = 0$ is (Equation 9.5):

$$PE = -\mu_l B \cos \theta.$$

The dipole moment of an electron in a semi-classical orbit can be expressed in terms of its angular momentum in that orbit by using Equation 9.21b:*

$$\mu_l = \left(\frac{e}{2M}\right)\mathbf{L}.$$

Therefore, the circulating electron current has magnetic orientation energy

$$PE_l = -\left(\frac{e}{2M}\right)BL \cos \theta. \tag{19.4}$$

Now of course the classical current loop model is merely suggestive. Nevertheless, a dipole moment proportional to orbital angular momentum can still be assigned to each

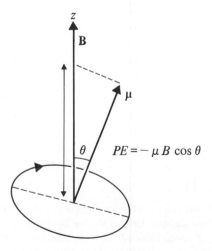

FIGURE 19.7 Magnetic orientation energy of a current loop with dipole moment **μ** in a magnetic field **B**. The direction of the dipole vector is the direction of the angular momentum vector, and the field direction defines the z-axis.

---

* N.B. In these expressions e is the charge of the electron, the *negative* of the fundamental charge $e = +1.6 \times 10^{-19}$ C.

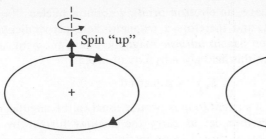

B seen by electron is
perpendicular to the page and outward

$$PE = -\mu_s B$$

$$PE = \mu_s B$$

FIGURE 19.8   Origin of the spin-magnetic orientation energy in the semiclassical model. The moving electron "sees" a moving proton, and thus a magnetic field **B** due to its motion. The electron's orientation energy in this field depends on whether the direction of its intrinsic dipole moment is up or down relative to the field of the "moving" proton, which is perpendicular to the orbital plane and out of the page.

electron state in an atom. In fact, a correct quantum mechanical treatment yields a magnetic orientation energy which is identical to the classical result. But we know that the direction of the angular momentum of an electron is quantized. If the magnetic field direction defines the z-axis then $L \cos \theta$ is simply L_z, the z-component of angular momentum, and Equation 19.4 becomes

$$PE_l = -\left(\frac{e}{2M}\right)L_z.$$

However, since L_z can only assume the values $m\hbar$ (Equation 19.3),

$$PE_l = -\left(\frac{e\hbar}{2M}\right)Bm. \tag{19.5}$$

If E_0 is the energy of an electron state in the absence of any external field, then if a field B is turned on, the energy of the state becomes

$$E = E_0 - \left(\frac{e\hbar}{2M}\right)Bm.$$

For each value of the orbital angular momentum quantum number there are $2l + 1$ possible values of the magnetic quantum number, m, ranging from $-l$ to $+l$. Therefore, in a magnetic field each such group of states splits into $2l + 1$ states with different energies. Since the orientation energy is small compared to E_0 even for very strong fields the separation of the states is also small relative to the separation of states with different values of l (Figure 19.6b).

Even in the absence of an external magnetic field a high resolution spectrometer reveals that most of the single spectral lines in hydrogen are really closely spaced pairs of lines, or doublets, suggesting that the states of hydrogen must be regarded as pairs of states differentiated by a new quantum number. In 1923 Wolfgang Pauli noted that the magnitude of this fine structure splitting is on the order of the Zeeman splitting and proposed an explanation by attributing intrinsic magnetic properties to the electron.

Using semiclassical language, an electron orbiting about a nucleus "sees" a moving positive charge, or current, and therefore a magnetic field perpendicular to its orbit (Figure 19.8). If the electron has an *intrinsic* magnetic dipole moment, μ_s, it will have orientation energy relative to this field given by Equation 9.5:

$$PE_s = -\mu_s B \cos \theta.$$

Now the dipole moment of a current loop is proportional to the angular momentum of the orbiting electron. Therefore, let us carry the analogy further by assuming the intrinsic dipole moment is proportional to an intrinisc *spin angular momentum*, **s** (see Equation 9.21b):

$$\mu_s = g\mathbf{s}, \tag{19.6}$$

where g is the constant of proportionality. Then,

$$PE_s = -gBs \cos \theta,$$

or letting $s \cos \theta = \pm s_z$,

$$PE_s = \pm gBs_z.$$

But since the spectral lines in hydrogen split into two components, it follows that there are but two possible values of PE_s and hence of s_z. There are $2l + 1$ values of m corresponding to every value of orbital angular momentum. Assuming that the same multiplicity rule is applicable to spin angular momentum, and referring to Equation 19.3,

$$s_z = \pm \tfrac{1}{2}h, \tag{19.7a}$$

and thus,

$$PE_s = \pm gB \frac{\hbar}{2}. \tag{19.7b}$$

In analogy with Equation 19.2, the magnitude of the total spin angular momentum is therefore

$$s = \sqrt{\tfrac{1}{2}(\tfrac{1}{2} + 1)}\, \hbar = \sqrt{\tfrac{3}{4}}\, \hbar. \tag{19.7c}$$

Finally, the constant g may be determined by measuring the fine structure splitting and applying Equation 19.7c with the result that $g = e/M$, or *twice* the classical value (Equation 9.21b).

Since these results can be derived from a correct quantum mechanical treatment, we conclude that the state of an electron is determined by an intrinsic quantum number called its spin angular momentum (or *spin*) quantum number as well as the quantum numbers determining its spatial distribution. Therefore, electron states in hydrogen are uniquely specified by the *four* quantum numbers n, l, m, and s_z. But whereas the first three numbers assume only *integral* values, s_z assumes only the half-odd integral values $\pm \tfrac{1}{2}$.

The *total* angular momentum of an electron, **J**, is the vector sum of its orbital and spin angular momenta **L** and **s**. Its magnitude is limited to the discrete set of values,

$$J = \sqrt{j(j + 1)}\, h, \tag{19.7a}$$

where the limits on the integer j are determined by the values of the orbital quantum number l.

Using the usual vector addition rules the z-component of **J** is the algebraic sum of the respective z-components of orbital and spin angular momentum. Hence for a particular value of l, J_z is restricted to the $2(2l + 1)$ values $J_z = m_j h$ (see Equation 19.3) with m_j determined by

$$m_j = m \pm \tfrac{1}{2}, \qquad -l \leqq m \leqq l. \tag{19.7b}$$

If $l = 0$ then $m_j = \pm \tfrac{1}{2}$. But for $l = 1$, m_j has the possible values

$$l = 1, \qquad m = 1, \qquad m_j = \tfrac{3}{2}, \tfrac{1}{2},$$
$$l = 1, \qquad m = 0, \qquad m_j = \tfrac{1}{2}, -\tfrac{1}{2},$$
$$l = 1, \qquad m = -1, \qquad m_j = -\tfrac{1}{2}, -\tfrac{3}{2}.$$

Now the quantum numbers m_j are related to j in the same way that a set of m's is related to a given value of l, i.e., they assume the $2j + 1$ values ranging in integral steps from $-j$ to $+j$. Since in our present example the maximum $m_j = +\tfrac{3}{2}$ and the minimum $m_j = -\tfrac{3}{2}$ it follows that $J = \tfrac{3}{2}$ is one possible value corresponding to $l = 1$. Indeed four of the six m_j assignments, $\tfrac{3}{2}, \tfrac{1}{2}, -\tfrac{1}{2}, -\tfrac{3}{2}$, clearly correspond to substates of $J = \tfrac{3}{2}(\tfrac{3}{2} + 1)h$ (Equation 19.7a). The two remaining values of m_j correspond to $j = \tfrac{1}{2}$. Thus the total angular momentum in a state with $l = 1$ is either $j = \tfrac{3}{2}$ or $j = \tfrac{1}{2}$, and can, in fact, be in six different substates each specified by a different value of m_j.

The *total* angular momentum of an atom in a particular state is often called its *spin* in that state and assigned a total magnetic dipole moment in analogy with Equation 19.6:

$$\mu_J = g\mathbf{J}.$$

Pursuing the analogy, an atom in an external field has the $2j + 1$ discrete values of orientation energy given by

$$PE_j = m_j gBh.$$

For a hydrogen atom in its ground state, $m_j = \pm\tfrac{1}{2}$ and

$$PE_j = \pm \left(\frac{e}{M}\right)B\frac{h}{2},$$

which agrees with Equation 19.7b since if $l = 0$ the spin of the atom is due to the intrinsic spin of the electron only.

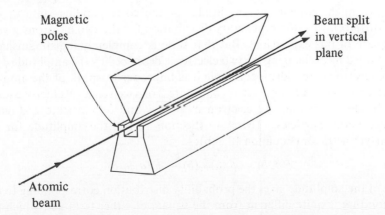

FIGURE 19.9 Principle of the Stern-Gerlach apparatus in which a beam of atoms passes through a region between specially shaped magnetic poles. These poles set up an inhomogeneous field which exerts a transverse force on the atoms, causing deflection in the vertical plane.

If a beam of neutral atoms is allowed to drift through a region in which there is a non-uniform magnetic field perpendicular to its direction of motion, then, since the force exerted by the field on each atom is proportional to its dipole moment, the deflection of an atom from its linear path is proportional to the z-components of its spin. Therefore, the single beam should be spatially separated into $(2j + 1)$ beams, each corresponding to a given value of m_j (Figure 19.9). For example, a beam of hydrogen atoms is split into two components. This technique, first introduced by Otto Stern and W. Gerlach in 1921 offers alternate experimental evidence for the ideas in this section, and in addition provides the basis for the most precise method of measuring atomic dipole moments.

▶▶ 19.3 States of multielectron atoms

An atom of an element with atomic number Z and atomic weight A may be regarded as a bound system with Z electrons each bearing the unit charge $-e$, and a nucleus with charge $+Ze$ and atomic weight A.* The attractive electrostatic interaction between the Z electrons and the nucleus is responsible for binding the system. However, the repulsive forces between the electrons cannot be ignored in determining the properties of its bound states.

If atoms were classical systems the probability amplitudes for a multielectron atom (say helium) could be found by first deducing the amplitudes for each electron bound by the electrostatic potential of the nucleus and then estimating the perturbations on these states caused by the electrostatic repulsion of the other electrons in the atom. For instance, since the helium nucleus has charge $+2e$, both of its electrons move in an electrostatic potential well twice as deep as the potential well in hydrogen but otherwise of the same form. Therefore, it should be possible to specify single electron states in helium with the four quantum numbers n, l, m, and s_z, and describe them with hydrogen-like probability amplitudes. So far the procedure is perfectly valid, and can even be interpreted by a semiclassical orbit model. However, the semiclassical approach breaks down when we construct amplitudes for the atom as a whole from the single electron amplitudes, since it ignores the indistinguishability of the two electrons (Section 18.10).

Suppose we know that electron a is in a single particle state described by the amplitude ϕ_1, and electron b in state 2 described by the amplitude ϕ_2. From the rules for combining amplitudes we might assume the amplitude for the corresponding state of the atom would be $\phi_1(a)\phi_2(b)$, with the probability distribution for the two electrons given by the absolute square of this expression. But that state is completely indistinguishable from the state obtained by exchanging the two electrons, described by the amplitude $\phi_2(a)\phi_1(b)$. Because the electrons are indistinguishable it is improper to speak of the amplitude for finding electron a in state 1 and electron b in state 2 or vice versa. Rather we must speak of the amplitude for finding one electron in state 1 and one in state 2 (Figure 18.4). Electrons are Fermi particles. Therefore (Section 18.10), the amplitude for the state must be antisymmetric or (Equation 18.34b):

$$\phi(a, b) = \phi_1(a)\phi_2(b) - \phi_2(a)\phi_1(b). \tag{19.8}$$

The square of the amplitude gives the probability distribution corresponding to the state, a distribution that is quite different from the square of either term and which therefore cannot be approximated by any set of semiclassical orbits.

---

* The atomic weight of the isotope $_6C^{12}$ is arbitrarily assigned the value $A = 12.000$ (Section 14.3). One atomic mass unit ($A = 1$) is approximately equal to 1.6×10^{-27} kg, while the rest energy M_0c^2 corresponding to $A = 1$ is 931 MeV (million electron volts).

Let us consider the construction of two-electron states in more detail.* The amplitude $\phi(a, b)$ (Equation 19.8) is said to be antisymmetric since the exchange of the indices a and b yields the amplitude $-\phi(a, b)$. As we noted in Section 18.10, all states of indistinguishable particles must either be symmetric under an exchange of the particle (Bose particles), or antisymmetric (Fermi particles). In fact, the antisymmetry requirement for Fermi particles is a generalization of the Pauli exclusion principle, for if states 1 and 2 are the same, then (Equation 19.8) the amplitude $\phi(a, b) = 0$.

Every single electron amplitude can be written as the product of a *spatial* amplitude, X_l^m, depending upon the quantum numbers n, l, m, and whose absolute square is equal to the spatial probability distribution, and a *spin* amplitude u^{s_z} which has the possible values $u^{+1/2}$ (or u^+), and $u^{-1/2}$ (or u^-). That is, $\phi = X_l^m u^{s_z}$. Likewise, a two-electron amplitude for helium can be written as the product of a two-electron spatial amplitude and a two-electron spin amplitude. Either part may be symmetric or antisymmetric under an exchange of indices according to whether it changes sign or not under that exchange. Since the total two-particle amplitude must be antisymmetric it can be the product either of a *symmetric* spatial part and an antisymmetric spin part, or an *antisymmetric* spatial part and a symmetric spin part.

To be more specific, let us write down several single-particle amplitudes for states with $l = 1$. If $m = 0$, we have

$$\phi_1 = X_1 u^+, \qquad \phi_2 = X_1 u^-.$$

Substituting into Equation 19.8,

$$\phi(a, b) = X_1^0(a)X_1^0(b)u^+(a)u^-(b) - X_1^0(b)X_1^0(a)u^+(b)u^-(a)$$
$$= X_1^0(a)X_1^0(b)[u^+(a)u^-(b) - u^+(b)u^-(a)], \tag{19.9a}$$

which is *symmetric* in its spatial part and *antisymmetric* in its spin part. Likewise, for $l = 1$, $m = +1$, we have

$$\phi_1 = X_1^{+1}u^+, \qquad \phi_2 = X_1^{-1}u^+,$$

which when substituted into Equation 19.8 yields

$$\phi(a, b) = [X_1^{-1}(a)X_1^{+1}(b) - X_1^{-1}(b)X_1^{+1}(a)]u^+(a)u^+(b). \tag{19.9b}$$

Finally, for $l = 1$, $m = -1$,

$$\phi_1 = X_1^{+1}u^-, \qquad \phi_2 = X_1^{-1}u^-,$$

which leads to

$$\phi(a, b) = [X^{-1}(a)X_1^{+1}(b) - X_1^{-1}(b)X_1^{+1}(a)]u^-(a)u^-(b). \tag{19.9c}$$

Both amplitudes are *antisymmetric* in their spatial parts and *symmetric* in their spin parts. We can write down one more amplitude with these symmetry properties, namely,

$$\phi(a, b) = [X_1^{-1}(a)X_1^{+1}(b) - X_1^{-1}(b)X_1^{+1}(a)][u^+(a)u^-(b) + u^+(b)u^-(a)]. \tag{19.9d}$$

Since the square of the *spatial* part of an amplitude determines the probability distribution of the electrons in space, it also is responsible for determining the energy of the corresponding state. Therefore, to the extent that the magnetic spin orientation energy can be neglected, the three states with antisymmetric spatial amplitudes (Equations

---

* The remainder of this section may be omitted without serious loss of continuity.

19.6b to 19.6d) have the same energy, which in general differs from the energy of the symmetric space state. (Equation 19.9a). In other words, the exchange symmetry of the *spin* states together with the requirement that the total amplitude for a two-electron state must be antisymmetric is instrumental in determining the energy of a state even in the approximation that the spin orientation energy is zero.

The total intrinsic spin of a multielectron system is the vector sum of the spins of its components. In the case of the three symmetric spin states (Equations 19.9b to 19.9d) the total z-components, s_z, are $+1$, -1, and 0, respectively, while the antisymmetric spin state (Equation 19.9a) has $s_z = 0$. Hence the three amplitudes given by Equations 19.9b to 19.9d differ only in the magnitude of the z-components of their total spins, while once again the amplitude, Equation 19.9a, is distinct. It is consistent to identify the three symmetric components with the three substates of total spin $s = 1$, since the latter has the three components -1, 0, and $+1$. Likewise, the single antisymmetric component $s_z = 0$ is associated with the total intrinsic spin $s = 0$. In other words, the total intrinsic spin states combine naturally into a *triplet* of states with $s = 1$ and a *singlet* state with $s = 0$. Each of the spin state amplitudes belonging to the same spin multiplet can be multiplied by the same spatial amplitude to obtain a total two-electron amplitude. Thus, to the extent that magnetic orientation energy may be neglected, each member of a spin-state multiplet is associated with a spatial state of the same total energy. In fact, in this approximation members of the same multiplet are indistinguishable. However, spin states belonging to different spin multiplets generally are associated with spatial states having different energies.

The grouping of states into equal energy multiplets according to the symmetry properties of their spatial and spin amplitudes is quite general and does not depend upon the specific functional forms assumed for the spatial amplitudes. Therefore, a considerable amount of information on the nature of specific states may be deduced from symmetry arguments alone. For instance, by generalizing the foregoing procedure it may be shown that of the nine totally antisymmetric two-electron states that may be constructed from single electron, $l = 2$ states, five states group together into a spatially symmetric quintuplet of equal energy states and three into a spatially antisymmetric triplet, leaving a unique spatially symmetric singlet state.

In later chapters the antisymmetrization procedure will be applied to the investigation of both nuclear states and the properties of the elementary particles.

▲▲ 19.4   The building up principle and electron shells in atoms

The remainder of the chapter deals with several macroscopic consequences of the quantum mechanical structure of atoms. In principle, the states of any atom may be determined by finding all possible single-particle amplitudes and then constructing antisymmetric amplitudes for the system as a whole. Of course the task becomes quite involved as the number of electrons and therefore the permutations of single-particle amplitudes contributing to each total amplitude increases. Therefore, we shall confine our discussion to the ground states of the atoms. If we assume that single-particle states in any atom can be labeled with the four quantum numbers n, l, m, s_z, then the ground state will be that state in which the electrons have their lowest possible quantum numbers. In the hydrogen atom, single-particle states with the same principal quantum numbers n, have the same total energy regardless of their total angular momentum (Section 19.1). However, due to the antisymmetrization requirement and to the noncentral repulsive interactions among the electrons (Section 19.3) the energy of an electron in a state of a

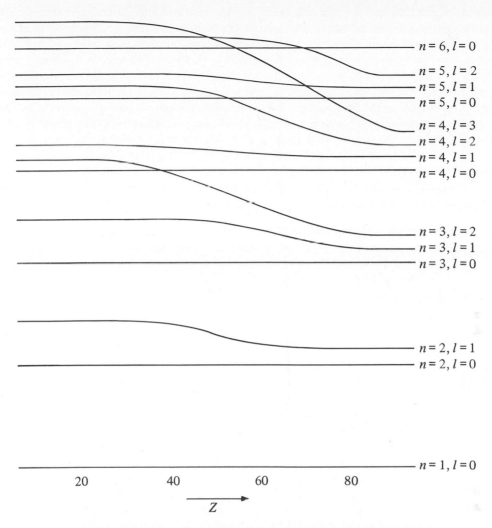

$n = 6, l = 0$
$n = 5, l = 2$
$n = 5, l = 1$
$n = 5, l = 0$
$n = 4, l = 3$
$n = 4, l = 2$
$n = 4, l = 1$
$n = 4, l = 0$

$n = 3, l = 2$
$n = 3, l = 1$
$n = 3, l = 0$

$n = 2, l = 1$
$n = 2, l = 0$

$n = 1, l = 0$

20   40   60   80

Z

FIGURE 19.10   Electron energy levels in an atom plotted as a function of atomic number Z in order to show the change in sequence with increasing atomic complexity. (Adapted from Derek L. Livesey, *Atomic and Nuclear Physics*, Blaisdell Publishing Co., Waltham, Mass., 1966.)

complex atom depends upon l as well as n. Therefore, each principal quantum number delimits a *group* of states that differ in their angular momentum quantum numbers.

Figure 19.10 plots the energies of several single electron states labeled by n and l as a function of Z, the number of electrons in the atom (and the charge of the nucleus in units of the fundamental charge, $+e$). For small values of the principle quantum number, n, the energy differences between groups of states with the same principle quantum number is greater than the energy differences between states with the same n but different orbital quantum numbers. But for n greater than 3 the energies of the states with different principle quantum numbers partially overlap.

If electrons were classically distinguishable particles (or Bose particles—Section 18.10) all electrons in the ground state of any atom would be in the lowest possible energy state, namely the state with $n = 1$, $l = 0$, and intrinsic spin orientation energy negative. In that event the external differences between atoms would be minimal. The energies of the twenty-six electrons in an iron atom would be more negative than the energies of the eight electrons in an oxygen atom, for instance, and thus the radii of the electron orbits in iron would be smaller than in oxygen. But that distinction alone would hardly account for the very different macroscopic properties of the two elements. However electrons are Fermi particles, subject to the Pauli principle that restricts the population of any state to one and *only* one member. Therefore, the number of states occupied by the electrons in any atom is equal to the number of electrons in the atom. It follows that the ground state configuration of an atom with Z electrons may be deduced simply by consulting an energy level diagram (Figure 19.10) and counting the Z states with lowest energy.

It is worthwhile summarizing the quantum mechanically derived rules for cataloguing single-particle states discussed in Sections 19.1 and 19.2:

1. The principal quantum number, n, may assume all integral values greater than zero.
2. For every value of the principal quantum number there are n possible angular momenta each specified by an orbital quantum number, l, that assumes all integral values from 0 to $n - 1$.
3. For each value of l there are $2l + 1$ states specified by the magnetic quantum number m.
4. In addition, an electron has two possible intrinsic spin states which are independent of the quantum numbers specifying its spatial amplitude.

Combining rules 3 and 4 it follows that there are $2(2l + 1)$ single-electron states corresponding to each value of l.

Given these rules we can immediately determine the ground state configuration of any atom. The lowest energy states all have principal quantum number $n = 1$. Hence $l = 0$, $m = 0$ and there are but two states differing in their z-components of intrinsic spin. Hydrogen has its single electron in one of these two states, whereas the two electrons of helium normally occupy both states. Because the helium nucleus has twice the charge of the hydrogen nucleus, the energy of its electrons should be more negative than the energy of the electron in the hydrogen ground state. In addition, the amplitude of the ground states in helium and hydrogen are quite different. Nevertheless, the same quantum numbers define the electron state in both instances (Figure 19.11).

The Pauli principle permits no more than two electrons to occupy the two states with $n = 1$. Therefore one of the lithium atom's three electrons must be in a higher energy

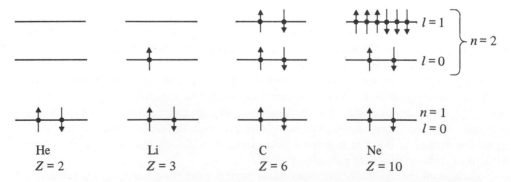

FIGURE 19.11   Electron configurations for the ground states of four light elements.

state. Turning to the above rules there are two possible angular momenta associated with the principle quantum number $n = 2$: $l = 1$ and $l = 0$. Again there are two states with $l = 0$, differing only in electron spin. But when $l = 1$ the magnetic quantum number m may assume three values -1, 0, $+1$ which, with the two states of intrinsic spin, specify six states. (This tally agrees with the conclusion drawn by combining rules 3 and 4 since $2(2l + 1) = 2(2 \times 1 + 1) = 6$.) One of the three electrons in lithium is in a state $n = 2$, $l = 0$ for the two states specified by these quantum numbers have lower energies than the six states with $n = 2$, $l = 1$. The four electrons of beryllium fill the states $n = 1$, $l = 0$, and $n = 2$, $l = 0$. Hence one of the five electrons in boron must be in a state with quantum numbers $n = 2$, $l = 1$. As there are six such states they are filled successively by the electrons of the next five atoms in order of atomic number, namely, carbon, nitrogen, oxygen, fluorine, and neon. However, sodium, with $Z = 11$, has one too many electrons to be accommodated in this manner. Hence one of its electrons must occupy a state with $n = 3$, in particular the state $n = 3$, $l = 0$.

Because of the relatively large energy gap between the groups of states with $n = 1$ and $n = 2$, and again between those with $n = 2$ and $n = 3$ (Figure 19.9), the electrons that occupy a group of states with the same principal quantum number are much more loosely bound than those in the preceding group. In addition, the binding energies of the electrons in states with the same principal quantum number are approximately equal, at least for low-lying states. Now the principal quantum number of a state determines the most probable mean distance between an electron and the nucleus, or, in classical terms, the mean radius of the electron's orbit (Figures 19.2 and 19.3). Therefore, electrons with the same principal quantum number are often said to occupy *shells*. The binding energy of the electrons within each shell decreases with increasing angular momentum. For this reason it is also possible to speak of subshells within a main shell, each subshell identified by its orbital angular momentum quantum number.

The distinction between the shells and subshells of an atom becomes blurred with increasing principle quantum number. The energy of both states with $n = 1$ is smaller than the energy of the $n = 2$ states, and likewise the $n = 2$ states all have lower energies than those with $n = 3$. However, the energies of ten states with $n = 3$, $l = 2$ overlap the energies of the two states with $n = 4$, $l = 0$ and the six with $n = 4$, $l = 1$ (Figure 19.10). In addition, the eighteen states in these three subshells are closer to each other than they are to the energies of both the next lowest subshell ($n = 3$, $l = 1$) and the next highest ($n = 4$, $l = 2$). In a very real sense the eighteen states constitute a group closer in spirit to the idea of a shell than either the entire group of states specified by $n = 3$ or the group with $n = 4$.

A very similar overlapping occurs with $n = 4$, $l = 3$ and $n = 5$, $l = 0$ and $l = 1$, and again with the high $n = 5$ and low $n = 6$ states. Therefore, the term *electron shell* is very often used to specify groups of states with energies separated from any other group, regardless of whether or not the states have the same principle quantum numbers. Subshells, however, always refer to groups with the same angular momenta, for in the absence of an external magnetic field (Section 19.2) the only difference between the energy of the states in the same subshell is the spin-orientation energy.

Ground state configurations of all the electrons in any atom up to the heaviest ($Z = 104$) are accommodated by seven major shells consisting of 2, 8, 8, 18, 18, 32, and 32 states, respectively. The first shell consists of the two states with $n = 1$, the second of the two in the subshell $n = 2$, $l = 0$, and the six with $n = 3$, $l = 1$. Shell three contains the first two subshells of $n = 3$, whereas shell four includes the subshell $n = 3$, $l = $ **2,** and the two lowest $n = 4$ subshells. The remaining three shells are shown in Figure **19.10**.

▲▲ 19.5 Periodicity of the elements. Ionic binding

At first glance the properties of the light elements exhibit no particular regularity when listed in order of increasing atomic number (Table 19.1). Hydrogen, a gas at room

TABLE 19.1 *Properties of the Eleven Lightest Elements*

Symbol	Name	Atomic Number (Z)	Atomic Weight (A)	Appearance at Room Temperature and Liquefaction (or Vaporization) Temperature	Chemical Reaction Characteristics
H	Hydrogen	1	1.008	Colorless gas, 20 °K	High reactivity. Enters readily into many compounds.
He	Helium	2	4.003	Colorless gas, 4 °K	None.
Li	Lithium	3	6.939	Soft metal, 1599 °K	Very high reactivity, especially with oxygen and the halogen group.
Be	Beryllium	4	9.012	Hard metal, 1556 °K	High reactivity, particularly with oxygen and the halogen group.
B	Boron	5	10.811	Brittle, nonmetallic solid	Low reactivity. All naturally occurring compounds are oxygen compounds.
C	Carbon	6	12.011	Graphite or diamond	Forms far more compounds than any other, but reactions are usually very subtle.
N	Nitrogen	7	14.007	Colorless gas (77 °K)	Low to moderate reactivity.
O	Oxygen	8	15.999	Colorless gas (90 °K)	High reactivity. Forms compounds with many other elements, especially with metals.
F	Fluorine	9	18.998	Corrosive gas (85 °K)	Very high reactivity, especially with metals.
Ne	Neon	10	20.183	Colorless gas (25 °K)	None.
Na	Sodium	11	22.990	Soft metal, 1156 °K	Very high reactivity, especially with oxygen and the halogen group.

temperatures, liquefies at 20 °K. Observational evidence indicates its propensity to exist in a diatomic state; hence its atoms readily interact with each other. We also know that hydrogen is a constituent of a very large number of compounds, the most common being water.

But the macroscopic properties of helium are quite different. The gas is normally monatomic and liquefies at 4 °K at atmospheric pressure, the lowest liquefaction temperature of any substance. Whereas hydrogen forms a large number of compounds, helium is chemically inert. We know that a hydrogen atom has one electron interacting with a singly charged positive nucleus, helium two electrons. However, it is not immediately obvious why the addition of one electron to an atom should alter substantially its ability to interact electromagnetically with other atoms. In fact, the difference can be attributed directly to the closed-shell structure of the helium atom.

Lithium, with $Z = 3$ (designated $_3$Li), is a soft, gray, metallic solid at room temperature, and enters into chemical reactions with gusto. When a small amount of the metal is immersed in water, for instance, its atoms replace hydrogen atoms in the water molecules to form lithium hydroxide and liberate hydrogen in the process:

$$2Li + 2H_2O \rightarrow 2LiOH + H_2.$$

The energy generated is usually sufficient to ignite the hydrogen gas evolved. The element also reacts readily with the halogen elements (fluorine, chlorine, bromine, and iodine) to form a series of characteristic compounds known as salts (lithium fluoride, LiF; lithium chloride, LiCl; etc.) which are white, crystalline substances with high melting points and appreciable solubilities in water. Evidently lithium atoms are exceedingly prone to interactions, a property which once again may be attributed to their shell structure.

Element 4, beryllium ($_4$Be) is a considerably harder, stronger metal than lithium. While it forms compounds with elements such as oxygen and the halogens it does not react with the violence of lithium. Boron, the fifth element is a brittle, nonmetallic, high melting-point solid. All of its naturally occurring compounds contain oxygen, and most of its chemical reactions can only be induced at high temperatures.

Carbon ($_6$C) is probably the most interesting of all the elements, for it is the fundamental constituent of all the exceedingly complex molecules of living matter. The element forms far more compounds than any other, many of which participate in the varied biochemical reactions that permit these living forms to function. But most of the reactions of carbon and its compounds are subtle rather than violent. That is, the atom interacts readily and forms molecules of unsurpassed stability against destruction by external agencies. In its pure state it may exist in two distinct forms: as graphite, a black, brittle solid which has a very high melting point and is a reasonably good conductor of electricity, or as diamond, the hardest known substance, with poor conduction properties. The hardness of a diamond again indicates that the bonds between its constituent atoms are very strong and not easily ruptured.

The next four elements are all gases at room temperature. Nitrogen ($_7$N) and oxygen ($_8$O) prefer to exist in diatomic form and have almost equal liquefaction temperatures. But oxygen enters more readily into chemical reactions. For instance, air is primarily a mixture of these two gases with almost five times as much nitrogen as oxygen. When substances are raised to high temperatures in air they often burn, forming compounds with oxygen rather than with the more abundant nitrogen. Animals breathe the mixture in order to obtain the oxygen required in the biochemical reactions that sustain them. The accompanying nitrogen performs no function in these processes except to dilute the oxygen.

Fluorine ($_9$F) is also a diatomic gas but with a considerably higher liquefaction temperature, indicating that its molecules have a greater affinity for each other. As we have noted, the gas belongs to the halogen family and readily forms stable salts with lithium and the other alkali metals—sodium, potassium, rubidium, and cesium. It also reacts readily with hydrogen to yield highly corrosive hydrofluoric acid (HF). The properties of the next element, neon ($_{10}$Ne) are much different than those of fluorine. A monoatomic gas with low liquefaction temperature, it forms no compounds whatsoever. Like helium it is chemically inert.

Concentrating for the moment on the list of elements from lithium through fluorine, we can make some sort of case for a continuous change in properties with increasing atomic number. The first two entries are decidedly metallic and form compounds with elements toward the end of the short list, i.e., oxygen and fluorine, although beryllium reacts less violently than lithium. Carbon, in the middle of the list, forms compounds with virtually all these elements but its reactions are usually subtle. Boron and nitrogen which flank it both form relatively few compounds, both react indifferently. However, oxygen enters readily into compounds with the elements below it (including carbon) and fluorine has marked reactive properties. Starting with lithium the reactive abilities of the elements decrease to carbon then increase to fluorine, with the elements above carbon reacting well with those below it.

The addition of the inert gases to the list destroys this seeming continuity, for a sharp break in chemical reactivity occurs between helium and lithium and again between fluorine and neon. However, the characteristics of the next element in order of atomic number, suggest a rationality in the sequence. Sodium, ($_{11}$Na), has properties very much akin to lithium: it is a soft, gray metal whose reactions are violent. We have already noted its explosive reaction with water for instance (Equation 14.5):

$$2Na + 2H_2O \rightarrow 2NaOH + H_2.$$

Again like lithium, sodium forms a characteristic series of salts with the halogens: sodium fluoride, sodium chloride, sodium bromide, and sodium iodine.

If we think of the break in reactivity between helium and lithium as analogous to the break between neon and sodium, a repetition or *periodicity* in the properties of the elements begins to suggest itself. Helium ($_2$He) and neon ($_{10}$Ne) are both inert gases, whereas lithium ($_3$Li) and sodium ($_{11}$Na) are alkali metals. The eight elements that constitute the group starting with sodium exhibit the same sort of continuity in reactivity that we noted in the eight elements from lithium through fluorine. Magnesium and aluminum ($_{12}$Mg and $_{13}$Al) are both metals, but aluminum does not react readily. Hence these elements have a great deal in common with beryllium and boron ($_4$Be and $_5$B). In the number of compounds it forms, silicon ($_{14}$Si) is second only to carbon. Again like carbon its compounds are very stable, its reactions subtle. Continuing through phosphorous and sulfur to chlorine, an increase in activity is again apparent, the latter gas belonging to the halogen family. It readily forms salts with the alkali metals and reacts with hydrogen to yield highly corrosive hydrochloric acid (HCl). Hence the properties of fluorine ($_9$F) repeat themselves in chlorine ($_{17}$Cl). Argon, the eighteenth element, in order of increasing atomic number, is an inert gas, a clear repetition of the outstanding chemical nonproperties of both helium and neon.

The Periodic Table of the Elements (Table 19.2) provides a convenient means for displaying these and other regularities. Elements are ordered in horizontal rows or *periods* according to atomic number. The first period contains hydrogen and helium. *By definition*, each of the remaining six periods starts with one of the alkali metals—lithium, sodium, potassium, rubidium, cesium, and francium. Hence the number of elements that intervene between each succeeding alkali metal determines the length of each period.

TABLE 19.2 *Periodic Table of the Elements Based on Atomic Number* (Z)

Group I	II	III	IV	V	VI	VII	0
$_1$H							$_2$He
$_3$Li	$_4$Be	$_5$B	$_6$C	$_7$N	$_8$O	$_9$F	$_{10}$Ne
$_{11}$Na	$_{12}$Mg	$_{13}$Al	$_{14}$Si	$_{15}$P	$_{16}$S	$_{17}$Cl	$_{18}$A
$_{19}$K	$_{20}$Ca	$_{21}$Sc	(First Transition Series)				
		$_{31}$Ga	$_{32}$Ge	$_{33}$As	$_{34}$Se	$_{35}$Br	$_{36}$Kr
$_{37}$Rb	$_{38}$Sr	$_{39}$Y	(Second Transition Series)				
		$_{49}$In	$_{50}$Sn	$_{51}$Sb	$_{52}$Te	$_{53}$I	$_{54}$Xe
$_{55}$Cs	$_{56}$Ba	$_{57}$La	(Lanthanides) (Third Transition Series)				
		$_{81}$Tl	$_{82}$Pb	$_{83}$Bi	$_{84}$Po	$_{85}$At	$_{86}$Em
$_{87}$Fr	$_{88}$Ra	$_{89}$Ac	(Actinides) . . .				

From Derek L. Livesey, *Atomic and Nuclear Physics* (Waltham, Mass.: Blaisdell Publishing Co., 1966), p. 494
NOTES
First Transition Series: $_{22}$Ti $_{23}$V $_{24}$Cr $_{25}$Mn $_{26}$Fe $_{27}$Co $_{28}$Ni $_{29}$Cu $_{30}$Zn.
Second Transition Series: $_{40}$Zr $_{41}$Nb $_{42}$Mo $_{43}$Tc $_{44}$Ru $_{45}$Rh $_{46}$Pd $_{47}$Ag $_{48}$Cd.
Lanthanides (Rare Earths): $_{58}$Ce $_{59}$Pr $_{60}$Nd $_{61}$Pm $_{62}$Sm $_{63}$Eu $_{64}$Gd $_{65}$Tb $_{66}$Dy $_{67}$Ho $_{68}$Er $_{69}$Tm $_{70}$Y $_{71}$Lu.
Third Transition Series: $_{72}$Hf $_{73}$Ta $_{74}$W $_{75}$Re $_{76}$Os $_{77}$Ir $_{78}$Pt $_{79}$Au $_{80}$Hg.
Actinides: $_{90}$Th $_{91}$Pa $_{92}$U $_{93}$Np $_{94}$Pu $_{95}$Am $_{96}$Cm $_{97}$Bk $_{98}$Cf $_{99}$E $_{100}$Fm $_{101}$Mv $_{102}$No $_{103}$Lw.

The atomic numbers of lithium, sodium, potassium, rhubidium, cesium, and francium are 3, 11, 19, 37, 55, and 87, respectively. Therefore the first period has two entries, the second and third eight each, the fourth and fifth, eighteen, and the sixth, thirty-two. The seventh period, starting with $_{87}$Fr is incomplete, but also has room for thirty-two entries.

The long form of the Periodic Table incorporates one complete period into each row. The short form, used for Table 19.2, has the advantage of saving page space. Here the elements in the last four long periods are not written out completely in the body of the table. Instead, only the first and last few elements whose properties place them unequivocally in a particular column are given, with the remaining elements listed below the table proper. Thus the elements of the first transition series, from $_{22}$Ti through $_{30}$Zn, are inserted in the gap between $_{21}$Sc and $_{31}$Ga. Likewise, the second transition series occupies the space between $_{39}$Y and $_{49}$In, while the lanthanide (or rare earth) elements, followed by the elements of the third transition series are inserted between $_{57}$La and $_{81}$Tl. Finally, the actinide series begins with the element $_{89}$Ac.

If the properties of the elements really do repeat themselves, then those with similar physical and chemical properties should be found together in the same column. It is not surprising that the alkali metals comply, for by definition each period commences with one of them. However, it is encouraging to find all the inert gases (helium, neon, argon, krypton, xenon, and emanation [or radon]) together in the last column, and the halogens (fluorine, chlorine, bromine, iodine, and astatine) in the next to the last. The semiconductors silicon ($_{14}$Si) and germanium ($_{32}$Ge), whose unique properties, neither unambiguously metallic nor unambiguously nonmetallic, make them the basis for transistor electronics, fall in the same column as carbon, a reasonable though not an excellent conductor of electricity. The common metals such as iron, copper, zinc, silver, gold ($_{26}$Fe, $_{29}$Cu, $_{30}$Zn, $_{47}$Ag, $_{79}$Au) as well as many that are less familiar, are members of one of the three transition series and are therefore more akin to the elements in the left than in the right half of the table. However, none of these familiar metals nor its neighbors has electrical conductivities as high as the alkali metals in the extreme left column. Finally, the properties of all the lanthanides are so similar to each other that they can be chemically separated only with difficulty. A similar statement is applicable to the actinides.

Only 63 of the present 103 elements were known to Dimitri Mendeleev and his contemporaries when the first periodic table was devised in 1869. At that time the Daltonian concept of the indivisible atom (Section 14.3) held sway. The planetary model was still fifty years in the future. Hence the known elements were ordered in terms of increasing atomic weight rather than in terms of the yet unconceived electron number. Despite the many striking regularities that were noted in Mendeleev's original table, disturbing inconsistencies were also apparent. For example, in order of atomic weight arsenic ($_{33}$As) followed gallium ($_{31}$Ga) in the list of known elements. Since the properties of gallium placed it in the same column as boron and aluminum, arsenic at first sight should have been grouped with carbon and silicon (Table 19.2). Yet its chemical properties suggested a far closer similarity to nitrogen and phosphorous. Faced with this seeming failure in his scheme, Mendeleev boldly asserted that arsenic really *did* belong in the latter column, and that a yet undiscovered element with properties akin to carbon and silicon would fill the gap thus created between gallium and arsenic. He even offered detailed predictions about the properties of this unknown element, basing his speculations upon the known properties of the nearby elements (silicon, tin, zinc, and arsenic). These predictions were verified with the discovery of the element germanium ($_{32}$Ge) in 1887.

Because the original periodic table permitted a rational classification of the elements, it also suggested gaps in the scheme and was thus an invaluable guide in the search for new elements. By the mid-1930's almost all gaps in the table had been filled, and the known elements ranged from hydrogen with atomic weight 1.008 and atomic number 1 to uranium with atomic weight 238.07 and atomic number 92. The status of remaining gaps as well as the elements beyond uranium will be discussed in Chapter 20.

The relationship between the seemingly diverse fields of chemistry and physics provided by a knowledge of atomic structure must be regarded as one of the more satisfying triumphs of quantum mechanics. Many features of the Periodic Table are directly related to the shell structure discussed in Section 19.4, whereas the properties of particular chemical compounds follow from detailed specifications of the amplitudes describing the states of their constituent atoms.

A vast majority of the physical and chemical properties of the elements and their compounds are comprehensible in terms of one general assumption: that the electrons in the outermost shell (or subshell) of an atom bear primary responsibility for its interactions with other atoms, both similar and dissimilar. It is worth noting that a number of properties and processes cannot be rationalized so simply. Indeed, some of the most interesting would be excluded if chemical activity were vested *entirely* in the outermost atomic shells. Nevertheless, the fruitfulness of the simple assumption cannot be denied.

The number of states in each of the seven major atomic shells is given in Section 19.4: 2, 8, 8, 18, 18, 32, 32. Because electrons are Fermi particles, no more than one may occupy a given state. Therefore helium ($_2$He) has just enough electrons to fill the first shell, neon ($_{10}$Ne) enough to close both the first and second shells, argon ($_{18}$A) enough to complete the first three shells. The thirty-six electrons of krypton ($_{36}$Kr) complete the first four shells, whereas xenon ($_{54}$Xe) and emanation, or radon ($_{88}$Em) also have their respective fifth and sixth shells filled. Closure of the seventh shell would occur for $Z = 118$, but that atom is yet to be discovered.

All of the inert gases are included in this list of perfect closed-shell atoms. Of course their outstanding common chemical property is really a nonproperty: they normally form no compounds at all.* Because their outermost shells are filled, rare gas atoms appear to other atoms not only as an electrically neutral systems, but also as an electrically symmetric systems (Figure 19.12). Therefore, another atom really cannot see an inert gas atom at all unless the two atoms are so close together that their electron shells overlap. The very low liquefaction temperatures of these gases indicate that their atoms refuse interaction with similar as well as dissimilar atoms. Over a wide range of temperatures and pressures they interact with each other only on direct contact. Hence they behave almost exactly like the classical, hard sphere atoms of Chapters 14 and 15.

Each atom of the alkali metal group has one electron outside a closed shell, while atoms of the halogen group require but one additional electron to complete their outer shells. For this reason the members of these two classes are the most highly reactive of the elements.

The binding energy of the excess electron in an alkali atom is small relative to the binding energies of its closed-shell electrons. For instance, the binding energy of the outermost electron in sodium is -5.1 eV. If a sodium atom could donate that electron to a chlorine atom then *both* species would attain perfect closed-shell status. In the process the sodium atom would become a singly charged positive *ion*, the chlorine atom singly charged negative ion.

---

* This statement requires some modification, since several inert gas compounds (principally xenon compounds) have been formed under special conditions. Thus the "rule" vesting all chemical activity in the outer electron shells should be regarded as a guiding principle instead.

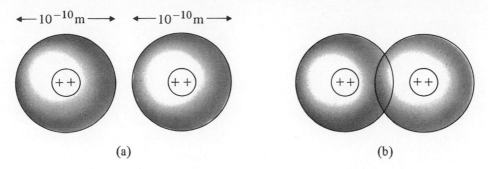

FIGURE 19.12 (a) The two electrons in helium form a closed, spherical shell centered upon the positive, doubly charged nucleus. Seen from the outside, no one part of the atom has a different charge from another part. Therefore, two helium atoms exert no net force on each other unless they are so close together that their electron shells overlap (b).

However, the binding energy of an *extra*, shell-closing electron in chlorine is -3.8 eV. Therefore, the transfer of an electron from sodium to chlorine requires an additional $5.1 - 3.8 = 1.3$ eV which is obtained from the mutual electrostatic attraction of the oppositely charged ions. Typically the ions will draw together until their outermost electron shells start to overlap. At that separation (about 4×10^{-10} m) they are bound to each other with an energy of -1.8 eV, exceeding the 1.3 eV required for electron transfer by 0.5 eV. Therefore, the transfer of an electron from sodium to chlorine and the consequent formation of an ion pair is energetically favorable and leads to a system with -0.5 eV binding energy (Figures 19.13a and 19.13b).

Because the reaction of sodium and chlorine yields $\frac{1}{2}$ eV per atom (opposed to the $\frac{1}{40}$ eV mean thermal energy at room temperature) the process is highly exothermic. We have illustrated the formation of the bond by restricting our attention to one pair of atoms. But of course many atoms are involved in the reaction of macroscopic quantities of the elements. Each positively charged sodium ion repels other sodium ions and attracts as many chlorine ions as possible; each chlorine ion tries to interact with as many sodium ions as possible. The resulting system may be envisioned, crudely, in terms of a large array of closely packed, dissimilar spheres. Each sphere of one type compromises in its attempt to be as close to as many of the other type as possible while maximizing the separation from those of its own kind (Figure 19.13c).

The result is a regular geometric pattern, the well-defined crystalline structure that characterizes sodium chloride and which may be easily seen by examining grains of table salt with a low-power magnifying glass. No single sodium ion can be associated preferentially with a particular chlorine ion. Therefore there are no molecules of sodium chloride, unless one complete crystal of the salt can be regarded as a giant molecule. Because of the complex of interconnecting bonds between the ions of a sodium chloride crystal, each requiring 0.5 eV for disruption, the salt is characterized by a high melting point.

▲▲ 19.6 Covalent binding. The hydrogen molecule

Sodium and chlorine interact to form a type of bond called (appropriately) the *ionic bond*. As we have seen, it is characterized by the complete transfer of electrons from the

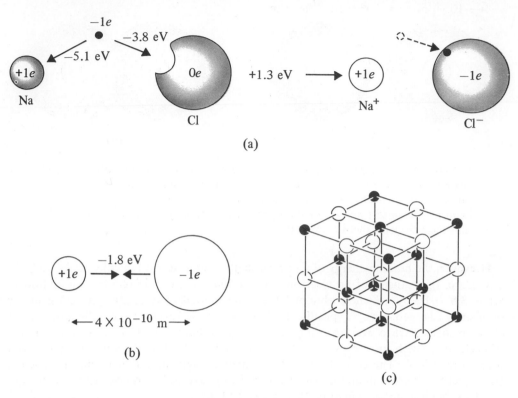

FIGURE 19.13   Formation of the ionic bond in sodium chloride. (a) If the loosely bound electron outside the closed shell in sodium is transferred to a chlorine atom, both sodium and chlorine attain closure. (b) The mutual electrostatic attraction of the resulting oppositely charged ions then constitutes a bond. (c) Position of the centers of the ions in a sodium chloride crystal.

atoms of one species to the atoms of another, a transfer which permits the resulting ions to interact electrostatically and arrange themselves into a regular crystalline array. All of the alkali metals can form ionic bonds with members of the halogen family by means of single electron transfer leading to the formation of compounds such as LiF, KBr, NaI, CsCl, etc. Ionic bonds are also formed between atoms with two electrons outside a closed shell or subshell (beryllium, magnesium, and many familiar metals such as copper, nickel, zinc), and atoms with two vacancies in their outermost shells. Since the formation of an ionic compound such as magnesium oxide (MgO) requires the transfer of two electrons from each magnesium to each oxygen atom, we would expect the resulting array of interacting ions (and hence the macroscopic properties of the compound) to differ in detail from an array of interacting, singly charged ions.

Most bonds between atoms are not ionic, simply because a complete transfer of one or more electrons between dissimilar species is usually not energetically favorable. However, two or more atoms may also interact by *sharing* some of the electrons in their outermost shells thus establishing *covalent* bonds. In these instances particular groups of atoms are identified with each other. Therefore, covalently bonded atoms constitute true molecules.

Diatomic hydrogen offers the simplest example. Because only two electrons may occupy the $n = 1$ shell, the hydrogen atom requires but one more electron for closure. However there is no reason why one hydrogen atom should transfer its electron to another hydrogen atom. The atoms are identical, indistinguishable systems, and the permanent loss of an electron by one would imply some other measurable difference between them. However, the atoms are able to compromise by *sharing* their electrons. Speaking crudely, the two electrons spend part of their time in the vicinity of one proton and part in the vicinity of the other. In other words, the protons *exchange* the electrons, and that exchange leads to an attractive interaction between them known as an exchange force.

There is no a priori reason why the exchange of electrons should lead to binding. In fact, the formation of the attractive covalent bond between two hydrogen atoms can only be understood in terms of a now familiar characteristic of quantum mechanical systems: that the properties of a composite system are different from the sum of the properties of its component parts. Let $\phi(A1)$ specify the ground state of a hydrogen atom with proton A and electron 1, and $\phi(B2)$ the corresponding state of another atom with proton labeled B and electron labeled 2. The square of the product amplitude $|\phi(A1)\phi(B2)|^2$ gives the joint probability of finding electron 1 in the vicinity of proton A and electron 2 in the vicinity of proton B as functions of the separation between the electrons and their respective protons (Figure 19.15). This state cannot be distinguished from the state with amplitude $\phi(A2)\phi(B1)$ in which electron 2 associates itself with proton A and electron 1 with proton B, i.e., the exchange state. Hence the amplitude for a hydrogen *molecule* expressed in terms of these *atomic* amplitudes must be

$$\phi_{H_2} = \phi(A1)\phi(B2) + \phi(A2)\phi(B1), \tag{19.10a}$$

(a)   (b)

FIGURE 19.14　Two types of ionic crystals. (a) Crystal of nitre (sodium nitrate). (b) Crystals of quartz. [From *Crystals and Crystal Growing*, by Alan Holden. Copyright © 1960 by Educational Services Inc. (Science Study Series). Reprinted by permission of Doubleday and Company, Inc.]

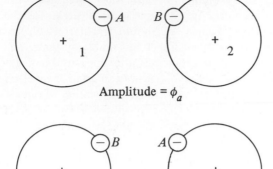

Amplitude = ϕ_a

Amplitude = ϕ_b

Probability of the state = $|\phi_a + \phi_b|^2$

FIGURE 19.15 Amplitude for a state in molecular hydrogen in terms of the amplitudes for the states of two hydrogen atoms.

and the probability of finding the electrons in the vicinity of the proton is

$$|\phi_{H_2}|^2 = |\phi(A1)\phi(B2)|^2 + |\phi(A2)\phi(B1)|^2 + 2\phi(A1)\phi(B2)\phi(A2)\phi(B1). \qquad (19.10b)$$

The first two terms give the result we would expect from a semiclassical treatment: that the probability of finding the molecule in a particular state is the sum of the products of two atomic states. The origin of third term, the interference term, is purely quantum mechanical, and shows that the molecule cannot be regarded simply as the sum of two atoms.

From a more basic point of view we should regard the molecule as an interacting system of four particles, two protons and two electrons, and try to deduce amplitudes defining the states of the system. Amplitudes for electron states in an *atom* are conveniently expressed as functions of the distance between the electron and the nucleus, and the angular momentum of the electron relative to the nucleus (Sections 19.1 to 19.3). However, since the hydrogen molecule has two protons we would expect to find a series of electron states associated with each possible separation between them. In addition, whereas in an atom the attractive interaction between the electrons and nucleus usually dominates over the repulsive interaction between electrons, the repulsive force between the protons of a hydrogen molecule may be appreciable. In a sense the exchanged electrons must shield the protons from each other if the attractive interactions between electrons and protons are to dominate over the repulsion. Both the strength of the repulsive force between the proton and the probability of finding the electrons associated with one proton in the vicinity of the other proton increase as the distance between the protons decreases. However, the increase in the repulsive force is the more rapid, a tendency that determines the minimum separation between the proton, typically about 0.74×10^{-10} m.

Figures 19.16a and b sketch the probability distributions corresponding to the two lowest energy states of *one* electron interacting with two protons. The total energy of the three interacting particles is negative in the first instance over a rather wide range of interproton distances,* but positive in the second. It is not hard to understand why these

---

* Motion of the protons relative to each other also changes the internal energy of the system, giving rise to the vibrational and rotational energies discussed in Chapters 16 and 17.

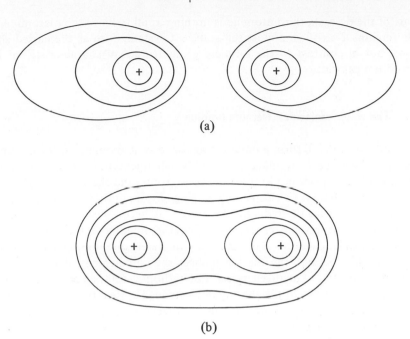

(a)

(b)

FIGURE 19.16   Contours representing equal probability distributions for the two lowest energy states of two protons (at a fixed separation) and two electrons. The second of these has negative energy and represents the electron configuration of the hydrogen molecule.

conclusions are plausible. Both distributions indicate that the electron spends equal amounts of time near each proton. But in the first state it is more likely to be found between the protons, shielding them from each other and attracting them both, whereas in the second state the electron prefers to be on one side of one proton or the other. In addition, the electron can move over a wider range in Figure 19.16b. Since its spatial confinement is reduced, then, by the uncertainty principle (or in analogy with the rectangular well calculation of Section 18.8), its momentum and consequently its kinetic energy can be lower.

Because of the Pauli principle the two electrons of the hydrogen *molecule* may both occupy the bound state whose probability distribution is represented by Figure 19.16b only when their intrinsic spins are opposite each other. If their spins are parallel the electrons cannot be in the same spatial state, and there is a high probability that each will remain associated with one proton or the other rather than being exchanged between the protons. In other words, the four particles constitute two *atoms* with probability distributions typified by Figure 19.16a rather than a hydrogen *molecule* with electron distributions as given by Figure 19.16b.

It is not difficult to understand why three hydrogen atoms have small probability of forming a bound system. At least two of the three electrons involved would have parallel intrinsic spins so that no more than two could occupy the lowest energy state of the system. Even in the absence of the additional repulsive force contributed by the third proton there is a small probability of finding the third electron between the two original protons. In a sense two electrons exclude a third from making any contribution to the system. By sharing their electrons two hydrogen atoms can each have closed outer shells part of the time. A third atom adds nothing at all. Hence the diatomic hydrogen molecule remains a satisfied, almost self-sufficient system, even as the closed shell, rare gas atoms, but in contrast to the limitless geometric array characteristic of ionically bonded sodium chloride.

►► 19.7 = The water molecule. Metallic binding

Two or more atoms will form a bound, composite system only if they can reduce their total energy in the process. We have discussed two distinct types of bond: the ionic bond, involving complete transfer of electrons between atoms, and the covalent bond in which two or more atoms share their electrons, attaining closure in their outer shells part of the time. In the former case the reduction of energy is accomplished by the electrostatic interactions between oppositely charged ions. On the other hand, the reduction in energy affected by the covalent sharing of electrons is completely quantum mechanical in origin. It arises principally because the sharing reduces the confinement of the electrons, and consequently lowers their kinetic energies. But without a detailed calculation there is no way to predict whether or not the sharing of electrons between two or more atoms leads to a negative total energy for the system, or, in other words, whether two or more atoms can form a stable molecule.

As we have seen, only one of the two lowest energy electron states in hydrogen is bound. Usually a group of atoms will form a molecule if each can close its outmost shell part of the time by sharing electrons with the others. However, the electron states in these molecules differ from molecule to molecule, and, as we know, are not related in a simple manner to the states of the composite atoms. In short, whereas nature strictly limits the ways in which particular atoms may interact, it nevertheless permits a rich variety of molecular systems whose detailed properties cannot be easily summarized in terms of a few rules.

When two hydrogen atoms share their electrons with an oxygen atom, a covalently bonded water molecule is formed. Since the macroscopic properties of hydrogen and water are very different, then so are the respective molecules of the substances. In particular, the interactions between water molecules must be considerably stronger than the interactions between hydrogen (or oxygen) molecules, otherwise water would also be gas at room temperature.

It is not immediately obvious that water should be covalent rather than ionic. Referring to the Periodic Table, an oxygen atom has two vacancies in its outer shell. If two hydrogen atoms each transferred their electrons to an oxygen atom the resulting doubly charged negative oxygen ion would certainly attract the two positively charged protons. However, the removal of an electron from the ground state of hydrogen requires 13.6 eV. A detailed calculation shows that the sum of the energy gained by the binding of two extra electrons to oxygen by the electrostatic binding of the resulting ions is less than $2 \times 13.6 = 27.2$ V. Therefore, the energy of two protons and one doubly charged oxygen ion must be positive relative to the energy of two hydrogen and one oxygen atoms. The formation of the ionic bond is just not energetically favorable.

On the other hand the covalent sharing of electrons between the three atoms *does* reduce their energy, as, again, a detailed calculation indicates. However, the character of the bond differs in detail from the covalent bond of a hydrogen molecule. Hydrogen atoms are indistinguishable. When two of them share their electrons with each other there is no way to identify either electron more with one proton than with the other.

Hence the hydrogen molecule must be symmetric. But since hydrogen and oxygen atoms are not identical there is no reason why the shared electrons should not be more closely identified with one species of atom more than with the other. In fact, the shared electrons have a higher probability of being nearer the oxygen atom than the hydrogen atoms. The outermost shell in oxygen attains closure more than half of the time. Hence the molecule is asymmetric with a net negative charge concentrated in the vicinity of the oxygen atom and net positive charge near the hydrogen atoms.

The six electron states of the outer subshell in oxygen have quantum numbers $n = 2$, $l = 1$; the two vacant states in the shell have the same intrinsic spin but different magnetic quantum numbers. As we would expect a symmetric spatial arrangement of states that differ only in magnetic quantum number, then, since the electrons shared with the hydrogen atoms* occupy only two of these three states, the hydrogen atoms should be arranged asymmetrically relative to the oxygen atom. Detailed investigations show in fact, that the bond angle in water (the angle between the two hydrogen atoms—Figure 19.17a) is about 105°.

Because water molecules have spatial asymmetries and, in addition, because more negative charge is associated with the oxygen than with the hydrogen atoms, the molecules

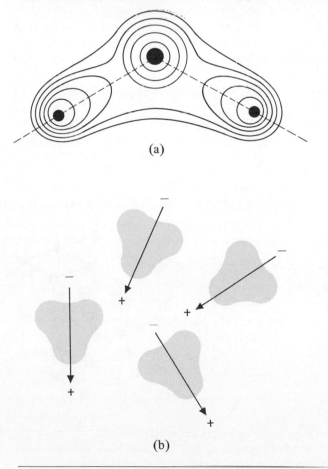

(a)

(b)

FIGURE 19.17 (a) The two shared electrons in a covalently bonded water molecule have a greater probability of being in the vicinity of the oxygen than the hydrogen nucleus. (b) Seen from the outside, the molecule resembles an electric dipole with excess positive charge at the hydrogen end, and excess negative charge at the oxygen end. Therefore it is able to exert a long-range electrostatic force.

---

* Strictly speaking it is incorrect to refer to hydrogen and oxygen atoms in this context since the properties of the water molecule as a whole are different from the sum of the properties of the three constituent atoms. But we continue to do so for convenience.

also have charge asymmetry even though they are electrically neutral. In the language of Section 9.1 water has an *electric* dipole moment. Thus its molecules interact with each other much more readily than symmetric molecules like hydrogen which do not have electric dipole moments. A group of water molecules with sufficiently low thermal energies will arrange themselves into a regular array with the negative part of each molecule as near as many positive parts of molecules as possible. Hence a regular crystalline pattern characterizes solid water, or ice. In addition the polarized molecules have the ability to disrupt the electrostatic bonds between the oppositely charged ion pairs in ionic compounds (Section 19.5), accounting for the high solubility of these substances in water.

A covalent bond between two identical atoms can be established only if at least half the electron states in the outermost subshells of the atoms are occupied. Otherwise the sharing of electrons cannot lead even to temporary closure for either atom. Nitrogen, oxygen, and fluorine, with three, two, and one vacancy, respectively, all exist as diatomic gases at room temperature.

In contrast, metallic atoms all have many vacancies in their outermost major shells. The alkali metals each have but one extra shell electron, magnesium and beryllium two electrons and two vacancies each. The situation with regard to the more familiar metals is slightly more involved. Iron, nickel, copper, and zinc are all members of the first transition series, a subgrouping of the fourth period that begins with potassium and ends with krypton. The major electron shell for these eighteen elements includes the states $n = 4, l = 0, n = 3, l = 2$, and $n = 4, l = 1$ (Figure 19.10). The first transition series elements are those for which the ten $n = 3, l = 2$ states are being filled. (Likewise, the second and third transition series includes those elements completing their $n = 4, l = 2$ and $n = 5, l = 2$ states, respectively.) The amplitudes for these $l = 2$ states are such that one or two, or at most three of the electrons in them are much more loosely bound than the remaining ones, and so behave very much as if they were outside a major shell.

Because metallic atoms have from one to three loosely bound electrons, they readily transfer these to atoms such as nitrogen, oxygen, or the halogens to form ionic compounds. Ionic bonds cannot be established between similar atomic species, for there is

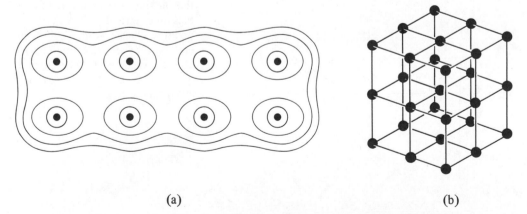

(a)   (b)

FIGURE 19.18 (a) Sketch representing the sharing of a single electron by eight copper ions. (b) The lattice structure of a cubic metal crystal resembles the structure of ionically bonded sodium chloride (Figure 19.13b). However, in the metal crystal the lattice centers are all positively charged ions and the shared electrons are free to migrate throughout the structure.

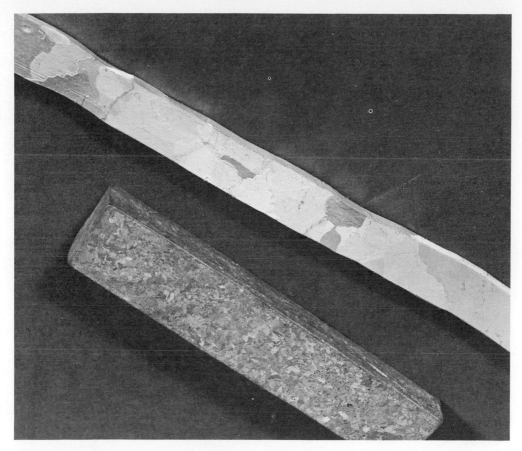

FIGURE 19.19   Bars of cast aluminum (above) and brass (below) annealed to enlarge grain size, then etched to reveal crystallinity. (Courtesy of Alan Holden, Bell Telephone Laboratories, Inc.)

no reason why seven copper atoms should each permanently transfer their excess electron to an eighth favored neighbor. But a group of eight atoms can *share* their electrons in such a way that each has a complete outer shell one-eighth of the time. In that case *none* of the shared electrons belongs to a particular atom. Rather, all of them belong in common to the group (Figure 19.18a). This transient exchange, a sort of extreme covalency, constitutes the *metallic* bond.

Extending the argument, there is no way to select particular favored groups of eight atoms from a large assembly of identical copper atoms and believe that each group jealously guards its eight free electrons. Detailed calculations of the energies involved verify the supposition that the outer-shell electrons in metals become the common property of the entire assembly of atoms and are confined only by the geometric limits of the assembly itself. Hence the kinetic energies of the electrons are much smaller than they would be if each were restricted to the vicinity of one atom. By contributing their outermost electrons to a common pool the array of atoms reduces its energy and becomes a bound system. The resulting ionized cores arrange themselves into a closely packed, regular geometric lattice, the characteristic crystal structure of the metal (Figure 19.19). As already noted, the outer electrons from the atoms may migrate over the entire lattice.

They constitute the free electrons responsible for both the electrical and thermal conduction properties of metals (Section 18.6).

▶▶ 19.8 Carbon chemistry. Notes on microbiology

Carbon atoms ($Z = 6$) have four electrons and hence four vacancies in their outermost shells. As a consequence they are able to establish covalent bonds with virtually all types of atoms: metallic atoms with less than half their full complement of outer shell electrons, atoms with more than half their outer shells occupied, as well as other carbon atoms. Each carbon atom can form bonds with four other atoms, some or all of which may be carbon. Hence the element forms a basis for a much greater number of molecules than any other. In particular, all the molecules composing the cells of biological systems are based on carbon, and for that reason the name *organic* is usually associated with carbon chemistry.

The properties of organic molecules almost always depend on their geometric characteristics. Therefore, a special notation has been developed to denote their structure schematically. A dash (—) joining the letter C (the chemical symbol for carbon) with the chemical symbol for some other element indicates one shared electron pair (or one covalent bond) between two atoms, a double dash (=) indicates that two electron pairs are formed, i.e., there are two covalent bonds between the atoms (Figure 19.20). This flexibility permits large aggregates of carbon atoms to arrange themselves into two distinct geometric patterns. In the first (Figure 19.21a), characteristic of graphite, the atoms are arranged in planes each consisting of a series of interlocking hexagonal rings.

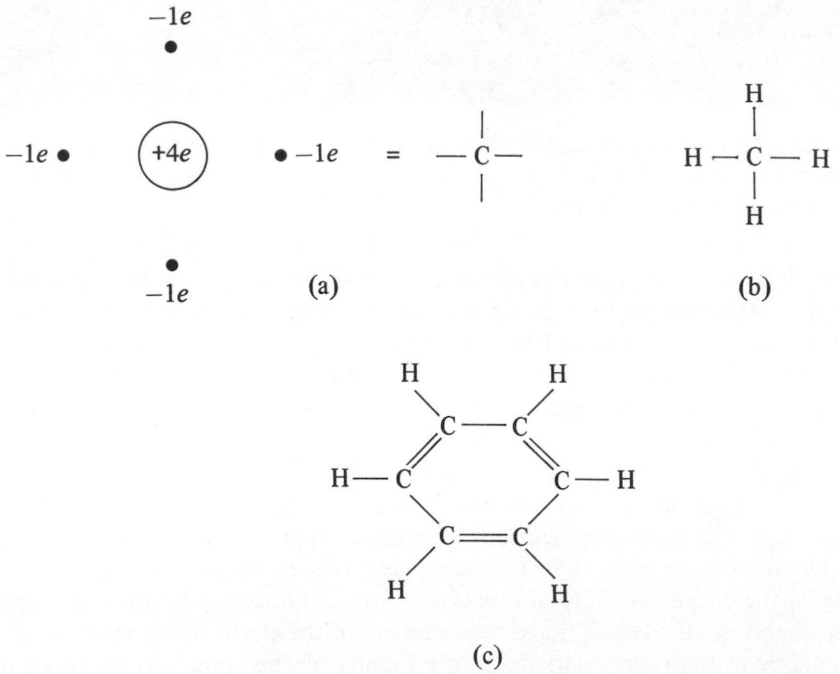

FIGURE 19.20 Notation used to represent the structure of organic molecules. (a) Carbon has four electrons and four vacancies outside its closed shell. Therefore, it can form as many as four covalent bonds with other atoms. (b) Structure of methane (CH_4). (c) Structure of benzene (C_6H_6).

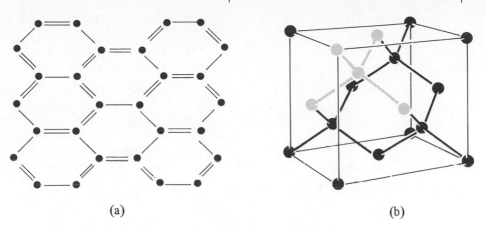

(a)   (b)

FIGURE 19.21   (a) The structure of graphite is essentially two dimensional with each carbon atom bound to three others in the same plane. (b) Diamond has a symmetric three-dimensional structure with each carbon atom bound to and equidistant from four others.

Since there is little interaction between the atoms in adjacent planes these planes readily slide over one another, which is consistent with the excellent lubricating properties of the substance. But under high temperature and pressure conditions one of the two bonds between adjacent atoms in the structure can be transferred to an atom in an adjacent plane. If all or most of the bonds are transferred in this way a rigid, regular three-dimensional structure is formed—diamond, the hardest substance that exists (Figure 19.21b).

The same bonding flexibility permits carbon to serve as the basis for exceedingly large, complex molecules. Three basic carbon skeletons are shown in Figure 19.22: the normal chain, the branched chain, and the ring. Each unconnected dash indicates that an opportunity exists for the carbon atom to form a covalent bond with another atom. Bonds with hydrogen, the halogens, phosphorous, oxygen, and nitrogen are typical, though others may also be formed. In addition, rings may bond to normal chains, branched chains to rings, and each remaining unsatisfied electron in the structure then may bond to some other atom or form a link to another structure and establish a three-dimensional array. Figures 19.23 show the structure of several different organic molecules. The subtle differences between some of them suggests something about the

(a)   (b)   (c)

FIGURE 19.22   The three basic carbon skeletons. (a) The normal chain. (b) The branched chain. (c) The ring.

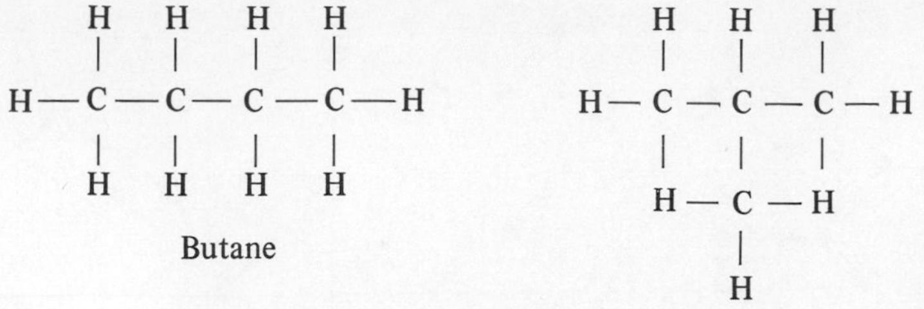

Butane

Isobutane

(a)

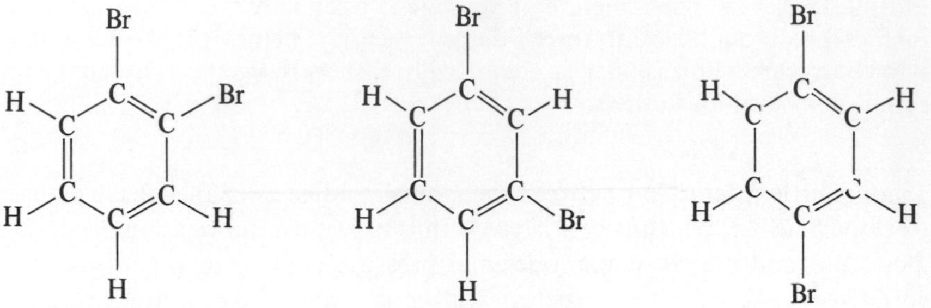

Ortho-dibromobenzene   Meta-dibromobenzene   Para-dibromobenzene

(b)

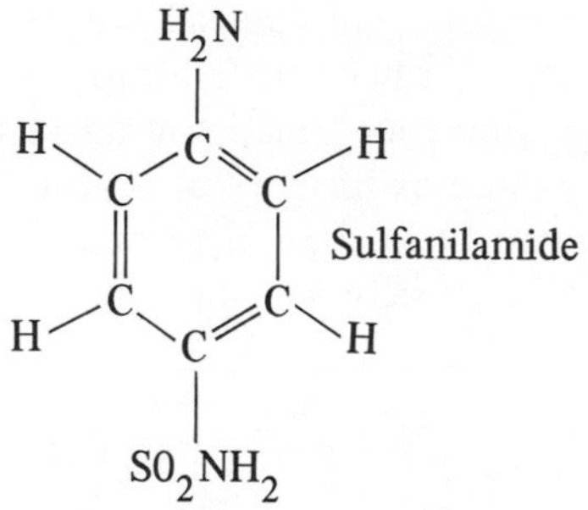

Sulfanilamide

(c)

FIGURE 19.23 (a) Molecules of the hydrocarbons butane and isobutane. Both have four carbon and ten hydrogen atoms. However, the former structure is based on a normal carbon chain, the latter on a branched carbon chain. (b) The molecules ortho-, meta-, and para-dibromobenzene all have six carbon and two bromine atoms, have structures based on the carbon ring, and differ only in the placement of the bromine atoms relative to each other. (c) A molecule of the drug sulfanilamide. (For simplicity, the structures of the groups H_2N and SO_2NH_2 are not shown in detail.)

number and variety of carbon compounds that are found in nature or fabricated in the laboratory.

The variety of conceivable carbon-based molecules also indicates why the chemical reactions of these compounds may often be quite subtle. Typical inorganic reactions are usually rather straightforward. The dissociation of water into hydrogen and oxygen requires that the two covalent bonds in each water molecule be broken and new covalent bonds formed between hydrogen atoms and oxygen atoms. The burning of an organic gas such as methane to yield carbon dioxide and water,

$$CH_4 + 2O_2 \rightarrow CO_2 + 2H_2O,$$

is an analogous, straightforward organic reaction. But the carbon-based compounds present other possibilities as well. A single hydrogen atom in a long chain can be replaced with a halogen atom, for instance. A molecule based on a ring structure can be unwound to yield a chain-based molecule. Several short chains may be combined into a complex branched chain.

Figure 19.24 shows the structural change resulting from a rather typical organic reaction: the fabrication of long, fibrous strands of the plastic polyethylene from gaseous ethylene, C_2H_6. Each molecule of the latter substance has a double covalent bond between its two carbon atoms (Figure 19.24a). If one of the double bonds in an ethylene molecule is broken the molecule can link itself covalently with another similar molecule (Figure 19.24b). The process can continue indefinitely with the result that many ethylene molecules become linked into a long, continuous-chain molecule, a chain whose properties are very different from the original separate molecules. This structural change is an example of polymerization—the linking of many (poly) similar molecules to each other. There should be no need to point out that understanding the structural changes that occur in polymerization is very different from finding ways to make the changes occur. The latter set of problems lie in the realm of experimental organic chemistry.

All living species are fashioned from highly complex, highly differentiated organic molecules. It follows that every biological process, the flowering of a plant, the contraction of a muscle in an animal, the memorization of a fact by a human being, is based

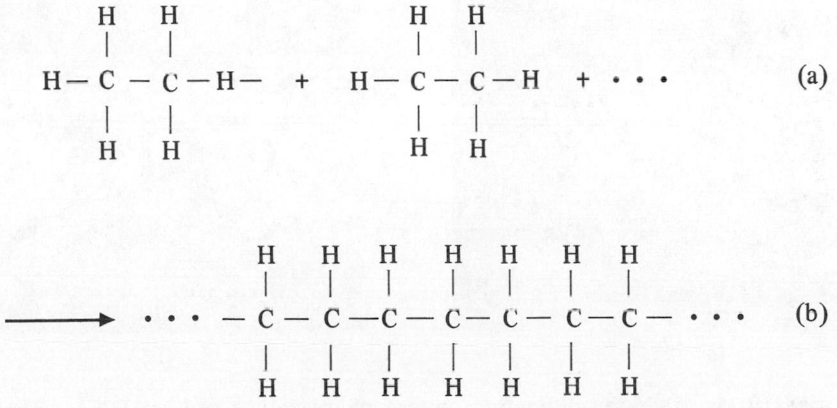

FIGURE 19.24 A polymerization reaction. Under the proper conditions ethylene molecules (a) may react to form chains of polyethylene (b) that contain several hundred thousand atoms. (Obviously hydrogen is evolved in the reaction.)

upon a sequence of organic chemical reactions resulting in particular changes in these molecules and in the larger patterns they form.

The chemical reactions characterizing even the simplest biological processes are both involved and subtle. But recent years have witnessed a considerable advance toward understanding many of them. We know the detailed organic structure of muscle fiber, for instance, and also know that the contraction of a muscle involves changes in the dimensions of these fiber molecules. But the associated chemical reactions have not been unraveled. The chemistry of thought remains an even deeper mystery. When a fact is learned, some structural alteration must occur in the neuron patterns of the brain. What are these changes? How are they brought about? At this writing no one can propose even a tentative answer.

Perhaps the most intriguing problems in biochemistry relate to questions of heredity and growth. Most of the matter composing the cells of living organisms is in the form of

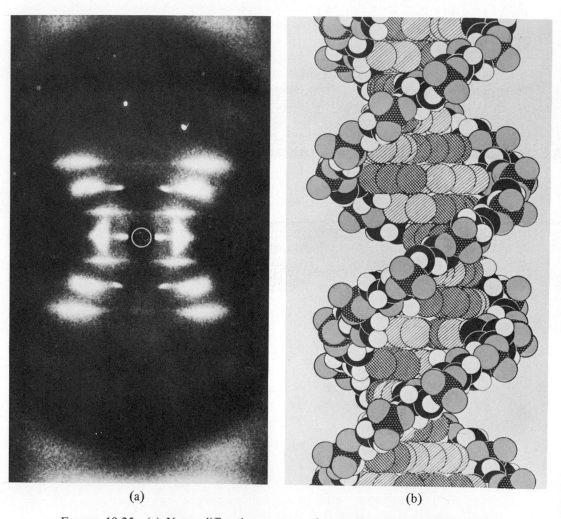

(a)   (b)

FIGURE 19.25   (a) X-ray diffraction pattern of crystalline sodium DNA. The position of the bright spots indicates a helical structure. (b) Model of the DNA molecule showing its twisted, helical structure. (Photographs courtesy of Dr. Leonard D. Hamilton and the Upjohn Company.)

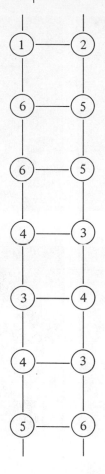

FIGURE 19.26 A highly simplified representation of a segment of a DNA molecule showing the bonds formed between each organic ring on the left and its complement on the right. The genetic code is vested in the ordering of the six ring types along the chains.

proteins, complex organic molecules whose nature depends upon their geometric structure as well as their atomic constituents.* All protein molecules are fashioned from combinations of amino-acid molecules, of which about twenty have been identified. Like all organic molecules the amino acids are based upon a carbon skeleton linked principally to oxygen and hydrogen atoms, although they also incorporate other elements such as nitrogen and phosphorus.

In general outline, the fundamental mechanism of growth is quite simple. Protein molecules are fabricated within a cell. As a result the cell grows and eventually divides into two cells which in turn fabricate more protein, grow, and divide. But since the basic materials in the protein of all cells is the same, how does the cell know what type of protein it must fabricate? Why does a cell in a particular human brain manufacture protein molecules appropriate to that brain and not to another brain? Why, for that matter, does it manufacture human brain cells rather than dog foot cells or radish leaf cells? In other words, what is the genetic code and how is that code impressed upon the raw materials ingested by an organism so that the growth of that organism will proceed coherently?

---

* Only the structure of the simpler proteins, whose atomic weights are about 700, have been completely unraveled.

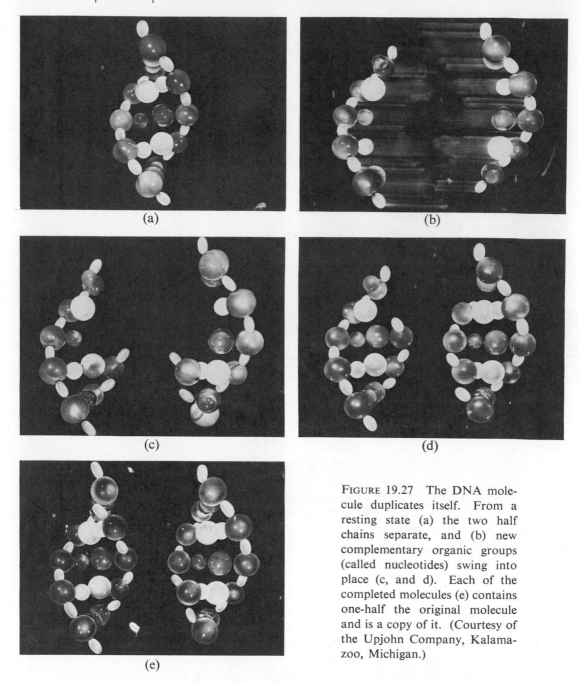

(a)

(b)

(c)

(d)

(e)

FIGURE 19.27 The DNA molecule duplicates itself. From a resting state (a) the two half chains separate, and (b) new complementary organic groups (called nucleotides) swing into place (c, and d). Each of the completed molecules (e) contains one-half the original molecule and is a copy of it. (Courtesy of the Upjohn Company, Kalamazoo, Michigan.)

A type of molecule called DNA (desoxyribose nucleic acid) is now recognized as the primary agent of heredity. (Figure 19.25) These molecules are located in the center or *nucleus* of a cell, and transmit specific fabrication instructions to the parts of the cell that manufacture protein. Each DNA molecule is a long, twisted double chain which differs from its fellows only in the way the types of organic rings that link its two chains together are ordered (Figure 19.26). Apparently the manufacturing blueprint, or the genetic code, vests itself in this ordering. Only six ring types have been identified, which for simplicity we designate as types 1 through 6. If a portion of the left chain of a particular molecule contains rings in the order 223165, for instance, the chain carries a different set of instructions than a portion whose order is 136542.

Since virtually the complete physiological pattern of an individual human being is determined at the moment of conception, then a set of blueprints, vested in DNA molecules, must be present at that moment.* How, then, do these reproduce themselves so that each cell of the fully developed individual will also carry its proper set of instructions for growth? As we have noted, each DNA molecule is a linked, twisted double chain. In addition, the two chains are the complements of each other. A type 1 ring always links with a type 2, a type 3 with a type 4, a type 5 with a type 6. If a portion of the left chain contains rings in the order 22461, the corresponding right hand links will be 11352. When a cell divides all DNA molecules unwind and the chains separate, the left chains going with one of the two daughter cells, the right chains with another. After cell division the half-molecules immediately cause the fabrication of new complementary chains from the raw material in the nucleus. Thus the chain 22461 has a 11352 fabricated and links with it to form a copy of its parent molecule, while the 11352 in the second daughter cell has a 22461 produced and follows suit. In this way the DNA molecules in the parent cell reproduce themselves in the daughter cell, and get on with their job of instructing the rest of the cell on how to fabricate protein.

Precisely how are instructions transmitted from DNA to raw material? What particular ring sequence leads to the manufacture of a particular protein? Why do DNA molecules have the special ability to unwind and cause their own reproduction (Figure 19.27) whereas other, only slightly different molecules, do not? Where, that is, can a line be drawn between living and inert matter? These and other similar questions remain unanswered, and we do not have time to explore any of the possible avenues of approach to their solutions. Perhaps it is sufficient to restate an obvious but important characteristic of complex matter: that it is more than the simple sum of its constituents. A hydrogen molecule has properties that differ from the properties of two noninteracting hydrogen atoms. The only fundamental difference between DNA molecules and polyethylene molecules is one of complexity. Both are based on carbon skeletons, both have other atoms bonded covalently to those carbon skeletons. Yet DNA molecules reproduce themselves and carry the code of heredity, while polyethylene molecules form a very useful plastic! The differences cannot be vested simply in the constituent atoms, but must lie in the details of their interactions. Again, the whole is more than the simple sum of its parts. Nature's endless variety of forms, the mystery of life itself bears witness to that obvious but endlessly intriguing fact.

SUGGESTIONS FOR FURTHER READING ▲▲▲

Several introductory texts in physics touch upon the relationship between atomic structure and the chemical properties of matter, for example:

K. R. ATKINS, *Physics*, John Wiley and Sons, Inc., New York, 1965, Chapter 29.

GERALD HOLTON AND DUANE H. D. ROLLER, *Foundations of Modern Physical Science*, Addison-Wesley Publishing Co., Inc., Reading, Mass., 1958, Chapter 35.

---

* Recent evidence suggests that a few hereditary characteristics may not be transmitted through the DNA molecules. However the substance of these remarks is not substantially altered thereby.

JAY OREAR, *Fundamental Physics*, John Wiley and Sons, Inc., New York, 1961, Chapters 13 and 14.

A monogram on a more advanced level also exists:

ALAN HOLDEN, *Bonds Between Atoms*, © Bell Telephone Laboratories, Murray Hill, N.J., 1966.

Textbooks in chemistry treat the topic in more detail. One of the best of these is:

LINUS PAULING, *The Nature of the Chemical Bond*, Cornell University Press, Ithaca, N.Y., 1960.

The story of the discovery of DNA is recounted in a book by one of the principals:

JAMES D. WATSON, *The Double Helix: a Personal Account of the Discovery of the Structure of DNA*, Atheneum, New York, 1968.

The same author has also written a very readable text on the biology of heredity:

JAMES D. WATSON, *Molecular Biology of the Gene*, W. A. Benjamin, Inc., New York, 1963.

The *Scientific American* regularly features articles on contemporary developments in chemistry and molecular biology. Among those that have appeared in recent years are:

Sept., 1957 issue, devoted entirely to the subject of giant molecules with articles by several authors.

Sept., 1961 issue, devoted entirely to the subject of cell structure with articles by several authors.

W. H. STEIN AND S. MOORE, "The Structure of Proteins," Feb., 1961, p. 81.

F. H. C. CRITCH, "The Genetic Code," Oct., 1962, p. 66.

M. W. NIRENBERG, "The Genetic Code, II," March, 1963, p. 80.

H. SELIG, et al., "The Chemistry of the Noble Gases," May, 1964, p. 66.

L. GARINI, "Antibiotics and the Genetic Code," April, 1966, p. 102.

F. H. C. CRITCH, "The Genetic Code," Oct., 1966, p. 55.

PROBLEMS AND EXERCISES ▲▲▲

19.1. Calculate and list the maximum values of orbital angular momentum in each of the first five states in hydrogen with different principle quantum numbers (n). Compare these values with the orbital angular momenta in the five lowest states in the Bohr model. Is there an exact correspondence between any two angular momenta in the two cases? If so do the states with the same angular momentum also have the same energy?

19.2. (a) The orbital angular momentum quantum number of a nitrogen atom in its ground state is 1. How many different orientations of the atom relative to a given arbitrary axis are there?

(b) In a macroscopic volume of nitrogen gas generally one-third of the atoms will be oriented with their angular momenta in the positive x-direction, one-third in the negative x-direction, one-third in the positive y-direction, one third in the negative y-direction, one-third in the positive z-direction, and one-third in the negative z-direction. How can all these statements be true simultaneously?

19.3. (a) Compare the positions of the maxima in the radial probability distribution functions for hydrogen in Figure 19.3 with the Bohr radii.

(b) Do the zeros in the probability density curves for $n = 2$ and $n = 3$ imply that if an electron is in the vicinity of one maximum it will never be found in the vicinity of another maximum? Explain.

(c) Is the existence of these maxima in the probability density for $n = 3$ consistent with Bohr theory? Need it be? Is it consistent with our basic ideas about quantum mechanical systems?

(d) Suppose an electron in the vicinity of the most pronounced maximum, the state $n = 3, l = 0$, later is found near one of the smaller radii maxima. Would there be any way to detect the change?

19.4. Calculate the orbital magnetic dipole moments corresponding to the maximum angular momenta for the three lowest energy states in hydrogen.

19.5. (a) Would you expect the total Zeeman splitting of a level in hydrogen with $l = 3$ to be smaller than, about equal to, or greater than the Zeeman splitting for a level with $l = 1$ in the same magnetic field?
  (b) Are there states in hydrogen in which there is no Zeeman splitting? Which ones?

19.6. Estimate the magnitude of the splitting (fine structure splitting) due to the interaction of the intrinsic electron spin with the magnetic field produced by the relative motion of the electron and proton for hydrogen in its ground state and in its first excited state. Assume the semiclassical model presented in the text, i.e., that in both cases the electron is in a circular Bohr orbit. Take $g = e/M$ in Equation 19.6.

[HINT: See Problem 17.15 and its answer.]

19.7. Calculate the magnetic field at the proton due to the circulating electron current for hydrogen in its ground state and first excited state. In both cases assume that the electron is in a circular Bohr orbit.

19.8. The proton, like the electron, has intrinsic spin $s = \hbar/2$ so that it also has two distinct orientation energies relative to a magnetic field. However, the ratio of the intrinsic dipole moments of the particles is roughly equal to the inverse ratio of their masses (i.e., in Equation 19.7b g_p is roughly e/M_p).

  (a) What is the difference between the magnetic orientation energies of the proton in its two spin states for hydrogen in its ground state? Its first excited state? (Use the results of Problem 7.)
  (b) What difference if any would you expect to see in the hydrogen spectrum as a result of the energy difference calculated in part a. (Be as quantitative as possible.)

19.9. Tabulate the single electron substates for the principle quantum numbers $n = 1, 2, 3$, and 4.

19.10. Draw electron configuration diagrams similar to Figure 19.11 for beryllium, sodium, aluminum, and argon ($Z = 4, 11, 13,$ and 18).

19.11. The rare earth elements ranging in atomic number from $Z = 57$ to 71 have properties that are very similar. Referring to Figure 19.10, can you give any reason why this might be the case?

19.12. Many properties of the elements exhibit a quantitative periodicity with Z. Look up the melting points and ionization energies of the elements in either *The Handbook of Physics and Chemistry* or *The American Institute of Physics Handbook* and plot each property as a function of Z. Are the observed periodicities consistent with the Periodic Table? Are they consistent with the basic properties of interatomic bonds discussed in this chapter? Explain.

19.13. The melting points of the four sodium halides NaF, NaCl, NaBr, and NaI increase with the atomic weight of the particular halogen element in the compound. What does this imply about the respective electron binding energies in the four halogen atoms? Is it reasonable? Why?

19.14. Of the four common halogen elements, fluorine and chlorine are gases at room temperature, bromine is a liquid, and iodine a solid. Is it reasonable to expect such differences among members of the same column in the Periodic Table? Explain.

19.15. Fluorine and chlorine at room temperature are diatomic, covalent molecular gases, yet they form ionic bonds with metals. Explain why both observations are reasonable.

19.16. Ionic compounds and metals both have regular crystalline structures. Yet the former are very brittle, while the latter are ductile and can be rolled into thin sheets, for instance.

Try to explain these differences in terms of the differences between the ionic and the metallic bond.

19.17. The energy required to convert a sodium chloride crystal into sodium and chlorine is about 3.6 eV per ion pair, while the dissociation energy for a hydrogen molecule is 4.5 eV. Yet hydrogen is a gas at room temperature and sodium chloride is a solid. Explain.

19.18. Carbon, silicon, and germanium have both metallic and nonmetallic properties. For instance, they conduct electricity much better than the true insulators but not nearly so well as the true metals (silicon and germanium are called semiconductors and are the basic elements used in transistors). On the other hand, all three elements form covalent bonds with elements like oxygen and hydrogen rather than the ionic bonds that true metals often form. How can these seemingly distinct types of behavior be reconciled?

19.19. Even though water is a covalent compound, ice is hard and has a definite crystal structure in contrast to waxes, for instance, which are also covalent yet soft and amorphous. How can the difference be explained?

19.20. Since water readily dissolves table salt then obviously a great many sodium ions can move about in it without suffering further interactions. Yet metallic sodium reacts violently with water. How do you account for the marked difference in behavior between sodium ions and sodium atoms vis-à-vis water molecules? Answer as quantitatively as possible.

19.21. The electrolysis of molten sodium chloride is a common method for obtaining both elements. What mass of chlorine (Cl_2) will be liberated at the anode and how much sodium is collected at the cathode if a current of 10^{-2} A is passed through molten sodium chloride for one hour?

19.22. The growth of green plants proceeds by means of a series of *photosynthesis* reactions induced when they absorb photons from sunlight, and which permit them to convert carbon dioxide, water, and nutrients from the soil into organic molecules. The photon energies required for many of these are slightly greater than 2 eV, i.e., in the green region of the spectrum. Is the fact that the peak of the sun's radiation spectrum also falls in this region a coincidence? If not what would the appearance of plants be if the peak of the sun's radiation spectrum were in another region, say the orange region?

19.23. Life as we know it depends critically upon the ability of carbon to form highly complex organic molecules, and for these molecules to enter into subtle chemical reactions. The binding energies of organic compounds are usually no more than 1 or 2 eV and often less. What approximate upper limit does this imply for the temperature of an environment in which carbon-based life is possible? What criterion (or criteria) might be applied in order to determine an approximate lower temperature limit?

The structure of the nucleus

20

▲▲ 20.1 Introduction and perspective

The internal structure of atomic nuclei make little explicit contribution to most of the macroscopic, chemical features of matter. As we have seen, these are determined primarily by the electrons in the outermost shells of interacting atoms, whereas the nuclei have the rather passive function of providing the atoms with mass and with the positive charge required to bind the planetary electrons into systems. Hence one might argue that the study of internal nuclear structure is something of a sideline.

On the other hand, the appearance of the physical universe depends quite as much upon the relative availability of the various atomic species as upon the bonds these species form with each other. For example, if carbon and oxygen were rare elements on earth, life, if it existed at all, would assume quite different forms than it does irrespective of the fact that those few carbon atoms which did exist *could* serve as the basis of complex molecules. Figure 20.1 shows the percentage abundances of the ten most common elements in the earth's crust as a function of their atomic number, Z. None of the remaining ninety-odd elements is sufficiently abundant even to show on the scale of the figure. In fact, they constitute *in toto* about 0.6% of the crust. The ten peaks in Figure 20.1 are not correlated in any obvious way with chemical periodicity, and hence it is reasonable to conclude that the electronic shell structure of an atom has little or no bearing upon its availability.

The latter part of Chapter 19 concentrated upon the connection between the outermost electron shell of an atom and its chemical behavior. By implication, its nucleus became an almost passive core. But we might also think of an atom as nothing more than a nucleus clothed in electrons, and be quite indifferent to the way those electrons interact with the electrons of other atoms.

Neither of these extreme viewpoints should be permitted to exclude the other completely. But even as it is convenient to concentrate upon electronic shell structure in discussing bonds between atoms, so there is merit in focusing attention on the nucleus for a time. In a very real sense that point of view will permit us to broaden our ideas about the nature of matter, for in truth the forms discussed in Chapter 19 are exceedingly rare in the universe. Neither sodium chloride crystals, nor hydrogen molecules, nor complex protein molecules could exist on the 6000 °K surface of the sun. At that temperature the mean thermal energy of an atom is about 0.5 eV, precluding the formation of most

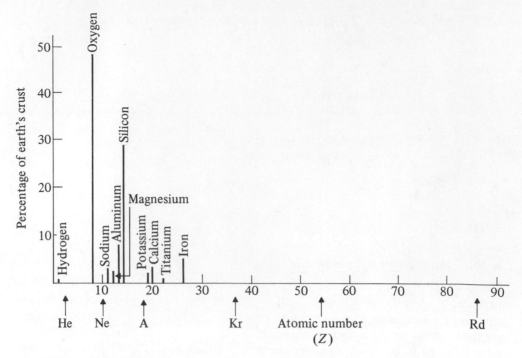

FIGURE 20.1 Percentage abundances of the ten most common elements in the earth's crust as a function of their atomic numbers. Arrows beneath the horizontal scale show the positions of the closed electron shell atoms.

interatomic bonds, since the potential energies of these bonds are rarely greater than a few electron volts. But if molecules cannot remain stable on the sun's surface, atoms themselves have only a very small probability of existing in its interior. There the temperatures reach up to sixteen million degrees, corresponding to mean thermal energies on the order of 1000 eV or more, energies that are more than sufficient to ionize all atoms completely. Hence matter in the interior of the sun and the other stars must be in the form of electrons and bare or almost bare nuclei rather than in the form of molecules or even atoms.

The Daltonian atom of the early eighteenth century was regarded as a fundamental, unchangeable entity. Chapter 19 recognizes the complex structure of atoms, and thus admits that they may change slightly by losing, gaining, or sharing electrons. In fact, these changes are the basis of most interatomic bonds. So long as the nucleus of an atom retains its charge, these alterations in electron structure cannot affect the chemical properties of the atom.

In 1896 Henri Becquerel accidentally discovered an entirely new phenomenon which he called *radioactivity*. By 1903 Ernest Rutherford and Frederick Soddy had demonstrated conclusively that radioactive decay signals drastic changes in the chemical nature of the decaying atom. Ten years later, after Rutherford and his colleagues had established the existence of the nucleus (Section 15.6), it became reasonable to equate radioactive decay with changes in the structure of nuclei themselves. Thereafter nuclei came to be regarded as complex rather than fundamental systems, a point of view implying that changes in their structure might not be limited to those associated with radioactive decay.

In this and the next chapter we shall discuss a number of the nuclear transmutation reactions now induced as a matter of course in laboratories in all parts of the world. There is convincing evidence that these reactions also proceed in the interiors of the stars, and that at least some of the complex nuclei that form the basis of complex terrestrial atoms were built up from hydrogen nuclei protons by a series of such reactions in stars that have long since vanished (Section 20.13).

▲▲ 20.2 Isotopes and nuclides. The mass spectrometer

All nuclei (save hydrogen whose nucleus is a single proton) are bound systems of inter-acting protons and neutrons, elementary particles to which we assign the collective noun *nucleon*. Later in the chapter we shall touch briefly upon the discovery of these two particles, but for the present let us take advantage of our retrospective vision.

The mass of a proton is 1.67×10^{-27} kg (to be compared with the 9×10^{-31} kg electron mass), or 1.0073 on the atomic mass scale, whereas the neutron's mass is 1.0087 on the same scale. Protons have one unit of positive charge ($e = +1.60 \times 10^{-19}$ C) while neutrons, as their name implies, are electrically neutral. Together, neutrons and protons combine to form over 200 strictly stable nuclei, and about a thousand other quasi-stable, radioactive species. Because there are (at this writing) 103 elements in the periodic listing, it is clear that not even every stable nucleus can serve as the core of an atom with unique chemical properties. Two or more atoms whose nuclei have the same number of protons (and therefore the same number of electrons) but different numbers of neutrons are called *isotopes* (Greek: same place) of the atom since their identical chemical properties put them in the *same place* on the Periodic Table. Only about twenty elements do *not* have more than one stable, naturally occurring isotope. Many have only two, several have as many as five, and xenon no fewer than nine.

The word *isotope* refers to an atom or occasionally to an aggregate of identical atoms. When referring to the *nucleus* of a particular atom the word *nuclide* is often employed. However, the terms isotope and nuclide are frequently used interchangeably although they are not quite synonymous.

A particular nuclide (or isotope of an element) is usually designated by writing its chemical symbol with its nucleon (or *baryon*) number (neutrons + protons) written as a right superscript and its proton number (or atomic number, Z) as a left subscript. Thus most oxygen is in the form of the isotope $_8O^{16}$ whose nucleus consists of sixteen nucleons, eight of them protons and therefore eight of them neutrons. The other two stable nuclides of oxygen are $_8O^{17}$ and $_8O^{18}$ with nine and ten neutrons, respectively.

There is another convention frequently encountered for designating nuclides in which the atomic number Z is written as a left superscript rather than as a left subscript, i.e., $^8O^{16}$ rather than $_8O^{16}$.

Atomic weights for a few stable isotopes are listed in Table 20.1. These are given on the scale that arbitrarily assigns the value 12.0000 to the atomic weight of $_6C^{12}$ *atom* (Section 14.3). Relative masses of the proton, neutron, and the electron on that scale are also given. In order to find the atomic weight of a particular *nuclide* the total atomic weight of the atom's planetary electrons must be subtracted from the atomic weight of the corresponding *isotope*. Significantly, the atomic weight of a particular nuclide is always smaller than the total atomic weight of the protons and neutrons that compose it (compare columns 2 and 3, Table 20.1). As we shall see presently these differences are directly related to nuclear stability.

TABLE 20.1   *Atomic Weights of Selected Stable Isotopes on the $_6C^{12}$ Scale*

Nuclide ($_ZX^A$)	Atomic Weight	$ZM_p + (A - Z)M_n$	Percentage Isotopic Abundance
Electron	5.48×10^{-4}	—	—
Proton	1.00728	—	—
Neutron	1.00866	—	—
$_1H^1$	1.00783	—	99.985
$_1H^2$	2.0141	2.0159	0.015
*Atomic weight of hydrogen = 1.0080			
$_2He^3$	3.0160	3.0232	10^{-4}
$_2He^4$	4.0026	4.0319	~ 100
*Atomic weight of helium = 4.0026			
$_6C^{12}$	12.0000	12.0956	98.89
$_6C^{13}$	13.0034	13.1043	1.107
*Atomic weight of carbon = 12.0011			
$_7N^{14}$	14.0031	14.1116	99.273
$_7N^{15}$	15.0001	15.1203	0.727
*Atomic weight of nitrogen = 14.0067			
$_8O^{16}$	15.9949	16.1275	99.52
$_8O^{17}$	16.9991	17.1362	0.07
$_8O^{18}$	17.9992	18.1448	0.41
*Atomic weight of oxygen = 15.9994			
$_{10}Ne^{20}$	19.9924	20.1594	90.92
$_{10}Ne^{21}$	20.9939	21.1681	0.26
$_{10}Ne^{22}$	21.9914	22.1767	8.82
*Atomic weight of neon = 20.4464			
$_{26}Fe^{54}$	53.9396	54.4318	5.81
$_{26}Fe^{56}$	55.9349	56.4491	91.64
$_{26}Fe^{57}$	56.9354	57.4577	0.34
*Atomic weight of iron = 55.847			
$_{82}Pb^{204}$	203.9701	205.6534	1.4
$_{82}Pb^{206}$	205.9745	207.6708	25
$_{82}Pb^{207}$	206.9759	208.6795	22
$_{82}Pb^{208}$	207.9766	209.6881	52
*Atomic weight of lead = 207.9530			
$_{92}U^{234}$	234.0409	235.8995	0.0057
$_{92}U^{235}$	235.0439	236.9081	0.7204
$_{92}U^{238}$	238.0576	239.9341	99.27

N.B.: All three of these uranium nuclides are slightly radioactive.

* Atomic weight of the naturally occurring isotopic mixture.

The percentage abundance of each isotope (the percentage normally found in a macroscopic sample of the corresponding element) is listed in column 4. With a few exceptions these remain constant regardless of where the element is found, suggesting a connection between the abundance of a nuclear species and the way it came into being. Atomic weights of the elements listed on the Periodic Table (and shown for comparison in Table 20.1) are normally determined by making chemical measurements on samples containing the natural isotopic mixtures. Hence they are averages of the isotopic weights given in

the table. For example, naturally occurring iron contains 5.81% $_{26}Fe^{54}$, 91.64% $_{26}Fe^{56}$, 2.21% $_{26}Fe^{57}$, and 0.34% $_{26}Fe^{58}$.
Therefore,

$$A_{mean} = 0.0581 \times 53.9396 + 0.9164 \times 55.9349 + 0.0221 \times 56.9354$$
$$+ 0.0034 \times 57.9333$$

$$= 55.847,$$

in agreement with the chemically determined average given in Table 20.1.

Because all isotopes of the same element have identical chemical properties, they obviously cannot be separated from each other by chemical means. Positive identification of an isotope, as well as a measurement of its relative abundance, must center upon its most distinctive property, its atomic weight. The first and still predominant method of isotope identification is the mass spectrometer, developed in 1919 by J. J. Thomson and F. W. Ashton, and used by them to separate the isotopes of neon in an experiment that marked the first identification of a stable isotope.

Construction of mass spectrometer is based upon the fact that a charged particle's radius of curvature in a magnetic field is a function of its charge to mass ratio, its velocity, and the field strength (Equation 9.18). Hence ions of two isotopes of the same element traveling with the same velocity have slightly different curvatures in the same magnetic field. In a simplified version of the instrument which, however, operates on the same general principles as Thomson's and Ashton's, the atoms to be separated are evaporated from a sample of the element of interest, then ionized and accelerated to a known velocity by a known potential difference. They subsequently enter a region with a magnetic field in the direction perpendicular to their velocity vectors, and are bent around in semicircles to a detector (Figure 20.2), where the ions of each isotope of the element leave a discrete line on a photographic emulsion. The position of these lines permits calculation of the radius of curvature of the ions in the magnetic field, and leads, therefore, to their masses. The relative intensities of the lines correspond to the number

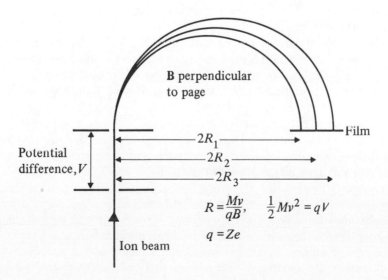

FIGURE 20.2   Principle of a mass spectrometer used to separate ions of three isotopes with the same charge, Ze.

of ions of each type deposited on the film, and hence to the relative abundances of the isotopes.

▲▲ 20.3 Sizes of nuclei. Nuclear binding. Internal nuclear states

Thus far we have avoided a fundamental question: why should *any* combination of neutrons and protons bind itself into a stable system? The eight protons and eight neutrons that constitute an $_8O^{16}$ nucleus are confined to a volume with linear dimensions smaller than 10^{-14} m. In the absence of a strong attractive force between these nucleons, the identically charged protons would drive each other out of the system, while the electrically neutral neutrons could not participate in the binding at all. Nuclear binding is, in fact, a manifestation of an interaction we have not previously encountered, called the *strong* interaction, which ranks with the gravitational and the electromagnetic as one of the fundamental interactions between the elementary particles. We shall be exploring the nature of the strong interactions (as well as the fourth fundamental interaction known as the *weak* interaction) in the next chapters. Part of our information about them comes from studying nuclear systems, more from the behavior of elementary particles at very high energies (Chapters 22 and 23).

The sizes of nuclei have been determined by precise scattering measurements similar to Rutherford's α-particle experiments (Section 15.6), but usually made with protons, neutrons, or electrons rather than α-particles incident upon target material containing the nuclei in question. These measurements indicate that the radius of any nucleus is approximated very well by the empirical expression

$$R = (1.4 \times 10^{-15})A^{1/3}\text{m}, \tag{20.1}$$

where A is the atomic weight of the nucleus (Figure 20.3). Because the radius of the nucleus is proportional to the cube root of its nucleon number its *volume* is directly proportional to the nucleon number itself.

Atoms do not share this feature with nuclei. A helium nucleus has twice the charge of a proton. Hence the force on an electron in helium is twice the force on the electron in a hydrogen atom and the (semiclassical) electron orbits in helium must therefore have about one-half the radius of the hydrogen orbits. By the same token the two electrons in the $n = 1$ shell of lithium have roughly one-third the radii of the hydrogen orbits, and the third ($n = 2$) electron's orbital radius is not very different from the radius of the single electron's orbit in hydrogen. In general, as the charge of the nucleus increases it binds its planetary electrons into tighter orbits. But the number of planetary electrons also increases with the nuclear charge, and because the Pauli principle requires that these additional electrons occupy higher orbits, they approximately compensate for the enhanced attraction of the nucleus. Thus, in summary, atomic sizes remain roughly constant with increasing atomic number primarily because the electrostatic force is a long range force that acts upon all the planetary electrons.

On the contrary, the variation in *nuclear* size with increasing atomic weight indicates that the addition of another neutron or proton to a nucleus does *not* appreciably alter the total force upon the nucleons already present. If each of the sixteen nucleons in $_8O^{16}$ interacted equally with the other fifteen the total force would be roughly proportional to the number of interactions, or 16×15, and the addition of another neutron to form $_8O^{17}$ would increase the number of interactions to 17×16. This would imply a more tightly bound and therefore a smaller system, in disagreement with Equation 20.1. Instead, the additional nucleon apparently interacts primarily with its nearest neighbors.

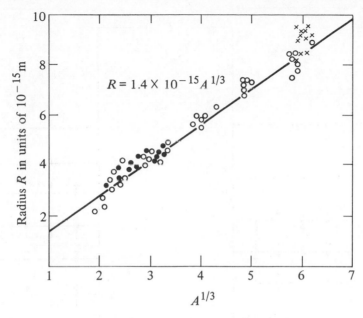

FIGURE 20.3 Nuclear radii plotted as a function of the cube root of the atomic weight A. The points are derived from experimental data, the straight line represents the best fit to these points and is described by the equation $R = 1.4 \times 10^{-15} A^{1/3}$ m.

Hence we conclude that the intranuclear force must have a short range that acts between nucleons only when they are sufficiently close to each other. From Equation 20.1 we can set that distance at about 1.4×10^{-15} m. The force between two nucleons separated by less than that distance must be strongly attractive, whereas two nucleons whose separation is greater than that repel each other electrostatically if they are both protons, and are quite indifferent to each other if either or both is a neutron.

In order to develop some stability criteria for nuclei let us assume a crude model in which each of the bound nucleons in a stable nucleus has a negative, potential energy derived from its interaction with the other nucleons as well as kinetic energy of more or less random motion throughout the nuclear volume. Absolute stability implies that the total energy of each constituent nucleon must always remain negative, although only the *sum* of the nucleon energies in the system need be constant. It is convenient to think of the nucleons as being in a potential energy well, even as we previously thought of atomic electrons in similar terms (Figure 20.4). The charge on the nucleus of an atom creates the well for the atomic electrons, whereas the interactions between the nucleons themselves are responsible for the nuclear well. Hence the detailed behavior of the systems is really quite different.

If our knowledge of the character of the strong interactions were as complete as our knowledge of the electromagnetic interactions we might be able to find the exact form of the nuclear potential well. Because we lack that knowledge and since in any case our present goal is a qualitative understanding of nuclear properties, we make the simplest possible assumption and regard the nucleons as being confined in a rectangular well about 10^{-14} to 10^{-15} m in extent. Since each nucleon is bound by the potential, its total

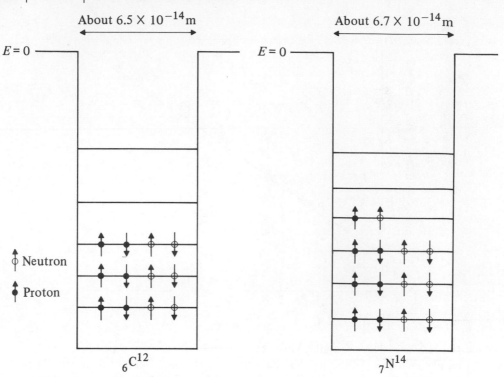

FIGURE 20.4 Qualitative, rectangular, potential well model for the ground states of two light nuclei. Since the nuclei are bound systems, their internal energy states are quantized. If the electrostatic repulsion between the protons is ignored the energies of the neutron and proton states are equal. Then since both neutrons and protons are Fermi particles subject to the Pauli exclusion principle two nucleons of each type, one with spin up, one with spin down, can occupy each level.

energy can assume only a discrete series of values. Thus in analogy with atomic systems (Sections 19.1 to 19.3) we expect to find a series of energy states within the nucleus, each representing a different possible combination of single-nucleon states. The amplitudes for these states as well as their associated energies depend upon the exact nature of the nuclear potential. But their existence is a general property of bound systems.

The ground state of a nucleus is that state in which all nucleons have their minimum possible energies. Following the atomic analogy the single-nucleon states should be distinguished from each other by a series of quantum numbers, perhaps a principal quantum number specifying total energy, certainly an orbital quantum number specifying the angular momentum of the nucleon relative to the rest of the system. In Chapter 18, Section 18.8, we concluded that the energy separation between bound, single particle levels increases as the size of the confining volume decreases. Therefore, nuclear level spacings should be much larger than the spacing between electron levels in atoms. The latter range from a few tenths to a few electron volts, the former from a few tens to a few hundred keV (thousand electron volts).

The emission spectrum of an atom represents a series of transitions from the various atomic states of the atom back to its ground state. Given the spacing between these levels it follows that a large portion of any particular spectrum is in the ultraviolet, visible, and infrared regions. Similarly, if a nucleus absorbs sufficient energy it should be able to make a momentary transition to an excited state, and emit a photon on returning to the ground state (Figure 20.5). Therefore, in principle it should be possible to study the character of nuclear states by measuring nuclear emission spectra. However, nuclear excitations require considerably larger energies than atomic excitations, energies that cannot be supplied with electric discharges but usually require bombardment by a beam of particles from an accelerator. Again, the energies of the photons emitted in transitions between nuclear levels place them in the very short wavelength γ-ray region. It follows that the techniques used for studying nuclear states differ considerably from the atomic case.

We shall pursue the exploration of excited nuclear states in Chapter 21. For the present let us concentrate upon a comparison of the ground state energies of different nuclei. In analogy with the atomic case we call the energy required to separate all the component nucleons from one another the *total* binding energy of the nucleus, and define the *average* binding energy of a nucleon in a particular nucleus (or the binding energy per nucleon) as the ratio of the total binding energy of the system to its nucleon number, A. Now the total disruption of a nucleus into a set of noninteracting nucleons requires the absorption of external energy greater than or equal to its total binding energy. Conversely, the process of assembling a stable nucleus in its ground state from an appropriate set of noninteracting nucleons would yield an energy equal to its binding energy. Hence, the total energy of a collection of nucleons when assembled into a stable nucleus is smaller than when all are completely free. Since special relativity equates rest mass and energy it follows that the total rest mass of a stable nucleus should be smaller than the sum of the

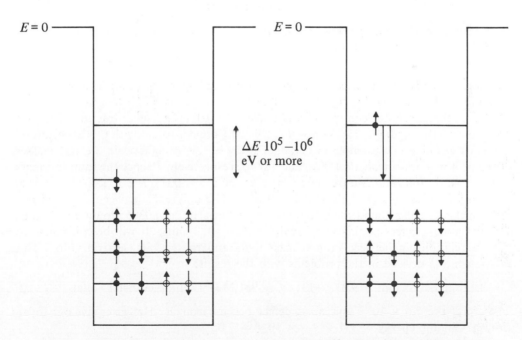

FIGURE 20.5 Two single-proton excitations in $_0C^{12}$. Since the energy level spacing is 10^5 to 10^6 eV or more, the energies of the photons emitted when an excited nucleus returns to its ground state are also on this order and therefore are very short wavelength γ-rays.

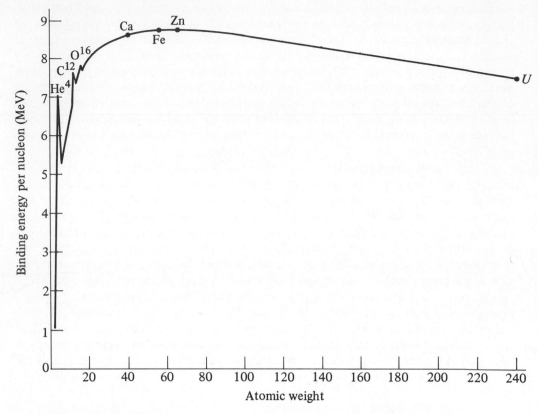

FIGURE 20.6 Binding energy per nucleon for the stable nuclides plotted as a function of atomic weight.

rest masses of its constituent neutrons and protons. In other words, the average mass of a bound nucleon should be slightly less than the average mass of a *free* nucleon. In a very real sense, each nucleon in a bound nucleus contributes a small fraction of its rest mass toward the binding. The entries in Table 20.1 are consistent with this expectation.

Let us examine one example in detail. On the atomic weight scale the rest masses of the proton and neutron are 1.0073 and 1.0087, respectively. Hence the total rest mass of two free protons and two free neutrons must be $2 \times 1.0073 + 2 \times 1.0087 = 4.0320$ whereas the mass of a $_2\text{He}^4$ nucleus is 4.0015.* The difference between the total rest mass in the free and bound states, the *mass defect* of $_2\text{He}^4$, is 0.0305 atomic mass units, yielding a mass defect per nucleon equal to 7.6×10^{-3} units. It will be convenient to have a relationship between atomic mass units and energies in electron volts. This relationship is derived in the problems with the result:

$$1 \text{ atomic mass unit} = 9.31 \times 10^8 \text{ eV} = 931 \text{ MeV (million electron volts)}. \quad (20.2)$$

Therefore, the 7.6×10^{-3} unit mass defect per nucleon in $_2\text{He}^4$ is equivalent to an average binding energy of $931 \times 7.6 \times 10^{-3} = 7.08$ MeV.

---

*The atomic weight of the He⁴ nucleus is obtained from the atomic weight of the corresponding atom listed in Table 20.1 by subtracting the atomic weights of the two planetary electrons. Thus $4.0026 - 2 \times 5.48 \times 10^{-4} = 4.0015$.

Figure 20.6 plots the binding energy per nucleon for the stable nuclei as a function of atomic weight. Except for the very lightest and the very heaviest nuclides, the equivalent average binding energies are roughly 8 MeV/nucleon, although there are definite fluctuations in the graph, especially at $_2He^4$, $_6C^{12}$, and $_8O^{16}$. The approximate constancy of these binding energies over such a broad range of atomic weights once again suggests the short-range nature of the internucleon binding forces. Six times as much force must be applied to lift a one kilogram mass from the earth's than from the moon's surface, for all matter on the earth or the moon interacts gravitationally with that mass. The removal of an electron from a helium atom requires twice as much energy as the removal of the single electron in a hydrogen atom, a reflection of the long-range nature of the electrostatic force. On the other hand, the amount of energy required to melt a sodium chloride crystal is proportional to its mass. Each sodium and each chlorine ion interacts primarily with its nearest neighbors. Hence the total binding energy of the crystal is proportional to the number of ions it contains. If each ion interacted with all others, the total binding energy of the crystal would be roughly proportional to the square of its mass. For similar reasons, the same amount of energy vaporizes an ounce of water in a saucepan or in the ocean: the forces between the water molecules are short-range forces. Since as Figure 20.7 indicates, the energies required to remove a nucleon from $_8O^{16}$ and $_{26}Fe^{56}$ are roughly equal, the internucleon forces are much more like intermolecular and interionic than intra-atomic forces. In fact, as we shall discover in Chapter 21, the analogy turns out to be very fruitful.

The rectangular potential energy wells that we have used to treat nuclear binding are oversimplified in at least one respect: they place neutrons and protons on exactly the

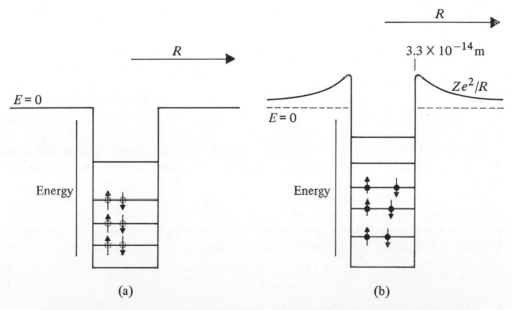

FIGURE 20.7 Improved potential energy wells for (a) the neutrons and (b) the protons in $_6C^{12}$. Because of the electrostatic repulsion among the protons their potential energy outside the well is positive and their energy levels inside the well are higher than the corresponding neutron levels. Both effects increase with atomic weight, i.e., with the number of protons in the nucleus.

same footing. But although there is convincing evidence for concluding that the *nuclear* part of the internucleon force does not distinguish between protons and neutrons, the additional electrostatic force acting between protons cannot be ignored. As a consequence, the binding energy of a proton in a nucleus usually differs from the binding energy of a neutron.

A more satisfactory approximation assumes that a proton in the nucleus is subject to a different total force than a neutron and therefore places the protons and neutrons in separate potential wells, each of them determined by the interactions of a single proton or neutron with all the other nucleons in the system. One of the differences between the two wells manifests itself beyond the short range of the nuclear forces. Since a neutron separated from a nucleus by more than about 10^{-14} m is indifferent to the presence of the nucleus, its potential energy is zero outside of that range (Figure 20.7a). However, a proton experiences an electrostatic repulsion at distances greater than 10^{-14} m. Hence its potential energy is positive and increases inversely as its distance from the nucleus until that distance is on the order of the nuclear force range (Figure 20.7b).

Another significant difference becomes increasingly important for the medium and heavy nuclei. The nuclear part of the interaction has a short range. Consequently, the total *nuclear* part of the potential energy should be proportional to the total number of nucleons, and the depth of the nuclear potential well seen by a nucleon independent of the total nucleon number. In contrast, the electrostatic repulsion between the protons is a long range force so that the total positive electrostatic potential energy of a nucleus varies approximately as the *square* of the number of protons. Therefore, in a nucleus with equal numbers of each type of nucleon a proton has a less negative potential energy than a neutron, with the difference in potential energies for the two particles increasing as the total nucleon number increases. It follows that a nucleus with more neutrons than protons should have a more negative total energy and hence should be more stable than a nucleus with the same total nucleon number but with protons dominating over neutrons.

This argument obviously leaves something out, for it implies that the number of neutrons in any stable nucleus should be completely unrestricted. But as a cursory glance at a list of stable isotopes indicates, only a very limited number of neutron-to-proton ratios is permitted for any given total nucleon number. That ratio is near unity for the light and medium isotopes ($_2\text{He}^4$, $_6\text{C}^{12}$, $_{10}\text{Ne}^{20}$). However, for the medium heavy and heavy nuclei ($_{26}\text{Fe}^{56}$, $_{82}\text{Pb}^{208}$, $_{92}\text{U}^{238}$) it is greater than unity and increases with increasing nucleon number.

What would happen if the neutron-proton balance in a stable nucleus were upset by the addition of one or more neutrons or protons? Would a series of new stable nuclides be formed, or would the original bound system reject the intruders out of hand? As it happens, the composite system frequently follows a middle course. New nuclides can often be formed provided no more than one or two protons are added to a stable nucleus. But these unbalanced systems have too much energy to be completely stable. Instead, they are only quasi-stable, and ultimately transmute themselves into stable species by radioactive decay.

▲▲ 20.4 Radioactive decay. Alpha, beta, and gamma radiation

The nucleus first revealed its existence directly in 1896 when Henri Becquerel noted that some photographic emulsions, wrapped in black paper and stored near some uranium-bearing minerals, had inexplicably been fogged just as if they had been exposed

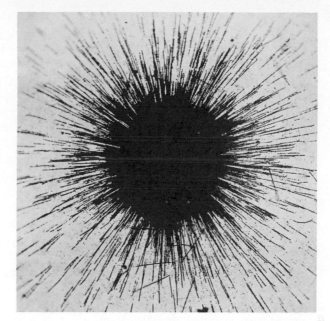

FIGURE 20.8 A specially prepared photographic emulsion fogged by the radioactivity from a nearby radium needle. (From C. F. Powell and G. P. S. Occhialini, *Nuclear Physics in Pictures*, The Clarendon Press, Oxford, 1947.)

to light (Figure 20.8). Upon further investigation he concluded that the atoms of uranium were emitting an unknown type of energetic ray capable of penetrating the opaque container in which the film was stored. Curiously enough, the radiation activity (or *radioactivity*) of uranium seemed to proceed spontaneously and was totally indifferent to external circumstances. Its intensity, as measured by its ability to fog film, depended only upon the amount of uranium, was altered neither by temperature nor pressure, and was unaffected by chemical changes in the uranium bearing compound. Provided the mass of uranium remained constant so did the radiation intensity.

Becquerel's work predated the discovery of the nucleus by more than a decade; hence he and his contemporaries did not know that chemical properties of the elements vest themselves in the outer electron shells of atoms, for none of them *knew* about electron shells. Nevertheless, they realized that radioactivity had no place in the view of the microworld as they conceived it, and could only grope toward a means of revising that conception. Two related avenues of further research suggested themselves: more complete investigations of the source (or sources) of radioactivity, and studies of the nature of the radiation itself.

Pierre and Marie Curie made the most significant early contributions toward understanding the sources of radioactivity. Becquerel's investigations were all carried out with uranium-bearing compounds (such as pitchblende) containing small percentages of the element. However, the residue remaining after chemical extraction of uranium from these minerals is also radioactive, indicating that that residue itself contains radioactive elements. The Curies devoted several years perfecting chemical techniques capable of separating these hypothesized elements from uranium-bearing minerals. Ultimately they succeeded in discovering and extracting two new elements: polonium ($Z = 84$) in 1898, and radium ($Z = 88$) in 1902. Their labors filled two of the gaps in the Periodic Table of the Elements. More significantly they identified two new sources of radioactivity, each having a much higher activity than pure uranium. In particular, the radiation intensity from radium turned out to be over a million times greater than the intensity from a pure uranium sample of the same mass.*

Coincidently with the work initiated by Becquerel and the Curies, a number of other investigators sought an understanding of the radiation itself. Although the radiation from uranium or radium easily penetrates thin paper (as Becquerel discovered), most of it is stopped by heavier materials, one inch of copper or one-half inch of lead, for example. Hence a small aperture in a metal plate collimates the radiation into a narrow, well-defined beam that blackens only a small spot on a photographic emulsion (Figure 20.9a). When the whole apparatus, source, collimator, and film detector, is placed in a magnetic field perpendicular to the beam direction, the single beam splits into three components. Two of the components deviate in opposite directions from the original beam path, the third is completely unaffected. Therefore, one of the three beams must consist of positively charged particles and one of negatively charged particles, whereas the third, undeviated beam is neutral. Early investigators labeled the three components α-rays, β-rays, and γ-rays, respectively.

The three types of radiation differ considerably in their ability to penetrate matter. Typically, α-rays stop in about $\frac{1}{100}$ in. of medium weight metals such as copper and iron. The penetrating ability (or *range*) of β-rays is ten to one hundred times greater, and the range of γ-rays, ten to one hundred times greater yet (Figure 20.9b). An energetic charged particle that penetrates matter interacts electromagnetically with the atoms along its path, transferring sufficient energy to ionize many of them. Approximately ten electron volts are transferred in each encounter, varying with the energy required to ionize the atoms in question. If the material is sufficiently thick, the primary particle makes enough encounters to divest itself of virtually all its kinetic energy and so comes to rest. The penetrating ability or *range* of a charged particle certainly should increase

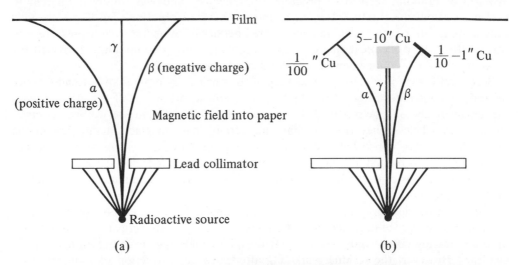

(a)   (b)

FIGURE 20.9 The three radiation components differ in (a) their curvatures in magnetic fields, and (b) their abilities to penetrate matter.

---

* Radium, polonium, and several other radioactive elements are always found in natural uranium-bearing minerals, though in small quantities compared with uranium and the nonradioactive elements of the mineral compound (typically oxygen or one of the halogens). Therefore, the dominance of uranium in naturally occurring minerals masks the more intense radiation per unit mass of elements such as radium.

with its initial energy since the more energy it has the more atoms it must ionize before coming to rest. In addition, we would expect the frequency of ionizing interactions to be proportional to the charge of the primary particle. Hence, given two particles with the same primary energies but different charges, the one with the smaller charge has the greater range.

Normally the range of a heavy particle of a given energy is independent of its mass. Protons and the nuclei of light atoms are all much heavier than electrons, and their ionizing abilities depend primarily upon their energy and their charge. But electrons behave differently. Because the velocity of an electron of a given kinetic energy is much greater than that of a proton with the same energy, the electron spends a much smaller time in the vicinity of each atom along its path, and has a much smaller interaction probability per atom. Consequently its range is also greater. Since electrons with energies greater than 1 MeV have a reasonably high probability of radiating x-rays when they interact with the charged nuclei and electrons (Section 10.4) and since this probability increases with energy, the range of an energetic electron in matter cannot be used to determine its primary energy to the same precision possible with a heavy particle.

How are these conclusions related to α-, β-, and γ-radiation? Since the negatively charged β-particles have a much greater range in matter than the positive α's, they either have much smaller charges or much greater energies. Alternately, the α-particles could be heavy particles, the β's electrons. Since the radiations all emanate from the same source, we might assume that the energies of the three components have roughly the same magnitudes, deferring a definitive test of that assumption for the time being. Then the latter hypothesis is favored, and β-particles tentatively identified as electrons—an identification that turns out to be correct. If so, the α-particles must be heavy charged particles. In fact, they are doubly charged helium ions, or, in modern terminology, $_2$He^4 nuclei. Rutherford devised a means to condense the α-particles emanating from a radioactive source in a glass vessel. When an electric arc was passed through the vessel he observed the emission spectrum of atomic helium. Apparently the stopped particles each clothed themselves with two electrons and became normal helium atoms. Hence he obtained direct proof that α-particles and helium nuclei are identical.

The velocity of a charged particle in a magnetic field of known strength follows from its radius of curvature in the field and its charge to mass ratio (Equation 9.18):

$$v = \frac{q}{M}\,BR.$$

Once the nature of α-particles and β-particles has been determined their velocities, and hence their kinetic energies, were measured by using an apparatus similar to the one shown schematically in Figure 20.9a. The results must have been more than a little shocking to early investigators who had measured binding energies in molecules on the order of a few tenths to a few electron volts. For the energies of the β-particles are a few hundred keV (kilo- or thousand electron volts), while α-particle energies range up to several MeV (million electron volts).

The third radioactive component, the γ-rays, are very energetic photons which lose energy in matter only by Compton scattering with electrons and, to a lesser extent, with nuclei (Section 10.5).* Because that process is considerably less probable than ionization

---

* A photon with energy greater than 1 MeV can also lose 1 MeV by producing an electron-positron pair.

by a charged particle, γ-rays have far greater ranges in matter than α- or β-particles with comparable energy.

The γ-rays emitted in radioactive decay are always monochromatic, although more than one discrete γ-ray energy may characterize a particular decay. In fact, the discrete nature of γ-ray spectra indicate that at least some of the ideas on nuclear energy levels presented in the last section are valid, for these spectra are somewhat analogous to the ultraviolet and optical spectra of atoms. If E_a and E_b are the respective energies of two states in a nucleus ($E_b > E_a$) then if the nucleus makes a transition from state b to a the energy of the emitted γ-ray will be $E_\gamma = E_b - E_a$, suggesting that the study of γ-ray spectra provides a means for determining the energy-level spacing in nuclei (Figure 20.5).

▶▶ 20.5 Alpha decay. The radioactive decay curve. Half-life of a radioactive nuclide

As Rutherford and Soddy first demonstrated in 1903, the decay of a radioactive nucleus is a transmutation reaction. When the nucleus $_{92}U^{238}$ ejects an α-particle it loses two protons and two neutrons, leaving behind a daughter nucleus with $Z = 90$ which, when clothed in its electron complement, has different chemical properties than uranium. Early investigators called that daughter nucleus UX_1. In terms of its modern designation, $_{90}Th^{234}$ (thorium), the decay of $_{92}U^{238}$ is written symbolically as

$$_{92}U^{238} \rightarrow {}_{90}Th^{234} + {}_{2}He^4. \tag{20.3}$$

Because the α-particle is ejected with a 4.18 MeV energy the rest mass of $_{92}U^{238}$ must be greater than the sum of the rest masses of $_{90}Th^{234}$ and $_2He^4$. Relative masses of the $_{92}U^{238}$ and $_2He^4$ atoms are listed in Table 20.1, while that of $_{90}Th^{234}$ is found in more complete listings. To find the masses of the corresponding nuclei, the masses of the planetary electrons must be subtracted from the entries in that table. Thus

$$M(_{92}U^{238}) = 238.0576 - 92M_e,$$
$$M(_{90}Th^{234}) + M(_2He^4) = (234.051 - 90M_e) + (4.0026 - 2M_e)$$
$$= 238.0536 - 92M_e.$$

Then ΔM, the difference between the rest masses in the initial and final states of the reaction, is

$$\Delta M = M(_{92}U^{238}) - M(_{90}Th^{234}) - M(_2He^4) = 0.0046.$$

Since 1 atomic mass unit = 931 MeV (Equation 20.2), the kinetic energy released in the reaction (called the Q value of the reaction) is $931 \times 4.6 \times 10^{-3} = 4.18$ MeV, as observed.

We may regard radioactive decay as an attempt by a system of nucleons to minimize its total energy. Evidently 92 protons and 146 neutrons have less total energy when separated into a noninteracting α-particle and a Th^{234} nucleus than when combined into a single U^{238} nucleus. But in that case why should $_{92}U^{238}$ be even quasi-stable? Why should the system be bound for any time at all?

The absolute stability of a nucleus requires that the total energies of all nucleons (or subgroups of nucleons) must always be less than zero (Section 20.3). However, there is no reason to expect that the energy of *each* nucleon will remain constant. If we conceive of the bound nucleons as being in constant motion within the nuclear volume, constantly interchanging their energies with each other, a model somewhat analogous to a liquid drop emerges. In the latter instance the molecules are in continual interaction with one another, but not yet frozen into a rigid pattern characterizing a solid. Individual molecules thus have considerable freedom, though they are constrained by their fellows from escaping the system. Hence, each molecule is in a potential energy well created by its interactions with the other molecules, and normally has insufficient kinetic energy to leave that well. But an occasional collision may give one molecule the energy required for escape. Then it evaporates, and, having taken away more than its average energy, leaves the molecules that remain with less average energy than before.

If nuclei were like water droplets, we would occasionally observe neutron evaporation (or neutron radioactivity) from say $_8O^{17}$ leaving behind $_8O^{16}$ (or proton evaporation yielding $_7N^{16}$). But apparently the character of the internucleon binding is more subtle, for such processes are never observed. The mass of an $_8O^{17}$ nucleus is $16.9991 - 17M_e$ (Table 20.1), while the total mass of an $_8O^{16}$ nucleus plus a free neutron is $(15.9949 - 16M_e) + 1.0087 = 17.0036 - 16M_e$. Hence the decay cannot occur from the ground state of $_8O^{17}$. There simply is insufficient energy available in the nucleus.

The evaporation model suggests how an α-particle decay might proceed, and also indicates why such a decay is so improbable. In the course of their continual interactions, bound groups of nucleons within a nucleus may form occasional very short-lived subgroups, most of which break up again very rapidly. Because there is a statistical energy distribution among the molecules in a drop of water a few receive anomalously large shares of total energy and are able to evaporate. Apparently the same sort of process occurs once in a while in α-unstable nuclei: a normally short-lived, bound two-proton, two-neutron cluster receives enough energy from the rest of the system to "evaporate."

Unfortunately, there are difficulties with this semiclassical evaporation model which can be understood by considering the energy required to induce the inverse of the α-decay reaction, capture of an α-particle by $_{90}Th^{234}$:

$$_2He^4 + {}_{90}Th^{234} \rightarrow {}_{92}U^{238}.$$

Because the α-particle expelled from a $_{92}U^{238}$ nucleus has 4.18 MeV kinetic energy, a 4.18 MeV α-particle incident upon a $_{90}Th^{234}$ nucleus should occasionally be captured by that nucleus to form $_{92}U^{238}$ in its ground state. If the nucleons of the α-particle are to bind themselves to the thorium nucleons they must approach within the range of the short-range nuclear forces. But until the α-particle approaches within that distance, the interaction between the charges of its two protons and the ninety protons of the thorium nucleus creates a repulsive, electrostatic potential barrier (Section 20.3). Calculations indicate that the energy required for an α-particle to surmount that barrier is considerably greater than 4.18 MeV. It follows that a particle with 4.18 MeV kinetic energy could never get into the nucleus. By the same token, a particle inside the nucleus could never get out if its energy were 4.18 MeV (Figure 20.10).

Classically, then, the α-decay of uranium can never occur. But from a quantum mechanical point of view a particle has a small but nonzero probability of *penetrating* a potential energy barrier (Section 18.9), which, according to Equation 18.30, decreases exponentially with the barrier width:

$$\frac{P(2)}{P(1)} = \exp\left(-2p_n \, \Delta X\right). \tag{18.30}$$

Thus the product of two statistical factors determines the α-decay probability for a particular nucleus: the probability that a particular subgroup can form within the nucleus,

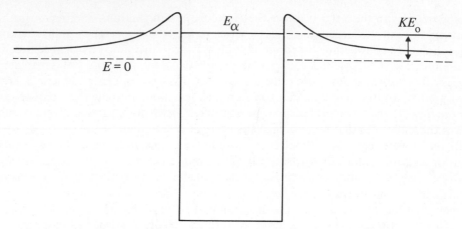

FIGURE 20.10   Barrier penetration and α-decay. Classically, an α-particle with the observed decay kinetic energy, KE_0, far from the residual nucleus would be unable to penetrate its repulsive electrostatic barrier and interact with the nucleons in the attractive well. Likewise, an α-particle with the same total energy inside the well could never escape. Thus α-decay offers a prime example of barrier penetration.

and the probability that the subgroup, once formed, can penetrate the potential barrier and appear outside the nucleus. Because that product is very small for nuclei such as U^{238} and Ra^{222} these species are virtually stable. In addition, since the penetration probability is such a sensitive function of barrier width, the total decay probability is expected to vary considerably among different nuclear species.

Of course the rest mass of a potential α-emitter must be greater than the sum of the rest masses of its potential daughter nucleus and $_2He^4$. Otherwise the decay would be energetically forbidden. All but two or three of the α-emitting nuclides have masses greater than 208 (lead), suggesting that the short-range nuclear forces are insufficient to bind more than about 200 nucleons into completely stable systems.

Although we know the probability of throwing a five on a die is one-sixth, we cannot predict which throw (if any) will yield a five. Similarly, even if we know the α-decay probability for a particular nucleus, we have no information about when (if ever) it will decay. But even as we have good reason to believe that if many dice are thrown about one-sixth will yield fives, so knowledge of the α-decay probability for uranium allows us to calculate the *fraction* of the nuclei in a large group that will decay during a particular time interval. That is, we can predict the number that will decay but cannot place labels in advance upon the individuals that later suffer that fate. To do so would imply some measurable difference between the members of the group of nuclei, and suggest that the nuclei were distinguishable.

Whatever the detailed decay mechanism, it is reasonable to assume that the number of nuclei in a sample that decay in any given time interval Δt is proportional to the number present at the beginning of the interval, even as we expect the number of fives that come up in many throws of a die to be proportional to the number of trials. If N radioactive nuclei are present in a sample at the beginning of an interval Δt, then ΔN, the loss in that number resulting from decay, is proportional both to N, the number available for decay, and to Δt, the time over which their decay is measured. That is,

$$\Delta N = -\lambda N \, \Delta t, \tag{20.4a}$$

where λ the constant of proportionality (called the decay constant of the nucleus) is related to the α-decay probability of the nucleus. Conversely, a measurement of λ provides information on the decay probability and hence on the characteristics of the original, undecayed nucleus.

For the reasons discussed previously, λ varies considerably among the various unstable nuclear species. As we noted in Section 20.4 the intensity of radiation from a given sample of radium is about one million times greater than the intensity from an equal number of uranium atoms. In other words, a million times as many radium atoms decay in a given time interval, indicating that the decay constant (λ) for radium must be a million times greater than the decay constant for uranium. Consequently the ratio of the relative probabilities of α-decay for the two nuclides must be a million to one.

The decay probability for a nuclear species is frequently specified in terms of its *half-life*, defined as the length of time required for one-half the nuclei in a sample to decay. If at some arbitrary time we have N nuclei then, by definition, only $N_0/2$ remain after one half-life. After another half-life one-half of these will have decayed so that only one-fourth of the original sample remain. In general, after n half-lives $(\frac{1}{2})^n$ of the original N_0 nuclei will *not* have decayed. A particular nuclear species with a short half-life has a correspondingly large decay probability, implying a higher radiation intensity from a sample of its atoms than from an equal number of atoms of a species with a longer half-life. Nuclear half-lives cover an enormous range—from milliseconds (10^{-3} sec) for many artificially produced β-active nuclei (Section 20.6) up to 4.5 billion years for $_{92}U^{238}$. The half-life of radium is 1620 years, less than a millionth the half-life of uranium, in agreement with the previously noted ratio of the radiation intensities from the two nuclei.

We may regard the passage of a nucleon across a nucleus as a measure of the nuclear time scale. Uranium nuclei have diameters on the order of 10^{-14} m (Equation 20.1) and a nucleon with a few MeV kinetic energy travels with about one-tenth the speed of light. Hence we have $\Delta t \sim 10^{-14}/(3 \times 10^7)$, or roughly 3×10^{-22} sec. In other words, a nucleon can make more than 10^{21} round trips across a nucleus per second, and presumably makes roughly the same number of collisions in that time. Yet short α-decay half-lives are measured in milliseconds, while the half-life of U^{238} is 4.5 billion years! Generalizing a remark made by Rutherford in reference to β-decay, we conclude that from the point of view of the nucleus radioactive decay hardly ever happens! In other words, we have a right to regard radioactive nuclei as almost-stable species.

An expression giving the number of radioactive nuclei that decay within any given time interval may be derived from Equation 20.4a.* The remainder of this section may be ommitted without serious loss of continuity. Dividing both sides of the equation by Δt then allowing the interval Δt to approach zero we obtain a differential equation relating the rate of change of N with time to N itself (see Appendix to Chapter 2):

$$\lim_{\Delta t \to 0} \frac{\Delta N}{\Delta t} = \frac{dN}{dt} = -\lambda N.$$

This relation gives a prescription for finding N, the number of atoms remaining in a given sample, as a function of time. We try a solution of the form

$$N = C \exp(-\lambda t). \tag{20.4b}$$

The first derivative of this function with respect to time (Equation 18.25a) is

$$\frac{dN}{dt} = -\lambda C \exp(-\lambda t),$$

---

* The remainder of this section may be omttted without serious less of continuity.

which when substituted into the differential equation gives

$$-\lambda C \exp(-\lambda t) = -\lambda C \exp(-\lambda t),$$

showing that the assumed form (Equation 20.4b) is indeed a valid solution.

In order to evaluate the constant C we note (see Appendix C to text) that at $t = 0$, $\exp(-\lambda t) = 1$ so that $N(0) = N_0$, the number of atoms in a sample present at time $t=0$ when measurements begin. Substitution into Equation 20.4b yields the final equation for the number of atoms remaining at a time t after measurements begin:

$$N = N_0 \exp(-\lambda t). \tag{20.4c}$$

By definition one-half the atoms remain after one half-life, T:

$$\frac{N}{N_0} = \exp(-\lambda T) = \frac{1}{2}.$$

This relation may be solved for λ in terms of the half-life T:

$$\lambda = \frac{0.693}{T},$$

which, substituted into Equation 20.4d, gives N in terms of the measured half-life of a species:

$$N = N_0 \exp\left[-\frac{0.693t}{T}\right]. \tag{20.4e}$$

Curves plotting the ratio N/N_0 against T are shown in Figure 20.11.

◣◣ 20.6 Induced transmutations. Discovery of the proton and neutron

Until the discovery of the neutron in 1932, nuclei could not be regarded with certainty as composite systems of interacting nucleons. Yet even before 1921, when protons were

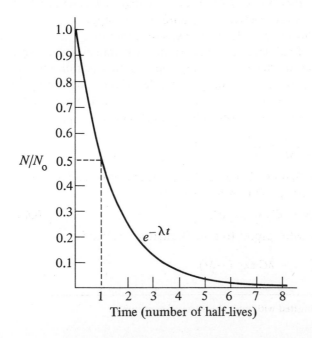

FIGURE 20.11 Decay curve giving the fraction of the radioactive atoms remaining in a sample with half-life T ($T = 0.693/\lambda$) after a time t measured in half-lives.

first identified as universal constituents of all nuclei, the observed instability of the very heavy species suggested that these, at least, were complex systems rather than fundamental particles. Both $_{92}U^{238}$ and $_{88}Ra^{226}$ decay by α-emission, which strongly implies that α-particles either exist (or can exist) as units within both species. A rather fascinating question arises at this juncture. The α-decay of $_{92}U^{238}$ into $_{90}Th^{234}$ is a transmutation reaction, the creation of an element by the destruction of another. However, the transmutation occurs spontaneously. No external intervention has any effect whatever upon it. But if nuclei are really complex systems with similar constituents, why shouldn't it be possible to *induce* transmutations.

Consider, for example, the possibility of inverting the U^{238} decay reaction by bombarding a sample of $_{90}Th^{234}$ with α-particles. The capture of an α-particle by one of the nuclei in the sample, leading to the formation of $_{92}U^{238}$, would constitute an induced transmutation reaction:

$$_2He^4 + {_{90}}Th^{234} \rightarrow {_{92}}U^{238}$$

Because of the mass difference involved, the decay of $_{92}U^{238}$ yields a 4.18 MeV α-particle (Section 20.5). Hence the α-particles incident upon $_{90}Th^{234}$ must have at least that energy, otherwise the inverse process will be energetically forbidden. If this condition is satisfied, we have every reason to believe that α-capture by $_{90}Th^{234}$ will be permitted by nature. The decay reaction involves $_{92}U^{238}$ in the initial state, $_{90}Th^{234}$ and a 4.18 MeV α-particle in the final state. These states are simply interchanged in the capture reaction. In the language of Section 6.8, the two reactions are connected by a time-reversal operation, and we believe that the fundamental laws of physics remain invariant with respect to that symmetry.

However, the experimental observation of α-capture by $_{90}Th^{234}$ presents a number of formidable technical difficulties, as we might have anticipated from the fact that the spontaneous decay of $_{90}U^{238}$ is so very improbable. If the capture reaction leads to $_{92}U^{238}$ in its ground state the kinetic energy of the incident α-particle should be 4.18 MeV. But the barrier penetration probability of an α-particle with that energy is exceedingly small. On the other hand a particle with sufficient energy to surmount the barrier carries much more energy than required, and may well pass through the thorium nucleus without entering into any significant interactions. Even if the α-particle is captured, the resultant $_{92}U^{238}$ nucleus if left in a highly excited state. It may emit its excess energy in the form of γ-rays and make the transition to its ground state. On the other hand, it may also break up in a more drastic fashion.

Other conceivable α-capture reactions should be more readily observable, for instance the reaction

$$_2He^4 + {_8}O^{16} \rightarrow {_{10}}Ne^{20}.$$

Since oxygen has eight units of positive charge, it presents a much lower barrier than thorium, and thus permits α-particles with lower energies to penetrate within the range of the intranuclear forces. Observation of the capture reaction is also more feasible technically simply because it is easier to obtain a suitable sample of oxygen for bombardment than rare, β-active $_{90}Th^{234}$. In addition α-capture on oxygen is really more interesting since the process is not the inverse of a decay reaction. Consulting a table of isotopic masses (Table 20.1),

$$M(_2He^4) + M(_8O^{16}) = (15.9949 - 8M_e) + (4.0036 - 2M_e) = 19.9975 - 10M_e,$$
$$M(_{10}Ne^{20}) = 19.9924 - 10M_e.$$

Hence $\Delta M = M(_2He^4) + M(_8O^{16}) - M(_{10}Ne^{20}) = 0.0051$, and $Q = 931\ \Delta M = -4.5$ MeV. Since $_{10}Ne^{20}$ has a smaller mass than $_8O^{16} + _2He^4$ it must be stable against α-decay, as observed. Conversely, the capture of an α-particle, with incident kinetic energy $(KE)_0$ by an $_8O^{16}$ nucleus should yield $_{10}Ne^{20}$ with excess energy equal to $(KE)_0 + 4.5$ MeV.

Is it possible to go one step further and use α-capture reactions to create nuclear species that are *not* found in nature? For example, α-capture by $_7N^{14}$ would yield a nucleus with nine units of positive charge and atomic number eighteen, $_9F^{18}$, a species that does not occur naturally. ($_9F^{19}$ is the sole stable fluorine nuclide.) The experiment might be performed by placing a radium source in a container of nitrogen. Most of the α-particles emitted would simply ionize a few nitrogen atoms and come to rest in the walls of the cylinder. Others would be scattered by the electrostatic force of the nitrogen nuclei (Section 15.6). But a few might penetrate within 10^{-14} m of these nuclei, and be captured to form $_9F^{18}$. That is,

$$_2He^4 + _7N^{14} \rightarrow _9F^{18}.$$

After a time, say a day or so, we would remove the radium source, and perform a chemical analysis in an attempt to find traces of fluorine mixed with the nitrogen.

Our efforts would be doomed to failure, for even quasi-stable $_9F^{18}$ cannot be fabricated by α-capture or any other method. For reasons that must hinge upon the detailed nature of the internucleon forces, nine protons and nine neutrons simply cannot form a bound stable system. However, a suitable chemical analysis of the α-bombarded nitrogen would reveal a trace of oxygen, indicating that the α-particles induce some other type of nuclear reaction even though they are not simply captured by the nitrogen nuclei.

This particular reaction actually has considerable historical importance, as the bombardment of $_7N^{14}$ by α-particles by Rutherford and his colleagues in 1921 led to their observation of the first induced transmutation and to experimental proof that protons are a constituent of $_7N^{14}$, and, by implication, of all nuclei.

A number of the transmutation reaction experiments performed by Rutherford and his colleagues made use of a Wilson cloud chamber, a device which encourages the formation of liquid droplets along the ion trail left behind by an energetic charged particle that passes through the chamber. Figure 20.12a shows the tracks of α-particles from radium sources located just outside and to the left of a cloud chamber containing nitrogen gas. A few of the tracks bend quite sharply, suggesting elastic scattering of an α-particle from a nitrogen nucleus (Section 15.6). A different type of event is seen in the right center of the chamber, where a track bends downward then stops, and a much lighter track goes off toward the top (see detail in Figure 20.12b).

The thickness of a cloud chamber track is proportional to the ionization left by the energetic particle. Hence the light track in Figure 20.12b was probably formed by a particle with a smaller charge than that of the incident α, by inference, one unit of charge. Presumably the α-particle is stopped by a $_7N^{14}$ nucleus, and a lighter, singly charged particle emerges from the encounter. (The short, heavy track emerging from the interaction is due to a recoiling $_8O^{17}$ nucleus. See below.) The curvature of the light track in a magnetic field could be used to show that the charge of the emerging particle is positive and also to give its charge-to-mass ratio as a function of its velocity (Equation 9.18). The particle's range in matter provides another relation between its mass, velocity, and charge (Section 20.4). Together, these data show that the mass of the emergent particle is close to unity on the C^{12} mass scale. More careful measurements

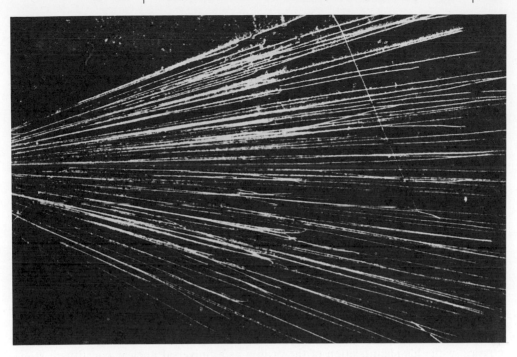

(a)

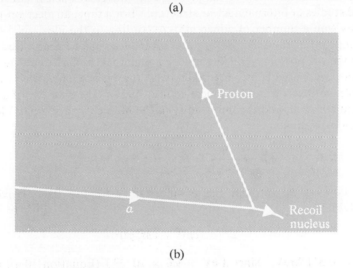

(b)

FIGURE 20.12 (a) The transmutation reaction $\alpha + {}_7N^{14} \rightarrow {}_8O^{17} + p$ in a Wilson cloud chamber. Alpha particles enter from the left, and the event of interest occurs near the right center of the chamber. (b) Sketch of the reaction. Both the outgoing proton and residual oxygen tracks are visible. [From P. M. S. Blackett and D. S. Lees, *Proc. Ray. Soc.*, London (A), Vol. 136, p. 325 (1932).]

(using a mass spectrometer as in Section 20.2) show that its mass is identical with that of the hydrogen nucleus.

Thus hydrogen nuclei can be ejected from ${}_7N^{14}$ when the latter are bombarded with α-particles. By inference, they are constituents of these nuclei, and thus elementary particles that deserve a special name—protons. Since an α-particle carries two positive charges into its reaction with a $_7N^{14}$ nucleus and a proton carries off only one, the residual nucleus must be an oxygen isotope with eight units of charge. Further, since three extra nucleons are left behind in the reaction, that nucleus must be $_8O^{17}$ whose short track is also visible in Figure 20.12a. Therefore, the reaction shown in Figure 20.12a was

$$_2He^4 + {_7N^{14}} \rightarrow {_8O^{17}} + {_1H^1}.$$

Let us apply the relativisitic mass-energy relation to this reaction. From Table 20.1 we calculate

$$M(_2He^4) + M(_7N^{14}) = (4.0026 - 2M_e) + (14.0031 - 7M_e) = 18.0057 - 9M_e,$$
$$M(_1H^1) + M(_8O^{17}) = (1.0078 - M_e) + (16.9991 - 8M_e) = 18.0069 - 9M_e,$$
$$\Delta M = -0.0012.$$

Since the total rest mass of the final state is greater than the mass of the initial state, the reaction cannot proceed unless an α-particle is incident with an energy greater than or equal to $931 \times 0.0012 = 1.1$ MeV. That is, the reaction is endothermic (energy absorbing) with a threshold energy of 1.1 MeV, and the relative kinetic energies of the particles in the final state are 1.1 MeV smaller than the relative initial state energies.

Rutherford's transmutation experiment opened a new field of investigation in nuclear physics, while his identification of the proton as a universal nuclear constituent stimulated detailed studies of internal nuclear structure. For a time, an electron-proton model of the nucleus won a number of adherents. According to the idea, $_7N^{14}$ (for instance) would be composed of fourteen protons and seven electrons to neutralize the charge on an equal number of protons. But the model was untenable for several reasons, one of the most important being its incompatibility with the Heisenberg uncertainty principle. (That principle, however, was not enunciated until 1926.) The diameter of a $_7N^{14}$ nucleus is smaller than 10^{-14} m, and the uncertainty in the momentum of a particle confined to those dimensions is thus:

$$\Delta p = \frac{h}{10^{-14}} = 6 \times 10^{-20} \text{ kg-m/sec.}$$

In order to convert Δp into an energy uncertainty we use the relativistic relation (Equation 11.25a):

$$E^2 = (cp)^2 + (M_0c^2)^2,$$

where $M_0c^2 = 0.511$ MeV. Since 1 eV $= 1.6 \times 10^{-19}$ J (Equation 10.4), the *minimum* possible energy of the bound electron (corresponding to the *minimum* possible momentum 6×10^{-20} kg-m/sec) would be

$$E = \sqrt{\frac{(2 \times 10^8 \times 6 \times 10^{-20})^2}{(1.6 \times 10^{-19})^2} + (0.511 \times 10^6)^2}$$

$$= \sqrt{(1.26 \times 10^8)^2 + (0.511 \times 10^6)^2}$$
$$\cong 126 \text{ MeV.}$$

But we know that nuclear binding energies are on the order of 8 MeV (Section 20.3). Thus the probability of confining an electron to a nuclear volume is very small.

During the late 1920's the conviction that nuclei must contain neutral particles as well as protons became increasingly, though by no means universally, persuasive. James Chadwick's discovery of the neutron in 1932 marked the culmination of a long series of careful experiments designed toward that end. One of the key experiments could be repeated using a cloud chamber as detector. If α-particles are incident upon a thin foil of $_4Be^9$ placed in the chamber, many scatter, as expected. Occasionally, an α-track will not reemerge from the foil. In fact, no track emerges at all. But further along in the chamber, often after a considerable gap, a proton track appears (Figure 20.13). Presumably the reaction $_2He^4 + {_4Be^9}$ yields a neutral particle which does not ionize and hence leaves no track, but later transfers all or part of its energy to a proton in the hydrogen of the chamber.

Chadwick's original experiments used nonvisual methods rather than a cloud chamber to detect the protons (Section 21.3). However, he arrived at the same experimental conclusion: namely than an α-particle can react with a $_4Be^9$ nucleus to yield a neutral particle.

Photons were the only neutral particles known in 1932. If Chadwick's neutral particle had been an γ-ray photon, that photon could have Compton scattered from a proton in his detector, even as x-ray photons scatter from atomic electrons (Section 10.5). Assuming this interpretation of the cloud chamber event of Figure 20.13 is correct, the measured energy and scattering angle of the proton gives the primary photon energy (Equation 10.5), which in Chadwick's experiment would have been more than ten times greater than the energy of any photon that had been observed until that time.

Another possible interpretation involved the production of a *neutron* in the reaction. When two equal mass billiard balls collide head on, the moving one stops, transferring all its momentum to the one initially at rest (Figure 4.2). In glancing collisions the incident ball shares its momentum and the two scatter at some angle relative to the incident direction. Assuming a neutron and proton have equal mass, the distribution of proton energies observed in many events of the type shown in Figure 20.13 should range from zero up to the incident neutron energy. The neutron energies so obtained are reasonable for the reaction, and hence the neutron hypothesis tenable.

Later experiments demonstrated the uniqueness of the neutron hypothesis, and also showed that is mass is slightly greater than the proton mass. The identity of the residual

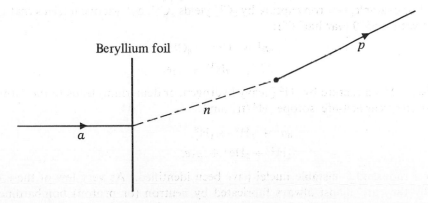

FIGURE 20.13 Neutron production in a Wilson cloud chamber. An α-particle track enters from the left and terminates in a beryllium foil. Further upstream a proton track appears, suggesting that a neutral particle emerged from the foil, followed the dotted line, and transferred all or part of its energy to the proton.

nucleus produced in Chadwick's neutron production reaction is obtained by balancing charge and nucleon number:

$$_2\text{He}^4 + {}_4\text{Be}^9 \rightarrow {}_6\text{C}^{12} + {}_0n^1.$$

▲▲ 20.7 Beta decay and the neutrino

Nucleons, like α-particles, induce nuclear reactions when they interact with the nuclei in suitably prepared targets. Protons interact electrostatically with nuclei long before they approach within distances sufficiently small to be subject to the short-range, attractive, intranuclear forces. Therefore, a proton incident upon a target has small probability of penetrating a nucleus unless its energy is high enough to surmount the electrostatic barrier presented by that nucleus. When such a proton enters a nucleus it brings far more energy than is required to form a new bound system in its ground state. As a result, the excited, compound system often breaks up immediately (Section 21.1).

Since neutrons have no charge they do not interact at all until within the range of the nuclear forces, and can therefore be captured by nuclei even if they have very small incident kinetic energies. The bound systems formed by slow neutron capture have less excess energy than the corresponding systems formed by proton capture. Hence they have much higher probabilities of divesting themselves of that energy by γ-emission rather than by a more drastic sort of breakup.

In the wake of Chadwick's discovery of the neutron Enrico Fermi devised a method for producing very slow neutrons, and used these to induce a series of neutron-capture reactions. A radium source embedded in a beryllium sheath produces fast neutrons by means of the reaction

$$_2\text{He}^4 + {}_4\text{Be}^9 \rightarrow {}_6\text{C}^{12} + {}_0n^1.$$

When the radium-beryllium complex is immersed in water, the emerging fast neutrons can make repeated "billiard-ball" collisions with protons in the water molecules and gradually lose most of their energies. If they make enough collisions they actually attain the same statistical energy distribution as the molecules and emerge from the water bath with fractional electron-volt energies.

Some of the isotopes formed by neutron capture are completely stable; others are radioactive β-emitters that decay with half-lives ranging from 10^{-3} sec to several thousand years. For example, neutron capture by $_6\text{C}^{13}$ yields $_6\text{C}^{14}$, a β^--active nucleus that decays to $_7\text{N}^{14}$ with a 5570 year half-life:

$$_0n^1 + {}_6\text{C}^{13} \rightarrow {}_6\text{C}^{14},$$
$$_6\text{C}^{14} \rightarrow {}_7\text{N}^{14} + {}_{-1}e.$$

Likewise, neutron capture by $_1\text{H}^2$ (heavy hydrogen, or deuterium) leads to the formation of the twelve-year half-life isotope $_1\text{H}^3$ (tritium):

$$_0n^1 + {}_1\text{H}^2 \rightarrow {}_1\text{H}^3,$$
$$_1\text{H}^3 \rightarrow {}_2\text{He}^3 + {}_{-1}e.$$

Over a thousand β-unstable nuclei have been identified. As very few of these occur naturally they are almost always fabricated by neutron (or proton) bombardment of suitably prepared targets, and for that reason are usually called artificial isotopes. Data on a few are given in Table 20.2.

At first sight the expulsion of an electron by a nucleus may appear to be a less drastic change than the expulsion of a much more massive α-particle. But actually β-decay must be regarded as the more fundamental process. Since electrons cannot be confined to volumes the size of nuclei (Section 20.6) it is necessary to assume that they are *created* at the moment of their expulsion by a mechanism that also converts a neutron into a proton. We now understand that mechanism as a manifestation of the *weak interaction*, the fourth of the basic interactions in nature (along with the strong, electromagnetic, and gravitational interactions).

TABLE 20.2   *Data on a Few Selected β-Emitters*

Decaying Nuclide	Daughter Nuclide	Type of Decay	Maximum Kinetic Energy of β (MeV)	Half-Life
$_0n^1$	$_1H^1$	β^-	0.778	12 min
$_1H^3$	$_2He^3$	β^-	0.018	12.4 yr
$_6C^{14}$	$_7N^{14}$	β^-	0.1567	5570 yr
$_{11}Na^{22}$	$_{10}Ne^{22}$	β^+	0.544	2.6 yr
$_{15}P^{34}$	$_{16}S^{34}$	β^-	5.100	12.4 sec
$_{26}Fe^{53}$	$_{25}Mn^{53}$	β^+	2.840	8.9 min
$_{27}Co^{60}$	$_{28}Ni^{60}$	β^-	0.314	27 yr
$_{55}Cs^{137}$	$_{56}Ba^{137}$	β^-	0.519	30 yr

Whatever detailed mechanism may be involved, the β-decay process leaves a daughter nucleus with positive charge one unit larger than its parent and rest mass smaller by at least the electron rest mass. Hence a nucleus is unstable against β-decay if its mass is greater than or equal to the sum of the rest masses of its potential daughter and a free electron. We may write the general decay reaction as:

$$_zX^A \rightarrow \,_{z+1}Y^A + \,_{-1}e. \tag{20.5a}$$

Provided $Q = 931 \, \Delta M = 931[M(X) - M(Y)]$ is greater than the electron rest energy, $M_0c^2 = 0.511$ MeV, then X can decay via Equation 20.5a.

For instance, let us examine the mass-energy balance in the β-decay of $_6C^{14}$:

$$_6C^{14} \rightarrow \,_7N^{14} + \,_{-1}e.$$

Since $M(_6C^{14}) = 14.0033 - 6M_e$ and $M(_7N^{14}) = 14.0031 - 7M_e$ we have $\Delta M = 0.0002 + M_e \cong 0.0007$ so that the decay yields a total energy of $0.0007 \times 931 = 0.652$ MeV. The rest energy of the electron is 0.511 MeV. Therefore, we expect all electrons emerging from the β-decay of a group of $_6C^{14}$ nuclei to have kinetic energies of 0.141 MeV (141 keV).* Instead, the measured electron energies range from zero up to the maximum kinetic energy permitted by energy conservation.

Again, a free neutron decays with an eighteen minute half-life into a free proton and an electron:

$$n \rightarrow p + e.$$

Applying mass-energy conservation to the decay reaction (see Table 20.1),

$$\Delta M = 1.0087 - 1.0073 = 0.0014,$$
$$Q = 931 \times 0.0014 = 1.303,$$
$$KE = 1.303 - 0.511 = 0.792 \text{ MeV}.$$

However, the measured kinetic energy of the electrons from neutron β-decay range from zero up to this maximum.*

When results such as these were first reported in the early 1930's they created considerable consternation in the ranks of nuclear physicists, for they seemed to indicate a breakdown in the long-established energy conservation principle. If an electron emerges from β-decay with less energy than prescribed by the conservation principle, then what becomes of the remaining energy?

As there is no classical precedent capable of describing the conversion of a neutron into a proton, it is conceivable that the energy conservation principle might fail. On the other hand, the principle is known to be applicable to such nonclassical problems as molecular binding and α-decay. Rather than accept the demise of energy conservation, Wolfgang Pauli suggested that a second, neutral particle is also created in the conversion of a neutron to a proton, and carries off the extra, undetected energy in the β-decay reaction. The following year (1934) Enrico Fermi took up Pauli's suggestion and incorporated it into a theory of the β-decay interaction, naming the new particle *neutrino*, "little neutral one." If β-decay involves the creation and expulsion of a neutrino (ν^0) as well as an electron, the general equation for the reaction (Equation 20.5a) must be modified:†

$$_{z}X^{A} \rightarrow _{z+1}Y^{A} + _{-1}e^{0} + _{0}\nu^{0}. \tag{20.5b}$$

Then the explicit $_{6}C^{14}$ decay reaction becomes

$$_{6}C^{14} \rightarrow _{7}N^{14} = _{-1}e^{0} + _{0}\nu^{0},$$

and the free-neutron decay reaction,

$$_{0}n^{1} \rightarrow _{1}p^{1} + _{-1}e^{0} + _{0}\nu^{0}.$$

The energy made available by the mass decrease $\Delta M = M(C^{14}) - M(N^{14})$ will be divided between the two particles created in the reaction. Given many decays, all possible divisions should be observed. In one type of extreme case the electron is created at rest and the neutrino takes all of the additional kinetic energy the electron would be expected to have if there were no competition from the neutrino. In the other extreme case the neutrino receives only its rest energy, leaving the remainder to the electron. Therefore, the rest energy of the neutrino must be the difference between the available energy in any particular β-decay reaction (931 ΔM MeV) and the maximum measured energy of the electron. Because electron energies range from 0.511 MeV (the electron rest energy) up to the maximum 931 ΔM available (Figure 20.14), the rest mass of the neutrino is zero within the experimental uncertainty of the measured energy spectra!

As we have already noted in dealing with photons (Chapter 11), special relativity easily accommodates the zero rest mass concept by merging mass (or inertia) and energy. We regard the total energy of an entity as the sum of its rest energy ($M_{0}c^{2}$) and its kinetic energy. Hence the energy of a zero rest mass particle must be completely kinetic. Combining the relation between the dynamic and rest masses of a particle traveling with velocity c (Equation 11.19),

---

* The measured maximum kinetic energies listed in Table 20.2 would have been obtained in these calculations had mass values been used that were correct to a greater number of decimal places.
† Actually negative (electron) β-decay involves an antineutrino ($\bar{\nu}_{0}$) rather than a neutrino, while positive β-decay (positron decay—Section 20.8) is accompanied by the neutrino. These distinctions are clarified in Chapter 22. Until then we refer to both particles by the generic name *neutrino*.

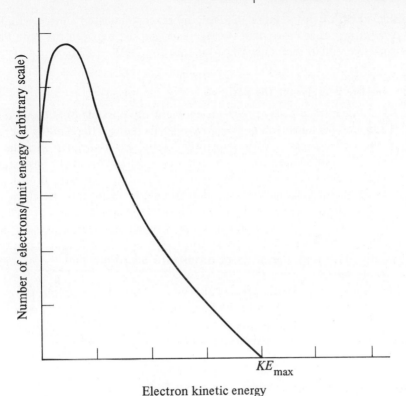

FIGURE 20.14 A typical β-decay spectrum showing the number of emerging electrons as a function of energy.

$$M = \frac{M_0}{\sqrt{1 - v^2/c^2}},$$

with the relativistic mass-energy equation (Equation 11.23a),

$$E = Mc^2,$$

we have

$$E = \frac{M_0 c^2}{\sqrt{1 - v^2/c^2}}.$$

Therefore, the total energy of a zero rest-mass particle vanishes unless the denominator as well as the numerator of the expression for total energy is zero. But $1 - v^2/c^2 = 0$ only if $v = c$. Therefore, we conclude that zero rest mass particles, whether neutrinos, photons, or any other variety, always travel with the velocity of light.

Neutrinos and photons have very little in common besides their zero rest mass and their common, constant velocities. The probability that a neutrino (or anti-neutrino) once created will interact with matter is infinitesimal. Whereas a 100 keV photon has about a 50% probability of being totally absorbed in one-half inch of lead, a neutrino of comparable energy has but 10% probability of being absorbed in passing through the entire volume of the earth! Therefore, it is not difficult to understand why the neutrinos produced in β-decay make no impression at all upon an electron detector, whether a photographic emulsion or a more modern, more sophisticated device. In fact, the neutrino is so elusive that more than twenty years elapsed between the time Pauli suggested its existence, and its direct identification (Section 22.11).

▲▲ 20.8 Positive beta decay. The positron

As has been noted, the β-decay process is energetically possible only because the substitution of a proton for a neutron in a β-active nucleus reduces the binding energy of the system and hence its rest mass. Very frequently β-activity is associated with the neutron imbalance mentioned in Section 20.3. For example, both $_6C^{12}$ and $_6C^{13}$ are stable even though the latter species has one more neutron than proton. An extra proton added to $_6C^{13}$ leads to $_7N^{14}$, for it equalizes the neutron-proton ratio and therefore becomes tightly bound into the composite system. In contrast, the addition of a neutron to $_6C^{13}$ increases the neutron excess further and is accepted reluctantly, yielding $_6C^{14}$. Since the neutron has a greater mass than the proton, this latter, unbalanced system can reduce its total energy by converting one of its neutrons into a proton, that is, by undergoing β-decay to stable $_7N^{14}$.

A nucleus with a proton imbalance may also be unstable. For example, the capture of a proton by stable $_{10}Ne^{20}$ can lead to the formation of $_{11}Na^{21}$, a species whose binding energy is more than 0.511 MeV greater than $_{10}Ne^{21}$ and which decays into $_{10}Ne^{21}$ by the emission of a positive electron or *positron*, and a neutrino. That is,

$$_{11}Na^{21} \rightarrow {}_{10}Ne^{21} + {}_{+1}e^0 + {}_0\nu^0.$$

P. A. M. Dirac's relativistic version of Schrödinger's equation (Section 22.4) requires the existence of an anti-electron, a particle with the electron mass but with a *positive* rather than a negative unit of charge. Carl Anderson's discovery of this particle in 1932 marked the first confirmation that antimatter could exist. Neutrinos created in positive and negative β-decay have also turned out to be different. An *anti*neutrino always accompanies an electron, while a neutrino always accompanies a positron.

Even as the negative β-decay of a complex nucleus requires the conversion of a bound proton into a neutron, positive β-decay signals the inverse process. But of the two particles the free proton has the smaller mass. Therefore, the existence of positron-emitting nuclei implies that a *bound* proton in such a nucleus sometimes has a larger mass than a bound neutron. We know that the rest mass of any nucleus, stable or radioactive, is less than the sum of the masses of its constituent nucleons. The nucleons give up some of their mass to effect the binding (Section 20.3). Hence in a very real sense the properties of free and bound nucleons are not precisely the same. Nor do the properties of a given bound *nucleon* remain constant. Its energy, and hence its mass, must fluctuate as it interacts with the other nucleons, just as the energy of a given molecule in a water droplet constantly changes. Occasionally a proton in a potential positron emitter has more than sufficient energy to create a positron and a neutrino, and therefore is able to convert itself into a neutron.

Free neutrons have an eighteen-minute half-life. But the half-lives of β-unstable complex nuclei, both positive and negative, range from milliseconds to thousands of years. Evidently the neutron's decay probability is enhanced in some species, repressed in others, consistent with the supposition that a nucleon suffers a change in its properties when bound into a system. We may regard the probability of β-decay as the product of the probability that a particular neutron (or proton) attains sufficient energy to be converted into a proton (neutron), times the probability that it actually *does* convert. Now as we noted in Section 20.5, the nuclear time scale is on the order of 10^{-22} sec. Energy fluctuations must be very rapid, implying that the probability of a nucleon's having sufficient energy to decay is large. We would expect this probability to be a rather sensitive function of the nuclear binding. Indeed, the maximum energy of the β's emitted by a particular nuclide is a rough determinant of half-life. Free neutron decay proceeds with an eighteen-minute half-life and yields a kinetic energy of 0.778 MeV, while C^{14} has a 5570-year half-life and yields only 0.157 MeV (Table 20.2). However, even the millisecond half-lives are far larger than the 10^{-22} sec nuclear time scale. Hence although a bound nucleon has a high probability of being *energetically* able to create an electron (positron) and a neutrino, the probability for that process to occur is very small.

▶▶ 20.9 Natural radioactivity. The transuranic elements

By the mid-1910's it was known that the decay of uranium into the element then called UX_1 (now $_{90}Th^{234}$) is but the first of a series of α- and β^--disintegrations that ultimately terminates with stable $_{82}Pb^{208}$ (lead). Two other natural decay series have also been discovered. One starts with $_{92}U^{235}$ and ends with $_{82}Pb^{207}$; the other starts with $_{90}Th^{232}$ and ultimately yields $_{82}Pb^{208}$.

It is interesting to list the first few decays in the $_{92}U^{238}$ series, together with their corresponding half lives, using the names given the isotopes by early investigators:

$$_{92}U^{238} \xrightarrow[4.5 \times 10^9 \text{ yr}]{\alpha} {}_{90}UX_1^{234} \xrightarrow[24\text{ d}]{\beta,\gamma} {}_{91}UX_2^{234} \xrightarrow[1.1\text{ min}]{\beta,\gamma} {}_{92}UII^{234}$$

$$\xrightarrow[2.5 \times 10^5 \text{ hr}]{\alpha} {}_{90}Io^{230} \xrightarrow[8 \times 10^4 \text{ yr}]{\alpha} {}_{88}Ra^{226} \longrightarrow \cdots$$

$$\longrightarrow {}_{84}Po^{210} \xrightarrow[138\text{ d}]{\alpha} {}_{82}Pb^{206} \quad \text{(stable)}.$$

Historically, the repetition of atomic numbers in this natural decay chain first prompted Frederick Soddy to suggest the existence of isotopes. Several of the elements in the series, radium (Ra), and UX_1 (thorium) among them, filled places in the Periodic Table that had been vacant, and were enthusiastically welcomed into the existing family of elements. But as the entire chain began to unravel it became clear that nature was providing an embarrassment of riches. The initial part of the series shown above contains two "elements" with atomic number 90 (UX_1 and ionium) and two with atomic number 92 (uranium and UII). Even though these "elements" differ in atomic weight, their chemical properties are identical. It now seems a short step from recognition of these duplications to the recognition of isotopes. But until 1932 the constituents of the nucleus were not known, nor indeed was the existence of the nucleus itself established until 1912. Hence the isotope hypothesis represented a considerable conceptual advance toward an understanding of the properties of matter.

If, as now seems reasonable, we assume that the nuclei of the sun, the earth, and the planets have not always existed in their present form but were fabricated within the stars by series of nuclear reactions, then most of the radioactive isotopes with half-lives much shorter than the age of the elements should not occur on earth today. Any of these that might have been formed along with the stable nuclei would long since have decayed to negligible traces.

On this hypothesis the few radioactive species that do occur naturally either are still being created by one reaction or another or else have half-lives on the order of the age of the elements themselves. For instance, $_6C^{14}$ is produced when a $_6C^{13}$ nucleus in atmospheric carbon dioxide captures a cosmic-ray neutron. When these radioactive nuclei are ingested into living plants they are incorporated into organic molecules along with the stable carbon isotopes where they continue to decay with their characteristic 5570-year half-lives. Hence a piece of wood from a 5570-year-old structure has only half as many $_6C^{14}$ nuclei per stable $_6C^{12}$ and $_6C^{13}$ as the wood in a living tree, for it has not ingested any newly formed radioactive carbon nuclei for one-half the life of the β-active species.

Most of the naturally occurring radioactive nuclei are links in one of the three natural decay chains. Except for the initial isotope in each of the sequences ($_{92}U^{238}$, $_{92}U^{235}$, and $_{90}Th^{232}$) these radioactive isotopes continue to exist on earth because they are themselves daughters of other emitters. But the supply of the three initial isotopes is not being replenished. Therefore, their half-lives must be comparable to the age of the nuclides themselves, and by implication to the age of the solar system. Otherwise neither they nor the subsequent unstable species in their decay chains could still be found on earth. The fact that all uranium-bearing minerals contain roughly equal numbers of $_{92}U^{238}$ and $_{82}Pb^{206}$ nuclei indicates that about one-half the earth's supply of the former isotope has already disintegrated, hence the $_{92}U^{238}$ must have been formed about 4.5 billion years ago, for that, in fact, is its half-life.

Virtually all isotopes heavier than lead are radioactive and decay with half-lives no longer than a few thousand years. Therefore, the three species with half-lives in the billion-year range—$_{92}U^{238}$, $_{92}U^{235}$, and $_{90}Th^{230}$—are really anomalies. It is reasonable to assume that if nuclei heavier than $_{92}U^{238}$ ever *did* exist on earth they too would have had half-lives much shorter than a billion years, and therefore would have completely vanished by now. Of course this argument cannot prove that transuranic elements (elements beyond uranium in the Periodic Table) ever *did* exist. But it provides a plausible rationale for the fact that uranium, with its anomalously long half-life, is the last naturally occurring element in the Periodic Table.

In 1934, Fermi (Figure 20.15) attempted the fabrication of transuranic isotopes by the slow neutron bombardment of uranium. He reasoned that the isotope $_{92}U^{239}$, formed when $_{92}U^{238}$ captures a neutron,

$$_0n^1 + {}_{92}U^{238} \rightarrow {}_{92}U^{239},$$

might well have too many neutrons for stability and decay by β-emission into a nucleus with atomic number 93:

$$_{92}U^{239} \rightarrow {}_{93}?^{239} + {}_{-1}e + \nu.$$

Fermi's experimental method had been perfected in his earlier slow neutron capture studies. A uranium sample, purified to remove the other elements in its decay chain, was exposed to neutrons produced by a radium-beryllium source and thence slowed down to thermal energies with a water moderator (Section 20.7). After a reasonable exposure the sample was examined for signs of the β^--activity that might be attributed to the decay of $_{92}U^{239}$ and would therefore signal the formation of element 93.

The initial results seemed to suggest that Fermi's success had been even greater than he might have hoped. Not one but four distinct β^--activities (distinguished by their different half-lives) were identified in the bombarded uranium sample, and it seemed possible that four transuranic elements had been produced. There was no particular reason to believe that $_{93}?^{239}$ would be stable. If it turned out to be a β^-- rather than an α-emitter, an isotope of element 94 would also exist in the sample, which, if a β^--emitter, would in turn decay into an isotope of element 95, etc.

FIGURE 20.15 Enrico Fermi. (Courtesy of the American Institute of Physics, Center for the History and Philosophy of Physics.)

Of course, other interpretations of the four half-lives were also possible. For instance $_{93}?^{239}$ might have been a short half-life α-emitter that decayed to $_{91}Pr^{239}$ (protactinium), and chemical separation of one of the β^--sources was required before the positive existence of even one transuranic isotope could be established. But that task was by no means trivial. The uranium sample contained only microscopic quantities of the new β-emitters, and no one knew precisely what the chemical properties of the presumed transuranic elements would be, as no one had ever seen a transuranic element before. Hence Fermi's results remained inconclusive despite his considerable effort to untangle the isotopes chemically.

In fact, Fermi may well have produced two transuranic elements, although their existence was not established for another five or six years. Uranium was named for Uranus, the seventh planet in the solar system. Hence consistency suggested naming the two elements immediately beyond uranium neptunium (Np) and plutonium (Pu), in honor of the eighth and ninth planets. Neptunium, which is formed in the 23.5 min half-life decay of $_{92}U^{239}$,

$$_{92}U^{239} \rightarrow {}_{93}Np^{239} + {}_{-1}e + \nu,$$

is indeed a short half-lived β^--emitter that decays into plutonium with a 56-hr half-life:

$$_{93}Np^{239} \rightarrow {}_{94}Pu^{239} + {}_{-1}e + \nu.$$

$_{93}Pu^{239}$, while radioactive, has quite a respectable half-life—24,000 years.

At this writing (1968), elements with atomic numbers up to 103 have been produced. The majority have more than one isotope, and all are radioactive. Almost all of the transuranic isotopes are very short-lived, $_{93}Pu^{239}$ with its 24,000-yr half-life being the most stable by far. (See the Periodic Table of the Elements, Table 19.2.)

▶▶ **20.10   Nuclear fission**

Until 1939, neither Fermi nor anyone else realized that the dominant β^--activity in his neutron-activated uranium signaled an entirely new and unanticipated reaction: the fission of $_{92}U^{235}$, an isotope occurring with a natural abundance of 0.7% relative to the dominant $_{92}U^{238}$ (Table 20.1). O. Hahn and F. Strassmann repeated Fermi's experiments in 1938, finding chemical evidence for the element barium ($Z = 56$) in their neutron-irradiated sample. This was a curious result indeed. By what conceivable means could an isotope with atomic number 56 be produced from one with atomic number 92? Early the next year Lise Mitner and Otto Frisch proposed a unique explanation: that the $_{92}U^{235}$ nuclei, formed by neutron capture on $_{92}U^{235}$, have a high probability of *fissioning*, that is, breaking up into two heavy, usually unequal-fragment nuclei. If one of the fragments in a particular fission reaction is an isotope of barium with atomic number 56, the other must have atomic number 36 and must therefore be an isotope of krypton.

The fission hypothesis was soon verified experimentally by Fermi himself, and created a sensation among knowledgeable physicists. As we noted in Section 20.3 the neutron-to-proton ratio in both stable and radioactive isotopes exceeds unity for all but the light species, and increases with atomic number. $_{92}U^{235}$ has a higher neutron-to-proton ratio than even short-lived isotopes of barium and krypton, and it is unlikely that all of the 144 neutrons of the uranium nucleus are bound to one or the other of the two heavy fragments. In other words, the fission of uranium should also yield several free neutrons. Hahn and Strassmann had probably identified $_{56}Ba^{141}$ from the reaction:

$$_{0}n^1 + {}_{92}U^{235} \rightarrow {}_{56}Ba^{141} + {}_{36}Kr^{92} + 3n^1.$$

The energy released in this particular reaction (determined as usual by calculating the mass difference between its initial and final states) turns out to be about 200 MeV!

Division into barium and krypton is but one possible result of uranium fission. Many other fragments have also been observed. On the average fission reactions each yield about 200 MeV and produce about two free neutrons per reaction. The slow decrease in the binding energy curve for heavy nuclei (Figure 20.6) implies that the total energy of a hundred or more nucleons is smaller when the nucleons congregate into two or more separate, stable systems than into one single, large system. Hence the breakup of a heavy nucleus should generally be exothermic, a conclusion consistent with fact that very heavy nuclei are almost invariable α-emitters. Fission reactions represent a more drastic rearrangement of the nucleons in a heavy nucleus, and, as noted, are much more exothermic, yielding on the order of 200 MeV rather than 4 or 5 MeV per reaction. More important, the two or three free neutrons released in the fission of one $_{92}U^{235}$ nucleus can, if captured by other nearby nuclei, induce them to fission too, release about 200 MeV apiece, and send their free neutrons to be captured by still other nuclei. If each fission reaction induces two others, the number of reactions occurring in a sizable piece of pure $_{92}U^{235}$ increases rapidly. The first reaction induces two others, and each of these induces two more for a total of four in the third generation. By the eleventh generation 1024 nuclei are fissioning, by the twentieth over a million (Figure 20.16).

Until the discovery of fission it seemed highly unlikely that large-scale power sources could ever be based upon the energies derived from nuclear transmutation reactions.

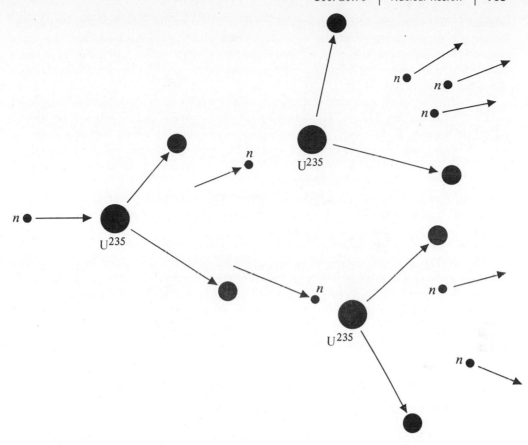

FIGURE 20.16   Beginning of a chain reaction in $_{92}U^{235}$. A neutron incident on a uranium nucleus induces fission which yields two radioactive fragment nuclei and two or three fast neutrons. These can induce additional fission reactions in their turn provided they do not escape from the uranium sample or interact with the nuclei of impurities that may be present.

But the free, fission-produced neutrons radically altered that expectation. Efficient power sources must be based upon self-sustaining processes that can involve large number of atoms, molecules, or nuclei. For instance, chemical power production requires the participation of many atoms and/or molecules. The burning of methane (a natural gas component) proceeds via the reaction

$$CH_4 + 2O_2 \rightarrow CO_2 + 2H_2O,$$

and yields about 23 eV or $23 \times 1.6 \times 10^{-19} = 3.6 \times 10^{-18}$ J per reaction (Section 16.3). Therefore, the complete combustion of $\frac{1}{1000}$ of a kilogram-mole of methane (16 g = 16×10^{-3} kg, since CH_4 has molecular weight 16) involves 6×10^{23} reactions, and produces a total energy of $3.6 \times 10^{-18} \times 6 \times 10^{23} = 2.2 \times 10^6$ J. The watt is a unit of power equal to 1 J/sec (Equations 8.20 and 8.21). Therefore, 2.2×10^6 J, if used with 100% efficiency, could power a one-hundred watt bulb for 22,000 sec, or about six hours.

Of course the energy released in a typical radioactive decay process is on the order of 10^5 times as great as the energy liberated in the reaction of a methane and an oxygen molecule. But relatively small numbers of nuclei in a sample undergo spontaneous decay. Hence the process is not suitable as a large-scale power source. However, the extra neutrons released in the fission of U^{235} *can* lead to a chain reaction involving large numbers of nuclei and therefore liberate far greater amounts of energy than are available from chemical reactions.

Consider the power available if even 1% of the nuclei in a ten-kilogram sample of pure $_{92}U^{235}$ undergoes fission. Ten kilograms of the isotope contains $\frac{10}{235} \times 6 \times 10^{26} = 2.6 \times 10^{25}$ nuclei so that a 1% efficient fission would involve 2.6×10^{23} reactions. If each of these releases an average of 200 MeV, the total energy released would be $2 \times 10^8 \times 1.6 \times 10^{-19} \times 2.6 \times 10^{23} = 6.8 \times 10^{12}$ J, equivalent to about 20,000 tons (of 20 kilotons) of TNT if released suddenly!

The rapid fission of U^{235} has implications beyond the potential power of the explosion. Most of the fragment nuclei resulting from the fission process are neutron-rich nuclei, and hence β^--emitters. Hence if ten kilograms of U^{235} undergo rapid fission with 1% efficiency, the shock wave resulting from the explosion scatters about one-tenth kilogram of radioactive material outward from the source of the blast. In addition, many of the neutrons produced in the last few generations of the chain reaction also leave the site of the explosion and are free to be captured by any material they may encounter.

On the other hand, if the 6.8×10^{12} J from the 1% efficient fission of ten kilograms of U^{235} were liberated slowly and used to produce electricity, the power generated would be equal to the amount required to power one million 100-watt bulbs for 68,000 seconds (about nineteen hours) each.

▶▶ 20.11 Historical notes on fission weapons

The fission of uranium was first recognized in 1939, a year of rising political tension in Europe and a growing awareness of the implications of that tension in the United States. Given only the barest outline of the facts concerning fission, any competent physicist could have performed the calculations in Section 20.10 and would have grasped at once the implications inherent in the process. In view of the timing of the discovery it was inevitable, perhaps, that the handful of American and refugee scientists in the United States who did know about fission should turn their thoughts toward its destructive potential and persuade their government to support a multifaceted project whose goal was the construction of fission bombs.

It may be difficult to understand, in retrospect, why the ultimate success of the project was ever in doubt. Calculating the energy that should be released if ten kilograms of pure $_{92}U^{235}$ undergoes fission with 1% efficiency presents no problem. But in 1939 no one had ever seen a chain reaction occur. No one had ever separated even one *atom* of $_{92}U^{235}$ from $_{92}U^{238}$, let alone ten kilograms. In fact, no one had ever seen more than one gram of pure, unseparated, elementary uranium, for little more than that existed in the entire world. Hence the initial major technical problems were obvious. Unprecedented quantities of pure uranium had to be chemically refined from naturally occurring ores, then techniques devised to separate the 0.7% abundant $_{92}U^{235}$ isotope from the pure, natural mixtures. In the meantime, experiments aimed toward understanding the details of chain reactions were obviously desirable.

Shortly after the initial discovery of fission in 1939 additional research had indicated that $_{92}U^{238}$ as well as $_{92}U^{235}$ was fissionable, but that its fission only occurred with appreciable probability when induced by slow neutrons. If $_{92}U^{238}$ captures an energetic neutron it has a higher probability of forming $_{92}U^{239}$ in its ground state which subsequently decays via β^--emission into $_{93}Np^{239}$ and thence into $_{94}Pu^{239}$ (Section 20.9). Hence the fast neutrons released in the fission of one $_{92}U^{238}$ nucleus form $_{94}Pu^{239}$ more often than they induce new fissions. It follows that a chain reaction cannot occur in $_{92}U^{238}$ *unless* most of the fission-released neutrons are slowed down (or moderated) before they interact with other uranium nuclei.

The reluctance of the heavier uranium isotope to undergo fission suggests its use in the controlled chain reactions from which power for constructive ends can be derived. Fermi reasoned that by interspersing blocks of pure metallic uranium with a moderator, or material that would slow down the neutrons from the fission process, a chain reaction might be induced. A satisfactory moderating material must be able to slow down neutrons without capturing many of them. Momentum conservation implies that the energy lost by a particle in a collision with another increases as the mass of the second, heavier-scattering particle approaches the mass of the first and is a maximum when the masses are equal. (Compare the collision of two ping-pong balls with a ping-pong ball and billiard ball. The ping-pong ball can lose much more energy in the former case.) Hydrogen would be the best neutron moderator if protons did not have a high neutron-capture probability. Heavy hydrogen ($_1H^2$ in the form of heavy water) is excellent, but was difficult to obtain in the early 1940's. Carbon was the lightest readily available material and was chosen on the basis of expediency.

Fermi constructed his first reactor in a squash court at the University of Chicago, calling it a pile because it was just that: a pile of interspersed uranium and graphite blocks. Cosmic ray neutrons constantly bombard the earth's surface and induce a few fission reactions in any sample of $_{92}U^{238}$. The problem was to create conditions that would lead to a self-sustaining chain reaction. As we have noted, a secondary neutron from a fission reaction need not induce another fission. It may be captured by $_{92}U^{238}$ and form $_{92}U^{239}$, for instance, or be captured by the nucleus of an impurity in the system. Again, it may escape from the assembly without undergoing any interaction at all.

Let $P(f)$ be the probability that a neutron undergoes fission capture in U^{238}, $P(nf)$ the probability of nonfission capture, $P(i)$ the probability of capture by an impurity, and $P(e)$ the escape probability. If N is the average number of secondary neutrons produced per fission, then the fraction of these that are available to induce new fission reactions is given by

$$n = N\left[\frac{P(f)}{P(f) + P(nf) + P(i) + P(e)}\right]. \tag{20.6}$$

When a self-sustaining chain reaction occurs, the number of fission reactions in each generation exceeds the number in the preceding generation, implying that n must be greater than one. Thus the construction of a working reactor requires that the probability of the competing reactions be minimized relative to the probability of fission capture. As we have already noted, the interactions of the secondary neutrons with the carbon moderator reduce their energies, thereby increasing $P(f)$ and decreasing (Pnf). The probability of impurity capture is minimized by using the element in its pure form, and the escape probability by increasing the dimensions of the pile beyond a minimum critical size so that the neutrons have a small probability of escaping without interacting.

In order to control the chain reaction, removable cadmium rods were inserted into Fermi's reactor (Figure 20.17). Since cadmium has a high neutron-capture probability these had the effect of increasing the impurity-capture probability in a controlled manner.

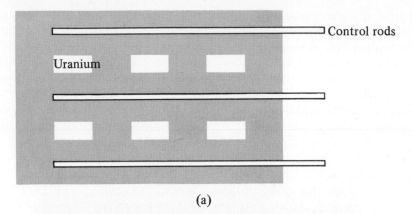

(a)

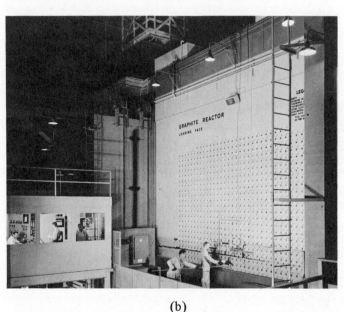

(b)

FIGURE 20.17   (a) Cross section of Fermi's first nuclear reactor. Blocks of uranium metal are embedded in a graphite moderator which slows down the neutrons from the fission reactions thereby increasing their probability of inducing new fission reactions when they enter another uranium block. The removable cadmium rods act as controlled impurities, absorbing sufficient fission-produced neutrons to keep the fission reaction from proceeding at an uncontrolled rate. (b) A reactor at Oakridge laboratory. Uranium slugs are inserted into the large graphite matrix (behind the wall) through any or all of the 1248 entrance channels shown. (Oakridge National Laboratory. Operated by Union Carbide Corporation for the U.S. Atomic Energy Commission.)

On December 2, 1942, Fermi, with a few associates and observers, removed the control rods one at a time, thereby increasing the fraction of the secondary neutrons available for fission reactions (Equation 20.6). As predicted, the removal of each rod increased the fission rate (as measured by neutron detectors in the pile). However, the rate remained steady until the last rod was removed, indicating that n was smaller than one. Finally with the last control rod partially removed, the neutron rate began to increase steadily and did not level off as before. Each generation of fission reactions had made more neutrons available for fission than its predecessor. The first self-sustaining chain reaction in history had thus been induced (Figure 20.18).

Fermi's experiments established the feasibility of self-sustaining chain reactions. Two and one-half years later, on July 16, 1945, a small group of observers on the New Mexico desert witnessed the first uncontrolled chain reaction, and three weeks later, on August 6, 1945, a twenty-kiloton fission bomb destroyed the Japanese city of Hiroshima. Detailed accounts of the bomb's development are given elsewhere. As already noted, the basic technical problem was obtaining quantities of pure $_{92}U^{235}$ sufficient to generate and sustain a chain reaction. Fission occurs with overwhelming probability whenever a $_{92}U^{235}$ nucleus captures a neutron, unlike the situation with $_{92}U^{238}$. Thus in producing a fission weapon there is no need to reduce the energies of the fission-produced neutrons, and $P(nf)$ in Equation 20.6 is negligible. If the fraction of secondary neutrons available for inducing more fission reactions is to be greater than one, impurity capture (including capture by $_{92}U^{238}$) must also be made negligible by using $_{92}U^{235}$ in a highly purified form. Finally, escape probability can be minimized by using a sufficiently large piece of material. When the material exceeds a particular critical mass (which no doubt varies with its shape and the way it is packed) the neutron multiplication factor of the assembly exceeds one, and a self-sustaining chain reaction occurs.

Apparently the core of the first fission bomb consisted quite simply of two, subcritical masses of pure $_{92}U^{235}$ which were automatically combined into a single supercritical unit at the appropriate time. Cosmic ray neutrons induced the primary fission reactions in the assembled supercritical mass. Since there was no control mechanism such as the cadmium rods in Fermi's pile each generation of fission reactions followed one another rapidly. Consequently the total energy of the historic chain reaction was liberated in a short, violent explosion. More sophisticated detonation methods which permit a large

FIGURE 20.18 Photograph of the sculpture "Nuclear Energy" by Henry Moore, taken on the day of its dedication, December 2, 1967, twenty-five years after Fermi's first successful reactor experiment, at the site of the squash court at the University of Chicago where the event took place. (Courtesy of the Public Relations Office, University of Chicago).

fraction of the uranium nuclei to undergo fission before the entire assembly is dispersed by the explosion are apparently used in modern fission weapons.

A good many of the $_{92}U^{238}$ nuclei in a reactor such as Fermi's prototype pile do not undergo fission when they capture neutrons, but instead form $_{92}U^{239}$ which β^--decays into $_{93}Np^{239}$ and thence into relatively stable $_{94}Pu^{239}$ (Section 20.11). When the Chicago pile had generated several micrograms of plutonium, it was extracted from the uranium and studied by a group headed by Glen Seaborg and E. M. McMillan. It had been suspected that $_{94}Pu^{239}$, like $_{92}U^{235}$, would have a high fission probability following fast neutron capture, and Seaborg's group confirmed that conjecture experimentally. It is far simpler to separate $_{94}Pu^{239}$ from uranium than it is to separate the two isotopes of uranium from each other, simply because uranium and plutonium have different chemical properties. For that reason $_{94}Pu^{239}$ rather than $_{92}U^{235}$ is the isotope used in most modern fission weapons. After its fissionable properties had been established, the isotope was manufactured in large reactors built primarily for that purpose. On August 9, 1945 a plutonium fission bomb destroyed the Japanese city of Nagasaki.

The two fission bombs dropped on Japan in August, 1945, were twenty-kiloton devices, each releasing the energy equivalent of 20,000 tons of TNT. Within two decades that once awesome sounding energy had come to be thought of as miniscule and ten- and twenty-megaton fusion bombs regarded as the norm. Each of the two mightiest of the world's nations had stockpiles of nuclear weapons sufficient to "overkill" the other as well as delivery systems of considerable sophistication, while three other nations had entered the nuclear "club." As this section suggests, the manufacture of a fission weapon requires the solution of problems that are technical rather than fundamental. It follows that even a small nation could develop at least a crude nuclear arsenal if it devoted sufficient funds to the project.

A discussion of the moral and political aspect of nuclear armaments would carry us far afield. However, in this age where twenty-megaton bombs can be discussed with equanimity by some, it is worth rereading statements concerning the first twenty-kiloton devices made by scientists, military men, statesmen, and journalists in late 1945, and then recalling that twenty-kilotons is only 0.02 megatons.

One of the most impressive of these statements was made by Brigadier General Thomas Farrell who witnessed the explosion at Alamogordo, New Mexico, on July 16 of that year from a concrete bunker one mile away. We quote his summary paragraph:

> . . . No man-made phenomenon of such tremendous power had ever occurred before. The lighting effects beggared description. The whole country was lighted by a searing light with the intensity many times that of the midday sun. It was golden, purple, violet, gray, and blue. It lighted every peak, crevasse and ridge of the nearby mountain range with a clarity and beauty that cannot be described but must be seen to be imagined. It was that beauty the great poets dream about but describe most poorly and inadequately. Thirty seconds after the explosion first came, the air blast pressing hard against the people and things, to be followed almost immediately by the strong, sustained, awesome roar which warned of doomsday and made us feel that we puny things were blasphemous to dare tamper with the forces heretofore reserved to the Almighty. Words are inadequate tools for the job of acquainting those not present with the physical, mental, and psychological effects. It had to be witnessed to be realized.*

---

* From the War Department Press Release on the New Mexico Test, July 16, 1945. Quoted in H. D. Smyth, *Atomic Energy for Military Purposes*, Princeton University Press, Princeton, N.J., 1945. p. 254.

▲▲ 20.12 Fusion reactions

During the 1930's Hans Bethe and George Gamow (among others) pointed out that the several million degree temperatures in the sun's interior would give a small but negligible fraction of its protons kinetic energies sufficient to overcome (or penetrate) the electrostatic barriers presented by other nuclei and react with them to form different species. They also showed that virtually all conceivable reactions would be exothermic, and suggested that these might well be the primary source of the sun's energy.

Bethe and Gamow originally thought that the principal reaction sequence would start with the capture of a proton by $_6C^{12}$. However, it is now known that $_1H^1$ dominates the sun's composition. Thus it is probable that protons react primarily with other protons.

Consider the reaction

$$_1H^1 + _1H^1 \rightarrow _1H^2 + _{+1}e^0 + \nu, \tag{20.7a}$$

which has a reasonable probability of occurring at temperatures greater than a few million degrees, when a reasonable fraction of the protons in a Maxwell-Boltzmann distribution (Equation 15.3) attain energies sufficient to approach within less than 10^{-14} m of each other. Referring to Table 20.1, each such reaction liberates a kinetic energy of 0.4 MeV. When sufficient heavy hydrogen ($_1H^2$) has been produced (or if enough already exists) it too can participate in reactions such as

$$_1H^1 + _1H^2 \rightarrow _2He^3 + \gamma, \tag{20.7b}$$

which releases 5.0 MeV (Table 20.1). Again, the $_2He^3$ can undergo reactions such as

$$_2He^3 + _2He^3 \rightarrow _2He^4 + _1H^1 + _1H^1, \tag{20.7c}$$

liberating 13.0 MeV. As a result of the three-step sequence, four protons disappear and one $_2He^4$ and two positrons are created. (Reactions 20.7a and 20.7b must each occur twice in order to produce the two $_2He^3$ nuclei required in Equation 20.7c.) More important, the net kinetic energy gain is $2 \times 0.4 + 2 \times 5.0 + 13.0 = 23.8$ MeV.

Any process leading to the formation of a nucleus from lighter component nuclei is called a *fusion* reaction. Figure 20.6 shows that the binding energy per nucleon tends to increase with atomic weight up to the iron group nuclei (centered around $_{26}Fe^{56}$) and thereafter slowly decreases. We have noted that this decrease for the heavy nuclei implies that *fission* reactions are generally exothermic in that region of atomic weight. In contrast, the form of the curve for the light and medium light nuclei shows that a group of fifty nucleons or less (roughly half of them protons and half neutrons) can minimize their total energy by forming one large bound system rather than two or more smaller systems. It follows that fusion reactions for nuclei lighter than the iron group are almost invariably exothermic. But of course the electrostatic barriers that all nuclei present to each other inhibit fusion reactions on a massive scale except under high temperature conditions such as those existing in stellar interiors.

Fission bombs also create the required high temperature conditions for short periods of time. Thus after Alamogordo it was reasonable to suppose that a fission device might be used to trigger a rapid, massive series of fusion reactions, even as the spark plug in an internal combustion engine triggers the burning of a compressed gas mixture in a cylinder (Section 16.3). There are a number of possible fusion reactions that yield more energy than any single step in the sequence Equations 20.7a to 20.7c. One or more might serve as the basis of a thermonuclear bomb. For example,

$$_1H^2 + {}_1H^2 \rightarrow {}_2He^4,$$
$$_1H^1 + {}_1H^3 \rightarrow {}_2He^4,$$
$$_1H^1 + {}_3Li^7 \rightarrow {}_2He^4 + {}_2He^4.$$

Each of these processes yields 20 MeV or more per reaction. The first would probably not be chosen since it would have to compete with the reaction

$$_1H^2 + {}_1H^2 \rightarrow {}_1H^3 + {}_1H^1,$$

which yields only 4 MeV. On the other hand the tritium ($_1H^3$) required in the second reaction is a twelve-year β^--emitter that must be fabricated by some nuclear process prior to its use in a bomb. Tritium bombs would have the added disadvantage of losing their potency if stockpiled for periods of time on the order of their half-lives. Obviously the problems of choosing one or more suitable reactions and obtaining the requisite amounts of the isotope have been solved in more than one country, although the details are still classified.

Fusion bombs have several clear advantages over pure fission devices. Although the energy released in a simple typical fusion reaction is only about one-tenth as great as the 200 MeV energy released in fission, the combined mass of one mole of tritium ($_1H^3$) and one mole of ordinary hydrogen is four kilograms—less than 2% the mass of a mole of U^{235}. Hence considerably more fusion than fission energy can be generated per unit mass of active material, if not per nucleus. More important, there is no fundamental limit on the size of a thermonuclear bomb. Cosmic-ray neutrons initiate a chain reaction in any piece of fissionable material larger than the critical mass. But even a very large volume of hydrogen and tritium remains inert until raised to a temperature of several million degrees.

Enrico Fermi's first reactor at the University of Chicago proved that nuclear chain reactions were feasible and thus led directly to Alamogordo, Hiroshima, and the existence of thermonuclear stockpiles. But it also pointed the way toward fruitful, constructive applications of nuclear technology. The development of nuclear reactors as power sources did not proceed as rapidly as might have been predicted in 1945, for the construction of such a power plant requires a considerable capital outlay. In many instances large-scale nuclear reactors first competed economically with conventional power sources in the less developed countries where the latter were expensive or in short supply. However, a considerable number are now operating in the United States and Western Europe as well. The dwindling world supply of conventional sources coupled with ever increasing demands for power will almost certainly lead to the widespread use of nuclear reactors within the next decade or two.

Fission reactors might conceivably satisfy the world's power demands for several centuries. However, uranium is a relatively rare element whose supply must ultimately be depleted. But a virtually unlimited supply of hydrogen exists in the sea and would seem to offer an endless source of power if used in fusion reactions. As yet the creation of a controlled miniature sun on earth remains an unattained dream. A fission bomb can generate the high temperatures required to initiate fusion, but only for a fraction of a second. The formidable technical problems involved in generating and sustaining controlled, million-degree temperatures and in confining the hydrogen at these temperatures within material containers have not yet been solved, although considerable effort has been devoted toward them in several countries, principally the United States, Great Britain, and the Soviet Union.

◣◣ 20.13   Notes on stellar evolution*

The study of nuclear reactions coupled with advances in the techniques of astronomical observation during the past few years has permitted the serious exploration of two fascinating problems: the evolution of the stars and the origin of the elements.

Figure 20.19, which plots the relative cosmic abundances of the isotopes as a function of atomic weight, is derived from spectroscopic studies made with optical and radio

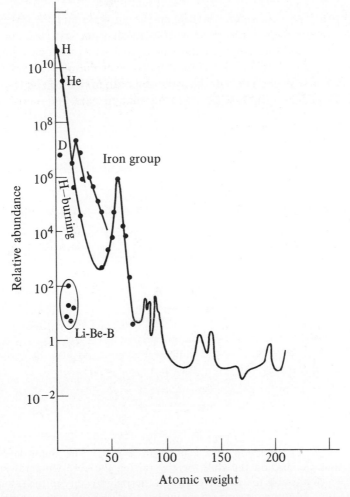

FIGURE 20.19   Mean relative cosmic abundances of the nuclides plotted as a function of their atomic weights. The solid line is drawn to show the trend of the data. Note that the vertical scale is logarithmic, not linear. That is, the distance from 10^{-5} to 10^{-4} is equal to the distance from 10^{-4} to 10^{-3} so that scale of the graph compresses toward the top. [Adapted from M. Burbidge, G. Burbidge, W. Fowler, and F. Hoyle, *Revs. Mod. Phys.*, Vol. 22, 153, p. 547 (1957).]

---

* I am indebted to Professor D. P. Goist for a particularly illuminating conversation on this topic.

telescopes* (terrestrial abundances are shown in Figure 20.1). The decrease in the cosmic abundance curve with increasing nucleon number is striking. (Note that the vertical scale is logarithmic rather than linear. That is, it is compressed toward the top so that the distances, from 0.1 to 1, 1 to 10, and 10 to 100 are equal.) Ninety-three percent of the atoms in the universe are hydrogen atoms, 6% are helium, and atoms heavier than zinc account for less than 0.0001%. A few peaks also appear against this background, i.e., $_6C^{12}$, $_8O^{16}$, $_{10}Ne^{20}$, $_{12}Mg^{24}$, and $_{14}Si^{28}$ are considerably more abundant than their immediate neighbors. Significantly (as it turns out) each of these nuclides is composed of an integral number of $_2He^4$ units. Isotopes in the vicinity of $_{26}Fe^{56}$ also appear with anomalously high abundances. Again, significantly, this region of nucleon number marks the peak of the nuclear stability curve (Figure 20.6).

Since hydrogen is the dominant material in the universe and the cosmic abundance curve exhibits a sharp, general decrease with increasing mass, it is tempting to assume that the other elements were created from hydrogen by thermonuclear reactions in the stars. The postulate is a fascinating one for it links the evolution of the elements with the evolution of the stars. A good deal of the hydrogen both in our local galaxy and in others appears in the form of large, diffuse clouds rather than in stars, and there is observational

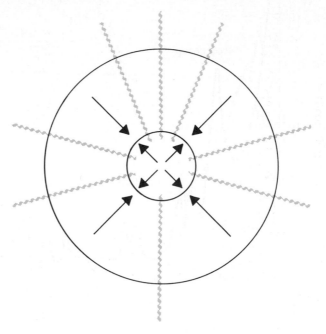

FIGURE 20.20 Compression and heating in a star. The outer layers exert gravitational pressure on the core thereby raising the core temperature to the point at which it is able to exert an outward, thermal pressure of the same magnitude. However, photons escaping from the hot core carry off energy, momentarily reducing the core temperature and the outward pressure it exerts. Thus the equilibrium with the outer layers is upset, leading to a further compression, a further temperature increase, and an accelerated energy loss.

---

* A radio telescope is basically a large antenna and receiver capable of detecting either the discrete, low-energy photons emitted from atoms when they make transitions between closely spaced energy levels or the continuous spectra of cold gas analogous to the continuous incandescent optical spectra that first led Planck to his quantum hypothesis (Section 17.3).

FIGURE 20.21 The Great Nebula in Orion photographed with the 100-in. telescope at Mt. Wilson. The bright spots in the gas cloud are thought to be hot, young stars no more than a few million years old. (Photograph from Mt. Wilson and Palomar Observatories.)

evidence in favor of the conjecture that this may well serve as the raw material from which new stars will ultimately be created.

The gravitational attraction between the atoms in these clouds is very small, of course. Nevertheless if the cloud is sufficiently massive one might imagine that under the proper conditions the sum of these gravitational interactions would result in a slow compression of the cloud toward its center. As detailed calculations indicate, an arbitrarily large cloud cannot forever remain stable as it compresses itself (Figure 20.20). Instead it ultimately breaks up into smaller fragments each of which then continues the processes of gravitational collapse and fragmentation until, finally, a number of semi-independent fragments remain, ranging in mass up to no more than about fifty solar masses. Many of these fragments of the original, more or less homogeneous gas cloud are destined to become stars (Figure 20.21).

From this point onward the entire history of a star can be regarded as a series of stratagems designed to delay its continuing gravitational collapse, a process that accelerates as the average distance between its atoms decreases and the total gravitational force between them increases. As the pressure on the inner core of a protostar increases so does its temperature (Section 14.7). Ultimately the mean kinetic energy of the core atoms becomes high enough so that the now frequent collisions between them result in ionization and internal excitations. Many of the photons emitted when the excited atoms return to their ground states are reabsorbed by other atoms. However, some escape, providing a mechanism of energy loss from the star. As a consequence the internal temperature of the core drops momentarily, but so does the outward thermal pressure exerted by the core upon the layers of gas surrounding it. Thus these layers are able to press down more vigorously and raise the interior temperature and pressure to an even higher level. In other words, the star's attempt to cool itself by getting rid of electromagnetic energy is a self-defeating attempt which inevitably leads to ever-increasing interior temperatures.

The rate at which the core temperature of a protostar increases clearly depends upon the gravitational pressure exerted by its outer layers, and therefore upon its total mass. If that mass is greater than about one-twentieth the solar mass, gravitational compression can produce temperatures that permit the series of exothermic fusion reactions of Section 20.12 (Equations 20.7a to 20.7c) to take place. These occur with small probability at temperatures on the order of few hundred thousand degrees; at temperatures in excess of several million degrees they constitute the major source of the star's energy. As these reactions begin in earnest the core temperature increases sharply, and so does the outward, thermal pressure it exerts. Expansion occurs until an equilibrium between the inward gravitational pressure and outward thermal pressure is achieved, and the star (for now it is a star) enters its longest period of stability. Several types of fusion reactions producing small amounts of $_4\text{Be}^7$, $_3\text{Li}^7$, and $_4\text{B}^8$ can occur during the period of its life:

$$_2\text{He}^3 + {_2}\text{He}^4 \rightarrow {_4}\text{Be}^7 + \gamma,$$

$$_{-1}e + {_4}\text{Be}^7 \rightarrow {_3}\text{Li}^7 + \nu,$$

$$_4\text{Be}^7 + {_1}\text{H}^1 \rightarrow {_5}\text{B}^8 + {_{+1}}e + \nu.$$

However, the conversion of $_1\text{H}^1$ into $_2\text{He}^4$ is the star's major occupation. Part of the resulting energy escapes through its surface, part heats the cooler layers surrounding the core. As a result the interior temperatures continue to rise slowly and additional layers are added to the region where the temperature is high enough for the fusion reactions to occur.

There is considerable observational evidence in favor of the broad outlines of this model. It is consistent with the fact that hydrogen and helium are the first and second most abundant elements in the universe, that there is much more hydrogen than helium, and that there is very little else. The age of the sun as estimated from geological evidence such as uranium dating (in addition to the assumption that the sun and earth are the same age) implies that fusion reactions must be its main source of energy. The total energy radiated from the sun per unit time can be calculated from measurements of the amount reaching the earth. If the gravitational compression mechanism were its only energy source the sun could not be more than a few tens of thousands of years old, whereas the geological evidence cited above indicates that it is at least four and one-half billion years old.

Eventually a time must be reached in the life of a star when virtually all the hydrogen in its core has been converted into helium. Hydrogen burning continues in layers near the surface of the star. But these too must ultimately exhaust their hydrogen supply. The course followed by a star from this point onward depends critically upon its mass and upon the anomalously high stability of $_2\text{He}^4$. Curiously enough there are no stable or even quasi-stable nuclides with nucleon number 5. Evidently the bound two proton-two neutron system is so stable and self-satisfied that it refuses to accept another nucleon of either type. If there were a stable mass 5 nuclide then reactions such as

$$_1H^1 + {}_2He^4 \rightarrow {}_3Li^5,$$

or

$$_1H^1 + {}_2He^4 \rightarrow {}_2He^5 + {}_{+1}e + \nu,$$

would have taken place during the hydrogen burning phase of the star's life, and the sequence of elements 6, 7, 8, ..., built up by further proton capture reactions.

Again, $_4Be^8$, the nucleus that would be formed by the fusion of two $_2He^4$ nuclei, is not even quasi-stable so that the reaction

$$_2He^4 + {}_2He^4 \rightarrow {}_4Be^8$$

cannot lead to the production of nuclei with higher atomic numbers. Thus the absence of the mass numbers 5 and the nonexistence of $_4Be^8$ terminate the hydrogen-burning sequence at $_2He^4$. There *is* a way out if the interior temperatures rise above one-hundred million degrees. However, as detailed calculations indicate, these cannot be attained unless the total mass of the star is somewhat greater than the solar masses. Thus the hydrogen-depleted core of a star like the sun is a hot, dead region where fusion reactions no longer take place. Deprived of its energy source the growing core region cannot maintain an outward, counter pressure against the gravitational compression of the outer layers and so becomes increasingly dense and increasingly hot. Ultimately when a major fraction of the star's interior is in this hot, dead state the system becomes unstable and throws off massive quantities of gas in a series of violent explosions. These spectacular events result in such an increase in the star's brightness as seen on the earth that a star previously not visible to the naked eye may become, for a few days or weeks, an obvious feature of the night sky. Hence a star in this stage of its career is called a *nova* (from the Latin for *new*). Alas, these outbursts mark the end of its active career. With all its hydrogen exhausted, the hot dense star (now called a white dwarf) can no longer produce energy at all. Thus it slowly dies, like a hot coal removed from a fire.

If the mass of a star is greater than about 1.5 solar masses, however, its fate is somewhat different, for the compression of the helium core can ultimately raise its temperature beyond one hundred million degrees. We have noted that the nonexistence of $_4Be^8$ prevents the fusion of two $_2He^4$ nuclei. But at these high temperatures the core density is about 10^5 times that of water and the mean distance between the nuclei is small enough so that the fusion of *three* $_2He^4$ nuclei to yield $_6C^{12}$ becomes probable. That is,

$$_2He^4 + {}_2He^4 + {}_2He^4 \rightarrow {}_6C^{12} + \gamma.$$

Thus the $_4Be^8$ impasse is circumvented, and fusion reactions begin once more. As the temperatures continue to rise additional reactions commence, such as

$$_2He^4 + {}_6C^{12} \rightarrow {}_8O^{16} + \gamma,$$
$$_2He^4 + {}_8O^{16} \rightarrow {}_{10}Ne^{20} + \gamma,$$
$$_2He^4 + {}_{10}Ne^{20} \rightarrow {}_{12}Mg^{24} + \gamma.$$

All of these nuclides—$_6C^{12}$, $_8O^{16}$, $_{10}Ne^{20}$, $_{12}Mg^{24}$—occur with anomalously high abundance, in the universe (Figure 20.19). In addition the few remaining protons in the core can be captured to form traces of other nuclei, which, in fact, have much smaller cosmic abundances:

$$_1H^1 + {}_6C^{12} \rightarrow {}_6C^{13} + {}_{+1}e + \nu,$$
$$_1H^1 + {}_8O^{16} \rightarrow {}_8O^{17} + \gamma.$$

Other capture reactions can lead to neutron production, for instance,

$$_1H^1 + {}_{10}Ne^{20} \rightarrow {}_{11}Na^{21} + {}_{+1}e,$$
$$_{11}Na^{21} \rightarrow {}_{10}Ne^{21} + {}_{+1}e,$$
$$_2He^4 + {}_{10}Ne^{21} \rightarrow {}_{12}Mg^{24} + {}_0n^1,$$

and *neutron* capture reactions can then yield a series of other nuclei. As a result of these many processes a rich variety of light and medium to medium-heavy nuclides are produced.

When, as a result of these exothermic reactions, the core temperature of a star exceeds one billion degrees or so, the energies are sufficient to remove nucleons from nuclei with reasonable probability in a process analogous to the ionization of an atom. Thereafter the core consists of nuclei, nucleons, γ-rays, and electrons in chaotic interaction. The detailed interactions become highly involved and the evolutionary model more speculative. But it is reasonable to assume that a statistical equilibrium of some sort is reached and that the amount of a particular species that exists depends upon its stability. Since the iron group nuclei are the most stable of all they no doubt are dominant (Figure 20.6).

At this juncture the star has reached another impasse from which it cannot escape. Previously it produced energy through fusion reactions, and the resultant outward pressure forestalled gravitational collapse. But with the formation of the iron group the star exhausts its supply of usable nuclear energy, for further fusion reactions would be *endothermic* rather than exothermic. In fact *all* reactions leading away from the iron peak are endothermic, but they must nonetheless occur, since the pressure of the outer layers upon the core continues, the interior temperature continues to rise, and the nuclear reaction rate increases. Since the endothermic reactions absorb energy from the core the outward pressure it exerts must decrease. But as a consequence the rate of compression and reheating accelerates! Eventually when the interior temperatures rise to about five billion degrees the core literally gives up the fight. Many of the nuclei built up so carefully over eons begin to break up in a virtual endothermic orgy, and the entire structure of the star collapses toward the center. Depending upon its total mass the time required for this collapse can range from several hours down to a few seconds! The rapid heating of the collapsing outer layers results in their sudden expansion, and fantastic quantities of matter are hurled into space in a process similar to, though many times more energetic than a nova explosion. The star has become a *supernova*, and for a few weeks dominates the night sky (Figure 20.22).

A supernova is a relatively rare phenomenon in a particular galaxy. Tycho Brahe saw one in 1572 and in fact first made his reputation as an astronomer through papers written about his observations of it. Kepler and Galileo both observed the supernova of 1604, and Chinese astronomers have left accurate and detailed accounts of a supernova observed in 1054. More recent supernovae have been seen in other galaxies. All of them appear suddenly then decrease in brilliance with half-lives of about fifty-five days, indicating that the whole process takes place rapidly on the cosmic scale.*

---

* Half-life in this context has the same meaning as for the decay of a radioactive sample. It is the time required for the light intensity from a supernova to decrease to one-half its maximum intensity.

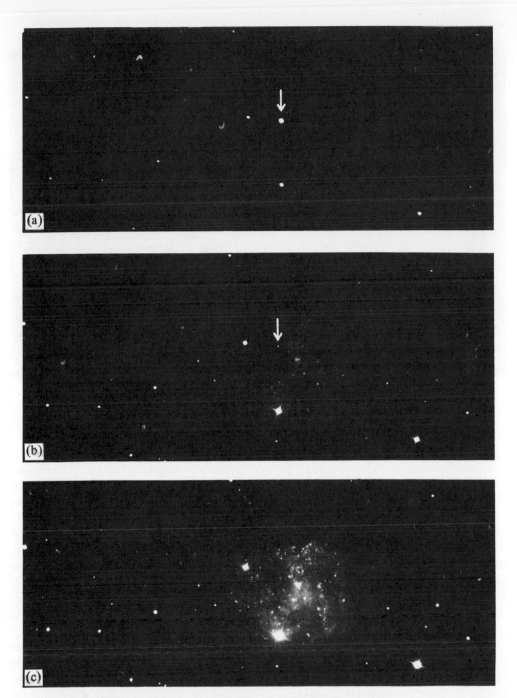

FIGURE 20.22 Supernova in the Galaxy IC4182 photographed with the Mt. Wilson 100-in. telescope at three different times and with exposures of increasing length. (a) August 23, 1937: Exposure 20^m; maximum brightness. (b) November 24, 1938: Exposure 45^m; faint. (c) January 19, 1942: Exposure 85^m; too faint to observe. The decrease in its brightness in fifteen months is striking. In the last photograph, taken four and one-half years after the first, the supernova is too faint to be seen against the background of the other stars. (Photograph from Mt. Wilson and Palomar Observatories.)

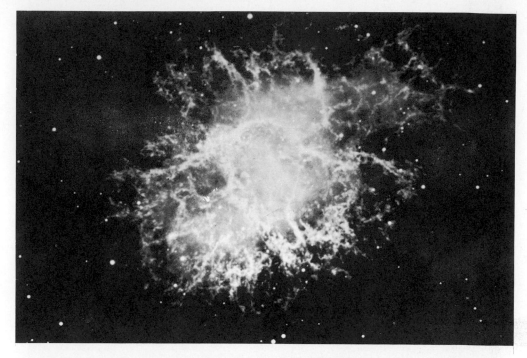

FIGURE 20.23 The Crab Nebula, the remains of the supernova of 1054, photographed with the 200-in. Hale telescope. (Photograph from Mt. Wilson and Palomar Observatories.)

During its final death agony a supernova contributes to its galaxy many of the complex medium and medium-heavy nuclei it has synthesized during the long eons of its career. But its work is not quite finished, for as the hot layers are hurled into space a great variety of proton, neutron, and α-captive reactions may well occur, thus building up the heavy nuclei beyond the iron group. Because the matter thrown off the star disperses rapidly, a stable nucleus, once formed, has a reasonable probability of surviving. The region of the sky where the Chinese reported seeing the supernova of 1054 now contains massive streams of gas rushing outward from a dense, dying core (Figure 20.23), the remnant of a once giant star that completed its task of synthesizing complex elements from hydrogen and, in a catastrophe that occurred nine hundred years ago, contributed some of these to the galaxy.

What, then, can we say about the solar system? The sun could not have evolved from pure hydrogen for it contains heavier nuclides as well. Very likely these were present in the primordial gas cloud from which it condensed. During the course of its final condensation small fragments may well have broken off the central protosun to become the protoplanets. The larger of these, such as Protojupiter, exerted a sufficient gravitational force to prevent their hydrogen from escaping, while the smaller ones, such as Proto-earth, lost most of their light elements.

Did the heavy elements from which the sun and planets were formed originate in the core of some long dead star that ended its life as a supernova? It is entirely possible, although, of course, it cannot be proved with absolute certainty. There is evidence to support the theory that the entire universe may have evolved from the explosion of a dense, primordial hydrogen core, and that traces of the elements were formed in the course of that event. But whatever their original source it seems reasonable to suppose that the elements composing the familiar forms we know, indeed the carbon that constitutes the foundation of all biological systems, was synthesized many eons ago in one or another series of large-scale astronomical processes.

Our survey of astrophysics, like our survey of biochemistry at the end of Section 19.8 has been cursory and has not even mentioned a number of fascinating contemporary problems. Rather it has emphasized the undoubted link between microscopic and macroscopic processes. The life cycle of a star is governed in detail by the properties of nuclei. For instance, because neither $_2He^5$, $_3Li^5$, nor $_4Be^8$ exist, stars of medium mass end their lives when they have consumed all their hydrogen. Again, the onset of a massive star's death agony is directly related to the stability of the iron group nuclei. Physics began as a quantitative science when Newton extracted his gravitational law from Kepler's planetary kinematics which the latter had deduced from Brahe's observational data. It is fitting that physics should repay its debt to astronomy by providing the nuclear data required to explore the internal processes of the stars themselves.

SUGGESTIONS FOR FURTHER READING ▲▲▲

Introductory texts containing chapters on nuclear structure include:

K. R. ATKINS, *Physics*, John Wiley and Sons, Inc., New York, 1965, Chapters 30 and 31.

GERALD HOLTON AND DUANE H. D. ROLLER, *Foundations of Modern Physics Science*, Addison-Wesley Publishing Co., Inc., Reading, Mass., 1958, Chapters 36–39.

JAY OREAR, *Fundamental Physics*, John Wiley and Sons, Inc., New York, 1961, Chapter 15.

The student interested in the early history of nuclear research should consult:

STEPHAN WRIGHT, *Classical Scientific Papers*, American Elsevier Publishing Co., Inc., New York, 1965.

J. B. BIRKS, *Rutherford at Manchester*, W. A. Benjamin, Inc., New York, 1963.

E. N. DACOSTA ANDRADE, *Rutherford and the Nature of the Atom*, Science Study Series, Doubleday and Co., Garden City, N.Y.

Many books also have been written on the development of the first atomic bomb and the potentialities of atomic energy including:

ROBERT JUNGK, *Brighter Than a Thousand Suns*, Harcourt, Brace and World, Inc., New York, 1958.

BERTRAND GOLDSCHMIDT, *The Atomic Adventure*, Pergamon Press, Oxford, 1964.

RALPH LAPP, *Atoms and People*, Harper and Brothers, New York, 1956.

HENRY D. SMYTHE, *Atomic Energy for Military Purposes*, Princeton University Press, Princeton, N.J., 1945.

(The last named reference is the official, unclassified history of the Manhattan project.)

The many readable, nontechnical books on astrophysics include:

FRED HOYLE, *Frontiers of Astronomy*, Harper and Row, New York, 1955.

FRED HOYLE, *Galaxies, Nuclei, and Quasars*, Harper and Row, New York, 1965.

ROBERT JASTROW, *Red Giants and White Dwarfs*, Harper and Row, Publishers, New York, 1968.

HERMAN BONDI, *The Universe at Large*, Science Study Series, Doubleday and Co., Garden City, N.Y.

VICTOR F. WEISSKOPF, *Knowledge and Wonder: The Natural World As Men Know It*, Science Study Series, Doubleday and Co., Garden City, N.Y., 1962.

The *Scientific American* has frequent articles on the history and current status of nuclear physics and astrophysics, for instance:

J. H. OORT, "The Crab Nebula," March, 1957, p. 52.

Sept., 1956, issue devoted entirely to the universe, with articles by several authors.

H. BROWN, "The Age of the Solar System," April, 1957, p. 80.

R. F. POST, "Fusion Power," Dec., 1957, p. 73.

OTTO HAHN, "The Discovery of Fission," Feb., 1958, p. 76.

G. T. SEABORG AND A. R. FRITSCH, "The Synthetic Elements," April, 1963, p. 68.

M. S. ROBERTS, "Hydrogen in Galaxies," June, 1963, p. 94.

J. L. GREENSTEIN, "Quasi-Stellar Radio Sources," Dec., 1963, p. 54.

A. R. SANDAGE, "Exploding Galaxies," Nov., 1964, p. 38.

L. BODASH, "How the Newer Alchemy Was Received," Aug., 1966, p. 88.

T. K. FOWLER AND R. F. POST, "Progress Toward Fusion Power," Dec., 1966, p. 21.

G. BURBIDGE AND F. HOYLE, "The Problem of the Quasi-Stellar Objects," Dec., 1966, p. 40.

PROBLEMS AND EXERCISES ▲▲▲

20.1. (a) How many protons and how many neutrons are there in each of the following nuclei: $_1H^3$, $_2He^4$, $_6C^{12}$, $_6C^{14}$, $_{26}Fe^{56}$, $_{82}Pb^{208}$, $_{82}Pb^{209}$, $_{92}U^{235}$, $_{92}U^{238}$?

(b) What are the approximate radii of $_2He^4$, $_6C^{12}$, $_{26}Fe^{56}$, and $_{82}Pb^{208}$?

20.2. Calculate the magnitudes of the electrostatic and gravitational forces between two protons in a nucleus. Take their separation as 1.4×10^{-15}.

20.3. (a) Neon ions, all of which have the same velocity, enter the magnetic field region in a mass spectrometer (Figure 20.2) and are deflected through 180° onto a photographic emulsion. If the radius of curvature of the $_{10}Ne^{20}$ ions is 0.5 m what is the separation between the lines on the film produced by the three isotopes. (Take their atomic weights as 20, 21, and 22, respectively.)

(b) If the spectrometer were used with uranium rather than neon ions and the magnetic field adjusted so that the $_{92}U^{238}$ ions would have a 0.5 m radius of curvature what would the separation at the film be for $_{92}U^{235}$ and $_{92}U^{238}$?

20.4. The isotopes of an element may also be separated by evaporation. For instance, as a tank of water evaporates, the concentration of the heavy water left in the residue increases. (One or both of the hydrogen atoms in heavy water are $_1H^2$ nuclei.)

Explain, on the basis of the statistical theory of matter, why this should be so.

Can 100% separation of ordinary from heavy water be accomplished by this technique? Why?

20.5. Why does the difficulty involved in separating two isotopes of the same element usually increase as their percentage mass difference decreases? (For example, it is much more difficult to separate the isotopes of uranium than the isotopes of hydrogen.)

20.6. Using the data in Table 20.1, determine the mass defect, the total binding energy, and the binding energy per nucleon of $_1H^2$, $_2He^4$, $_7N^{14}$, $_{26}Fe^{56}$, and $_{92}U^{238}$.

20.7. (a) Estimate and compare the electrostatic potential energies (in MeV) of a proton in $_{26}Fe^{56}$ and $_{92}U^{238}$ by assuming that the average distance between the proton of interest and the remaining protons is equal to the respective nuclear radii.

(b) Compare your answer to part a with the differences in the binding energies per nucleon for the two nuclei given in Figure 20.6. Why should the positive electrostatic energy of the protons contribute to the observed difference? What other factors do you think should contribute?

20.8. Justify the numerical relation (Equation 20.2) 1 atomic mass unit = 931 MeV.

20.9. (a) If a proton and an α-particle with the same kinetic energy penetrate matter which would you expect to stop first? Why? (There are two reasons.)

(b) If a neutron and a proton of the same kinetic energy penetrate matter which should stop first? Why?

20.10. (a) Estimate the probability of barrier penetration from a $_{88}Ra^{226}$ nucleus by noting the 1620-yr half-life of the nuclide, and assuming that on the average at least one α-particle exists in the nucleus at all times and travels back and forth across its diameter with a velocity 0.1 c.

(b) The α-particle emitted from the decay of $_{88}R^{226}$ and $_{92}U^{238}$ have comparable kinetic energies (4.8 and 4.2 MeV), yet the half-lives of the nuclides are 1620 yr and 4.5×10^9 yr, respectively. Is the half-life difference reasonable? Explain.

20.11. (a) Complete the following equations by identifying the missing decay product on the right (i.e., α, β^-, β^+, or γ. Of course a neutrino must accompany each $\beta^\pm$.)

i. $_{84}Po^{210} \rightarrow {}_{82}Pb^{206} + ?$
ii. $_{13}Al^{26} \rightarrow {}_{12}Mg^{26} + ?$
iii. $_{6}C^{12} \rightarrow {}_{6}C^{12} + ?$
iv. $_{14}Si^{31} \rightarrow {}_{15}P^{31} + ?$
v. $_{38}Sr^{90} \rightarrow {}_{39}Y^{90} + ?$

(b) The accompanying table gives the atomic masses of the daughter nuclei and the *kinetic* energies released in four of the above reactions. Use these data to calculate the masses of the respective decaying nuclei.

N.B.: The table lists the nuclear masses, not the masses of their corresponding atoms.

Reaction	Energy	Mass of Final State Nucleus
i	5.3 MeV	205.9296
ii	4.02 MeV	25.9750
iv	1.48 MeV	30.9655
v	0.54 MeV	89.8840

20.12. The products of several α-emitters in the three natural radioactive decay chains are β^--emitters, but none are β^+-emitters. Can you think of any reason why?

20.13. At 9 a.m. a sample of a certain radioisotope emits 20,000 decay electrons per second. By 10 a.m. the rate has fallen to 14,000 per second, and by 11 a.m. to 10,000 per second. What is the half-life of the nuclide? What decay rate is expected at 1 p.m.? At 5 p.m.?

20.14. An archaeologist analyzes the wood in a prehistoric structure and finds that the ratio of radioactive carbon ($_6C^{14}$) to stable carbon ($_6C^{12}$ and $_6C^{13}$) is only one-fourth the ratio found in the cells of living plants. How old is the structure (that is, when were the trees cut down to build it)? The half-life of $_6C^{14}$ is 5570 yr.

20.15. $_{38}Sr^{90}$, a β^--emitter with a twenty-eight-year half-life, is one of the common fragment nuclei from the fission of $_{92}U^{238}$ or $_{94}Pu^{239}$, and is thus found in the fallout from nuclear bombs. Being chemically akin to calcium it frequently displaces that element in milk and thus finds its way into bone cells.

Suppose a certain number of $_{38}Sr^{90}$ atoms concentrate in the bones of a one-year-old child. How old will he be when only 25% of the original dose remains?

20.16. (a) The biologically useful radioisotope $_{15}P^{32}$ is produced by neutron capture on $_{16}S^{32}$. What do you think its decay mode is? Why?

(b) What is the probable decay mode of $_{11}Na^{22}$? Why?

20.17. The reaction in which Chadwick first observed the neutron is

$$_2He^4 + {}_4Be^9 \rightarrow {}_6C^{12} + {}_0n^1.$$

Each incident α-particle (obtained from a radium source) had kinetic energy 4.8 MeV. What was the kinetic energy of each of the neutrons? (The mass of a $_4Be^9$ atom is 9.012 atomic units. Other necessary data are given in Table 20.1.)

20.18. One possible fission reaction of $_{92}U^{235}$ is

$$_0n^1 + {}_{92}U^{235} \rightarrow {}_{38}Sr^{90} + {}_{54}Xe^{126} + \text{? neutrons.}$$

(a) How many secondary neutrons are produced?

(b) How much energy is released in the reaction? (The masses of the $_{38}Sr^{90}$ and $_{54}Xe^{136}$ atoms are 89.909 and 135.909. The mass of the neutron and of $_{92}U^{235}$ are given in Table 20.1.)

20.19. (a) Calculate the total energy yield in any series of fusion reactions resulting in the conversion of four protons into an α-particle (and two positrons).

(b) What total energy would be evolved if 10.073 kg of hydrogen fused with 1% efficiency?

(c) How much hydrogen would have to burn with 100% efficiency to produce the same energy by chemical means? (The necessary data for this part of the problem are found in Section 16.2.)

20.20. According to the model presented in Section 20.13 the beginning of the end of a massive star's existence occurs when the mean temperature of its core is on the order of the binding energy of a nucleon in the medium to medium heavy nuclei. About how high is this temperature?

20.21. The temperatures at which the various thermonuclear reactions of Section 20.12 and 20.13 occur with reasonable probabilities are actually somewhat smaller than the temperatures calculated from the relation $KE = \frac{3}{2}kT$, where KE is the energy required to initiate the reaction. How can this be possible?

20.22. As we have used it in this text, temperature is a statistical concept intimately related to the observed behavior of matter. Thus, for instance, temperatures less than absolute zero are usually thought of as meaningless.

Can you think of a way in which a *maximum* conceivable temperature might be defined?

20.23. Comment on the probable appearance of the sun if:

(a) The gravitational constant G were twice as large as it is, but the strengths of the electromagnetic and nuclear interactions remained unaltered.

(b) The electromagnetic interactions were twice as strong as they are, but the strengths of the gravitational and nuclear interactions remained unaltered.

20.24. If the outlines of the astrophysical model of Section 20.13 are correct, does β-decay make (or has it made) any important contribution to the macroscopic appearance of the sun and planets or is it to be regarded as a completely incidental process?

Nuclear reactions and the
nucleon-nucleon interaction 21

▲▲ 21.1 The purpose of nuclear reaction studies. Illustrative examples

Our discussion of nuclear reactions in Chapter 20 centered upon energy yield (as in fission and fusion reactions) or upon the nature of the residual nuclei produced (as in the formation of β^--active $_6C^{14}$ by neutron capture on $_6C^{13}$, or fusion products in the stars, for instance). Rutherford's α-scattering measurements (Section 15.6) and the experiments that led to the identification of the proton and neutron (Section 20.6) concentrated instead upon the behavior of the light outgoing particles, and are prototypes of reaction experiments, whose purpose is to cast light upon internal nuclear structure.

The results that follow the bombardment of a target made of the isotope whose nuclei are being probed with particles whose energies are at least a few million electron volts are rarely simple, for the incident particles usually induce several reactions concurrently in different nuclei. We have already mentioned two reactions that are induced by α-particles incident upon $_7N^{14}$: α-scattering, and proton production. That is,

$$_2He^4 + {_7N^{14}} \rightarrow {_2He^4} + {_7N^{14}}, \tag{21.1a}$$

and

$$_2He^4 + {_7N^{14}} \rightarrow {_1H^1} + {_8O^{17}}. \tag{21.1b}$$

Actually each of these equations represents a series of possible reactions, for the outgoing light particle need not take all the kinetic energy available in the final state. Instead the residual nucleus can be left in one of its excited states, and subsequently make a transition to its ground state by emitting a γ-ray photon, in complete analogy with the deexcitation of an excited atom by optical photon emission (Figure 20.5). The relative probability for each possible series of reactions to occur is related in detail to the nature of the interaction between the incident particle and target nucleus. In quantum mechanical language the initial states in both Equation 21.1a and 21.1b are identical. By measuring the ratio of the number of incident α-particles that scatter from $_7N^{14}$ relative to the number that produce protons, we determine the relative transition probabilities into two different series of final states (Section 18.9). Hopefully some information about the transition amplitudes can be deduced from these data, and that information used to learn something about the interaction between α-particles and $_7N^{14}$ nuclei.

783

Virtually all of our knowledge of nuclear structure and nuclear interactions is derived from these and similar reactions induced with incident protons, neutrons, electrons, or γ-ray photons. Incident nucleons react with bound protons and neutrons primarily through the short-ranged nuclear interactions. The interactions of electrons, and photons are purely electromagnetic. Hence the character of the excitation and the type of information deduced about the nuclear states differ with the type of incident particle used to induce the reaction.

If an incident particle is to serve as a suitable probe it must have a reasonable probability of penetrating a nucleus and interacting with its bound nucleons. Thus, for instance, an incident proton must have sufficient kinetic energy to surmount the electrostatic potential barrier presented by the target nuclei and approach to within about 10^{-14} m of their centers (Figure 20.7b) for its barrier penetration probability is small. Referring to Equation 18.13, the potential energy of a nucleus with charge Ze ($Z =$ atomic number) and a proton with charge e separated by R meters is

$$PE = \frac{1}{4\pi\epsilon_0} \frac{(Ze)e}{R}.$$

Substituting $e = 1.6 \times 10^{-19}$ C, $R = 10^{-14}$ m, and using nitrogen ($Z = 7$) as an example,

$$PE = \frac{9 \times 10^9 \times 7 \times (1.6 \times 10^{-19})^2}{10^{-14}},$$

$$= 1.6 \times 10^{-13} \text{ J} \simeq 1 \text{ MeV},$$

which provides an estimate of the minimum kinetic energy a proton requires to induce a nuclear reaction on nitrogen. Because the height of the electrostatic barrier is proportional to Z the incident energy must increase with the atomic number of the target nucleus.

It should be noted that the electrostatic barrier criterion gives an estimate of the energy a proton requires if it is to react at all with the target nucleus. It does *not* imply that a proton with that energy can induce all conceivable reactions. In general the minimum threshold energy for a reaction is determined by applying mass-energy conservation. For example, if the final state particles have greater total rest mass than those in the initial state as they do in the proton production reaction (Equation 21.1b; see Section 20.6), the reaction is endothermic and proceeds only if the mass defect is balanced by the kinetic energy of the incoming particle. Again, if it is desired to excite a target nucleus to an energy level 5 MeV above its ground state, then clearly the incident particle's kinetic energy must be at least 5 MeV.

There are basically two ways in which a proton may induce a reaction (Figure 21.1). If it penetrates a nitrogen nucleus it may interact with the composite bound nucleons, remain in the vicinity long enough to share its energy with them, and form the compound nucleus $_8O^{15}$ in a highly excited state. On the other hand, a proton can also react with a nucleus without forming a compound nucleus. It might simply be scattered by the nuclear and electromagnetic forces:

$$_1H^1 + _7N^{14} \rightarrow _7N^{14} + _1H^1;$$

or it might interact with the surface nucleons alone by picking up a neutron and becoming a deuteron (i.e., a $_1H^2$ nucleus):

$$_1H^1 + _7N^{14} \rightarrow _7N^{13} + _1H^2.$$

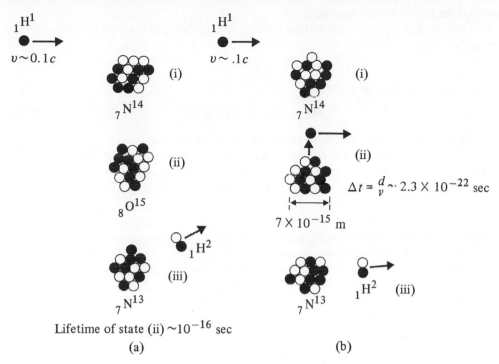

FIGURE 21.1   Two mechanisms for the reaction $_1H^1 + _7N^{14} \rightarrow _7N^{13} + _1H^2$. (a) Compound nucleus formation. The incident proton is captured by the nucleus and amalgamates with it to yield $_8O^{15}$ in a highly excited state. After a time on the order of 10^{-16} sec the system divests itself of its excess energy by expelling a deuteron $(_1H^2)$. (b) In a direct reaction the incident proton interacts only with the surface nucleons during the time it crosses the nuclear diameter. In the case illustrated it picks off a neutron leaving $_7N^{13}$ behind.

The compound nucleus formation process and the direct interaction processes differ drastically in their characteristic times. In the latter cases the reactions occur while the proton crosses the nuclear diameter. Since the proton's velocity will be on the order of 0.1 c, and the diameter of $_7N^{14}$ about 7×10^{-15} m (Equation 20.1), the reactions occur in times on the order of:

$$\Delta t = \frac{7 \times 10^{-15}}{3 \times 10^7} \cong 2.3 \times 10^{-22} \text{ sec.}$$

In contrast, a newly formed compound nucleus usually exists in its excited state for about 10^{-10} sec, which is about a million times longer than the 10^{-22} direct reaction time scale. Thus the newly captured proton can make almost a million excursions back and forth across the nucleus, sharing its energy with the other nucleons so that after a time nothing distinguishes the original incident proton from its neighbors.

We may summarize the formation of the compound system by the equation

$$_1H^1 + _7N^{14} \rightarrow [_8O^{15}],$$

using brackets to denote the transitory existence of the highly excited state. By observing the way various particles emerge from a nitrogen target bombarded with protons, we observe, in part, the decay modes of the compound system, and therefore extract information related to its internal structure.

The compound system might make a transition to the ground state of $_8O^{15}$ by emitting a γ-ray photon:

$$[_8O^{15}] \rightarrow {_8O^{15}} + \gamma.$$

In that event the observed reaction would be

$$_1H^1 + {_7N^{14}} \rightarrow {_8O^{15}} + \gamma. \tag{21.2a}$$

Even in a highly excited, transitory state, $_8O^{15}$ is a bound system with quantized energy levels. Hence its probability of formation by proton capture on $_7N^{14}$ should be appreciable only if the total energy in the initial state ($_1H^1 + {_7N^{14}}$) corresponds to the energy of an internal state in $_8O^{15}$. It follows that proton capture and subsequent γ-decay occurs with high probability only for a given set of incident proton energies. Therefore, a measurement of the reaction rate of Equation 21.2a as a function of incident proton energy provides one rather direct means of determining the energies of the highly excited states in $_8O^{15}$. To perform the experiment a proton beam with variable energy and known intensity is required as well as a means of identifying and counting the photons produced when a nitrogen-filled target is bombarded with that proton beam. The results of a series of such experiments are shown in Figure 21.2a.

Again, the excited compound system may decay by ejecting a proton with energy equal to the incident proton energy, so that we would observe the reaction

$$_1H^1 + {_7N^{14}} \rightarrow {_7N^{14}} + {_1H^1}. \tag{21.2b}$$

Of course the same final state is also observed when a proton scatters elastically from a $_7N^{14}$ nucleus without forming an intermediate $[_8O^{15}]$ state. The results of measurements of the probability of proton elastic scattering (Equation 21.2b) as a function of incident proton energy at 150° are shown in Figure 21.2b. The dashed curve gives the results that would be expected if the $_1H^1$-$_7N^{14}$ interaction were purely electrostatic (i.e., if the scattering were pure Rutherford scattering). Since the measured curve is considerably more complicated than the dashed curve it is apparent that the incident protons interact at least in part via the nuclear forces, and that some of them probably penetrate the $_7N^{14}$ nucleus.

More detailed measurements are required to disentangle the direct and compound nucleus contributions to an observed elastic scattering process. For example, most of the directly scattered protons are probably not deflected through very large angles. Therefore, they should be concentrated within a fairly narrow cone centered about the incident direction. In contrast, any directional preference shown by protons ejected from a decaying compound nucleus should be far less pronounced. By measuring the angular distribution for elastic scattering the probability of compound nucleus formation relative to direct scattering can be deduced, a datum that is evidently very sensitive to the details of the interaction between a proton and $_7N^{14}$.

FIGURE 21.2   (a) Measured probability of the reaction $_1H^1 + {_7N^{14}} \rightarrow {_8O^{15}} + \gamma$ as a function of incident proton energy. [D. B. Duncan and J. E. Perry, *Phys. Rev.*, Vol. 82, p. 809 (1951).] (b) Measured probability for the elastic scattering of protons by $_7N^{14}$ at 150° as a function of incident proton energy. The dashed curve shows the probability for pure Rutherford scattering. [E. W. Tautfest, J. R. Havill, and Sylvan Rubin, *Phys. Rev.*, Vol. 98, p. 280A, (1955).]

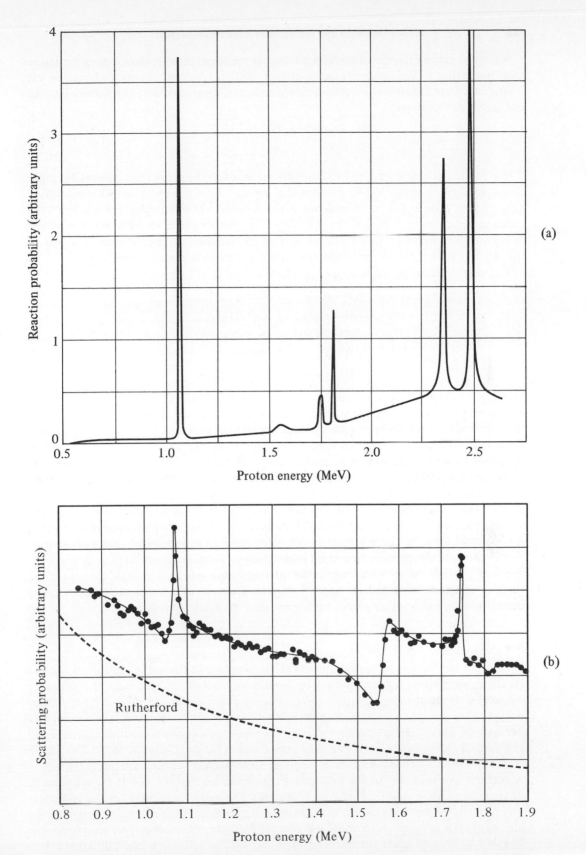

(a)

(b)

A proton ejected from a compound nucleus or scattered directly from a target nucleus need not retain its full incident kinetic energy. Rather, the residual nucleus may be left in one of its excited states and subsequently return to its ground state by γ-emission. In our particular example,

$$_1H^1 + {_7N^{14}} \rightarrow {_7N^{14}} + {_1H^1}$$
$$\hookrightarrow {_7N^{14}} + \gamma. \tag{21.2c}$$

These particular reactions may be distinguished from all the other reactions taking place concurrently by identifying the photons that emerge from a bombarded nitrogen target at the same time as (or in coincidence with) protons whose energies are less than the incident beam energy. Measurements of the energies of the emergent γ-rays from the decay of $_7N^{14}$ will then give the same sort of information about the excited states of the nucleus that optical photon spectra give about excited atomic states.

For completeness we list several other reactions induced by protons on $_7N^{14}$:

$$_1H^1 + {_7N^{14}} \rightarrow {_8O^{14}} + {_0n^1},$$
$$_1H^1 + {_7N^{14}} \rightarrow {_6C^{11}} + {_2He^4},$$
$$_1H^1 + {_7N^{14}} \rightarrow {_7N^{13}} + {_1H^2},$$
$$_1H^1 + {_7N^{14}} \rightarrow {_7N^{12}} + {_1H^3},$$
$$_1H^1 + {_7N^{14}} \rightarrow {_6C^{12}} + {_2He^3}.$$

Of these five sets, the first two almost always proceed via the compound $[_8O^{15}]$ system, and may, therefore, be used to study the formation and decay of that system. The latter three can also occur directly with the incident proton picking up one or two nucleons from the surface of a target nucleus. All of the reactions can also leave the residual nuclei in excited states so that measurements of the energies of the γ-rays emerging in coincidence with a particular light particle offer a means of determining the energy levels in the respective final state nucleus.

We shall not examine nuclear reaction mechanisms in detail. But from this brief survey it should be evident that these reactions can yield considerable information about the internal structure of complex nuclei. It should also be evident that two general technical problems are involved in all such studies. First, it is necessary to produce an incident particle beam with reasonable intensity and sufficient energy to induce the reactions that are to be studied. Second, detectors capable of distinguishing the outgoing particles from one another and of measuring their energies are required.

◤◤ 21.2 Particle accelerators

Prior to the advent of the first practical accelerators in the early 1930's, all nuclear reactions were either induced directly by α-particles from natural radioactive sources, or by secondary neutron or (occasionally) secondary proton beams produced by the interaction of these α-particles with suitable nuclei (Section 20.6). However, such secondary beams have very small intensities. In addition, since their energies are directly related to the natural α-decay energies, they rarely exceed 4 or 5 MeV and cannot be selected at will or easily varied. Hence the utility of such beams in nuclear reaction studies is limited.

As their names imply, particle accelerators are machines that increase the kinetic energy of charged particles and thus produce beams of those particles suitable for use in nuclear and elementary particle reaction experiments. Regardless of their detailed design or the energy they attain, *all* accelerators use electric fields to accomplish their purpose. The simplest types accelerate the particles in a single stage. If a potential difference V is

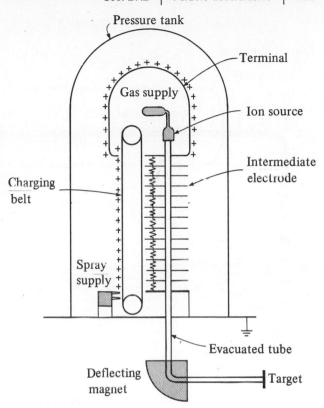

FIGURE 21.3 Schematic diagram of a Van de Graaff generator designed to accelerate positive ions from the source down the evacuated tube. A magnet then deflects the accelerated beam onto an experimental target. (From Derek L. Livesey, *Atomic and Nuclear Physics*, Blaisdell Publishing Co., Waltham, Mass., 1966.)

established between two electrodes, a particle with charge $e = +1.6 \times 10^{-19}$ C will be accelerated from the positive to the negative electrode, its kinetic energy increasing by V electron volts in the process.

The only single stage accelerator in widespread common use today is the Van de Graaff generator, essentially a device for producing and maintaining a large, negative potential difference between an insulated electrode and ground (Figure 21.3). Free protons with several electron volts energy are produced by passing hydrogen gas over a hot, ionizing electric arc. (The same technique yields free deuterons or α-particles if heavy hydrogen or helium is used instead.) The ion source in a Van de Graaff generator is located at the positive electrode. Therefore, the newly ionized positively charged nuclei see a large positive potential difference, and are immediately accelerated through an evacuated tube to the electrode at ground potential. The particles emerge through an aperture in the latter electrode and constitute a beam suitable for inducing nuclear reactions in an external target.

The only restriction upon the energy of a proton beam from this accelerator is set by the practical upper limit in the potential difference that can be maintained between the positive electrode and ground, normally about five or six million volts. However, a working scheme has been developed for using two Van de Graaff's in tandem, thereby increasing this energy limit by a factor of two (Figure 21.4). When diatomic hydrogen molecules flow over an electric arc a few are dissociated into a free proton and a *negative* hydrogen ion, a proton with two bound electrons. These are accelerated *toward* a positive electrode, then pass through a thin metallic foil where a number of them lose both electrons and become free protons, ready for another stage of acceleration toward a second negative electrode.

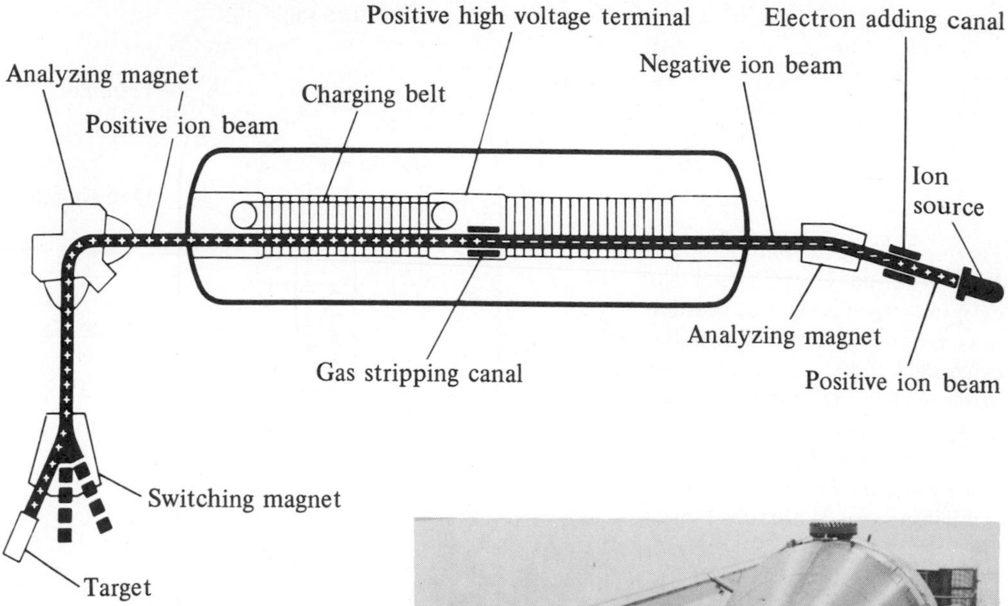

(a)

(b)

FIGURE 21.4 (a) Schematic diagram of a two stage-tandem Van de Graaff. Positive ions from the source pick up electrons to become negatively charged ions. These are accelerated to the positive high voltage terminal at the center of the accelerator, stripped of their electrons and, as positive ions once again, accelerated the rest of the way. The analyzing magnet deflects the accelerated beam to a switching magnet which in turn deflects the beam onto one of three targets, depending on its field. (b) Output end of the tandem Van de Graaff at the Yale University Nuclear Structure Laboratory. The evacuated beam tube, analyzing magnet, and switching magnet, which directs the beam to a target, are visible in the foreground. (Drawing and Photograph Courtesy of the Yale Nuclear Structure Laboratory.)

Because the electric field in a Van de Graaff generator is constant in time, all accelerated particles are subject to the same potential difference regardless of when they leave the region where they are produced. Hence all particles in the outgoing accelerated beam have the same energy to within a few electron volts, a distinct advantage in experiments requiring a precise knowledge of the incident energy. In addition, beams from Van de Graaff generators are more intense than those from the multistage accelerators we consider next, for in the latter some fraction of the particles is usually lost at each stage. Be that as it may, the single stage accelerator is unsuitable for many applications simply because its energy is limited to 5 or 6, or, in the case of a tandem Van de Graaff, to 10 or 12 MeV.

Figure 21.5 shows the basic features of one type of multistage accelerator, the linear accelerator, or *linac*. We may regard the accelerator as a series of parallel plate capacitors, each constituting an accelerating stage, connected by metal tubes that shield the particles from the electric field and permit them to drift between each stage of

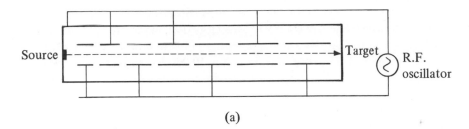

(a)

(b)

FIGURE 21.5   (a) A drift tube linear accelerator. The electric field direction between adjacent tubes varies periodically with time. Thus a proton emerging from a tube at the proper time in the cycle is accelerated across the gap, as it would be accelerated across a parallel plate capacitor gap. During the unfavorable part of the cycle the protons coast in the tubes where they are shielded from the changing field. (From Derek L. Livesey, *Atomic and Nuclear Physics*, Blaisdell Publishing Co., Waltham, Mass., 1966.) (b) View into a linear accelerator showing the drift tubes. (Courtesy of Brookhaven National Laboratory.)

acceleration. The electric field in a linac, as in all multistage accelerators, varies periodically as a function of time. During one-half of each periodic cycle the field direction across all of the capacitor gaps is positive from left to right, and can accelerate positively charged particles in that direction.

Suppose a proton, newly stripped of its electron by an electric arc, enters the first capacitor gap just as the left-hand plate comes positive. If the field varies sinusoidally with time, it will be positive and increasing during one-quarter of the cycle, positive and decreasing during the next one-quarter cycle, and then negative for the next half-cycle. Hence the proton must cross the gap and enter the first drift tube in a time no greater than one-half the period of the field. Otherwise it will remain in the gap when the field becomes negative and be decelerated. If the proton coasts along in the drift tube shielded from the field during the negative part of the cycle, it will enter the second capacitor gap when the potential difference across that gap is favorable for another acceleration stage. Again, however, the proton must have crossed the gap and be in the second, fieldfree drift region before the field becomes negative once more.

By arranging a sufficient number of properly designed capacitor-drift tube sections in series, the proton can be accelerated, in stages, to an energy that, in principle, is unlimited. Suppose a linac is designed so that the average potential difference across each capacitor gap during the positive part of the electric field cycle is 10,000 V. In that case a proton gains $10 \text{ keV} = 10^5 \times 1.6 \times 10^{-19} = 1.6 \times 10^{-14} \text{ J}$ in each stage. Its velocity at the end of the first stage is

$$v = \sqrt{\frac{2KE}{m}} = \sqrt{\frac{2 \times 1.6 \times 10^{-15}}{1.6 \times 10^{-27}}} = 1.4 \times 10^6 \text{ m/sec.}$$

If the electric field varies with a frequency of 5 megacycles (5×10^6 cycles/sec) the proton must remain in each drift tube for at least $\frac{1}{2} \times \frac{1}{5} \times 10^{-6} = 10^{-7}$ sec if it is to be shielded from the field during the unfavorable half of each cycle. Thus the length of the first tube must be $1.4 \times 10^6 \times 10^{-7} = 0.14$ m.

A linear accelerator built according to these specifications would require 100 acceleration stages to produce a 1 MeV proton beam. Because the velocity of the protons would increase in each gap, the length of each succeeding drift tube would also have to increase. After the tenth gap a proton would have velocity 4.5×10^6 m/sec requiring a 0.45 m drift tube. Likewise the length of the fiftieth drift tube would be 1 m, the length of the last about 1.4 m. The entire accelerator, including capacitor gaps, would be well over 100 m long, far too unwieldy a device to serve as a practical source of 1 MeV proton beam, especially in comparison with Van de Graaff generators.

An increase in the potential difference across each gap or an increase in its frequency or both would permit a decrease in the total length of our linac. For example, by using fifty thousand volts per gap, protons could be accelerated to 5 MeV in one hundred stages. If, in addition, the frequency were 50 rather than 5 megacycles, those hundred stages would have a total length of about 10 m instead of 100.

Linear accelerators were discussed and investigated in the late 1920's. However, they only became practical with the availability of the high frequency vacuum tubes developed to power radar transmitters during World War II. A good many of the linacs in current use accelerate electrons rather than protons, partly because it is easier to build a very high energy electron linear accelerator than a proton linear accelerator which delivers a comparable energy, partly because there are more efficient ways to accelerate protons. The velocity of a particle whose kinetic energy is equal to its rest energy is more than 85%

the velocity of light. Its velocity is more than 95% of that limiting velocity when its kinetic energy is three times its rest energy (Equations 11.25, 11.26, and 11.28). Hence the velocity of a 2 MeV electron (rest energy 0.511 MeV) can never increase by more than 5% regardless of how much its energy increases. It follows that the required drift tube lengths in an electron linac remain constant after the 2 or 3 MeV stage and that thereafter the accelerator can be constructed from identical segments. In contrast, a proton has rest energy 938 MeV and would have to be accelerated to 4 or 5 BeV in a proton linac before the remaining sections of the accelerator could be of identical construction.

By far the longest and most energetic linear accelerator in existence is the 20 BeV (billion electron volts) accelerator located at Stanford University (Figure 21.6). Electrons boiled off a hot filament, as in an x-ray machine, are preaccelerated by a single stage device before being injected into the linac proper. Here they are accelerated to their final, 20 BeV energies by a number of identical sections whose total length is two miles.

The first cyclotron, progenitor of the best known as well as the most energetic of all accelerators, was constructed by Ernest Lawrence and M. S. Livingston at the University of California in 1932. The linear accelerator principle had already been discussed and a few experimental models constructed and tested. But as we have noted, the lack of high frequency power sources in the late 1920's made that type of accelerator unwieldy. The basic innovation introduced by Lawrence and Livingston is quite simple in principle. In order to overcome the length problem implicit for any multistage accelerator, the particles are constrained in spiral orbits by a constant *magnetic* field while they are being accelerated by a periodically varying *electric* field (Figure 21.7). The ready applicability of the scheme turns on the rather remarkable fact already noted in our discussion of the cyclotron in Section 9.4: although the radius of curvature of a circular particle trajectory in a uniform magnetic field depends upon its velocity, the *time* the particle requires to complete one revolution is independent of both its velocity and that radius of curvature.

FIGURE 21.6 Stanford University's two-mile electron linear accelerator. The acceleration tube itself is the small tube rigidly mounted to the large one at the bottom of the photograph. Alignment is achieved by adjusting the jacks beneath the large tube and is checked by directing a laser beam down its length.(Courtesy of Brookhaven National Laboratory.)

For convenience we shall summarize the pertinent relations derived in Section 9.4. The orbital frequency of a particle with charge e and mass M in a uniform magnetic field of strength B is

$$f = \frac{1}{T} = \left(\frac{e}{M}\right) \frac{B}{2\pi}. \tag{9.19}$$

Thus the high voltage across the gap between the dees of the cyclotron must vary with the same frequency. The velocity of the particle is directly related to its radius of curvature by Equation 9.18. Therefore, the maximum velocity attainable in a particular cyclotron is related to its maximum radius by

$$v_{\max} = \left(\frac{e}{M}\right) B R_{\max}. \tag{9.20a}$$

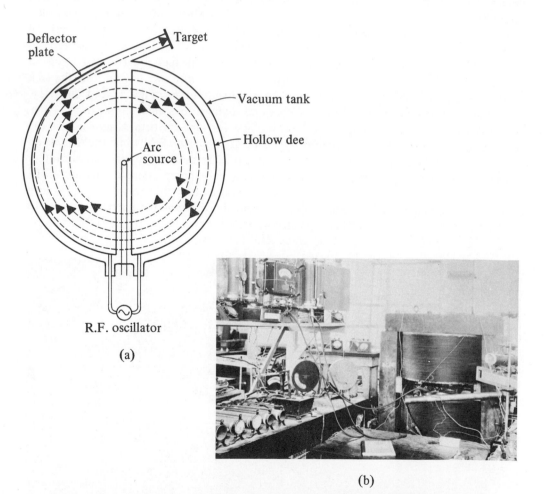

(a)

(b)

FIGURE 21.7 (a) Principle of the cyclotron. Positive ions, produced at an arc source in the center, are maintained in spiral orbits by a magnetic field perpendicular to the plane of the page while being accelerated by an alternating electric field across the gap between two dees. (From Derek L. Livesey, *Atomic and Nuclear Physics*, Blaisdell Publishing Co., Waltham, Mass., 1966.) (b) The first practical cyclotron, built by E. O. Lawrence and M. S. Livingstone early in 1932. It accelerated protons to 1.2 MeV. (Courtesy of M. S. Livingston.)

Finally, if the final velocity is small relative to the velocity of light the maximum attainable kinetic energy is

$$KE = \tfrac{1}{2}Mv^2 = \frac{e^2}{2M}(BR_{max})^2. \tag{9.20b}$$

A numerical example will indicate why cyclotrons were more practical than linear accelerators in the late 1930's. As in the previous hypothetical linac let the frequency of the alternating high voltage be 5 megacycles/sec. Then the field strength required if the orbital frequency of the protons in the cyclotron is also 5 megacycles/sec follows from Equation 9.19:

$$B = 2\left(\frac{M}{e}\right)f$$

$$= \frac{2 \times 3.14 \times 1.6 \times 10^{-27} \times 5 \times 10^6}{1.6 \times 10^{-19}}$$

$$= 0.31 \text{ Wb/m}^2.$$

If the radius of the magnet is 0.5 m (about $19\tfrac{1}{2}$ in.) the energy of the protons emerging from the cyclotron is (Equation 9.20b):

$$KE = \frac{(1.6 \times 10^{-19})^2}{2 \times 1.6 \times 10^{-27}}(0.31 \times 0.5)^2$$

$$= 1.8 \times 10^{-13} \text{ J} = 1.1 \text{ MeV}.$$

That is, the protons have roughly the same energy they would have had if accelerated in the 100-m, 5-megacycle linac considered previously.

Uniform magnetic field strengths up to about 1.5 Wb/m² can be produced by large electromagnets. According to Equation 9.19 such a field, if used in a cyclotron, would require an alternating high voltage with a frequency of 25 megacycles to accelerate protons. Since the final energy is proportional to the *square* of the field strength (Equation 9.20b), the maximum energy attainable with a 1-m diameter, 1.5 Wb/m² field strength magnet is about 25 MeV. Alternately, a larger diameter magnet with a smaller field strength could be used to accelerate protons to the same energy, provided, of course, that the frequency of the alternating potential across the accelerating gap were related to the magnetic field strength by Equation 9.19.

The applicability of the simple cyclotron principle, summarized by the constancy of a particle's orbital frequency in a fixed magnetic field, is limited by the relativistic mass increase that begins to become apparent for protons with kinetic energies greater than about 20 MeV. The total energy of a particle, E (kinetic energy plus rest energy) is Mc^2 and its rest energy M_0c^2. Therefore,

$$\frac{E}{E_0} = \frac{KE + M_0c^2}{M_0c^2} = \frac{Mc^2}{M_0c^2} = \frac{M}{M_0}, \tag{21.3}$$

the ratio of total energy to rest energy is equal to the ratio of relativistic mass to rest mass. A proton with 20 MeV kinetic energy (and 938 MeV rest energy) has a relativistic mass 3% greater than its rest mass, i.e.,

$$\frac{M}{M_0} = \frac{958}{938} = 1.03,$$

whereas the ratio is 1.10 for a 100 MeV kinetic energy proton. According to Equation 9.19, the orbital frequency of a particle in a constant magnetic field varies inversely as its mass. Thus, when the outward spiraling protons in a cyclotron attain energies on the order of 20 or 30 MeV, they no longer arrive at the accelerating gap at just the moment when the electric field is a maximum in the proper direction for acceleration. Instead, they lag behind the alternating field. After a few turns they may actually arrive at the worst possible moment, when the field is in the proper direction for *deceleration* across the gap. Hence the simple cyclotron principle cannot be used to accelerate particles to energies greater than 20 or 30 MeV.

Two different methods are used to overcome this relativistic limitation. In a *synchrocyclotron* the strength of the magnetic field increases toward the periphery of the system so that the ratio B/M, and therefore, the orbital frequency of the accelerated particle, will remain constant as its energy increases. A *frequency modulated* or *FM cyclotron* retains the constant magnetic field of the conventional cyclotron, but reduces the frequency of the alternating voltage applied across the dees as the orbital frequency of the particles decreases. Proton energies up to 500 or 600 MeV can be attained by using one method or the other, provided sufficiently large magnets are used.

The largest of the circular accelerators, known as *synchrotrons*, are also based upon the cyclotron principle, but incorporate both of these modifications in addition to others. We state here without proof a relativistically correct relation between the radius of curvature of a particle with *total* energy E in moving in a magnetic field of strength B given in webers/meter^2 (see Problems):

$$R = 3.3 \times 10^{-3} \frac{E}{B} \frac{v}{c} \text{ m,} \tag{21.4}$$

where v/c is the ratio of the particle's velocity to the velocity of light, and may be obtained from its total energy by using Equation 11.19:

$$E = \frac{M_0 c^2}{\sqrt{1 - v^2/c^2}}.$$

For a 6 BeV proton in a magnetic field of strength 1.2 Wb/m^2,

$$R = 3.3 \times 10^{-3} \left(\frac{6 \times 10^3}{1.2}\right) \frac{v}{c} = 16.5 \left(\frac{v}{c}\right) \text{ m.}$$

From Equation 11.19,

$$\sqrt{1 - v^2/c^2} = \frac{M_0 c^2}{E} = \frac{938}{6000} = 0.156,$$

yielding $(v/c) = 0.98$. Therefore, $R = 16.5 \times 0.98 = 16.1$ m, or about 50 ft, and it follows that a synchrotron magnet must have at least that radius in order to confine 6 BeV protons within the accelerator. The quantity of iron required to build a solid one-hundred-foot diameter magnet would be prohibitively expensive, even if such a magnet could be constructed and supported. However, the same electromagnet used to confine 6 BeV total energy protons to a radius of 16.1 m also confines 20 MeV kinetic energy protons (total energy 958 MeV) to the same radius of curvature at a lower field, specifically (Equation 9.19) at 0.17 Wb/m^2.

Synchrotron designs take advantage of the foregoing considerations by using a circular *ring* of magnets in place of the solid magnet of a conventional cyclotron (Figure 21.8).

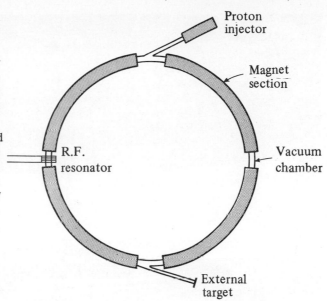

FIGURE 21.8   Outline diagram of a proton synchrotron. Protons are injected into an orbit in the chamber enclosed in the magnet ring. Energy is supplied by varying both the magnetic field strength and the frequency of the radio frequency electric field applied to the resonator. (From Derek L. Livesey, *Atomic and Nuclear Physics*, Blaisdell Publishing Company, Waltham, Mass., 1966.)

Particles pre-accelerated in a linac to 20 MeV kinetic energy or more are injected into a doughnut-shaped, evacuated chamber within the ring while the field in the magnets is low. As they circle about the ring their energies are increased by alternating electric fields applied at gaps located between several of the magnets, and the magnetic field is increased continuously to keep the accelerating particles in orbits of constant radius. In addition, the frequency of the alternating accelerating electric field also varies so that it will always be in the right direction to accelerate the particles when they arrive at the gaps.

Presently, the world's most energetic particle accelerator is the proton synchroton located at Serpukov in the Soviet Union. It first accelerated protons to 70 BeV in October, 1967, and may eventually attain energies in the 80 to 90 BeV range. The second and third most energetic synchrotrons are the 33 BeV Alternating Gradient Synchrotron at the Brookhaven National Laboratory, Long Island, New York (Figure 21.9) and the 28 BeV proton synchrotron operated by the Central European Laboratory for Nuclear Research (CERN) at Geneva, Switzerland. In the former of these two synchrotrons, protons are pre-accelerated to 50 MeV by a linac before injection into the synchrotron proper, whose fifty ring magnets give it an overall diameter of about 600 ft. Three seconds are required for the fields in the magnets to increase from their minimum, injection values to their maximum, 33 BeV values, and return again to their minima. During each of these three-second cycles the synchrotron can accelerate about 10^{12} protons. The accelerator has been in operation since 1960.

Electron synchrotrons are also useful research instruments. The most energetic of these, at Cornell University, attained an energy of 10 BeV early in 1968. Three 6 BeV electron synchrotrons, at Cambridge, Mass., Hamburg, Germany, and Yerevan, Soviet Armenia, have been in operation for several years.

Detailed studies for the construction and operation of a 200 BeV proton synchrotron to be located at a new National Accelerator Laboratory at Batavia, Illinois, were completed by mid-1968 (Figure 21.10). Acceleration is to be accomplished in three stages. In the first, protons will be accelerated to about 50 MeV by a linac then injected into a relatively small, 500-ft diameter synchrotron, called a *booster ring*. Here they will be

(a)

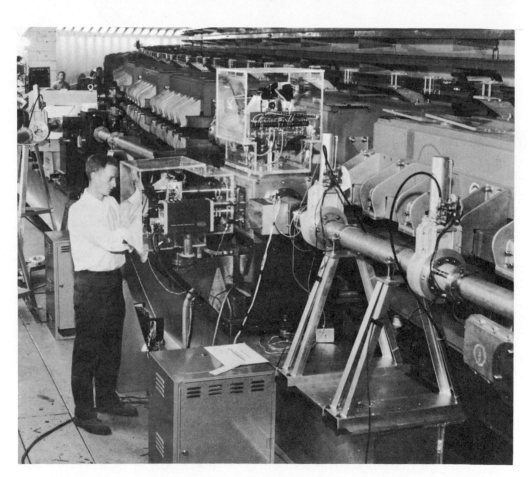

(b)

FIGURE 21.9 (a) The Brookhaven Cosmotron, a proton synchrotron which
first attained an energy of 3 BeV in 1953. (b) A section of the Brookhaven
alternating gradient synchrotron showing part of the ring magnet and an external
beam tube. The synchrotron first attained an energy of 33 BeV in 1961. (Courtesy of Brookhaven National Laboratory.)

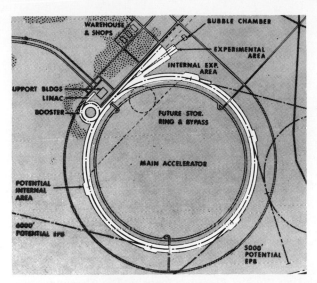

FIGURE 21.10 Plan view of the proposed synchrotron and experimental facilities to be located at Batavia, Illinois. Protons will be injected from a linac into the "small" 500-ft diameter booster ring then accelerated to 10 BeV before injection into the 1.25 mile diameter main ring. (The "small" booster ring is only slightly smaller than the Brookhaven alternating gradient synchrotron.) (Courtesy of the National Accelerator Laboratory.)

accelerated to 10 BeV before injection into the 1.25 mile (2 km) diameter main ring, composed of about 1000 magnets. Thirteen injections from the booster will be required to fill the main ring with protons. Since the former will accelerate to its maximum, 10 BeV energy fifteen times per second, about one second will be required for the protons to accumulate in the main ring. During that time they will circle about at that energy, and thereafter be accelerated to their full 200 BeV in about three seconds.

The cost of the project is estimated at $240 million, compared with the $30 million required for the 33 BeV Brookhaven synchrotron and the $120 million for the Stanford two-mile linac. Official ground breaking ceremonies for the 200 BeV accelerator took place on December 1, 1968.

▲▲ 21.3 Particle detectors

The design of all particle detectors is based upon the transfer of electromagnetic energy from a charged particle passing through matter to the atoms along its path (Section 20.4). We may distinguish between two broad classes of particle detectors: those that leave a visible record that may either be observed directly or photographed, and those that mark the passage of a particle by producing an electric pulse.

Photographic emulsions are the oldest of all particle detectors (Figure 21.11). Indeed, the most common types find their principal use in the detection of a very special type of particles—photons with associated wavelengths in the visible region of the electromagnetic spectrum. The formation of a photographic image involves a relatively complex series of chemical reactions. However, for our purposes it is sufficient to note that the grains of silver bromide suspended in an emulsion undergo chemical changes when they absorb energy from photons, and that the altered grains are blackened when the film is developed. Since the silver bromide in an emulsion cannot distinguish the source of the energy inducing its change, an energetic charged particle will have the same effect on the grains along its path as a photon whose associated wavelength is in the visible region of the electromagnetic spectrum. Special, highly refined emulsions have been developed for charged particle detection with grain size small enough to resolve the tracks due to individual charged particles. Since the ionization caused by a charged particle passing

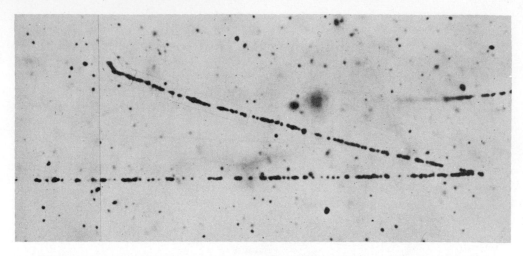

FIGURE 21.11   Particle tracks in a thick, specially prepared emulsion. (From C. F. Powell and G. P. S. Occhialini, *Nuclear Physics in Pictures*, The Clarendon Press, Oxford, 1947).

through matter is a function of its energy, the relative density of a track provides a rough measurement of that primary energy.

Figure 21.12 suggests a method for using emulsions to measure the number of protons scattered by a particular species of target nucleus as a function of scattering angle.   The

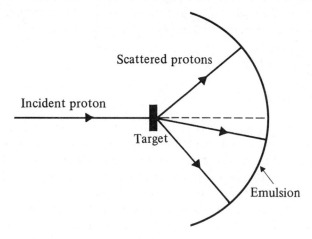

FIGURE 21.12   Measurement of the angular distribution of scattered protons by means of an emulsion technique.

FIGURE 21.13   (a) Principle of the Wilson expansion cloud chamber. The gas is suddenly expanded by means of a piston and the chamber becomes supersaturated with vapor, which condenses preferentially on ions along the tracks of charged particles. (From Derek L. Livesey, *Atomic and Nuclear Physics*, Blaisdell Publishing Co., Waltham, Mass., 1966.) (b) Some of Wilson's first published cloud chamber photographs. [From C. T. R. Wilson, "On an expansion apparatus for making visible the tracks of ionizing particles in gases and some results obtained by its use," *Proc. Roy. Soc.*, Vol. *A 87*, 277–92 (1912).]

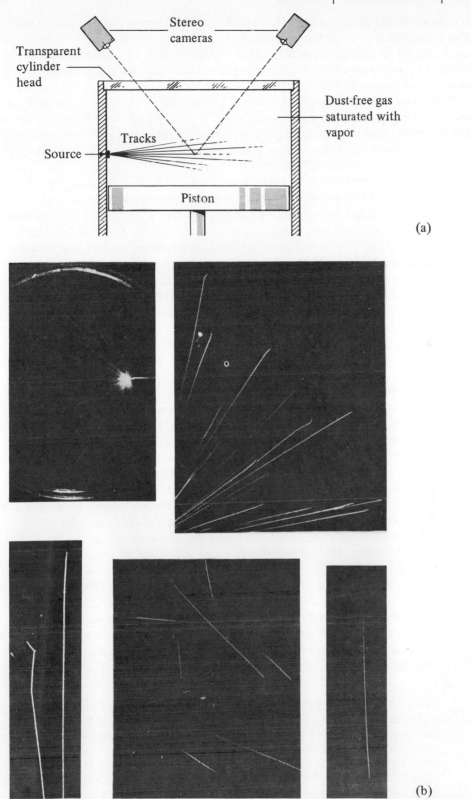

Stereo cameras

Transparent cylinder head

Dust-free gas saturated with vapor

Tracks

Source

Piston

(a)

(b)

emulsions are arranged in a semicircle centered upon the target so that each small strip of film corresponds to a specific small range of scattering angles. The number of particle tracks found in each of these strips after a proton beam of known intensity has been incident upon the target for a specific length of time measures the scattering probability into each of the angular intervals defined by the film.

Photographic emulsions preserve visual records of all charged, subatomic particles that pass through them while they are exposed to a source of such particles. But they do not record the time at which each particle leaves its imprint. Three other visual detectors are much better both in that respect and in their ability to make extended, three-dimensional records of charged particle tracks.

The *cloud chamber* (Figure 21.13) invented by C. T. R. Wilson during the 1910's, was used in some of the very earliest nuclear reaction experiments (Section 20.4).

A vapor, reduced to its liquefaction temperature, can often remain in its gaseous state until some sort of disturbance induces its molecules to cluster and liquefy. Turbulence in the vapor qualifies as a potential catalyst for liquefaction, as does the presence of an impurity or electric charge. The simplest types of cloud chambers (Figure 21.13a) maintain an organic vapor (alcohol or ether, for instance) at liquefaction temperature. A charged particle passing through the vapor ionizes the molecules in its wake, and the disturbed vapor liquefies along that ion trail, leaving a vapor trail that may be observed directly or photographed for later, more careful study.

Expansion cloud chambers operate on a similar principle, but are only sensitive for relatively short time intervals. The chamber volume contains the working substance in gaseous form together with a second, permanent gas with a lower liquefaction temperature. When the volume is expanded suddenly the pressure and therefore the temperature of the two gases drop. The cooled, permanent gas facilitates the cooling of the active substance so that the latter is left in a supersaturated state ready to liquefy along any trail of ions that may then be present in the chamber.

Just as liquefaction is triggered in a vapor by an external disturbance, boiling can be induced in a liquid maintained at the requisite temperature. In the most widely used types of *bubble chambers*, an expansion mechanism periodically reduces the pressure on a refrigerated volume of liquid hydrogen (or a heavy organic liquid) to the point where boiling can start along an ion trail left behind in the unstable liquid by a fast charged particle (Figure 21.14). Thus a trail of bubbles marks the passage of the charged particle through the chamber. Both cloud chambers and bubble chambers take advantage of the instability of a substance hovering between the gaseous and liquid states. In one instance the creation of an ion trail forces the substance along the trail into the liquid state, in the other case, the ions induce a transition to the opposite direction.

The trail of a charged particle through a spark chamber is marked by a series of high voltage discharges between electrical conductors along its path, a situation once again induced by the ion trail left in the wake of an energetic charged particle. The potential difference between two closely spaced conductors cannot be increased indefinitely, for

FIGURE 21.14. (a) The Brookhaven 80-inch liquid hydrogen bubble chamber during assembly, showing the coils of the magnet which are to enclose it. The high energy particle beam enters the chamber through a thin window covered with plastic in the photograph, and tracks are photographed through a plate glass window which will cover the large open aperture. (b) High energy π-mesons (incident from the left) and a π-meson induced reaction in the Brookhaven 30-inch liquid hydrogen bubble-chamber. (Courtesy of Brookhaven Laboratory.)

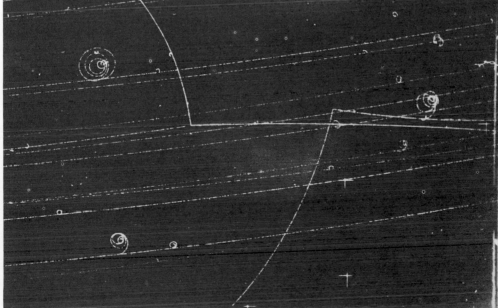

(a)

(b)

ultimately the insulating material between them, be it air, another gas, a liquid, or a nonmetallic solid, becomes a momentary conductor, and the resulting discharge across the gap usually reduces the potential on the conductors to the same level. Electrical breakdown (sparking) through an insulator can be induced at a potential difference

(a)

(b)

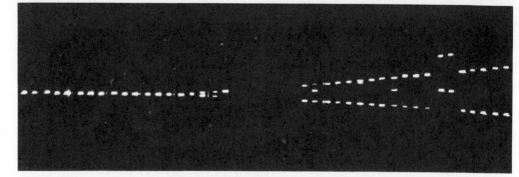

FIGURE 21.15.   (a) A set of spark chambers viewed along their conducting plates. The particles emerge from the magnet whose coils are visible to the right of the first chamber, and pass through the chambers in a direction perpendicular to the plates. The high voltage connections can be seen in the upper part of the picture. (Courtesy of Brookhaven National Laboratory.) (b) The production of a pair of muons in a spark chamber plate by a high energy π^--meson incident from the left.

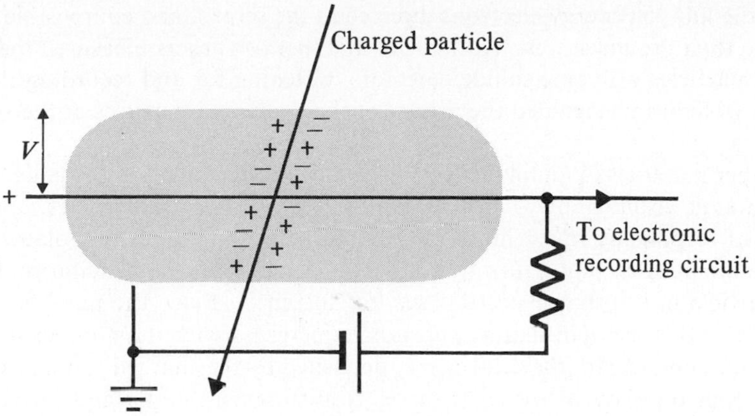

FIGURE 21.16. Principle of the Geiger counter. An energetic charged particle passing through the counter ionizes the gas along its trail. Electrons, accelerated toward the central collector wire which is maintained at a high positive potential difference relative to ground, ionize other atoms along their paths. When all these electrons are collected they constitute a current which is recorded in an external unit.

somewhat below the breakdown level by introducing electric charge into the gap between two conductors. Figure 21.15 shows the essence of a typical spark chamber. The potential difference between alternate pairs of a series of parallel conducting plates is raised to a value slightly less than the breakdown voltage, and the entire chamber filled with an insulating gas at low pressure, usually a mixture of helium and neon. An ion trail forms along the path of an energetic charged particle through that gas, and the charge thus injected induces a breakdown between the plates, leaving a series of sparks to mark the particle's passage.

Geiger counters, the best known of the nonvisual detectors, operate upon an extension of the electrical discharge principle. The body of the counter is a metallic conductor filled with an organic gas and maintained at a high, negative potential difference relative to a wire that runs along its axis (Figure 21.16). Electrons freed from the gas molecules by an energetic charged particle are accelerated toward the central wire, whereas the residual positive ions migrate toward the outer, negative conductor. Before reaching the central wire many of the accelerated electrons acquire sufficient energy to ionize additional molecules, releasing more electrons which also accelerate toward the negative conductor and can liberate more free ions in their turn. Hence a virtual avalanche of electrons follows the creation of the original ion trail. Collected at the central wire, these electrons constitute a current that flows through an external circuit and may be used to light a neon lamp, for example, or to activate a mechanical register of some sort.

Geiger counters are exceedingly sensitive devices since they yield large, external current pulses even when triggered by a relatively small number of ions. But by their very nature they cannot distinguish between a heavily ionizing and a lightly ionizing primary particle, and many applications require that precisely that distinction be made. Modern scintillation counters are nonvisual detectors based upon a visual technique frequently employed in early nuclear reaction experiments. Many materials scintillate (or phosphoresce) under the impact of fast, charged particles. Zinc sulfide molecules deposited on the surface of a cathode ray tube in an oscilloscope or television receiver are excited by absorbing the kilovolt energy electrons directed at the screen, and emit visible light upon returning to their ground states. Rutherford and his co-workers measured the scattering angles of α-particles with zinc sulfide detectors, watching for and recording the momentary flashes of light that signaled the arrival of these charged particles at the scintillating material.

Many other materials (sodium and cesium iodide and a number of organic liquids and solids) also emit visible light when they are excited by charged particles, and have the advantage of responding much more rapidly than zinc sulfide. The molecules in some special organic plastics may return to their ground states to await excitation by another charged particle in less than 3×10^{-9} sec, for instance. Since the number of photons emitted by one of these scintillating substances increases with the number of molecules excited, and, therefore with the total energy deposited by the charged primary, a measurement of output intensity of the light serves to distinguish lightly and heavily ionizing primaries.

Light intensity measurements can be made by using very sensitive photoelectric detectors, known as photomultiplier tubes, that yield short electrical current pulses proportional to the amount of light they absorb, and can respond reliably to as few as ten or twenty photons. Light incident upon a photocathode coated with one of the alkali metals results in the ejection of electrons via the photoelectric effect, the number of electrons ejected being proportional to the incident photon intensity. These photoelectrons are then accelerated through a positive potential difference toward a specially treated metal electrode, each gaining a sufficient energy on the way to eject several more electrons from that electrode upon impact, thus effecting a multiplication in the number of electrons traveling along the tube (Figure 21.17). These are in turn accelerated toward another electrode where once again each of them ejects several more electrons. The technique is usually repeated ten or more times. Ultimately the cascading, multiplying electrons are collected at an anode following their final acceleration stage, and used to activate an external electrical or electromechanical device, such as a light or a mechanical register.

A scintillation counter, then, consists of a piece of scintillating material with its light output directed onto the photosensitive, alkaline surface of a photomultiplier tube. When in operation, each successive electrode stage of the tube is normally maintained at a 200 to 300 volt potential difference relative to the next stage. Because scintillation counters respond to light as well as to charged particles, the entire assembly, scintillator and photomultiplier tube, must be enclosed in a light tight container.

Neutral particles do not directly ionize atoms in matter. Therefore their detection requires methods that are even more indirect than those used in the detection of charged particles. For instance, a neutron passing through hydrogen or a hydrogen-bearing material, such as the organic plastic of a scintillation counter, can transfer all or part of its energy to a proton in a "billiard ball" collision, and the resultant proton detected by means of the ion trail it leaves in its wake. Photons may eject electrons from atoms along their path by Compton scattering, or, if their energies exceed 1 MeV, may produce electron-positron pairs (Section 22.4). In either case, detection of the charged secondary particles records the passage of the primary photon. Since the probability for a neutron or a photon to interact with matter by the means we have cited is much smaller than the probability that a charged particle of comparable energy will ionize an atom, the efficient identification of neutral particles usually requires considerably larger detectors.

The detector or combination of detectors chosen for a particular application depends upon the detailed nature of the processes being studied: the types of particles involved, their energies, the probability of the process relative to other, competing processes induced by the incident beam particles, for instance. The subject is very involved and we shall not go into it in detail. However, it is worth noting that our survey of detectors has

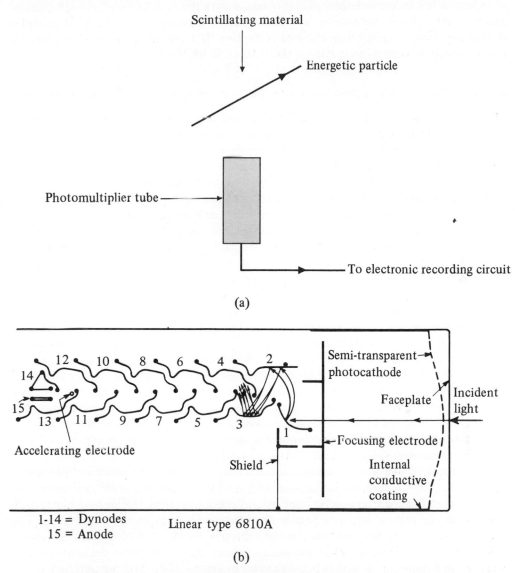

(a)

(b)

FIGURE 21.17. (a) Principle of the scintillation counter. An energetic particle excites the atoms in a piece of scintillating material. When they return to their ground states, the atoms emit light which is incident in turn on the face of a photomultiplier tube. (b) Operation of a photomultiplier. Light incident on an alkali photocathode causes the emission of electrons which are accelerated to the first dynode (1) by a positive potential difference. Here they eject more electrons which are accelerated to dynode 2. The group cascades from dynode to dynode, increasing in number at each stage, until at the anode (15) it constitutes a considerable current pulse capable of actuating an external recording circuit. (Drawing Courtesy of the Electron Tube Division, Radio Corporation of America.)

included two, the bubble chamber and spark chamber, whose applications are confined almost exclusively to the study of elementary particle processes. In these instances the energies of the particles are usually in excess of 100 MeV. Therefore, many have ranges of at least a few inches in bubble chamber liquid or in the metallic spark chamber plates and produce easily identifiable tracks. In contrast, the energies involved in the complex nuclear reactions such as those outlined in Section 21.1 and the foregoing chapters are usually less than (and often much less than) 40 or 50 MeV.

▲▲ 21.4 The nucleon-nucleon interaction. Range of the interaction. Charge independence

By making use of some of the acceleration and detection techniques outlined in the foregoing sections, it is possible to determine in considerable detail the way complex nuclei behave when they are excited by energetic incident particles. These reaction studies, in turn, cast light upon the internal properties of nuclei. In Section 21.1 we discussed several reactions induced by bombarding $_7N^{14}$ nuclei with protons. That target nucleus could be replaced by any other stable or quasi-stable nucleus, and the reactions induced in each studied with incident neutrons, deuterons, α-particles, electrons, or photons rather than protons. Given, in addition, the range of incident energies available from accelerators, a virtually endless series of reaction studies is conceivable. Not all of these studies have been, or probably ever will be, undertaken. Some are simply not technically feasible; others would yield information either too difficult to interpret or too similar to the information derived from other reactions.

On the other hand, nuclei are complicated, multiparticle systems whose structure is determined primarily by an interaction whose nature is not yet completely understood. Hence it is not surprising that the study of nuclear reactions in what is now called the low energy regions (from a few to around 40 or 50 MeV) continues to be a field of intense activity. We shall not attempt to review contemporary knowledge of nuclear structure, for the subject is too vast, too complicated, indeed in many ways too tentative to submit itself to a rapid, coherent summary. However, one question is certainly fundamental to virtually any other question that might be asked about internal nuclear structure: what is the nature of the interaction that binds nucleons together in these complex systems? Surely, that problem should be explored in further detail.

Let us recall the few general features about the nucleon-nucleon interaction outlined in Chapter 20. First, the interaction must be attractive (or at least not always repulsive) and stronger than the electromagnetic interaction between protons. Otherwise nuclei with more than one proton would be totally unstable simply because the magnitude of the electrostatic repulsion between two protons separated by 10^{-14} to 10^{-15} m is enormous.

Second, and by the same token, the force must act between protons and neutrons, and neutrons and neutrons, as well as between protons and protons. If it did not, then nuclei would be totally indifferent to the presence of neutrons, when in fact, the light, stable nuclei contain roughly equal numbers of protons and neutrons, while neutrons dominate the heavy nuclei.

Third, the nuclear interaction must have a short, finite range. If its range were infinite, like the gravitational or the electromagnetic interactions, then every nucleon in a nucleus would interact with every other, and the binding energy of a nucleus per nucleon would increase with atomic weight. In fact, it remains roughly constant as the nucleon number increases, indicating that each nucleon interacts primarily with its nearest neighbors. The short range of the force can also be deduced from the fact that the volume of a nucleus is proportional to its nucleon number (Equation 20.1), unlike the situation encountered in atomic structure where the atomic radius actually decreases within each major shell as the electron number increases. From the empirical relation between the radius of a nucleus and its atomic number (Equation 20.1):

$$R = 1.4A^{1/3} \times 10^{-15} \text{ m},$$

we conclude that the range of the interaction is a few times 10^{-15} m.

Of course nucleons, and nuclei, must be described in quantum mechanical terms, and therefore the range of the force cannot be precisely delimited. But for our purposes it is sufficient to note that at separations much greater than about 5×10^{-14} m two nucleons have very small probabilities of interacting by means of the internucleon force, whereas for separations smaller than 10^{-15} m their probability of attracting each other is large. These conclusions are completely consistent with more detailed information drawn from nuclear structure and reaction experiments. In particular, the behavior of systems composed of two interacting nucleons has been studied extensively, for the internucleon force should certainly manifest itself more simply in these two-particle systems than in any multinucleon system.

There are three different dinucleon configurations: the proton-proton (diproton), neutron-neutron (dineutron), and proton-neutron systems. Of the three, only the deuteron ($_2\text{H}^2$) a proton-neutron system, has more than a transitory existence. The properties of the others must be derived from nucleon-nucleon and nucleon-deuteron scattering experiments. For example, protons incident upon a hydrogen target with sufficient energy may interact directly with, and be scattered by, the target protons. Energetic neutrons, produced by bombarding a suitable target with protons, will likewise interact and scatter from the protons in a hydrogen target. In both cases measurements of the number of nucleons scattered from the protons as a function of their incident energies and scattering angle provide information about the appropriate nucleon-proton scattering interaction.

The neutron-neutron interaction cannot be studied as directly, for no pure neutron substance, analogous to hydrogen, exists as a suitable target material. However, data on the system is obtained most simply through the neutron-induced break-up of deuterium (heavy hydrogen):

$$n + {}_1\text{H}^2 \rightarrow n + n + p^*.$$

One of the outgoing neutrons in the reaction corresponds to the incident particle, the other to the neutron initially bound in the target deuteron, although quantum mechanics offers no way of spelling out the correspondence more explicitly. Whenever the outgoing proton in the break-up reaction receives a minimal share of the total available energy, the primary interaction that caused the break-up must have been between the incident and the bound neutrons. Hence data on the neutron-neutron system can be extracted from that restricted subclass of interactions.

Nucleon-nucleon scattering experiments lead to the far reaching conclusion that the nuclear force is *charge independent*. That is, if the electromagnetic interaction could be suspended, the remaining, *nuclear* part of the force between two nucleons would be the same regardless of the identity of the interacting nucleons. The diproton, dineutron, and proton-neutron systems would be indistinguishable, and, in fact, so would the two nucleons themselves. Hence with respect to the *nuclear* interaction the proton and neutron may be regarded as two different states of the same entity, the nucleon.

---

* Henceforth for simplicity we designate the proton as p rather than as $_1\text{H}^1$.

Of course the *total* force between two nucleons does depend upon their identity (or, alternately) their charge states. Protons exert an electrostatic repulsion upon each other. In addition neutrons, though electrically neutral, have small intrinsic magnetic dipole moments (analogous to the intrinsic magnetic dipole moment of the electron introduced in Section 19.2) so that they too enter into minimal, though not completely insignificant electromagnetic interactions. Finally, of the three possible dinucleon systems, only the deuteron is bound and stable, a significant fact that requires a brief consideration of a nucleon property we have thus far ignored: intrinsic spin.

▲▲ 21.5 Intrinsic spin of the nucleon. Charge independence and the deuteron. Charge independence and beta decay

Let us consider for a moment a possible quantum mechanical description of internal nuclear states. If (as in Section 20.3) we assume that the force upon a nucleon can be approximated by a potential energy well whose form depends on the interaction of the nucleon with all others in the system, then the atomic analogy serves as a useful guide (Section 19.1 to 19.3). Although the amplitudes of the single nucleon states as well as their corresponding energies depend upon the precise nature of the nuclear potential, it is reasonable to assume that nuclear states, like atomic states, can be labeled by sets of quantum numbers. For instance, if we assume the orbital angular momentum of each proton and neutron is conserved, an orbital angular momentum quantum number, l, may be assigned to each state. Again, it should be possible to assign a set of quantum numbers, m, specifying the components of total angular momentum relative to some axis, with $(2l + 1)$ values ranging in integral steps from $-l$ to $+l$.

In addition to their orbital angular momenta protons and neutrons also have intrinsic or *spin* angular momenta related to their intrinsic magnetic properties (Section 19.2). The orientation energy of a particle with magnetic dipole moment μ relative to a magnetic field of strength **B** is (Equation 9.5):

$$PE_B = \mu B \cos \theta,$$

where θ is the orientation angle between the field and the dipole vector. As in the electron case we assume that the magnetic moments of the proton and neutron are proportional to their intrinsic angular momenta (Equation 19.6):

$$\mu_p = g_p \mathbf{s},$$
$$\mu_n = g_n \mathbf{s}.$$

Then for each of the nucleons the magnetic orientation energy can be written:

$$PE_B(p) = g_p B s \cos \theta,$$
$$PE_B(n) = g_n B s \cos \theta.$$

But $s \cos \theta$ is just the component of the intrinsic angular momentum, $\mathbf{s}$, in the direction of the field (Figure 21.18), which we write as s_z. Thus,

$$PE_B(p) = g_p B s_z,$$
$$PE_B(n) = g_n B s_z.$$

Classically s_z can assume any value between $-s$ and $+s$. However, measurements show that for a fixed value of B there are but two possible values of magnetic orientation energy for each nucleon: one corresponding to $s_z = +\hbar/2$, the other to $s_z = -\hbar/2$.

FIGURE 21.18. The proton and neutron both have intrinsic magnetic dipole moments about their spin axes, and therefore, potential energy due to their orientation in a magnetic field. Since only two magnetic energy states exist for each particle they must both have $s_z = \pm \hbar/2$.

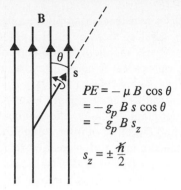

$$PE = -\mu B \cos \theta$$
$$= -g_p B s \cos \theta$$
$$= -g_p B s_z$$

$$s_z = \pm \frac{\hbar}{2}$$

Therefore,

$$PE_B(p) = \pm g_p B \frac{\hbar}{2},$$

$$PE_B(n) = \pm g_n B \frac{\hbar}{2}.$$

Therefore, protons and neutrons, like electrons, are said to have intrinsic spin angular momentum (or more simply spin) $\frac{1}{2}$, which implies that their total intrinsic angular momentum is (Equation 19.2):

$$s = \sqrt{\tfrac{1}{2}(\tfrac{1}{2} + 1)}\, \hbar = \sqrt{\tfrac{3}{4}}\, \hbar,$$

and also that the z-component of their spin can assume only two values: $+\hbar/2$ and $-\hbar/2$. Given these conclusions the proportionality constants g_p and g_n can be determined by measuring the difference between the two possible magnetic orientation energies in a field of known strength. Significantly the constant g_n is not zero even though the neutron has no net electric charge, a fact which suggests that the neutron is a more complex entity than the electron.

Intrinsic spin is a property of all the elementary particles fully as fundamental in distinguishing them from one another as their charge or mass. All have measured spin angular momenta equal either to *integral* multiples of $\hbar$, i.e.,

$$0, \hbar, 2\hbar, 3\hbar, \ldots,$$

or to one-half odd integral multiples of $\hbar$:

$$\tfrac{1}{2}\hbar, \tfrac{3}{2}\hbar, \tfrac{5}{2}\hbar, \ldots.$$

For our purposes a spin $n\hbar$ means that there are $(2n + 1)$ possible orientations of intrinsic angular momentum ranging in integral steps from $-n$ to $+n$. Significantly, if the spin of a particle is integral it obeys the *Bose* statistics, if half-odd integral the *Fermi* statistics (Section 18.10). Photons (spin 1), and π-mesons (spin 0) fall into the Bose category, electrons and nucleons (spin $\frac{1}{2}$) into the Fermi class. Since the antisymmetric form of the identical particle amplitude for Fermi particles is tantamount to the Pauli Exclusion Principle we conclude that photons and π-mesons are *not* subject to that principle, but that nucleons, like electrons, are.

These considerations have a direct bearing upon the structure of complex nuclei, in particular the di-nucleon systems. If we knew the amplitudes for all possible single-particle states in a nuclear potential well we could presumably construct amplitudes for nucleon states just as we constructed amplitudes for atomic states from single electron states in Section 19.3, labeling them by a total angular momentum quantum number l, a magnetic quantum number m, and a spin quantum number $s_z = \pm\hbar/2$. Lacking such detailed information we can nevertheless draw a number of conclusions regarding the character of dinucleon systems (Figure 21.19).

Although the dineutron system has only transitory existence, it still qualifies as an interacting quantum mechanical state. The two neutrons have the largest probability of being close together, and therefore of interacting most strongly when they are both in the state $l = 0$ (with angular momentum measured relative to the center of mass of the two particle system). But if $l = 0$ then also $m = 0$, since the latter quantum number ranges in integral steps from $-l$ to $+l$. Since the two interacting neutrons are identical Fermi particles and must therefore be in different states, one must have spin $s_z = +\hbar/2$, the other $s_z = -\hbar/2$. That is, the neutron spins are antiparallel. But no stable dineutron system exists. Thus we conclude that the dineutron state with $l = 0$, $m = 0$, and total spin $S = s_z(1) + s_z(2) = 0$, cannot be a bound state.

Similar considerations are applicable to the diproton system. Since the particles are identical Fermi particles then their spins must be opposite in the state $l = 0$, $m = 0$. But the two particles in a neutron-proton system are *not* identical. Therefore, there are *two* available spin substates with $l = 0$, $m = 0$. In one of these, the nucleons are in different states of s_z, and the total spin of the system has magnitude 0. In the other the nucleons are in the *same* state of s_z (i.e., their spins are parallel) and the magnitude of the spin's system is $\hbar/2 + \hbar/2 = \hbar$. According to the charge independence principle the energy of the first of these states should be equal to the energy of the dineutron system and, to the extent that the electromagnetic interaction can be neglected, to the diproton energy as well, while in general the parallel spin state will have a different energy.

From the foregoing analysis we conclude that since the deuteron is the only bound (i.e., negative energy) dinucleon system its nucleons cannot have antiparallel spins. Otherwise bound dineutron and diproton systems would also exist. Therefore, the parallel spin state must be a bound, negative energy state, and must, in fact, be the ground state of the deuteron. We also conclude that the deuteron has total spin $\hbar$ (i.e., it is in a spin 1 state, since $s = n\hbar$). Finally, the system can have no bound excited states for the lowest of these would be the state with the two nucleons in different spin states which, as we know, is an unbound, positive energy state. Both these conclusions are in accord with experimental data.

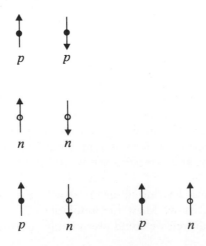

FIGURE 21.19. The four possible dinucleon states with $l = 0$. Since nucleons are Fermi particles the nucleons in the diproton and dineutron states have antiparallel spins. However, a proton and neutron in an $l = 0$ state can have their spins either parallel or antiparallel. According to the charge independence principle the three antiparallel states would be completely identical in the absence of the electromagnetic interaction.

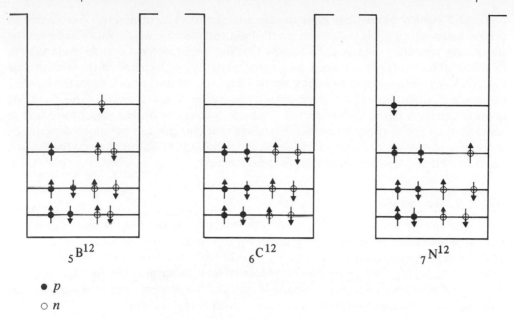

● *p*

○ *n*

FIGURE 21.20. In the absence of electromagnetic interactions the single nucleon states in $_5B^{12}$, $_6C^{12}$, and $_7N^{12}$ would be identical. But because of the Pauli principle one neutron in $_5B^{12}$ and one proton in $_7N^{12}$ must be in the fourth state, whereas all nucleons in $_6C^{12}$ can be accomodated in three states. Thus the energy of a nucleus with an unequal number of neutrons and protons is generally greater than the ground state energy of a nucleus with equal numbers of protons and neutrons. Both $_5B^{12}$ and $_7N^{12}$ can reduce their ground state energies by β-decay to $_6C^{12}$, i.e., by reversing the identity of the excess nucleon.

By extending these charge independence arguments, we can begin to understand why the light and medium atomic mass stable nuclei have about equal numbers of neutrons and protons. We can represent at least some of the states of a nucleus by energy levels in a potential well (Figure 21.20). If we neglect the electromagnetic repulsion between the protons, as many as four nucleons, two protons with opposite spin and two neutrons with opposite spin, can occupy each level. In terms of this crude model it is easy to understand why $_6C^{12}$ is stable, for example, while $_5B^{12}$ and $_7N^{12}$ are both quasi-stable β-emitters. The lowest three levels in $_6C^{12}$ are each fully occupied. If one of its neutrons were replaced by a proton to form $_7N^{12}$, that proton would have to go into a higher energy state than the neutron it replaced, for the third level in $_6C^{12}$ already has its full proton complement. Therefore the total internal energy of the system would increase. Conversely, the conversion of a proton in $_7N^{12}$ into a neutron by β^+-emission permits the nucleon to occupy a lower state, and decreases the internal energy of the system.

By the same argument, $_5B^{12}$ must also have a higher internal energy than $_6C^{12}$ and, if we are justified in neglecting electromagnetic effects, the internal energies of $_5B^{12}$ and $_7N^{12}$ in their ground states should be about equal. In addition, $_6C^{12}$ should have an excited state with total energy approximately equal to the ground states of $_5B^{12}$ and $_7N^{12}$, differing from its ground state configuration by the promotion of a nucleon to the fourth level. The agreement between these expectations and observation is quite good, considering the very approximate nature of the model.

A more refined model that does not ignore electromagnetic interactions considers proton and neutron states separately. In the light and medium weight nuclei these sets of states have very nearly the same energies so that the lowest internal energies for a system of N nucleons is usually obtained with equal numbers of nucleons in the proton and neutron levels. But the repulsive electrostatic force on a proton increases with the number of protons, while the attractive nuclear force, being a short-ranged force, remains approximately constant. Therefore, in the heavy nuclei the proton states have higher energies than the neutron states, and lower internal energies can be attained by filling more of the latter states than by keeping the number of occupied states equal for the two particles. Hence neutrons should dominate in the heavy nuclei, as indeed they do.

▲▲ 21.6 Isotopic spin

Because the nuclear part of the force between any two nucleons in the same state is the same regardless of the identity of the nucleons, it follows that the nuclear force cannot distinguish between a neutron and proton. In other words, the two particles are *identical* with respect to the nuclear force. This identity may be formulated by regarding the proton and neutron as two electromagnetic states of the *same* particle, the nucleon, for only the electromagnetic interaction can distinguish between them.

Let us assign a quantum number T_3 defined by

$$T_3 = Q - \tfrac{1}{2} \tag{21.5}$$

to each of the two states, where Q is the charge of the state. For the proton $Q = +1$ so $T_3 = +\tfrac{1}{2}$, while for a neutron $Q = 0$ and $T_3 = -\tfrac{1}{2}$.

Thus the state of a nucleon can be labeled with *four* quantum numbers: l and m, which give its total angular momentum and the component of angular momentum along some arbitrary axis, $s_z = \pm\tfrac{1}{2}$ which specifies its spin state, and $T_3 = \pm\tfrac{1}{2}$ which tells whether it is a proton or neutron.

The *formal* analogy between intrinsic spin and the T_3 number is striking. A particle with intrinsic spin $\tfrac{1}{2}$ has two orientation states; in the absence of an interaction that distinguishes between these orientations these states are identical in every respect. Likewise, in the absence of electromagnetic interactions, the two charge states of the nucleon are completely identical. Therefore, let us pursue the analogy and assume that the two charge states can both be labeled with the same quantum number T which has $(2T + 1)$ electromagnetic substates, even as a state with spin s has $(2s + 1)$ substates. In the present instance we are considering two substates with $T_3 = \pm\tfrac{1}{2}$. Therefore, we conclude that $T = \tfrac{1}{2}$ for a single nucleon. Because of the formal analogy on which it is based, the quantum number T is called *isotopic spin* and T_3 the third component of isotopic spin. We can state the charge independence of the nuclear interactions as a symmetry law by using this formal concept:

•   States with the same total isotopic spin, T, behave identically with respect to the nuclear interactions, provided the other quantum numbers of the states (i.e., l, m, and s_z, for instance) are also equal.

The utility of the isotopic spin formulation becomes apparent when it is applied to states with more than one nucleon.* For two nucleons, a and b, there are four possible combinations of $T_3(a)$ and $T_3(b)$, corresponding to four different dinucleon states:

---

* The remainder of this section may be omitted without serious loss of continuity.

	$T_3(a)$	$T_3(b)$	$T_3(ab) = T_3(a) + T_3(b)$
1	$\frac{1}{2}$	$\frac{1}{2}$	1
2	$\frac{1}{2}$	$-\frac{1}{2}$	0
3	$-\frac{1}{2}$	$\frac{1}{2}$	0
4	$-\frac{1}{2}$	$-\frac{1}{2}$	-1

In the first state both nucleons are protons, in the second a is a proton and b a neutron, etc.

According to our convention a system with isotopic spin T has $(2T + 1)$ substates labeled by values of T_3 ranging in integral steps from $-T$ to T. Since the maximum and minimum T_3 values for the two nucleon state are ± 1 they must specify substates of total isotopic spin $T = 1$. Thus if we restrict attention to situations in which all other possible quantum numbers are also equal, states 1 and 4 behave identically with respect to the nuclear interactions. These are the diproton and dineutron states, respectively. Therefore, this conclusion is consistent with the verbal statement of charge independence given in Section 21.5.

Since particles a and b are regarded as indistinguishable as far as the nuclear interactions are concerned, neither state 2 or 3 corresponds to a physically measurable state, for in quantum mechanics it is improper to ask for the probability that a specific member of an indistinguishable set of particles is in a given state. Rather, we must determine the probability that one or the other is in the state in question. In other words, the measurable states corresponding to $T_3(ab) = 0$ are superpositions of states 2 and 3.

Let p and n designate the amplitudes corresponding to the single nucleon states with $T_3 = +\frac{1}{2}$, and $= -\frac{1}{2}$, respectively (i.e., the proton and neutron states). Then the amplitudes corresponding to two simple superposition states may be formed:

$$V_s = p(a)n(b) + n(a)p(b),$$

and

$$V_u = p(a)n(b) - n(a)p(b).$$

The first of these amplitudes is a *symmetric* exchange amplitude, since it remains unaltered if the states of the particles are interchanged. (See Section 18.10, and Section 19.3). Likewise, states 1 and 4 are also symmetric, as may be easily seen by writing their amplitudes:

$$V_1 = p(a)p(b),$$
$$V_4 = n(a)n(b).$$

Thus on the basis of exchange symmetry we identify the symmetric superposition state V_s with $T_3 = 0$ as the third, indistinguishable member of the $T = 1$ triplet. Finally, by the process of elimination we are left with the single antisymmetric exchange state which, since it has $T_3 = 0$, must also have $T = 0$ and is therefore distinguishable from the three symmetric states with $T = 1$.

These formal results are directly applicable to the deuteron problem. If we regard nucleons as identical Fermi particles then no more than one can be in a given quantum mechanical state. That is, we require that the total amplitude for the system be antisymmetric under exchange of the particles (Section 18.10). The total amplitude may be expressed as the product of a spatial part, a spin part, and an isotopic spin part. The spatial amplitude corresponding to $l = 0$ turns out to be symmetric. Therefore, the permissible dinucleon amplitudes either have symmetric spin amplitudes and antisymmetric isotopic spin amplitudes, or vice versa. The symmetric spin amplitudes correspond to parallel spin states ($s = 1$), the antisymmetric spin amplitude to antiparallel spin ($s = 0$). It follows that the triplet of isotopic spin state with $T_3 = 1, -1, 0$ have antiparallel spins and specify the diproton, dineutron, and the unbound, excited deuteron state, while the unrelated state with isotopic spin amplitude V_A goes with the spin 1 amplitude and specifies the deuteron ground state.

▲▲ 21.7 Yukawa's meson exchange model of the nucleon-nucleon interaction

In at least one respect the interactions between nucleons is analogous to the interactions between atoms in a molecule. Two neutral hydrogen atoms do not interact until they are close enough together to share their electrons, or, speaking semiclassically, until their electron orbits overlap and it becomes necessary to speak of electron states of the diatomic molecule instead of electron states of the individual atoms (Section 19.7). If we had no idea that hydrogen atoms are interacting proton-electron systems we might nevertheless deduce a great deal about interatomic forces by studying chemical reactions and/or the behavior of gases at high pressures and low temperatures. In particular, we would conclude that the interaction between two hydrogen atoms is virtually nonexistent for interatomic separations greater than about 10^{-10} m, is attractive at smaller distances, and ultimately becomes repulsive when the force between the protons dominates the electron exchange force. Except for the much larger scale involved, the description is also applicable to the internucleon force.

In 1937 H. Yukawa suggested that the short-range interaction between two nucleons could be carried by a new particle, the *meson* (now designated as the π-meson), that is exchanged between nucleons, even as the bonding in covalent molecules can be attributed to electron exchange. On the Yukawa model a nucleon assumes a complex structure which we may envision, crudely, as a core enveloped by a bound meson cloud (Figure 21.21a). When two nucleons are sufficiently close together their meson clouds overlap, or (in less pictorial language) they share or exchange their π-mesons (Figure 21.21b). This sharing increases the limits of the region to which the mesons are confined and, according to the Heisenberg Principle, reduces their momentum and therefore, their

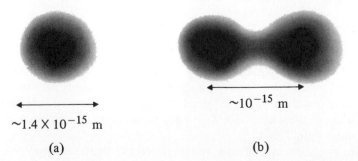

$\sim 1.4 \times 10^{-15}$ m

(a)

$\sim 10^{-15}$ m

(b)

FIGURE 21.21. (a) According to the Yukawa model a nucleon can be envisioned as a core surrounded by a meson cloud. (b) When two nucleons are close together they interact by exchanging or sharing their mesons, very much like two hydrogen atoms which form a covalent bond by sharing their electrons.

energies, in complete analogy with covalent electron exchange bonding (Section 19.7). Conversely, if the meson clouds do not overlap there is no interaction. At least qualitatively, then, the meson exchange model is consistent with the short-range character of the nuclear force.

Since the nucleon-nucleon interaction only becomes significant for distances less than about 10^{-15} m, the meson cloud surrounding a nucleon must have a radius of that order. Assuming a circular configuration, the location of a π-meson is determined to about $2\pi R = 2\pi \times 10^{-15}$ m. Hence their *minimum* momentum follows from the Heisenberg Principle:

$$p = \frac{h}{2\pi R} = \frac{6 \times 10^{-34}}{2\pi \times 10^{-15}} \cong 10^{-19} \text{ (mks units).}$$

Of course we do not know the meson's velocity, but might guess that it is large, probably a few tenths the velocity of light. We surely overestimate the velocity by letting $p = M_0 c$. On the other hand, we also underestimate is mass which at a velocity a few tenths c is greater than the rest mass. However, the product represents a reasonable compromise and we have

$$M_0 c \cong 10^{-19} \text{ (mks units).}$$

Thus, $M_0 = 3 \times 10^{-28}$ kg, about 300 times the rest mass of the electron or, in terms of rest energy ($M_0 c^2$), about 150 MeV. Actually the π-meson rest energy turns out to be slightly less than 140 MeV, roughly 280 electron masses or somewhat less than one-sixth the nucleon mass.

If π-mesons really are exchanged between nucleons then occasionally one should be ejected by a proton or neutron that absorbs energy greater than or equal to the 140 MeV π-meson rest energy. (Analogously, a hydrogen atom can be ionized by absorbing energy greater than or equal to the binding energy of its electron.) Indeed, the particles are copiously produced when nucleons (or nuclei) are bombarded with high-energy incident particles, other nucleons, electrons, high energy photons; for instance,

$$p + p \rightarrow p + n + \pi^+,$$
$$p + p \rightarrow p + p + \pi^\circ,$$
$$n + p \rightarrow p + p + \pi^-,$$
$$\gamma + p \rightarrow n + \pi^+,$$

etc. C. F. Powell and C. P. Occhialini first identified π-mesons in 1947 as one component of the secondary cosmic rays that continually bombard the earth's surface. This radiation is created when nuclei in the upper atmosphere are bombarded by protons accelerated to high energies in the solar system and the galaxy by a variety of mechanisms that are still not completely understood. Today the production of π-mesons with particle beams from high energy accelerators is commonplace. As indicated in the sample production reactions (above) the mesons may either be neutral or carry one unit of positive or negative charge. Presumably the neutral mesons carry the nuclear interaction between any two pairs of nucleons, whereas the charged mesons can only be exchanged between a proton and neutron. In the latter instances the members of the interacting pair exchange their roles, for a proton that emits a π^+-meson to become a neutron, while the neutron that absorbs it becomes a proton.

Charged π-mesons have rest energies of 139 MeV, while the rest energy of the neutral member of the triplet is 135 MeV. All three particles are unstable in their free states.

The neutral meson decays with a half-life about 10^{-16} sec into two photons:

$$\pi^\circ \to 2\gamma,$$

while each charged meson decays with a 2×10^{-8} sec half-life into a charged muon ($\mu^{\pm}$) and a neutrino (or antineutrino):

$$\pi^+ \to \mu^+ + \nu,$$
$$\pi^- \to \mu^- + \bar{\nu}.$$

We shall have more to say about these somewhat mysterious muons in the next chapter. Here we note only that they have 106 MeV rest energies and are also unstable, decaying into electrons (positrons) and neutrino-antineutrino pairs in 2×10^{-6} sec:

$$\mu^{\pm} \to e^{\pm} + \nu + \bar{\nu}.$$

◣◣ 21.8 Exchange models of the electromagnetic and nucleon-nucleon interactions. The role of the Heisenberg principle. Ranges of the interactions

The assumption that a π-meson moves in a well-defined classical orbit within a nucleon obviously has no quantum mechanical justification. A more consistent approach starts by equating the range of the nuclear force with the most probable location of the meson relative to the center of the nucleus, and deduces its amplitude as a function of distance by following the analogy offered by the covalent, electron-exchange model. Surprisingly enough, this more consistent treatment leads to very much the same estimate of the π-meson mass as the semiclassical estimate of the last section, even as the Bohr and the quantum mechanical models yield identical, quantitative values for the energy levels of the hydrogen atom.

Even though the covalent, exchange model of the nucleon-nucleon interaction provides a valuable insight into the nature of that interaction, the analogy should not be overdrawn. The binding energy of the electron in a hydrogen atom is 13.6 eV, whereas the binding energy of a π-meson in a nucleon is its 140 MeV rest energy. More basically, hydrogen atoms are composite systems, but both nucleons and π-mesons must still be regarded as fundamental particles. Remove the electron from a hydrogen atom, and a proton remains; remove a π-meson from a nucleon, and a nucleon remains! In this sense π-mesons have more in common with photons than electrons, for the ejection or absorption of a photon by a charged particle changes its internal energy but does not (or at any rate *need* not) alter its fundamental character.

Actually, the analogy can be pursued with considerable profit. The π-meson was postulated for the explicit purpose of carrying the nuclear interactions. In a like manner we may regard photons, exchanged between charged particles, as carriers of the *electromagnetic* interaction (Section 12.4). Unlike electrons and nucleons, photons and π-mesons need not be conserved in interactions between the elementary particles. Any number may be created, any number destroyed, provided no other conservation laws such as those of charge, momentum, and energy are violated. In contrast, the creation of an electron requires the simultaneous creation of an anti-electron (positron), the creation of a nucleon, the simultaneous creation of an antinucleon* (Section 22.4).

The nonconservation of mesons (and photons) is directly related to the fact that they are Bose rather than Fermi particles. Hence an unlimited number may exist in any

---

* These two conservation laws are actually somewhat less restrictive, as we shall see in Section 22.10.

quantum mechanical state. As we saw in Section 18.10, Bose particles actually prefer to occupy states with many other identical particles. Suppose we could deduce the possible bound states of a meson in a nucleon. Presumably there would be a ground state and a number of excited states, equivalent to, though far more tightly bound than the electron states in an atom. (In fact there is abundant experimental evidence for the existence of these excited states, as we shall see in the next chapter.) How many mesons can occupy each state? An unlimited number! From another point of view, there is no way to determine how many mesons are bound to a nucleon if that nucleon has no excess internal energy. At best we can state that all mesons are in the ground state. Hence there can be no distinction between the *ejection* of a meson from a nucleon by the absorption of sufficient energy, and the *creation* of a meson by the conversion of energy to mass. Do mesons *really* surround a nucleon or are they created when the nucleon interacts with other particles? The question admits to no answer. Yukawa's exchange model accounts for some, though not all of the observed features of the internucleon interaction, and free π-mesons are certainly produced in high energy particle reactions. But we cannot distinguish between creation and ejection any more than we can decide whether photons are created when charged particles interact, or are bound to these particles all the while and are simply ejected in these interactions.

At any rate, the ability of nucleons to exchange π-mesons must be regarded as one of their basic properties, for it permits them to form bound systems with other nucleons. However, that property is comprehensible only in quantum mechanical terms. The relationship between the uncertainty in the position and momentum of a particle that we have called the Heisenberg principle ($\Delta p \, \Delta x \geqq h$) and used so often is, in fact, only the best known aspect of that principle. More generally, Heisenberg's basic formulation shows that there are many *pairs* of classical variables which bear the same relationship to each other as momentum and position. That is, their products are uncertain to at least $h = 6 \times 10^{-34}$ J-sec.

For instance, the uncertainty ΔE in the energy of a quantum state, and Δt, the time the system exists in that state, are related by

$$\Delta E \, \Delta t \geqq h. \tag{21.6}$$

Since $h = 4 \times 10^{-15}$ eV, we also have

$$\Delta E \geqq \frac{h}{\Delta t} = \frac{4 \times 10^{-15}}{\Delta t} \text{ eV,}$$

that is, the precision with which the energy of a state can be determined varies inversely with its lifetime. For example, an atom that makes a transition to an excited state usually remains in that state for about 10^{-8} sec. Hence the energy of the state cannot be determined to a precision greater than about 3×10^{-17} eV.

As a direct consequence of the Heisenberg principle, the conservation of energy, heretofore regarded as an absolute principle, can be suspended over time intervals consistent with Equation 21.6. For if the change in the energy of a system can be determined only within given limits, there is no way to decide whether or not that energy is conserved from moment to moment. All methods of measuring the 938 MeV rest energy of a proton require substantial fractions of a second. But according to the Heisenberg principle, its rest energy may exhibit short-term fluctuations, ejecting a π^+-meson and becoming a system with energy $938 + 139 = 1077$ MeV (or more if the π-meson has kinetic energy relative to the nucleon) *provided* the nucleon either reabsorbs the meson within a time interval consistent with Equation 21.6, or else transfers it to another nucleon.

Let us estimate the distance a π-meson can travel within the time allotted by the suspended energy conservation principle (Figure 21.22). Since

$$\Delta E = \frac{4 \times 10^{-15}}{\Delta t} \text{ eV},$$

the interval decreases with energy. For a π-meson created with its 139 MeV rest energy,

$$\Delta t = \frac{4 \times 10^{-15}}{1.39 \times 10^{-8}} \sim 3 \times 10^{-23} \text{ sec}.$$

Let us assume (as in our estimate of the π-meson mass) that the particle travels with almost the velocity of light. Then the distance it covers in 3×10^{-23} sec is

$$d = c \, \Delta t \sim 10^{-14} \text{ m},$$

a few times the range of the nuclear force. Usually the energy of a π-meson will exceed its rest energy; otherwise it could not travel with velocity approaching c. Hence the time interval during which it can remain free will be smaller than 3×10^{-23} sec, and its travel-distance correspondingly less.

In any event, we can begin to understand why nucleons remain nucleons even while emitting and absorbing π-mesons. Presumably an isolated nucleon continually emits and reabsorbs mesons within the time permitted by the Heisenberg principle. When another nucleon is close enough to absorb one of the π-mesons an exchange bond can be established.

Conversely, it is clear that *any* force carried by a nonzero rest mass particle must have a finite range. For since a particle cannot be created with energy smaller than its rest energy, it must be reabsorbed in a finite time interval after traveling a finite distance. Otherwise measurable violations of energy conservation would occur. But photons have

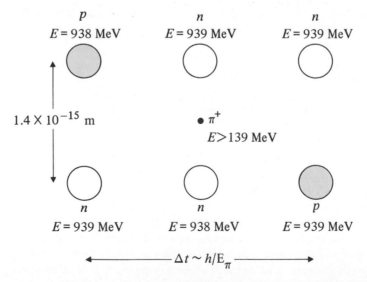

FIGURE 21.22. Meson exchange and the Heisenberg principle. Since exchange of a π-meson between two nucleons at rest implies that the energy of the system increases by at least the π-meson rest energy during the exchange, the process must occur within a time interval Δt given by the uncertainty relation for energy and time.

zero rest mass, and thus may be emitted with energies approaching zero. A photon with virtually zero energy can exist as a free particle for a virtually infinite time, and during that time travel a virtually infinite distance. It follows that the interaction carried by photons, the electromagnetic interaction, has a virtually infinite, or (as the photon energy approaches zero) an infinite range.

SUGGESTIONS FOR FURTHER READING ▶▶▶

The introductory texts cited at the end of Chapter 20 touch upon accelerators and detectors. Two paperback books on topics related to the subject matter of this chapter are:

DONALD J. HUGHES, *The Neutron Story*, Science Study Series, Doubleday and Co., Garden City, N.Y.

ROBERT R. WILSON AND RAPHAEL LITTAUER, *Accelerators: Machines of Nuclear Physics*, Science Study Series, Doubleday and Co., Garden City, New York.

Pertinent articles from the *Scientific American* include:

MARIA G. MAYER, "The Structure of the Nucleus," March, 1951, p. 228.

HANS A. BETHE, "What Holds the Nucleus Together," Sept., 1953, p. 201.

W. H. K. PANOFSKY, "The Linear Accelerator," Oct., 1954, p. 234.

D. A. GLASSER, "The Bubble Chamber," Feb., 1955, p. 68.

V. F. WEISSKOPF AND E. P. ROSENBAUM, "A Model of the Nucleus," Dec., 1955, p. 261.

R. R. WILSON, "Particle Accelerators," March, 1958, p. 64.

R. E. PEIERLS, "Models of the Nucleus," Jan., 1959, p. 235.

G. K. O'NEILL, "The Spark Chamber," Aug., 1962, p. 36.

G. K. O'NEILL, "Particle Storage Rings," Nov., 1966, p. 107.

D. YOUNT, "The Streamer Chamber," Oct., 1967, p. 38.

PROBLEMS AND EXERCISES ▶▶▶

21.1. Why can low energy neutrons (a few hundred electron volts or less) induce nuclear reactions if protons with similar energies cannot?

21.2. What is the minimum energy proton that can be expected to induce nuclear reactions on $_6C^{12}$? On $_{26}Fe^{56}$?

21.3. A sample of the positron emitter $_7N^{12}$ is to be produced by bombarding a $_6C^{12}$ target with protons. Write down an equation for the production reaction.

21.4. (a) Write down some of the reactions that might be induced when protons of sufficient energy bombard an $_8O^{16}$ target.
   (b) When γ-ray photons bombard the same target.

21.5. The probability that a γ-ray with energy ranging from a few hundred thousand electron volts to several million electron volts will be absorbed by a given nucleus exhibits a series of sharp pronounced maxima when plotted as a function of γ-ray energy.
   Explain this behavior. What information can such γ-absorption studies yield regarding the internal structure of nuclei?

21.6. Design a cyclotron capable of accelerating protons to 10 MeV if the radius of the dees is 0.5 m. (Magnetic field intensities in cyclotrons are usually no greater than about 1.5 Wb/m². However, you may choose a smaller field if you desire.)

21.7. A Van de Graaf generator is designed to accelerate protons to 5 MeV. To what energy will it accelerate dueterons ($_1H^2$)? α-particles?

21.8. A cyclotron is designed to accelerate protons to 10 MeV. If the hydrogen arc source is replaced by a helium source can it accelerate α-particles with no further changes in operating conditions? If not what changes must be made? If the magnetic field and magnet radius of the cyclotron remain fixed, to what energy can the cyclotron accelerate the α-particles? (Other changes in operating conditions are permitted.)

21.9. Explain why simple, unmodified cyclotrons are almost never used to accelerate electrons.

21.10. Derive Equation 21.4.

21.11. (a) What is the approximate mass of a proton with a kinetic energy of 470 MeV?
(b) If protons are to be accelerated to 470 MeV in a synchrocyclotron by what percentage must its magnetic field increase from the beginning to the end of each acceleration cycle?

21.12. Why are the tracks of protons in emulsions and cloud chambers less dense than α-particle tracks of comparable energy?

21.13. How might a high energy neutron reveal its presence in a bubble chamber or spark chamber?

21.14. Would the properties of the diproton and dineutron systems (*pp* and *nn*) be different than they are if the spin of the deuteron were zero (i.e., if its neutron and proton spin were antiparallel rather than parallel)? If the deuteron had more than one internal energy state?

21.15. It is possible to produce neutron beams with all or almost all spins aligned in one direction, and likewise to align the spins of the protons in a target in one direction.

Suppose neutrons with their spins up were incident first upon a hydrogen target in which the proton spins were up and then upon another in which they were down. Would you expect to observe any differences in the two scattering probabilities as functions of incident energy? Explain.

21.16. (a) What is the third component of isotopic spin (T_3) for the system *ppp*? *pnp*? *npp*?
(b) What is the total isotopic spin (T) of a triproton system? What other trinucleon combination definitely belongs to the same total isotopic spin grouping? How many other trinucleon states also belong in the group?
(c) What other total isotopic spin state is available to three nucleons? How many substates of T_3 does it have?

21.17. (a) The kinetic energies of the particles emitted in the decays

$$_7N^{12} \rightarrow {_6C^{12}} + \beta^+ + \nu,$$

and

$$_5B^{12} \rightarrow {_6C^{12}} + \beta^- + \bar{\nu},$$

are 16.4 and 13.4 MeV, respectively. Predict the approximate energy of one of the excited states of $_6C^{12}$.
(b) According to the simple model presented in the text the two β-decay energies in part a should be the same. Give a probable resaon for the discrepancy.

21.18. Using the form of the amplitude for a free particle and your knowledge of special relativity as a guide, present an argument for the plausibility of the Heisenberg relation.

$$\Delta E \, \Delta t \gtrsim h.$$

21.19. The lifetimes of certain elementary particles (Chapter 22) are as short as 10^{-23} sec. What is the minimum precision to which the rest mass of such a particle can be measured?

21.20. How would the properties of nuclei differ if the π-meson mass were twice what it is?

21.21. How is it possible for π-mesons to play a dominant role in the nucleon-nucleon interactions when they have 2×10^{-8} sec (or for the neutral π-meson 10^{-16} sec) half-lives?

21.22. There has been speculation concerning the existence of a particle called the *graviton* that carries the gravitational interaction even as the photon carries the electromagnetic interaction.

   What would its rest mass be? With what speed would it travel?

The fundamental particles and their interactions | 22

▲▲ 22.1 What is an elementary particle?

The attempt to understand the physical universe in terms of a small number of fundamental constituents has no doubt been the dominant, recurrent theme in the history of natural philosophy. But even as our understanding of the universe evolves, so the particular set of entities we designate as "elementary" changes, for our viewpoint toward natural process is necessarily determined, in part, by what we regard as fundamental.

For instance, the verification of John Dalton's hypothesis in the late eighteenth century established atoms as the fundamental constituents of matter and led to a quantitative understanding of chemical change. A shift in emphasis occurred when it became evident that Dalton's "elementary" atoms could be regarded as systems composed of "elementary" electrons, protons, and neutrons. This new concept of elementarity led not only to an understanding of the Periodic Table and the character of interatomic bonds, but also to a broader understanding of the nature of matter by admitting processes (such as the transmutation of nuclei) that had no place at all in the Daltonian scheme.

It might be comforting to believe that we have finally reached the goal of comprehending the physical universe in terms of a few of the interactions among well-understood fundamental particles. But, alas, we are nowhere in sight of that understanding. From a superficial point of view we may regard an atom as an interacting system of electrons, protons, and neutrons, and hence might believe that we have reduced the universe to these three constituents. But atoms emit and absorb electromagnetic radiation, requiring that photons be added to our list of elementary particles. The β^--decay of nuclei yields a fifth entry, for a decaying neutron emits a neutrino in addition to an electron. Positron decay provides a sixth candidate, and the extension of Dirac's theory of antimatter to all Fermi particles (Section 22.4) adds the antiproton, antineutron, and antineutrino as well. Finally, the identification of the π^+-, π°-, and π^--mesons as the exchange particles in the Yukawa theory of the internucleon interaction (Section 21.7) brings the number of particles to twelve.

We have listed only a small fraction of the particles which at this writing are in one sense or another candidates for the title "elementary." As recently as 1960 the number stood at about thirty. Today we recognize more than one hundred basic states of matter, though that number may be reduced considerably by referring to the three charged π-mesons as one particle rather than three, by relating the particles and their antiparticles (Section 22.4) and by thinking of the neutron and proton as two states of a nucleon, for instance (Section 21.6). The fact that we *can* find relations between the particles such as the electron and positron or the neutron and proton indicates that we have at least some comprehension of the nature of these particles. On the other hand, since we must continue to speak of a great many classes of particles even after we have taken advantage of all the relations we know, it is very likely that there may be other, as yet unidentified relations that would further reduce the list.

More bluntly, the existence of so many unrelated "elementary" particles is in a real sense a measure of our ignorance about the fundamental nature of the universe. In the early years of the present century the number of elementary particles stood at 92, for there were then ninety-two places in the Periodic Table (even though all of them were not filled), and atoms were regarded as fundamental entities. When the quantum mechanical model of the atom was developed, the basic relationship among these ninety-two separate entities became clear, and it also became evident that the number 92 had been based upon an ignorance of internal atomic structure. Likewise, we might hope that our attempts to relate the entries in the contemporary table of elementary particles to each other will also lead to a deeper understanding of nature. For that reason, among others, we continue to pursue the age-old goal of trying to comprehend the physical universe in terms of a fundamental set of constituents.

▶▶ 22.2 Classes of particles and interactions

The criteria used for deciding whether or not a particular entity is fundamental rest in part upon pragmatic grounds, depending as they do upon the current state of our knowledge. Quantum mechanically we regard any particle, composite or elementary, as a state of matter whose properties are defined in terms of its interactions with the rest of the universe and whose behavior is describable in terms of a probability amplitude. If its properties cannot be understood, even in principle, in terms of the interactions of another set of entities, then we must regard the state of matter as elementary.

Thus, for example, a hydrogen atom in its ground state has a different amplitude from a hydrogen atom in an excited state. But for at least two reasons these states are not regarded as different fundamental particles. First, we can understand either one in terms of the other; second, we can understand both in terms of the electromagnetic interaction of a proton and an electron. On the other hand, although the neutron is unstable and decays with a twelve-minute half-life into a proton-electron-antineutrino system, it cannot be completely described in terms of the interactions of its decay products and hence must be regarded as fundamental. In addition, since a proton bound in a nucleus can decay into a neutron-positron-neutrino system, it is clear that we cannot think of the proton as being more fundamental than the neutron. But we have also noted that if we disregard their electromagnetic interactions, both particles appear to be identical (Sections 21.5 and 21.6). Therefore, we might hope to describe both of them as states of a more basic entity, the nucleon, although as yet that description is by no means totally satisfactory.

Of all the elementary particles only seven, the electron, the proton, the neutrino, their antiparticles, and the photon, are completely stable in their free states. All of the others are produced either in the interactions of several hundred million electron volt nucleons, electrons, photons, or mesons with the nucleons of matter, or appear as products in the decay of heavier particles. These particles decay in their turn with half-lives ranging from 12 min for the neutron down to 10^{-22} or 10^{-23} sec.

Throughout this text we have regarded all changes in physical systems, whether the acceleration of falling bodies toward the earth, the increase in the gas pressure in a container, or the absorption of photons by atoms, as manifestations of the interactions of the constituents of those systems. We shall approach the production and decay of the elementary particles in the same spirit. Here, then, we have the basic reason for studying elementary particles. Since by definition the elementary particles are the simplest, most fundamental states of matter we know about, it follows that a study of their properties is tantamount to an attack upon the simplest, most unadorned manifestations of the basic interactions themselves. Indeed, from this point of view the fundamental interactions and the fundamental particles are quite inseparable from one another. The description of any physical entity ultimately reduces to a description of the way it interacts with the rest of the universe. Hence in a very real sense its properties *are* its interactions. In principle, then, the study of elementary particles permits us to relate the most fundamental properties of matter to the most fundamental interactions of the physical universe.

We now believe that all processes in the physical universe, both microscopic and macroscopic, can be related to four fundamental types of interactions named, in order of decreasing strength, the *strong, electromagnetic, weak,* and *gravitational* interactions. Of these only the second and the fourth have infinite range and, consequently are the only ones observable in macroscopic processes, whereas the importance of the strong and the weak interactions is restricted to the nuclear and subnuclear levels. The internucleon binding force is the most familiar example of the strong interaction. However, the interaction also plays the dominant role in the production of particles in nucleon-nucleon and meson-nucleon collision, and is responsible for the decay of the very short-lived particles. In contrast, virtually all the decay interactions from the 5570-yr half-life decay of $_6C^{14}$ down to the less than 10^{-14} sec decay of the Σ° particle occur via the weak interactions.

In order to estimate the relative strengths of the strong and the weak interactions we may compare the typical time intervals they require to manifest themselves. Because of the finite range of the strong, internucleon interaction, a high energy proton traveling with virtually the velocity of light can only interact with another proton while the two particles are within about 10^{-15} m of each other. Therefore, the interaction must occur in a time no greater than the range of the interaction divided by c, or about 10^{-23} sec. On the other hand, the decay of the charged π-meson (a typical weak interaction) requires 2×10^{-8} sec. It follows that high energy nucleon-nucleon interactions occur with characteristic rates 10^{14} to 10^{15} faster than typical weak decays, and we conclude that the former must be stronger than the latter by roughly that factor.

Similarly, the relative strengths of the strong and the electromagnetic interactions may be determined by measuring the times required for typical excited states in atoms and nuclei to decay by photon emission, and turns out to be on the order of $\frac{1}{137}$, making the electromagnetic interactions about 10^{12} times stronger than the weak interactions. Finally, we may relate the strength of the gravitational interaction to the other three by comparing the electrostatic force between two protons, calculated from Coulomb's law to the gravitational force between the same two protons calculated from Newton's gravitational law (Equation 8.2):

$$\frac{F_E}{F_G} = \frac{(1/4\pi\epsilon_0)(e^2/R^2)}{G(M_p^2/R^2)} = \left(\frac{1}{4\pi\epsilon_0 G}\right)\frac{e^2}{M_p^2} = 1.35 \times 10^{36}.$$

That is, the gravitational interaction has less than 10^{-22} the strength of the weak and less than 10^{-38} the strength of the strong interactions. For that reason it is usually disregarded when elementary particle interactions are considered.

TABLE 22.1 *Properties of the Quasi-Stable Particles*

Name	Symbol	Anti-particle	Rest Energy (MeV)	Charge (units of e)	Lifetime	Typical Decay Modes
			PHOTON CLASS			
Photon	γ	γ	0	0	Stable	—
			LEPTON CLASS			
Electron	e	$\bar{e}$ (positron)	0.511	-1	Stable	—
Muon	μ^-	μ^+	106	-1	2.2×10^{-6} sec	$e^- + \nu_e + \nu_\mu$
Electron Neutrino*	ν_e	$\bar{\nu}_e$	0	0	Stable	—
Muon Neutrino*	ν_μ	$\bar{\nu}_\mu$	0	0	Stable	—
			MESON CLASS			
π-meson	π^+	π^-	139	$+1$	2.6×10^{-8} sec	$\left[\begin{matrix}\mu^+ + \nu_\mu \\ e^+ + \nu_e\end{matrix}\right.$
π-meson	π^0	π^0	135	0	10^{-16} sec	$\left[\begin{matrix}\gamma + \gamma \\ \gamma + e^+ + e^-\end{matrix}\right.$
K-meson	K^+	K^-	494	$+1$	1.2×10^{-8} sec	$\left[\begin{matrix}\pi^+ + \pi^0 \\ \pi^0 + \mu^+ + \nu_e \\ \pi^+ + \pi^0 + \pi^0\end{matrix}\right.$
K-meson	K^0	$\bar{K}^0$	498	0	$\left.\begin{matrix}10^{-10} \text{ and} \\ 5.3 \times 10^{-8} \\ \text{sec}\end{matrix}\right]$†	$\left[\begin{matrix}\pi^+ + \mu^- + \pi^0 \\ \pi^\pm + \mu^\mp + \nu_\mu \\ \pi^+ + \pi^-\end{matrix}\right.$
			BARYON CLASS			
Proton	p	$\bar{p}$	938	$+1$	Stable	—
Neutron	n	$\bar{n}$	939	0	12 min	$p + e^- + \bar{\nu}_e$
Lambda	Λ^0	$\overline{\Lambda}^0$	1115	0	8×10^{-11} sec	$p + \pi^-$ $n + \pi^0$
Sigma	$\Sigma^\pm$	$\overline{\Sigma}^0$	1189	± 1	10^{-10} sec	Nucleon $+ \pi$
Sigma	Σ^0	$\overline{\Sigma}^0$	1192	0	10^{-14} sec	$\Lambda^0 + \gamma$
Xi	Ξ^-	$\overline{\Xi}^-$	1321	-1	1.7×10^{-10} sec	$\Lambda^0 + \pi^-$
Xi	Ξ^0	$\overline{\Xi}^0$	1315	0	2.9×10^{-10} sec	$\Lambda^0 + \pi^0$
Omega‡	Ω^-	$\overline{\Omega}^-$	1672	-1	10^{-10} sec	$\left[\begin{matrix}\Xi^0 + \pi^- \\ \Xi^- + \pi^0 \\ \Lambda^0 + K^-\end{matrix}\right.$

* The distinction between the muon and electron neutrinos was first established in 1962 (Section 22.10).
† For reasons that are touched upon in Chapter 23 (Section 23.6) the neutral K-meson is unique in having two distinct half-lives.
‡ The Omega minus (Ω^-) was discovered in 1964. At this writing only seven have been seen. Its antiparticle has not yet been identified but presumably exists.

Using the fundamental interactions as a guide, all the known particles may be divided into four classes: the *baryons*, the *mesons*, the *leptons*, and the *photon*. Members of the first two classes may participate in all four interactions. The baryons (from the Greek word for heavy) are *Fermi* particles with half-odd integral intrinsic spin ($\hbar/2, 3\hbar/2, \ldots$; Section 21.5) and range in mass from the proton (rest energy 938 MeV) upward, whereas the mesons (Greek for medium) are *Bose* particles with integral spin ($0, \hbar, 2\hbar, \ldots$) whose masses range upward from the 135 MeV neutral π-meson mass. In contrast, leptons (Greek for light) are *Fermi* particles which do *not* participate in the strong interactions. At present the class contains four members: two types of neutrino (zero rest energy), the electron (rest energy 0.511 MeV), and the muon (rest energy 106 MeV), plus their corresponding antiparticles. Finally, the photon class contains only the familiar, massless, spin 1 (or $\hbar$) Bose particle which participates only in the electromagnetic interactions, and is, in fact, the carrier of that interaction.

Table 22.1 summarizes the properties of the elementary particles with half-lives greater than 10^{-16} sec, that is, those whose lifetimes are at least a million times greater than the characteristic strong interaction time. Since only two particles (the π° and Σ°) have half-lives shorter than 10^{-11} sec, these particles are virtually stable as far as the strong and (but for the two exceptions) the electromagnetic interactions are concerned. With two exceptions which are explicitly noted, all particles in the table had been identified by 1960. In the remainder of this chapter and in the next we shall discuss a few of the many approaches to the problem of understanding the role these particles play in the fundamental interactions that have been put forward in the last two decades. In doing so we shall discuss some of the newer members of the baryon and meson classes which have been discovered in the meantime, and which, in many ways have clarified the nature of the problem at hand.

◂◂ 22.3 Quantum theory of the electromagnetic interaction. Feynman diagrams

Of the four classes of interactions, the electromagnetic is unique in its ability to manifest itself significantly on both the microscopic and macroscopic levels. Hence it is also the best understood of the four.

All of the elementary particles bear one of three charges, $+e$, 0, or $-e$ ($e = 1.6 \times 10^{-19}$ C), regardless of their masses, regardless of their other properties. In Chapter 8 we defined charge as a property of matter that permits its participation in the electromagnetic interactions, even as we had previously given an analogous definition of gravitational mass (Chapter 5). Although our comprehension of the electromagnetic interaction has evolved considerably since we first spoke of the affinity of pith balls for amber rubbed vigorously with animal fur, the spirit of the original definition remains unaltered. Hence the statement that there are but three basic charge states, one of them the negative of another, the third zero, implies that at least to a first approximation all the elementary particles that *can* participate in the electromagnetic interaction, participate in the same way. In Chapter 21 we concluded, somewhat analogously, that the nuclear part of the force between two nucleons does not depend upon whether the participating nucleons are protons or neutrons. However, our conclusion regarding the electromagnetic interaction is considerably broader, applying as it does to *all* charged particles.

Our contemporary view of the electromagnetic interaction is based upon a theory known as quantum electrodynamics developed in the late 1940's by a number of physicists, primarily Julian Schwinger and Richard Feynman. Classical or Maxwellian electrodynamics describes the interaction between charged matter in terms of continuous

FIGURE 22.1. Richard Feynman. (Courtesy of the American Institute of Physics, Center for the History and Philosophy of Physics.)

electromagnetic fields which are induced by and act upon the charges. Thus the magnitude of a charge is measured in terms of its ability to interact with the electromagnetic field. Of course the classical continuum theory breaks down when applied to atomic processes, and we speak instead of the emission and absorption of quanta of electromagnetic energy, or photons. But we have really not reconciled the photon idea with the total range of classical electromagnetic phenomena, the electrostatic interaction between two charges at rest or the radiation from an accelerating free charge, for instance, although we have touched upon the problem (Section 12.4). Quantum electrodynamics reestablishes the electromagnetic field as a construct of fundamental importance. However, it assumes that the energy of the field is quantized rather than continuous, and identified photons as the quanta of the field. Whenever a charge interacts with the field its energy changes, or, in other words, it emits or absorbs one or more photons. Hence the theory is certainly consistent with our simpler description of radiation processes in atoms and nuclei. However, it is considerably broader since it places *all* electromagnetic processes on the same footing.

Classically, we measure the charge of a particle in terms of its ability to interact with the electromagnetic field. Equivalently, quantum electrodynamics attributes to a charged particle a particular probability for interacting with the field. Let us imagine that the quantized electromagnetic field pervades all space, or, more prosaically, that photons of all possible energies are everywhere available. A free electron traveling through space eventually interacts with the field, or, in other words, emits or absorbs a photon. In the process it changes both its energy and its momentum, so that both the electron and photon make transitions from one energy-momentum state to another. Therefore, in the spirit of Section 18.9, the entire process should be describable in terms of a transition probability between the initial and final sets of energy-momentum states.

The diagram in Figure 22.2a, of a type introduced by Feynman, provides a convenient means of representing this and many analogous processes. The solid lines show the spatial position of the electron as a function of time, with the arrowheads indicating the direction of its motion (i.e., from left to right, or forward in time). Initially (from point a to b) the velocity of the electron is constant and given by the slope of the solid line, just as the slope of the line on the first spacetime graph we ever discussed in Chapter 2 gave us the velocity of an automobile on a toll road. At point b the electron emits a photon whose subsequent motion is indicated by the irregular line. Since the energy and momentum of the electron decrease after emission of the photon, the slope of electron line must change.

Figure 22.2b is an analogous Feynman graph for the absorption of a photon by an electron at b and shows the consequent change in the electron's velocity. Classically both Figures 22.2a and 22.2b represent strictly forbidden processes, for energy and momentum

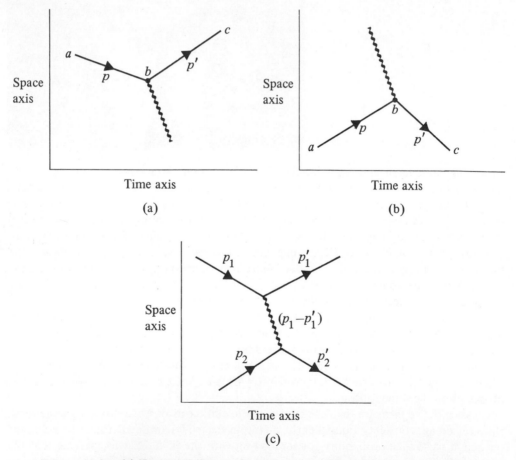

FIGURE 22.2. (a) Feynman diagram for the emission of a photon by an electron. (b) The absorption of a photon by an electron. (c) Interaction of two electrons by means of one photon exchange.

cannot both be conserved if nothing occurs save the emission or absorption of one par-ticle by another. But as we saw in our discussion of the Yukawa model for the inter-nucleon force (Section 21.8), the Heisenberg principle permits a temporary suspension of the energy conservation principle. If a process occurs during a time interval Δt the un-certainty in its energy is $\Delta E = h/\Delta t$ (Equation 21.6). Hence an electron may emit a photon with any energy whatsoever *provided* the energy balance is redressed within the time limit set by the uncertainty principle. For example, in Figure 22.2c a photon is emitted by one electron and absorbed by another so that no net, long-term energy change occurs. However, there is a transfer of energy and momentum between the two electrons. In other words, they interact via the exchange of a photon even as, on the Yukawa model, two nucleons interact via π-meson exchange.

Figure 22.2c represents the interaction (or scattering) of two electrons and is known as a one-photon exchange diagram. The entire process can be described in terms of a transition probability from an initial state with two free electrons with the respective momenta $\mathbf{p}_1$ and $\mathbf{p}_2$, to a final state in which their momenta are $\mathbf{p}_1'$ and $\mathbf{p}_2'$, with the re-quirement that $\mathbf{p}_1 + \mathbf{p}_2 = \mathbf{p}_1' + \mathbf{p}_2'$. The actual transition occurs through an intermediate state (Figure 22.2c) in which a photon with momentum $\mathbf{p}_1 - \mathbf{p}_1'$ has been emitted by the first electron but not yet absorbed by the second. The transition amplitude between the initial and final states, and thus the probability of the two-electron interaction, depends on the probability for the first electron to emit a photon and for the second to absorb it. Because charge measures the ability of a particle to interact with the electromagnetic field, the amplitude for emission and/or absorption of a photon should be constant and should involve the fundamental charge $e = 1.6 \times 10^{-19}$ C in some way. In addition, the probability that a photon once emitted by an electron will be absorbed by another should be a function of the photon's energy and the distance between the electrons, for the separation between the electrons determines the time lapse between emission and absorption, and thus sets an upper limit on the photon energy. Therefore, we conclude that the *intrinsic* strength of the interaction between two electrons depends upon their ability to emit and absorb photons. Also, since the maximum energy of the photons that may be transferred between two electrons decreases with their separation, it follows that the interaction also decreases as a function of distance.

These conclusions are, of course, consistent with all we have learned about the electro-magnetic interaction, both micro- and macroscopically. Indeed, all of the quantitative details of both classical electrodynamics and elementary quantum mechanics may be derived from the photon exchange model, for all of these processes may be represented by combinations of the basic emission and absorption graphs of Figure 22.2, and their amplitudes calculated by combining the basic amplitudes according to the usual quantum mechanical rules. For example, Figure 22.3a is a Compton scattering diagram showing the absorption of a photon by an electron followed by the remission of another photon.* Again, energy need not be conserved in the intermediate state (from *b* to *c*) provided the lifetime of that state is no longer than the limit set by the uncertainty principle. The Compton diagram differs in detail from Figures 22.2, for now there is an electron rather than a photon in the classically "forbidden" intermediate state. But the principle involved in calculating the probability for the process to occur is no different. Here an

---

*The fact that photons are emitted and absorbed at particular points on these diagrams does not imply that the processes are completely localized in space. Since we are dealing with definite momentum states such an implication would clearly violate the Heisenberg principle. Feynman graphs provide a convenient means for representing detailed processes. However, they are certainly not photographs in any sense of the word.

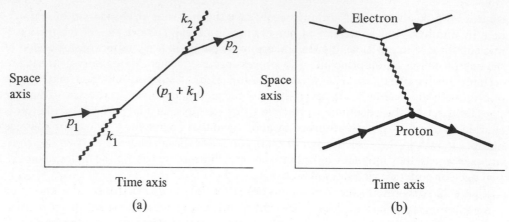

FIGURE 22.3. (a) Diagram for the scattering of a photon by an electron (Compton scattering). (b) Interaction of a proton and an electron via one photon exchange.

electron with momentum $\mathbf{p}_1$ and a photon with energy k_1 make a transition to a state in which the electron has momentum $\mathbf{p}_2$ and the photon energy k_2. The transition occurs via the intermediate state in which the electron has absorbed the initial state photon. Thus again the complete transition probability depends in good measure upon the emission and absorption probabilities.

Figure 22.3b suggests an interpretation of the Coulomb interaction between the proton and electron in a hydrogen atom in terms of photon exchange, and is clearly related to the diagrams 22.2c and 22.3a.

If quantum electrodynamics did no more than yield the results of classical electrodynamics and elementary quantum mechanics we would probably conclude that the photon exchange viewpoint is interesting but unnecessary. But in fact, it permits us to go considerably further by unifying a number of seemingly distinct processes. The fact that both the repulsive interaction between two electrons and Compton scattering are related to the same basic set of diagrams (and therefore to combinations of the same amplitudes) illustrates the point. Figure 22.4a reproduces the basic photon emission

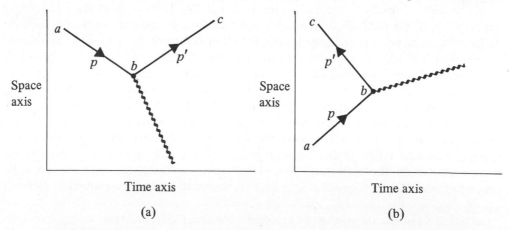

FIGURE 22.4 (a) Feynman diagram for the emission of a photon by an electron. (b) The emission diagram rotated 90° so that one of the electron lines goes backward in time.

diagram of Figure 22.2a. Superficially, Figure 22.4b looks very much the same; a photon is emitted by an electron at point *b* and consequently the slope of the electron line changes. However, the slope of the line has changed so much that the electron travels *backward* in time "after" emitting the photon. Does such a diagram have any physical meaning?

In Chapter 6 we discussed the rather difficult question of symmetry under time reversal, and concluded that none of the fundamental equations of classical physics depends on which direction of time we choose to call forward and backward. Hence a motion picture of an undamped pendulum would look the same regardless of which direction the film ran, a ball thrown upward reverses its motion exactly on returning to earth from its highest point. By extending these arguments to quantum electrodynamics, Feynman was able to give a physical meaning to the idea of an electron moving backward in time. However, in order to understand his interpretation it is desirable to take a brief look first at P. A. M. Dirac's relativistic formulation of quantum mechanics.

▲▲ 22.4 Dirac's relativistic quantum mechanics. Antiparticles

In Chapter 18 (Section 18.6) we assumed that the amplitude for a free particle with definite momentum p_n and definite energy E_n is

$$\phi_n = \bar{a}_n \exp\left[\frac{i}{\hbar}(p_n x - E_n t)\right]. \tag{18.19}$$

Subsequently we found that this assumption was consistent with the free particle solutions of the one-dimensional Schrödinger equation (Equation 18.23). However, that equation is only valid in the nonrelativistic approximation that all velocities are small relative to c. In 1928 P. A. M. Dirac generalized the equation so that its solutions correctly described the electron as a relativistic particle. His generalized equation also predicted the existence of antiparticles.

In order to understand this latter consequence of Dirac theory let us assume that the free-particle amplitude is still given by Equation 18.19, but that p_n and E_n are related by the correct relativistic expression (Equation 11.25a) rather than by the nonrelativistic expression used by Schrödinger. That is,

$$E_n^2 = c^2 p_n^2 + M_0^2 c^4,$$

or

$$E_n = \pm\sqrt{c^2 p_n^2 + M_0^2 c^4}.$$

As Dirac pointed out this relation implies that Equation 18.19 can describe *two* free particle states with definite momentum p_n, one with positive total energy, the other with negative total energy.

But what is the physical meaning of negative *total* energy? If the *potential* energy of a particle is negative relative to its free state the particle is subject to an attractive force. But kinetic energies are always greater than zero. Hence classically a free particle, with zero potential energy, cannot have negative *total* energy. Nevertheless, Dirac's equation, which follows from the combined logic of quantum mechanics and special relativity, asserts that once again the classical prediction is too limited in scope.

An electron confined to a large box of length L can assume only a discrete set of momentum states (Section 18.8). If L is very large these states are very close together. However, if the total energy of a system of electrons is finite then so is the number of available electron states, even for a volume greater than the size of the solar system or the galaxy, though of course in the latter cases the number of available states is exceedingly large.

Both the positive and the negative energy states available to an almost free electron confined in a very large volume are shown schematically in Figure 22.5. Because the minimum total energy states correspond to zero momentum states, all of the states have energies greater than the electron rest energy, $E_0 = M_0 c^2$, or less than the negative of the electron rest energy, $-M_0 c^2$. Except for these restrictions the particle may assume virtually any total energy. If the negative energy states exist we would expect an electron in the lowest positive energy state $M_0 c^2$ to have a reasonable probability of making a transition to one of them. Because the rest energy of an electron is 0.511 MeV its energy would decrease by at least $2M_0 c^2 = 1.02$ MeV in making the transition; hence one or more photons with total energy greater than 1 MeV (million electron volts) would be emitted in the process.

Why aren't these spontaneous transition processes commonly observed? Shortly after Dirac first published his equation it was suggested that the answer was related to the Pauli exclusion principle. Since electrons are Fermi particles, no more than one can occupy a given state. Therefore, if we assume that the negative energy states are already filled (at least in this part of the universe) then no more electrons can be accommodated, and spontaneous transitions from the positive energy states are therefore forbidden. For the same reason an electron in one negative energy state normally cannot make a transition to another. Thus negative energy electrons are normally unobservable. It might be argued that since we have always lived with this lifeless sea of negative energy electrons, we have never been aware of its existence, even as a fish might well consider a continuum of water as the normal condition.*

The negative energy electron sea is, however, not quite closed to our view. If one of the electrons in that sea absorbs a million electron volts energy or more it can make a transition to one of the unfilled *positive* energy states (Figure 22.6a), leaving a vacancy or a "bubble" in the sea. The existence of the vacant state means that another negative energy electron is now able to make a transition, filling the original vacancy but leaving another vacancy in its initial state (Figure 22.6b). Thus the state which is vacant may

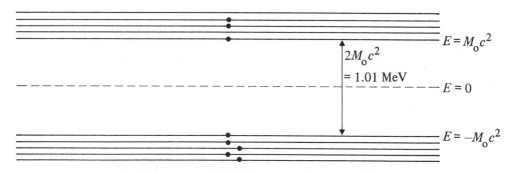

FIGURE 22.5. The positive and negative energy states predicted by Dirac. If the negative states are all filled, an electron with positive energy cannot make a translation into one of them.

---

* If this parallel seems far-fetched we have only to note that the concept of the vacuum is a reasonably sophisticated one simply because human beings normally do not consider air very remarkable. In fact, Aristotle went to considerable pains to deny the possible existence of the vacuum on both philosophical and physical grounds.

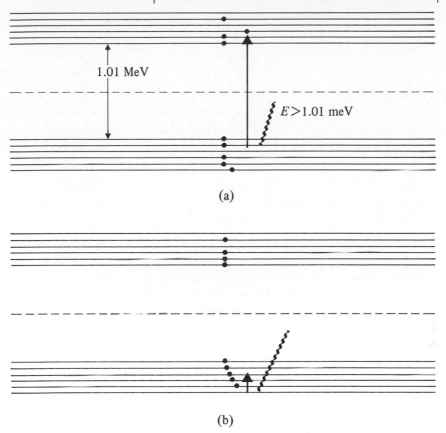

FIGURE 22.6.   (a) A negative energy electron absorbs a photon with energy greater than 1.01 MeV, making a transition into a positive energy state and leaving a vacancy behind. (b) Another negative energy electron absorbs a photon making a transition into the vacant state. Therefore, the energy of the vacancy becomes more negative.

change, or, from another point of view, the vacancy *itself* may move so that in a very real scnse we may regard the vacancy as a particle.

However, the vacancy is a particle with rather curious properties, for in many ways its behavior is precisely opposite to the behavior of the surrounding electrons. Suppose a group of electrons in the negative encrgy states are subject to an electric field. Because of their negative charge each would be accelerated in the direction opposite to the field direction, provided vacancies existed in the sea. If by filling such a vacancy an electron moves in one direction under the influence of the field a vacancy would be crcated in its old state. Hence the vacancy moves in the same direction that a *positively* charged particle would move if subject to the field (Figure 22.7). In much the same way a fish, watching a bubble rise in his sea, might conclude that he was observing a particlc which obeys antigravitational laws.

A detailed quantum mechanical analysis shows that a vacancy in the negative-energy sea has all the qualities of an electron except for the fact that the sign of its charge must be taken as *positive*. The vacancy acts exactly as if it were the charge symmetric counterpart of an electron, or its *antiparticle*, and is explicitly called a *positron*. Because this conclusion follows from the general rules of quantum mechanics and relativity, the

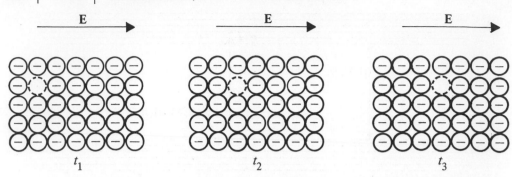

FIGURE 22.7. Motion of a vacancy (second row from the top) in an electric field. As each electron moves to the left to fill the vacancy, the vacancy itself moves to the right as if it were a positively charged electron.

Dirac equation predicts the possible existence not only of anti-electrons, but of charge symmetric antiparticles corresponding to *all* of the fundamental particles. On the basis of the model, whenever an undetectable electron in a negative energy state absorbs a photon with energy greater than $2M_0c^2 = 1.01$ MeV it appears in a positive energy state, becomes measurable, and also leaves a vacancy behind (Figure 22.6a). Experimentally, an electron and a positron should be *created* (Figure 22.8). Likewise, when an electron in a positive energy state makes a transition to a vacant *negative* energy state not only the electron, but also the vacancy disappears. The electron and positron *annihilate* each other leaving two photons with total energy at least one million electron volts.*

Positrons were first observed in 1932 by Carl Anderson (Section 20.8) who thus confirmed the existence of Dirac's antiparticles. The creation of an antiproton with *negative* charge and rest mass 938 MeV was not observed until the six billion electron volt proton accelerator at the University of California was completed in 1955. Antineutrons were observed the following year. Of course neutrons have zero charge, and hence so do their antiparticles. Therefore an antineutron manifests itself as an antiparticle only in its mutual annihilation with a neutron to yield π-mesons or photons with a total energy greater than two billion electron volts. The ability of an antiparticle to annihilate a particle is its primary property rather than the fact that the sign of its charge, if nonzero, is opposite that of the particle.

Is an antiproton "really" a bubble in a negative energy proton sea? We have asked similar questions before. Do moving clocks really slow down? Do electrons really have wavelike properties? The logic of quantum mechanics and relativity implies the existence of negative energy states. One interpretation of those states can be made in terms of the vacancy-as-particle model, a model whose predictions are in accord with experiment. Hence the model gives a consistent description of a series of natural processes. We can ask no more than that from a physical theory. An alternate interpretation of the negative energy states that involves time reversal invariance was given by R. P. Feynman in 1949, and is considered in the next section.

The vacancy model for elementary particles has at least one more important implica-

---

* Momentum conservation does not permit an electron-positron pair to annihilate into one photon. If the pair annihilates at rest its total momentum is zero. One photon would then have energy $2M_0c^2$ and hence momentum $p = E/c = 2M_0c$, obviously greater than zero. But since momentum is a vector, the total momentum of two photons each with energy M_0c^2 will be zero if the photons travel in the opposite directions. Similarly a pair can only be created near a nucleus that is able to recoil slightly and hence conserve momentum in the creation reaction.

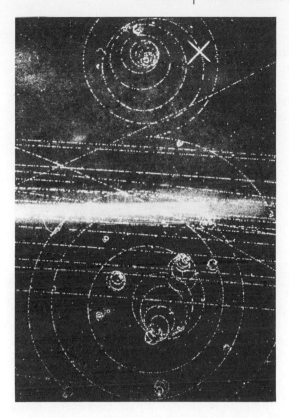

FIGURE 22.8. Pair production in a bubble chamber. A photon (not visible) enters the chamber from the left. The opposite curvatures of the resulting electron and positron show that their charges are also opposite, while their inward spiraling orbits show that they lose energy rapidly. (Courtesy of Brookhaven National Laboratory.)

tion. If we assume that no particle is ever "really" destroyed but merely disappears by making a transition into an unobservable negative energy state, we conclude that an electron can appear to be destroyed only if a positron also appears to be destroyed simultaneously, or created when a positron is created. Hence we are led to a new conservation law: *the total number of electrons minus the total number of anti-electrons in a closed system remains constant.* We also arrive at an analogous law for protons and for neutrons.

These conservation laws are not quite correct, for a neutron may decay into a proton, an electron, and an antineutrino via the weak interactions. However, the electron conservation law is correct if generalized to include neutrinos, and the proton-neutron conservation law valid if generalized to include all baryons, as we shall see in a later section. Nevertheless the spirit of the simpler laws forbidding the conversion of the electron, neutron, or proton masses completely into kinetic energy without the simultaneous annihilation of the corresponding antiparticles remains valid. Hence atoms and nuclei are ultimately stable against complete spontaneous transformations into energy, for there are relatively few anti-electrons, antiprotons, and antineutrons in this part of the universe.

The Pauli exclusion principle is a keystone in the vacancy model of anti-Fermi particles, for without it the negative energy states could never be filled regardless of the number of particles that existed. Bose particles also have negative energy states available to them. Hence anti-Bose particles also exist and may also be created and annihilated in pairs. However, since these particles are *not* subject to the Pauli exclusion principle they need not obey conservation laws analogous to the electron-neutrino and proton-neutron laws.

Given sufficient energy any number of bosons should be able to make transitions from negative to positive energy states *without* leaving any vacancies behind.

In fact, the fundamental Bose particles are not conserved. A hydrogen atom absorbs a single photon in making a transition to a higher energy state, and emits a photon when it returns to its ground state. Similarly, the π-meson can be created and destroyed (or emitted and absorbed) without the simultaneous creation or destruction of their antiparticles—provided no other conservation laws (energy, momentum, charge, for instance) are violated. Even as the conservation of the several classes of Fermi particles is important to the ultimate stability of matter, so the nonconservation of the Bose particles permits us to approach the problem of the fundamental interactions among the Fermi particles in terms of the exchange of Bose particles between them.

22.5 Feynman's description of antiparticles. The generalizing power of quantum electrodynamics

In 1949 Feynman offered an alternative interpretation of the relation between particles and antiparticles which has the distinct advantage of being easily incorporated into the interaction scheme we started to develop in Section 22.3. He noted that the free-particle amplitude (Equation 18.19) involves energy and time as the product Et. Now if t is changed to $-t$ the conventional order of time is reversed. If in addition E is changed to $-E$ then since $(-E)(-t) = Et$, Equation 18.19 is completely unaltered. That is, the *same* amplitude that describes a *positive* energy electron going *forward* in time also describes a *negative* energy electron, or a positron going *backward* in time. Therefore, whenever a graph (such as Figure 22.4b) shows an *electron* of a particular energy going *backward* in time, we are to interpret that line of the graph as a *positron* of the same energy going *forward* in time. Similarly, a positron going backward in time becomes an electron going forward in time.

We are now in a position to interpret Figure 22.9a: it represents the annihilation of an electron and a positron to yield a photon. Actually the diagram is incomplete for the same reasons that Figures 22.2a and 22.2b are, for it does not conserve energy and momentum. However, Figure 22.9b represents a real physical process provided the usual uncertainty criterion is satisfied for the intermediate state. Thus we have an interpretation of antimatter quite different and in many ways more satisfying than the Dirac hole model, for the amplitude for the process may be related directly to the amplitude for emission (or absorption) of a photon by an electron (Figure 22.2a). The positron and electron amplitudes for the same momentum are equal, and annihilation, emission, and absorption are seen as variants of the same basic process. Hence the amplitude for each diagram is the product of the same factors. It is also simple to relate the production of an electron-positron pair to these processes, for the basic diagram (Figure 22.9c) is nothing more than the annihilation diagram turned upside down.

The fundamental equivalence of the diagrams of Figures 22.2 and 22.9 suggests that the words "emission" and "absorption" are somewhat misleading. While we can conceivably speak of emission in Figure 22.2a, the word has little meaning in Figure 22.9a, where an electron and a positron disappear and a photon appears. Points on the diagrams at which photon and electron lines intersect are called *vertices*. If we reinterpret a vertex as a point on the graph at which the incoming particles are annihilated and the outgoing particles created, then the electron in Figure 22.2a is annihilated at b and *another* electron and photon created. Of course the two verbal descriptions are physically in-

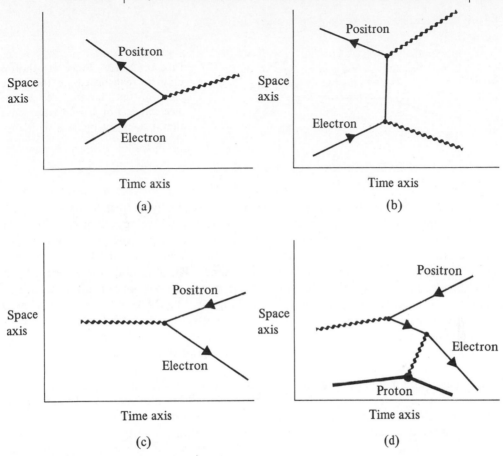

FIGURE 22.9. (a) Diagram for the annihiliation of an electron-positron pair into a photon. (Compare with Figure 22.2a.) (b) Energy and momentum conserving annihilation into two photons. (c) Basic diagram for pair creation by a single photon. (d) Energy and momentum conserving pair production in matter. Two photons, one of them obtained from the electrostatic field of the proton, disappear and the electron-positron pair appears. The pair shown in the bubble chamber photograph of Figure 22.8 was created in this way.

distinguishable. But the latter places the electron and photon on a more equal footing and is more consistent with the fundamental framework of quantum electrodynamics. We may think of electrons and photons pervading all space, since they cannot be detected unless they interact. Both particles, however, *do* have a particular probability of interaction—a probability that measures charge, or, synonymously, the strength of the electromagnetic interaction. Further, that interaction is always catastrophic with the participants vanishing and new particles appearing at the interaction vertices in accord with the basic diagrams of Figures 22.2 and 22.9, and with a set of symmetry principles we shall discuss in Chapter 23.

We have not yet exhausted the implications of quantum electrodynamics. Suppose the electron in Figure 22.10 is so far away from all other particles that the photon it emits cannot reach another charged particle within the time limit set by the uncertainty principle. In that event energy can only be conserved if the original electron reabsorbs

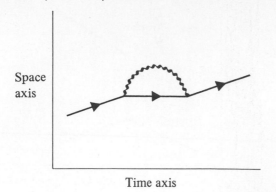

Space axis

Time axis

FIGURE 22.10. Since a photon may be reabsorbed by the same electron that emitted it, a free electron is not free in the sense that it does not interact with anything.

the photon. It follows that a "free" electron can never really be free. Rather, it always has a definite probability of interacting with a photon and of being accompanied by that photon for a short interval of time. Using more picturesque, though somewhat less precise language, we can envision a photon "halo" surrounding an electron with the extent and energy of the halo fluctuating with time. The amplitude for Figure 22.10b (and therefore the properties of the "halo") is in principle no more difficult to determine than the two-particle interaction amplitudes of Figures 22.2, 22.3, and 22.9, for it is based upon the same basic emission-absorption (or creation-annihilation) processes.

Applying similar arguments to the behavior of a "free" photon, it immediately becomes evident that we have by no means exhausted the contents of the electron halo. A photon has a definite amplitude for creating an electron-positron pair (Figure 22.11). But again, since energy and momentum cannot both be conserved in the basic diagram, something else must occur within the time, for example, the absorption of another photon by one member of the pair (Figure 22.9d). Alternately, the pair may annihilate to yield another photon of the original energy. Therefore, even as we think of a free electron as spending a fraction of its time as an electron and photon, so we regard a photon as spending part of its time as an electron-positron pair. More generally, we cannot hope to understand either electrons or photons by considering them in isolation from the rest of the universe (as we once considered the motion of falling bodies) for the properties of both particles are intimately related to each other.

Figure 22.12 emphasizes the point. Part of the time a "free" electron is accompanied by a photon (Figure 22.10), part of the time a photon exists as an electron-positron pair (Figure 22.11). It follows that a free electron has a definite probability of spending part of its time as an electron plus an electron-positron pair. Presumably the amplitude describing the intrinsic properties of the "free" electron is the sum of all amplitudes

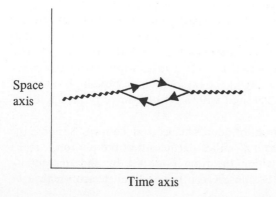

Space axis

Time axis

FIGURE 22.11. Since an electron-positron pair created by a photon may annihilate to produce another photon, the properties of electrons and photons are intimately related.

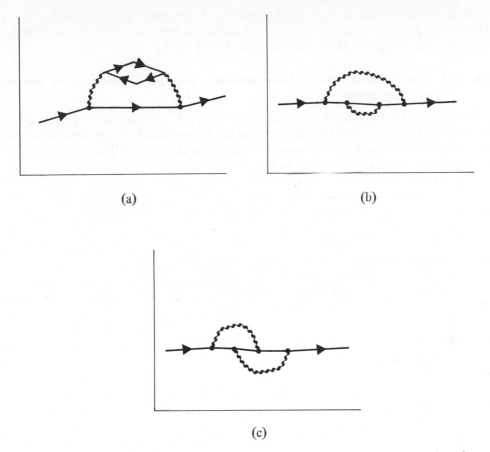

FIGURE 22.12. Four-vertex diagrams contributing to the intrinsic properties of a "free" electron.

describing its interactions with the electromagnetic field; that is, it is the sum of the amplitudes corresponding to all possible diagrams of the types illustrated in Figure 22.12. Obviously there are an infinite number of these, for every photon in an intermediate state has a nonzero probability of existing for a time as an electron-positron pair, and every electron and positron a definite probability of emitting or absorbing another photon.

Fortunately, the magnitude of a particular diagram's contribution to the total amplitude decreases rapidly with increasing complexity so that to an excellent approximation the amplitude may be obtained if diagrams of complexity greater than those in Figure 22.12 are omitted from the sum. The probability amplitude for any interaction vertex in a Feynman diagram is often called the *strength* of the vertex, and is a measure of the intrinsic strength of the interaction. As detailed calculations show, the strength of an electron-photon vertex is proportional to the dimensionless number:

$$\frac{e^2}{\hbar c} = \frac{1}{137}$$

where e is the fundamental charge, $\hbar$ = Planck's constant divided by 2π, and c is the velocity of light. Since the probability of a complex electromagnetic process is proportional to the product of all its basic photon-electron interaction amplitudes, then if a particular diagram has n vertices its amplitude is proportional to $(e^2/\hbar c)^n = (\frac{1}{137})^n$. Hence a diagram with four vertices has an amplitude less than 10^{-4} times as large as the basic, two-vertex self absorption diagram (Figure 22.10).

▲▲ 22.6 Electromagnetic mass of the electron. Conceptual difficulties in quantum electrodynamics

The ideas of the last section, when developed in detail, lend themselves to a number of experimental tests. One of the first involved the measurement of very small changes in the energy levels of the hydrogen atom. To determine these energy levels by the methods of elementary quantum mechanics we first express the electrostatic and magnetic inter-action between the proton and electron in terms of a classically-derived potential, and then deduce the amplitude for finding an electron bound in that potential (Sections 19.1 and 19.2). In quantum electrodynamics, the interaction between the electron and proton is mediated by the exchange of photons. Indeed, the amplitude calculated by taking account of the simplest exchange diagrams (Figure 22.3b) leads to results in accord with the more elementary calculations. But of course part of the time the exchanged photons can exist as electron-positron pairs, and while they exist these charged particles interact with both the orbital electron and the proton. As a result, the energy levels calculated using quantum electrodynamics differ very slightly from the levels determined from elementary quantum mechanics. Exceedingly precise measurements of these levels have been made, and are in complete agreement with the quantum electrodynamic expectations.

If we take the interaction viewpoint to its ultimate, logical conclusion, we should be able to understand *all* of the properties of a particle in terms of its interactions. This program has met with some success for the electron. For example, the magnitude of its intrinsic magnetic moment (Section 19.2) is certainly an electromagnetic property, and should be related to its charge and mass in some way. Indeed, a magnetic moment whose magnitude is in complete agreement with measurement has been calculated by taking the proper self-emission and absorption diagrams into account.

An even more ambitious program would relate the electron's inertial mass to its inter-actions. From the most basic point of view, inertial mass is the measure of a body's inertia, its resistance to changes in its motion (Chapter 4). Since the interactions of an electron are overwhelmingly electromagnetic then its mass, too, should be overwhelm-ingly electromagnetic. As we have noted, a free electron is never really free. Hence an electron "at rest" must in reality undergo a more or less random motion as it recoils from self-emission and absorption processes, and consequently must have kinetic energy greater than zero. Presumably this kinetic energy should follow from a proper sum over all appropriated Feynman diagrams (Figure 22.12) and lead through the relativistic mass-energy relation to the electron rest mass.

Unfortunately, technical difficulties continue to plague all attempts to relate the rest mass of the electron to its interactions, although a few partial successes have been achieved. But we should also note a singular failure of the program that is, in fact, one of the major unsolved problems in quantum electrodynamics. Of all the charged elementary particles, there are but the two charged leptons, the electron and the muon, which by definition do *not* participate in the strong interactions. The latter particle with a rest energy of 106 MeV is one of the decay products of the charged π-meson (Section 21.7):

$$\pi^+ \rightarrow \mu^+ + \nu,$$
$$\pi^- \rightarrow \mu^- + \bar{\nu},$$

and in turn decays in 2×10^{-6} sec into an electron and a neutrino-antineutrino pair:

$$\mu^+ \rightarrow e^\pm + \nu + \bar{\nu}.$$

Except for its instability and its mass, the muon appears to be identical in virtually every respect to the electron. Its decay occurs via the weak interactions which, as noted in Section 22.2, are about 10^{12} times weaker than the electromagnetic interactions. Therefore, the muon's interactions, like the electron's, are overwhelmingly electromagnetic. But if all properties are related to interactions, why does the muon have a mass more than 200 times larger than the mass of another particle whose interactions are virtually identical? At this writing no one has any idea how to solve the problem. Considerable effort has been expended in trying to discover some difference in the behavior of the two particles, but so far to no avail.

One further difference between the muon and electron has been discovered: the fact that the neutrino accompanying the muon and the neutrino accompanying the electron are different particles (Section 22.10). Although the existence of two neutrinos might contain the clue to the riddle of the muon-electron mass difference, at this writing no one has been able to use that clue to good advantage.

It would be well to note one remaining conceptual problem in quantum electrodynamics. We know that the range of the electromagnetic interaction is infinite so that two charged particles separated by a very large distance still interact with each other. But can the form of the interaction remain unaltered at arbitrarily small separations? As the separation between two charged particles decreases, so does the time required for a photon to travel between them. Consequently, the maximum allowable energy of the exchanged photons increases with decreasing separation, becoming infinite for zero separation. Obviously there are logical problems involved in talking about infinite interaction energies. Therefore, when calculations are made, an arbitrary upper limit is usually set on the exchange energy, corresponding to a minimum separation between the interacting particles, and it is assumed that at smaller separations the interaction must somehow change so that the exchange of infinite energy photons will be inhibited. From a slightly different point of view, it is assumed that the electron-photon vertices cannot be points, or that the interaction at the vertices, and thus in effect the electron itself, must have some structure.

If the formalism of quantum electrodynamics *does* break down at small distances, what is that breakdown distance and how does the strength of the electron-photon vertex change? These questions have been investigated by measuring the probability for pair-production at high energies as a function of angle. If N is some nucleus then the reaction studied is

$$\gamma + N \rightarrow e^+ + e^- + N.$$

Figure 22.9d shows the basic diagram corresponding to the process. A free, incoming photon can exist for a time as a high energy electron-positron pair. If either member of the pair exchanges a photon with the nucleus, then the process conserves energy, and the electron and positron can exist as free particles. Of course the probability of the process depends upon the strength of the vertex, which specifies the electron-positron-photon interaction. If the particles have high energies they also have large momenta, and thus by the uncertainty principle can interact over small distances. Hence measurements of the probability of the process as a function of outgoing momentum yields information on the character of the interaction at small differences.

Experiments of this nature have now been carried out with photon energies up to six billion electron volts and have thus far yielded no convincing evidence for an alteration of quantum electrodynamics at small distances. At this writing the finite interaction region, if it exists, must be smaller than 10^{-16} m. Completely analogous experiments to measure the probability of muon pair production have also been made with the expressed aim of seeking some difference between the muon and electron at small interaction distances. Once again the results show an exact correspondence between the particles down to distances on the order of 10^{-16} m.

◣◣ 22.7 Charge structure of the proton and neutron

Neutrons and protons participate in the strong as well as the electromagnetic interactions. Thus any mathematical description of their properties is certain to be more involved than the corresponding description of the electron. Nevertheless, since the proton and electron have charges of equal magnitude, and since we interpret charge in terms of the ability to interact with the electromagnetic field, at least some features of the photon exchange model should be applicable to the electromagnetic properties of the proton.

Figure 22.13a represents the exchange of a photon between an electron and a proton. The left-hand part of the diagram is just the basic electron-photon emission graph familiar from the foregoing sections. For large separations the electromagnetic interaction between two electrons is equivalent (but for a change in sign) to the electromagnetic interaction between an electron and a proton. Hence, the strength of the proton-photon vertex should be equal in magnitude to the electron-photon vertex, and the amplitude for an electron-proton interaction follows at once from the corresponding electron-electron amplitude.

However, we should not expect the equivalence to persist for interaction distances on the order of the range of the nucleon-nucleon force. The Yukawa model (Sections 21.7 and 21.8) requires that a nucleon continuously emit and absorb both charged and neutral π-mesons. Speaking rather crudely, we envision a nucleon surrounded by a π-meson cloud extending out to the range of the nuclear force (10^{-15} m), a distance often called the

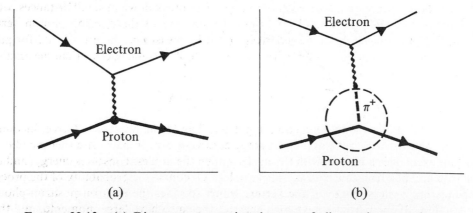

(a)   (b)

FIGURE 22.13. (a) Diagram representing the sum of all one photon exchange, electron-proton interaction diagrams. (b) Photon exchange between an electron and a π^+-meson in the proton's meson halo: one particular diagram contributing to the interaction shown in part a.

radius of the nucleon. Therefore, at distances less than about 10^{-15} m, a photon no longer "sees" a proton as just a point of charge. Instead it is enveloped in the nucleon's π-meson cloud, a modification represented on a typical Feynman graph by drawing the photon-proton vertex as a circle to indicate that the proton-photon interaction takes place over an extended region instead of a point. The circle is also a partial admission of ignorance, for it suggests the possibility of considerable complication. Charged π-mesons as well as nucleons and electrons have the ability to emit and absorb protons. Therefore the amplitude of the proton-photon vertex must depend in part upon all amplitudes for the interactions of photons with π-mesons. The diagram corresponding to one such amplitude is shown in Figure 22.13b. It is, so to speak, one of the graphs that would be seen if the circle at the vertex in Figure 22.13a were placed under a microscope: a proton momentarily emits a π^+-meson which absorbs a photon emitted (for instance) by the electron.

Because the amplitudes at the proton-photon and electron-photon vertices are equal for interactions at large distances, the sum of all the meson-absorption terms must be constant and proportional to the fundamental charge e for the low energy photons exchanged over such distances. But for higher energy photons exchanged over distances on the order of 10^{-15} m or less the strength of the vertex is clearly a function of exchange energy, or, equivalently, of distance.

Information related to the amplitude for the emission and absorption of a photon by a proton, or, equivalently, the variation of the density of a proton's π-meson cloud as a function of distance from its center may be determined by measuring the electron-proton scattering probability as a function of incident electron energy and scattering angle and comparing it with the scattering probability that would be expected if the proton were a

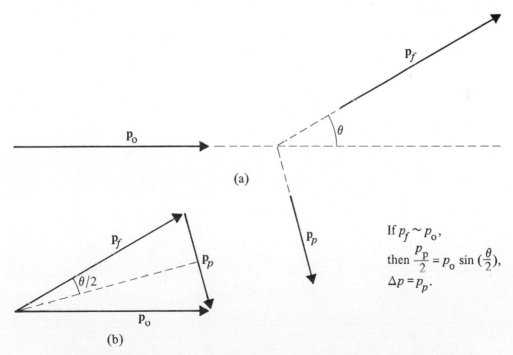

FIGURE 22.14. (a) Geometric diagram of electron proton scattering. (b) Calculation of the momentum transfer Δp in the approximation that the electron's energy loss is negligible.

point charge of magnitude *e*. Initially the scattering proton is at rest, and all the momentum ($\mathbf{p}_0$) of the electron-proton system is in the direction of the incident electron (Figure 22.14a). The momentum vector of the recoil proton $\mathbf{p}_p$ may be calculated from the initial and final state electron momenta by applying the vector addition rule. If the electron's energy loss is negligible then (Figure 22.14b) to a good approximation $p_p = 2p_0[\sin(\theta/2)]$. Since the proton is originally at rest this is also the momentum Δp transferred to it by the electron, which may be regarded as the characteristic momentum of the elastic scattering process. The Uncertainty Principle then gives an estimate of the distance (i.e., $\Delta x = h/\Delta p$) at which the interaction occurs. If it is assumed that the electron is a point particle and that the heavy proton remains stationary during the interaction, $\Delta x = \Delta r$. That is, it measures the electron's maximum penetration distance into the proton. Of course the latter assumption is never quite valid and becomes increasingly bad with increasing energy. Nevertheless, by using more sophisticated mathematical procedures, electron-scattering measurements can be used to provide something resembling a profile of the proton's charge structure.

Figure 22.15, due to Robert Hofstadter, shows a profile of the proton's charge density which is consistent with the electron-scattering data up to several hundred million

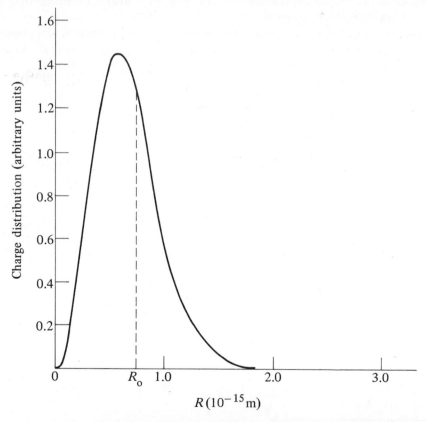

FIGURE 22.15. Charge distribution profile consistent with electron-proton scattering measurements up to several hundred million electron volts. The curve plots the fraction of the total charge in a sphere of radius *R* as a function of *R*. R_0 is defined as the "radius" of the proton (see text). (Adapted from Robert Hofstadter, "Electron Scattering and Nuclear Structure," *Revs. Mod. Phys.* Vol. 28, p. 214 (1956).)

electron volts. As noted in the last paragraph there are certain ambiguities involved in deriving this sort of distribution in r from the scattering data in Δp so that Figure 22.15 is not a "photograph" by any means. (If it were it would be inconsistent with the fundamental assumptions of quantum mechanics.) Nevertheless it does indicate that the charge associated with the proton is not concentrated at a single point, but rather that it is extended over a finite volume and decreases with increasing distance from the center. If the proton does not appear as a point to the electron it is equally clear that it does not appear as a hard sphere. Therefore, the term "proton radius" may appear somewhat ambiguous. The proton radius (or more strictly its charge radius) is defined as the radius of a hypothetical sphere containing 70% of its charge. Electron-scattering measurements assign it a value on the order of 0.7–0.8×10^{-15} m. From the definition (and Figure 22.15) it is clear that the proton does not terminate abruptly at its "radius."

Figure 22.15 suggests that the general meson-halo idea of Yukawa is a valid one. However, it is well to note that the specific rather simple form of the halo assumed by Yukawa is *not* consistent with electron-scattering measurements. Higher energy measurements make that conclusion even more emphatic and indicate, for example, that interactions among the mesons in the halo have an important bearing on the structure and interactions of the proton (Section 22.8). By measuring the probability of electron-deuteron ($_1H^2$) scattering and comparing it with the electron-proton measurements it is possible to obtain information on the structure of the neutron. The general conclusions are quite analogous, i.e., the neutron is an extended rather than a point object, the general meson cloud model is certainly tenable, but its structure is considerably more complex than Yukawa first assumed.

▲▲ 22.8 Strong interaction exchange diagrams. Nucleon resonances

Although the term "meson cloud" provides a rather graphic, qualitative description of nucleon structure, it also carries a number of unfortunate classical implications. A more consistent and rigorous representation of the strong interactions can be developed by using the analogy offered by quantum electrodynamics. We begin by assuming the existence of a "strong" field that transmits the strong interaction between nucleons, even as the electromagnetic field transmits the electromagnetic interaction. Again, we assign to a nucleon a property that may be called "strong charge," corresponding to ordinary (or electromagnetic) charge, and identify that property with the nucleon's ability to interact with the strong field.

We expressed quantization of the energy in the electromagnetic field by assuming that charged particles interact by creating and destroying (or emitting and absorbing) photons. We also expect that the energy in the strong field will be quantized, and make the tentative assumption that interactions with the field proceed via the creation and destruction of the quantized energy units of the field. If these energy units are called particles they obviously cannot be conserved. Hence they must be Bose particles with integral spins (0, 1, 2) rather than Fermi particles. There is no a priori way to assign rest masses to them. However, since π-mesons fit the description of the exchanged entities we tentatively assume that they do, in fact, represent the quantization of the strong field. Ultimately we shall learn that this assumption is too simple, for there are other mesons that can serve equally well as exchanged entities and presumably do. Hence there is more than one strong field, or, perhaps, more than one way to quantize the strong field. But for the present we restrict our attention to π-meson exchange.

Figure 22.16 shows the Feynman graphs corresponding to the basic processes assumed by the model: the emission and absorption of a π-meson by a nucleon with a consequent change in the nucleon's energy and momentum. Neither diagram represents an energy conserving process. Therefore the π-meson emitted in Figure 22.16a cannot exist for a time interval greater than $\Delta t = h/E$, where E is its total energy. If another nucleon absorbs the π-meson within that time interval (Figure 22.16c) then both the energy and momentum of the system may be conserved. In addition, since a change occurs in the energy and momentum of the individual nucleons, the π-meson exchange mechanism is tantamount to an interaction between them.

Although the meson-exchange model is based on an analogy with photon exchange, there are, of course, important differences. First, π-mesons exist in all three charge states. Therefore, by exchanging a charged meson a neutron and proton reverse their identity. More important, perhaps, the range of the electromagnetic interactions is infinite, while the range of the strong interactions is limited to about 10^{-15} m. We have already noted the connection between range and the mass of the particle representing a quantized field

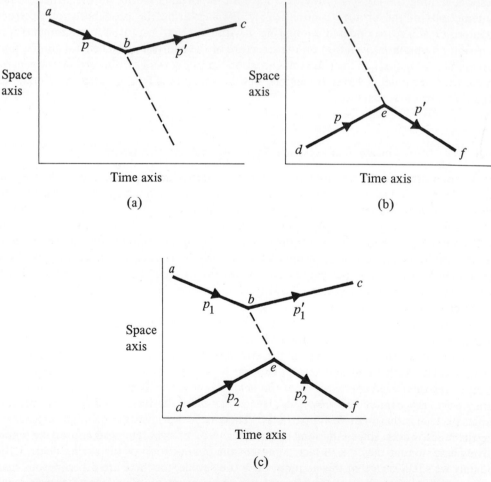

FIGURE 22.16. (a) Basic Feynman diagram for the emission of a π-meson by a nucleon. (b) Basic Feynman diagram for the absorption of a π-meson by a nucleon. (c) Two nucleons interacting via π-meson exchange.

(Section 21.8). The energy of the photon exchanged between two electrons can be arbitrarily small. Hence the photon may exist for an indefinitely long time and travel an indefinitely large distance. In contrast, the energy of a π-meson cannot be smaller than its rest energy (135 MeV for the π^0, 139 MeV for the charged π-mesons). It follows that energy nonconserving states such as those represented by the basic emission and absorption graphs cannot exist for a time greater than $\Delta t = h/E_0$, or about 3×10^{-23} sec.

The probability amplitude for any π-meson exchange interaction (such as Figure 22.16c) should follow from the amplitudes for the basic diagrams (Figures 22.16a and 22.16b). These are in turn proportional to the strength of the π-meson-nucleon vertices (b and e in the basic diagrams) or, equivalently, to the magnitude of the nucleon's strong charge. Unfortunately, the short range of the meson-exchange interaction precludes the possibility of making a macroscopic determination of this quantity. Rather, the strength of the vertex, like virtually all other features of the strong interactions, must be determined indirectly by means of particle reactions at high energies. One such reaction is the production of a π-meson by a proton incident upon a hydrogen target with an energy of several hundred million electron volts:

$$p + p \to p + n + \pi^+, \tag{22.1a}$$

a process which is analogous to the electromagnetic reaction

$$e + e \to e + e + \gamma. \tag{22.1b}$$

There are many detailed mechanisms through which two protons might conceivably interact to yield a proton, neutron, and π^+-meson in the final state. Presumably the amplitude for Equation 22.1a is the sum of the amplitudes corresponding to all such processes. Two possibilities, based on the π-meson exchange model, are shown in Figure 22.17 (for comparison a diagram representing a process leading to Equation 22.1b is also shown). Let us concentrate on Figure 22.17a. The incident proton exchanges a π^0-meson with the target proton, transferring energy and momentum in the process so that the total energy of the latter particle is greater than its 938 MeV rest energy. After a short time the energetic target proton divests itself of its excess energy by radiating a free π-meson.

The amplitude for the process shown in Figure 22.17a depends on several factors such as the strengths of the vertices and the energies of the particles in the initial, final, and (classically forbidden) intermediate state. In addition, Equation 22.1a can proceed via a number of other mechanisms (one of them shown in Figure 22.17b), implying that its total amplitude is the sum of a number of terms. Other complications will become apparent in later sections. Nevertheless, by measuring the probabilities of such reaction processes as functions of energy and scattering angle, it is possible to isolate the contribution to the amplitude due to the meson-nucleon vertices, and therefore to deduce the magnitude of the nucleon's strong charge. Even as the strength of an electromagnetic vertex is equal to $e^2/\hbar c = 1/137$, so we may relate the strong charge, g, to the strength of a π-meson-nucleon vertex by defining the strength as $g^2/\hbar c$, a number whose experimental value is roughly unity. Any observable exchange interaction has at least two vertices (one for emission, one for absorption). Therefore, the basic exchange amplitudes involve the squares of the vertex strengths, or $(1/137)^2$ and 1, respectively, for the electromagnetic and strong interactions. The ratio of these expressions, $(e^2/\hbar c)/(g^2/\hbar c) = \frac{1}{137}$, may be regarded as a measure of the relative strengths of these two fundamental interactions. (Section 22.2.)

Yukawa's π-meson exchange model for the nucleon-nucleon force (Sections 21.7 and

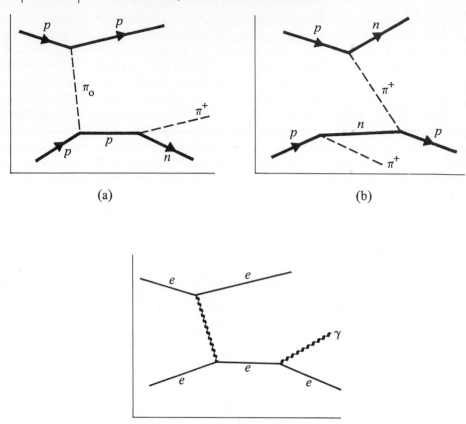

(a)

(b)

(c)

FIGURE 22.17. (a) One possible exchange process leading to the production of a π^+-meson. (b) Another possible π-meson production diagram. (c) Diagram analogous to part a for the emission of a photon in an electron-electron interaction.

21.8) is, of course, at least qualitatively consistent with the foregoing strong field representation. However, the latter model is capable of a considerably greater degree of generalization. For example, superficially the two Feynman diagrams shown in Figures 22.18a and b are identical save for the difference in their orientation relative to the space and time axes. However, the direction of the nucleon from b to c in Figure 22.18b is backward in time, whereas, Figure 22.18c represents the emission of a π-meson and a consequent change in the momentum of the nucleon. Of course the pair of diagrams is completely analogous to the photon-emission and electron-positron annihilation diagrams shown in Figure 22.9. Pursuing the analogy between the strong and electromagnetic interactions, we interpret a nucleon going backward in time as an antinucleon going forward in time. Therefore, Figure 22.18b represents the annihilation of a nucleon-antinucleon pair into a π-meson. Furthermore, the equivalence of the emission and the annihilation diagram implies a direct relationship between the amplitudes for the processes since both are proportional to the strength of the nucleon-π-meson vertex. Neither process shown in Figure 22.18a or 22.18b is energy-conserving. Figure 22.18c is an energy-conserving diagram for annihilation into two π-mesons, based upon a combination of two basic annihilation diagrams while Figure 22.18d is a corresponding diagram for the creation of a nucleon-antinucleon pair by two π-mesons.

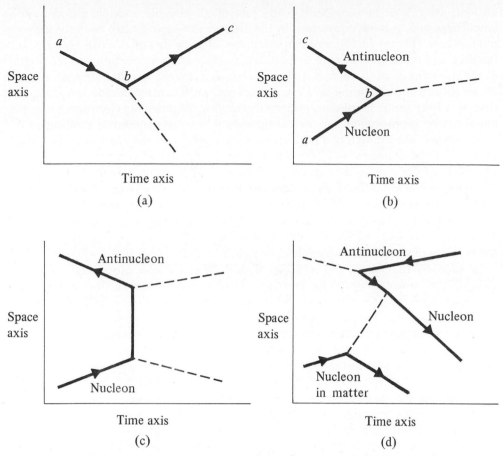

FIGURE 22.18. (a) Basic π-meson emission diagram. (a) Basic nucleon-anti-nucleon annihilation diagram. (c) Energy conserving diagram for the annihilation of a nucleon-antinucleon pair into a pair of π-mesons. (d) Creation of a nucleon-antinucleon pair in matter via the interaction of a free π-meson and a π-meson from the halo of another nucleon.

Even as quantum electrodynamics attempts to equate all properties of the electron to its electromagnetic interactions, so the strong field description of nucleon-nucleon forces suggests a similar correlation between the properties of nucleons and their ability to emit and absorb π-mesons. However, the nucleon problem presents far greater difficulties.

Figure 22.19 shows a basic π-meson self-absorption diagram for a nucleon analogous to the electron-photon self absorption diagrams in Figure 22.10. It implies that since a free nucleon has a probability of dissociating briefly, spending part of its time disassociated into a nucleon and π-meson, a proton spends part of its time as a neutron and π^+-meson, while a neutron spends part of its time as a proton and π^--meson. In more graphic language, a nucleon is surrounded by a "halo" or "cloud" of π-mesons whose number, energy, and distance from the nucleon fluctuate with time. We cannot in any sense think of this cloud as dissociated from the nucleon, for it is intimately related to the strong interactions of the nucleon and therefore, to its basic properties.

The intimate association of π-mesons and nucleons suggests one reason why the quantitative study of strong interaction is so complicated. Presumably all properties of a nucleon are related in some way to the sum of all possible multiple self-absorption amplitudes such as those represented by the diagram in Figure 22.20. As in the electron-photon case (Figure 22.12), an infinite number of such diagrams exist. In the latter instance we argued that since the amplitude for a diagram is proportional to the product of the strengths of all its vertices, and since the electromagnetic vertex strength is 1/137, an amplitude corresponding to a six vertex diagram has a magnitude less than 10^{-4} that of a four vertex amplitude. Hence the total amplitudes for electromagnetic processes can be approximated very well as the sum of the relatively simple amplitudes.

In contrast, the strength of a nucleon-π-meson vertex is on the order of unity. Therefore, *all* of the diagrams in Figure 22.20, have amplitudes of comparable importance *regardless* of the number of vertices. It follows that an approximate total amplitude involving only a few of these amplitudes can at best give a very rough description of the nucleon. Several powerful mathematical techniques have been devised to deal with various aspects of the interaction of nucleons without summing over all possible diagrams. These have met with considerable quantitative success. However, our understanding of the problem remains very incomplete.

In addition to making the problem of describing nucleon properties enormously difficult, the intimate relationship between π-mesons and nucleons complicates all other processes involving strong interactions between two particles. Figure 22.21a suggests one possible mechanism for the interaction of two π-mesons. Each dissociates briefly into a nucleon-antinucleon pair; a member of each pair interacts via π-meson exchange; there after the two pairs recombine to yield two π-mesons again. Although the diagram has six vertices, its amplitude (and therefore the probability for two π-mesons to interact) is roughly equal to the amplitude for direct nucleon-nucleon interaction. In contrast, the analogous six-vertex diagram for a photon-photon interaction is negligible relative to the four-vertex diagram.

Figure 22.21b represents a two-meson exchange process between two nucleons. This process has an amplitude of roughly equal importance to the one-meson exchange amplitude. However it is considerably more difficult to calculate since the nucleons in the intermediate states, like the π-mesons, need not conserve energy. In addition, the inter-mediate mesons can themselves interact. Again, for the reasons already cited, the corresponding, four-vertex amplitude for the two-photon exchange interaction between two electrons is usually neglected relative to the fundamental one-photon exchange process.

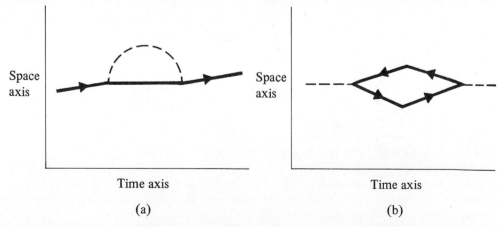

Space axis   Time axis   (a)   Space axis   Time axis   (b)

FIGURE 22.19. (a) Basic self-absorption diagram for a nucleon. (b) A diagram whose amplitude contributes to the properties of a free π-meson.

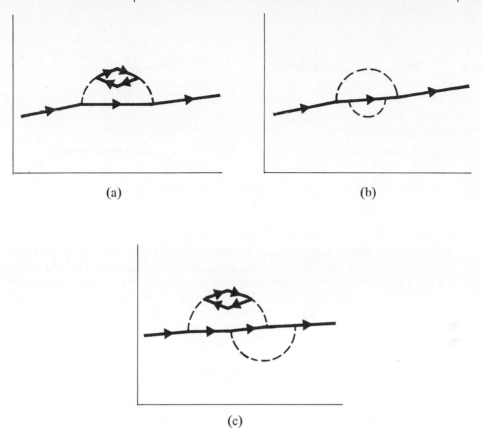

FIGURE 22.20.   Three processes which contribute to the intrinsic properties of the nucleon.

These last considerations seem to imply that the task of obtaining a coherent, quantitative description of the strong interactions among the particles is completely impossible rather than just enormously difficult. But in fact we have oversimplified the details of the π-meson exchange process, or, perhaps, have forgotten some of the restrictions

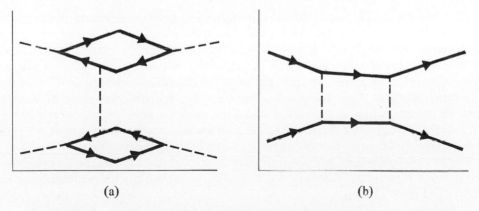

FIGURE 22.21.   (a) One possible mechanism for the interaction of two π-mesons. (b) A two-meson-exchange interaction between two nucleons.

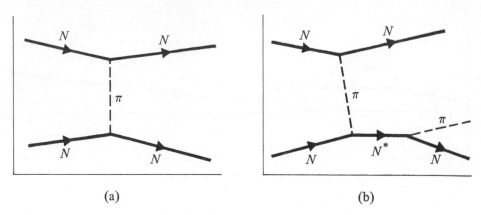

(a)   (b)

FIGURE 22.22. Two related π-meson exchange interactions between two nucleons. (a) The energy supplied by the exchanged π-meson increases the *kinetic* energy of the absorbing nucleon. (Compare with Figure 22.16c.) (b) The energy supplied by the exchanged π-meson increases the *internal* energy of the absorbing nucleon for a brief time interval. The short-lived excitation is denoted as N^*. (Compare with Figure 22.17a.)

imposed upon systems of interacting particles by quantum mechanics. Two π-meson exchange diagrams are reproduced in Figure 22.22. In the first, the *kinetic* energy of the absorbing nucleon is increased by the energy and momentum carried by the exchanged meson. In the second, that nucleon exists briefly with excess internal energy, and eventually divests itself of that energy by emitting a free meson. We have hitherto assumed that the only restrictions placed on the intermediate exchange states are imposed by the uncertainty principle, and therefore, that the exchanged mesons in Figures 22.19a and 22.19b, as well as the excited nucleon state in Figure 22.23b, can have all energies up to a given maximum with equal probabilities. But both processes involve interacting particles, and systems of interacting particles do *not* have equal probabilities of existing at all energies. Indeed, this general feature of quantum mechanical systems leads directly to the quantized energy states in complex nuclei, atoms, and molecules. (Sections 18.8 and 18.9.)

Of course the specific interactions that leads to short-lived intermediate meson-nucleon states might be exempt from the bound state restriction. But if in fact mesons *are* exchanged preferentially with a given set of energies it should be possible to find experimental situations in which only a few of the infinity of conceivable exchange diagrams are dominant. A somewhat coherent picture of the strong interactions might follow from a detailed study of those situations. From a somewhat different point of view, the preferential interaction of a π-meson and a nucleon at a given set of discrete energies implies the existence of a discrete set of excited nucleon states, designated as N^* states, just as there are a discrete number of excited states of the hydrogen atom.

The existence of excited nucleon states can be investigated experimentally by means of a number of high energy reactions. For example, the probability for the reaction process shown in Figure 22.22b,

$$p + p \rightarrow p + n + \pi^+,\tag{22.2a}$$

can be studied as a function of incident proton energy and outgoing neutron and π-meson momentum. However, it is simpler to study the elastic scattering of π-mesons and nucleons, for instance,

$$\pi^+ + p \rightarrow \pi^+ + p \tag{22.2b}$$

as a function of incoming π-meson energy, for as Figure 22.23a clearly indicates, the reaction should proceed in part through formation of an excited nucleon state (Figure 22.23a is the lower part of the diagram of Figure 22.22b except that the first π-meson is an energy conserving π-meson incident on a proton rather than a π-meson emitted by another nucleon).

If, as we suspect, excited nucleon states exist at a discrete set of energies, then one of these states will be formed with high probability in a π-proton interaction only when the sum of the π-meson's total energy and the proton rest energy corresponds to the total energy of the excited state. (We assume the π-mesons are incident upon protons initially at rest, in a liquid hydrogen bubble chamber, for instance.) Therefore, if excited nucleon states exist, the π-p elastic scattering probability measured as a function of incident π-meson energy should exhibit a series of maxima at those energies which correspond to the excited states.

Figure 22.23b summarizes the π^+-p and π^--p elastic scattering probabilities up to incident energies of two billion electron volts, and provides evidence for the existence of two excited nucleon states. The lowest and most pronounced of these, which appears in both the π^--p and π^+-p curves, was first discovered by Fermi and his coworkers in 1953, has a total energy of 1238 MeV, and exists in four charge states: N^{++}, N^+, N^0, and

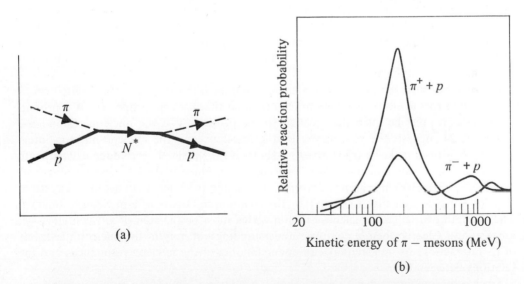

(a)

(b)

FIGURE 22.23. (a) Elastic scattering of a π-meson by a nucleon via the formation of an excited nucleon state. (b) Measured elastic scattering probability for $\pi^+ p$ and $\pi^- p$ as a function of π-meson energy up to one billion electron volts. The maxima suggest the existence of excited nucleon states. (From J. D. Jackson, *The Physics of Elementary Particles*, Princeton University Press, Princeton, N.J., 1958.)

N^-.* Many other excited nucleon states have been discovered since 1953. In fact, as the available accelerator energies increase, so does the number of these states, and there is no apparent end in sight.

Measured scattering probability curves such as Figure 22.25 also provides a measure of the lifetimes of the excited nucleon states. The width of each maximum corresponds to an uncertainty in the value of the rest energy of the state, and the Heisenberg uncertainty principle links the energy uncertainty of a process with the time interval over which it occurs. In the present instance the "process" is the π-nucleon interaction in an intermediate state. Hence the lifetime of each state is given by $t = h/\Delta M_0 c^2$, and is on the order of 10^{-22} to 10^{-23} sec, i.e., the characteristic strong interaction time (Section 22.2).

▶▶ 22.9 Excited states of the nucleon. Meson resonances. The baryon and meson families

The existence of bound nucleon-π-meson states implies that a free nucleon has excited states roughly analogous to the excited states of an atom. Given the detailed electromagnetic interaction between an electron and a proton, the rules of quantum mechanics lead to probability amplitudes relating the excited states of the hydrogen atom to the ground state. Presumably complete knowledge of the strong interactions would likewise lead to a unique set of predictions about the bound nucleon-meson states. Lacking such knowledge we must regard each of the observed bound states as a unique state of matter, or, synonymously, as a separate particle, called a nucleon *resonance* (or *isobar*), each with an empirically determined rest energy.

At this writing at least fifteen nucleon isobars have been positively identified with rest energies extending to more than 3.0 BeV. Even though there is still no completely satisfactory theory relating these masses to each other through an interaction, nevertheless we can assume they *are* related to the strong interaction and try to discern empirical relations between them that might bring us closer to the desired theory. The situation is reminiscent of the early twentieth century before the Bohr model of the hydrogen atom and, later, quantum mechanics led to a fundamental understanding of the observed emission spectra of the atoms.

Even as the hydrogen atom was not understood until the energies of its excited states were related to the electromagnetic interaction, so the intrinsic properties of a ground state nucleon must be intimately related to the properties of the nucleon resonances. Figure 22.24 suggests the role played by the resonances in the nucleon-nucleon interaction. A proton makes a transition to a short-lived, classically forbidden excited state which dissociates into a neutron and π^+-meson. Subsequently the π^+-meson is absorbed by a neutron which then becomes a proton. This diagram spells out in detail one possible way for π-meson exchange to occur—by the creation and decay of a nucleon resonance. The strength of the basic nucleon-π-meson vertex must be the sum of all such emission amplitudes. Clearly, then, a complete understanding not only of the nucleon itself, but of its interactions as well, requires an understanding of the nucleon resonances and the relations between them.

Since π-mesons interact with each other as well as with nucleons, it is not surprising that bound, short-lived states of two and three π-mesons with discrete energies have also

---

* The difference in the magnitudes of the π^+-p and π^--p curves at this energy is related to the fact that the doubly charged N^{++}, formed in a π^+-p interaction, can decay only to π^+-p, while the neutral N^0, formed in a π^--p interaction, can decay either into π^--p or π^0-n.

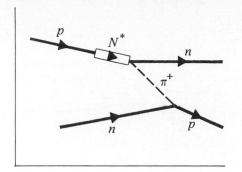

FIGURE 22.24. One possible nucleon-nucleon interaction process involving the formation and decay of a nucleon resonance state.

been identified. The experimental determination of the energies of these states is analogous to the identification of nucleon resonance states. For instance, if the reaction

$$\pi^- + p \rightarrow n + \pi^+ + \pi^- \tag{22.3}$$

proceeds via the creation and decay of the intermediate meson V^0:

$$\pi^- + p \rightarrow n + V^0,$$

followed by

$$V^0 \rightarrow \pi^+ + \pi^-,$$

then in a manner of speaking the two final state π-mesons should stick together on emerging from the reaction.

In order to investigate the possible existence of short-lived mesons the probability for reactions such as Equation 22.3 are measured as functions of the outgoing π-meson energies and the angle between them (Figure 22.25a). The final state energies lead, through energy conservation, to the energy of the hypothetical short-lived state:

$$E_V = E_{\pi^+} + E_{\pi^-}.$$

Knowledge of the opening angle between the final state particle permits the calculation of their momentum vectors, and leads, through momentum conservation, to the momentum vector of the decaying state:

$$\mathbf{p}_V = \mathbf{p}_{\pi^+} + \mathbf{p}_{\pi^-}.$$

Finally, the rest mass of the decaying state follows from the relativistic relation between its energy and momentum:

$$E_V^2 = c^2 p_V^2 + M_0^2 v c^4.$$

Therefore, the results of measurements of the probabilities for reactions such as that of Equation 22.3, taken as functions of the outgoing π-meson momenta, can be displayed as graphs of reaction probabilities versus the masses of the hypothetical decaying states. These should exhibit maxima at mass values corresponding to any such states that do, in fact, exist. Figure 22.25c shows the experimental data that first suggested the existence of the ρ^0- and ρ^--mesons with rest masses equal to 765 MeV. From the width of the peak and the Heisenberg Principle, the lifetimes of these mesons is on the order of 10^{-23} sec.

By 1968 at least a dozen of these multimeson resonances had been positively identified through such multi-π-meson (and K-meson) production studies. All of them fall into the meson class, along with the π-meson (and K-meson—Section 22.11 and Table 22.1).

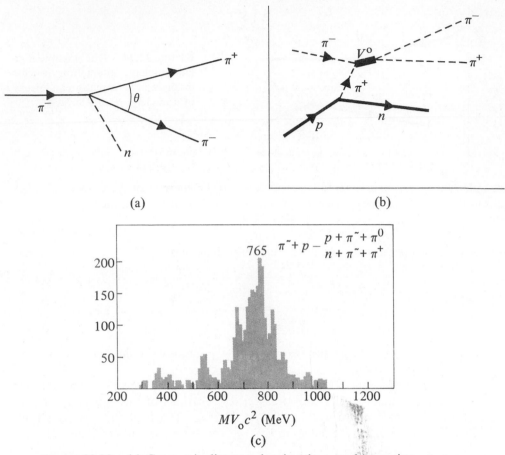

FIGURE 22.25. (a) Geometric diagram showing the way the reaction $\pi^- + p \to n + \pi^+ + \pi^-$ would appear in a bubble chamber. (b) Feynman diagram for reaction a via the formation of an intermediate V° state. (c) Combined probabilities for the two reactions $\pi^- + p \to n + \pi^+ + \pi^-$ and $\pi^- + p \to p + \pi^+ + \pi^\circ$ plotted as a function of the rest energy of the hypothetical decaying state V_0. The peak at 765 MeV suggests the existence of such a state with that rest energy which is now called the ρ-meson and which may have charge $+1$, 0, and -1. (Adapted from A. R. Erwin, R. March, W. D. Walker, and E. West, "Evidence for a π–π Resonance in the $I = 1$, $J = 1$ State," *Phys. Rev. Letters*, Vol. 6, p. 628, 1961.)

Like the nucleon resonances, they play an important role in the strong interactions for they are quite obviously related to the properties of the π-meson (and the K-meson). Again, a complete theory of the strong interactions would presumably lead to a unique determination of the energies of these states. Lacking that knowledge, we regard all of them as separate members of the meson family on an equal footing with the π-mesons, just as the nucleons and nucleon resonances must be regarded as equllay fundamental baryons.

It is now evident that both the Yukawa model of the nucleon-nucleon force and our model that quantized the strong field into π-mesons alone were too simple. Since π-mesons can form short-lived bound states with each other, then clearly the halo surrounding a nucleon must contain ρ- and ω-mesons, for instance, as well as π-mesons. If these mesons exist in the nucleon cloud then they can also be exchanged between two nucleons, and therefore are responsible in part of the internucleon force.

There is a natural temptation to regard π-mesons and nucleons as the most fundamental members of their respective classes simply because they are the least massive and have the longest lifetimes. But there is really no justification for such an assumption. Rather, we must generalize our view of the strongly interacting particles by assuming that the strong field has many different quantized modes, each corresponding to a different meson, and that there are a number of baryons which interact with one another by emitting and absorbing mesons from this field. At first glance the existence of so many particles makes the problem of understanding the strong interactions seem hopeless. But since the baryons may be regarded as excited nucleon states, and a number of the mesons as bound π-meson states, we really have much more empirical evidence on the strong interactions than the Yukawa model provided. Hopefully, we shall continue to make progress in translating this empirical data into a more fundamental understanding of the interactions themselves.

◣◣ 22.10 Weak interactions. Baryon and lepton conservation

The strong interactions relate, or couple, the baryons and mesons to one another. Likewise, the electromagnetic interactions provide a coupling between all charged particles, leptons as well as baryons and mesons. Since we think of the neutral baryons and mesons as spending part of their existence dissociated into charged particles, they too participate indirectly in the electromagnetic interactions.

Members of the lepton, meson, and baryon classes are also related to one another by the weak interactions, which normally manifest themselves in decay processes, for example, the β^--decay of the neutron with a twelve-minute half-life:

$$n \rightarrow p + e^- + \bar{\nu}, \tag{22.4a}$$

or of the muon with 2×10^{-6} sec half-life:

$$\mu^\pm \rightarrow e^\pm + \nu + \bar{\nu}. \tag{22.4b}$$

We have already considered several strong and electromagnetic decay interactions; for instance, the decay of a nucleon isobar into a nucleon and π-meson:

$$N^* \rightarrow p + \pi^-,$$

or of a ρ^0-meson:

$$\rho^0 \rightarrow \pi^+ + \pi^-,$$

proceed via the strong interactions, while the decay of an excited state of a hydrogen atom into a ground state atom and a photon:

$$H^* \rightarrow H + \gamma,$$

is electromagnetic. Indeed, Feynman graphs for *all* strong and electromagnetic processes are based upon emission and absorption diagrams, and there is no reason why the former type of graph cannot be reinterpreted as a decay graph.

Thus there is nothing particularly novel about an interaction that leads to the decay of a particle. However, the particles in the final state following a strong decay reaction are baryons or mesons or both, while an electromagnetic decay invariably involves one or more photons. In contrast, leptons and antileptons are often created in weak decay processes. Moreover, the half-lives for these processes are always many orders of magnitude greater than the corresponding half-lives in strong and electromagnetic decay. Nucleon and meson resonances are produced in high energy particle reactions such as Equations 22.2a and 22.3. These must take place during the time the initial state particles are within 10^{-15} m of each other, or about 10^{-22} to 10^{-23} sec, and decay with comparable lifetimes since the production and decay interactions are the inverses of each other. Therefore, the ratio of lifetimes of the ρ^0-meson and the muon (Equation 22.4b) is about $10^{-23}/10^{-6} = 10^{-17}$, which is roughly the ratio of one second to three billion years! It should be obvious, then, that the latter decay proceeds via a much different, much less probable, and hence much weaker interaction.

Although both neutron β-decay (Equation 22.4a) and muon decay (Equation 22.4b) proceed via the same interactions, the latter process involves no baryons or mesons and may therefore be regarded as a purer manifestation of that interaction. The bubble chamber photograph in Figure 22.26a shows the creation and decay of a muon. A π^--meson enters the chamber from the left, and decays into a muon and a neutrino:

$$\pi^- \rightarrow \mu^- + \nu. \tag{22.5}$$

Only the charged muon leaves a visible track; the presence of the accompanying neutrino is deduced from energy and momentum conservation arguments, even as its existence was originally deduced by applying similar arguments to nuclear β-decay (Section 20.7). After traveling a very short distance the muon itself decays into a particle identified as an electron by its curvature in the chamber's magnetic field and the rate at which it loses energy as it travels.

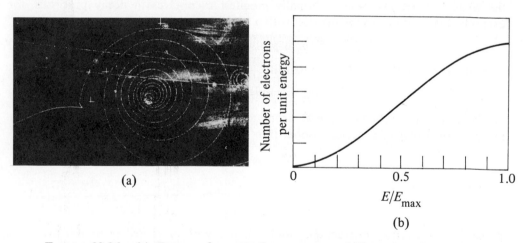

(a)

(b)

FIGURE 22.26. (a) Decay of a negative π-meson which enters the bubble chamber from the left and comes almost to rest before decaying into a slow negative muon (short track) and a neutrino which is not visible in the picture. The muon subsequently decays into an electron (and a pair of neutrinos) identified by the curvature of its track and the rate at which it loses energy. (Courtesy of Brookhaven National Laboratory.) (b) The number of electrons produced in the decay of several hundred muons plotted as a function of the ratio of their energy to their maximum possible energy, i.e., the total energy of the decaying muon. (From J. D. Jackson, *The Physics of Elementary Particles*, Princeton University Press, Princeton, N.J., 1958).

Figure 22.26b shows a typical distribution in the total energies of the electrons from several hundred negative muons which decayed while at rest. It is clear at a glance that energy conservation requires that one or more neutral particles must have been produced in each decay, for usually the total energy of the electron is less than the muon rest energy. However, since Figure 22.26b indicates that in some instances the electron *does* take all the available energy, it follows that the total rest mass of the neutrals must be zero. Hence we tentatively call these missing particles neutrinos, although we have not demonstrated that they are the same neutrinos produced in neutron β-decay. In fact as we shall see presently they are not the same neutrinos at all.

Arguments based on the spins of the muon, positron, and neutrino, and upon the detailed shape of the electron energy distribution in Figure 22.24b, lead to the conclusion that *two* massless neutrals with spin $\frac{1}{2}$ are produced in muon decay. Another set of experiments shows that one of the neutrals must be an antineutrino rather than a neutrino. Therefore, we are justified in writing

$$\mu^+ \to e^+ + \nu + \bar{\nu}, \tag{22.6a}$$

and, from an analogous set of experiments,

$$\mu^- \to e^- + \nu + \bar{\nu}. \tag{22.6b}$$

The latter process is shown graphically in Figure 22.27a. A muon is annihilated and an electron and a neutrino-antineutrino pair created in the region enclosed by the open circle. Using the language of the foregoing sections, the open circle represents a four-particle vertex, the region at which the particles interact. Presumably, the characteristics of the weak interactions are in a large degree determined by such vertices. If the amplitude for a particle to go backward in time is precisely equivalent to the amplitude for its antiparticle to go forward in time, and vice versa, then the description of an antineutrino *leaving* a weak decay vertex should be no different from the description of a neutrino *entering* the vertex. This assumption permits us to relate the negative muon decay interaction directly to the reaction

$$\bar{\nu} + \mu^- \to e^- + \bar{\nu}, \tag{22.7a}$$

a process whose Feynman diagram is shown in Figure 22.27b. By reversing all the arrows in the graph we change all particles into antiparticles and have a diagram (Figure 22.27c) for the reaction

$$\nu + \mu^+ \to e^+ + \nu. \tag{22.7b}$$

Likewise, by equating the incoming $\bar{\nu}$ to an outgoing ν, we obtain a diagram for positive muon decay. Finally, by rotating the diagrams through 180° we are led to graphs representing the reactions

$$\bar{\nu} + e^- \to \bar{\nu} + \mu^-, \tag{22.8a}$$

$$\nu + e^+ \to \nu + \mu^+. \tag{22.8b}$$

Although Figures 22.27b and 22.27c are directly related to the decay diagram (Figure 22.27a) they are much more reminiscent of the strong and electromagnetic diagrams that we have already discussed at some length (such as Figure 22.27e, in which a π^--meson and proton enter an interaction region and a π^0-meson and neutral nucleon resonance

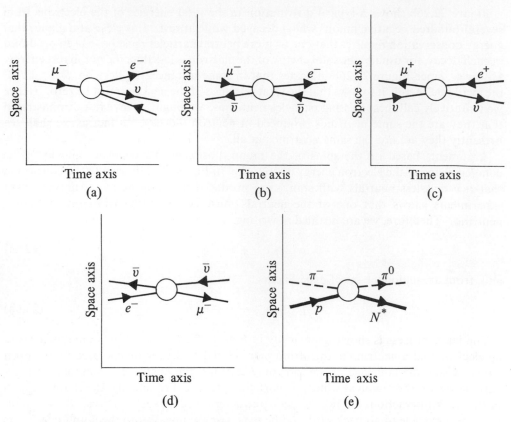

FIGURE 22.27.   (a) Diagram for the process $\mu^- \rightarrow e^- \; \nu + \bar{\nu}$. (b) Diagram for the process $\bar{\nu} + \mu^- \rightarrow \bar{\nu} + e^-$. (c) Diagram for the process $\nu + \mu^+ \rightarrow \nu + e^+$. (d) Diagram for $\bar{\nu} + e^- \rightarrow \bar{\nu} + \mu^-$. (e) Diagram for the strong interaction process $\pi^- + p \rightarrow N^* + \pi^0$.

emerge*). This similarity suggests a description of the weak interactions analogous to our description of the strong and electromagnetic interactions. We assume that members of the lepton class (muons, electrons, and neutrinos) pervade all space. If there were no electromagnetic or weak interactions these particles would be completely free and therefore completely unobservable. However, electrons and muons interact via photon exchange. In addition, the three particles also interact by means of a "weak" field, even as baryons and mesons interact via a "strong" field. Presumably, then, leptons have "weak charge" which is a measure of their coupling (or interaction) with the weak field, even as baryons possess strong charge and "charged" particles electromagnetic charge. Clearly weak charge must be much weaker than either electromagnetic or strong charge, for the time scale of the weak interactions implies that the leptons have a very small probability of coupling to each other via the weak field.

---

*In the latter case we have usually indicated the mechanism of the interaction more explicitly. For example, the interaction of Figure 22.27e might proceed by ρ-meson exchange. Indeed, there is speculation that the weak interactions are also carried by an exchanged particle. For the moment, however, we concentrate upon the blanked out, four-particle interaction vertices, and thereby effectively sum over all possible detailed exchange processes.

Of course the weak interactions are not confined to the leptons. We have already referred to the decays

$$\pi^+ \rightarrow \mu^+ + \nu,$$

and

$$\pi^- \rightarrow \mu^- + \bar{\nu},$$

which occur with half-lives of 2×10^{-8} sec, as well as to the twelve minute half-life free neutron β-decay:

$$n \rightarrow p + e^- + \bar{\nu}.$$

Hence our description of the weak interaction field must be generalized by permitting baryons and mesons to interact with leptons (and conceivably with each other) via that field. Using time reversal arguments, we can relate the neutron β-decay reaction to the inverse reaction

$$\nu + n \rightarrow p + e^-, \tag{22.8c}$$

whose diagram appears in Figure 22.28a. If we assume that neutrons and protons differ only in their electromagnetic charge we can also relate the process to (Figure 22.28b):

$$\bar{\nu} + p \rightarrow n + e^+. \tag{22.8d}$$

Quantitative determinations of the amplitudes for the weak decays of baryons and mesons are complicated by the strong interactions of these particles. A neutron spends part of its existence as a proton and π^--meson, for instance, and the π^--meson in turn has a definite amplitude for existing as an antiproton and neutron. Therefore, a neutron couples to the weak field both directly and by means of its strong coupling to the π-meson. In addition, the differences between the rest masses of the initial and final state particles in muon, π-meson, and neutron decay imply different total kinetic energies in the final states. For these reasons the half-lives for the decay processes are expected to differ from one another. However, all detailed measurements and calculations are consistent with the assumption that muon decay, π-meson decay, and neutron β-decay are all manifestations of the same basic interaction.

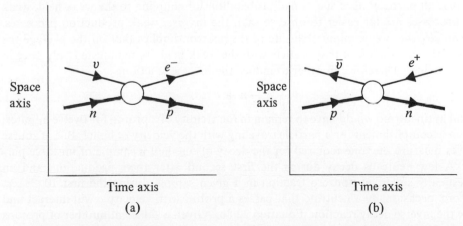

FIGURE 22.28. Two basic weak interaction diagrams that couple nucleons to electrons and neutrinos.

Each of the three types of weak decay interaction we have considered involves the annihilation of at least one lepton or antilepton and the creation of another. For instance, in the basic inverse muon decay reaction,

$$\bar{\nu} + \mu^- \rightarrow e^- + \bar{\nu},$$

a muon appears to be converted into an electron, while in the inverse β-decay reaction,

$$\nu + n \rightarrow p + e^-,$$

a neutrino changes into an electron while the neutron becomes a proton. The first of these reactions illustrates the empirically-based law of lepton conservation; the second illustrates, in addition, the law of baryon conservation.

LEPTON CONSERVATION. The number of leptons minus the number of antileptons in the universe remains constant.

BARYON CONSERVATION. The number of baryons minus the number of antibaryons in the universe remains constant.

Significantly, there is no equivalent meson conservation law, for of course the exchange model of the strong interactions could not have been put forward if there were. When we encountered the Dirac negative energy sea description of positrons in Section 22.4, we remarked that that model together with the Pauli exclusion principle implies that positrons and electrons, and therefore, all other charged particle-antiparticle pairs, are created and annihilated together. The weak interaction apparently modifies the process by allowing one type of lepton (or antilepton) to be converted into another type. But it does not permit a lepton to appear or disappear entirely. In the same vein both the strong and the weak interactions permit a baryon to be converted into another type of baryon. For instance, a proton may absorb a π^--meson to become a nucleon resonance, or a neutron may convert itself into a proton in β-decay. But the baryon itself cannot disappear entirely. This empirical law guarantees the ultimate stability of matter, for if there were no such conservation law all nucleons might ultimately disintegrate into mesons, electrons, and photons.

►► 22.11 Neutrino interaction experiments

Because all particles have such small probabilities of coupling to the weak field, weak decay processes are far easier to observe than the inverse, weak production processes. For example, the twelve-minute half-life of the neutron implies that on the average the results of the interaction of that particle with the weak field are manifested only once in twelve minutes. Therefore, in order to induce the inverse reaction,

$$\bar{\nu} + p \rightarrow n + e^+,$$

a typical antineutrino would have to remain in the vicinity of a proton for twelve minutes, no mean accomplishment for a particle traveling with the velocity of light! But of course half-lives measure the time required for the decay of one-half a sample of unstable particles. A few neutrons decay during the first second after their production, and an infinitesimally small yet nonzero fraction in a given sample during the first 10^{-22} sec. Therefore, occasionally a neutrino that passes a proton with velocity c will interact and initiate the inverse decay reaction, Equation 22.8b. Given a sufficient number of protons in a target and enough antineutrinos incident upon that target, a free neutron and positron should occasionally be produced.

An approximate calculation will indicate just how infrequently such an event occurs. A two-billion-electron-volt π-meson has about a 50% chance of interacting in eight inches of iron. Thus, if a million π-mesons per second were incident upon an iron slab we would expect to observe roughly half a million strong interaction processes. Weak interaction processes are typically 10^{14} times less probable. Hence 10^{14} neutrinos would have to be incident upon the iron before the probability of initiating a *single* weak interaction process would be 50%. At an incident rate of 10^6/sec we would have to wait 10^6 sec or three years for each event!

Of course the expected neutrino interaction rate can be increased by using a larger target and more intense incident beams. F. Reines, C. L. Cowan and their coworkers first observed the inverse β-decay reaction in 1956 using a very large tank of scintillating liquid as both target and detector of the expected neutron and positron from the inverse reaction process, Equation 22.8b. The tank was irradiated with antineutrinos from the β-decay of fission fragments at the Savannah River nuclear reactor. Once or twice a month the apparatus produced an electronic signal indicating that inverse β-decay had indeed occurred.

High energy neutrino interactions were first studied at the Brookhaven National Laboratory's alternating gradient synchrotron in 1962 by L. Lederman, M. Schwartz, and J. Steinberger. The thirty-three billion electron volt circulating proton beam, incident upon a thick target, produced π-mesons which drifted for several hundred feet until most of them had decayed into muons and neutrinos. Charged particles were filtered out of the resultant beam by passing it through several feet of concrete and steel where all of them were certain to lose virtually all of their kinetic energy by repeated interactions with the electrons and nuclei in the material. Finally the remaining, filtered neutrino beam was incident upon a series of large, thick plate spark chambers containing, *in toto*, about ten tons of matter (Figure 22.29).

During a run lasting several months the experimenters observed about one hundred interactions induced by neutrinos in the spark chamber plates. Many of these were muon production events:

$$\nu + n \rightarrow \mu^- + p.$$

Significantly, *no* examples of the presumably analogous inverse β-decay reaction,

$$\nu + n \rightarrow e^- + p,$$

were found. But Reines and Cowan had already observed the latter reaction (induced by antineutrinos) in 1956. Hence it was concluded that the neutrinos incident upon the Reines-Cowan apparatus which were produced by nuclear β-decay were *not* the same particles incident upon the Lederman-Schwartz-Steinberger spark chamber system. Apparently there are at least *two* types of neutrinos (and two antineutrinos). One of them, called the electron neutrino (ν_e) is always associated with an electron, while the other, the muon neutrino (ν_μ), accompanies the muon.

Both the weak interaction diagrams and the equations they represent must be revised in the light of the two neutrino discovery; e.g.,

$$\bar{\nu}_\mu + \mu^- \rightarrow e^- + \bar{\nu}_e, \tag{22.9a}$$

$$\mu^- \rightarrow e^- + \bar{\nu}_e + \nu_\mu, \tag{22.9b}$$

$$\pi^- \rightarrow \mu^- + \bar{\nu}_\mu, \tag{22.9c}$$

$$\nu_e + n \rightarrow p + e^-, \tag{22.9d}$$

$$n \rightarrow p + e^- + \bar{\nu}_e. \tag{22.9e}$$

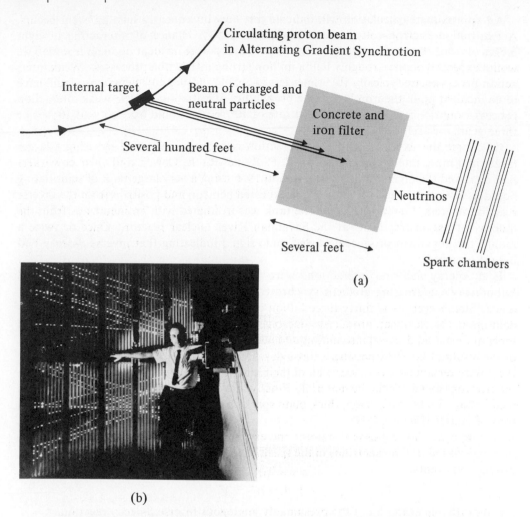

Circulating proton beam
in Alternating Gradient Synchrotion

Internal target

Beam of charged and
neutral particles

Concrete and
iron filter

Several hundred feet

Neutrinos

Several feet

Spark chambers

(a)

(b)

FIGURE 22.29. (a) Layout of the two-neutrino experiment of Lederman, Schwartz, and Steinberger. The circulating proton beam in the Brookhaven alternating gradient synchrotron strikes an internal target and produces a number of different types of particles, among them charged π- and K-mesons, which constitute an external beam. Neutrinos are produced as decay products of these mesons as the beam drifts for several hundred feet. A thick concrete and steel filter then stops all particles except the neutrinos which are incident upon an array of spark chambers. (b) Composite photograph showing Professor Melvin Schwartz with the spark chambers used in the experiment. The photograph was taken with a long time exposure so that many charged particle tracks would appear in the chambers. (Courtesy of Brookhaven National Laboratory.)

Furthermore, the lepton conservation law becomes more stringent, as the equations suggest, applying separately to the electron and electron-neutrino and to the muon and muon-neutrino:

● The sum of the electrons and electron neutrinos minus the sum of the positrons and anti-electron neutrinos is constant; and *in addition* the sum of muons and muon neutrinos minus the sum of their respective antiparticles remains constant.

It is interesting to speculate about the consequences of the symmetry implied by the existence of two charged and two neutral leptons and by the close association of a particular neutral member of the set with each charged member. If, as suggested in Section 22.6, the entire rest mass of an electron is a consequence of its electromagnetic interactions, the electron-neutrino might be nothing but a neutral electron. Then we could talk about a single lepton (plus an antilepton) with two charge states, neutral and negative, that could change its state only by means of the weak interactions. Likewise, the muon-neutrino would be the neutral state of a second lepton and the negative muon its charged state.

Unfortunately, this appealing model has not yet answered an obvious and perplexing question: since both of the neutral lepton states presumably have zero rest mass why does the charged state of the second (the muon) have over two hundred times the rest mass of the first? We might assume that the muon is really an excited electromagnetic state of an electron, even as nucleon resonances are excited states of nucleons. If that is the case we would expect the excited state to decay to its ground state by photon emission. But that process has never been observed. In addition, we would also expect to find some other difference between the states. Finally, in view of the fact that many nucleon excited states have been observed, it would be strange if the electron had only one. Clearly there are difficulties inherent in the idea, and indeed in all attempts to solve the problem of the muon-electron mass difference. Since at this writing there is no hint of a solution to the problem, we must continue to think of the two particles as distinct and thus admit that we do not fully understand either the weak or the electromagnetic interactions.

The difference between the three-particle vertices of electromagnetic and strong interaction diagrams and the less explicit detailed four-particle interaction vertices has already been noted. It is natural to try bringing the latter into correspondence with the general scheme of assuming the existence of an exchange Bose particle as the carrier of the interaction. Because of the known, detailed characteristics of the observed weak decays, this particle, usually called a W particle (for weak) would have to have spin 1 and would be the quantized unit of the weak field. Presumably the basic weak processes could be represented by emission and absorption diagrams just as in the strong and electromagnetic cases. For example, a negative muon would disappear at a weak vertex, and a W^- and a free muon-neutrino would appear. Subsequently, the W^- would annihilate with an electron-neutrino to produce a free electron (Figure 22.30). Analogous diagrams would be applicable to other weak interaction processes.

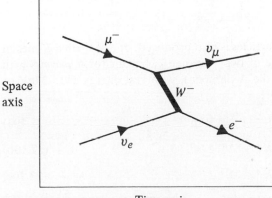

FIGURE 22.30. Exchange diagram for the decay of a negative muon via the exchange of a hypothetical W^- particle.

Time axis

If the weak exchange particle really exists, then a high energy neutrino should occasionally interact with the nucleons in matter to create the particle in its free state:

$$\nu_\mu + n \rightarrow p + \mu^- + W^+.$$

The free W would have a very short half-life, however, decaying in 10^{-16} sec or less via one of several modes:

$$W^+ \rightarrow \mu^+ + \nu_\mu,$$
$$W^+ \rightarrow e^+ + \nu_e,$$

so that the detected reactions would be

$$\nu_\mu + n \rightarrow p + \mu^- + \mu^+ + \nu_\mu,$$

or

$$\nu_\mu + n \rightarrow p + \mu^- + e^+ + \nu_e.$$

Observation of the first of these would strongly suggest the existence of the W particle, whereas the second would confirm its existence beyond a doubt since there is no other known way for that process to occur. A number of experimental searches for the W have been carried out. All have yielded negative results. At this writing we can only conclude that if the weak exchange particle really does exist its rest energy must be at least two billion electron volts.

▲▲ 22.12   Strange particles. Complexity of the strongly interacting particles

For the sake of simplicity Sections 22.8 and 22.9 omitted reference to a subclass of mesons and a subclass of baryons that were collectively christened "strange" particles after their discovery in the early 1950's (see Table 22.1).

When a π-meson or a nucleon with an energy of several hundred million electron volts or more interacts with a proton in a bubble chamber (for instance), a great many different types of processes occur. For instance,

$$p + p \rightarrow N^* + n$$
$$\llcorner \rightarrow p + \pi^+,$$
$$\pi^- + p \rightarrow n + \rho^0$$
$$\llcorner \rightarrow \pi^+ + \pi^-.$$

Occasionally, also, a pair of "strange" particles is also produced, one of them a K-meson with rest energy 495 MeV, the other one of two "strange" baryons (or *hyperons*) with rest energies greater than the nucleon: the Λ (lambda), with rest energy 1115 MeV or the Σ (sigma), with rest energy 1190 MeV:

$$p + p \rightarrow K^+ + \Sigma^+ + p + \pi^-, \tag{22.10a}$$

$$\pi^- + p \rightarrow K^0 + \Lambda^0 + \pi^0, \tag{22.10b}$$

$$\pi^- + p \rightarrow K^+ + \Sigma^-. \tag{22.10c}$$

The Λ has only a neutral charge state, while all three states of the Σ have been observed.

All of the "strange" particles are unstable with lifetimes ranging from 10^{-8} down to 10^{-15} sec, and decay by various modes. Hyperon decays always involve nucleons; for instance,

$$\Lambda^0 \to p + \pi^-, \tag{22.11a}$$

$$\Sigma^- \to n + \pi^-, \tag{22.11b}$$

$$\Sigma^0 \to \Lambda^0 + \gamma \tag{22.11c}$$
$$\quad \downarrow p + \pi^-,$$

whereas the K-mesons decay into π-mesons or leptons:

$$K^+ \to \pi^+ + \pi^0, \tag{22.12a}$$

$$K^+ \to \pi^0 + \mu^+ + \nu, \tag{22.12b}$$

$$K^0 \to \pi^+ + \pi^-, \tag{22.12c}$$

etc. Because the particles usually have velocities at least a few tenths the velocity of light, they can travel distances ranging from a few inches to a few feet before decaying. Hence bubble chamber photographs of the production and decay of neutral strange particles have the typical "V" appearance shown in Figure 22.31.

The disparity between the times required for the production and for decay of the "strange" particles led to their being christened as such when they were first discovered in the early 1950's. For although the production of a Λ^0 in a strong, π^--p interaction requires only about 10^{-23} sec, the decay of a Λ^0 into the same two particles requires 10^{-10} sec, a fact that appears completely inconsistent with the assumption of symmetry under time reversal. However, a more detailed examination of any strong production reaction initiated by π-mesons or nucleons indicates that if a hyperon appears in the final state than either a K-meson or an antihyperon is also present. Likewise, a final state K-meson is always accompanied either by a hyperon or an anti-K-meson. In contrast, the decays of the hyperons and K-mesons yield only π-mesons, nucleons, or leptons.

Murray Gell-Mann devised a simple, consistent scheme based on the experimental data for determining whether or not a particular strong production reaction involving strange particles is possible. If each of the baryons and mesons is assigned a quantum number, S, called *strangeness*, then, according to Gell-Mann's rule, in the strong and electromagnetic interaction the total strangeness never changes. Nucleons and π-mesons are assigned $S = 0$, K^+- and K^0-mesons $S = -1$, anti-K's (K^- and $\overline{K}^0$) $S = -1$, Λ and Σ hyperons $S = -1$, and their antiparticles $S = -1$. Two other hyperons with $S = -2$ (the Ξ^0) and $S = -3$ (the Ω^-) have also been discovered (Table 22.2).

Let us apply Gell-Mann's strangeness conservation rule to reaction 22.9a:

$$p + p \to K^+ + \Sigma^+ + p + \pi^-.$$

The total strangeness in the initial state is zero. Therefore, the total strangeness must also be zero in the final state. Since $S(K^+) = +1$, $S(\Sigma^+) = -1$, the requirement is obviously satisfied. However, the reaction $\pi^- + p \to \Lambda^0$ violates the rule, for $S = -1$ in the final state. In fact this reaction has never been observed. Likewise the reaction

$$K^- + p \to \Lambda^0 + \pi^+ + \pi^-$$

conserves strangeness and is observed, whereas the reaction

$$K^+ + p \to \Lambda^0 + \pi^+ + \pi^-$$

is forbidden.

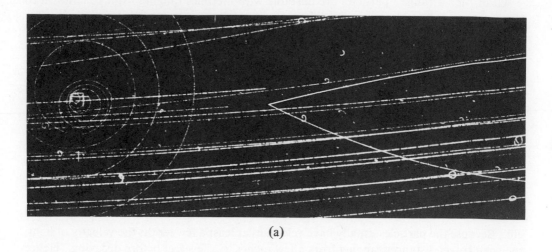

(a)

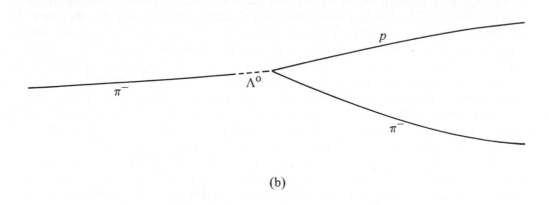

(b)

FIGURE 22.31. Production and decay of a Λ^0. A π^--meson track incident from the left terminates about a third of the way through the chamber, and a proton and a π^- track emerge from a point a small distance downstream. The observed disparity between the times required for the production and decay of the Λ^0 led to its designation as a strange particle. A K^0-meson which must have been produced along with the Λ^0 evidently left the chamber before it decayed. (Courtesy of Brookhaven National Laboratory.)

The Gell-Mann strangeness conservation rule is clearly not applicable to the *decay* of hyperons and K-mesons, for the reactions

$$\Lambda^0 \rightarrow p + \pi^-, \tag{22.11a}$$

$$\Sigma^- \rightarrow n + \pi^-, \tag{22.11b}$$

$$K^+ \rightarrow \pi^0 + \mu^+ + \nu, \tag{22.12b}$$

are among the principally observed decay modes of these particles. Since Equations 22.11 and 22.12 occur with half-lives ranging from 10^{-8} to 10^{-10} sec we assume that they

TABLE 22.2   *The Quasi-Stable Strange Particles*

Particle	Antiparticle	Rest Energy (MeV)	Strangeness*
		MESONS†	
K^+	K^-	494	$+1$
K^0	$\bar{K}^0$	498	-1
		BARYONS	
Λ^0	Λ^{-0}	1115	-1
$\Sigma^{\pm 0}$	$\bar{\Sigma}^{\pm 0}$	1190	-1
Ξ	$\overline{\Xi 0}$	1320	-2
Ω^-	$\bar{\Omega}$	1672	3

* An antiparticle has strangeness opposite that of its corresponding particle. See Table 22.1 for data on lifetimes and decay modes.
† Meson and baryon resonances have the same strangeness as their quasi-stable counterparts.

proceed via the weak interactions. Therefore, the Gell-Mann scheme suggests that since the empirically assigned total strangeness of a particle system is conserved for strong and electromagnetic but *not* for weak interactions, it is related to a common, basic property of the strongly interacting particles. We have defined strong charge as a measure of participation in the strong interactions. Hence it is natural to conclude that the strong charge of a particle is determined, at least in part, by its strangeness. From this point of view we can think of hyperons as the strange counterparts of nucleons, and K-mesons as the strange counterparts of π-mesons.

The parallel between hyperons and nucleons and between K- and π-mesons is reinforced by the existence of short-lived excited hyperon states (or hyperon resonances) with $S = -1$ and -2 which are analogous to the excited nucleon states and must still be regarded as unique states of matter. Likewise there are a number of meson resonances analogous to the ρ which decay into several K-mesons or K- and π-mesons. Like their nonstrange counterparts these states decay rapidly via the strong, strangeness-conserving interactions. For instance, the hyperon resonance called Σ^{*+} (1385) which is an excited state of the Σ^+ with $S = -1$ and rest energy 1385 MeV decays via:

$$\Sigma^{*+} (1385) \to \Lambda^0 + \pi^+,$$

while the 888 MeV rest energy K^{*+} ($S = -1$) has a principle decay mode

$$K^{*+} (888) \to K^0 + \pi^+.$$

The strange particles and their excited states completes the list of particle types that exist in the current catalogue. Their existence requires a revision, or at least a generalization, of several ideas about the interactions of the fundamental particles. For instance, the baryon conservation law now embraces the entire group of particles: nucleons, nucleon resonances, hyperons, and hyperon resonance. Although the types of baryons and antibaryons that participate in a reaction may be changed by that reaction, the complete disappearance of a baryon has never been observed.

Even as the lepton conservation law (Section 22.10) led us to speculate on a possible intimate relationship between the neutrinos, the electron, and the muon, the baryon conservation law leads us into a similar speculation on a connection among all the baryons. Indeed, in view of the assumption that the properties of all the particles are determined by their interactions, we can scarcely avoid such speculations. Previously we spoke about nucleons, nucleon resonances, π-mesons, and π-meson resonances pervading all space, coupling to each other via the basic strong creation and annihilation vertices. For example, one possible mechanism for the reaction

$$\pi^- + p \rightarrow N^{*0} + \pi^0$$

is ρ^--meson exchange, represented by Figure 22.32a. But we must now add the strange baryons, the K-mesons, and their resonances to the particles pervading space, and therefore increase considerably the number of basic creation-annihilation processes. For instance, we might then attempt to describe the reaction

$$\pi^- + p \rightarrow \Sigma^+ + K^-$$

in terms of the exchange of the 888 MeV K^*-meson resonance (Figure 22.32b). Now, if a proton and K-resonance can annihilate to form a Σ^+ baryon as in the lower vertex in Figure 22.32b, we must assume that a free proton spends part of its existence dissociated into a K^*-resonance and a Σ^+ (Figure 22.32c) even as it spends part of its existence as a neutron and π^+-meson.

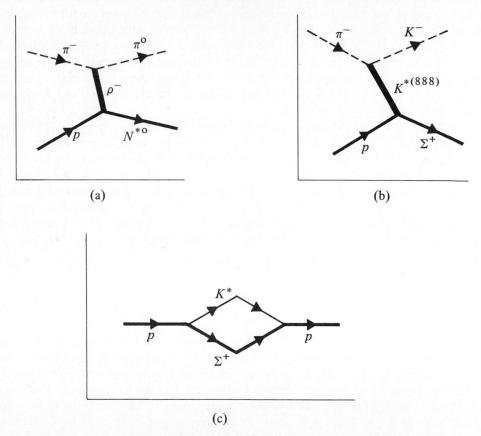

FIGURE 22.32. (a) ρ^--meson exchange contribution to the reaction $\pi^- + p \rightarrow N^{*0} + \pi^0$. (b) K^{*0}-meson exchange contribution to the reaction $\pi^- + p \rightarrow K^- + \Sigma^+$. (c) One of the diagrams contributing to the intrinsic properties of the proton: the formation and annihilation of a Σ^+ and K^*.

Clearly, then, the properties of all the baryons and mesons are intimately bound to each other by the strong interactions so that we cannot hope to understand the properties of a nucleon, say, in isolation from the other strongly interacting particles. Nor can we understand the particles themselves separately from the strong interaction. The task is enormously complicated, but physicists with their faith in the ultimate simplicity of the universe have not given it up as impossible. Complexity has yielded to simplicity in the past. Perhaps it will do so again.

SUGGESTIONS FOR FURTHER READING ▲▲▲

A few introductory physics texts include one or two chapters on elementary particles; for example:

K. R. ATKINS, *Physics*, John Wiley and Sons, Inc., New York, 1965, Chapters 32 and 33.

JAY OREAR, *Fundamental Physics*, John Wiley and Sons, Inc., New York, 1961, Chapter 16.

In addition there are at least two paperback books on the subject:

KENNETH W. FORD, *The World of Elementary Particles*, Blaisdell Publishing Co., Waltham, Mass., 1964.

DAVID H. FRISCH AND ALAN M. THORNDIKE, *Elementary Particles*, Momentum Series, D. Van Nostrand and Co., Princeton, N.J., 1964.

Many articles of interest have also appeared in the *Scientific American*:

E. SEGRE AND C. E. WIEGAND, "The Antiproton," June, 1956, p. 37.

G. BURBIDGE AND F. HOYLE, "Anti-Matter," April, 1958, p. 34.

S. B. TREIMAN, "The Weak Interactions," March, 1959, p. 72.

S. PENMAN, "The Muon," July, 1961, p. 46.

P. MORRISON, "Neutrino Astronomy," Aug., 1962, p. 90.

R. D. HILL, "Resonance Particles," Jan., 1963, p. 38.

L. M. LEDERMAN, "The Two Neutrino Experiment," March, 1963, p. 60.

G. F. CHEW, M. GELL-MANN, AND A. H. ROSENFELD, "The Strongly Interacting Particles," Feb., 1964, p. 74.

F. REINES AND J. P. F. SELLSCHOP, "Neutrinos from the Atmosphere and Beyond," Feb., 1966, p. 40.

V. W. HUGHES, "The Muonium Atom," April, 1966, p. 93.

V. D. BARGER AND D. B. CLINE, "High-Energy Scattering," Dec., 1967, p. 76.

PROBLEMS AND EXERCISES ▲▲▲

22.1. Brief summaries of experimental data on three particles are given below. To which of the four classes does each particle belong? Can you place a plausible lower limit on its rest energy?

(a) Particle A is produced copiously when very high energy nucleons interact with matter. Its charge may be positive, negative, or neutral. Any number of the three charge states may be produced in a given interaction provided sufficient energy is available and charge is conserved.

(b) Particle B is produced in nucleon-nucleon interactions. One of the two interacting nucleons always disappears when B is produced; furthermore a nucleon is always among its decay products.

(c) Particle C is charged and is produced along with its antiparticle when ultra high energy photons interact with matter. Its decay products always include a muon or an electron but never both.

22.2. Which types of interactions are represented by the following decay processes?

    (a) The decay of a particle into two photons with a 10^{-16} sec half-life.
    (b) The decay of a particle into π-mesons and nucleons with a 10^{-22} sec half-life.
    (c) The decay of a particle into nucleons and π-mesons with a 10^{-8} sec half-life.
    (d) The decay of $_6C^{14}$ into $_7N^{14}$.
    (e) The decay of a hydrogen atom from an excited state to its ground state.

22.3. Why must an electron-positron pair annihilate into two photons rather than one?

[HINT: Assume the pair is at rest immediately before annihilation. If only one photon was produced what would its energy be? Its momentum? How are the energy and momentum of a photon related?]

22.4. (a) An electron positron pair always annihilates into two photons, while a proton-antiproton pair may annihilate into photons or mesons. Explain the difference.
    (b) What would some of the possible annihilation products of a neutron-antineutron pair be?
    (c) What would the annihilation products of a $\mu^+\mu^-$ (muon-antimuon) pair be?

22.5. Since the antiproton and antineutron can both exist, then so can diantinucleon systems.

    (a) Would you predict that there are bound diantineutron and diantiproton states?
    (b) What is the ground state spin of the antideuteron? Does it have excited states?
    (c) What are the third components of isotopic spin (T_3) of the antineutron and antiproton? Of the diantineutron, diantiproton, and the antideuteron?

22.6. What are the energies of the ground and first excited states in an antihydrogen atom (a bound antiproton-positron system)?

22.7. So far it has not been possible to perform any experiments to determine whether antiparticles enter into gravitational or antigravitational interactions; that is, whether they are attracted to or repelled by the gravitational mass of a particle. Which prediction follows from the most basic postulate of general relativity?

22.8. (a) A proton and a muon with energies of several billion electron volts are both incident upon a thick lead wall. Which has a higher probability of stopping first? Why?
    (b) Soon after Yukawa proposed the existence of a meson as the carrier of the nuclear interactions a cosmic ray particle with approximately the predicted rest mass was discovered. However, since the particle penetrated several inches of lead it was concluded that it could *not* be Yukawa's meson. Why? (In fact, it was the muon.)

22.9. Sketch one or more Feynman diagrams for each of the following processes and rank them in order of their relative probabilities (one or more may have approximately the same probability).

    (a) $p + p \rightarrow p + p$.
    (b) $p + p \rightarrow p + n + \pi^+$.
    (c) $\gamma + p \rightarrow p + \pi^+$.
    (d) $p + p \rightarrow p + p + \gamma$.
    (e) $e + p \rightarrow e + p + \pi^0$.
    (f) $\pi^+ + p \rightarrow N^* \rightarrow \pi^0 + n$.
    (g) $\gamma + p \rightarrow N^* \rightarrow \pi^+ + n$.

22.10. In very high energy proton-proton interactions both π-mesons and γ-rays (among other things) may be produced. What is the approximate ratio of the probabilities for the two types of processes?

22.11. The probable existence of the ρ-meson (rest mass 765 MeV) was first proposed when it was noted that the shape of the nucleon's meson cloud, determined from electron-proton scattering data, could in part be rationalized by assuming a high probability for two π-mesons in the cloud to exist in a state with a total energy of 765 MeV. In 1960 the predicted ρ-meson was discovered through its dominant two π-meson decay mode. Since the existence of the particle had been suggested on the basis of electron-proton scattering data, however, it was predicted that the neutral ρ would decay into e^+e^- and $\mu^+\mu^-$ pairs as well. Why was that prediction reasonable?

[HINT: Draw a Feynman diagram for the interaction of an electron with a ρ^0-meson in a proton's meson halo.]

22.12. The decay of a ρ^0-meson into e^+e^- or $\mu^+\mu^-$ is a electromagnetic process and has a probability of about 5×10^{-5} relative to the dominant strong decay mode $\rho^0 \to \pi^+ + \pi^-$. Explain why that relative probability is reasonable.

22.13. Since K- and ρ-mesons (rest energies 494 and 765 MeV, respectively) are presumably constituents of the nucleon clouds, they also participate in the nucleon-nucleon interaction. What are the approximate ranges of the interaction due to the exchange of these two particles?

22.14. The proton, the $\pi^\pm$-mesons, and the electron are the charged particles with the smallest rest masses in their respective classes (baryon, meson, lepton). The proton and electron are stable while the π-meson is not. Comment on the distinction.

22.15. Even though charged π- and K-mesons have half-lives on the order of 10^{-8} sec, beams of these particles which drift for many meters and are used to induce reactions (in bubble chambers for instance) are commonly produced at high-energy accelerator laboratories. Why is this possible?

22.16. A particle traveling with virtually the speed of light travels almost three meters in 10^{-8} sec. What must the total energy of (a) a π^+-meson, (b) a K^+-meson, and (c) a Λ^0-meson be such that only one-half the particles in a beam of each type decays in a flight path of 150 m? Necessary data are given in Table 22.1.

[HINT: Recall that

$$E = Mc^2 = \frac{M_0 c^2}{\sqrt{1 - v^2/c^2}}.$$

22.17. Muons and $\pi^\pm$-mesons both carry electromagnetic charge and therefore both interact electromagnetically with protons in matter. Howefer, one type of beam is better than the other for studying high energy *electromagnetic* production processes. Which is it and why?

22.18. As noted in the text, the nucleon-nucleon interaction is complicated by the fact that if two π-mesons are exchanged between nucleons the interactions of the mesons themselves may be appreciable. On the other hand, if two photons are exchanged between charged particles the photon-photon interaction is usually not mentioned. Can there be a photon-photon interaction? If so draw a possible diagram for it and explain why it is ignored relative to the π-π interaction.

22.19. The system known as *muonium* is a bound μ^+-electron system. A study of its energy levels should give purer information on the electromagnetic interactions than a study of energy levels in the hydrogen atom. Why? Predict the four lowest energy levels in muonium.

22.20. (a) Which of the following processes are forbidden by the conservation of strangeness? (Necessary data are given in Table 22.2.)

     i. $\pi^- + p \to \Sigma^+ + \pi^-$.

    ii. $\pi^- + p \to \Sigma^+ + K^-$.

   iii. $\pi^- + p \to \Lambda^0 + \pi^0$.

   iv. $K^- + p \to \Sigma^+ + \pi^-$.

    v. $\pi^- + p \to \Xi^- + K^+$.

   vi. $K^- + p \to \Xi^- + K^+$.

  (b) For each process that *is* forbidden add a sufficient number of particles on the right to conserve strangeness, being careful to conserve charge, baryon number, and lepton number in so doing.

22.21. If the *W*-particle exists as the carrier of the weak interactions, then presumably the properties of the nucleon are in part determined by its coupling to the *W*. Would you expect this coupling to make an important contribution to the nucleon mass relative to the contribution due to its coupling to photons and π-mesons? Why?

22.22. (a) Electron positron pairs normally annihilate into pairs of photons. It has been suggested that they might occasionally annihilate into $\nu_e \bar{\nu}_e$ pairs as well. Estimate the relative probabilities of the two annihilation modes.

  (b) The process $e^+ + e^- \to \nu_e + \bar{\nu}_e$ could have important astrophysical consequences, for when the interior temperature of a star is high enough there is sufficient energy to produce $e^+ e^-$ pairs. If these occasionally annihilate into $\nu_e \bar{\nu}_e$ pairs then, since the interaction of a neutrino with matter is highly improbable, a mechanism exists by which energy can escape from the interior of a star, leading to further compression, heating, and an accelerated rate of energy loss which would culminate in a supernova explosion.

    What temperature corresponds to the minimum energy at which this process could occur?

Symmetry principles and the fundamental interactions 23

▶▶ **23.1 Introduction: symmetry principles, conservation laws, and particle classification**

At this writing the catalogue of elementary particles contains over one hundred entries. By 1975 that number may well stand at more than two hundred, for in the past an increase in the maximum energy available from particle accelerators has led to the discovery of new particles, and there is no reason to expect that trend to change as accelerator energies in excess of 200 BeV become available.

But as the foregoing chapter suggests, the hundred or more known particles are by no means independent of one another. For instance, the three π-mesons may be regarded as three charge states of the same particle rather than as three distinct particles, and the neutron and proton as the two charge states of the nucleon. Hence a mere catalogue listing of one or two hundred particles can be misleading, for it seems to imply a lack of knowledge of the relationships between them.

We have already explored the intimate connections between the particles and the fundamental interactions. We shall now discuss the more general problem of relating the particles to each other without reference to specific, detailed interaction mechanisms. During the fifteenth and sixteenth centuries Copernicus, Brahe, Galileo, Kepler, and their many forgotten contemporaries sought a revision of the Ptolemaic system of the heavens, for they regarded the sequence of circles upon circles as a scandal. Their labors led to a coherent view of planetary motion, and, more important, to the law of gravitation which provided a rationale for the planetary system and for so many other phenomena as well. Likewise, we now seek a coherent, systematic point of view toward the elementary particles not only because the existence of over one hundred fundamental entries is a scandal, but also because such a systematic viewpoint could well lead to a deeper understanding of the fundamental interactions themselves.

The general concept of symmetry in nature is a very old one. Since the advent of quantum mechanics, the generalizing and organizing power implicit in that concept has been indispensable in suggesting basic relationships among the particles. We first encountered the explicit idea of symmetry or invariance principles in Chapter 6 where we discussed the important connection between these symmetry principles and the empirically derived conservation laws. For instance, momentum conservation follows from the homogeneous character of space, energy conservation from the homogeneity of time. Although there are many empirical conservation laws such as baryon and lepton conservation (Section 22.10) that have not yet been identified with symmetry principles, the idea that the two sets of principles are fundamentally connected has been so fruitful and is of such a fundamental character that most physicists now accept, as a matter of faith, the proposition that there is a symmetry principle corresponding to every conservation law.

It is not hard to understand why the conservation laws are so much more central to quantum than to classical physics. Classical physics is fundamentally deterministic. Hence its basic laws are stated as imperatives. For instance, when a force of a particular magnitude is applied to a certain mass, that mass *must* accelerate at a particular, well-determined rate. In contrast, the conservation laws are permissive: when two particles interact, any result may occur *provided* it does not violate the conservation laws—energy, momentum, angular momentum, for example. As a consequence, these principles are applicable to a far broader class of problems than the more deterministic, imperative laws. By the same token, the conservation laws provide less explicit information in any given detailed situation. Since momentum is conserved in all interactions, for instance, application of the momentum conservation law alone cannot distinguish between, say, a gravitational and an electromagnetic interaction.

However, imperatively stated laws are inconsistent with the basic spirit of quantum mechanics. In addition, the types of problems normally encountered in elementary particle physics often involve facets of the interactions that are neither simple nor completely understood. Hence the symmetry principles and the related conservation laws provide a natural starting point for interpreting experimental data, for seeking general relationships between the particles, and for studying the fundamental interactions.

▶▶ 23.2 Partial and absolute symmetries

A good number of contemporary physicists believe that virtually *all* the detailed mechanisms of the fundamental interactions could be interpreted in terms of symmetry principles provided we knew all of them. Obviously this conjecture endows the principles with a deeper significance than has thus far emerged in our discussions. Nevertheless, we have had numerous examples of the relationships between seemingly diverse phenomena suggested by the symmetry principles. For instance, the requirement that physical laws be invariant with respect to transformations between inertial systems yields the result that both projectile motion and satellite motion are related to free fall (Section 4.7). By applying the special relativistic generalization of that same principle, it becomes apparent that the classic electric and magnetic fields are but two different aspects of a single field (Section 12.1).

Turning to elementary particle physics, the identity of the proton and neutron with respect to the strong interactions can be formulated as a symmetry principle, *the principle of charge independence*, which states that the strong interactions neither recognize nor care about a particle's electromagnetic charge (Sections 21.4 to 21.6). That is, we regard the proton and neutron as electromagnetic states of the nucleon, the π^+-, π^--, and π^0-meson as three states of a single particle, the Σ^+, Σ^-, Σ^- hyperons as three states of a single particle, etc. By adding charge independence to our list of symmetry principles we have extended the idea to encompass partial or broken symmetries, for, quite obviously, charge independence is *not* applicable to the electromagnetic interactions. But in fact the concept of broken symmetries turns out to be exceedingly fruitful. If a symmetry which is absolute for one type of interaction is broken by another, then the symmetry itself provides a basic distinction between the interactions. Furthermore the exact way in which it is broken should have a direct bearing on the character of the interaction that breaks it. Finally, the fact that a symmetry-breaking interaction leads to different quantum mechanical states of the same basic system suggests that *all* quantum mechanical states might be related to broken symmetries.

The conservation of strangeness, introduced in Section 22.12, provides a further example of a broken symmetry. For instance, the reactions

$$\pi^- + p \rightarrow \Lambda^0,$$

and

$$\Lambda^0 \rightarrow p + \pi^-,$$

cannot proceed via the strong or electromagnetic interactions since the proton and π-meson both have $S = 0$, whereas the Λ^0 has $S = -1$. However, both processes can and do proceed via the weak interactions.

Since we know of several partial symmetries and since apparently the existence of these symmetries can have an important bearing on our understanding of the basic interactions, it is clearly worthwhile to search for any additional symmetry principles that might reveal themselves in experimental data on elementary particle interactions. The strangeness-conservation law was originally formulated in exactly this way, that is, as an empirical rule to rationalize a series of otherwise inexplicable observations. By the same token it cannot be assumed a priori that there are any absolute, unbroken symmetries, for all of the principles are ultimately based on observations of the fundamental processes.

Each of the four fundamental interactions appears to be subject to at least six "absolute" conservation principles: energy, momentum, angular momentum, charge, baryon number, and lepton number. The first four of these were known in classical physics, and are linked, respectively, to the homogeneity of time, the homogeneity and isotropy of space (Sections 6.3 and 6.6), and the observation that absolute electrostatic potentials do not exist. It does not necessarily follow that a classical conservation law must be valid in quantum mechanics. However, no violations of these four conservation principles have ever been observed. Obviously an established violation of one of these virtually sacrosanct principles would have spectacular consequences for the entire logical structure of physics. Nevertheless, even they are based upon experimental data and cannot be regarded as absolute in any a priori sense.

The baryon and lepton conservation laws (Section 22.10) have not yet been connected with any obvious symmetry principles, although in a restricted way they are related to Dirac's theory of antimatter and the Pauli Exclusion Principle. Strictly speaking, neither law has a macroscopic counterpart. Yet in a sense they are the contemporary successors to the law of conservation of matter (Section 14.2) which once underwrote the ultimate stability of the material universe. Einstein's mass-energy equation, with its implication that all matter might ultimately be converted into kinetic energy, seemed to undermine that stability. But although we must now regard matter and energy as equivalent, the baryon and lepton conservation laws inhibit a free, unlimited conversion. Given the overwhelming preponderance of matter over antimatter (at least in this part of the universe) these two laws restore a measure of material stability. If the related symmetry principles could be deduced they would no doubt provide considerable insight into the nature of matter. Elementary particles can exist in but three charge states. Their spins are either integral or half-odd-integral multiples of $h/2\pi$. In contrast, attempts to rationalize the observed mass spectrum of all the particles have met with no more than a limited success.* Special relativity permits us to equate inertial mass and energy, but offers no clues to the undoubted distinctions between the concepts. The symmetry principles underlying the baryon and lepton conservation laws might offer a reason why a particular discrete set of rest energies, the rest energies of the baryons and lepton, have a special status.

▲▲ 23.3 Charge independence, isotopic spin, and hypercharge

We first encountered the principle of charge independence (Section 21.4–21.6) when we noted that the *nuclear* parts of the proton-proton, neutron-neutron, and proton-neutron interactions are identical, and concluded, therefore, that the internucleon force is indifferent to a nucleon's electromagnetic properties. In other words, the proton and neutron can be regarded as two electromagnetic states of the same particle, the *nucleon*, labeled by a different value of a quantum number, T_3, called the third component of isotopic spin (Section 21.6). This quantum number is related to Q, the number of unit charges carried by the nucleon, by

$$T_3 = Q - \tfrac{1}{2}, \tag{21.5}$$

so that $T_3 = +\tfrac{1}{2}$ for the proton, $-\tfrac{1}{2}$ for the neutron. Pursuing the analogy between isotopic spin and angular momentum we assigned the nucleon itself a total isotopic spin $T = \tfrac{1}{2}$. Since a particle or composite system with isotopic spin T has $2T + 1$ electromagnetic substates ranging in integral steps from $-T$ to $+T$, it follows that the nucleon must have two such substates with $T_3 = \pm\tfrac{1}{2}$, respectively, in agreement with observation.

The charge independence principle can be stated concisely and quantitively by requiring that *all* particles or composite systems belonging to the same total isotopic spin multiplet must behave identically relative to the strong interactions. As we have already noted, the usefulness of the isotopic spin formulation only becomes apparent when we deal with composite systems. Thus if the respective symbols p and n are used to denote the proton and neutron amplitudes we can write down four different two-nucleon amplitudes proportional to

$$pp,$$
$$nn,$$
$$(pn + np),$$

and

$$(pn - np).$$

The total T_3 quantum number of a composite system is the sum of the individual T_3's of its components. Therefore, the four two-nucleon states have $T_3 = 1, -1, 0,$ and 0, respectively (Section 21.6). The first three amplitudes do not change sign when the proton and neutron amplitudes are interchanged. They are said to be symmetric under such an exchange, and therefore, form a triplet of electromagnetic substates with total isotopic spin $T = 1$. On the other hand, the fourth state reverses its sign under a proton-

---

* See Section 23.4, however.

$$\bullet \;\; \bullet \qquad T_3 = \tfrac{1}{2} + \tfrac{1}{2} = 1 \qquad \text{Diproton}$$

Proton $\bullet \quad T_3 = \tfrac{1}{2}, T = \tfrac{1}{2}$ $\qquad\qquad \bullet \;\; \circ \qquad T_3 = \tfrac{1}{2} - \tfrac{1}{2} = 0 \qquad \text{Proton-neutron}$

Neutron $\circ \quad T_3 = -\tfrac{1}{2}, T = \tfrac{1}{2}$ $\qquad\qquad \circ \;\; \bullet \qquad T_3 = -\tfrac{1}{2} + \tfrac{1}{2} = 0 \qquad \text{Neutron-proton}$

$$\circ \;\; \circ \qquad T_3 = -\tfrac{1}{2} - \tfrac{1}{2} = -1 \quad \text{Dineutron}$$

(a)

(b)

Symmetric states $\qquad\qquad\qquad$ Antisymmetric state

$$\bullet \qquad \bullet \qquad T_3 = 1, T = 1 \qquad\qquad \tfrac{1}{2}(\bullet\circ - \circ\bullet)\; T_3 = 0, T = 0$$

$$\tfrac{1}{2}(\bullet\circ + \circ\bullet)\; T_3 = 0, T = 1$$

$$\circ \qquad \circ \qquad T_3 = -1, T = 1$$

(c)

FIGURE 23.1. (a) Isotopic spin assignments for the two single nucleon states. (b) The four dinucleon states and the third component of isotopic spin for each. (c) Four dinucleon states divided into a triplet of states with amplitudes symmetric under particle exchange, and a singlet state with amplitude antisymmetric under particle exchange.

neutron interchange, is therefore antisymmetric, and must be the lone member of an isotopic spin singlet with $T = 0$ (Figure 23.1).

In summary, then, the isotopic spin formalism leads quite naturally to a separation of the four two-nucleon states into a triplet with $T = 1$ and a singlet with $T = 0$. Likewise the eight possible three nucleon states separate into three multiplets whose members are identical relative to the strong interactions: a quadruplet with $T = \tfrac{3}{2}$ and two distinct doublets each with $T = \tfrac{1}{2}$.

All experimental evidence is consistent with the generalization of the charge independence principle to include all strongly interacting particles and systems of strongly interacting particles. Thus for instance, we are able to speak of three electromagnetic substates of the π-meson. In order to generalize the isotopic spin formalism to include mesons, strange particles, and their antiparticles, we first assign to each of them a *baryon number*, B, which assumes the value $B = +1$ for the baryons, $B = -1$ for the antibaryons, and $B = 0$ for the mesons.[*]

The third-component of isotopic spin of a strongly interacting particle is defined in terms of its charge, its baryon number, and its strangeness, S, by

$$T_3 = Q - \frac{B}{2} - \frac{S}{2}. \tag{23.1}$$

---

[*] Because the number of baryons minus the number of antibaryons cannot change in any interactions, it is clear that the total baryon number of a system must remain constant.

For nucleons $B = +1$, $S = 0$ and Equation 23.1 reduces to Equation 21.5. The three-charge states of the π-meson (with $B = 0$ and $S = 0$), have $T_3 = -1, 0, +1$, respectively. Thus they form a triplet with $T = 1$ and must be indistinguishable to the strong interactions. Likewise, the Λ^0 hyperon with $B = +1$, $Q = 0$, and $S = -1$ has $T_3 = 0$ and is the sole member of a singlet; the Σ^+, Σ^-, Σ^0 hyperons with $B = +1$ and $S = -1$ have $T_3 = +1, 0, -1$, respectively, and therefore belong to a triplet with $T = 1$.

K-mesons present a special problem. The K^+ has $S = +1$, $B = 0$, $Q = +1$. Therefore it has $T_3 = +\frac{1}{2}$ and should belong to a doublet with $T = \frac{1}{2}$. We identify the other member of the doublet (with $T_3 = -\frac{1}{2}$) as a neutral K-meson. Similarly, the K^-, the antiparticle of the K^+, has $Q = -1$, $S = -1$, therefore $T_3 = -\frac{1}{2}$ and $T = \frac{1}{2}$. But what is the second member of the doublet—the member with $S = -1$, $T_3 = +\frac{1}{2}$? According to Equation 23.1 it must have $Q = 0$. But we have already paired a neutral K^0 with the K^+. Therefore if the charge independence principle is to be applicable to K-mesons there must be not one but rather *two* distinct neutral K-mesons. One of them pairs with the K^+ and has $S = -1$. The other must be an anti-K^0 ($\overline{K}_0$) that pairs with the K^- and has $S = -1$. In fact, both of these neutral K-mesons predicted by the charge independence principle have been identified.

It is useful to define a quantum number Y, called *hypercharge*,[*] which combines baryon number and strangeness:

$$Y = B + S. \tag{23.2}$$

Thus π-mesons have hypercharge 0, nucleons hypercharge $+1$, the Λ^0 hypercharge 0. Clearly an antiparticle has opposite hypercharge from its corresponding particle. Using hypercharge, the baryon and strangeness conservation laws may be combined into a single statement:

> The hypercharge of a system is conserved for the electromagnetic and strong interactions.

Hypercharge is not conserved for the weak interactions, but of course baryon number is.

The baryon numbers, total isotopic spins, strangenesses, and hypercharges of the quasi-stable mesons and baryons are summarized in Table 23.1.

TABLE 23.1 *Baryon Number, Total Isotopic Spin, Strangeness, and Hypercharge Quantum Numbers of the Quasi-Stable Mesons and Baryons*

Particle[*]	B	T	S	Y
MESONS				
π	0	1	0	0
K	0	$\frac{1}{2}$	$+1$	$+1$
BARYONS				
Nucleon	1	$\frac{1}{2}$	0	1
Λ	1	0	-1	0
Σ	1	1	-1	0
Ξ	1	$\frac{1}{2}$	-2	-1
Ω	1	0	-3	-2

[*] Antiparticles have all quantum numbers opposite those of their counterparts.

---

[*] The hypercharge quantum number Y should not be confused with the property we called strong charge in Chapter 22.

▶▶ 23.4 Unitary symmetry and the quark model of baryons and mesons

As the foregoing section suggests, the microscopic world would be far simpler if charge independence symmetry were *not* broken by the electromagnetic interactions, or, in other words, if there *were* no electromagnetic interactions. In that case we would not have to distinguish between neutrons and protons, or between the charge states of π- and K-mesons. Conversely, we expect that differences in the properties of charge states of the same particle (for instance the neutron-proton mass difference) should be attributable to the electromagnetic interaction. Detailed calculations bear out this expectation moderately well, though not completely.

Are there still other symmetry principles that could lead to further simplifications in our view of the fundamental particles? Even as the electromagnetic interactions break charge independence symmetry, so we might conceive of a higher symmetry which is absolute for a yet undetected superstrong interaction. Then, presumably, we might attribute differences between nucleons and strange baryons (Λ, Σ), or between π- and K-mesons, to the breaking of this higher symmetry by the *strong* interactions.

In the early 1960's Gell-Mann (Figure 23.2) and Y. Ne'eman independently discovered a grouping of the strongly interacting particles that seems to indicate the existence of such a symmetry. Their scheme, known as unitary symmetry, rests upon extension of the isotopic spin formulation to incorporate hypercharge.

The charge independence symmetry exhibited by nucleons and combinations of nucleons may be displayed graphically by plotting the third components of a given isotopic spin multiplet along a horizontal axis called, conveniently, the T_3-axis (Figure 23.3). Such a plot for $T = \frac{1}{2}$ has points at $\pm\frac{1}{2}$, the T_3-numbers of the proton and neutron. Charge independence implies that the graph should remain unchanged if the points on it were interchanged, as it obviously does in this trivial instance. Similar plots for all possible dinucleon systems are obtained by taking all possible sums of the points on two

FIGURE 23.2. Murray Gell-Mann. (American Institute of Physics, Center for the History and Philosophy of Physics.)

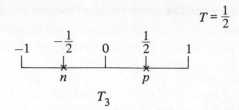

FIGURE 23.3. The two T_3 substates of the nucleon displayed on a one-dimensional plot.

single-nucleon graphs, a procedure leading to a graph with points at $T = \pm 1$ and two points at $T_3 = 0$ (Figure 23.4). In order to divide these four points into sets with equal T, we need only ask which combinations are symmetric about $T_3 = 0$ so that the two-nucleon plots will retain their character upon a reflection of the axis about the origin. Clearly there are two possibilities: the triplet ($T = 1$) with points at ± 1 and 0, and the singlet ($T = 0$) whose lone element can only be changed into itself. Hence we immediately divide the four points in Figure 23.4 into a set of three and a set of one with members of each set having the same behavior relative to the strong interactions. This is completely consistent with our earlier algebraic conclusions.

The unitary symmetry scheme of Gell-Mann and Ne'eman groups together particles with different third components of isotopic spin and different hypercharges but with the same intrinsic spins and baryon numbers. Even as particles with different electromagnetic charge have the same total isotopic spin and are therefore identical with respect to the strong interactions, so the unitary symmetry classification assumes that particles with different hypercharges are identical relative to some hypothetical *super*-strong interaction. Since it is not obvious how the known baryons and mesons are grouped so that the

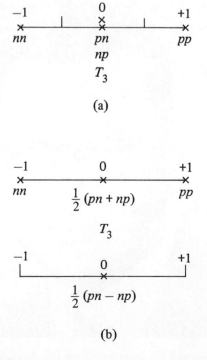

(a)

(b)

FIGURE 23.4. (a) The four T_3 substates of the dinucleon system displayed on a one-dimensional plot. (b) Separation of the dinucleon states into two plots (with $T = 1$ and 0, respectively) both of which are symmetric under reflection about zero.

members of each multiplet *would* be identical with respect to that unidentified inter-action, we start with the simplest possible generalization of the T_3-classification, extend-ing the one-dimensional representation of Figures 23.3 and 23.4 to two dimensions by plotting T_3 horizontally and Y vertically. Just as two points equidistant from the origin constitute the simplest one-dimensional symmetry, the simplest two-dimensional arrange-ment places three points at the vertices of an isosceles triangle with the lines connecting the midpoints of the three sides to the vertices intersecting at the origin. These three points specify the third components of isotopic spin and the hypercharges of a set of three hypothetical spin-$\frac{1}{2}$ particles which Gell-Mann calls *quarks* and to which we assign the labels q_1, q_2, and q_3. If we assume that the difference between the hypercharges of any two quarks is ± 1 and the differences in the third components of isotopic spin $\pm \frac{1}{2}$ or ± 1 then the altitude and the base of the triangle are equal, and the arrangement shown in Figure 23.5a is obtained. That is, q_1 and q_2 have $Y = +\frac{1}{3}$, $T_3 = \pm \frac{1}{2}$, while q_3 has $Y = -\frac{2}{3}$, $T_3 = 0$. Of course other assignments could be made which would also preserve the symmetry about the origin, but these are the simplest assignments that maintain the differences between the hypercharges and half-integral differences between the isotopic spin components. A fundamental triplet of antiquarks having Y and T_3 assignments opposite those of the quarks is also postulated (Figure 23.5b).

In the unitary symmetry scheme the *mesons* exhibit the symmetry properties of quark-antiquark combinations while the baryons have the symmetry properties of triquark systems (and antibaryons the symmetry properties of tri-antiquark systems). Since baryons have baryon number 1 each quark has baryon number $\frac{1}{3}$ so that (referring to Equation 23.2), the strangeness assignments of q_1, q_2, and q_3 are 0, 0, -1, respectively. Finally, referring to Equation 23.1 the charges of the triplet must be $-e/3$, $-e/3$, and $-2e/3$, respectively (and $+e/3$, $+e/3$, and $-2e/3$ for the antitriplet).

The total third component of isotopic spin of any composite quark or quark-antiquark system can be determined by adding the respective third components and hypercharges of its constituent quarks. There are six possible combinations of a quark with a *different*

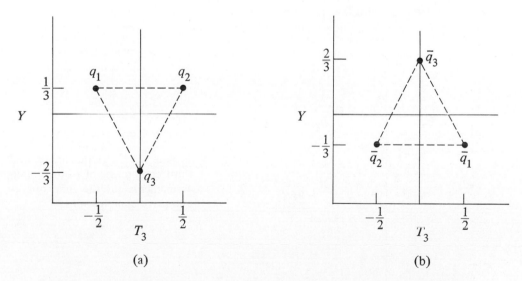

(a)   (b)

FIGURE 23.5. (a) The basic quark triplet displayed on a two-dimensional graph with hypercharge and the third component of isotopic spin as axes. (b) The basic antiquark triplet is obtained by reflecting part a about both the T_3 and the Y-axes.

antiquark. If we let q_1, $\bar{q}_2$, etc., represent the amplitudes for the corresponding quark or antiquark, then the respective T_3 and Y quantum numbers for the six combinations are:

Combination	T_3	Y
$q_1\bar{q}_2$	-1	0
$\bar{q}_1 q_2$	1	0
$q_1\bar{q}_3$	$-\frac{1}{2}$	1
$\bar{q}_1 q_3$	$\frac{1}{2}$	-1
$q_2\bar{q}_3$	$\frac{1}{2}$	1
$\bar{q}_2 q_3$	$-\frac{1}{2}$	-1

In addition there are three combinations $q_1\bar{q}_1$, $q_2\bar{q}_2$, and $q_3\bar{q}_3$ which each have $T_3 = 0$ and $Y = 0$.

A two-dimensional T_3-Y plot for the nine quark-antiquark combinations is shown in Figure 23.6. Before trying to correlate points on the plot with known mesons we must recall that the isotopic spin and hypercharge quantum numbers do not uniquely specify a system, for the constituent quarks can have intrinsic spins either parallel or antiparallel to each other and different orbital angular momenta about their centers of mass. The charge independence principle states that two particles or composite systems with the same total isotopic spin T are identical relative to the strong interactions *provided* all their other quantum numbers (such as spin) are also the same. Likewise, the unitary symmetry scheme connects systems with the same intrinsic spin. The π- and K-mesons all have spin 0. Therefore, we shall try to identify them with the members of a set of quark-antiquark combinations with antiparallel spins and zero orbital angular momentum relative to their centers of mass, even as, in our discussion of dinucleon states in Sections 21.5 and 21.6 we restricted our attention to zero orbital angular momentum states with the nucleon spins either parallel or antiparallel.

Let $u(0)$ be the amplitude corresponding to a $q\bar{q}$ combination with intrinsic spin 0. Then it is possible to write down the amplitudes for all four of the K-mesons and two

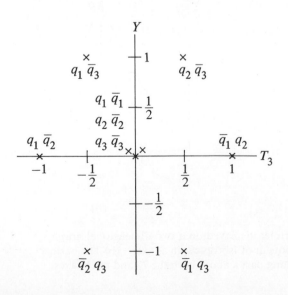

FIGURE 23.6. Hypercharge and third component of isotopic spin assignments for the nine quark-antiquark combinations.

of the three π-mesons in terms of quark-antiquark amplitudes simply by comparing the T_3 and Y quantum numbers for the mesons and the $q\bar{q}$ systems:

$$\phi(\pi^+) = q_2\bar{q}_1 u(0) \tag{23.4a}$$

$$\phi(\pi^-) = q_1\bar{q}_2 u(0) \tag{23.4b}$$

$$\phi(K^+) = q_2\bar{q}_3 u(0) \tag{23.4c}$$

$$\phi(K^-) = q_3\bar{q}_2 u(0) \tag{23.4d}$$

$$\phi(K^0) = q_1\bar{q}_3 u(0) \tag{23.4e}$$

$$\phi(\bar{K}^0) = q_3\bar{q}_1 u(0) \tag{23.4f}$$

The positions of these six mesons on the T_3-Y plot are shown in Figure 23.7.

In the absence of the electromagnetic interactions all differences between particles in a specific total isotopic spin multiplet must vanish. We may impose a hypothetical higher symmetry on the strongly interacting particles by assuming that in the absence of *both* the strong and the electromagnetic interactions all three quarks would be identical. In other words, we assume the strong and electromagnetic interactions split a single quark into a triplet. It follows that any composite system that could be changed into another by interchanging quarks would remain unchanged relative to the superstrong interaction. Hence the K- and π-mesons, for instance, would be identical in the absence of the strong interactions. If the unitary symmetry approach has any validity it should be possible to attribute observed differences between these particles to the symmetry-breaking properties of the interactions, and, more important, discover consistencies in properties such as mass difference among *all* members of the group.

We have not yet identified the systems $q_1\bar{q}_1$, $q_2\bar{q}_2$, $q_3\bar{q}_3$ with any known mesons. Since all three combinations have $T_3 = 0$, $Y = 0$, they are indistinguishable relative to the strong and electromagnetic interactions. Therefore, in analogy with our treatment of the dinucleon systems, known meson amplitudes must be identified with superpositions

FIGURE 23.7. Hypercharges and third components of isotopic spin for the nine spin-0 mesons. The six mesons at the vertices of the hexagon, the π^0, and the η^0 have the same exchange symmetry and are grouped together as an octet. In the absence of the strong and electromagnetic interactions all members of the octet would be identical. The X^0 has different exchange symmetry properties and thus is regarded as a unique state.

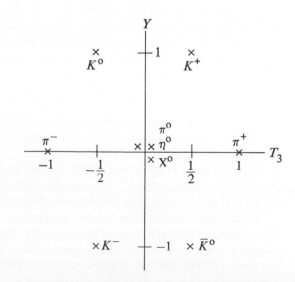

of these amplitudes, and the resulting amplitudes classified according to their exchange symmetry properties. For instance the combination

$$(q_1\bar{q}_1 + q_2\bar{q}_2 + q_3\bar{q}_3)u(0)$$

has the same symmetry properties under exchange of quarks as the amplitudes (Equations 23.4a to 23.4f) and may be identified with the π^0-mesons. Two other unique combinations are possible: one of them having the same exchange symmetry as the seven previous systems and one with a unique symmetry. Hence the nine quark-antiquark combinations divide into a set of eight (an octet) whose members change into each other under an interchange of quarks, and an unrelated singlet that changes into itself, even as, under charge independence symmetry, the four two-nucleon systems divide into a triplet and a singlet (Section 23.3).

When the unitary symmetry scheme was first proposed only seven spin zero mesons were known—the four K-mesons and the three π-mesons. On the basis of the symmetry, Gell-Mann predicted the existence of two more, both with $T = 0$ and $Y = 0$. One of these missing mesons was needed to complete the symmetric octet, the other to serve as the unrelated singlet. By studying the systematic mass differences among the seven known particles in the octet, Gell-Mann predicted the mass of the undiscovered eighth entry. The subsequent identification of the very short-lived η^0-meson with approximately the predicted mass (550 MeV) was an early triumph of the symmetry scheme. A ninth meson with spin 0, the X^0 with a mass of 960 MeV, has also been discovered. Presumably it is the unrelated singlet member of the original set of nine. At this writing no additional spin-0 mesons have been found.

Of course we have not exhausted all possible quark-antiquark combinations, for we have only considered those with total angular momentum equal to zero. If we now let the total intrinsic spin of the quark-antiquark systems be 1 and write the corresponding spin amplitude as $u(1)$ we can write down total amplitudes such as

$$q_1\bar{q}_2u(1), q_1\bar{q}_3u(1), \text{etc.},$$

suggesting that there should be nine spin-1 mesons which like the spin-0 mesons divide into an octet whose members have similar properties, and a ninth, unrelated singlet.

Indeed, nine and only nine of these mesons have been identified; indeed they do group into an octet and a singlet; indeed the mass differences between the octet members are consistent with the assumption that they are related to a symmetry-breaking interaction (Figure 23.8). A number of otherwise inexplicable observations fall into a pattern if we assume that there can be no more than nine mesons with a given spin. We mention only one of them here. The K^*-mesons (mass 888 MeV) decay via

$$K^* \to K + \pi,$$

and therefore may be regarded as an excited state of the K-mesons. Since both the K- and π-mesons have spin 0, however, there seems to be no a priori reason why an excited state with spin 0 could not also exist. However, the fact that there are already nine spin-0 mesons apparently excludes that possibility so that the lowest excited state must be one in which the K- and π-mesons have orbital angular momentum $l = 1$ relative to their center of mass, and therefore total spin 1.

Several other nine-meson families are also predicted by the unitary symmetry scheme, each family being differentiated from the others by the relative spin orientation of its composite quark and antiquark and by their orbital angular momenta relative to their centers of mass. Although none of these additional families has yet been completely identified,

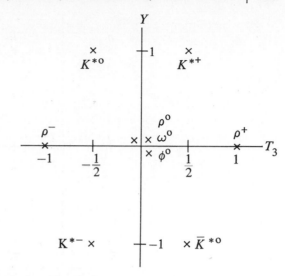

FIGURE 23.8. Hypercharges and third components of isotopic spin for the nine spin-1 mesons (or meson resonances). The six mesons at the vertices of the hexagon together with the ρ^0 and ω^0 form an octet whose members have the same exchange symmetry, the ϕ^0 is a singlet state with unique exchange symmetry.

and although the quantitative predictions of the theory do not agree completely with observation, at this writing no discrepancy has been found that is sufficiently serious to destroy the basic underlying assumptions of the scheme.

Baryons, in the unitary symmetry scheme, have the symmetry properties of *triquark* systems. As in the case of the mesons, we could write down all the twenty-seven possible combinations, then, by examining their symmetry under exchange of one type of quark for another, decide how the set of twenty-seven divides into subgroups with the same symmetry properties. Except for the additional technical difficulties nothing new is involved. We would conclude that each set of twenty-seven systems with the same total angular momentum splits into a group of one (a singlet), two groups of eight (octets), and a group of ten (a decuplet). Also, presumably, a distinct set of each of these four groups should correspond to each set of spin orientations and orbital angular momenta of the triquark systems.

In the simplest set of composite systems, two of the quark spins would be parallel, the third antiparallel to the other two, and the total orbital angular momentum for the three, zero, giving the system spin $\frac{1}{2}$ (Figure 23.9). At this writing no full set of twenty-seven baryons has been completely identified, though two of the octets and one decuplet

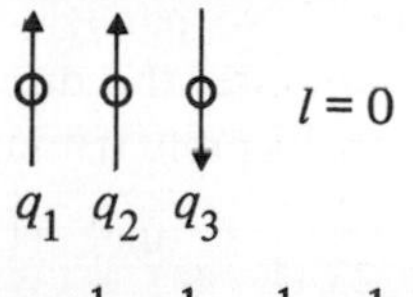

FIGURE 23.9. One of the twenty-seven possible triquark combinations with orbital angular momentum $l = 0$ and intrinsic spin $\frac{1}{2}$. The set of twenty seven has the same symmetry properties as the spin-$\frac{1}{2}$ baryons.

$$l = 0$$

$$q_1 \quad q_2 \quad q_3$$

$$\text{Spin} = \frac{1}{2} + \frac{1}{2} - \frac{1}{2} = \frac{1}{2}$$

$$Y = \frac{1}{3} + \frac{1}{3} - \frac{2}{3} = 0$$

$$T_3 = -\frac{1}{2} + \frac{1}{2} + 0 = 0$$

$$\text{Baryon number} = \frac{1}{3} + \frac{1}{3} + \frac{1}{3} = 1$$

$$\text{Charge} = -\frac{e}{3} - \frac{e}{3} + \frac{2e}{3} = 0$$

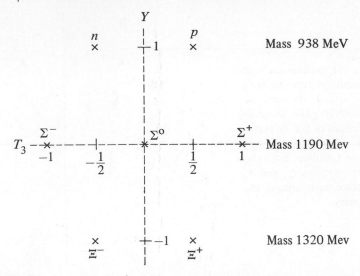

FIGURE 23.10. The octet of spin-$\frac{1}{2}$ baryons containing the neutron and proton. Members of the group have the same properties under the exchange of two quarks, and in the absense of the strong and electromagnetic interactions would be identical. Thus whereas charge independence groups the neutron and proton together, unitary symmetry extends the group to eight members.

belonging to spin-$\frac{1}{2}$ are filled. The octet that incorporates the nucleon is shown in Figure 23.10. Mass differences among the members of the octet, derived on the basis of more detailed considerations of the symmetry properties of the group, agree with observation to a remarkable precision.

Following the quark model one step further, we assume that baryons with spin-$\frac{3}{2}$ (nucleon and strange particle isobars) are composed of three quarks with orbital angular momentum $l = 1$, two spins parallel, and the third antiparallel. Again there are twenty-seven such combinations, again they divide into a decuplet, two octets, and a singlet on the basis of their exchange symmetry. The nine spin-$\frac{3}{2}$ baryons with $Y = +1, 0$, and -1 shown in Figure 23.11a were known in 1963 when Gell-Mann first proposed his symmetry scheme. (The four N^* states with mass 1236 MeV were discovered in 1953; see Figure 22.23.) These nine fit naturally into nine of the ten places in the spin-$\frac{3}{2}$ decuplet. By considering their mass differences Gell-Mann was able to predict the mass of the missing tenth baryon with hypercharge -2 and therefore, strangeness -3 which he named the Ω^-. No particle with such a high strangeness assignment had ever been observed. Therefore, the discovery of the Ω^- with the predicted mass a few months later was a considerable triumph for the unitary symmetry scheme (Figure 23.11b).

FIGURE 23.11. (a) A decuplet of spin–3/2 baryons. Nine known baryons fell naturally into place when Gell-Mann first proposed his unitary symmetry scheme. The tenth, the Ω^- with strangeness -3, at the apex of the inverted triangle, was predicted by Gell-Mann and discovered a few months later. (b) Discovery of the Ω^-. In this bubble chamber photograph K^--mesons are incident from below. Since the initial K^-p system has strangeness -1, the particle produced along with the K^+- and K^0-mesons (whose total strangeness is $+2$) must have strangeness -3. The mass of the Ω^- follows from a determination of the momentum vectors of the particles in its decay chain and knowledge of the incident K^- energy. (Courtesy of Brookhaven National Laboratory.)

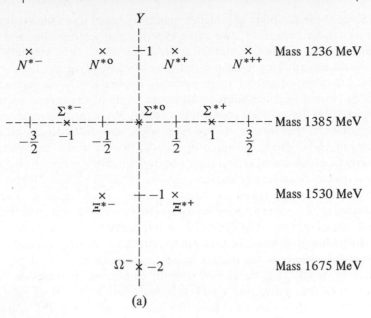

Y

$\times$ N^{*-} $\times$ N^{*0} $+1$ $\times$ N^{*+} $\times$ N^{*++} Mass 1236 MeV

Σ^{*-} Σ^{*0} Σ^{*+} Mass 1385 MeV

$-\frac{3}{2}$ -1 $-\frac{1}{2}$ $\frac{1}{2}$ 1 $\frac{3}{2}$

$\times$ Ξ^{*-} $+$ -1 $\times$ Ξ^{*+} Mass 1530 MeV

Ω^{-} $\times$ -2 Mass 1675 MeV

(a)

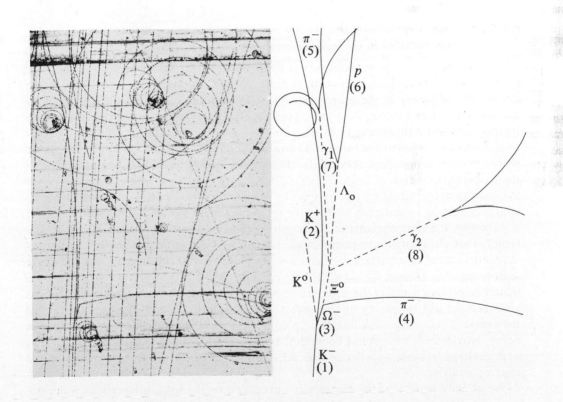

π^{-}
(5)

p
(6)

γ_1
(7)

Λ_o

K^{+}
(2)

γ_2
(8)

K^{o}

Ξ^{o}

π^{-}
(4)

Ω^{-}
(3)

K^{-}
(1)

(b)

Since the assumption of a higher symmetry based upon the existence of a fundamental quark triplet appears to have some experimental justification, and since that symmetry leads to such a dramatic simplification of our view of the strongly interacting particles, it would be satisfying to have direct, unambiguous evidence for the existence of quarks. The fractional charge of these particles implies that their interactions with ordinary matter would be quite unique. However, none of the several experiments designed to detect them has yielded convincing results. We can only state, on the basis of these experiments, that quarks, if they exist, must have rest energies greater than two billion electron volts. Because composite quark systems would be bound by the superstrong interactions we would expect their negative binding energies to be very large, leading to total masses considerably less than the sum of the constituent free quark masses—in fact, on the order of the meson and baryon masses. Since considerable energy would thus be required to dissociate a bound quark system into its constituents, the fact that free quarks have not as yet been identified need not imply that they do not exist.

But although it would be pleasant to reduce all strongly interacting particles to a set of three, the validity of the unitary symmetry scheme does not depend upon the real existence of quarks, for the known strongly interacting particles *do* exhibit the symmetry properties that composite quark systems *would* have. Real quarks would provide a rational, satisfying physical basis for the symmetry, but the symmetry itself does not depend on their existence.

▶▶ 23.5 Broken symmetries and the hierarchy of interactions. Reflectional noninvariance in the weak interactions

The symmetry concept probably offers the most satisfying set of distinctions between the basic interactions, for it permits us to relate each of the interactions with a particular degree of complexity in the microworld. If there were no interactions save the hypothetical superstrong interactions then, presumably, there would be but one particle—a quark—and one antiparticle, and only total rest energy and total angular momentum would serve to differentiate between the various composite quark systems. The world would be very simple (and very dull!). But strong interactions break the unitary symmetry, permitting us to distinguish the hypercharge of the quarks and of their composite systems, thereby increasing the complexity of the universe. Indeed, the idea of hypercharge would be meaningless without the strong interactions.

Likewise, the electromagnetic interactions break charge independence symmetry and require that we specify the third component of isotopic spin, or, equivalently, the electromagnetic charge of a particle. In addition, the electromagnetic interactions introduce leptons into the scheme, for if only the strong and superstrong interactions existed there would be no way to detect the latter group of particles. The electromagnetic interactions also increase the complexity of the lepton class by splitting it into neutral and charged members. Finally, the weak interactions couple the members of the lepton class to each other, provide another coupling between the class as a whole and the baryons and mesons, and, perhaps, provide a distinction between muons and electrons, muon neutrinos and electron neutrinos.

We already know that the complexity introduced by the weak interactions is accompanied by the breaking of hypercharge invariance (strangeness conservation). Of course this is not surprising since the strangeness concept was introduced explicitly to differentiate between the observed production and decay rates of the strange particles (Section 22.12). However, these interactions also destroy a symmetry that is usually

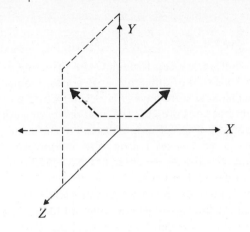

FIGURE 23.12. A vector, viewed in a mirror in the *yz*-plane at the origin of a Cartesian coordinate system, appears with its *x*-component reversed but its *y*- and *z*-components unaltered. The reflectional invariance principle states that the mirror image of any physical system is also a possible physical system.

considered self-evident—symmetry under spatial reflection, or parity conservation. We discussed this particular symmetry from the classical viewpoint in Section 6.7. Physically it implies that a mirror image of any physical system is also a possible physical system, and that the two systems cannot differ in any fundamental way. The principle can be formulated mathematically by considering the way a Cartesian coordinate system would appear in a mirror in the *yz*-plane held perpendicular to the *x*-axis at the origin. All the *x*-coordinates would be changed to $-x$, all *y*- and *z*-coordinates would remain unaltered (Figures 23.12a and 6.6). Hence classical reflectional invariance requires that physical laws be invariant when $+x$ is changed to $-x$. Since the mirror image of right is left and vice versa, the symmetry law also implies that the ideas of right and left have no absolute significance.

The quantum mechanical formulation of the principle is a bit more subtle. Suppose the amplitude for a particular process is given as a function of x in some coordinate system. There are two distinct ways that *amplitude* might be affected by the substitution of $-x$ for x without changing the *probability* for the process: it might be unchanged or it might be equal to its own negative. That is,

$$\phi(-x) = \phi(x), \tag{23.5a}$$

or

$$\phi(-x) = -\phi(x). \tag{23.5b}$$

Amplitudes that transform like Equation 23.5a are said to have *even* or *positive* parity, those that transform like Equation 23.5b have *odd* or *negative* parity. (See the rectangular well amplitudes of Section 18.8, for instance.) If a quantum mechanical state is described by an amplitude with definite parity, either even or odd, the measurable *square* of its amplitude remains invariant under spatial reflection. However, consider the mathematical properties of an amplitude which is a supposition of amplitudes with both parities:

$$C(x) = \phi_1(\text{even}) + \phi_2(\text{odd}).$$

The probability density corresponding to the state is

$$P(x) = |CC^*| = |\phi_1\phi_1^* + \phi_2\phi_2^* + \phi_1\phi_2^* + \phi_1^*\phi_2|,$$

where the asterisks denote complex conjugates of the respective amplitudes. Under spatial reflection the amplitude becomes

$$C(-x) = \phi_1 - \phi_2,$$

leading to

$$P(-x) = |CC^*| = |\phi_1\phi_1^* + \phi_2\phi_2^* - \phi_1\phi_2^* - \phi_1^*\phi_2|,$$

which is quite different from $P(x)$. Therefore, we can formulate the principle of reflectional symmetry by forbidding the superposition of different parity states, requiring that an amplitude describing a quantum mechanical state have *either* even *or* odd parity, but not both. Further, we require that all interactions preserve the total parity of a system.

No violation of the parity conservation law has ever been observed in the strong or the electromagnetic interactions, and there is no *a priori* reason why anyone would have predicted its breakdown in the weak interactions. As we noted in Chapter 22 our knowledge of the strong and weak interactions is still much too incomplete to permit us to write down explicit expressions for these interactions as we can in the electromagnetic case. Hence the restrictive properties of the conservation laws offer an indispensable set of guidelines in formulating theories of the strong and weak processes. For example, energy, momentum, angular momentum, charge, baryon number, and lepton number must be conserved. In addition, the interactions must conform to the symmetry implied by the special theory of relativity. For more than twenty years all mathematical expressions for the β-decay interaction also assumed that the interaction could not alter the parity of the baryon and lepton amplitudes involved in the process, and this requirement placed a further, severe restriction on the form of the interaction.

(a)   (b)

FIGURE 23.13. (a) T. D. Lee. (American Institute of Physics, Center for the History and Philosophy of Physics.) (b) C. N. Yang. (American Institute of Physics, Meggers Gallery of Nobel Laureates.)

However, the observed decays of the *K*-mesons discovered in the early 1950's led C. N. Yang and T. D. Lee (Figure 23.13) to question the validity of parity conservation for the weak interactions. One of these mesons, then called τ (tau) with mass 495 MeV decayed into two π-meson, while the θ (theta) particle with the same mass decayed into three π-mesons. Now it can be shown that a two π-meson state must have even parity, a three π-meson state odd parity. Hence if parity were conserved in the weak interactions, the τ and θ would have opposite intrinsic parities and would therefore be different particles.

No doubt most physicists who knew about the τ-θ problem realized at once that a considerable simplification would be achieved if parity were *not* conserved for weak interactions. For then the τ and θ mesons could be regarded quite simply as alternate decay modes of the *K*-meson. But most of them regarded parity conservation as a well-established principle. Lee and Yang showed that, on the contrary, the principle never *had* been confirmed for the weak interactions, and suggested several direct experimental tests. The first and most famous of these, carried out by C. S. Wu and E. Ambler in 1956, showed that in fact reflectional symmetry is not valid for the weak interaction.

The Wu-Ambler experiment is discussed at length in several other sources, and we content ourselves with a brief résumé here. When a sample of an isotope whose nuclei have nonzero intrinsic spin is placed in a strong magnetic field the nuclei tend to align themselves in the field direction. At ordinary temperatures the net alignment is small, however, for the random thermal energy of the atoms and molecules is usually far greater than the nuclear magnetic orientation energy (Section 21.5). But at temperatures near absolute zero the thermal energies become very small, and in several isotopes it is possible to align virtually all of the nuclei. Wu and Ambler measured the angular distribution of electrons emitted in the β-decay of cobalt-60 whose nuclei were aligned in a magnetic field:

$$_{27}\text{Co}^{60} \rightarrow {}_{28}\text{Ni}^{60} + \beta^- + \bar{\nu}.$$

The direction of the magnetic field defined a direction in space relative to which the emission angles of the electrons could be measured, and it was observed that most of the electrons were emitted in the opposite direction (Figure 23.14a).

If the β's had been emitted upward or downward with equal probability the result would have been consistent with reflectional symmetry. Figure 23.14b shows why it was not. In the original apparatus (Figure 23.14a) the current in the solenoid flows into the page on the right so that the magnetic field direction is up. In the mirror image (Figure 23.14b) the current in the coils is reversed so that the magnetic field and the alignment direction of the cobalt nuclei is *downward*. But the preferential emission direction is *not* reversed in the mirror image so that the β's are emitted *in* the direction of the field. Therefore, since the mirror image experiment would yield different results than the original experiment the mirror system is *not* physically observable. It follows that the β-decay interaction, and by implication the weak interactions in general, do not conserve parity.

A detailed quantitative analysis of these rather surprising results shows not only that reflectional symmetry is broken for the weak interactions, but that it is broken as much as it possibly can be. That is, if $\phi_e(x)$ is an even parity amplitude describing the interaction, and $\phi_0(x)$ an odd parity amplitude, then in general the β-decay interaction is described as a superposition of these states:

$$\phi_{\text{total}} = \bar{a}\phi_e + \bar{b}\phi_0,$$

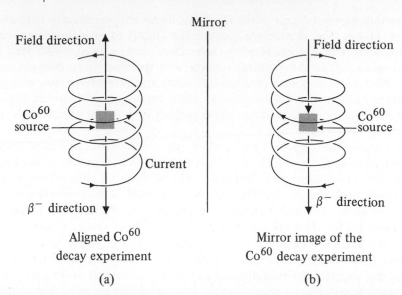

FIGURE 23.14.   (a) Essential features of the experiment to measure the direction of the electrons from the decay of $_{27}Co^{60}$ nuclei aligned in a magnetic field. (b) Mirror image of the apparatus in part a. Since the current is reversed so is the magnetic field. Therefore, electrons are emitted *in* the field direction rather than opposite to it.

where $\bar{a}$ and $\bar{b}$ are arbitrary complex constants. If either $\bar{a} = 0$ or $\bar{b} = 0$ the total amplitude has definite parity. As it happens $|\bar{a}| = |\bar{b}| = 1/\sqrt{2}$. Therefore, the contributions from the two amplitudes are equal, the interference between them is a maximum, and so is the violation of reflectional symmetry.

▲▲ 23.6 Charge conjugation and time reversal invariance. TCP theorem. Evidence for CP noninvariance in the weak interactions

The nonconservation of parity for the weak interactions calls into question two other related symmetry principles: time reversal and charge conjugation invariance. The first of these principles is very much akin to invariance under spatial reflection and states that physical processes cannot depend upon an assumed direction in time. Therefore, if all the t-coordinates in an equation representing a physical process are changed to $-t$ the resulting equation describes also a possible physical process (Section 6.8). As in the case of reflectional symmetry, if the amplitude describing a quantum mechanical system is either even or odd under time reversal—that is, if

$$\phi(-t) = \phi(t) \qquad \text{(even)},$$

or

$$\phi(-t) = -\phi(t) \qquad \text{(odd)}$$

the square of the amplitude remains invariant. However, the superposition of an odd and an even amplitude leads to an interference between the even and odd amplitudes and to a probability that in general is not invariant under time reversal. Hence the symmetry principle requires that all amplitudes describing quantum mechanical states must be either completely even or completely odd under time reversal, and that all interactions preserve the even or odd character of these amplitudes.

The charge conjugation symmetry principle states that if all the particles in a system are replaced with their antiparticles, the resulting system is also a possible physical system differing in no fundamental way from the original. Again, an amplitude may be either even or odd under charge conjugation—i.e., either

$$\phi(-q) = \phi(q),$$

or

$$\phi(-q) = -\phi(q).$$

We formulate the principle by requiring that all amplitudes describing quantum mechanical systems be either even or odd under charge conjugation, and that all interactions preserve the even or odd character of the states.

These three discrete symmetries, time reversal, charge conjugation, and parity, are often referred to as T, C, and P, respectively. There is no a priori reason why any of them should hold for quantum mechanical systems, though P and T appear to be valid in classical physics (C has no classical analogue). However, there is a very general principle called the TCP theorem which lies at the foundations of quantum mechanics and states that *all* interactions must be invariant with respect to the combination of the three symmetries. That is, if for any system time is reversed, particles changed into antiparticles, and left changed into right, the resulting system and the original system will be indistinguishable.

The best present measurements indicate that all three of these invariance principles are applicable separately to the strong and electromagnetic interactions, although many experiments searching for possible breakdowns in these principles have been and are being performed. But since the weak interactions are *not* invariant under spatial reflections then either time reversal invariance or charge conjugation invariance must also fail for these interactions. Otherwise they could not be invariant under the combination of T, C, and P.

Following the Wu-Ambler experiment on the β-decay of $_{27}Co^{60}$, many other experiments were performed to ascertain the full implications of parity nonconservation. One of these by R. Garwin, L. Lederman, and their coworkers studied the decay of π^+-mesons brought to rest in a block of carbon, and proved that the weak interactions are also not invariant under charge conjugation.

Both the muon and the muon neutrino from the decay,

$$\pi^+ \rightarrow \mu^+ + \nu_\mu,$$

have intrinsic spin $\frac{1}{2}$, while the π^+-meson has spin 0. If the π-meson decays while at rest, the linear momentum vectors of the two decay products must be equal and opposite. Furthermore, their spin angular momenta must be opposite so that the total angular as well as linear momentum of the system will be zero (Figure 23.15a). The direction of the muon's spin axis need have no special a priori relation to its momentum direction. But measurements show that the two axes are always the same axis, and furthermore that (in semiclassical language) the μ^+ "spins" to the left as it moves directly away from an observer. (That is, it "spins" in the direction a left-handed screw would turn as it advanced.) It follows that the neutrino spin axis must also coincide with its momentum direction, and, further, that the particle "spins" to the *right* as it recedes from an observer.

If the system in Figure 23.15a is charge conjugated, a left-spinning negative muon and a right-spinning antineutrino (seen receding from an observer) emerge in opposite directions from a decaying π^--meson. But if *both* positive and negative muons had the same spin direction then angular momentum would not be conserved in many other processes involving muons—for example, in the annihilation reaction:

$$\mu^+ + \mu^- \rightarrow 2\gamma,$$

with both particles approaching the reaction region with equal and opposite momenta. We conclude that the μ^- emerging from π^--decay must spin to the *right* and the antineutrino to the *left*. Therefore, Figure 22.15b does *not* represent a possible physical process, and it follows that the reaction is not invariant under charge conjugation. However, if we apply *both* C and P to Figure 22.15a the particles are changed into antiparticles and *in addition* their spin directions are reversed to yield the observed right-handed neutrino and left-handed antineutrino (Figure 22.15c). The system is invariant under a combination of C and P, and, from the *TCP* theorem, it is presumably invariant under time reversal as well.

Similar, consistent conclusions have also been reached for most other weak interactions. Negative muons, electrons and both types of neutrinos appear to have right-handed spins, their antiparticles left-handed spins. As of this writing all weak interactions. that do not involve strange particles seem to be invariant under the CP operation Hence the results of measurements on the *positron* decay of anti-Co^{60} in a magnetic field produced by a current flowing *clockwise* in a solenoid would be indistinguishable from results on the electron decay of Co^{60} in a field produced by a current flowing *counter-*

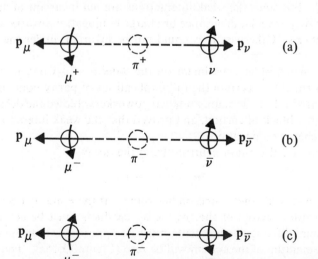

FIGURE 23.15. Invariance of the decay $\pi \rightarrow \mu + \nu$ under the combined operations of charge conjugation and parity inversion. (a) In the decay $\pi^+ \rightarrow \mu^+ + \nu$ the μ^+ spin is left-handed, the neutrino spin right-handed. (b) If part a is charge conjugated the μ^- spin is left-handed and the antineutrino spin left-handed, in disagreement with observation. (c) In the mirror image of part b the μ^- is right-handed, the antineutrino left-handed, in agreement with observation.

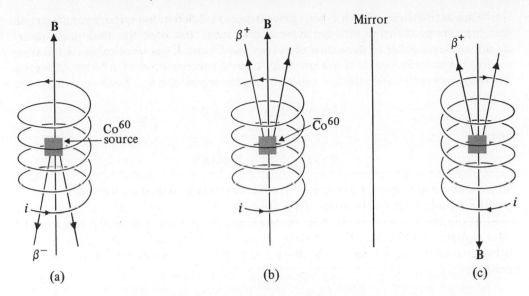

FIGURE 23.16. Invariance of the aligned Co^{60} decay experiment under the combined operations of charge conjugation and parity inversion. (a) Results of the Wu-Ambler experiment (Figure 23.14a). (b) Charge conjugate system: the anti-Co^{60} spin is aligned opposite the field and the positrons emitted in the field direction. The system is not observable. (c) In the mirror image of part b the current and field both reverse but the direction of the positrons do not. Therefore, they are emitted opposite the field direction, as in the Wu-Ambler experiment (part a).

clockwise in a solenoid (Figure 23.16). Although the original Co^{60} experiment of Wu and Ambler at first seemed to provide an absolute criterion for distinguishing left from right, that distinction is meaningful only if we accept the conventional designation of "particle" and "antiparticle." If in some part of the universe antimatter is dominant, then the latter convention would doubtless be reversed, and with it the meaning of left and right.

The invariance of weak interactions under the combination of charge conjugation and spatial reflection, and, therefore also under time reversal, seemed to be well established by 1960. However, in 1964, V. Fitch, J. Cronin, and their coworkers observed a particular decay mode of the neutral K-meson which is forbidden by CP invariance. The effect is a rather subtle one, and we shall not discuss the original experiment in detail. Although other investigators have confirmed the Fitch-Cronin measurement, at this writing CP noninvariance has yet to be observed in a clearcut way for any reaction that does not involve K-meson decay. Indeed, the origin of CP noninvariance in K-decay is by no means certain since it can be attributed either to the weak or to the electromagnetic interactions.

Even though the origin of the observed CP violation in K-meson decay is not yet understood, the TCP theorem implies that either the weak or the electromagnetic interactions (or perhaps both) are *not* invariant under time reversal. Therefore, an absolute distinction can be made between matter and antimatter, and thus also between left and right. As noted in Section 23.3 there are two distinct neutral K-mesons, the K^0 and $\bar{K}^0$, which are antiparticles of each other. Since they have different hypercharge and isotopic spin they are produced in different types of reactions. But since the weak interactions do not conserve either of these quantities they see K^0 and $\bar{K}^0$ as identical particles. For this reason neutral K-mesons always decay from a superposition of K^0 and $\bar{K}^0$ states. There are two such states: the first called the K_1, the second the K_2. Their amplitudes are

$$\phi(K_1^0) = \bar{a}\phi(K^0) + \bar{b}\phi(\bar{K}^0),$$

and

$$\phi(K_2^0) = \bar{a}\phi(K^0) - \bar{b}\phi(\bar{K}^0),$$

where $\bar{a}$ and $\bar{b}$ are complex constants. The K_1^0 state has a lifetime on the order of 10^{-10} sec, the K_2^0 a lifetime on the order of 10^{-8} sec.

Most of the CP violations observed to date (including the original Fitch-Cronin result) have involved the decay of the K_2^0 state. If our goal is to find an absolute distinction between matter and antimatter the most direct criterion can be given in terms of the decays

$$K_2^0 \rightarrow \pi^- + e^+ + \nu_e,$$

and

$$K_2^0 \rightarrow \pi^+ + e^- + \bar{\nu}_e.$$

If the decay interaction were CP invariant then (for reasons we shall not discuss in detail) a given sample of K_2^0-mesons would decay via the two modes with equal probability. But measurements first performed in 1967 by J. Steinberger and his colleagues, and independently by M. Schwartz and his group, show that a slightly greater number of K_2^0-mesons decay via $\pi^- e^+ \nu_e$ than via $\pi^+ e^- \bar{\nu}_e$.

Why does this result permit an absolute distinction between matter and antimatter? Feynman has suggested a graphic interpretation of invariance principles. We imagine that we are communicating by short wave radio with an intelligent being in another corner of the galaxy, and then try to decide whether or not we can instruct him on a number of our conventions by means of the laws of physics. Numbers present no problem. We need only tap the microphone once to indicate "one," twice for "two," etc. Likewise, we can tell him what we mean by one meter, since nature is *not* invariant with respect to changes in scale. Therefore, his hydrogen atoms (or antihydrogen atoms as the case may be) will be the same size as ours. But because space is isotropic there is no way for us to communicate our meaning of north and south to him. Nor can we communicate any information that depends on the assumption of an absolute location in space.

In the absence of CP violations there would also be no way to instruct him on what we mean by right and left. We might try to do so with a $_{27}Co^{60}$ experiment, giving him instructions like this:

> Take a sample of the isotope with atomic weight 60 and atomic number 27. Align it by means of a magnetic field in a solenoid. Now look for the direction in which the charged particles are emitted. Call that direction "down" and the opposite direction "up." If you look toward the "up" direction then the direction the current flows in your solenoid is what we call "right."

Unfortunately, since both *C and P* invariance are violated for β-decay while CP seems to be an invariant, the instructions would lead to an ambiguity if antimatter predominated in the world of our communicant. For in that case he would perform the suggested experiment with *anti-*$_{27}$Co^{60}, observe *positron* decay, and, following our instructions would identify "right" with left. But the K_2^0-decays offer a way out of the ambiguity. The new instructions would be something like this:

Go build a synchrotron and obtain a beam of neutral K-mesons. (These are the mesons with mass $\frac{498}{938}$ times the mass of the nucleus of the isotope with atomic weight 1 and atomic number 1. We call it hydrogen.) Now look for the component (we call it K_2^0) with a 10^{-8} sec lifetime, and examine its decay into a π-meson, electron, and neutrino (identified by means of their rest masses). There are two ways this decay occurs. In one mode the electron has one charge, in the other mode the opposite charge. Do a careful experiment to determine the probability for each decay. Now the sign of the electron for the mode with the higher probability is what we call "positive." If that is also the charge on the nucleus of your hydrogen atom (we call it a proton), then matter predominates in your world as in ours. If it is the *opposite* charge, your "proton" is what we call an "antiproton." Now that we have clarified these two distinctions go back to the $_{27}$C^{60} decay experiment, and you'll learn what we mean by "right" and "left."

◤◤ 23.7 Unsolved problems. Place of the gravitational interaction in the basic scheme

The foregoing sections suggest the important role played by the concept of symmetry in giving shape and coherence to our view of the fundamental particles and their inter-actions. We have not yet succeeded in relating every known symmetry principle to a conservation law, nor every empirical conservation law to a symmetry. We are even further from the ideal of being able to formulate all observed interactions in terms of symmetry principles. No manifestation of the superstrong interaction relative to which all members of an octet of mesons or of baryons are identical has been observed. Further, there are discrepancies between the measured properties of octet members and the properties predicted on the basis of symmetry breaking by the strong interactions. The electromagnetic interactions are far better understood than either the weak or the strong interactions. Yet the magnitude of the proton-neutron mass difference, calculated by assuming that it is due completely to the breaking of charge independence symmetry by the electromagnetic interactions, does not completely agree with observation.

Even if the higher unitary symmetry scheme of Gell-Mann and Ne'eman yielded results in complete accord with observation, even if the differences between charged and neutral members of the same isotopic spin multiplet were completely understood, the weak interactions would still present problems. Leptons are left out of the unitary symmetry scheme, and in any case no one even knows how to approach the mystery of the muon-electron mass difference in terms of the basic assumption relating the properties of a particle to its interactions. Finally, the manner in which *CP* invariance occurs remains an open question.

Despite the many unresolved problems, the power and appeal implicit in the symmetry approach to the fundamental interactions should be obvious. Without it we are faced with one hundred or more individual entities and a discouragingly large number of possible interaction modes. If the properties of a particle are to be understood in terms of its interactions, and if we cannot comprehend the interactions of one strongly inter-acting particle in isolation from all the others, it is clear that the situation would be hope-less in the absence of some guiding principle enabling us to identify groups of these particles whose properties and interactions are virtually identical. The symmetry principles offer such a set of guidelines. Even with these principles we do not begin to have a complete understanding of the fundamental processes. Without them, however, it is questionable whether or not we could even approach the problem of comprehension.

The last of the four fundamental interactions, the gravitational interaction, has been noticeably absent from our considerations of elementary particles, and for a very obvious reason: it is weaker by a factor of 10^{-40} than the strong interactions, weaker by roughly a factor of 10^{-26} than the weak interactions. Hence we expect it to play a negligible role in the structure of the microscopic world. Of course there is no reason why a quantum mechanical theory of the interaction cannot be formulated in analogy with quantum electrodynamics. Even as we regard the fundamental interaction between two charged particles as a photon exchange process, so we can regard the basic gravitational process as a particle exchange process, christening the exchanged boson a *graviton* (Figure 23.17). From the known properties of the gravitational interaction these particles would have to be massless (due to the infinite range of the interaction) and have intrinsic spin 2. The gravitational field can be quantized in terms of gravitons just as the electromagnetic field is quantized in terms of photons. Finally, the property called gravitational mass would be defined in terms of the ability of a particle to emit and absorb gravitons, completing the analogy with quantum electrodynamics.

Although the graviton model is very appealing, there is virtually no possibility of observing free gravitons in the foreseeable future. Quantum effects are readily apparent only on the microscopic level, and at that level the effects of the gravitational interaction between two particles is totally masked by the effects of the other interactions. Nevertheless, it is interesting to speculate on the role of symmetry in the gravitational interactions. The number of symmetry principles applicable to the other three interactions decreases with the strength of the interactions. Electromagnetic interactions are not charge independent, weak interactions do not conserve hypercharge, nor are they invariant under spatial reflection and charge conjugation. Might not the gravitational interactions continue the trend and break even one of the sacrosanct symmetry laws such as energy or momentum conservation? Such effects would hardly be noticed on the microscale. But then the importance of the gravitational interaction lies elsewhere—namely in its role in binding the planets to the sun, the stars into galaxies, the galaxies into a universe. Hence even a small gravitational violation of some "absolute" symmetry law could have an important effect upon the nature of the universe as a whole.

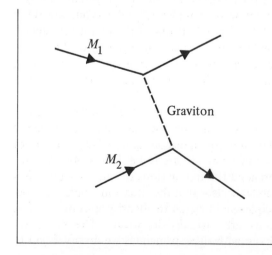

FIGURE 23.17. Diagram for the interaction of two particles with gravitational masses M_1 and M_2 via the exchange of a graviton.

SUGGESTIONS FOR FURTHER READING ▲▲▲

An excellent discussion of the place of symmetry principles in physics appears in:

R. P. FEYNMAN, R. B. LEIGHTON, AND M. SANDS, *The Feynman Lectures On Physics*, Vol. 1., Addison-Wesley Publishing Co., Inc., Reading, Mass., 1963, Chapter 52.

In addition, the two paperback references cited at the end of Chapter 22 both discuss the status of the symmetry principles at the time of their publication.

Pertinent *Scientific American* articles include:

P. MORRISON, "The Overthrow of Parity," April, 1957, p. 45.

W. B. FOWLER AND N. P. SAMIOS, "The Ω^- Experiment," Oct., 1964, p. 36.

E. P. WIGNER, "Violations of Symmetry in Physics," Dec., 1965, p. 28.

M. GARDNER, "Can Time Go Backward?" Jan., 1967, p. 98.

PROBLEMS AND EXERCISES ▲▲▲

23.1. Give at least one conservation law that forbids each of the following reactions from occurring:

    (a) $n + p \rightarrow n + n + \pi^+ + \pi^-$.

    (b) $\Sigma^- \rightarrow n + K^-$.

    (c) $n + p \rightarrow n + \bar{n} + p$ ($\bar{n}$ = antineutron).

    (d) $\pi^- + p \rightarrow \mu^- + p$.

    (e) $\pi^+ + p \rightarrow K^0 + n$.

23.2. The decay of Λ^0 at rest (rest energy 1115 MeV) via

$$\Lambda^0 \rightarrow p + K^-$$

is forbidden by energy conservation. Could the decay occur if the Λ^0 were moving so rapidly that its mass was greater than the combined rest masses of the proton and K^--meson? Explain.

23.3. Recently (1967–68) several different experiments have indicated that a series of baryons with strangeness $S = +1$ may exist. Write down one possible production reaction for such baryons (call them Z-particles) using K-mesons incident on protons.

23.4. Explain why:

    (a) The assignment of total isotopic spin $T = 1$ to the K-mesons and $T = \frac{1}{2}$ to the π-mesons implies that whereas there is only one neutral π-meson, there are two distinct neutral K-mesons one of which is the antiparticle of the other.

    (b) The assignment $T = \frac{1}{2}$ to the Ξ implies that physicists believe only the negative and neutral particles exist (see Table 23.1).

23.5. Why aren't isotopic spins assigned to the electron and the muon?

23.6. Charge independence states that two members of the same total isotopic spin multiplet behave identically with respect to the strong interactions. Yet the proton and neutron masses are different as are the masses of the neutral and charged π- and K-mesons, and the neutral and charged Σ's and Ξ's. Are these differences consistent with charge independence? Explain.

23.7. The table below lists the total isotopic spin, T, and the third component of isotopic spin, T_3, for the six possible π-meson-nucleon systems.

    (a) Verify the table by showing that

        i. each T_3 component is the algebraic sum of the T_3 components of its constituents, and

        ii. there are $2T + 1$ substates of T_3 corresponding to each value of T.

(b) The nucleon resonance with energy 1236 MeV (Figure 22.23b) is produced in π-nucleon elastic scattering. Its probability of being produced in $\pi^+ p$ scattering is about nine times larger than its probability of being produced in $\pi^- p$ scattering. What is its total isotopic spin?

(c) Another nucleon resonance at 1518 MeV is produced in $\pi^- p$ elastic scattering but not in $\pi^+ p$ scattering. What is its total isotopic spin?

State	T	T_3
$\pi^+ p$	$\frac{3}{2}$	$\frac{3}{2}$
$\pi^+ n$		$\frac{1}{2}$
$\pi^0 p$	Superposition of $\frac{3}{2}$ and $\frac{1}{2}$	$\frac{1}{2}$
$\pi^0 n$		$-\frac{1}{2}$
$\pi^- p$		$-\frac{1}{2}$
$\pi^- n$	$\frac{3}{2}$	$-\frac{3}{2}$

23.8. Suppose the existence of the neutron had not yet been established, but that all other contemporary information on nuclear systematics such as the atomic weights and numbers of the stable and β-active nuclides, the energies released in various β-decays, and the energy levels of the nuclei were available.

Make as strong a case as you can for the existence of a fundamental charge independent doublet (called n and p if you wish) as the basic constituents of the light nuclei using such nuclear systematics data alone.

23.9. The accompanying diagram shows one mechanism for the scattering of π^--mesons by protons, namely via the exchange of a ρ^0-meson. Draw the diagram you would expect to be most simply related to it by unitary symmetry for the reaction

$$K^- + p \rightarrow \pi^- + \Sigma^+.$$

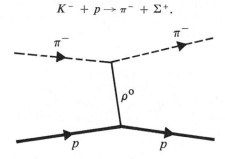

23.10. Interactions between the π^0 and proton or the K^- and Σ^+ cannot be investigated directly because in the first instance the 10^{-16} sec half-life of the π^0 precludes the possibility of utilizing a π^0 beam,* while in the latter case stable Σ^- targets do not exist.

However, both interactions are related by charge independence and/or unitary symmetry to the interactions of other particles that can and have been studied directly. List one or more directly observable reactions related to interactions between each of these pairs of particles by a symmetry principle, and identify the principle.

---

* Calculate the π^0 total energy such that one-half of the particles in a beam would decay in a one-meter flight path.

23.11. The mass differences between the π- and K-mesons are considerably larger than the mass differences between the charged and neutral members of each meson group; similarly, the mass differences between the nucleons and the Σ's are considerably greater than the mass differences between the charged and neutral members of each baryon group. Are these observations consistent with the basic assumptions of the quark model?

23.12. If quarks exist their free state rest energy is at least two billion electron volts. Use this fact to determine the minimum binding energy per quark in a π-meson, and compare it to the binding energy per nucleon in the nucleus.

23.13. The W particle and the graviton have been postulated as the respective carriers of the weak and gravitational interactions. Would their discovery upset the unitary symmetry scheme? Explain.

23.14. The accompanying sketch represents the production and decay of Λ^0 in a liquid hydrogen bubble chamber. For a large sample of events in which the incident π^--meson and Λ^0 lie in the plane of the page, the decay proton is usually emitted in a direction into the page while the π^--meson is out of the page. Show that this observation implies the nonconservation of parity for the decay $\Lambda^0 \rightarrow p + \pi$. Would you expect parity to be conserved for the decay?

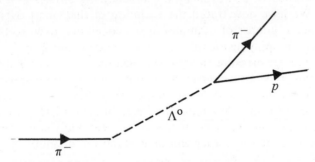

23.15. Show directly that parity is not conserved for a superposition of a sine- and cosine-dependent square well amplitude (Section 18.8).

23.16. What are the charge conjugates of the reactions:

(a) $\pi^+ + p \rightarrow K^+ + \Lambda^0$.
(b) $\mu^- + p \rightarrow \nu_\mu + n$.
(c) $\bar{n} + p \rightarrow \pi^0 + \pi^0 + K^0 + K^+$.

23.17. The conversations with the extragalactic communicant (Section 23.6) assume the universal validity of several laws of nature. List some of these assumptions. What other assumptions about universality might you make that would permit you to convey further information about the world to your communicant?

Chapter 1 followed R. P. Feynman in characterizing physics as a quest for the rules of the game. We have now traced the evolution of that quest over several centuries, and have studied a number of examples of the coherence given to the investigation of natural processes by applying the rules as we now understand them.

This book is in large measure an argument against the oft repeated assertion that only professionals can hope to understand anything about contemporary science. Most physicists would be outraged at the suggestion that they were not equipped to visit an art gallery, or listen to a symphony, or engage in a political discussion because they lacked Ph.D.'s in art, music, or political science. Yet many nonscientists are convinced that there is no level at which they can understand the developments in contemporary science.

It is true that the day of the gifted amateur who could make significant, original contributions to science is probably over, for in most cases searching for the rules of the game as well as studying the application of those rules are highly specialized, expensive, and time-consuming undertakings. However, one need not master a particular field in order to understand something about the way its rules are sought and applied, and to appreciate the relevance of its subject matter. A respected professor in the humanities once told the author that many of the best humanists he knew were scientists. He meant, perhaps, that an intelligent, sympathetic person viewing a field from the outside may be better able to keep its basic goals in mind than a professional working in one specialized region of that field.

It is reasonable to assume that science will continue to evolve and will continue to play an important role in the development of contemporary society. If it is to remain healthy and contribute to that society in the most beneficial manner, then it must have its well-informed friends and critics as well as its dedicated professionals. Hopefully, then, many of the non scientists who have been introduced to the rules of the game will want to follow the developments in physics by pursuing the subject in one or more of the excellent nontechnical books and journals devoted to science, and will feel that they are equipped to do so.

Exponents and powers of ten notation

The expression:

$$a = c^n, \tag{A.1}$$

for positive, integral values of n means quite simply that a is obtained by multiplying c by itself n times. Thus if

$$a = 8^3,$$

then clearly $a = 8 \times 8 \times 8 = 512$.

The meaning of Equation A.1 can be extended to negative integers by defining

$$a = c^{-n} = \frac{1}{c^n}. \tag{A.2}$$

Thus $a = 8^{-3}$ implies $a = 1/8^3 = 1/512$.

For rational fractional exponents,

$$a = c^{m/n} = \sqrt[n]{c^m} \tag{A.3}$$

so $a = 8^{1/3}$ implies $a = \sqrt[3]{8} = 2$.

In order to extend the meaning of Equation A.1 to irrational exponents it is necessary to introduce the idea of *logarithms*. Thus if

$$a = c^n, \tag{A.4a}$$

then *by definition* n is the logarithm of a to the base c written:

$$n = \log_c a. \tag{A.4b}$$

For example, since $512 = 8^3$, $3 = \log_8 512$. Likewise, $2 = 8^{1/3}$ implies $\frac{1}{3} = \log_8 2$.

Two systems of logarithms are in use and have been extensively tabulated: logarithms to the base 10 (so called common logarithms) and logarithms to the base $e = 2.718\ldots$ (the so-called natural or Naperian logarithms). Thus both 10 and e may be raised to any power whatsoever by consulting the appropriate table and applying Equations A.4.

Algebraic manipulations with numbers written in exponential form are particularly simple.

In order to multiply two numbers written as the *same* number to different powers the respective exponents are added. Thus if

$$a = c^n \quad \text{and} \quad b = c^m,$$

then

$$ab = c^n c^m = c^{(n+m)}. \tag{A.5a}$$

To find the ratio of two such numbers write

$$\frac{a}{b} = \frac{c^n}{c^m} = c^n c^{-m} = c^{(n-m)}. \tag{A.5b}$$

Thus, since $4 = 2^2$, $8 = 2^3$, then

$$4 \times 8 = 2^2 \times 2^3 = 2^5 = 32.$$

Also,

$$\frac{4}{8} = \frac{2^2}{2^3} = 2^{2-3} = 2^{-1} = \frac{1}{2}.$$

Equation A.5a is easily applied in raising a number written in exponential form to a power. Since $a = (c^n)^m$ implies that c^n is to be multiplied by itself m times, then

$$a = (c^n)^m = c^{nm}. \tag{A.6}$$

For example, $(2^2)^3 = 2^5 = 32$.

Any number may be raised to any power by combining Equations A.4 and A.6. Thus since by consulting a table of logarithms a number p can be found such that

$$c = 10^p,$$

it is possible to write

$$a = c^n = (10^p)^n = 10^{np},$$

and, given np, to find a by again consulting the table, since

$$np = \log_{10} a.$$

The ease of manipulating exponents leads naturally to a very convenient method of writing large and small numbers, namely, as the product of a decimal number between 1 and 10 and an appropriate power of 10. For instance,

$$23946 = 2.3946 \times 10,000 = 2.3946 \times 10^4,$$

$$1374 = 1.374 \times 1000 = 1.374 \times 10^3,$$

$$0.0294 = \frac{2.94}{100} = 2.94 \times 10^{-2},$$

etc. Then, for example,

$$392 \times 0.0043 = (3.92 \times 10^2) \times (4.3 \times 10^{-3})$$
$$= (16.856) \times 10^{-1} = 1.6856,$$

$$\frac{4734}{29.2} = \frac{4.734 \times 10^2}{2.92 \times 10^1} = 1.62 \times 10^{-1} = 0.162,$$

$$2684 \times 0.0015 = (2.684 \times 10^3) \times (1.5 \times 10^{-3})$$
$$= 4.026 \times 10^0 = 4.026.$$

The last step follows from the definition of a number raised to the zeroth power:

$$c^0 = 1. \tag{A.7}$$

EXERCISES ▲▲▲

A.1. Express the following in powers of 10 notation:

$$168,473, \qquad 2,983,572,$$
$$0.000568, \qquad 0.0000094.$$

A.2. Express the following in ordinary decimal notation:

$$3.86 \times 10^3, \qquad 9.74 \times 10^6,$$
$$7.87 \times 10^{-2}, \qquad 4.63 \times 10^{-5}.$$

A.3. Carry out the following arithmetic operations:

(a) $(2.4 \times 10^3) \times (1.2 \times 10^2)$.

(b) $(2.4 \times 10^4) \times (1.2 \times 10^5)$.

(c) $\dfrac{2.4 \times 10^3}{1.2 \times 10^2}$.

(d) $\dfrac{2.4 \times 10^4}{1.2 \times 10^5}$.

(e) $(2.4 \times 10^4)^2$.

(f) $(2.4 \times 10^4)^{-2}$.

Angular measurement and trigonometry

The angle θ in *radians* subtended by an arc s of a circle of radius R is defined as the ratio of the arc to the radius (Figure B.1):

$$\theta = \frac{s}{R}.$$

(B.1)

Thus if $s = 0.4$ m and $R = 2$ m then $\theta = 0.4/2 = 0.2$ radians (rad). Conversely, if $\theta = 0.15$ rad and $R = 6$ m then $s = 0.15 \times 6 = 0.9$ m.

If $s = 2\pi R =$ the entire circumference of a circle, then

$$\theta = \frac{2\pi R}{R} = 2\pi \text{ rad.}$$

But also in this case $\theta = 360°$ and therefore, $180° = \pi$ rad, or

$$1 \text{ rad} = 57.29 \text{ degrees.}$$

$$1 \text{ degree} = 1.75 \times 10^{-2} \text{ rad.}$$

Any triangle is uniquely specified if two sides and one angle, or two angles and one side, or all three sides are given. The trigonometric functions, sine, cosine, and tangent, of an acute angle are each defined as a specific ratio of two sides of a right triangle. Referring to Figure B.2,

$$\sin \theta = \frac{a}{c},$$

(B.2a)

$$\cos \theta = \frac{b}{c},$$

(B.2b)

$$\tan \theta = \frac{a}{b}.$$

(B.2c)

The tangent of an angle may be expressed in terms of the sine and cosine by noting that:

$$\tan \theta = \frac{a}{b} = \frac{a/c}{b/c} = \frac{\sin \theta}{\cos \theta}.$$

(B.3)

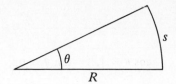

FIGURE B.1. Definition of the angle θ in radians.

In addition, the sine and cosine are related by the Pythagorean theorem. Since

$$a^2 + b^2 = c^2,$$

then

$$\left(\frac{a}{c}\right)^2 + \left(\frac{b}{c}\right)^2 = 1,$$

or

$$\sin^2 \theta + \cos^2 \theta = 1. \tag{B.4}$$

It also follows from the definitions (and Figure B.2) that

$$\sin \theta = \cos (90° - \theta), \tag{B.5a}$$

$$\cos \theta = \sin (90° - \theta). \tag{B.5b}$$

The functions cotangent, secant, and cosecant are defined as the reciprocals of the tangent, cosine, and sine, respectively:

$$\operatorname{ctn} \theta = \frac{1}{\tan \theta},$$

$$\sec \theta = \frac{1}{\cos \theta},$$

$$\csc \theta = \frac{1}{\sin \theta}.$$

The values of the functions for a few angles may be derived from elementary geometric

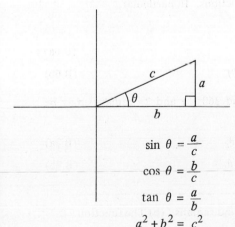

$$\sin \theta = \frac{a}{c}$$

$$\cos \theta = \frac{b}{c}$$

$$\tan \theta = \frac{a}{b}$$

$$a^2 + b^2 = c^2$$

FIGURE B.2. Definitions of the trigonometric functions.

considerations. Thus,

(1) If $\theta = 0$, then $a = 0$, $b = c$.

$$\therefore \sin \theta = 0, \quad \cos \theta = 1, \quad \tan \theta = 0.$$

(2) If $\theta = 30°$ $\left(\text{or } \dfrac{\pi}{6} \text{ rad}\right)$, then $a = \dfrac{c}{2}$, $b = \sqrt{c^2 - a^2} = \dfrac{\sqrt{3}}{2}$ $c \cong 0.866c$.

$$\therefore \sin \theta = 0.500, \quad \cos \theta = 0.866\ldots, \quad \tan \theta = 0.577\ldots.$$

(3) If $\theta = 45°$ $\left(\text{or } \dfrac{\pi}{4} \text{ rad}\right)$, then $a = b$, $c = \sqrt{a^2 + b^2} = \sqrt{2}\, a$.

$$\therefore \sin \theta = \cos \theta = \dfrac{\sqrt{2}}{2} = 0.707\ldots, \quad \tan \theta = 1.$$

(4) If $\theta = 60°$ $\left(\text{or } \dfrac{\pi}{3} \text{ rad}\right)$, then $90 - \theta = 30°$ and using Equation B.5b,

$$\sin \theta = 0.866, \quad \cos \theta = 0.500, \quad \tan \theta = 1.732\ldots.$$

(5) If $\theta = 90°$ $\left(\text{or } \dfrac{\pi}{2} \text{ rad}\right)$, then $a = c$, $b = 0$.

$$\therefore \sin \theta = 1, \quad \cos \theta = 0, \quad \tan \theta = \tfrac{1}{0} = \infty.$$

These results are summarized below:

$\theta(°)$	$\theta(\text{rad})$	$\sin \theta$	$\cos \theta$	$\tan \theta$
0	0	0.000	1	0
30	$\pi/6$	0.5	0.866	0.577
45	$\pi/4$	0.707	0.707	1.00
60	$\pi/3$	0.866	0.500	1.732
90	$\pi/2$	1.00	0.000	∞

Values of the functions for other angles have been extensively tabulated. For most of the problems in this text it is sufficient to read the functions from the accompanying graphs (Figures B.3a and B.3b), and, for the tangent, to use Equation B.3 in addition.

Figures B.3 exhibit the well-known periodicity of the functions. In particular,

1. If $90° < \theta \leq 180°$:

$$\sin \theta = \sin (180° - \theta), \tag{B.6a}$$

$$\cos \theta = -\cos (180° - \theta). \tag{B.6b}$$

2. Values of the functions for angles between $180°$ and $360°$ (π and 2π radians) may be obtained by using the equations

$$\sin (180° + \theta) = -\sin \theta, \tag{B.7a}$$

$$\cos (180° + \theta) = -\cos \theta. \tag{B.7b}$$

FIGURE B.3. (a) The function $\sin\theta$ for θ in degrees and radians. (b) The function $\cos\theta$ for θ in degrees and radians.

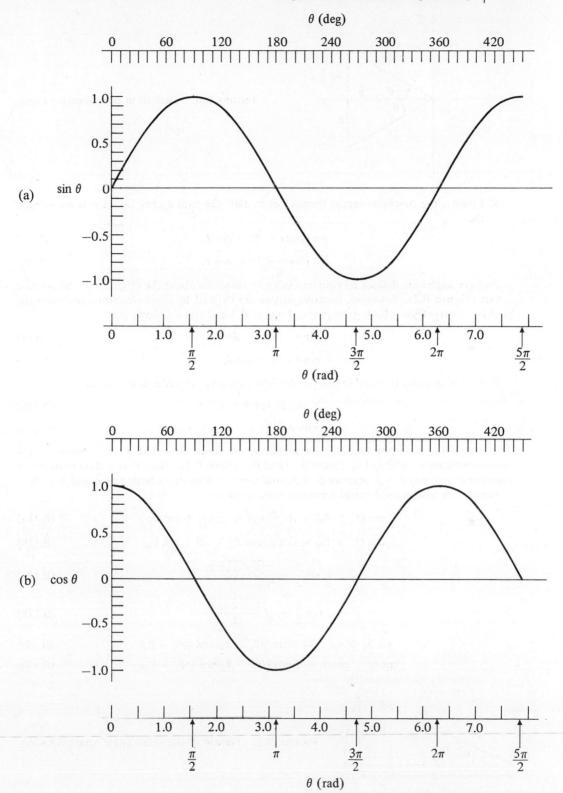

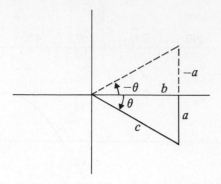

FIGURE B.4. Definition of a negative angle.

3. Finally, the functions repeat themselves in 360° (2π rad) cycles, i.e., if n is an integer, then

$$\sin(360n + \theta) = \sin\theta, \tag{B.8a}$$

$$\cos(360n + \theta) = \cos\theta. \tag{B.8b}$$

Positive angles are defined by counterclockwise rotations about the origin from the positive x-axis (Figure B.2). Likewise, negative angles are defined by *clockwise* rotations from the positive x-axis (Figure B.4). Comparing Figures B.2 and B.4 it follows that

$$\sin(-\theta) = -\sin\theta, \tag{B.9a}$$

$$\cos(-\theta) = \cos\theta. \tag{B.9b}$$

For small angles *expressed in radians* the following approximations are useful:

$$\sin \cong \tan\theta \cong \theta, \tag{B.10a}$$

$$\cos\theta \cong 1. \tag{B.10b}$$

These are valid to better than 1% for angles up to about 0.1 rad (6°). The nature of the approximations is indicated by Figure B.5 (and Equations B.2). Since $\theta = s/R$ then $\sin\theta = \theta$ assumes $a = s$, $\cos\theta = 1$ assumes $b = R$, and $\tan\theta = \theta$ assumes both $s = a$ and $b = R$.

Finally, we give several useful formulas without proof:

$$\sin(\theta_1 \pm \theta_2) = \sin\theta_1 \cos\theta_2 \pm \sin\theta_2 \cos\theta_1, \tag{B.11a}$$

$$\cos(\theta_1 \pm \theta_2) = \cos\theta_1 \cos\theta_2 \mp \sin\theta_1 \sin\theta_2, \tag{B.11b}$$

$$\sin\frac{\theta}{2} = \sqrt{\frac{1 - \cos\theta}{2}}, \tag{B.12a}$$

$$\cos\frac{\theta}{2} = \sqrt{\frac{1 + \cos\theta}{2}}. \tag{B.12b}$$

$$\sin\theta_1 + \sin\theta_2 = 2\sin\tfrac{1}{2}(\theta_1 + \theta_2)\cos\tfrac{1}{2}(\theta_1 - \theta_2), \tag{B.13a}$$

$$\cos\theta_1 + \cos\theta_2 = 2\cos\tfrac{1}{2}(\theta_1 + \theta_2)\cos\tfrac{1}{2}(\theta_1 - \theta_2). \tag{B.13b}$$

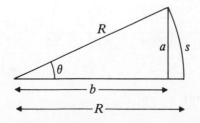

FIGURE B.5. Nature of the small angle approximation.

The exponential function

For convenience we summarize several properties of the exponential function that appear scattered throughout the text.

The differential equation

$$\frac{dy}{dx} = y$$

can be solved numerically (Chapters 4 and 5) to yield a table giving y as a function of x such that the numerically calculated value of the first derivative of the function (Appendix to Chapter 2) is equal to the function itself. The resulting table of values is known as the *exponential function*, i.e.,

$$y(x) = e^x.$$

The value of the number e is clearly the tabulated value of the function for $x - 1$ and turns out to be

$$e = 2.718\ldots.$$

As implied by the above, the frequency with which the exponential function is found in equations in physics derives in part from the fact that the defining differential equation is encountered in many different situations. The values of the functions e^x and $e^{-x} = 1/e^x$ are plotted in Figure C.1. Values not given on the graphs may be related to those that are by applying Equation A.6 in the form:

$$e^x = (e^{x/n})^n.$$

with $e^{x/n}$ given.

For reasonably small values of x the functions may be approximated by the first terms in the infinite series expansions:

$$e^x = 1 + x + \frac{x^2}{2} + \frac{x^3}{6} + \cdots,$$

$$e^{-x} = 1 - x + \frac{x^2}{2} - \frac{x^3}{6} + \cdots.$$

915

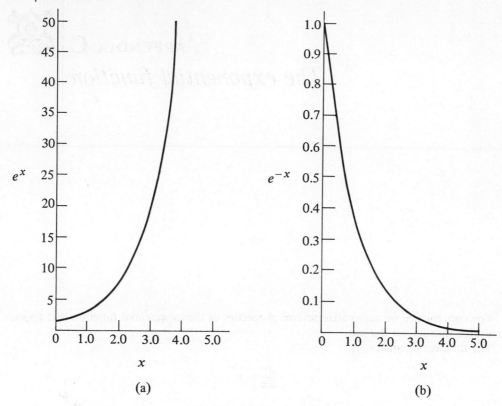

FIGURE C.1. (a) The function e^x. (b) The function e^{-x}.

If the exponent of e is an imaginary number then the Euler relation is applicable:

$$e^{\pm ix} = \cos x \pm i \sin x.$$

Thus,

$$\text{Real}\ (e^{\pm ix}) = \cos x,$$

$$\text{Im}\ (e^{\pm ix}) = \pm \sin x.$$

Finally, if $\bar{a} = a_1 + ia_2$ is complex then:

$$e^{\bar{a}} = e^{a_1}e^{ia_2} = e^{a_1}(\cos a_2 + i \sin a_2).$$

The binomial expansion

It may be shown that the sum of two numbers, a and b, raised to the nth power may be written as the series

$$(a + b)^n = a^n + na^{n-1}b + \frac{n(n-1)}{2}a^{n-2}b^2 + \frac{n(n-1)(n-2)}{6}a^{n-3}b^3 + \cdots.$$

If n is a positive integer then the series has $n + 1$ terms; otherwise the number of terms is infinite.

We give the explicit expansions for positive integral values of n up to 6:

$$(a + b)^2 = a^2 + 2ab + b^2,$$
$$(a + b)^3 = a^3 + 3a^2b + 3ab^2 + b^3,$$
$$(a + b)^4 = a^4 + 4a^3b + 6a^2b^2 + 4ab^3 + b^4,$$
$$(a + b)^5 = a^5 + 5a^4b + 10a^3b^2 + 10a^2b^3 + 5ab^4 + b^5,$$
$$(a + b)^6 = a^6 + 6a^5b + 15a^4b^2 + 20a^3b^3 + 15a^2b^4 + 6ab^5 + b^6.$$

If b is much smaller than a then the value of $(a + b)^n$ for nonpositive and/or nonintegral n may be approximated by the first few terms in the appropriate series expansion. These are given for $n = \pm\frac{1}{2}$, $n = -1$, and $n = -2$ for the special case $a = 1$, b much less than 1.

$$(1 + b)^{1/2} = 1 + \tfrac{1}{2}b - \tfrac{1}{8}b^2 + \tfrac{1}{16}b^3 + \cdots,$$
$$(1 + b)^{-1/2} = 1 - \tfrac{1}{2}b + \tfrac{3}{8}b^2 - \tfrac{5}{16}b^3 + \cdots,$$
$$(1 + b)^{-1} = 1 - b + b^2 - b^3 + \cdots,$$
$$(1 + b)^{-2} = 1 - 2b + 3b^2 - 4b^3 + \cdots.$$

In order to obtain the first terms in the expansions $(1 - b)^n$ replace b by $-b$ in the appropriate series.

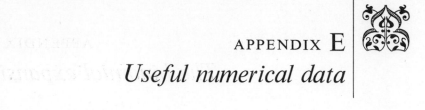

APPENDIX E

Useful numerical data

FUNDAMENTAL CONSTANTS

c	Speed of light in vacuum	3.00×10^8 m/sec
h	Planck's constant	6.63×10^{-34} J-sec
		4.15×10^{-15} eV-sec
$\hbar$	$h/2\pi$	1.06×10^{-34} J-sec
		6.63×10^{-16} eV-sec

TERRESTRIAL AND ASTRONOMICAL DATA

g	Acceleration due to gravity at the earth's surface	9.8 m/sec²
G	Universal gravitational constant	6.67×10^{-11} N-m²/kg²
R_e	Mean radius of the earth	6.37×10^6 m
R_{es}	Mean radius of the earth's orbit	1.50×10^{11} m
R_{me}	Mean radius of the moon's orbit	3.84×10^8 m
M_e	Mass of the earth	5.98×10^{24} kg
M_s	Mass of the sun	1.99×10^{30} kg

ELECTROMAGNETIC DATA

$1/4\pi\epsilon_0$	Coulomb's law constant	8.99×10^9 N-m²/C²
$\mu_0/4\pi$	Magnetic force constant	10^{-7} N/A²
e	The fundamental charge	1.60×10^{-19} C

MOLECULAR DATA

R	Universal gas constant	8.31×10^3 J/°K-kg mole
N_o	Avogadro's number	6.02×10^{26} /kg mole
k	Boltzmann constant	1.38×10^{-23} J/°K

ATOMIC DATA

M_e Mass of the electron 9.11×10^{-31} kg
                                               0.511 MeV
                                               5.48×10^{-4} atomic mass units

M_p Mass of the proton 1.67×10^{-27} kg
                                               938 MeV
                                               1.00728 atomic mass units

CONVERSION UNITS

1 kg = 2.20 lb   1 mile = 1.61×10^3 m
1 lb = 0.454 kg   1 light year = 9.5×10^{15} m
1 m = 3.28 ft   1 day — 8.64×10^4 sec
1 in. = 0.0254 m   1 eV — 1.60×10^{-19} J
1 ft = 0.305 m   1 atomic mass unit = 9.31×10^8 eV = 931 MeV
                               1 year = 3.16×10^7 sec

PURE NUMBERS

$\pi = 3.14159\ldots$
$e = 2.71828\ldots$
$\sqrt{2} = 1.414\ldots$
$\sqrt{3} = 1.732\ldots$

APPENDIX F

The Greek alphabet

A	α	alpha
B	β	beta
Γ	γ	gamma
Δ	δ	delta
E	ϵ	epsilon
Z	ζ	zeta
H	η	eta
Θ	θ	theta
I	ι	iota
K	κ	kappa
Λ	λ	lambda
M	μ	mu
N	ν	nu
Ξ	ξ	xi
O	o	omicron
Π	π	pi
P	ρ	rho
Σ	σ	sigma
T	τ	tau
Υ	υ	upsilon
Φ	ϕ	phi
X	χ	chi
Ψ	ψ	psi
Ω	ω	omega

Answers to selected odd-numbered problems

Chapter 2

2.1.   36 miles/hr, 30 miles/hr. The answers should not be equal.

2.7.   (a) 1.47 m/sec in all three cases.
       (c) 1.80 m/sec in all three cases.

2.9.   (a) $x(30) = 2880$, $\Delta x = x(60) - x(30) = 14{,}400 - 2880 = 11{,}520$.
       (b) $x(30) = 0.5$, $\Delta x = x(60) - x(30) = 0.866 - 0.5 = 0.366$.

2.13. $a(1) = 24$ m/sec².
       $a(3) = 72$ m/sec².

2.15. $v = \frac{1}{2}kt^2$.

2.17. (a) 9.65 sec.
       (b) 65 m/sec.

2.19. (b) 0.025 m.
       (c) 1600 m.
       (d) 26.7 m/sec.
       (e) 1.5×10^{11} m.
       (f) 0.465 m².

2.21. (a) About 0.02 radians.
       (b) 0.06 radians.
       (c) 0.0041 radians.

2.23. (a) 0.26 radians.
       (b) 1050 miles.

2.25. (a) 5 units long. Tan $\theta = 0.75$.
       (b) $x = 12.1$ units. $y = 7$ units.

2.27. (a) $v_x = 500$ m/sec, $v_y = 866$ m/sec.
       (b) $v = 15.8$ miles/hr.
       tan $\theta = 0.33$, where θ is the angle relative to the perpendicular to the banks of the stream.

2.29. (a) 45 m/sec² toward the center of the circle.
       (b) 5 m.
       (c) 21.2 m/sec.

2.31. (a) 2.6×10^{-3} m/sec² toward the earth.
       (b) 9.8 m/sec².

Chapter 3

3.1. 8×10^{-6} radians.
3.7.   About 83,000 miles.
3.9.   About 28 days.
3.11. Moon 2, $T = 3.52$ days.
       Moon 3, $T = 7.06$ days.
3.13. (a) The satellite in the circular orbit.
       (b) The satellite with the greater semiminor axis.
3.15. 0.68%.

Chapter 4

4.1.   (a) Midway between the particles.
       (b) 0.5 m from the more massive particle.
       (c) $x = +2.33$, $y = -1.20$.
       (d) $x = +1.4$, $y = -1.28$.
       (e) The center of the sphere.
       (f) The point on the axis of the cylinder midway between its ends.
4.3.   (a) Twice its speed before collision.
       (b) Twice its original speed and in the direction opposite its incident direction.
4.5. $-30°$.
4.7. $v_0 - \frac{4}{234}v_1$ in the direction of v_0. $-\frac{4}{234}v_1$.
4.9.   Velocity = nmv forward. Acceleration during the 30 sec = $nmv/30$ m/sec, afterwards zero.
4.11. (a) $V = x\sqrt{g/2d}$.
       (b) $v = \dfrac{m + M}{m} V = \left(\dfrac{m + M}{m}\right)x\sqrt{g/2d}$.
4.15. (a) 25.5 sec.
       (b) 3180 m.
       (c) 11,000 m.
4.17. 11,000 m, 12,900 m, 11,000 m.
       Maximum range for $\theta = 45°$.
4.19. (a) 5.1 and 30.6 sec: 127 and 762 m; 440 and 2640 m.
       (b) 1620 m/sec.
4.23. 9.9 m/sec.
4.15. (a) Increases by a factor of $\sqrt{2}$.
       (b) Decreases by a factor of $\sqrt{2}$.
       (c) Unaffected.
       (d) Unaffected.
4.27. (a) At a time such that $\frac{1}{2} = \sin(100t)$, so that $100t = \pi/6$ radians, or $t = \pi/500$ sec.
       $v/v_0 = \cos(\pi/6) = 0.866$.
       (b) At a time such that $v/v_{mx} = \frac{1}{2} = \cos(100t)$, so that $100t = \pi/3$ radians, or $t = \pi/300$ sec; $x = x_0 \sin(\pi/6) = 0.0866$ m from the maximum amplitude position, $x_0 = 0.1$ m.
4.29. (a) It remains at rest at that point.
       (b) It continues to move toward and past equilibrium with constant velocity = $0.866\, v_{mx}$ (see Problem 4.27b).
       (c) It continues to move past equilibrium with constant velocity $v = v_{mx} = 2\pi x_0/T = 10$ m/sec (see Problem 4.26b).

Chapter 5

5.1. (a) The magnitude of the force would increase by a factor of four, while the magnitude of the acceleration would increase by a factor of two.

(b) Both the magnitude of the force and of the acceleration would decrease by factors of four.

5.3. Because of the rotation of the earth on its axis, the acceleration due to gravity at the equator is smaller than at the poles. Hence the total gravitational force on a particle due to the remainder of the earth is also smaller at the equator.

5.5. $F_c/F_g = v^2/gR = 4\pi^2 R/gT^2 = 3.5 \times 10^{-3}$.

5.7. $\Delta t = \sqrt{2d/g_1} - \sqrt{2d/g_2} = \sqrt{2d}\,(1/\sqrt{g_1} - 1/\sqrt{g_2})$. If $g_1 = g_2 - \Delta g$ then, $\Delta t = \sqrt{2d/g_2}\,(1/\sqrt{1 - \Delta g/g_1} - 1)$. Using the binomial expansion (Appendix D to text) $\Delta t \cong \sqrt{2d/g_2}\,(1 + \frac{1}{2}\Delta g/g_1 - 1) = \frac{1}{2}\Delta g/g_1\sqrt{2d/g_2}$.
$\Delta g/g_1 = 0.05/9.8 = 5 \times 10^{-3}$, $d = 1000$ m/sec, $g_2 \cong 9.8$ m/sec^2, so $\Delta t \cong 0.5$ sec.

5.9. (a) Assuming $M_1 = M_2 = 70$ kg, $R_{12} = 1$ m, $F = 3.3 \times 10^{-7}$ newtons.

(b) 5.3×10^{-10} newtons.

(c) 2×10^{20} newtons.

5.11. (a) 1.35×10^{30} kg.

(b) About 220 m/sec^2.

5.15. $T = 2\pi\sqrt{R/g} = 1.23 \times 10^5$ sec $= 1.4$ days.

5.17. The mass of Jupiter, and therefore the centripetal force exerted on its satellites, is much greater than the earth's mass.

5.19. Semimajor axis of the orbit is about $\frac{1}{2}$ that of the moon's orbit. Therefore, $T_s \cong T_m(\frac{1}{2})^{3/2} \cong 10$ days. Time to reach moon's orbit is about 5 days, if the attraction of the moon for the vehicle is not taken into account, which of course is a serious omission.

5.21. The light particles would obey Kepler's laws of motion relative to the central, positively charged particle, which is assumed to have charge of a much greater magnitude than any of the light particles, so that its motion can be neglected relative to theirs. (In the analogous gravitational situation the motion of the massive central body is neglected relative to that of its light satellites.)

5.23. (a) The ratios of the magnitudes of the forces on the sun due to the four planets are $F_V:F_E:F_M:F_J = 1.58:1.00:0.043:10.9$. Therefore, the net momentum transfer to the sun is toward Earth, Mars, and Jupiter.

(b) The ratio of the magnitude of the forces on Earth due to Mars and Jupiter is $F_M:F_J = 0.3:18.0$. Therefore, Jupiter produces the larger perturbation on Earth's motion.

5.25. (a) About 7.8×10^8 m from the center of the sun.

(b) The sun's center describes an approximate circle with a 7.8×10^8-m radius in 11.86 years. In one-half that time the sun shifts by a distance of about 1.56×10^9 m relative to the center of mass of the sun and Jupiter.

(c) 1.7×10^{-8} radians, or about 3.5×10^{-3} seconds of arc.

5.29. (a) 14 m/sec.

(b) 31 m/sec at the rim.

5.31. Since the gravitational force exerted by the earth per unit *inertial* mass would be greater on the aluminum than on the iron satellite, the former would have to travel with a greater orbital speed to maintain a stable circular orbit of the same radius as the latter. Therefore, the inner aluminum satellite would ultimately collide with the forward inner edge of the outer hollow satellite.

Quantitatively, let M_i and M_g be the respective inertial and gravitational masses of either of the satellites, R the radius of their circular orbits, v either orbital speed, and M_e the mass of the earth. Equating the centripetal force to the gravitational force on a satellite: $M_i v^2/R = GM_e M_g/R^2$, or $v = \sqrt{GM_e/R}\,\sqrt{M_g/M_i}$. **Substituting**

$G = 6.7 \times 10^{-11}$ N-m^2/kg^2, $M_e = 6 \times 10^{24}$ kg, and $R = 2.4 \times 10^4$ miles $= 3.9 \times 10^7$ m, $v = 3.2 \times 10^3 \sqrt{M_g/M_i}$ m/sec.

Then the difference between the orbital speed of the two satellites would be $\Delta v = v_{A1} - v_{Fe} = 3.2 \times 10^3 (\sqrt{1.01} - 1) = 3.2 \times 10^3 \times 0.005 = 16$ m/sec. That is, the inner aluminum satellite would travel 19 m and collide with the outer iron shell in a little over one second.

Chapter 6

6.1. (a) $x_B = +3$, $y_B = 2$; $x_B = +8$, $y_B = 0$; $x_B = -2$, $y_B = 7$; $x_B = -7$, $y_B = 2$.
   (b) $x_A = -1$, $y_A = 1$; $x_A = 2$, $y_A = 2$; $\Delta x = 6$.

6.3. (a) $x_B = 1.73$ m, $y_B = 1.0$ m.

6.9. Strength of the joint varies as the square of the scale factor and is the same on the moon. Weight of the beam varies as the cube of the scale factor and is one-sixth as great on the moon for a beam of a given size. Therefore, the ability of the system to support itself is proportional to the scale factor so that all dimensions on the moon could be increased by a factor of six.

6.11. g on the earth's surface would increase by a factor of 2. The moon's period would be only $\frac{1}{4}$ as large.

6.13. (a) 5×10^5 kg-m^2/sec.
   (b) 3×10^8 kg-m^2/sec.
   (c) 4.5×10^{15} kg-m^2/sec.

6.15. One-half its previous value.

6.17. Equal in magnitude to the incident spin and clockwise.

6.21. (a) 10 m.
   (b) 6 m.
   (c) -12 m.
   (d) 3 m/sec.
   (e) -6 m/sec.
   (f) 2.6 m/sec^2.

6.23. (a) $v_x = 6.95$ m/sec, $v_y = 4$ m/sec.
   (b) $v'_x = 2.95$ m/sec, $v'_y = 4$ m/sec.
   (c) $v' = \sqrt{v'^2_x + v'^2_y} = 4.97$ m/sec.
       $\tan \theta' = v'_y/v'_x = 4.00/2.95 = 1.35$.

6.25. (a) 0.98 newtons toward the rear of the train.
   (b) 0.98 newtons toward the floor of the train.
   (c) $g_{\text{eff}} = \sqrt{2} \times 0.98/0.1 = 13.9$ m/sec^2 at an angle 45° to the "true" vertical.

6.27. (a) 160 newtons.
   (b) 61 m.

Chapter 7

7.1. (a) 11.1 joules.
   (b) 0.75 m.
   (c) No, otherwise no work would be required to move the mass at constant velocity.

7.3. (a) 2000 newtons.
   (b) 5900 joules/sec.

7.5. (a) 780 newtons/m.
   (b) 4.45 m/sec.

7.7. (a) 19.9 m/sec.
   (b) 17.8 m/sec.
   (c) 3.92×10^4 J, -1.57×10^5 J.

(d) 9.9 m/sec.

(e) 21.5 m/sec.

7.9.　(a) 40.8 m.

　　　(b) 10 m.

7.11.　(a) $v = \sqrt{\dfrac{M_2}{M_1 + M_2}\, gy}$.

　　　(b) Some of the potential energy of M_2 would be transferred into rotational kinetic energy of the pulley.

7.17.　$v_m/v_e = 0.2$.

7.19.　$\sqrt{5/6}$ times escape velocity $= 7.25 \times 10^3$ m/sec.

7.21.　Momentum conservation, momentum conservation, energy conservation.

7.25.　(a) $V = \sqrt{2gy}$, $v = (M_1 + M_2)/M_1$, $V = (M_1 + M_2)/M_1\sqrt{2gy}$.

　　　(b) $\Delta E = \frac{1}{2}M_1 v^2 - (M_1 + M_2)gy = M_2[1 + (M_2/M_1)]gy$.

Chapter 8

8.1.　(a) Doubles.

　　　(b) Quadruples.

　　　(c) Decreases by a factor of four.

8.3.　(a) 3.6×10^4 N/C in the positive x-direction.

　　　(b) $E_x = 1.27 \times 10^4$ N/C, $E_y = 3.82 \times 10^4$ N/C, $E = \sqrt{E_x^2 + E_y^2} = 4 \times 10^4$ N/C, $\tan\theta = 3.82/1.27 = 3.0$, $\theta = 73.5°$.

　　　(c) 7.2×10^{-2} and 8×10^{-2} N in the field direction.

　　　(d) 10.8×10^{-2} and 12.0×10^{-2} N opposite the field direction.

8.5.　(a) Zero.

　　　(b) $(q/d^2)[4 + \frac{1}{2}(\frac{4}{5})^{3/2}]$, parallel to the side and directed toward the negative charge.

8.7.　(a) In 0.2 sec.

　　　(b) 0.1 m from its starting point.

8.9.　(a) 0.02 m.

　　　(b) No. The electrical device functions as it does because the two particles have different charge to mass ratios, whereas the gravitational to inertial mass ratio is always unity.

8.11.　(a) 0.196 and 0.392 N. Both are at rest relative to the elevator.

　　　(b) $E = 980$ N/C downward.

　　　(c) Yes. Give the other particle an equal charge and observe its acceleration.

8.13.　(a) -8 J.

　　　(b) 126 m/sec.

　　　(c) 126 m/sec.

8.15.　(a) 2 J.

　　　(b) 5×10^{-4} m.

　　　(c) $v_{2f} = 20$ m/sec, $\theta_2 = 30°$, momentum conservation.

8.17.　(c) $T = 2\pi/\sqrt{5} = 3.6$ sec.

8.19.　8×10^{-4} A in the negative x-direction.

8.21.　(a) 3.13×10^{10}/sec.

　　　(b) 119 m/sec.

8.23.　The longer wire has sixteen times the resistance of the shorter one.

8.25.　(a) $3\frac{1}{3}$ ohms.

　　　(b) $\frac{5}{6}$ A, $1\frac{2}{3}$ A, 5 A.

　　　(c) 20.8 watts, 41.6 watts, 125 watts, 187.4 watts.

8.27.　In series.

8.29.　0.91 A, 120 ohms.

8.31.　75 A.

Chapter 9

9.1.   (a) 50 A.
       (c) 10^5 watts.
9.3. $B_s/B_p = \frac{1}{2}$, $P_s/P_p = \frac{1}{4}$.
9.5.   (b) $T = 2\pi\sqrt{Ml/2\mu B}$.
9.7.   (a) 22 A.
       (b) Opposite.
       (c) 4.9×10^{-3} J.
9.9.   (b) 2.5×10^{-2} A-m², direction perpendicular to the plane of the loop in the sense given by the right-hand screw convention.
       (c) 2.5×10^{-2} J.
       (d) 2.5×10^{-2} J.
9.11. (a) 9.9×10^6 m/sec.
       (b) 5×10^{-32} A-m.
       (c) $\Delta\omega = \mu B(\cos 0 - \cos 30) = 1.34 \times 10^{-32}$ J.
9.13. $\Delta i/i = 2/102 \cong 2\%$.
       $\Delta i/i = 2/1002 \cong 0.2\%$.
9.15. (a) 0.1 N in the negative z-direction, 100 m/sec² in the negative z-direction.
       (b) The force will reverse its direction.
       (c) The force will again reverse its direction.
       (d) The magnitude of the force will be halved.
9.17. 4.9×10^{-3} Wb/m² in the negative z-direction, where the positive direction of y is taken as vertically upward.
9.19. 12.5 m.
9.23. One possible design: $R_0 = 1.0$ m, $B = 0.5$ Wb/m², $f = 4 \times 10^6$/sec.
9.25. (a) 376 volts.
       (b) 3.76 A.
       (c) 1420 watts.
9.27. (a) $\mathscr{E} = \Delta B/\Delta t = \pi \times 10^{-2}/5 = 2\pi \times 10^{-3}$ volts.
           $i = \mathscr{E}/R = 2\pi \times 10^{-4} = 6.28 \times 10^{-4}$ A.
       (b) $\mathscr{E} = 4\pi \times 10^{-2}$ volts. $i = 4\pi \times 10^{-3} = 1.26 \times 10^{-2}$ A.
9.29. 9×10^{-4} Wb/m².

Chapter 10

10.1. 20°, 28°, 36°.
10.3. (a) 45.5°, 36°, 49°.
       (b) No, since light is always bent toward the perpendicular on entering a medium with a higher refractive index.
10.5. (a) 19.05° and 19.3°.
       (b) 8×10^{-3} m.
10.7. (a) $\theta_2 = 34.9°$.
       (b) $\theta_1' = 25.1°$.
       (c) $\theta_2' = 39.9°$.
       (d) 70.8°.
           Separation at the second glass-air interface $\cong 2.5 \times 10^{-2}$.
           $(\theta_2$ blue $- \theta_2$ red$) \cong 2.2 \times 10^{-4}$ m.
           Additional separation after 0.5 m $\cong 0.5$.
           $(\theta_2'$ blue $- \theta_2'$ red$) \cong 1.3 \times 10^{-2}$ m.
10.9. (a) $\sin \theta_1 = n \sin \theta_2$.
       (b) $A = 2\theta_2$.
       (c) $n = \sin \theta_1/\sin (A/2)$.

10.11.   (a) 2500 eV = 4×10^{-16} J.
   $\Delta v = 3 \times 10^7$ m/sec.
   (b) 2500 eV = 4×10^{-16} J.
   $\Delta v = 2.24 \times 10^5$ m/sec.

10.13. -2.18×10^{-18} J. The negative sign indicates that the kinetic energy of the electron is smaller than the absolute magnitude of its potential energy so that the system is bound. (See the potential energy diagrams of Sections 7.5 and 7.6.)

10.15.   (a) About 2.2×10^{10} photons/sec.
   (b) About 1.1×10^9 electrons/sec corresponding to a current of about 1.8×10^{-10} A.

10.17. $10^{-2} M_e c^2 = 5.1 \times 10^3$ eV.

10.19.   About 5 MeV. About 50 MeV.

10.21.   On copper, 2.9×10^{-7} m (ultraviolet).
   On sodium, 5.1×10^{-7} m (yellow).

10.23.   (a) 8×10^{-4} m (0.8 mm).
   (b) 9.7×10^{-4} m (0.97 mm).
   (c) A series of overlapping, dispersed spectra with each spectrum corresponding to a different value of n in Equation 10.7a.

Chapter 11

11.3.   (a) $\Delta l = 0.211$ in.
   (b) $\Delta t / t = 5 \times 10^{-9}$.

11.5.   (a) $0.707\,c = 2.1 \times 10^3$ m/sec.
   (b) 0.5 m.

11.11. c.

11.13.   (a) 2.16×10^4 sq m, timelike.
   (b) -6.75×10^2 sq m, spacelike.
   (c) 0 sq. m, lightlike.
   Only (a) and (c) could be causally connected.

11.15.   (a) 1.5×10^{-30} kg.
   (b) 2.1×10^{-30} kg.
   (c) 2.9×10^{-30} kg.
   (d) 6.5×10^{-30} kg.

11.17.   (a) $E = 850$ keV, $T = 340$ keV, $p = 685$ keV/c.
   (b) $E = 1190$ keV, $T = 680$ keV, $p = 1080$ keV/c.
   (c) $E = 1650$ keV, $T = 1140$ keV, $p = 1570$ keV/c.
   (d) $E = 3700$ keV, $T = 3190$ keV, $p = 3640$ keV/c.

11.19. $2 M_e c^2 = 1.022$ MeV.

11.21.   About 3×10^{-8} kg.

11.23.   (a) About 4×10^4 in both cases.
   (b) About 0.26 in. long if the electron had the full 20 BeV energy over the entire two-mile length.

11.25.   (a) About 20 and 1.01, respectively.
   (b) About 5.4×10^{-21} kg-m/sec, and 7.2×10^{-20} kg-m/sec, respectively.
   (c) 0.034 and 0.45 m, respectively, with curvatures in the opposite directions.

11.27.   At $R = 5$ m.
   (a) $C/D = \pi / \sqrt{1 - v^2/c^2} = 3.4$.
   (b) $F = M v^2 / R = M_0 v^2 / R \sqrt{1 - v^2/c^2} = 4 \times 10^{14}$ N.
   (c) $\Delta t = 1.1$ sec.
   At $R = 10$ m:
   (a) $C/D = 7$.
   (b) $F = 1.6 \times 10^{17}$ N.
   (c) $\Delta t = 2.2$ sec.

11.29. $r = R \sin \theta$.

$C = 2\pi r = 2\pi R \sin \theta$.

For $\theta = 90°$, $c = 2\pi R$; the circumference of the great circle and of the sphere itself are equal at the equator.

For $\theta = 180°$, $C = 0$. The circumference of the sphere which encloses the entire surface area and whose radius is equal to πR, the half-circumference of the sphere, is zero, a decidedly non-Euclidean result.

Chapter 12

12.1. (b) The width of the gap decreases by a factor of 1.66, so that the magnitude of the field is unaltered.

(c) The x-dimension of the plate contracts by a factor of 1.66, so that the magnitude of the field increases by this factor.

12.3. (a) The positive x-direction.

(b) The positive x-direction.

12.5. (a) $0.1/c = 3.3 \times 10^{-10}$.

(b) $0.8/c = 2.6 \times 10^{-9}$.

(c) $0.9/c = 3 \times 10^{-9}$.

(d) $0.95/c = 3.2 \times 10^{-9}$.

(e) $0.99/c = 3.3 \times 10^{-9}$.

12.7. (a) 75 N/C tangent to the circle in the direction the current originally flowed.

(b) 7.5×10^{-5} N.

12.9 $B = 10^{-6}$ Wb/m².

Therefore, $i = 0.4$ A.

12.15. (c) 10^{-8} sec.

12.17. (a) 10^4/sec.

(b) Area of entire spherical surface $= 4\pi R^2 = 16\pi m^2$. Therefore, number intercepted by 10^{-2} m² area $= 10^{-2}/16\pi \times 10^4 \cong 2$/sec.

(c) $F = \Delta p/\Delta t = 2 \times 10^{-4} \times 10^6/1 = 200$ N.

(d) $\sim \frac{1}{2}$/sec. 50 N.

Chapter 13

13.3. (a) $\lambda = 0.05$ m, $f = 200$/sec, $v = 10$ m/sec.

(b) 100 N.

13.5. (c) As R increases, the circumference of the disturbance increases. Therefore, in order to conserve energy its amplitude decreases.

13.7. (a) $\lambda_1 = 1$ m, $\lambda_2 = 0.5$ m, $\lambda_3 = 0.33$ m, $\lambda_4 = 0.25$ m.

(b) $f_1 = 440$ sec, $f_2 = 880$/sec, $f_3 = 1320$/sec, $f_4 = 1760$/sec, $v = 440$ m/sec in all cases.

13.9. (a) 1.2 N.

(b) 4.8 N.

(c) 0.1 m.

13.11. (a) 5×10^3 cycles/sec.

13.13. 1000, 1250, and 1500 cycles/sec (corresponding to the modes 100, 010, and 001).

13.15. (a) 700 cycles/sec.

(b) 500 cycles/sec.

13.17. 1000 cycles/sec.

13.19. About 5×10^{-7} m, in the green region of the electromagnetic spectrum.

13.21. (a) 1.43×10^4/sec.

(b) 1.43×10^4/sec.

(c) 2.1×10^4 m.

13.23. Let R_1 be the distance from source 1 to x_1, $R_2 = \sqrt{R_1^2 + d^2}$ the corresponding distance from source 2. Maxima and minima are determined by the condition:

$$\Delta R = \sqrt{R_1^2 + d^2} - R_1 = n\lambda,$$

$n = 1, 2, 3, \ldots$, for maxima, $n = \frac{1}{2}, \frac{3}{2}, \ldots$, for minima, or (solving) $R_1 = (d^2 - n^2\lambda^2)/2n\lambda$.

Thus for the first three maxima (corresponding to $n = 1, 2$, and 3): $R_1 = 0.225$ m, 0.09 m, and 0.035 m.

For the first two minima ($n = \frac{1}{2}$ and $\frac{3}{2}$): $R_1 = 0.475$ m and 0.138 m.

13.25. (a) Assuming the aperture of the eye has a radius of about 1.5×10^{-3} m, the radius of the comparable radio telescope would have to be about 500 m.

(b) 16.6×10^6 m—twice the diameter of the earth.

13.27. (a) 10^{-10} m or less because of diffraction effects.

(b) A 10^{-10} m wavelength corresponds to a 12.5 keV photon energy. Thus $\Delta E = 300$ eV.

(c) About 22.

Chapter 14

14.1. (a) 2 and 1, respectively.

(b) Cu_2O and CuO, respectively.

(c) $2Cu_2O \rightarrow 4Cu + O_2$, $2CuO \rightarrow 2Cu + O_2$.

14.3. (a) Ferrous oxide, 1 iron atom; ferric oxide, 2 iron atoms.

(b) FeO (ferrous oxide) and Fe_2O_3 (ferric oxide).

(c) $2FeO \rightarrow 2Fe + O_2$, $2Fe_2O_3 \rightarrow 4Fe + 3O_2$.

14.5. (a) 1.7726.

(b) 35.453.

(c) $2HCl \rightarrow H_2 + Cl_2$.

14.7. (a) $CH_4 + 2O_2 \rightarrow 2H_2O + CO_2$.

(b) 0.45 kg of H_2O, 0.55 kg of CO_2.

(c) 0.8 kg of O_2.

14.9. 8.1×10^4 N.

(b) 6.67 atm.

14.11. (a) A decrease by a factor of 2.5.

(b) A decrease by a factor of 1.25.

14.13. (a) $p = \rho g \, \Delta h$.

(b) 2.66×10^4 N/m^2.

14.15. (a) Both pressure and temperature increase by a factor of 4.

(b) The pressure doubles while the temperature remains constant.

(c) The pressure is reduced by a factor of 2 while the temperature remains constant.

14.17. 33 kg.

14.19. (a) 1.55×10^3, 6.25×10^3, and 3.60×10^5 m/sec.

(c) 4.9×10^2, 1.97×10^3, and 1.14×10^5 m/sec.

Chapter 15

15.1. (a) $\frac{1}{6} \times \frac{1}{6} = \frac{1}{36}$.

(b) $\frac{1}{6} \times \frac{1}{6} = \frac{1}{36}$.

15.3. (a) $5 \times \frac{1}{6} = \frac{5}{6}$.

(b) $\frac{5}{6}$.

15.5. (a) $\frac{1}{6} \times \frac{5}{6} \times \frac{1}{6} = \frac{5}{216}$.

(b) $3 \times \frac{5}{216} = \frac{15}{216}$.

15.7. (a) Let the specific aces be spades and diamonds (S and D). Then in three trials there are three ways in which S and D may each be drawn once and only once in three trials with S drawn before D, and three ways with D drawn before S. Therefore,

$$P = 2 \times 3 \times \left(\frac{1 \times 1 \times 51}{52^3}\right) = 2.2 \times 10^{-3}.$$

Likewise in four trials,

$$P = 2 \times 6 \times \left(\frac{51^2}{52^4}\right) = 4.5 \times 10^{-3}.$$

(b) There are three ways to draw two and only two specific aces in a particular order in three trials, four ways to choose the first, and three ways to choose the second. Therefore,

$$P = 4 \times 3 \times 3 \times \left(\frac{51}{52^3}\right) = 1.32 \times 10^{-2}.$$

Likewise in four trials,

$$P = 4 \times 3 \times 6 \times \left(\frac{51^2}{52^4}\right) = 2.7 \times 10^{-2}.$$

15.9. (a) $10 \times (\frac{1}{6})^3(\frac{5}{6})^2$.
 (b) $35 \times (\frac{1}{6})^3(\frac{5}{6})^4$.

15.11. (a) $0.0185/0.0385 = 0.48$.
 (b) $0.115/0.125 = 0.97$.
 (c) Although the *absolute* asymmetry represented by $x = N_H - N_T$ between 10 and 15 is the same for both parts a and b, the *fractional* asymmetry, $x/(N_H + N_T)$ is ten times larger in part a.

15.15. (a) In order to be found outside the container after 100 collisions the molecule must be $2 \times 10^{-2}/10^{-3} = 20$ units in x from its starting point. Referring to Figure 15.13a, the area under the curve between $x = 0$ and $x = 20$ is about 0.455 (this part of the curve may be approximated as a triangle resting upon a rectangular base 20 units wide by 0.0055 units high). The entire area of the curve to the right of $x = 20$ is 0.500. Therefore, the probability of finding the molecule outside the container (beyond $x = 20$) after 100 collisions is $0.500 - 0.455 = 0.045$. Likewise the probability of finding it outside the container after 1000 collisions is about 0.287.
 (b) Virtually 0 after 100 collisions, about 0.070 after 1000.
 (c) Although it is assumed that a molecule can move in either the $+x$ or $-x$ direction following a collision, the answers to parts a and b indicate that a given molecule has a definite probability of *not* being at its starting point after N collisions. In addition, the probability of a molecule's being a given distance away from its starting point evidently increases with the number of collisions. The members of a large group of molecules that interact only by collision (i.e. an ideal gas) have a tendency to diffuse out of a container.

15.17. About 82 at 90° and 36 at 120°.

15.19. (a) The mean energy is defined such that one-half the molecules have greater energies and one-half smaller energies. The most probable energy is the energy that more molecules have than any other.
 (b) The horizontal scale for the Gaussian distribution is the asymmetry of some division of trials. Both positive and negative asymmetries are defined, and it is reasonable to assume that the probability of a given positive asymmetry is equal to the probability of the same negative asymmetry. On the other hand, energy is

the horizontal scale for the Maxwell-Boltzmann distribution. Thus the distribution is defined for positive values of the horizontal scale only, and there is no reason to expect symmetry about the nonzero, most probable energy. In fact, since small energy transfer collisions are more probable than very large energy collisions it is reasonable to expect many more molecules with small energies than with large energies relative to the most probable value, as borne out by Figure 15.9.

15.21. Refer to Figure 15.10:
- (a) About $5.3/9.1 = 0.58$, and about $1.6/9.1 = 0.175$.
- (b) About $21/23 = 0.91$, and about $5/23 = 0.22$.
- (c) Evidently there is a much greater spread in speeds about the most probable speed for a group of light molecules than for a group of heavier ones. This has a direct bearing on the composition of planetary atmospheres, for instance, as outlined in Section 15.8.

Chapter 16

16.1. (a) They are equal.
   (b) The ratio of the total energy of the second to that of the first is two.
16.3. $\Delta W = 2.46 \times 10^5$ J, $\Delta Q = 61.5 \times 10^5$ J.
16.5. (a) 0.14 kg.
   (b) 8.5×10^{-3} and 5.6×10^{-2} m^3.
16.7. (a) 0.2 m.
   (b) 3.6 J.
16.9. (a) 2.56×10^{-7} m.
   (b) In the ultraviolet.
16.11. (a) 9.5×10^7 J.
   (b) Yes, since the energy released in each replacement reaction (2×11.4 eV) is more than sufficient to disassociate two hydrogen molecules and one oxygen molecule.
16.13. (a) 3.3×10^4 J.
   (b) 0.6 A.
   (c) Power = 18.3 watts; $R_{eff} = 510$ ohms.
16.15. $\Delta M = M_{2H} - M_{H_2} = \Delta E/c^2 = 8.7 \times 10^{-36}$ kg; $\Delta M/M = 2.7 \times 10^{-9}$.
16.17. (a) No. In an elastic collision between equal mass billiard balls the speeds before and after the collision are equal.
   (b) The second was taken first. Evidently the rod is being heated from the left end.
   (c) [HINT: Compare the answers to parts a and b from the viewpoint of the second law of thermodynamics.]

Chapter 17

17.1. (a) 6.25×10^6 J in both cases.
   (b) 10.4×10^6 J.
   (c) By 6 °K.
17.3. [HINT: Consider the second law of thermodynamics.]
17.5. 3700 °K. A body need not be this hot to emit in the red region of the spectrum, since the Wien law refers only to the *peak* of the spectrum.
17.7. About 1.0 eV, $P_2/P_{max} = 0.4$, $P_{1/2}/P_{max} = 0.65$.
17.9. (a) 6.5×10^{-7}, 4.8×10^{-7}, and 4.3×10^{-7} m.
   (b) 1.89, 2.55, and 2.85 eV.
17.11. (a) About $0.83\,c$.
   (b) About 3.4×10^{-7} m.

17.13. (a) $E_1 = -3.4$ eV.
(b) $0.26 = 10^{-10}$ m.
(c) First "Balmer" wavelength $= 1.62 \times 10^{-7}$ m.
First "Lyman" wavelength $= 3.0 \times 10^{-8}$ m.

17.15. (a) 0.94×10^{-23} and 1.88×10^{-23} A-m².

(b) $B = \dfrac{\mu_0 i}{2R_0}$,

$$ i = \frac{ev}{2\pi R_0} = \frac{eL}{2\pi M R_0^2} = \frac{\mu_l}{R_0^2}. $$

Therefore, $B = \dfrac{\mu_0 \mu_l}{2\pi R_0^3}$.

(c) $\Delta E = -\mu_s B(\cos 180° - \cos 0°)$,

$$ = 2\mu_s B = \frac{\mu_0 \mu_s \mu_l}{\pi R_0^3}. $$

(d) $\Delta E = \dfrac{\mu_0}{\pi R_0^3} \left(\dfrac{eh}{4\pi M}\right)^2 = 2.88 \times 10^{-22}$ J $= 1.8 \times 10^{-3}$ eV.

(e) The energy levels calculated on the Bohr model should each be split into two closely spaced components.

17.17. (a) λ(photon) $= 1.2 \times 10^{-9}$m, λ(electron) $= 3.6 \times 10^{-11}$ m.
(b) λ(neutron) $= 9.2 \times 10^{-13}$ m, λ(electron) $= 3.6 \times 10^{-11}$ m.
(c) λ(neutron) $= 1.4 \times 10^{-15}$ m, λ(electron) $= 2.4 \times 10^{-12}$ m.

17.19. [HINT: What would be the momentum uncertainty of an electron confined to a nuclear volume? To what (relativistic) energy uncertainty would it correspond?]

17.21. (a) 10^{-10} m or less.
(b) 1.2×10^4 eV.
(c) 280 eV.
(d) $280/13.6 = 21$.

Chapter 18

18.1. 0.06 m.
18.5. (a) Two superimposed single slit patterns—one red, one green.
(b) Two superimposed diffraction patterns.
18.7. (a) $\bar{\phi}_{abc} = \bar{\phi}_a + \bar{\phi}_b + \bar{\phi}_c$.
(b) $P(x) = |\bar{\phi}_{abc}|^2$,
$$ = P_a(x) + P_b(x) + P_c(x) + (\bar{\phi}_a^*\bar{\phi}_b + \bar{\phi}_a\bar{\phi}_b^* + \bar{\phi}_a^*\bar{\phi}_c + \bar{\phi}_a\bar{\phi}_c^* + \bar{\phi}_b^*\bar{\phi}_c + \bar{\phi}_b\bar{\phi}_c^*). $$
18.9. (a) $8(2 + i)$, $-2(2 + i)$, $15(3 + 4i)$.
(b) $6 - 3i$ and $10 - 5i$.
(c) 54 and 125; 7.35 and 15.
18.11. (a) 0.
(b) π radians (180°).
(c) $3\pi/2$ radians (270°).
(d) $\pi/4$ radians (45°).
(e) $2\pi/3$ radians (60°).
(f) $\pi/3$ radians (30°).
18.13. (a) 10.
(b) Let $\bar{E}_a = \bar{E}_0 \exp (iS_a/\lambda)$,
$\bar{E}_b = 10\bar{E}_0 \exp (iS_b/\lambda)$.

Then: $I_{ab}(x) = |\bar{E}_a + \bar{E}_b|^2$,

$$= E_0^2 \left\{ 101 + 10 \left[\exp i \left(\frac{S_A - S_B}{\lambda} \right) + \exp -i \left(\frac{S_A - S_B}{\lambda} \right) \right] \right\},$$

$$= E_0^2 \left[101 + 20 \cos \frac{\Delta s}{\lambda} \right].$$

(c) $I_{max}/I_{min} = \frac{121}{81} = 1.5$.

18.15. It is completely uncertain, since $|\bar{\phi}(x, t)|^2 = |\exp [(i/\hbar)(xp - Et)]|^2 = 1$.

18.17. (a) $\bar{\phi}(x) = a_0 \left[\exp \left(i \frac{p_1 x}{\hbar} \right) + 2 \exp \left(i \frac{p_2 x}{\hbar} \right) \right]$.

Therefore, $P(x) = |\bar{\phi}(x)|^2 = a_0^2 \left[5 + 4 \cos \frac{\Delta p x}{\hbar} \right]$, where $\Delta p = p_1 - p_2$.

18.19. (a) $F = Mg$,

$$M \frac{d^2 y}{dt^2} = F.$$

Therefore, $\frac{d^2 y}{dt^2} = g$.

(b) $y = y_0 + v_0 t + \frac{1}{2} g t^2$,

$$\frac{dy}{dt} = v_0 + gt,$$

$$\frac{d^2 y}{dt^2} = g.$$

Q.E.D.

18.21. They would be one hundred times further apart than previously.

18.23. No. It has zero probability of being found at certain locations, but not of crossing from one region of nonzero probability to another. The model gives no information about the motion of the particle in the well, but rather predicts where it is likely to be found.

18.25. Let

$$\bar{\phi}_0(x) = \bar{\phi}_e(x) + \bar{\phi}_0(x),$$

where $\bar{\phi}_e(-x) = \bar{\phi}_e(x)$ and $\bar{\phi}_0(-x) = -\bar{\phi}_0(x)$.
Then

$$\bar{\phi}_{e0}(-x) = \bar{\phi}_e(-x) + \bar{\phi}_0(-x),$$
$$= \bar{\phi}_e(+x) - \bar{\phi}_0(x).$$

$$P(x) = |\bar{\phi}_{e0}(x)|^2 = P_e^2 + P_0^2 + (\bar{\phi}_e^* \bar{\phi}_0 + \bar{\phi}_e \bar{\phi}_0^*),$$

$$P(-x) = P_e^2 + P_0^2 - (\bar{\phi}_e^* \bar{\phi}_0 + \bar{\phi}_e \bar{\phi}_0^*).$$

Therefore, $P(-x) \neq P(x)$.

18.27. Let $\bar{\phi}_u$ and $\bar{\phi}_d$ be the respective amplitudes for upward and downward scattering of a single particle, and a and b the two particles. Then the amplitudes corresponding to the two diagrams are $\bar{\phi}_u(a)\bar{\phi}_d(b)$ and $\bar{\phi}_u(b)\bar{\phi}_d(a)$, respectively. The detection probabilities are

for distinguishable particles,
$$P = |\phi_u(b)\phi_d(a)|^2 + |\phi_u(a)\phi_d(b)|^2;$$
for Bose particles,
$$P = |\phi_u(b)\phi_d(a) + \phi_u(a)\phi_d(b)|^2;$$
for Fermi particles,
$$P = |\phi_u(b)\phi_d(a) - \phi_u(a)\phi_d(b)|^2.$$
Because of the geometric symmetry $\phi_u = \phi_d = \phi$. Therefore,
for distinguishable particles,
$$P = 2|\phi(a)\phi(b)|^2;$$
for Bose particles,
$$P = 4|\phi(a)\phi(b)|^2;$$
for Fermi particles,
$$P = 0.$$

Chapter 19

19.1.

n	L(Q.M.)
1	0
2	$\sqrt{2}\,\hbar$
3	$\sqrt{6}\,\hbar$
4	$\sqrt{12}\,\hbar$
5	$\sqrt{20}\,\hbar$

The orbital angular momenta in the Bohr model are integral multiples of $\hbar$. Therefore, none of them correspond exactly to the correct quantum mechanical values.

19.3. (b) No. The probability density plots give no information on the radial motion of the electron. Rather, they show where it is likely to be found.

(c) Not completely. No. Yes, for it implies an uncertainty in the radial position of the electron.

(d) No, for neither its energy nor angular momentum would have changed.

19.5. (a) Greater, since the splitting between the extreme components of a level is proportional to its orbital angular momentum.

(b) Yes. Those with $l = 0$.

19.7. $B = \mu_0 i/2R$ (Equation 9.10); $\mu_0/4\pi = 10^{-7}$ mks units. $i = ev/2\pi R = eL/2\pi MR^2$. Therefore, $B = (\mu_0 e/4\pi M)(L/R^3)$. But (on the Bohr model) $L = nh/2\pi$, $R = n^2 R_0$ ($R_0 = 0.5 \times 10^{-10}$ m). So:

$$B = \left(\frac{\mu_0 e h}{8\pi^2 M R_0^3}\right)\frac{1}{n^5}.$$

For $n = 1$, $B = 60$ Wb/m²; for $n = 2$, $B = 1.9$ Wb/m².

19.9. $n = 1$

| $l = 0,$ | $m = 0,$ | $s_z = \pm\frac{1}{2}$ (2 states). |

$n = 2$

| $l = 1,$ | $m = \pm 1, 0,$ | $s_z = \pm\frac{1}{2}$ (6 states). |
| $l = 0,$ | $m = 0,$ | $s_z = \pm\frac{1}{2}$ (2 states). |

$n = 3$

$l = 2,$	$m = \pm 2, \pm 1, 0,$	$s_z = \pm\frac{1}{2}$ (10 states).
$l = 1,$	$m = \pm 1, 0,$	$s_z = \pm\frac{1}{2}$ (6 states).
$l = 0,$	$m = 0,$	$s_z = \pm\frac{1}{2}$ (2 states).

$n = 4$

$l = 3,$	$m = \pm 3, \pm 2, \pm 1, 0,$	$s_z = \pm\frac{1}{2}$ (14 states).
$l = 2,$	$m = \pm 2, \pm 1, 0,$	$s_z = \pm\frac{1}{2}$ (10 states).
$l = 1,$	$m = \pm 1, 0,$	$s_z = \pm\frac{1}{2}$ (6 states).
$l = 0,$	$m = 0,$	$s_z = \pm\frac{1}{2}$ (2 states).

19.11. The energies of the $n = 4$ and $n = 5$ states overlap for these values of Z so that the distinctions between the outer-shell structures of atoms with nearly the same number of electrons is not too pronounced.

19.13. The binding energy of the outer shell electrons of the halogen atoms increases with increasing atomic number. It is reasonable since the increasingly attractive Coulomb force of the nucleus binds the electron shells more tightly.

19.15. Ionic bonds are formed only between dissimilar atoms with small numbers of vacancies on the one hand and extra electrons on the other in their outer shells. Covalent bonds are formed when similar or dissimilar atoms can reduce their total energy by sharing electrons.

19.17. The interaction between hydrogen *molecules* at room temperature, which determines the macroscopic appearance of the aggregate, is very small, and not directly related to the molecular dissociation energy. In contrast, the average 3.6 eV dissociation energy for sodium chloride, together with the ionic nature of the compound, implies that the sodium and chlorine ions have appreciable interactions with *all* their near neighbor ions.

19.19. Water molecules have a decided charge asymmetry so that at low temperatures they arrange themselves in definite patterns. Apparently the charge asymmetry of the wax molecules is not so pronounced.

19.21. 1.3×10^{-5} kg.

19.23. Taking $\overline{KE} = \frac{3}{2}kT$, $\overline{KE} = 1$ eV yields 8000 °K. But $\overline{KE}$ is an average so that many molecules have much higher energies. Therefore, an upper limit on the order of 1000 °K is more reasonable. A lower temperature limit could be found in terms of the mean energy required to initiate the fundamental chemical reactions upon which life processes depend.

Chapter 20

20.1. (a) $_1H^3$: $1p$, $2n$; $_2He^4$: $2p$, $2n$;
$_6C^{12}$: $6p$, $6n$; $_6C^{14}$: $6p$, $8n$;
$_{26}Fe^{56}$: $26p$, $30n$; $_{82}Pb^{208}$: $82p$, $126n$;
$_{82}Pb^{209}$: $82p$, $127n$; $_{92}U^{235}$: $92p$, $143n$;
$_{92}U^{238}$: $92p$, $146n$.
(b) 2.2×10^{-14} m, 3.2×10^{-15} m, 5.4×10^{-15} m, 8.3×10^{-15} m.

20.3. (a) 0.025 m between $_{10}Ne^{20}$ and $_{10}Ne^{21}$;
0.025 m between $_{10}Ne^{22}$ and $_{10}Ne^{21}$.
(b) 0.006 m.

20.5. Because all isotope separation techniques must of necessity rely on mass difference alone.

20.7. (a) For $_{26}Fe^{56}$, $V = 6.9$ MeV.
For $_{92}U^{238}$, $V = 15.2$ MeV.
(b) The repulsive coulomb potential represents a disruptive force, in contrast to the attractive, nuclear part of the potential. The total binding energy is the algebraic sum of these potentials and the kinetic energy of the nucleons. The neutron-proton mass difference should also contribute to the differences in binding energies.

20.9. (a) The α-particle, because it is double charged and has a smaller velocity (being more massive), and thus has a higher probability of ionizing the atoms along its path.
The proton, since it can interact both with the atomic electrons and nuclei, whereas the neutron interacts with nuclei only when within about 1.4×10^{-15} m.

20.11. (a) (i) α, (ii) β^+, (iii) γ, (iv) β^-, (v) β^-.
(b) (i) 209.9368, (ii) 25.9799, (iii) 30.9676, (iv) 89.8851.

20.13. The half-life is 2 hr; 5000/sec at 1 p.m.; 1250/sec at 5 p.m.

20.15. 56 years old.

20.17. 10.8 MeV.

20.19. (a) Total energy yield, including positron rest energies, $= 25.7$ MeV. Total kinetic energy $= 25.7 - 2M_e = 24.7$ MeV.

 (b) 6.2×10^{13} J.

 (c) 2.3×10^5 kg.

20.21. $\frac{3}{2}RT$ is the *mean* translational energy per mole of an ideal gas; many atoms have considerably higher energies.

Chapter 21

21.1. A neutron need not overcome the repulsive electrostatic barrier of a nucleus in order to penetrate and interact.

21.3. $p + {}_6C^{12} \rightarrow {}_7N^{12} + n$.

21.5. A photon has large absorption probability only if its energy corresponds to the energy difference between the ground state and an excited state of the nucleus so that by absorbing it the nucleus can make a transition to an excited state.

 The energies of excited nuclear states can be studied by the γ-ray absorption.

21.7. To 5 MeV. To 10 MeV.

21.9. Because its mass is small, the velocity of a 1 MeV electron is already more than 80% the velocity of light.

21.11. (a) 1.5 times its rest mass.

 (b) By 50%.

21.13. By transferring all or part of its energy to a proton in a "billiard ball" collision. The energetic proton would then leave a track.

21.15. Yes, since the *np* interaction depends in part on the relative spin alignment of the nucleons.

21.17. (a) About 14.9 MeV.

 (b) Because of the repulsive electrostatic interaction between the protons in a nucleus, and the neutron-proton mass difference, the energy levels for the two types of nucleon differ slightly, even in the light nuclei.

21.19. About 40 MeV.

21.21. The properties of a tightly bound particle differ from those of a free particle.

Chapter 22

22.1. (a) The meson class; 139 MeV, the π-meson rest energy.

 (b) The baryon class; 938 MeV, the proton rest energy.

 (c) The lepton class; 106 MeV, the muon rest energy.

22.3. Total energy for a pair at rest $= 1.02$ MeV, total momentum $= 0$. Thus, for a pair annihilating at rest, momentum and energy are conserved only if two 0.511 MeV photons are produced and travel outward in opposite direction.

22.5. (a) No.

 (b) 1; no.

 (c) $\frac{1}{2}$, $-\frac{1}{2}$, 1, -1, 0.

22.7. The principle of equivalence assumes that gravitational and inertial masses are equal. It therefore predicts that antiparticles have normal gravitational interactions. Otherwise *any* attractive force would repel them.

22.9. [HINT: The probability for a process decreases with the number of *electromagnetic* vertices, but is approximately independent of the number of strong vertices.]

22.11. Since electrons interact predominately via electromagnetic interactions, the original prediction of the ρ°-meson from electron scattering data implied that the latter particle had electromagnetic properties. Its decay via the electromagnetic interaction into predominantly electromagnetic particles was thus a reasonable hypothesis.

22.13. 0.4×10^{-15} and 0.25×10^{-15} m.

22.15. Because of the relativistic time dilation experienced by a very high energy particle that increases considerably their lifetimes as observed in the laboratory.

22.17. Muons, because it is difficult to disentangle the effects of the π-meson's electromagnetic interaction from its dominant strong interactions, whereas the predominant interactions of the muon are electromagnetic.

22.19. The electron in hydrogen interacts electromagnetically with the mesons in the proton's halo, although these effects are small relative to its dominant single-photon exchange interaction with the proton as a whole. However, the muon does not have an associated meson cloud. Therefore, its electromagnetic interactions with the electron should be much simpler. The energy levels of muonium should be almost the same as those of hydrogen.

22.21. No, since the relative probability that a nucleon would spend part of its time disassociated into a nucleon and W particle would be on the order of the strength of the weak interactions.

Chapter 23

23.1. (a) Charge conservation.
  (b) Strangeness conservation.
  (c) Baryon conservation or angular momentum (spin) conservation.
  (d) Lepton conservation or angular momentum (spin) conservation.
  (e) Charge and strangeness conservation.

23.3. $K^+ + p \rightarrow Z^+ + \pi^+$.

23.5. The isotopic spin formalism is intimately related to the properties of the strong interactions, and leptons do not participate in these interactions.

23.7. (b) $T = \frac{3}{2}$ (the $\pi^+ p$ system has total isotopic spin $\frac{3}{2}$, whereas the $\pi^- p$ system is in a mixed state of $T = \frac{3}{2}$ and $T = \frac{1}{2}$).
  (c) $T = \frac{1}{2}$.

23.9. A K^* exchange diagram.

23.11. Yes, since the π-K and N-Σ mass differences are presumably due to symmetry-breaking by the strong interactions, where the $\pi^\pm$-π°, n-p, and $\Sigma^\pm$-Σ° mass differences are due to symmetry-breaking by the electromagnetic interactions.

23.13. No, since unitary symmetry is concerned only with the strongly interacting particles.

23.15. [HINT: The cosine-dependent amplitudes have even parity, the sine-dependent amplitudes odd parity.]

INDEX

Subject Index